COMPARATIVE BIOCHEMISTRY

A Comprehensive Treatise

COMPARATIVE BIOCHEMISTRY

VOLUME IV: CONSTITUENTS OF LIFE—PART B

COMPARATIVE BIOCHEMISTRY

A Comprehensive Treatise

Edited by

Marcel Florkin
Department of Biochemistry
University of Liège
Liège, Belgium

Howard S. Mason
University of Oregon Medical School
Portland, Oregon

Volume IV

CONSTITUENTS OF LIFE—PART B

1962

ACADEMIC PRESS • New York and London

ACADEMIC PRESS INC.
111 FIFTH AVENUE
NEW YORK 3, N. Y.

United Kingdom Edition
Published by
ACADEMIC PRESS INC. (LONDON) LTD.
BERKELEY SQUARE, LONDON W. 1

Library of Congress Catalog Card Number 59–13830

PRINTED IN THE UNITED STATES OF AMERICA

CONTRIBUTORS TO VOLUME IV

THOMAS PETER BENNETT,* *Department of Chemistry, Florida State University, Tallahassee, Florida*

GEORGE BRAWERMAN, *Cell Chemistry Laboratory, Department of Biochemistry, College of Physicians and Surgeons, Columbia University, New York*

J. S. BRIMACOMBE, *The Chemistry Department, University of Birmingham, Edgbaston, Birmingham, England*

C. E. DALGLIESH, *Miles Laboratories, Ltd., London*

HUGH S. FORREST, *Genetics Foundation, The University of Texas, Austin, Texas*

SIDNEY W. FOX, *Oceanographic Institute, Florida State University, Tallahassee, Florida*

EARL FRIEDEN, *Department of Chemistry, Florida State University, Tallahassee, Florida*

R. K. GHOLSON, *Department of Biochemistry, Oklahoma State University, Stillwater, Oklahoma*

T. W. GOODWIN, *Department of Agricultural Biochemistry, University College of Wales, Penglais, Aberystwyth, United Kingdom*

CHARLES GRÉGOIRE, *Institut Léon Fredericq, Department of Biochemistry, University of Liège, Belgium*

L. M. HENDERSON, *Department of Biochemistry, Oklahoma State University, Stillwater, Oklahoma*

G. Y. KENNEDY, *Cancer Research Unit, The University of Sheffield, Sheffield, England*

A. GEDEON MATOLTSY, *Department of Dermatology, Boston University, School of Medicine, Boston, Massachusetts*

F. F. NORD, *Laboratory of Organic Chemistry and Enzymology, Fordham University, New York*

M. G. M. PRYOR, *Department of Zoology, Cambridge University, England*

* Present address: Graduate School, The Rockefeller Institute, New York, New York

C. RIMINGTON, *Department of Chemical Pathology, University College Hospital Medical School, London, England*

K. M. RUDALL, *Department of Biomolecular Structure, The University of Leeds, England*

WALTER J. SCHUBERT, *Laboratory of Organic Chemistry and Enzymology, Fordham University, New York*

HERMAN S. SHAPIRO, *Cell Chemistry Laboratory, Department of Biochemistry, College of Physicians and Surgeons, Columbia University, New York*

M. STACEY, *The Chemistry Department, University of Birmingham, Edgbaston, Birmingham, England*

H. B. STEINBACH, *Department of Zoology, University of Chicago, Chicago, Illinois*

HENRY J. TAGNON, *Department of Medicine and Clinical Investigation, Institut J. Bordet, University of Brussels, Belgium*

T. L. V. ULBRICHT,* *Department of Organic and Inorganic Chemistry, University of Cambridge, England*

ALLEN VEGOTSKY, *Oceanographic Institute, Florida State University, Tallahassee, Florida*

* Present address: Twyford Laboratories Ltd., Twyford Abbey Road, London, N.W. 10, England

PREFACE

In order to provide a systematic comparison of the biochemical phenomena of life throughout the phylogenetic scale, Comparative Biochemistry has been organized as follows: Volumes I and II are primarily concerned with the biological transformations of energy, Volumes III and IV with the biological transformations of matter, and Volumes V and VI with the properties of the organized systems occurring in living organisms.

Thus, the present volumes, III and IV, are devoted to the principal classes of constituents of cells and organisms, their distribution, and the comparative enzymology of their biogenesis and metabolism. The comparison of structure and distribution, on the one hand, and metabolism, on the other, require different types of specialized knowledge; we have asked two different authors, when necessary, to describe these different aspects of the composition of living organisms.

In the main, organisms are made up of fatty acids and lipids, mono- and polysaccharides, amino acids and proteins, nucleotides and nucleic acids, and water. This is an aspect of biochemical unity to which, on earth at least, there appears to be no exception. It is logical to arrange the chapters in these volumes to emphasize this unity. There are also numbers of other structural classes of metabolic components which occur only in portions of the phylogenetic scale; these less usual components illustrate the diversity of life. A number of chapters in Volume IV are devoted to amino acids and proteins. Some of these chapters deal with special forms of adaptation of protein structure: keratin, sclerotized proteins, silk; or protein transformations during the coagulation of blood, or during amphibian metamorphosis. This group of chapters offers ample material for comparison in the field of the molecular biology of proteins.

The editors, although they have preferred to delay publication of individual volumes rather than have chapters appear out of their organized context, have been confronted with serious difficulties arising from the necessity of translating manuscripts written in languages other than English, and of insuring the publication of texts already received without too long a delay. They have therefore decided not to postpone the printing of chapters already on hand. This somewhat upsets the original plan of organization which, nevertheless, continues to underlie the treatise as a whole.

As in the case of previous volumes, the publishers have provided us with prompt, competent, and reliable assistance. We wish again to express our gratitude to them.

M. FLORKIN
Liège, Belgium

H. S. MASON
Portland, Oregon

June, 1962

CONTENTS

COMPARATIVE BIOCHEMISTRY

A Comprehensive Treatise

Volume I: Sources of Free Energy

Volume II: Free Energy and Biological Function

Volume III: Constituents of Life—Part A

Volume V: Constituents of Life—Part C

Volume VI: Cells and Organisms

* Most of the names refer to phyla, except in a few cases where some of the smaller taxonomic groups are shown. Capitalized names written across lines are groups including all forms above the name.

NOTE: Charts I, II, and III were prepared by Helen A. Stafford, Reed College, Portland, Oregon. For further information see "A Guide to the Nomenclature and Classification of Organisms," by Dr. Stafford, in Vol. I of this treatise.

CHART I
HYPOTHETICAL PHYLOGENETIC RELATIONSHIPS
BETWEEN EXTANT MAJOR GROUPS
OF ORGANISMS*

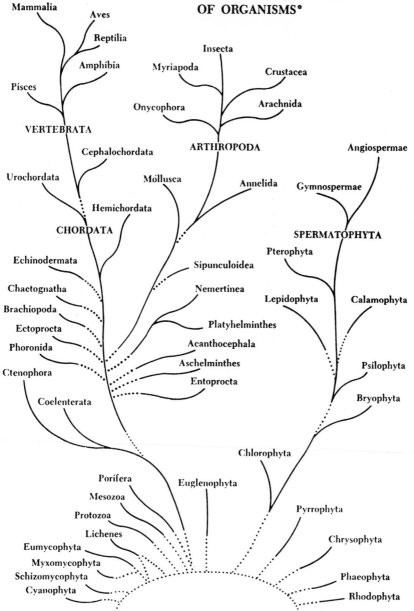

CHART II: ANIMAL KINGDOM

Divisions	Estimated Number of Species[d]	Taxonomic Classifications			
Protozoa (acellular animals)	15,000				
Mesozoa	—				
Porifera (sponges)	5,000				
Coelenterata (coelenterates)	10,000				Radiata
Ctenophora (comb jellies)	100				Radiata
Platyhelminthes (flat worms)	6,000	Acoelomates		Protostomia	Bilateria
Nemertinea (nemertine worms)	500	Acoelomates		Protostomia	Bilateria
Aschelminthes[a], Acanthocephala[a]	7,000	Pseudocoelomates		Protostomia	Bilateria
Entoprocta[b], Ectoprocta[b] (moss animals)	3,000	Eucoelomates	Schizocoela	Protostomia	Bilateria
Phoronida	15	Eucoelomates	Schizocoela	Protostomia	Bilateria
Brachiopoda (lamp shells)	120	Eucoelomates	Schizocoela	Protostomia	Bilateria
Mollusca (mollusks)	70,000	Eucoelomates	Schizocoela	Protostomia	Bilateria
Sipunculoidea	—	Eucoelomates	Schizocoela	Protostomia	Bilateria
Annelida[c] (segmented worms)	6,500	Eucoelomates	Schizocoela	Protostomia	Bilateria
Arthropoda (arthropods)	750,000	Eucoelomates	Schizocoela	Protostomia	Bilateria
Chaetognatha (arrow worms)	30	Eucoelomates	Enterocoela	Deuterostomia	Bilateria
Echinodermata (echinoderms)	5,000	Eucoelomates	Enterocoela	Deuterostomia	Bilateria
Hemichordata, Chordata (including vertebrates)	60,000	Eucoelomates	Enterocoela	Deuterostomia	Bilateria

[a] Includes Rotifera, Gastrotricha, Kinorhyncha, Nematoda, Nematomorpha, Priapuloidea. Formerly called Nemathelminthes.

[b] Formerly in Bryozoa.

[c] Includes Echiuroidea.

[d] Taken from "Handbook of Biological Data" (*4*), p. 533.

CHART III: PLANT KINGDOM

Divisions	Estimated Number of Species[d]	Major Synonymous Terms		
Euglenophyta (euglenoids)	340	Algae	Thallophyta	Cryptogamia
Chlorophyta (green algae)	5,700	Algae	Thallophyta	Cryptogamia
Pyrrophyta (cryptomonads, dinoflagellates)	1,000	Algae	Thallophyta	Cryptogamia
Chrysophyta (yellow green algae, diatoms)	5,700	Algae	Thallophyta	Cryptogamia
Phaeophyta (brown algae)	900	Algae	Thallophyta	Cryptogamia
Rhodophyta (red algae)	2,500	Algae	Thallophyta	Cryptogamia
Cyanophyta[a] (blue-green algae)	1,400	Algae	Thallophyta	Cryptogamia
Schizomycophyta[a] (bacteria)	1,300[e]	Fungi	Thallophyta	Cryptogamia
Myxomycophyta (slime molds)	430	Fungi	Thallophyta	Cryptogamia
Eumycophyta (true fungi)	74,000	Fungi	Thallophyta	Cryptogamia
Lichenes (lichens)	15,500		Thallophyta	Cryptogamia
Bryophyta (mosses and liverworts)	23,800		Bryophyta	Cryptogamia
Psilophyta[b] (whisk ferns)	3	Psilopsida	Tracheophyta	Cryptogamia
Calamophyta[b] (horsetails)	30	Sphenopsida	Tracheophyta	Cryptogamia
Lepidophyta[b] (lycopods)	1,300	Lycopsida	Tracheophyta	Cryptogamia
Pterophyta[b, c] (ferns)	10,000	Pteropsida	Tracheophyta	Cryptogamia
Spermatophyta (seed plants)	201,000	Pteropsida	Tracheophyta	Phanerogamia

[a] Sometimes grouped as Schizophyta.
[b] Formerly classed as Pteridophyta.
[c] Formerly classed as Filicineae in Pteropsida.
[d] Taken from "Handbook of Biological Data" (*4*), p. 533.
[e] There is much disagreement concerning designation of species here.

CHAPTER 1

The Optical Asymmetry of Metabolites

T. L. V. ULBRICHT*

*Department of Organic and Inorganic Chemistry,
University of Cambridge, England*

"Who would have thought that God would turn out to be a weak left-hander?"†

I. Introduction

In this discussion of the optical asymmetry of metabolites, no attempt has been made to embrace all aspects of the problem or to present a

* *Present address:* Twyford Laboratories Ltd., Twyford Abbey Road, London N.W. 10, England.
† W. Pauli, on hearing that parity was not conserved in β-decay.

1

complete literature survey. Rather, it is hoped that by concentrating on some of the more important work of recent years in the light of certain fundamental ideas, the significance of optical asymmetry and its role in living systems may emerge more clearly. This we can do only by restricting our attention to those metabolites the importance of whose stereochemical configuration we begin to understand.

II. The Significance of Optical Purity

A. LIFE AND ORDER

Life cannot help but appear to be an extremely improbable phenomenon since, as Lecomte du Noüy put it, evolution has produced less and less likely states, in apparent contradiction to the second law of thermodynamics (1). Although the evolution of life remains to be precisely explained, we are now at least able to explain the *maintenance* of life, using the thermodynamics of irreversible processes and the concept of living things as open, steady state systems (2), which du Noüy neglected to consider. Living organisms work against the law of increasing disorder and concentrate order within themselves. This is possible not merely because organisms absorb energy from their environment (for this alone would not prevent their entropy from increasing), but because the sources of energy are complex, highly ordered molecules (derived, ultimately, from the sun). Food may be regarded as negative entropy (3).

In discussing such phenomena as enzyme action, antibody-antigen interaction, and the self-duplication of genes and viruses, it has been said: "I believe that it is the molecular size and shape, that are of primary importance in these phenomena, rather than the ordinary chemical properties of the substances" (4). The secret of biological organization surely lies just in that word *organization*—an ordered molecular structure which is the precise equivalent of the *necessary life-information* [ultimately stored, as far as we know, in the base sequences of the deoxyribonucleic acids (DNA)]. In the living processes deriving order from order, as distinct from nonliving processes in which order leads to disorder, *information* is equivalent to negative entropy.

B. OPTICAL PURITY AS A MANIFESTATION OF ORDER

Despite the great increase in recent years of our knowledge of the structure of proteins and nucleic acids, it is not sufficiently appreciated that the optical asymmetry of metabolites is absolutely essential to life;

that optical purity is one of the most fundamental aspects of the order of which we have been speaking. Imagine a molecule of DNA in which half the molecules of 2-D-deoxyribose have been replaced by 2-L-deoxyribose; an ordered structure, such as the one from which a base-paired, twin-stranded helix is derived (5), would be quite impossible. We shall return to this point later, particularly in connection with protein structure.

In theory, life as we know it would be equally possible if *all* optical configurations were inversed.* What is certain is that optical purity is essential to life, first in those metabolites which are built up into polymers (enzymes, nucleic acids), since an ordered structure would otherwise be impossible, and, as a consequence of this, in all metabolites involved in enzyme reactions.

C. The Maintenance of Optical Purity

What consequences would follow if the monomeric metabolites of a living system were racemic? The main reason why this question is difficult to answer is that it never happens because a number of factors prevent it.

1. Unwanted isomers are eliminated:

a. By excretion. D-Amino acids are more rapidly excreted than the L-isomers (7), but it is not altogether clear whether this is actually due to a differentially more rapid excretion, or simply slower metabolism (8).

b. By being built up into stable polymeric structures not involved in metabolism, e.g., the cell walls of certain bacteria (see below).

c. By optically specific destruction. All animals investigated (not only mammals) contain D-amino acid oxidase, a stereospecific enzyme which oxidizes all D-amino acids (except glutamic and aspartic acid, for which there is a separate enzyme). Common views on the role of this enzyme are as follows: "It is a curious fact that this enzyme acts only upon the non-natural D-series of amino acids. . . . As far as is known, D-amino acids are relatively uncommon in nature, and it may be that this enzyme has some other as yet unknown important biological function" (9); "The physiological role of D-amino acid oxidase, if any, is unknown" (10); and "Despite the widespread occurrence of D-amino acid oxidases, their physiological role is unknown at present" (11). These views echo those of the discoverer of the enzyme (12). It

---

* We do not know enough to be sure of this. If a neutrino could look at itself in the mirror it would see nothing (6). There may be a more fundamental relationship between the structure of matter and the structure of life than we yet understand (see Section VII, B).

has even been suggested that the enzyme represents an evolutionary vestige (*13*).

In contrast, Kuhn (*14*) argues cogently that the degree of optical purity is related to the process of aging and the natural life span. It is not necessary to agree with all his arguments to admit that, at least, the maintenance of ordered structure—in other words, the maintenance of life—depends on optical purity.

Natural processes are never rigorously exclusive or complete; the equilibrium constant of a reaction may be very large, but it is never infinity; an enzyme may be highly stereospecific, but it is never absolutely so. The laws of the universe are statistical and rest, finally, on an element of chance (*15*); it is not possible, for example, to predict exactly when a particular radioactive atom will decay. Predictions are therefore statements of probability. There is a finite probability that a D-amino acid will be built into an enzyme, a probability which is so very small only because normally no D-amino acids are present. It should not be forgotten in this connection that racemization is thermodynamically irreversible and, in the absence of factors specifically acting against it, is bound to occur in time. [The total entropy of mixing for D- and L-tartaric acid to the racemic form is about 2 kcal. per mole (*16*)].

2. Most enzymatic reactions, and certainly all the most important ones, have high rate constants. Enzymes are catalysts and do not affect the position of equilibrium of a reaction. Hence, the more an enzyme speeds up the reaction, say, of a keto acid to an L-amino acid, the less D-amino acid will be formed.

3. In an isolated, closed system, the same enzyme would eventually bring about the formation of equal amounts of the D- and L-isomers. Since the equilibrium constant is finite, a small amount of keto acid (in our example) is not aminated by the enzyme and will slowly react in random fashion to give both the L- and the D-products. Since the amount of keto acid is thereby reduced, the enzyme will catalyze the reverse reaction, converting L-amino acid to keto acid. Thus the final result, which is thermodynamically inevitable in a closed system, is to produce a racemic mixture. It is readily apparent that the most important factor in this process is time. Initially, owing to the rapid enzymatic reaction, a product of very high optical purity (which to all intents and purposes will seem complete, though never in fact quite complete) will be produced, but ultimately this will fall (*14*). Examples of this have been known for some time (*17*).

However, in living systems an enzymatic reaction does not constitute a closed, isolated system, but is part of an integrated metabolic network —part of the ordered structure which seems to center on the particulate elements of the cytoplasm. Consequently, as soon as an enzymatic reaction is complete, the product finds itself involved in a coupled process—the next step in a synthesis, involving another enzyme; active transport to another part of the cell; or whatever it might be. In all cases, there is in living systems no prolonged contact of a product with the enzyme which catalyzed its synthesis—and hence racemization is avoided, since there is no time for it to occur.

Obviously the presence of the wrong isomers in living cells is not damaging *ipso facto*, but if such metabolites were built up into structures that regulate other processes—proteins (see Section V) and nucleic acids (Section VII)—then it would be damaging.

Even in simple diastereoisomers the physical properties are often radically different. This is true, for example, of the dissociation constants of the four isomeric alanylalanines (*17a*) and of the leucyltyrosines (*17b*); for the latter, the formation constants of the cobalt complexes, the positions and intensities of absorption bands of the oxygenated cobaltous chelates, and the rates of oxygen uptake by the chelates are also markedly different for the diastereoisomeric forms.

III. Absolute Configuration

The absolute configuration of the L-series of amino acids is related to that of L(−)-serine (I), and that of the D-series of sugars to D(+)-glyceraldehyde (II). The configurations assigned were arbitrary, but that (II) is correct was shown by the X-ray crystallographic analysis of tartaric acid (*18*).

$$
\begin{array}{cc}
\text{COOH} & \text{CHO} \\
| & | \\
\text{H}_2\text{N}\!-\!\!-\!\!-\!|\!-\!\!-\!\text{H} \qquad \text{H}\!-\!\!-\!|\!-\!\!-\!\text{OH} \\
| & | \\
\text{CH}_2\text{OH} & \text{CH}_2\text{OH} \\
\text{(I)} & \text{(II)}
\end{array}
$$

The two series were related (*19*) when D-glucosamine, in which C-2 is as in D-glyceraldehyde, was converted, without inversion of the carbon atom bearing the amino group, to L-alanine. Because of the interchange of reference groups, this related L-glyceraldehyde to L-alanine (and therefore to L-serine). This was confirmed when subsequently the two reference compounds, (I) and (II), were related by a series of controlled stereochemical reactions, which showed that they had the opposite configuration (*20*).

IV. The Natural Occurrence of D-Amino Acids and L-Sugars

A. L-SUGARS

Both D-glucose and L-gulose may be converted to D-gluconic acid, and D-xylose may be converted to L-gluconic acid; no inversions are involved in these reactions. The most important natural sugars all have several asymmetric centers, but the compounds are assigned to the D- or the L-series on the basis of the configuration at one carbon atom; this sometimes leads to results like those quoted. At the present time, it does not seem possible to come to definite conclusions about the significance of the configuration of particular sugars and their interrelationship; we need to know much more about the stereochemistry of their interaction with enzymes.

L-Sugars are relatively more common in nature than D-amino acids. In plants, L-sugars are sometimes found in glycosides, particularly L-rhamnose, whereas D-rhamnose has not been found, and L-arabinose occurs more frequently than D-arabinose. But L-sugars are rarely found in animals: L-fucose in a blood group substance (21, 22), L-galactose in snails (23), and both these sugars in echinoderms (24) represent isolated examples. The L-isomers of such universally important metabolites as D-glucose and D-ribose have never been found in nature, in plants or animals, though a derivative of L-glucosamine occurs in streptomycin (see Table I).

B. OCCURRENCE OF D-AMINO ACIDS AND L-SUGARS IN ANTIBIOTICS

A list of L-sugars and D-amino acids occurring in antibiotics is given in Table I. The most common of the amino acids found are D-isomers of essential amino acids, whereas all the sugars and a few of the amino acids (e.g., penicillamine) have never been found elsewhere.

It is believed that the presence of D-amino acids and L-sugars in these compounds is linked with their activity; the penicillin derived from L-penicillamine is inactive (61). One day we may understand the precise mode of action of these compounds; it should tell us a great deal about the stereochemistry of living systems.

C. D-AMINO ACIDS IN BACTERIA

1. Occurrence in Cell Walls

D-Amino acids occur relatively more frequently in bacteria than elsewhere in living organisms, and particularly in bacterial cell walls. Numerous species are involved, mainly gram-positive Eubacteriales

TABLE I
ANTIBIOTICS

Antibiotic	Origin	L-Sugars	Reference
Neomethmycin (and methymycin, narbomycin, pikromycin)	*Streptomyces* sp.	Related to L-glyceraldehyde	(25)
Novobiocin	*Streptomyces spheroides, Streptomyces niveus,* and *Streptomyces griseus*	Noviose (lyxose derivative)	(26)
Oleandomycin	*Streptomyces antibioticus*	Oleandrose	(27)
Streptomycin	*Streptomyces griseus*	N-methylglucosamine, Streptose	(28) (29)

Antibiotic	Origin	D-Amino acids	Reference
Actinomycins I–V	*Actinomyces* sp., and	Val	(30–34)
Actinomycin VI	*Streptomyces antibioticus*	Val, alloisoleu	(31)
Actinomycin VII		Alloisoleu	(31)
Amicetin	*Streptomyces vinaceusdrappus, Streptomyces fasciculatus*	α-Methylserine	(35)
Amidomycin	*Streptomyces* sp.	Val	(36)
Aspartocin	*Streptomyces griseus* var. *spiralis, S. violaceus*	α-Pipecolic	(36a)
Bacitracin	*Bacillus licheniformis*	Phe, Asp, Glu	(37–39)
Cephalosporin C	*Cephalosporium* sp.	Orn, α-aminoadipic	(40)
Cephalosporin N	*Cephalosporium* sp.	Penicillamine	(41)
Chloramphenicol	*Streptomyces* sp.	Related to D-serine	(41a)
Duramycin	*Streptomyces cinnamomeus* forma *azacoluta*	Lanthionine, β-Methyllanthionine	(42)
Echinomycin	*Streptomyces echinatus*	Ser	(43)
Enniatin A and B	*Fusarium* sp.	Val	(44)
Etamycin	*Streptomyces* sp.	Leu, allohydroxyPro	(45)
E₁₂₉B (ostreogrycin B)	*Streptomyces ostreogriseus*	α-Aminobutyric	(46)
Gramicidin J	*Bacillus brevis*	Leu, Orn	(47)
Gramicidin S	*Bacillus* sp.	Phe	(48, 49)
Micrococcin P	*Bacillus pumilus*	Related to D-alanine	(49a)
Oxamycin	*Streptomyces orchidaceus*	Cycloserine	(50)
Penicillin	*Penicillium* sp.	Penicillamine (dimethylcysteine)	(51)
Polymixin B₁	*Bacillus polymixa*	Phe; α,γ-diaminobutyric	(52, 53)
Polypeptin	*Bacillus krzemieniewski*	Val, Phe	(54)
Staphylomycin S	*Streptomyces virginiae*	α-Aminobutyric	(55)
Subtilin	*Bacillus subtilis*	Lanthionine, β-methyllanthionine	(56, 57)
Thiostrepton	—	Cysteine	(57a)
Tyrocidin A	*Bacillus brevis*	Phe	(58)
Tyrocidin B	*Bacillus brevis*	Phe	(59)
Valinomycin	*Streptomyces fulvissimus*	Val	(60)

and Actinomycetales (62). α,ε-Diaminopimelic acid is widely distributed, most commonly as the *meso* isomer, though the LL- and, rarely, the DD-isomer also occur; an *Escherichia coli* variant contains a racemase which converts the LL-acid to the *meso* form, but leaves the DD-acid unaffected (63). Fairly common also are D-glutamic acid and D-alanine; D-lysine is less common. D-Glutamic acid is found as a γ-linked polypeptide in the capsules of *Bacillus anthracis* (64) and *B. subtilis* (65), and D-alanine in the recently studied teichoic acids from the cell walls of *B. subtilis* (66).

The relative amounts of the L- and D-glutamic acids in the polypeptides from *B. subtilis* are affected by the concentration of Mn^{2+} in the medium; the polypeptides are predominantly of either the D or the L configuration, for those containing appreciable amounts of both isomers are found to be mixtures of D- and L-peptides (67).

Penicillin, which itself contains a D-amino acid, interferes with cell wall synthesis, and in *Staphylococcus aureus* cultures, leads to the accumulation of certain nucleotide compounds which appear to be cell wall precursors. They are uridine derivatives, some of which contain D-alanine and D-glutamic acid (68).

The occurrence of D-amino acids in bacterial cell walls raises a number of questions. Is this a protective device, developed as resistance to proteolytic (L-specific) enzymes? Or is it a method of utilizing unwanted D-isomers and placing them, so to speak, out of harm's way? Although the latter hypothesis hardly seems very likely, in view of the relatively wide presence of D-amino acids and various racemases in bacteria, it cannot be ruled out. But there is another problem which may be more closely defined; cell walls and polypeptides containing D-amino acids also often contain L-amino acids; how are they built up into a composite structure? Unless one configuration predominates over the other, a stable helical structure is impossible (see Section V, A), and consequently we must assume that, if a desired structure exists, the L- and D-isomers must be predominantly in distinct molecular chains, as indeed found in the *B. subtilis* peptides. One interesting suggestion is that the *meso* form of diaminopimelic acid could link such chains together (62).

2. Bacterial Metabolism

The growth of numerous bacteria [for example, *Lactobacillus arabinosus* (69), *E. coli* (70, 71), *Salmonella typhimurium* (72–74)] is inhibited by a variety of D-amino acids; spore germination in *Bacillus subtilis* is inhibited by D-alanine (75); D-serine inhibits the formation of tetanus toxin (76); and, as already mentioned, penicillin interferes with the synthesis of cell walls. It has recently been shown that several D-amino acids, including D-methionine, induce abnormal forms (crescents) in an *Alcaligenes faecalis* strain, similar to those induced by penicillin, i.e., the cell walls are affected (77); it also appears that exogenous D-methionine prevents the incorporation of exogenous L-methionine into *A. faecalis* protein, though it does not interfere with endogenous incorporation (78). Earlier work on the effect of D-amino acids on bacterial metabolism is discussed in a recent paper on the inhibition of cell division and growth in a species of *Erwinia* by a variety of D-amino acids (78a).

Novobiocin and bacitracin (Table I) also interfere with cell wall synthesis in *Staphylococcus aureus* (79), causing the accumulation of uridine nucleotide cell wall precursors. Interesting results have been obtained with oxamycin (D-cycloserine), which has a similar effect on *S. aureus* and causes the accumulation of an unusual nucleotide, containing D-glutamic acid and L-alanine, but no D-alanine. It was shown that oxamycin was a competitive antagonist of the incorporation of D-alanine (80), but did not interfere with the incorporation of L-alanine. On the other hand, L-cycloserine does not induce nucleotide accumulation (79).

It appears, therefore, that D-amino acids in some cases interfere with cell wall synthesis, and in other instances the effects may be related to inhibition of certain enzyme systems. It is known, for example, that D-leucine greatly decreases the hydrolytic activity of peptidases (81) and the effects found in the inhibition of *L. arabinosus* (69) correspond closely to the hydrolyzability of peptides from these amino acids by proteases, as found in work on the specificity of dipeptidase, where it was shown that the peptides of small D-amino acids could still be hydrolyzed (82).

On the other hand, it is now known that D-amino acids are present not only in cell walls, as was once thought, but sometimes also within the cells; thus, D-phenylalanine and D-aspartic acid are found in *Bacillus brevis*, partly in relatively simple peptides (83). Furthermore, there are cases in which it has been shown that D-amino acids are essential for growth; *Streptococcus faecalis* R requires D-alanine (84), and several lactic acid bacteria require D-aspartic acid, which is released by them on hydrolysis (85).

The D-amino acids found in bacteria do not necessarily arise from exogenous D-amino acids. D-Valine inhibits actinomycin synthesis in *Streptomyces antibioticus*, and this effect is partially reversed by L-valine, suggesting that the L rather than the D acid is the precursor of the D-valine in the antibiotic (86). Similarly, it seems probable that

L- and not D-valine is the precursor of D-penicillamine (87). These facts can be explained only if bacteria are able to convert L- into D-amino acids, and this was first specifically shown in S. *faecalis*, in which D-alanine is formed from L-alanine (or vice versa) by an enzyme (alanine racemase) for which, as expected, pyridoxal phosphate is the cofactor (88). The enzyme is specific for alanine and occurs in a number of bacteria.

Other bacterial racemases have been found (see Section V, C), and there is no doubt that the utilization of D-amino acids depends either on such enzymes or on deamination to the keto acid followed by stereo-specific amination to the L-isomer; the latter explanation is supported by the ability of α-keto acid analogs of certain amino acids to support growth.

D. D-AMINO ACIDS IN ANIMALS

D-Amino acids are not particularly toxic; they are often less toxic than the corresponding L-isomers (in any case, toxicity is always higher for individual acids than for a mixture, for obvious reasons), and they are excreted more rapidly. It is possible to summarize a great deal of information on D-amino acids in animal nutrition by saying that their utilization seems to depend entirely on deamination and reamination to the L-isomers. For a review, see (8). It is well known that a number of metabolites related to or derived from amino acids are active in only one configuration; for example, natural thyroxine is the L-isomer and D-thyroxine is inactive (88a).

As regards the actual occurrence of D-amino acids in animals, authenticated cases are very rare. The main difficulty is that one cannot be certain that racemization does not take place during protein hydrolysis. Also, methods of isolation based on fractional crystallization are unreliable. Kuhn made use of the great difference in solubility of a certain pair of disastereoisomeric salts of leucine to isolate small quantities of D-leucine in the presence of L-leucine (89, 90) in the hydrolyzate of horsehair; he also showed that neither L-leucine nor leucylleucine were racemized under the reaction conditions. However, it may still be objected that in the natural protein the secondary structural features may labilize the molecule to racemization.

Octopine, a substance isolated from the sea scallop *Pecten magellanicus* (91), seems to be a derivative of D-alanine (92), and D-alanine itself occurs in the blood of the milkweed bug *Oncopeltus fasciatus* (93). From a homogenate of rat intestinal mucosa incubated with pyruvic acid and ammonium salts, the alanine formed was shown to contain 2% of the D-isomer (94) (Section VI). The compound lombricine, isolated from earthworms, *Megascolides cameroni,* is a derivative of D-serine (*95*), derived biosynthetically from D-serine ethanolamine phosphodiester (*96*). In two other species of earthworms, *Allobophora caliginosa* and *Octalasium cyaneum,* D-serine occurs as 25% of the free serine isolated (*96a*). The presence of D-amino acids in neoplastic tissues will be discussed in Section VI.

E. D-AMINO ACIDS IN PLANTS

D-Amino acids have never been found in plants.

V. Optical Asymmetry and Protein Structure

A. THE STRUCTURE OF PROTEINS*

Very interesting results have been obtained by Blout, Doty, and their co-workers from experiments on the polymerization of γ-benzyl-L-glutamate-N-carboxyanhydride. Two different polymers are formed; the rate for the formation of the one having an α-helical structure is higher than that for the nonhelical β-polypeptide (*97*), showing that an ordered structure, once formed, would have an advantage during further growth.

Substitution of DL- for pure D- or pure L-monomer (in the methoxide-initiated reaction) caused a fall in the reaction rate to one-twentieth (*98*). A simple preference of a growing chain for its own isomer should have reduced the rate to only one-half. One possible explanation is that the polypeptide helixes which are formed have a preferred screw direction for each isomer, and that the rate of incorporation of the opposite isomer is lower owing to steric hindrance; but this does not explain the magnitude of the effect.

A study of the same polymerization, but initiated with *n*-hexylamine, showed the same effect when DL-isomer was used (*99*). Assuming that selectivity depends only on the terminal residue, one can calculate the rate expected if the reaction took place only with the same isomer. The experimental rate is lower still, i.e., reaction with *both* isomers is reduced. Hence interaction must occur between monomer and other residues apart from the terminal ones.

The changes in optical rotation which take place when the polymerization of the D-anhydride is initiated with a primer of L-polymer indicate that D-residues first add in a normal way to the α-helix, but after about four residues have been added the helix inverts (the L-polymer forms a right-handed helix, and vice versa). It has also been

---

* The application of optical rotatory dispersion studies to the structure of proteins and polypeptides is discussed by Blout (*96b*).

shown that in such DL-copolymers, the stability of the helical structure is reduced. In aqueous solution, in which the α-helical structure is weak in any case, it could not be maintained if significant amounts of D-residues were present (100). Even small amounts of the isomeric monomer lower both the rate of polymerization and the molecular weight of the polypeptide formed (101).

A number of conclusions may be drawn from this work, some of which are of particular concern to us. (a) The incorporation into a polymer of amino acids of the opposite configuration *can* occur non-enzymatically, and, providing this proportion is not too high and that there is not at any place a long sequence of such residues, a helical structure of the original screw-sense is retained. However, the stereochemistry of certain portions of the polymer is obviously profoundly affected, and as a consequence the stability of the helical structure is markedly reduced. (b) Optical purity has a very large effect on the rate of synthesis.

Although these conclusions are derived from purely chemical experiments, they are certainly relevant to our previous arguments (see Section II). A recent study made it possible to correlate the differences in dissociation constants, the stability constants of metal complexes, and rates of hydrolysis at different pH values with the optical configuration (and possibility of folding in the chain) of a number of LL-, DL-, LD-, and DD-dipeptides, e.g., alanylalanine (101a).

The X-ray analysis of myoglobin (101b) has shown that two-thirds of the L-amino acid residues are present in right-handed α-helical chains, and this also appears to be true of haemoglobin (101c). This work has provided a striking demonstration of the importance of the α-helical structure in key biological compounds.

B. ENZYMATIC AND SEROLOGICAL SPECIFICITY

This is a vast subject, quite beyond the scope of this chapter, but one or two suggestive facts are worth mentioning. Greenstein and his co-workers have carried out valuable studies on a number of enzymes, using amino acids and amino acid derivatives containing two asymmetric centers, to see the effect of the second asymmetric center on the reaction rate at the primary one. Experiments with the amino acid oxidases (102, 103) showed that the β-center exerted quite a marked effect, i.e., α-D-amino acids in which the β-center was L were less susceptible to D-amino acid oxidase than such amino acids in which the β-center was D; and similarly with α-L-amino acid derivatives and L-amino acid oxidase. However, comparable effects were not observed with α-hydroxyacid oxidase (103). On the other hand, renal aminopeptidase, which hydrolyzes peptides such as glycylalanine, shows a high requirement for the L configuration in the acyl group, but is relatively indifferent to the configuration of the terminal amino acid (104).

A striking case of stereospecificity has been shown in the interaction of purified antibody with optically active haptens (105). The haptenic groups studied were the D- and L-isomers of phenyl-(p-azobenzoylamino) acetate, and it was found that the binding affinity constant of purified anti-D serum for L dye was 1/35 of that for the D dye. With purified anti-β-lactoside antibody (106), the association constant for cellobiose was 400 times less than for lactose; these sugars differ only in the position of one hydroxyl group. There was a factor of 50 between the constants for β- and for α-glycosides. γ-Irradiation of ovalbumin leads to a breakdown of the molecule, and the loss of serological specificity is correlated with the unfolding of the protein chains, as shown by changes in optical rotation (106a).

Even these few examples are sufficient to show that (a) stereospecificity varies considerably from system to system—in some cases this can be related to the importance of the substrate concerned (cf. amino acids and α-hydroxyacids); and (b) it is sometimes very high (see also the following section).

C. ENZYMES SPECIFIC FOR D-AMINO ACIDS

1. D-Amino Acid Oxidase

We have already discussed the role of this enzyme (Section II). Data on its occurrence, specificity, and inhibition have been reviewed (107), and its concentration is known to be reduced in the presence of transplantable tumors (see Section VI). An interesting observation which has not so far been followed up is that, in general, the highest concentrations of the enzyme are found in carnivorous, the lowest in herbivorous, and intermediate concentrations in omnivorous, species (108)— that is, animals feeding on the primary synthesizers of optically active products have least enzyme; those that feed on other animals, in which such products have been involved in many more reactions and transformations (with consequently greater possibility of racemization— which may also take place after death), have the most enzyme.

2. Racemases

After the discovery of alanine racemase (Section IV, C), the same enzyme was found in B. subtilis and B. anthracis, which also contain D-specific transaminases (109–111). A number of amino acids are active in the latter system, mainly with pyruvic acid, giving D-alanine; and

D-alanine (or D-aspartic acid) can transaminate with α-ketoglutaric acid to give D-glutamic acid (which occurs in the capsules of these species). It seems probable that alanine racemase is responsible for the original D-configuration, and in this way the synthesis of D-alanine and D-glutamic acid in these organisms is satisfactorily explained. A lysine racemase has been found in a few *Escherichia* and *Proteus* species (*111a*), and possibly in a *Pseudomonas* species (*111b*).

Interconversion of L- and D-glutamic acid occurs in *L. arabinosus* (*112, 113*), but it was not clear at first whether this is due to a true glutamic acid racemase, or to a combination of alanine racemase with transaminase enzymes. The pathways of L- and D-glutamic acid and of L-glutamine utilization, some of which are inhibited by aspartic acid, are rather complicated in this organism (*114*). Recently glutamic acid racemase from *L. arabinosus* has been purified, and it definitely appears to be a unique enzyme (*114a*).

The enzyme in *E. coli* which converts LL-α,ε-diaminopimelic acid to the *meso* isomer (i.e., only one asymmetric center is affected) has already been mentioned (Section IV, C).

3. *Other Enzymes*

Two new D-amino acid oxidases have been discovered, one from rabbit kidney and liver, specific for D-aspartic acid (*115, 116*), and another from the cephalopod *Octopus vulgaris* Lam. (*117*) acting primarily on D-glutamic acid and to some extent on D-aspartic acid. These findings are of particular interest, as ordinary D-amino acid oxidase has little activity for these two compounds.

An unusual occurrence is the isolation of two distinct enzymes from the same source, each catalyzing the same reaction, but with the different optical isomers of one metabolite as substrate: aerobic yeast contains a lactic dehydrogenase ("enzyme O") specific for L-lactic acid; anaerobic yeast has a different lactic dehydrogenase ("enzyme N"), specific for D-lactic acid (*117a*). Previously, there was evidence of two optically specific lactic dehydrogenases in the lactic acid bacteria (*117b*).

A D-serine dehydrase has been discovered in *Neurospora crassa* (*118*) and in an *E. coli* strain (*119*), and a specific D-aspariginase in smooth *Brucella abortus* (*120*). An enzyme in *B. subtilis* transfers a γ-glutamyl radical from L- or D-glutamine to D-glutamic or glutamyl-glutamic acid (*121*) and may be concerned in the synthesis of the capsular polypeptides. An enzyme responsible for the activation of D-alanine has been discovered in a number of organisms (*B. subtilis*, *L. arabinosus, L. casei,* and *Staphylococcus aureus* H); this activation may represent the first step in a cell-wall component synthesis (*121a*). Finally, some years ago, a number of dipeptidases were described (*122*) that split peptides containing D-amino acids, e.g., D-leucylglycine, glycyl-D-leucine, and glycyl-D-alanine.

Enzymes stereospecific for D-amino acids must have characteristic structural and stereochemical features quite different from those in the corresponding enzymes specific for the L-amino acids, but this has not yet been investigated. It is tempting to speculate whether D-amino acids occur in such enzymes; rigorous purification of some of these enzymes would make it possible to answer this question.

VI. Optical Asymmetry and Cancer

It is a characteristic of cancer cells that they dedifferentiate; i.e., during the neoplastic process, cells with originally highly specialized morphology gradually disappear and are replaced by cells often almost embryonic in appearance.* This change is observed histologically (*123*). At the same time, a corresponding biochemical dedifferentiation takes place; a study of enzymes in tumors has revealed a common enzyme pattern with loss of specialized activity (*124*), including a reduction in the level of D-amino acid oxidase. The neoplastic process is therefore one which leads to the formation of a less ordered system from a more ordered one (with increase in entropy); it follows that, as a living system, cancer represents a more probable state than does normal growth.

Since the change from normal to neoplastic growth does not spontaneously take place all the time, one may assume that, as always, the transition even from a less probable state to a more probable one involves an energy barrier, or a series of energy barriers; the agents (carcinogens) which effect the transition must therefore either supply the necessary activation energy or increase the effective rate of the change by acting as catalysts, i.e., by lowering the activation energy. It is of interest that Schmidt (*125*) long ago pointed out that carcinogenic hydrocarbons have excited states of comparatively low energy, i.e., states that are easily reached and might effect a quantum jump in a neighboring molecule. This could lead to racemization (Reaction 1) in a protein chain (loss of asymmetry at C^*):

$$
\begin{array}{ccc}
\overset{|}{NH} & & \overset{|}{NH} \\
| & & | \\
C{=}O & \rightleftharpoons & C{-}OH \\
| & & \| \\
R{-}\overset{|}{C^*}{-}H & & R{-}\overset{|}{C^*} \\
| & & |
\end{array}
\qquad (1)
$$

* We do not mean by this that a cancer cell is like a normal, undifferentiated cell.

Miescher (16) has defined a series of properties, vital to life, as *biopotentials* (intensive, as opposed to extensive, energy factors). These include body temperature, blood pressure, osmotic pressure, various electric potentials, etc., *and optical asymmetry*. As regards the latter, it would be more accurate to say *optical purity*. The maintenance of "normal" life processes requires a minimum degree of optical purity (corresponding to a maximum entropy); if this minimum cannot be met (if the maximum entropy is exceeded) the consequences in time may be cancer and/or death (17).

Kögl's claims to have isolated D-amino acids from tumor tissue are not generally accepted (126, 127). It has already been pointed out that results depending on protein hydrolysis are necessarily ambiguous, since variations in stereochemical environment may make amino acids in some proteins more susceptible to racemization during hydrolysis than in others. There are, however, just two unambiguous results.

Homogenates of various tissues have been incubated with pyruvic acid and ammonium salts and assayed for D-amino acids with purified D-amino acid oxidase; the dinitrophenylhydrazones of the resulting keto acids were prepared and chromatographed (94). No D-amino acids were produced by muscle, liver, or kidney, and the alanine formed, with intestinal mucosa, contained only about 2% of the D-isomer; but when rat epithelioma was used, the proportion in the D-form was 10%.

D-Pyrrolidene carboxylic acid has been isolated from the urine of rats fed with human liver metastases, and, in one case, a glutamyl dipeptide was obtained, consisting mainly of D-glutamic acid. In control experiments (with normal liver) only small quantities of D-glutamic acid could be isolated (128).

It is a pity that, for most people, the subject of D-amino acids and cancer is so firmly associated with the work of Kögl, which merely proved that certain techniques cannot be used in this problem. The subject certainly warrants further investigation.

VII. The Origin of Optical Activity and the Origin of Life

A. GENERAL COMMENTS

Today, we cannot define life very much more precisely than did Schopenhauer in 1850: "The state of a body in which it always maintains its essential form through continuous change in its constituents" (129)—a concept that is obviously the basis of the present-day model of the open, steady-state system (2). But although we now have a fair understanding of how life maintains itself, how it *evolved* from non-living matter remains mysterious; theories about it are based on analogies. Part of the confusion that prevails in this field is due to the presentation of a false alternative: either the origin of life is explained by vitalist arguments or, if these are rejected (as they must be by a scientist), then life must be explained by the known laws of physics and chemistry. This conclusion, however, is false. Life represents an organization of matter which is *qualitatively* quite different from that of matter in other forms, and we already know from physics that new, different laws are required to explain phenomena involving, for example, the very large or very small; hence it should not surprise us to find new laws in the realm of living matter. Schrödinger came to the conclusion that "from all we have learnt about the structure of living matter, we must be prepared to find it working in a manner that cannot be reduced to the ordinary laws of physics" (3), not because of any "new force," but because of the difference in construction. Similarly, Heisenberg reports (130) Pauli's skepticism regarding the assumption of contemporary biology that the combination of the known laws of physics and chemistry with Darwin's theory and the idea of "chance" mutations can satisfactorily explain life and evolution.

Unfortunately, the real and inevitable limitations of science are obvious only in a highly developed discipline like physics, as witness modest (and accurate) statements such as: "the incomplete knowledge of a system must be an essential part of every formulation in quantum theory" (131); the limitations are less obvious in biology (132, 133).

All explanations of the origin of optical asymmetry*—which, from all that has been said, must be intimately linked with the origin of life—may be classified as follows. (i) Optical asymmetry developed in some degree before life arose: (a) by physical induction; or (b) by chance. (ii) Optical asymmetry developed only as life evolved. We shall consider these in turn.

B. The Origin of Optical Activity by Physical Induction

The induction of optical activity by physical agents has been reviewed (6). It is clearly established that circularly polarized light can be used to produce optical activity, either by asymmetric decomposition or by true asymmetric synthesis. Byk (134) argued that the linearly polarized light which reaches the sea is converted to elliptically polarized light and this, in combination with the magnetic field of the earth, could give rise to light circularly polarized more in one direction than another. Despite assumptions to the contrary (135), the statistical pre-

---

* An over-all asymmetry is here meant. Obviously, asymmetry existed in countless individual molecules.

dominance of a determinate sense of rotation has never been reported and, if any exists, must be very small and may vary with time; hence this explanation really does not merit further consideration.

The other argument, equally well worn with familiarity, is that optical asymmetry derives from naturally asymmetric crystals, e.g., quartz. Here at least there is some positive experimental evidence (though none for pure quartz itself); for example, racemic butan-2-ol could be selectively dehydrated at 400–500° on a catalyst consisting of metallic copper, platinum, or nickel deposited on quartz (136). Although local unequal distribution of the D- and L-crystals of quartz may be assumed, there would be no over-all asymmetry. Further, such arguments always overlook the problem of the *coordination in time;* it is necessary to explain the presence of some degree of optical purity *at the time when the crucial live-evolving processes were taking place.* Any effect that is subject to fluctuation is therefore unsatisfactory; nor must it be forgotten that optical purity is thermodynamically unstable in the absence of life (Section I, C).

The idea that the earth's magnetism alone could produce optical activity rests on a misconception regarding the nature of asymmetry, which necessarily requires two vectors (6, 137). We are left with the suggestion that the optical asymmetry found on earth is related to the structure of matter itself—in other words, that it is a reflection of the asymmetry of our part of the universe. Our world is composed of protons, neutrons, and electrons, and the electrons from radioactive β-decay and from meson decay in cosmic rays are predominantly left handed; hence the Bremsstrahlung produced is circularly polarized in one sense. That much is experimentally established (6), though it has not been possible, so far, to induce optical activity with polarized electrons in the systems investigated (138, 139). The effect, if it exists, is certainly very small; but this hypothesis regarding the origin of optical activity differs from the others in that the effect, if true, is constant and has always existed. This means that a very small predominance of one isomer could have been increased by a large number of reactions. For example, let us suppose that under the influence of polarized electrons, transamination is a reaction which yields a product with an anisotropy factor (L:D ratio) of a, where a is negligibly larger than 1. After n transaminations, the anisotropy factor is a^n, which may be significantly larger than 1.

According to this view, the particular optical asymmetry we find among the metabolites on earth is not an accident, and one would expect to find life based on D-amino acids in an anti-matter world (140).

C. THE ORIGIN OF OPTICAL ACTIVITY BY CHANCE

Essentially there are two hypotheses: (a) The beginning of life depended on the formation of the first autocatalytic molecule; this arose by chance, and so a chance asymmetry was propagated. The concept of life merely as an "autocatalytic molecule" is absurd; reproduction implies the existence of a complicated, *organized* network of metabolic reactions, making biosynthesis possible. This kind of explanation can be altogether rejected (see Oparin, *132*). (b) Optical asymmetry arose before life by spontaneous resolution during crystallization. Undoubtedly such crystallizations can occur (for discussions, see Oparin, *132;* The Moscow Symposium, *135;* Pirie, *141*), but there are many objections: the phenomenon presupposes supersaturation; it has been found to occur only in a *few* simple compounds—most optical enantiomers form mixed crystals—and it could never have taken place in peptides, colloidal substances, etc.; and (again!) only local fluctuations and no over-all, lasting asymmetry could have been produced.

D. THE EVOLUTION OF OPTICAL ACTIVITY

"Racemic life is no more than a speculative idea" (*142*)—but are not all ideas regarding the origin of life speculative?

Nevertheless, there are grave objections to the idea that there once existed "racemic life." Not only is it impossible for us to imagine life processes on a racemic basis (neither enzymes and other proteins, nor nucleic acids, could have had an ordered structure), but the whole idea presupposes that asymmetry evolved from symmetry. We are therefore led to the idea that life developed from certain polymeric substances, which, of necessity, were asymmetric, because of some stereospecificity during the polymerization process. There are two possibilities here.

(1) *Polymerization initiated with an asymmetric catalyst.* The work of Price with propylene oxide provides an excellent example (*143, 144*). The polymerization of L-propylene oxide with a ferric chloride-propylene oxide complex catalyst gave in very high yield a crystalline, optically active polymer. Polymerization of racemic propylene oxide under the same conditions gave a mixture of two products: (a) a liquid, amorphous polymer; and (b) a crystalline polymer which had the same melting point, viscosity, and X-ray diffraction spacings as the crystalline L-polymer, but was optically inactive. This product, therefore, either consists of a mixture of pure L- and pure D-polymer chains, or, at least (to account for the physical properties), the sequence of L- and D-units

along the chains must be very long (a hundred or more). Many similar examples could be given from the field of isotactic polymers.

If we apply these facts to our problem, we come back to an explanation by chance—it was chance that a catalyst of a certain configuration was used, or that a chain of a particular screw sense became involved in vital reactions.

(2) *Proteins and nucleic acids.* Our final possibility is that the stereospecificity we have already noted in the ordinary nonenzymatic polymerization of amino acid derivatives (Section V, A) would inevitably mean that, under conditions in which long peptide chains could be formed, asymmetric configurations would be favored, particularly if the reaction occurred under reversible conditions, which would enable the most stable (optically pure α-helix) to be built up. In a similar way, a nucleic acid polymerization that occurred in a medium containing derivatives of both L- and D-ribose would also show stereospecificity, as the helical form is stabilized by internal hydrogen bonding. This view, which has also been put forward by Wald (145), obviates any necessity for explaining a large preponderance of one isomer among compounds of low molecular weight before life began; such a preponderance would only have been produced later, as a result of selection by living organisms.

We consider this to be the most attractive hypothesis to date, and it may be combined with our idea of the possible origin of a preferred configuration among certain compounds (Section VII, B); however, Wald believes that the preference for L or D forms was a matter of chance.

Akabori (146) has suggested that if polyglycine was absorbed on the surface of, for example, kaolin, it might have a preferred (cis) configuration which would react stereospecifically with aldehydes, giving derivatives of various amino acids. The drawback to this ingenious argument is that it applies to only *one* reaction (polyglycine with aldehydes), and one would wish for some more general mechanism.

VIII. Conclusions

A great many things remain unexplained. Among mollusks, the widespread dextrotropic form is more susceptible to $(-)$-acriquine than to $(+)$-acriquine, whereas the levotropic form is more susceptible to the $(+)$-isomer (147). There is also the curious fact that in each recorded instance of spontaneous resolution by crystallization, each series of experiments always showed a strong bias in favor of one isomer. Perhaps there are highly asymmetric contaminants, all of the same configuration in one laboratory—or of the same configuration in many laboratories—living organisms—the experimenters themselves (*145*)? There can be no doubt that, as biochemistry develops and our knowledge becomes more precise, the fundamental importance of the optical asymmetry of metabolites will continue to become clearer and better understood. Life probably exists on many other planets in the universe and we can predict that if it has evolved to any degree of complexity there, we shall find many examples of stereospecificity in its biochemical systems, especially in those concerned with the transfer of information.

ACKNOWLEDGMENT

The author is indebted to Professor Sir Alexander Todd, F.R.S., for his interest. This work was carried out during the tenure of an Imperial Chemical Industries Fellowship.

References

1. Lecomte du Noüy, "Human Destiny." Longmans, Green, New York, 1947.
2. L. von Bertalanffy, "Das biologische Weltbild." A. Franke, Berne, Switzerland, 1949.
3. E. Schrödinger, "What is Life?" Cambridge Univ. Press, London and New York, 1945.
4. L. Pauling, *Nature* **161,** 707 (1948).
5. I. D. Watson and F. H. C. Crick, *Nature* **171,** 737, 964 (1953).
6. T. L. V. Ulbricht, *Quart. Revs.* (*London*) **13,** 48 (1959).
7. S. M. Gartler and R. E. Tashian, *Science* **126,** 76 (1957).
8. C. P. Berg, *in* "Protein and Amino Acid Nutrition" (A. A. Albanese, ed.), Academic Press, New York, 1959.
9. E. Baldwin, "Dynamic Aspects of Biochemistry," 3rd ed. Cambridge Univ. Press, London and New York, 1957.
10. A. Meister, "Biochemistry of the Amino Acids." Academic Press, New York, 1957.
11. J. S. Fruton and S. Simmonds, "General Biochemistry," 2nd ed. Wiley, New York, 1959.
12. H. A. Krebs, *Biochem. J.* **29,** 1620 (1935); *in* "The Enzymes: Chemistry and Mechanism of Action." (J. B. Sumner and K. Myrbäck, eds.), Vol. II, Part 1, p. 510. Academic Press, New York, 1952.
13. D. E. Atkinson and S. W. Fox, *Arch. Biochem. Biophys.* **31,** 220 (1951).
14. W. Kuhn, *Experientia* **11,** 429 (1955).
15. E. Schrödinger, "Science Theory and Man." Dover Publns., New York, 1957.
16. K. Miescher, *Experientia* **11,** 417 (1955).
17. W. Kuhn, *in* "Handbuch der Enzymologie" (F. F. Nord and R. Weidenhagen, eds.), Akad. Verlagsges., Leipzig, 1940.
17a. E. Ellenbogen, *J. Am. Chem. Soc.* **78,** 369 (1956).
17b. G. W. Miller, B. T. Gillis, and N. C. Li, *J. Biol. Chem.* **235,** 2840 (1960).
18. J. M. Bijvoet, A. F. Peedeman, and A. J. van Bommel, *Nature* **168,** 271 (1951).
19. M. L. Wolfrom, R. U. Lumieux, and S. M. Olin, *J. Am. Chem. Soc.* **71,** 2870 (1949).

20. P. Brewster, E. D. Hughes, C. K. Ingold, and P. A. D. S. Rao, *Nature* **166**, 178 (1950).
21. A. Bendich, E. A. Kabal, and A. E. Bezer, *J. Am. Chem. Soc.* **69**, 2163 (1947).
22. D. Aminoff and W. T. J. Morgan, *Biochem. J.* **46**, 426 (1950).
23. E. Baldwin and D. J. Bell, *J. Chem. Soc.* p. 1461 (1938); 125 (1941).
24. E. Vasseur and J. Immers, *Arkiv Kemi* **1**, 39, 253 (1949).
25. C. Djerassi and O. Halpern, *J. Am. Chem. Soc.* **79**, 2022 (1956).
26. C. H. Chunk, C. H. Stammer, E. A. Kaczka, E. Walton, C. F. Spence, A. M. Wilson, J. W. Richter, F. W. Holly, and K. Folkers, *J. Am. Chem. Soc.* **78**, 1770 (1956).
27. R. B. Woodward, *in* "Festschrift A. Stoll." Birkhäuser, Basel, 1957.
28. F. A. Kuehl, E. H. Flynn, F. W. Holly, R. Mozingo, and K. Folkers, *J. Am. Chem. Soc.* **68**, 536 (1946).
29. F. A. Kuehl, E. H. Flynn, N. G. Brink, and K. Folkers, *J. Am. Chem. Soc.* **68**, 2679 (1946).
30. H. Brockmann and G. Pampus, *Angew. Chem.* **67**, 519 (1955).
31. H. Brockmann, G. Bohnsack, B. Frank, H. Grone, H. Muxfeldt, and C. H. Süling, *Angew. Chem.* **68**, 70 (1956).
32. E. Bullock and A. W. Johnson, *J. Chem. Soc.* p. 3258 (1957).
33. H. Brockmann and J. H. Manegold, *Naturwissenschaften* **45**, 310 (1958).
34. A. W. Johnson and A. B. Manger, *Biochem. J.* **73**, 535 (1959).
35. E. H. Flynn, J. W. Hinman, E. L. Caron, and D. O. Wolf, *J. Am. Chem. Soc.* **75**, 5867 (1953).
36. L. C. Vining and W. A. Taber, *Can. J. Chem.* **35**, 1109 (1957).
36a. J. H. Martin and W. K. Hausmann, *J. Am. Chem. Soc.* **82**, 2079 (1960).
37. L. C. Craig, W. Hausmann, and J. R. Weisiger, *J. Biol. Chem.* **199**, 865 (1952).
38. W. Hausmann, J. R. Weisiger, and L. C. Craig, *J. Am. Chem. Soc.* **77**, 721, 723 (1955).
39. I. M. Lockhart and E. P. Abraham, *Biochem. J.* **62**, 645 (1956).
40. E. P. Abraham and G. G. F. Newton, *Biochem. J.* **62**, 658 (1956).
41. G. G. F. Newton and E. P. Abraham, *Biochem. J.* **58**, 103 (1954).
41a. D. Fleš and B. Balenović, *J. Am. Chem. Soc.* **78**, 3072 (1956).
42. O. L. Shotwell, F. H. Stodola, W. R. Michael, L. A. Lindenfelser, R. G. Dworschack, and T. G. Pridham, *J. Am. Chem. Soc.* **80**, 3912 (1958).
43. W. Keller-Schierlein, M. L. Mihailovic, and V. Prelog, *Helv. Chim. Acta* **42**, 305 (1959).
44. P. A. Plattner and U. Nager, *Helv. Chim. Acta* **31**, 665, 2192 (1948).
45. Q. R. Bartz, *Antibiotics Ann.* **2**, 777, 784 (1954–1955).
46. F. W. Eastwood, B. K. Snell, and Sir A. R. Todd, *J. Chem. Soc.* p. 2286 (1960).
47. S. Otani and Y. Saito, *Angew. Chem.* **67**, 665 (1955).
48. R. L. M. Synge, *Biochem. J.* **39**, 363 (1945).
49. A. R. Battersby and L. C. Craig, *J. Am. Chem. Soc.* **73**, 1887 (1951).
49a. M. P. V. Mijovic and J. Walker, *J. Chem. Soc.* p. 909 (1960).
50. F. A. Kuehl, F. J. Wolf, N. R. Trenner, R. L. Peck, E. Howe, B. D. Hunnewell, G. Downing, E. Newstead, K. Folkers, R. P. B. Buhs, I. Putter, R. Ormond, J. E. Lyons, and L. Chaiet, *J. Am. Chem. Soc.* **77**, 2344 (1955).
51. H. T. Clarke, J. R. Johnson, and R. Robinson, "The Chemistry of Penicillin." Princeton Univ. Press, Princeton, New Jersey, 1949.
52. W. Hausmann and L. C. Craig, *J. Am. Chem. Soc.* **76**, 4892 (1954).
53. W. Hausmann, *J. Am. Chem. Soc.* **78**, 3663 (1956).

54. W. Hausmann and L. C. Craig, *J. Biol. Chem.* **198**, 405 (1952).
55. H. Vanderhaeghe and G. Parmentier, *Bull. soc. chim. Belges* **68**, 716 (1959).
56. G. Alderton, *J. Am. Chem. Soc.* **75**, 2391 (1953).
57. A. Stracher and L. C. Craig, *J. Am. Chem. Soc.* **81**, 696 (1959).
57a. M. Bodansky, J. T. Sheehan, J. Fried, N. J. Williams, and C. A. Birkheimer, *J. Am. Chem. Soc.* **82**, 4747 (1960).
58. A. C. Paladini and L. C. Craig, *J. Am. Chem. Soc.* **76**, 688 (1954).
59. T. P. King and L. C. Craig, *J. Am. Chem. Soc.* **77**, 6627 (1955).
60. H. Brockmann and G. Schmidt-Kastner, *Ann.* **603**, 216 (1957).
61. V. du Vigneaud, F. H. Carpenter, R. W. Holley, A. H. Livermore, and J. R. Rachele, *Science* **104**, 431 (1946).
62. E. Work, *Nature* **179**, 841 (1957).
63. L. E. Rhuland, *Nature* **185**, 224 (1960).
64. V. Bruckner, J. Wein, M. Kajtar, and J. Kovacs, *Naturwissenschaften* **42**, 463 (1955).
65. A. C. Chibnall, M. W. Rees, and F. M. Richards, *Biochem. J.* **68**, 129 (1958).
66. J. Armstrong, J. Baddiley, and J. G. Buchanan, *Nature* **184**, 248 (1959).
67. C. B. Thorne and C. G. Leonard, *J. Biol. Chem.* **233**, 1109 (1958).
68. J. T. Park and J. L. Strominger, *Science* **125**, 99 (1957).
69. M. Fling and S. W. Fox, *J. Biol. Chem.* **160**, 329 (1945).
70. Y. Kobayashi, M. Fling, and S. W. Fox, *J. Biol. Chem.* **174**, 391 (1948).
71. B. D. Davis and W. K. Maas, *J. Am. Chem. Soc.* **71**, 1865 (1949).
72. J. Nicolle, *Compt. rend. acad. sci.* **229**, 252 (1949).
73. J. Nicolle, *Compt. rend. acad. sci.* **231**, 1002 (1950).
74. J. Nicolle, *Compt. rend. acad. sci.* **237**, 668 (1953).
75. C. R. Woese, H. J. Morowitz, and C. A. Hutchinson, *J. Bacteriol.* **76**, 578 (1958).
76. J. H. Mueller and P. A. Miller, *J. Am. Chem. Soc.* **71**, 1865 (1949).
77. C. Lark and K. G. Lark, *Can. J. Microbiol.* **5**, 369 (1959).
78. K. G. Lark, *Can. J. Microbiol.* **5**, 381 (1959).
78a. E. A. Grula, *J. Bacteriol.* **80**, 375 (1960).
79. J. Ciak and F. E. Hahn, *Antibiotics & Chemotherapy* **9**, 47 (1959).
80. J. L. Strominger, R. H. Threnn, and S. S. Scott, *J. Am. Chem. Soc.* **81**, 3803 (1959).
81. E. Abderhalden and R. Abderhalden, *Fermentforschung* **16**, 445 (1942).
82. M. Bergmann, L. Zervas, J. S. Fruton, F. Schneider, and H. Schleich, *J. Biol. Chem.* **109**, 325 (1935).
83. C. M. Stevens, R. P. Gigger, and S. W. Bowne, *J. Biol. Chem.* **212**, 461 (1955).
84. E. E. Snell, *J. Biol. Chem.* **158**, 497 (1945).
85. M. N. Camien, *J. Biol. Chem.* **197**, 687 (1952).
86. E. Katz, *Nature* **184**, 1666 (1959).
87. H. R. V. Arnstein and H. Margreiter, *Biochem. J.* **68**, 339 (1958).
88. W. A. Wood and I. C. Gunsalus, *J. Biol. Chem.* **190**, 403 (1951).
88a. F. C. Larson, K. Tomita, and E. C. Albright, *Endocrinology* **65**, 336 (1959).
89. K. Weil and W. Kuhn, *Helv. Chim. Acta* **27**, 1648 (1944).
90. W. Kuhn and K. Vogler, *Z. Naturforsch.* **6b**, 232 (1951).
91. E. Moore and D. W. Wilson, *J. Biol. Chem.* **111**, 573 (1937).
92. R. M. Herbst and E. A. Swart, *J. Org. Chem.* **11**, 368 (1946).
93. J. L. Anclair and R. L. Patton, *Rev. can. biol.* **9**, 3 (1950).
94. P. Boulanger and R. Osteux, *Compt. rend. acad. sci.* **236**, 2177 (1953).
95. I. M. Beatty, D. I. Magrath, and A. H. Ennor, *Nature* **183**, 591 (1959).

96. R. J. Rossiter, T. Gaffner, H. Rosenberg, and A. H. Ennor, *Nature* **185**, 383 (1960).

96a. H. Rosenberg and A. H. Ennor, *Nature* **187**, 617 (1960).

96b. E. R. Blout, in "Optical Rotatory Dispersion" (C. Djerassi, ed.) McGraw-Hill, New York, 1960.

97. M. Idelson and E. R. Blout, *J. Am. Chem. Soc.* **79**, 3948 (1957).

98. E. R. Blout and M. Idelson, *J. Am. Chem. Soc.* **78**, 3857 (1956).

99. R. D. Lundberg and P. Doty, *J. Am. Chem. Soc.* **79**, 3961 (1957).

100. E. R. Blout, P. Doty, and J. T. Yang, *J. Am. Chem. Soc.* **79**, 749 (1957).

101. M. Idelson and E. R. Blout, *J. Am. Chem. Soc.* **80**, 2387 (1958).

101a. N. C. Li, G. W. Miller, N. Solony and B. T. Gillis, *J. Am. Chem. Soc.* **82**, 3737 (1960).

101b. J. C. Kendrew, R. E. Dickerson, B. E. Strandberg, R. G. Hart, D. R. Davies, D. C. Phillips, and V. C. Shore, *Nature* **185**, 422 (1960).

101c. M. F. Perutz, *Biochem. Soc. Symposium on the Structure and Synthesis of Macromolecules*, London, March, 1961.

102. M. Winitz, S. M. Birnbaum, and J. P. Greenstein, *J. Am. Chem. Soc.* **77**, 3106 (1955).

103. M. Winitz, L. Bloch-Frankenthal, N. Izumiya, S. M. Birnbaum, C. G. Baker, and J. P. Greenstein, *J. Am. Chem. Soc.* **78**, 2423 (1956).

104. D. S. Robinson, S. M. Birnbaum, and J. P. Greenstein, *J. Biol. Chem.* **202**, 1 (1953).

105. F. Karush, *J. Am. Chem. Soc.* **78**, 5519 (1956).

106. F. Karush, *J. Am. Chem. Soc.* **79**, 3380 (1957).

106a. H. Fricke, W. Landmann, C. A. Leone, and J. Vincent, *J. Phys. Chem.* **63**, 932 (1959).

107. H. A. Krebs, in "The Enzymes: Chemistry and Mechanism of Action" (J. B. Sumner and K. Myrbäck, eds.), Vol. II, Part 1, p. 499. Academic Press, New York, 1952.

108. L. Birkhofer and N. Wetzel, *Z. physiol. Chem.* **264**, 31 (1940).

109. D. M. Molnar and C. B. Thorne, *Bacteriol. Proc.* (*Soc. Am. Bacteriologists*) p. 123 (1955).

110. C. B. Thorne, C. G. Gomez and R. D. Housewright, *J. Bacteriol.* **69**, 357 (1955).

111. C. B. Thorne and D. M. Molnar, *J. Bacteriol.* **70**, 420 (1955).

111a. H. T. Huang and D. W. Davisson, *J. Bacteriol.* **76**, 495 (1958).

111b. P. S. Thayer, *J. Bacteriol.* **78**, 150 (1959).

112. P. Ayengar and E. Roberts, *J. Biol. Chem.* **197**, 453 (1952).

113. S. A. Narrod and W. A. Wood, *Arch. Biochem. Biophys.* **35**, 462 (1952).

114. M. N. Camien and M. S. Dunn, *J. Biol. Chem.* **217**, 125 (1955).

114a. L. Glaser, *J. Biol. Chem.* **235**, 2095 (1960).

115. J. L. Still, M. V. Buell, W. E. Knox, and D. E. Green, *J. Biol. Chem.* **179**, 831 (1949).

116. J. L. Still and E. Sparling, *J. Biol. Chem.* **182**, 585 (1950).

117. E. Rocca and F. Ghiretti, *Arch. Biochem. Biophys.* **77**, 336 (1958).

117a. F. Lateyric, P. P. Slonimski, and L. Naslin, *Biochim. et Biophys. Acta* **34**, 262 (1959).

117b. E. L. Tatum, *J. Biol. Chem.* **192**, 301 (1951).

118. C. Yanofsky, *J. Biol. Chem.* **198**, 343 (1952).

119. D. E. Metzler and E. E. Snell, *J. Biol. Chem.* **198**, 363 (1952).

120. R. A. Altenbern and R. D. Housewright, *Arch. Biochem. Biophys.* **49,** 130 (1954).
121. W. J. Williams and C. B. Thorne, *J. Biol. Chem.* **210,** 203 (1954).
121a. J. Baddiley and F. Neuhaus, *Biochem J.* **75,** 579 (1960).
122. E. Maschmann, *Biochem. Z.* **313,** 129 (1943).
123. E. V. Cowdry, "Cancer Cells." Saunders, Philadelphia, 1955.
124. J. P. Greenstein, "The Biochemistry of Cancer," 2nd. ed. Academic Press, New York, 1954.
125. O. Schmidt, *Naturwissenschaften* **29,** 146 (1941).
126. D. Rittenberg and D. Shemin, *Ann. Rev. Biochem.* **15,** 250 (1946).
127. F. Kögl, *Experientia* **5,** 173 (1949).
128. G. Hillmann, A. Hillmann-Elies, and F. Methfessel, *Z. Naturforsch.* **9b,** 660 (1954).
129. Quoted by W. Troll, "Das Virusproblem in ontologischer Sicht." Steiner, Wiesbaden, 1951.
130. W. Heisenberg, *Naturwissenschaften* **46,** 661 (1959).
131. W. Heisenberg, "The Physicist's Conception of Nature." Hutchinson, London, 1958.
132. A. I. Oparin, "The Origin of Life on the Earth," 3rd ed. Academic Press, New York, 1957.
133. A. I. Oparin *et al.*, eds., "Proceedings of the First International Symposium on the Origin of Life on the Earth, Moscow" (Engl. transl. edited by F. Clark and R. L. M. Synge). Pergamon, London, 1960.
134. A. Byk, *Z. physiol. Chem.* **49,** 641 (1904).
135. A. P. Terent'ev and E. I. Klanubovskii, *in* "Proceedings of the International Conference on the Origin of Life on the Earth, Moscow" (I. A. Oparin *et al.*, eds.; Engl. transl. edited by F. Clark and R. L. M. Synge), p. 95. Pergamon, London, 1960.
136. G. M. Schwab, F. Rost, and L. Rudolph, *Kolloid-Z.* **68,** 157 (1934).
137. P. Curie, *J. physique* **3,** 409 (1894).
138. F. Vester, T. L. V. Ulbricht, and H. Krauch, *Naturwissenschaften* **46,** 68 (1959).
139. T. L. V. Ulbricht and F. Vester, in preparation.
140. F. Vester, Seminar on "Parity Non-conservation and Optical Activity." Yale University, New Haven, Connecticut, February, 1957; Habilitationsschrift, Universität des Saarlandes, Saarbrücken, Germany, 1961.
141. N. W. Pirie, *Trans. Bose Research Inst. Calcutta* **32,** 111 (1958).
142. M. Volk'nstein, *in* "Proceedings of the International Conference on the Origin of Life on the Earth, Moscow" (I. A. Oparin *et al.*, eds.; Engl. transl. edited by F. Clark and R. L. M. Synge), p. 174. Pergamon, London, 1960.
143. C. C. Price, M. Osgan, R. E. Hughes, and C. Shambelan, *J. Am. Chem. Soc.* **78,** 690 (1956).
144. C. C. Price and M. Osgan, *J. Am. Chem. Soc.* **78,** 4787 (1956).
145. G. Wald, *Ann. N. Y. Acad. Sci.* **69,** 352 (1957).
146. S. Akabori, *in* "Proceedings of the International Conference on the Origin of Life on the Earth, Moscow" (I. A. Oparin *et al.*, eds.; Engl. transl. edited by F. Clark and R. L. M. Synge), p. 189. Pergamon, London, 1960.
147. E. I. Klanubovskii and U. V. Patrikeev, *in* "Proceedings of the International Conference on the Origin of Life on the Earth, Moscow" (I. A. Oparin *et al.*, eds.; Engl. transl. edited by F. Clark and R. L. M. Synge), p. 175. Pergamon, London, 1960.

CHAPTER 2

Cellulose, Starch, and Glycogen

J. S. Brimacombe and M. Stacey

The Chemistry Department, University of Birmingham,
Edgbaston, Birmingham, England

I. Cellulose: General Introduction

Although the enzymatic synthesis of starch and dextran-type poly-saccharides by transglycosylation reactions is widely known and the mechanism of such syntheses established (1), such is not the case with the enzymatic synthesis of cellulose. The synthesis of cellulose from glucose by certain *Acetobacter* species is accompanied by oligosaccharide formation (2), and since mutant organisms grown on the same synthetic medium did not produce these oligosaccharides, they may be inter-related to cellulose synthesis. Much work still remains to be done here before unequivocal proof of the mechanism of the biosynthesis of cel-lulose can be given. The enzymatic degradation of cellulose, undoubt-edly owing to its greater industrial significance, has received a great deal of attention, and many recent reviews (3) have appeared on this subject. Two important questions still require conclusive answers. The first concerns the mode of enzymatic attack—whether, in fact, it is a random cleavage of the cellulose chain removing cellobiose and higher cello-oligosaccharides, or an "endwise" attack removing cellobiose or larger units from the reducing or nonreducing chain ends. Secondly, the number of enzymes involved in the breakdown is still a point of argument. Both unienzymatic and multienzymatic hydrolysis have been postulated, and evidence is forthcoming to support both points of view.

From whatever source it is derived, cellulose has basically the same chemical structure and consists of several thousand β-1,4-linked D-gluco-pyranose units. The presence of modified linkages in cellulose, particularly cross linking of the chains, has been forwarded, but no chemical evidence has substantiated these views. Certainly, if present, they represent a very small percentage of the total linkages.

A. ENZYMATIC SYNTHESIS OF CELLULOSE

As early as 1866, Brown (4, 5) observed that *Acetobacter xylinum* synthesized cellulose from carbohydrate substrates; since then, other types of *Acetobacter* have shown the same ability. Among these are *Acetobacter acetigenum* (6, 7), *A. pasteurianum*, *A. rancens* (8), and *A. kützengianum* (6). Hibbert and Barsha (9, 10) carried out the first thorough chemical study of the cellulose of *A. xylinum*. The isolation of 2,3,6-tri-O-methyl-D-glucose by hydrolysis of the methylated poly-saccharide, and of cellobiose octaacetate by acetolysis of the polysaccharide itself, demonstrated that it was a β-1,4-linked polyglucose. The membranes produced by *A. xylinum* from sucrose (11), and from glucose, fructose, glycerol, galactose, and mannitol (9, 10) gave X-ray diagrams similar to those of cotton cellulose. Later work (7) corroborated that the polysaccharide synthesized from D-glucose by cultures of *A. acetigenum* was cellulose. Methylation and end-group assay revealed that the average chain length of its trimethyl ether was of the order of 600 glucose units. Infrared studies (12, 13) on bacterial cellulose established that the glucose units were β-linked, showing adsorption peaks at 766, 894, 914, and 933 cm.$^{-1}$, identical with the peaks given by cotton cellulose.

In its ability to utilize carbohydrate substrates as its sole source of carbon, *A. acetigenum* was found to have a more complete cellulose-synthesizing enzyme system than *A. xylinum*. Thus, whereas *A. acetigenum* could utilize ammonium lactate, methyl α- and β-D-glucopyranoside, dipotassium α-D-glucose-1-phosphate, three pentoses, erythritol, and ethylene glycol, none of these compounds supported the growth of *A. xylinum*. Many attempts have been made to determine the mechanism of cellulose synthesis. Resting cells of both *A. acetigenum* (7) and *A. xylinum* (14), freed from preformed cellulose, synthesized cellulose when incubated with glucose. Furthermore, the cell debris from smashed *A. acetigenum* cells was found capable of synthesizing cellulose from glucose in phosphate buffer (7). A study of the utilization of DL-(carboxy C^{14})-lactic acid by *A. acetigenum* and of the ultimate distribution of the labeled atoms in the cellulose was completed by Bourne and Weigel (15). The results, shown in Table I, revealed that the carbon chain was labeled symmetrically. Such a distribution suggests that the glucose units of cellulose arise by a fusion of two three-carbon fragments. Greathouse (16) studied the biosynthesis of cellulose by A. xylinum utilizing D-glucose-6-C^{14} and glycerol-1,3-C^{14}. The hydrolyzate of the cellulose-C^{14} synthesized from D-glucose-6-C^{14} showed that approximately 82% of the activity remained in the C-6 position. When glycerol-1,3-C^{14} was the sole carbon source, the labeling was as follows: C-1, 12%; C-2, 4%; C-3, 22%; C-4, 29%; C-5, 3%; and C-6, 30%. The biosynthesis

TABLE I

DISTRIBUTION OF C^{14} IN CELLULOSE FROM DL-(CARBOXY-C^{14}-LACTIC ACID

Carbon position of glucose	Specific activity (μc per mole carbon)	Percentage distribution
1–6	139.9^a	100
1	2.6	2
2	16.6	12
3	50.2	36
4	51.7	37
5	15.4	11
6	1.1	1

^{a} Microcuries per mole glucose.

of cellulose-C^{14} from D-glucose-1-C^{14} added 24 hours after inoculation, as compared with that added initially, produced a 10–12% higher concentration of radioactivity in C-1. These results indicated that the polymerization of D-glucose, as such, without prior cleavage, is favored by adding the radioactive sugar after the bacteria had initiated growth. At least two major mechanisms appear from these studies (16) (Fig. 1):

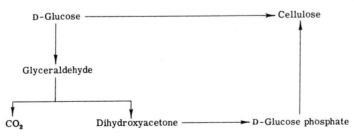

FIG. 1. Major routes of cellulose synthesis proposed by Greathouse (16).

(a) direct polymerization, possibly involving phosphorylases; and (b) cleavage of the hexose and resynthesis of hexose phosphate from trioses such as glycerol. Hexose phosphates have been isolated and identified as intermediates by Greathouse (16) in the biosynthesis of cellulose from D-glucose. The same worker also reported (16) that a cell-free enzyme system from A. xylinum synthesized cellulose from D-glucose-1-C^{14} and that analysis of the labeling showed that 90% remained at C-1. These data suggest that glucose-1-C^{14} was synthesized to cellulose directly by the cell-free enzyme.

Schramm, Gromet, and Hestrin (17), from a study of the C^{14}-distribution in cellulose produced by incubating resting cells of A. xylinum with specifically labeled glucoses, concluded that cellulose was formed directly from hexose phosphate derived from glucose-C^{14} in the sense that after its formation it did not require intermediary cleavage of the carbon skeleton but might require either modification or replacement of the phosphate group. However, it appeared that only a minor fraction of the glucose undergoes phosphorylation as such, and that the bulk of the glucose carbon is introduced into the hexose phosphate pool indirectly via a pentose cycle which is operating on gluconate.

The enzymatic synthesis of cellulose by a cell-free particulate system from A. xylinum has been achieved by Glaser (18). Incubation of the enzyme with C^{14}-glucose-labeled uridine diphosphoglucose gave rise to a radioactive, water-insoluble, alkali-insoluble polysaccharide which was identified as cellulose by partial hydrolysis and isolation of cellobiose of constant specific activity. Both C^{14}-labeled α-glucose-1-phosphate and C^{14}-labeled glucose were inactive when incubated with the enzyme under the same conditions. The formation of insoluble cellulose was stimulated greatly by the addition of high molecular weight, soluble cellodextrins. The enzyme responsible for the synthesis of cellulose was freed from any enzyme catalyzing the formation of uridine diphosphoglucose (UDPG) from glucose-1-phosphate and uridine triphosphate (UTP). It would thus appear that cellulose synthesis is achieved by the utilization of UDPG as substrate and cellodextrins as receptors.

Colvin (19) has recently shown that an ethanolic extract of an active culture of A. xylinum cells contain a compound which is rapidly converted to cellulose in the complete absence of cell walls. The formation of cellulose is accelerated by a heat-labile extracellular substance (presumably an enzyme) in the medium of an active culture. Prior autoclaving of the extract destroyed cellulose fibril formation, but this was restored by addition of a portion of extracellular medium of active cells. Autoradiographs of the ethanolic extracts of an active culture metabolizing uniformly C^{14}-labeled glucose showed no spots corresponding to cellobiose, cellotriose, cellotetraose, and UDPG. This suggests that neither UDPG nor short-chain β-glucosans are immediate precursors of bacterial cellulose. However, the synthesis of cellulose from glucose by certain *Acetobacter* species is accompanied by formation of oligosaccharides (2), and these include cellobiose, cellotriose, cellotetraose, and oligosaccharides containing fructose residues and phosphorylated sugar residues. Since mutant organisms, unable to synthesize cellulose, did not produce these oligosaccharides when grown on the same synthetic medium, cellulose synthesis and oligosaccharide formation may be interrelated.

B. ENZYMATIC DEGRADATION OF CELLULOSE

1. Enzymes Involved in Hydrolytic Degradation

The hydrolysis of cellulose ultimately yields soluble sugars able to pass through the cell walls, but until this stage is reached the digestion remains extracellular. The principal enzymes involved in the hydrolysis of cellulose are variously referred to as β-glucosidases, cellobiases, and cellulases. The term "cellulase" has often been applied to impure enzymes that catalyze not only the hydrolysis of cellulose to cellodextrins, cellobiose, and glucose, but also the hydrolysis of other β-glycosides. Many have also been shown to contain transglucosidases. Frequently cellulolytic organisms secrete additional enzymes to assist in the breakdown of smaller molecules, and these enzymes often vary with the strain of the organism and the conditions under which it is grown.

a. β-Glucosidase. The occurrence of β-glucosidases is widespread, notably in almonds, and by definition such enzymes should catalyze only the hydrolysis of carbohydrates containing one or more glucose units linked to each other (or to an aglycon) in the β-configuration. However, even purified samples of β-glucosidases catalyze the hydrolysis of β-xylosides (20). In the breakdown of cellulose by enzymatic hydrolysis, β-glucosidases of various specificities have been shown to play important parts and the transferase activity of such enzymes must be considered when interpreting results if oligosaccharides and cellodextrins are produced. A partially purified enzyme system from *A. niger* (21) catalyzed the transfer of a glucosyl residue from cellobiose and other oligosaccharides of the cellulose series leading to higher saccharides, although prolonged incubation gave glucose. Similar transferase activities have been detected in other extracts (including *Myrothecium verrucaria* and *Aspergillus aureus*), and growing cultures of *Aspergillus niger* acting on cellobiose led to the formation of mixtures of trisaccharides; the principal linkage formed was β-1,6-, but some β-1,2-, β-1,3-, and β-1,4-linkages were also synthesized (22).

b. Cellobiase and Cellulase. The preparation of a β-glucosidase of such specificity that only cellobiose can act as substrate has not yet been achieved. In most preparations from cellulose-degrading organisms β-glucosidases have been found; the activity of such enzymes has been determined using a number of substrates containing the β-linkage, such as cellobiose, salicin, and p-nitrophenyl-β-cellobioside. Many of the cellobiases reported in the literature must be regarded as relatively unspecific β-glucosidases until it has been proved that only the hydrolysis of β-1,4-linkages, as in cellobiose or even cello-oligosaccharides, is catalyzed. A cellobiase without action on other β-glucosides has been found in malt extract (23), and in this case the holosidic bond of p-nitrophenyl-β-cellobioside is cleaved, but not the aglycon bond.

The nature of cellulose as a substrate involving such factors as crystallinity, accessibility, degree of polymerization, degree of substitution, and solubility makes it unlikely that a single enzyme (cellulase) is involved in the hydrolysis. Thus, no single definition can readily be provided for the term "cellulase," and other terms (see later) have been invoked to account for the various changes observed in cellulose during enzymatic action.

2. Nature of Cellulose as Substrate

A typical molecule of cellulose consists of a long chain of β-1,4-linked glucose units, but the so-called "fine structure" of cellulose is also important in determining the properties of cellulose as a substrate. Cellulose is laid down in cell walls and some bacterial membranes as microfibrils. In some regions the effect of hydrogen bonds and van der Waals' forces between adjacent segments of chains results in a close, regular packing resembling that of a crystal lattice; in other regions the packing is less regular (24). Segments within the "crystalline regions" are separated by only a few angstrom units and are less readily accessible to hydrolytic agents. Heterogeneous acidic hydrolysis of cellulose, for instance, proceeds rapidly at first but slows down once the linkages readily accessible to the reagent are cleaved. X-ray diffraction patterns (25, 26) reveal that acidic hydrolysis occurs preferentially in the amorphous regions. With molecules in the molecular weight range of the cellulases (12,000–100,000) the problem of penetration through capillary spaces in the substrate is also an important criterion, and it is not surprising therefore that the hydrolysis of cellulose by enzymes tends to be rather slow (27).

The length of the cellulose molecule varies considerably, and this variation would be expected to affect hydrolysis, especially if attack commenced at the ends of molecules. However, no correlation has been found between the degree of polymerization (DP) and enzymatic cleavage in the range DP 100–700 (28, 29). However, Gilligan and Reese (30) have reported the chromatographic separation of three components from a crude filtrate of *Trichoderma viride* which differ in their activities toward two regenerated cellulose samples with DP 500 and DP 50. It was suggested that the components of a cellulolytic enzyme system may differ in their preference or affinity for chains of a particular length.

3. Mode of Action of Cellulolytic Enzymes

Two important questions related to the enzymatic hydrolysis of cellulose still require conclusive answers: (a) whether the cleavage of the cellulose chain is random, or whether cellobiose or other units are removed from the reducing or nonreducing ends of chains; and (b) the number of enzymes involved in the hydrolysis. Some understanding of the mechanism of hydrolysis might be obtained from the intermediates produced during enzymatic attack of cellulosic polymers. Few reports have presented evidence for the presence of cellodextrins and higher cello-oligosaccharides between cellulose and cellobiose or glucose. Cellobiose, -triose, -tetraose, and -pentaose were detected by paper chromatography (31) during the hydrolysis of a cellodextrin with a cellulase from *Myrothecium verrucaria*. Paper chromatographic evidence for the existence of the same oligosaccharides among the products of hydrolysis of cellodextrins, acid- and alkali-swollen celluloses, and cellulose precipitated from cuprammonium hydroxide solution has been presented (32). The oligosaccharides arising during the hydrolysis of the various forms of cellulose were considered to arise from random splitting of the bonds by a single enzyme. Hash and King (33) have reported tracer amounts of cellotetraose in the hydrolyzate of a phosphoric acid-swollen cellulose, but other workers (34) have suggested that this is in fact cellotriose. Reese, Smakula, and Perlin (34) have shown that *Streptomyces* (sp. QMB 874) acting on cellulose gives cellobiose as the dominant reducing sugar, but that cellotriose also accumulates in the digest. These sugars were thought to arise from the absence or near-absence of enzymes capable of hydrolyzing them. Cellotriose, in addition to glucose and cellobiose, has been detected in the hydrolysis of cellodextrins (35) and during the early stages of hydrolysis of swollen cellulose (36). During the hydrolysis of cellophane and carboxymethylcellulose by a preparation from rumen microorganisms it was probable that both cellotriose and cellotetraose were produced (37), while other intermediates in the hydrolysis of carboxymethylcellulose had the structure of substituted sugars (38).

Whitaker (39) has reported the formation of both glucose and cellobiose from cellulose using a purified enzyme system from *Myro-thecium verrucaria* although the enzyme had very low activity toward cellobiose. Thus it appeared that both sugars were produced directly by random cleavage. Cellobiose alone has been reported as the end product by various workers, some of whom (40, 41) claim that the enzyme acts by removing disaccharides from the chain ends. The degradation of cello-oligosaccharides has been studied in some detail by Whitaker (42–44) using a purified cellulase from *M. verrucaria*. During hydrolysis of cellotriose the glucosidic linkage adjacent to the nonreducing end was preferentially cleaved, the rate of hydrolysis of this linkage being five times greater than that of the other linkage. A study of the breakdown of a series of oligosaccharides from cellotriose to cellohexaose revealed that increase in molecular weight was accompanied by increased rate of hydrolysis, the effect being particularly marked as the degree of polymerization increased from 2 to 4. The central ether linkage of cellotetraose was broken preferentially to the two terminal linkages, and a similar preference was shown in cellopentaose, but at least one of its terminal linkages was cleaved at a higher rate than that for either of the terminal linkages of cellotetraose. Very little evidence was obtained for any preferential cleavage in cellohexaose; it appeared that as the chain length increased, hydrolysis became more random. Upward mutarotation was observed by Whitaker (44) during the hydrolysis of cellopentaose with a purified cellulase from *M. verrucaria*. This provides evidence that the cellulase catalyzed the hydrolysis of a β-glucosidic linkage to give a reducing end group in the β-configuration, i.e., with retention of configuration, and so parallels the action of α-amylase on amylose.

Much of the evidence accumulated suggests a purely random attack during enzymatic hydrolysis, notably from the systematic work of Whitaker (42–44) cited earlier. Other more indirect evidence has been obtained which lends support to this view, namely: (a) the reduction in viscosity of soluble cellulose derivatives before appreciable increase in the reducing sugar concentration; (b) the formation of oligosaccharides during hydrolysis where this cannot be accounted for by transglycosylation; (c) the formation of glucose and cellobiose using a cellulase devoid of cellobiase activity; and (d) the apparent independence of the rate of hydrolysis on the initial degree of polymerization of the substrate.

The belief that enzymatic action proceeded "endwise" was held by Clayson (45), and this was supported more recently by Nishizawa and Kobayashi (40). The latter workers found that cellobiose was formed from a hydrocellulose by the action of *Irpex lacteus* cellulase freed from cellobiase activity. The copper value of the hydrocellulose recovered after enzymatic attack had increased almost proportionally to the decrease in weight of the substrate. The action of this cellulase on p-nitrophenyl-β-D-cellobioside was also significant. Cleavage occurred at both aglucon and holosidic bonds giving rise to a mixture of p-nitrophenol, cellobiose, p-nitrophenyl-β-D-glucoside, and glucose.

This preparation was free from cellobiase, amylase, and aryl-β-glucosidase activity, and the findings that units were split from a β-cellobioside in pairs was forwarded as evidence that hydrolysis by this enzyme occurred by the cleavage of cellobiose units from the ends of cellulose chains (40, 46). An endwise cleavage of cellulose was also reported in the presence of a cellulase from Corynebacterium fimi (41).

It may well be that both random and endwise types of action exist, and the analogy with amylose must be emphasized when both types of action are known.

Evidence for the number of enzymes involved in hydrolytic attack on cellulose is conflicting, and several factors have been invoked to account for observed changes. Whereas the ability to hydrolyze modified celluloses is widespread, the catabolism of native cotton is more restricted (47). It was suggested therefore that two enzymes were involved in the production of low molecular weight compounds from native celluloses (38, 47, 48). The first enzyme, termed C_1, converted cellulose to linear chains, which in turn were degraded by a second enzyme, termed C_x, to soluble products. This second enzyme is also active in the case of linear chains produced during modification of cellulose by reprecipitation or substitution. Kooiman (49) in a study of several Aspergillus species could not corroborate the C_x–C_1 theory. A unienzymatic degradation is generally supported by Kooiman (49), except that a cellobiase is invoked for the conversion of cellobiose to glucose.

Marsh et al. (50) have found that pretreatment of intact cotton fibers with culture filtrates of various fungi increased the extent to which the fiber was swollen by concentrated alkali. The factor(s) involved was termed "S factor" and is referred to by Reese and Gilligan (51) as a "swelling factor." The evidence of the latter workers suggests that the effect is concerned with damage to the primary wall of the fiber, which, when intact, restricts the swelling of fibers by alkali. The S factor activity of M. verrucaria could be precipitated with acetone, was active over a wide range of pH, and had considerable thermal stability. Reese and Gilligan (51) have measured both S factor and C_x activities from several microorganisms, and both enzymes were shown to be inducible. Separation of the two enzymes was not possible, but the ratio of activities (S/C_x) varied with the microorganism producing them, the conditions of growth, and the method of purification. Chromatographic studies provided further evidence for the separate characters of S factor and C_x enzyme. While several C_x components have been demonstrated in *M. verrucaria* filtrates (52), the rate of migration of S factor was low and was associated with only the slowest-moving C_x components. In filtrates from *Pestalotia palmarum*, containing three C_x components, S factor was separated into two fractions, neither of which corresponded in mobility to any of the C_x components (51).

If the reaction is multienzymatic in character, the question of the number of enzymes involved and how their actions differ arises. The findings of Reese et al. (51, 52) were explained by enzymatic components differing largely in their preference for substrates of different chain lengths. The enzyme C_1, for instance, may merely be a C_x component acting only on the longest chains, and Reese (53) has recently suggested a "multiple C_x-theory." Those components showing a preference for shorter chains of cellulose may, in fact, act by endwise hydrolysis.

II. Starch: Structure of Amylose and Amylopectin

Starch, the reserve carbohydrate of many plants, contains two distinct polysaccharides, amylose and amylopectin, the former constituting 20–30% of the total. A few starches, such as those derived from waxy maize and waxy sorghum, are exceptional inasmuch as they are practically devoid of amylose, whereas in others, such as wrinkled pea starch, amylose is the principal component. Amylose (I) is a polyglucose in

(I)

which the glucose units are joined by α-1,4-linkages, to form chains several hundred units in length; there is little or no branching of the chains. Amylopectin (II) is a highly branched molecule composed of several hundred unit chains, each of which comprises 20 to 25 α-1,4-linked glucose residues; the unit chains are interlinked principally by α-1,6-glucosidic linkages (54). Some workers have reported the presence of linkages other than α-1,4- and α-1,6-linkages in starch. The presence

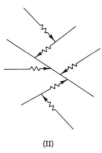

(II)

of a small number of α-1,3-linkages in amylopectin was shown by the isolation of nigerose (3-*O*-α-D-glucopyranosyl-D-glucose III) from the acid hydrolyzate of amylopectin (*55*). Nigerose has also been isolated

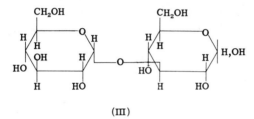

(III)

(*56*) from acid and enzyme hydrolyzates of the Floridean starch from *Dilsea edulis*, and it was concluded that the α-1,3-linkages are an integral part of its structure.

A. ENZYMATIC SYNTHESIS OF STARCH

Over the last twenty years or so, much work has been done on the starches of higher plants and on the structurally related glycogens in the animal kingdom. This work was early stimulated by the fractionation of starches into two distinct components, and the isolation of enzymes responsible for syntheses of these polysaccharides. There are four known enzymatic processes for the synthesis of amylose from simple sugars: (*a*) the phosphorylase-catalyzed conversion of salts of α-D-glucopyranose-1-phosphoric acid (*57–59*); (*b*) the amylomaltase-catalyzed synthesis from maltose (*60*); (*c*) the transformation of sucrose by means of amylosucrase (*61*); and (*d*) the synthesis from malto-oligosaccharides using D-enzyme (*62*). Of these syntheses, that catalyzed by phosphorylase seems to be the most prevalent in nature, but all are transglycosidation reactions involving an exchange of a glycosidic linkage in the substrate for another in the polysaccharide product (*63*). Each step in such a process entails the reversible addition of a monosaccharide residue to a growing polysaccharide chain, and it is necessary, in the first three processes (a), (b), (c)—, to have an amylosaccharide "primer," particularly where a purified enzyme system is used. The nature of the primer, as will be discussed later, varies with the enzyme system used. One fundamental equation (1) will be encountered frequently in such syntheses:

$$G_t—O—X + H—O—G_r \rightleftharpoons G_t—O—G_r + X—O—H \tag{1}$$

where G_tO and X are, respectively, the sugar residue and the aglycon portion of a glycoside ($G_t—O—X$) which serves as the substrate for an enzyme, and $G_r—O—H$ is a carbohydrate receptor molecule, the products being a higher saccharide ($G_t—O—G_r$) and a hydroxy compound ($X—O—H$). Amylopectin, the branched component of starches, requires two enzymes, namely, phosphorylase, which catalyzes the formation of amylose-type chains, and another enzyme (Q-enzyme) which converts these chains into a branched polysaccharide.

1. *Synthesis of Amylose from Glucose-1-phosphate.*

In 1937, Cori, Colowick, and Cori (*64, 65*) showed that a salt of α-glucopyranose-1-(dihydrogen phosphate) was formed when a solution of glycogen, inorganic phosphate, and adenylic acid was incubated with a dialyzed muscle extract. Subsequent investigations by a number of workers (*58, 59, 66–70*) using phosphorylases, derived from a variety of sources, established that the reaction was reversible, and could be represented in the over-all Eq. 2:

$$n \, C_6H_{11}O_5 \cdot O \cdot PO_3K_2 \rightleftharpoons (C_6H_{10}O_5)_n + n \, K_2HPO_4 \tag{2}$$

At equilibrium, the ratio of total inorganic phosphate to total glucose-1-phosphate is dependent on the pH value of the system, but the ratio of the bivalent ions $[HPO_4]^{2-}/[C_6H_{11}O_5 \cdot O \cdot PO_3]^{2-}$, is independent of pH and is always constant at 2.2 (*58, 59, 71*).

Hanes (*58, 59*) recognized that the product synthesized from glucose-1-phosphate by the agency of potato phosphorylase differed from natural potato starch inasmuch as it was less soluble in water, was stained more deeply blue by iodine, and gave an almost theoretical amount of maltose when treated with β-amylase. Subsequently, polysaccharides synthesized *in vitro* by phosphorylases were submitted to methylation and end group assay (*72–75*) and to a variety of chemical and biochemical tests (*1*). These methods, which were able to distinguish clearly between amylose and amylopectin, proved beyond doubt that the synthetic product was an unbranched polyglucose of the amylose type.

a. Conditions and Mechanism of the Synthetic Reaction. So far as is known at present, α-D-glucose-1-phosphate is the only substrate on which phosphorylase can display its synthetic function, and the enzyme has no action on a variety of other substrates (*1*), including the β-anomer (*76, 77*), α-D-galactose (*66, 78*), and α-maltose (*78*). Many workers (*59, 79*) observed that there was an induction period during the incubation of the phosphorylase with glucose-1-phosphate, and that the effect was more marked with some highly purified enzyme systems. Synthesis could be initiated by the introduction of starch or dextrins derived therefrom, and it was apparent that a "primer" was necessary for the synthesis of amylose. Unless special precautions are taken to purify the enzyme and phosphate ester, there is usually sufficient primer present as impurity to initiate the reaction.

All phosphorylases catalyzing the conversion of glucose-1-phosphate into amylose require the presence of a α-1,4-glucosan primer containing nonreducing chain ends, but differ as regards the most suitable molecular size for the primer. In the case of potato phosphorylase, for instance, the molecular size of the primer is not critical; higher linear homologs of maltose (but not maltose itself) containing three, four, five, or six glucose units are effective (*80, 81*), as are also starch, amylose, and amylopectin (*64, 65, 82, 83*). Comparison of the relative efficiencies of α-1,4-glucosans as primers for the potato enzyme has shown that there are at least two controlling factors. The priming power is related to the number of nonreducing end groups available (*83*). This finding explains why amylopectin (5% end groups) is more effective than amylose (<0.5% of end groups) and why the cyclic Schardinger dextrins are devoid of priming activity (*82, 84*); it seems also that there is a certain chain length at which priming activity reaches an optimum, probably at about twenty glucose units (*83*). Muscle phosphorylase resembles potato phosphorylase inasmuch as it displays its synthetic activity only in the presence of a primer containing nonreducing terminal glucose units (*85–87*). On the other hand, muscle phosphorylase requires these end groups to be supplied as part of a macromolecule, as is shown by two facts: (*a*) that it is not primed by higher homologs of maltose containing fewer than eight glucose units (*87*); and (*b*) that the priming power of glycogen is rapidly destroyed when the polysaccharide is treated mildly with acid, in spite of the fact that such a treatment increases the number of nonreducing terminal glucose units (*87, 88*). It is not surprising that minor differences of this sort arise, because it is well established that the enzymes themselves are not identical chemically. The phosphorylases of muscle (*89*) and adipose tissue (*90*), for instance, require adenylic acid before they display full activity, whereas those from potato (*82*) and jack bean (*91*) do not. The phosphorylases of muscle will be discussed in more detail later.

Two synthetic reaction patterns can be envisaged; these are described as *single-chain* and *multichain*. In the former, a molecule of phosphorylase continuously increases the length of a single chain until the molecules become immune to further action (for example, by precipitation from solution) before transferring its activity to a second molecule of primer. In the multichain type of action, random synthesis occurs and all the primer chains grow at approximately equal rates. Recent experiments (*92*) have shown that the action pattern of potato phosphorylase is completely multichain both in the synthesis and phosphorolysis of amylose.

2. Synthesis of Amylose from Maltose

The synthesis of an iodophilic polysaccharide from maltose by means of a cell-free extract of *Escherichia coli* has been described by Monod and Torriani (*60, 93, 94*). The enzyme, termed amylomaltase, was shown to catalyze the reversible over-all Reaction 3.

$$n \text{ Maltose} \rightleftharpoons (\text{Glucose})_n + n \text{ Glucose} \tag{3}$$

It is an adaptive enzyme inasmuch as it is produced only when the organism is grown in maltose, but not, for example, on glucose or lactose (*95*); it shows a high measure of substrate specificity, being without action on methyl α- or β-D-glucoside, cellobiose, lactose, sucrose, melibiose, or glucose-1-phosphate (*60, 93*). Equilibrium, in the forward reaction, is normally established after 60% of the maltose has been converted, but the addition of glucose oxidase (notatin) to the system results in the complete conversion of maltose. Under normal conditions, the polymeric material gives a faint red stain with iodine suggesting that the average chain length is about ten glucose units (*60, 93–95*), but an amylose-like polyglucose (blue stain with iodine) is obtained on addition of notatin. The reverse reaction proceeds when the synthetic polysaccharide is incubated with amylomaltase in the presence of glucose (*60, 63, 95*), but the enzyme does not attack the polysaccharide in the absence of glucose. Using a mutant of *Escherichia coli* (strain W-327), Hassid *et al.* (*96*) obtained a series of dextrins containing four to six glucose units, susceptible to hydrolysis by β-amylase. In a similar experiment with *Escherichia coli* (Monod strain ML), Barker and Bourne (*97*) fractionated the saccharides on a charcoal column and proved by both chemical and biochemical methods that they consisted of the higher homologs of maltose, three to five units in length. Some

35% of the glucose units present initially in the maltose appeared as higher saccharides.

Using Eq. 1, it will be seen that each stage in the synthesis of amylose entails a transfer of a $C_6H_{11}O_5$ unit (G_t) from maltose $(G_t—O—X)$ to an amylosaccharide molecule $(H—O—G_r)$ with the elimination of a molecule of glucose $(X—O—H)$ (Eqs. 4, 5).

$$\text{Maltose} + \text{Maltose} \rightleftharpoons \text{Maltotriose} + \text{Glucose} \qquad (4)$$
$$(\textit{first step})$$

$$\text{Maltose} + (\text{Glucose})_n \rightleftharpoons (\text{Glucose})_{n+1} + \text{Glucose} \qquad (5)$$
$$(\textit{later step})$$

It has yet to be established whether the glucose unit (G_t), which is transferred by amylomaltase to the receptor molecule, must be furnished as maltose. It is possible, for example, that Eq. 5 is really a special case and that each step in the reaction could be written in the more general form of Eq. 6 (where $x > 1$).

$$(\text{Glucose})_x + (\text{Glucose})_n \rightleftharpoons (\text{Glucose})_{n+1} + (\text{Glucose})_{x-1} \qquad (6)$$

3. Synthesis of Amylose by D-Enzyme

In 1953, Peat, Whelan, and Rees (62) reported the isolation of an enzyme from potato which affects the synthesis of short amylose-type chains by transglucosylation. This enzyme, termed D-enzyme, synthesized iodophilic material from a series of maltodextrins, the substrates being disproportionated into products of higher and lower molecular weight. For example, maltotriose is acted on to give, as the first product of the reaction, glucose and maltopentaose; and at equilibrium a whole series of maltodextrins are present. The smallest donor substrate on which D-enzyme exerts a rapid action is maltotriose, and there is some doubt whether it has any action at all on maltose. Maltose can nevertheless act as a acceptor for the transferred maltodextrinyl units, as can glucose and several mono- and disaccharides, and also monosaccharide derivatives such as methyl α-glucoside (98, 99).

The reaction between starch and glucose, catalyzed by D-enzyme, leads to the production of maltodextrins in high yields. D-Enzyme preparation was shown to contain the debranching R-enzyme (100); from the total amount of maltodextrins produced, it was apparent that the α-1,6-linkages of the amylopectin component had been broken. Purified D-enzyme appeared to be without action, as judged by the diminution of intensity of the iodine stain or by the liberation of reducing groups, on either of the separated components of starch (101). If an acceptor such as glucose is present, the transferring action of

D-enzyme is at once detected by a diminution of intensity of the iodine stain. When starch and glucose-C^{14} are incubated with D-enzyme, the maltodextrin products are labeled with radioactivity exclusively in the reducing-end glucose unit (*102*). The mechanism, resulting from such labeling, proposed by Walker and Whelan (*102*), is as shown in Eq. 7

$$N-R + G \rightleftharpoons N-G + R \tag{7}$$

where glucose (G) is the acceptor for the donor substrate (N—R) and where R is the part of the molecule containing the free reducing group. Recently these workers (*103*) have shown that D-enzyme incubated with maltodextrins in the presence of a suitable glucose-removing system brings about amylose synthesis. Maltotetraose, for instance, which with D-enzyme alone does not give iodine-staining products, under these conditions gave an iodophilic product.

4. Synthesis of Amylopectin

The branched-polysaccharide component of starch arises from the joint action of two enzymes. In 1944, Haworth, Peat, and Bourne (*104*) isolated from potato juice an enzyme fraction which synthesized a poly-saccharide, giving a reddish purple stain with iodine from glucose-1-phosphate in the presence, but not in the absence, of potato phosphorylase. The active principle of this fraction, termed Q-enzyme, was later purified (*105*) and crystallized (*106, 107*). The nature of the polysaccharide synthesized by the joint action of these two enzymes is dependent on the relative activities of the enzymes (*108*). When a high proportion of Q-enzyme is used, the product is indistinguishable from natural potato amylopectin except that it has a somewhat smaller molecular weight than the native polysaccharide. Hydrolysis of the methylated polysaccharide afforded 2,3,4,6-tetra-O-methylglucose, 2,3,6-tri-O-methylglucose, and 2,3-di-O-methylglucose, thereby establishing that the principal glucosidic linkage involves positions 1 and 4, while the branch linkages were of the 1,6-type (*75*). Q-Enzyme is now known to be quite widespread in nature; sources of it include wrinkled pea (*Pisum sativum*) (*110*), broad bean (*Vicia faba*) (*110*), green gram (or mung bean, *Phaseolus aureus*) (*111*), *Neisseria perflava* (*112*), and *Polytomella caeca* (*113, 114*).

The conversion of amylose to amylopectin entails the liberation of little or no reducing sugar ($<2\%$, expressed as maltose) (*105–107, 115–117*) and proceeds equally well in the absence and presence of large portions of inorganic phosphate (*118*), provided that the Q-enzyme is

already fully activated by the addition of salts, such as sodium acetate
and ammonium chloride, to the digest (*118, 119*). Thus it seems that
Q-enzyme is a transglucosidase, operating by a nonphosphorolytic
mechanism, which converts about one in every twenty α-1,4-linkages of
amylose into the α-1,6-linkages, which constitute the branch points in
amylopectin (*118, 120, 121*). The suggested mechanism (*1*) is shown
in Fig. 2, in which the arrows signify chains of α-1,4-glucopyranose units,

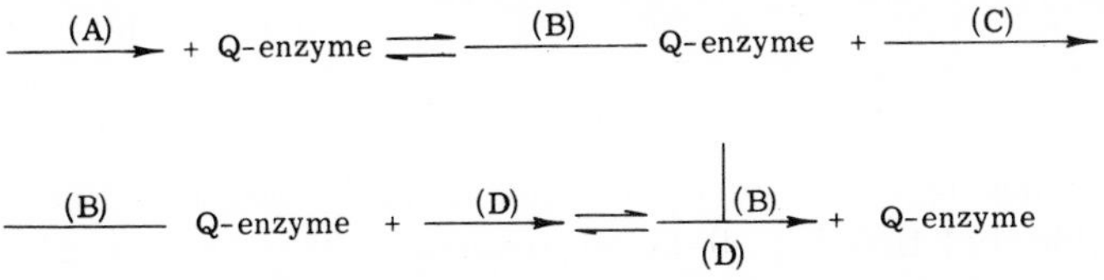

FIG. 2. Schematic representation of the action of Q-enzyme.

the reducing groups being indicated by the arrowheads, and the branch
points being of the α-1,6-type.

Studies with potato Q-enzyme have shown that the amylose-type
substrate (A) must contain at least 42 glucose units before it is attacked
by the enzyme (*122, 123*). The initial attack probably involves fission
of an α-1,4-linkage in the substrate, with the formation of an amylosaccharide (B)–enzyme complex and dextrin fragment (C). The complex
could then react with a second amylosaccharide molecule (D) to give a
branch product (BD), together with the free enzyme. The receptor
molecule (D) might be, for example, an intact amylose molecule, the
residual dextrin (C), or a branched product formed in an earlier stage
of the reaction. Under the experimental conditions so far employed, the
equilibrium favors strongly the synthesis, rather than the fission, of the
branch points; no conclusive evidence has been found to show that
Q-enzyme can cleave the α-1,6-linkages of amylopectin or β-dextrin.

Recently, Abdullah and Whelan (*124*) have isolated from potato a
second enzyme, termed T-enzyme, which is capable in simple substrates
of both transforming α-1,4-linkages into α-1,6-linkages (Eq. 8) and of
redistributing α-1,6-linkages (Eqs. 9–11). T-Enzyme acts on maltose
(Eq. 8)

$$2 \text{ Maltose} \rightarrow \text{Panose (IV)} + \text{Glucose} \qquad (8)$$

and reactions shown in Eqs. 9–11 are also catalyzed

$$2 \text{ Panose (IV)} \rightarrow 6^2\text{-}\alpha\text{-Isomaltosylmaltose (V)} + \text{Maltose} \qquad (9)$$

$$2 \text{ Isomaltose} \rightarrow \text{Isomaltotriose} + \text{Glucose} \qquad (10)$$

$$2 \text{ Isomaltotriose} \rightarrow \text{Isomaltotetraose} + \text{Isomaltose} \qquad (11)$$

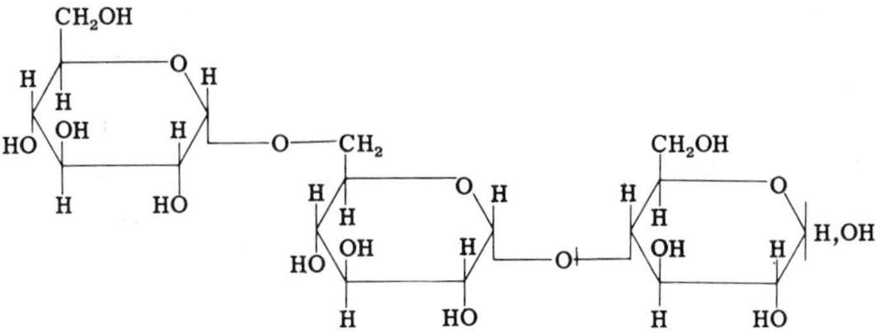

(IV)

The evidence reported by these workers (*124*) suggests that Eq. 8 is irreversible, but that Eqs. 9–11 are reversible. This type of catalysis has

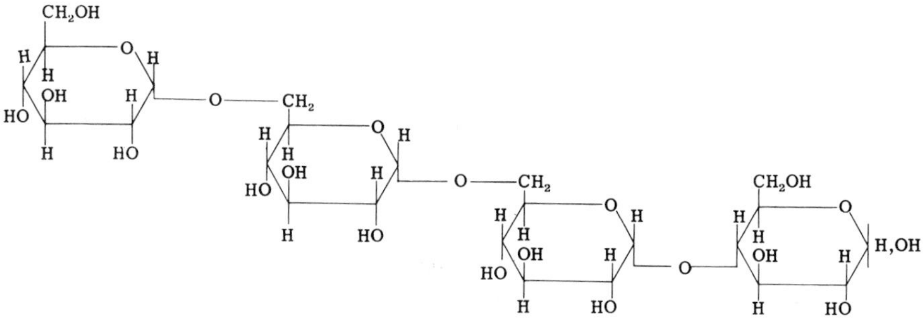

(V)

previously been encountered in enzyme preparations from *Aspergillus* species (*125–127*), in *Penicillium chrysogenum* (*128*), *Cladophora rupestris* (*129*), and *Tetrahymena pyriformis* (*130*).

5. Synthesis of an Amylopectin-type Polysaccharide from Sucrose

In 1946, Hehre and Hamilton (*61, 131*) reported the synthesis from sucrose of a polyglucose resembling amylopectin in properties using washed cells of *Neisseria perflava*. The enzyme was inactive toward maltose, lactose, trehalose, melibiose, raffinose, melezitose, or methyl α-D-glucoside, and toward a mixture of glucose and fructose. With glucose-1-phosphate a trace of an iodophilic polysaccharide was produced, but this synthesis (attributed to phosphorylase) was suppressed by addition of excess mineral phosphate, whereas that from sucrose was unimpaired. From the thirty-nine strains of *Neisseria perflava* synthesizing this polysaccharide, a cell-free enzyme, termed amylosucrase, was obtained (*132*), which catalyzed the conversion

$$n \text{ Sucrose} \rightleftharpoons (\text{Glucose})_n + n \text{ Fructose} \qquad (12)$$

The amylosucrase was distinguished from the bacterial phosphorylases by its stability to heat and to gas treatment, and by the fact that the synthesis was not suppressed by mineral phosphate.

The synthetic polysaccharide, which was virtually free from fructose, was shown to be of the amylopectin-glycogen class by α- and β-amylolysis, by phosphorolysis, by its iodine stain, by potentiometric titration with iodine, by its failure to give an insoluble butanol complex, and by negative serological tests for dextran. Barker, Bourne, and Stacey (133) using *Neisseria perflava* (strain II-1) were able to show that the polysaccharide synthesized from sucrose had properties intermediate between those of amylopectin ·and glycogen. Methylation and end-group assay established that the chains of α-1,4-glucopyranose units, averaging 11–12 glucose units in length, were joined by branches of the 1,6-type. Hehre and Hamilton (132) showed that the amylosucrase was contaminated with a second enzyme, which was responsible for the synthesis of the branch points, and this was. verified when it was shown that the enzyme sample exhibited Q-enzyme activity inasmuch as it converted amylose into a glycogen-type polysaccharide without the formation of reducing sugar. The function of amylosucrase appears to be to convert sucrose into an unbranched polysaccharide of the amylose class by a glucose-transferring mechanism involving the exchange of the biose linkage for an α-1,4-glucosidic bond (132).

B. Enzymatic Degradation of Starch

The hydrolysis of starch is catalyzed by two principal enzyme systems, α- and β-amylases, and also by debranching enzymes, and enzymes that catalyze a stepwise hydrolysis of all α-1,4-linkages.

1. *Action of α-Amylases*

α-Amylases have been isolated in a purified form (134, 135) from many sources (e.g., barley, malt, salivary secretions, and several bacterial and fungal extracts), and several α-amylases have been crystallized (136–138). Whelan (139) has recently summarized the action of several α-amylases on amylose and has accounted for the variations observed in their activities. The α-amylases fragment amylose by hydrolysis, the end products being maltose and glucose. Two stages occur in the salivary α-amylolysis of amylose. The first stage is a rapid hydrolysis to maltose and maltotriose, but in the second stage the maltotriose is slowly hydrolyzed to maltose and glucose (140). Pig-pancreatic and *Aspergillus oryzae* α-amylases were reported to be similar in their actions to salivary α-amylase. The ratio of maltose and glucose in the digests after hydrolysis by these enzymes suggests a random attack on nonterminal linkages. The retardation observed at an early stage of hydrolysis of amylose by malt and *Bacillus subtilis* α-amylases, results from the low affinity of these two enzymes for maltodextrins containing less than about seven glucose units. Maltohexaose, for instance, is hydrolyzed by malt α-amylase at about one-sixth the rate of starch (*141*), whereas salivary α-amylase attacks both substrates with equal ease. Further, with malt and *B. subtilis* α-amylases, the proximity of linkages to end groups has a much more marked effect in retarding hydrolysis than for other α-amylases and the final stages of hydrolysis are much slower. Both these enzymes are capable of liberating glucose from the reducing ends of relatively large maltodextrins, a property that distinguishes them from other α-amylases (*139*).

The α-limit dextrins, arising from the amylopectin component of starch, may be assumed to contain α-1,6-linkages which constitute the points of branching in the dendritic structure of this polysaccharide. Recent investigations (*142, 143*) have indicated that the α-1,6-branches of amylopectin confer resistance to α-amylolysis on α-1,4-linkages in their vicinity. Structural analysis of a pentasaccharide in the α-amylolysis digest of amylopectin by salivary α-amylase has shown that the branching occurred at the nonreducing-end glucose unit (*144*). Under the conditions employed, salivary α-amylase rapidly hydrolyzed nonterminal α-1,4-linkages of starch but did not attack the terminal linkages at the reducing or nonreducing chain ends. Maltotriose, containing only terminal linkages, is therefore resistant to α-amylolysis and only begins to break down under conditions of prolonged enzyme action or with a relatively high concentration of enzyme (*140*). An α-limit dextrin formed under chosen experimental conditions will therefore be one in which the α-1,4-linkages are resistant to amylolysis either by reason of their proximity to the 1,6-linkage or because they occupy terminal positions.

2. Action of β-Amylases

The action pattern of β-amylase, unlike that of α-amylase, does not appear to depend on the enzyme source (for example, wheat, barley, and soybean). β-Amylolysis consists of stepwise hydrolysis of alternate linkages in the glucose chains, commencing at the nonreducing end, with the liberation of maltose. Enzyme action is arrested by the presence of anomalous linkages in the chain (for example, interchain linkages or ester-phosphate linkages) and, unlike α-amylases, β-amylase cannot bypass such linkages and units between two branch points are not attacked. β-Amylolysis of amylopectin yields maltose and a β-dextrin of high molecular weight which differs from amylopectin in that the outer chains of the amylopectin branches contain only two or three glucose units.

The action of purified β-amylase on most samples of amylose is incomplete, since only 65–80% conversion into maltose is observed (145). For complete hydrolysis a second enzyme, named Z-enzyme (146, 147), is required; this occurs together with β-amylase in soybeans and barley (146, 147), and has no action on α-1,3- or α-1,6-glucosidic linkages or on β-glucosidic linkages (145–147). Recently, several workers (148) have reported the similarity in reaction of Z-enzyme and α-amylase, and Cunningham et al. (149) have found that β-amylase preparations from soybean, barley, and emulsin are contaminated with α-amylase. The Z-enzyme (α-amylase) contaminant in a barley β-amylase preparation has no action on the anomalous linkages in amylose, but catalyzes the random hydrolysis of a small number of α-1,4-glucosidic linkages. This slight random hydrolysis exposes a sufficient number of nonreducing end groups to enable further β-amylolysis to take place. The ability of Z-enzyme to increase the phosphorolysis limit of amylose, from 70 to 95% conversion into glucose-1-phosphate (149) can now also be explained in terms of slight α-amylolytic activity.

The nature of the structural anomalies in amylose is not yet known; the proportion of these anomalies is extremely low, probably less than 0.1%. These may include one or more of the following possibilities: (a) an anomalous linkage (other than the α-1,4-type) in the amylose chain or as a branch point; (b) an anomalous residue, i.e., an α-1,4-linked hexose residue derived from D-glucopyranose by substitution with a phosphate group, or by acylation or oxidation at position 2,3 or position 6; (c) both a residue and its linkage may be anomalous. Recent evidence (150) suggests that a small number of glucose residues in amylose may become modified by oxidation during isolation of the polysaccharide. Since Z-enzyme is an α-amylase, its action will be to bypass such structural anomalies rather than their removal by selective hydrolysis.

The specific mode of action of β-amylase has been in dispute (145), but recent experiments (151) have tended to clarify this situation. Maltose, for instance, may be produced by the enzyme either (a) by attachment to one amylose molecule and then by stepwise removal of maltose units result in complete degradation before attack on another amylose molecule ("single-chain" action), or (b) by removal of one maltose unit on each random collision with an amylose molecule with the result that all chains in the system are shortened simultaneously ("multichain" action). Manners et al. (151) have shown that with potato amylose hydrolysis proceeded by an essentially single-chain mechanism as there was no evidence of molecules intermediate in degree of polymerization between the original amylose and maltose in the digest, as shown by sedimentation studies. Nevertheless, the action pattern appears to differ for short-chain amyloses. Studies by Bird and Hopkins (152) have shown that amylodextrins, with DP 16–30, were degraded by multichain action, whereas Bailey and French (153) have found that short-chain synthetic amyloses were attacked by an intermediary mechanism, whereby several glucosidic linkages are hydrolyzed during the enzyme-substrate reaction.

French in a recent communication (153a) has indicated that hitherto insufficient attention has been paid to the nature of the chain-length distribution of the original amylose, as well as that of the amylose remaining at intermediate stages of hydrolysis. If the molecular weight distribution of amylose is the "most probable" distribution (153b), as some workers have indicated (153c), then any of the suggested reaction patterns for β-amylase will lead to precisely the same average molecular weights and size distributions of the residual amylose as those for the original amylose. On the other hand, Gaussian or Kraemer-Lansing type distribution of the original amylose will lead to products of substantially lower molecular weight if a multichain action pattern is operative. French suggests that high-molecular-weight amyloses, differing significantly in molecular size from the "most probable" distribution (prepared by synthesis or by fractionation), are best suited for definitive studies of the action pattern of β-amylase.

The existence of amylases that yield glucose as the primary product of their action on starch have been reported. These enzymes catalyze a stepwise hydrolysis of every linkage in a chain of α-1,4-linked glucose units beginning at the nonreducing terminal linkages. One such amylase, from the mold *Rhizopus delemar*, liberated over 90% of the glucose from amylose, amylopectin, glycogen, and a β-dextrin (154). Although the enzyme is not able to hydrolyze α-1,6-linkages, it can bypass them and so attack interior chains. Recently, Japanese workers (155) have isolated two amylases from *Rhizopus delemar* and *Aspergillus niger* in crystalline form. Both enzymes were free from α-amylase activity and hydrolyzed starch and maltose to glucose, but were without action on isomaltose. The enzyme from *Rhizopus delemar* showed much stronger hydrolytic activity than did the other toward panose (IV), starch, and glycogen. Its ability to hydrolyze starch may be due to its ability to hydrolyze panose (IV) since starch may be initially hydrolyzed to α-1,6-linked oligosaccharides similar to panose. Similar results were reported for an enzyme, termed glucamylase, isolated from a cell-free extract of *Aspergillus niger* (156, 157) by Barker and Fleetwood. This enzyme gave glucose as the major product of its action on starch, and attack on various amylosaccharides was multichain and consisted of a stepwise removal of single units from the nonreducing ends of chains. The so-called "maltase" from *Clostridium acetobutylicum* (*158*) also appears to be a glucose-producing enzyme since it converts maltose, maltoheptaose, isomaltose, and starch almost quantitatively into glucose and is capable of hydrolyzing both α-1,4- and α-1,6-linkages.

3. *Action of R-Enzyme*

During the last decade important advances have been made in studies of enzymes that catalyze the hydrolysis of α-1,6-interchain linkages in starch-type polysaccharides. The debranching enzyme, termed R-enzyme, from potato and broad bean (*100, 159*) hydrolyzes the interchain linkages in amylopectin or β-dextrin, as shown by the increase in the β-amylolysis limits of amylopectin or β-dextrin when incubated with R-enzyme. The α-1,6-linkages in branched α-dextrins are also hydrolyzed by R-enzyme, giving a mixture of linear maltosaccharides (*100, 142, 159, 160*). The earlier observation by Peat *et al.* (*159*) that the majority of the α-1,6-linkages in glycogen were inaccessible to R-enzyme, thus providing a simple means of differentiating between glycogen and amylopectin, has recently been reviewed by Fleming and Manners (*161*). The latter workers have shown that the specificity of R-enzyme is controlled not by the degree of branching in the substrate, or the exterior chain length, but by the average length of the interior chains. It appears that R-enzyme will hydrolyze the outermost interchain linkages in a branched α-1,4-glucosan, irrespective of source, in which the branch points are separated by a minimum of five glucose residues. Maruo and Kobayashi (*162, 163*) have obtained a debranching enzyme (isoamylase) from a brewers' yeast that hydrolyzes the interchain linkages in glutinous rice starch producing a more linear polysaccharide of lower molecular weight. Both isoamylase and R-enzyme hydrolyze nonterminal α-1,6-linkages. A second type of debranching enzyme which can hydrolyze only terminal α-1,6-linkages has been isolated from rabbit muscle (*164*). It is without action on amylopectin or glycogen but can hydrolyze those α-1,6-linkages that are exposed by the action of muscle phosphorylase on these polysaccharides (see below). It is of interest here to examine the successive and the simultaneous action of R-enzyme and β-amylase on starch (*165*). The degree of β-amylolysis of waxy-maize starch is 52% before, and 64% after, treatment with R-enzyme, and the corresponding values for the β-dextrin are 0 and 73%. Clearly R-enzyme has a great debranching activity on the β-dextrin than on the parent amylopectin, an indication that at least some of the outer chains of the amylopectin (which are degraded by β-amylase) constitute a barrier to R-enzyme. When, however, R-enzyme and β-amylase act simultaneously on waxy-maize starch, conversion to maltose and maltotriose is complete. This contrast between the successive and the simultaneous action of R-enzyme and β-amylase is explicable if it is assumed: (a) that the R-enzyme attacking the amylopectin molecule at its surface penetrates inward only as the surface is eroded by the removal of some of the outer branches; and (b) that a further number of branch linkages become accessible to R-enzyme when the outer chains are degraded by β-amylase. Complete debranching occurs when β-amylase and R-enzyme act simultaneously because R-enzyme exposes what were previously inner chains to the action of β-amylase which, in turn, degrades these newly exposed chains and thus allows R-enzyme to penetrate to the innermost branches.

III. Glycogen: Structural Studies

The chemical studies of Haworth and Percival (166, 167) of methylation and hydrolysis led them and other workers (168) to postulate a laminated structure for glycogen. Haworth, Hirst, and Smith (169) found that three specimens of glycogen from various sources contained a repeating unit of twelve α-1,4-linked glucopyranose residues. Further light on the nature of the branch linkage in glycogen was shed by Wolfrom et al. (170, 171) by fractionation, on a carbon column, of the acid hydrolyzate of a beef liver glycogen into disaccharide and trisaccharide fractions. Separation of the acetylated disaccharide mixture on Magnesol-Celite gave crystalline β-maltose octaacetate, β-isomaltose octaacetate, and β-nigerose octaacetate. Separation of the trisaccharide fraction by paper chromatography afforded crystalline panose (IV) and amorphous isomaltotriose (171). From the relative amounts of each obtained, it was firmly established that the major branch points in glycogen were constituted by joining the adjacent chains of α-1,4-linked glucopyranose units with α-1,6-glucosidic linkages, and to a very minor extent with α-1,3-glucosidic linkages. Adaptation of a method of Halsall, Hirst, and Jones (172, 173) using periodate oxidation gave further information as to glycogen structure. The principle involved postulates that in glycogen each glucose unit except those linked at the branch points through either the 1,2,4- or the 1,3,6-position will be oxidized by periodate and on hydrolysis yield a dialdehyde; if periodate oxidation is complete the presence of glucose in the hydrolyzate will indicate interchain linkages of the 1,2- or 1,3-type. Gibbons and Boissonnas (174) found that with one glycogen the ratio of the number of interchain linkages at C-2 or C-3 to those at C-6 was not greater than 1:42. Whereas Bell and Manners

(175) found that the hydrolyzate of a periodate-oxidized cat glycogen contained no glucose, Abdel-Akher *et al.* (176) obtained about 1% glucose from the hydrolyzate of hydrogenated periodate-oxidized glycogen, results suggesting that not all the branch points were of the 1,4,6-type.

The β-amylolysis of amylopectin-type polysaccharides has been previously discussed (page 46). Such studies have revealed that most glycogens have exterior chain lengths of about 8 glucose units, and interior chain lengths of about 4 glucose units, although quite a large degree of variation was apparent in glycogen from the same type of animal tissue (177–180). Similarly, Roberts and Whelan (143) have shown that treatment of glycogen with α-amylase yields maltose, maltotriose (ratio 2.03:1) together with α-limit dextrins, the smallest of which is a pentasaccharide. No cleavage of α-1,6-linkages was detected. A small amount of maltulose (4-O-α-D-glucopyranosyl D-fructose) was detected among the products of α-amylolysis of rabbit liver glycogen. Examination of the α-dextrins (142), together with the evidence obtained by stepwise degradation of glycogen by phosphorylase and amylo-1,6-glucosidase (181), have supported the dendritic type of structure for glycogen proposed by Meyer and Bernfeld (182).

A. THE ENZYMATIC SYNTHESIS OF GLYCOGEN

The enzymes known to be specifically related to glycogen synthesis in mammalian cells are listed as follows:

(a) Phosphorylase which, as previously described, effects the synthesis and destruction of α-1,4-glucosidic linkages by catalyzing the reversible reaction

$$\text{Glucose-1-phosphate} + \text{Polysaccharide primer} \rightleftharpoons \text{Inorganic phosphate} + \text{Glucosyl } (\alpha\text{-1,4}) \text{ primer} \quad (13)$$

(b) Uridine diphosphoglucose-glycogen transferase, which catalyzes the reaction

$$\text{UDPG} + \text{Polysaccharide primer} \rightarrow \text{UDP} + \text{Glucosyl } (\alpha\text{-1,4}) \text{ primer} \quad (14)$$

(c) Amylo-(1,4 → 1,6)-transglucosidase, the branching enzyme, which under suitable conditions transfers glycosyl residues from α-1,4- to α-1,6-linkages.

1. *Muscle Phosphorylases*

In 1943 Cori, Cori, and Green (86, 183–187) obtained phosphorylase from muscle in two forms: as phosphorylase a, which crystallized readily and which had activity without addition of adenylic acid, and as a much more soluble protein, phosphorylase b, which required adenylic acid for activation. It was reported that muscle and other tissues contained an enzyme, termed PR enzyme, which converted phosphorylase a to phosphorylase b. Both phosphorylase a and b were subsequently obtained crystalline (187–191), and molecular weight determinations by Madsen and Cori (192, 193) established that phosphorylase a had a molecular weight of 480,000, and phosphorylase b of 240,000. Phosphorylase a is held to contain four subunits of molecule weight 120,000, whereas phosphorylase b is thought to contain two such subunits.

Unequivocal evidence for the existence of pyridoxal 5-phosphate in crystalline muscle phosphorylase was advanced by Cori and Green (185) and Baranowski et al. (194), who compared its reactions, spectrum, chromatographic and electrophoretic properties with the standard synthetic compound. Treatment of the enzyme with acid liberated two or more molecules of pyridoxal 5-phosphate per mole of phosphorylase b, and twice this amount of phosphorylase a.

The conversion of phosphorylase a to phosphorylase b is catalyzed by a specific PR enzyme (185). The total reaction catalyzed by PR enzyme may be written

$$\text{Phosphorylase a} \xrightarrow{\text{PR enzyme}} 2 \text{ Phosphorylase b} + 4 \text{ Inorganic phosphate} \qquad (15)$$

The conversion of phosphorylase b to phosphorylase a has been accomplished in cell-free muscle extracts (189) and is catalyzed by a distinct enzyme termed phosphorylase b kinase. The requirements for the reaction of phosphorylase b → a include a divalent metal ion and, under certain circumstances, adenosine triphosphate (ATP). ATP is by far the most effective nucleotide and Mn^{2+} appears to be the most effective divalent cation (195–197) for this reaction. The over-all reaction may be expressed

$$2 \text{ Phosphorylase b} + 4 \text{ ATP} \xrightarrow[\text{kinase}]{Mn^{2+}} \text{Phosphorylase a} + 4 \text{ ADP} \qquad (16)$$

If the conversion of phosphorylase b to a is carried out in the presence of P^{32}-labeled ATP, incorporation of at least 2 moles of P^{32} per mole of phosphorylase a is found to occur (196).

The mechanism of degradation of the outer chains of glycogen and amylopectin by crystalline muscle phosphorylase has been studied by Larner (198). The results indicated that resynthesis of the units of the limit dextrin to longer chains took place during the over-all degradation, as is indicated by the decreased yield which occurs with increased phosphorolysis. In a further study (199) the distribution of molecular weights in a single sample of glycogen was calculated from sedimentation and diffusion data; from the changes in the distribution after treatment with crystalline muscle phosphorylase it was concluded that the enzyme preferentially attacked the larger molecules of the polydispersed population. The effect of molecular weight of glycogen upon its reactivity with isolated phosphorylases of muscle and liver was also studied by Stetten and Stetten (200). Each phosphorylase showed a preference for polysaccharide molecules of a specific size, and, whereas liver phosphorylase preferred the smallest molecules of the glycogen population, muscle phosphorylase reacted preferentially with the largest of the glycogen molecules.

2. Liver Phosphorylases

Sutherland has reviewed earlier experiments (201) showing that the decreased quantity of glycogen in liver or diaphragm when incubated with epinephrine, and in liver slices when incubated with either epinephrine or glucagon, was attributable to an increase in phosphorylase activity. In studies with rat diaphragm, addition of epinephrine to the incubation medium resulted in a marked increase in the ratio phosphorylase a : phosphorylase b, but with no significant changes in the total phosphorylase concentration. The homogeneous, soluble enzyme from dog liver was found to have a molecular weight of 237,000 (202). At the same time an enzyme from dog liver was reported (203) which catalyzed the conversion of liver phosphorylase to an inactive form whose activity was not restored by adenosine-5-phosphate. Products of the enzymatic inactivation were inactive liver phosphorylase and inorganic phosphate. This enzyme, like the PR enzyme in muscle, was shown to be a phosphatase. The inactive dephosphophosphorylase sedimented at the same rate as the active form, and there did not appear to be a gross change in the phosphorylase molecule, as was reported when phosphorylase a from rabbit muscle was incubated with the phosphorylase-rupturing enzyme (PR) (204).

Yet another related activity was found in dog liver (205), which catalyzed the reactivation of dephosphophosphorylase. This enzyme, termed phosphokinase, requires a cofactor for its activation (206); the formation of this cofactor is enhanced markedly by addition of epinephrine or glucagon. Later work established that the cofactor was identical with adenosine-3',5'-phosphate (207).

3. *Uridine Diphosphoglucose-Glycogen Transferase*

In 1957 Leloir and Cardini (*208*) reported the existence of an enzyme in rat liver homogenates which catalyzed the reaction

$$\text{UPDG} + \text{Primer} \rightarrow \text{UDP} + \text{Glucosyl } (\alpha\text{-1,4}) \text{ primer} \qquad (17)$$

An absolute requirement for primer was indicated; whereas glycogen and starch could serve in this capacity, glucose, maltose, and other oligosaccharides could not. An analogous enzyme was prepared from muscle homogenate (*209*) and its activity was separated from that of phosphorylase, but even the best preparations were heavily contaminated with the latter enzyme. The reaction required the presence of a polysaccharide primer and was strongly activated by hexose-6-phosphate. Using UDPG labeled in the glucose moiety, it was found that the radioactivity was transferred to the primer (glycogen) from which it could be removed as maltose with β-amylase or as glucose-1-phosphate with phosphorylase. Thus it seems that the glucose residue becomes linked α-1,4 to the polysaccharide.

Villar-Palasi and Larner (*210*) reported two enzyme activities in skeletal muscle and diaphragm, which together constituted a reaction sequence for the conversion of glucose-1-phosphate (G-1-P) to glycogen through uridine coenzyme-linked reactions. Uridine diphosphoglucose pyrophosphorylase catalyzed the reaction

$$\text{UTP} + \text{G-1-P} \rightleftharpoons \text{UDPG} + \text{PP} \qquad (18)$$

which supplied the needed percursor for glycogen synthesis (Eq. 18). The synthetic route suggested by these workers (Eq. 19), renders glycogenesis independent

$$\text{Glucose} \rightarrow \text{G-6-P} \rightarrow \text{G-1-P} \rightarrow \text{UDPG} \rightarrow \text{Polysaccharide} \qquad (19)$$

of inorganic phosphate and circumvents the unfavorable equilibrium by the phosphorylase route. Preliminary experiments also indicated that the system favored synthesis rather than glycogen breakdown in muscle under physiological conditions.

More recently Hauk and Brown (*211*) have isolated a soluble enzyme from rabbit muscle homogenates. The purification procedure used, as well as the inability of pure phosphorylase a and b to utilize UDPG, confirmed the existence of an independent transferase activity. It was concluded that UDPG-glycogen transferase adds glucose units in α-1,4-linkage to the terminal units of pre-existing primer chains. It is of interest that in the transferase reaction no net inversion of glucose configuration occurs.

4. Branching Enzyme

Since the actions of known animal phosphorylases and UDPG-glycogen transferase are limited to formation and breakdown of α-1,4 glucosidic linkages, the presence of α-1,6-linkages in glycogen require special consideration. In studies of glycogenesis *in vitro*, the action of muscle phosphorylase yielded a polysaccharide resembling amylose, whereas liver phosphorylase yielded a product resembling glycogen (*212*). Two years later Cori and Cori (*213*) were able to show that muscle phosphorylase supplemented by an extract of heart or of liver, yielded a glycogen-like product on incubation with glucose-1-phosphate. They suggested the existence of an independent branching mechanism that synthesized and degraded the α-1,6-linkages of glycogen (*213–215*).

Enzymes responsible for the establishment, by an independent mechanism, of branch points in polysaccharides of the starch-glycogen family are now known to be fairly widely distributed in nature (*98, 109, 216, 217*). The mechanism of action of mammalian branching enzyme, termed amylo-(1,4 → 1,6)-transglucosidase, derived from liver or muscle has been studied by Larner (*218*). Using as substrate glycogen which contained α-1,4-linked C^{14}-labeled glucose units in the outer chains, it was established that radioactive 1,6-linked glucose units were formed by the above enzymes. This rearrangement occurred in the absence of free glucose and inorganic phosphate. In the case of the liver enzyme, a glycogen with an average outer chain length of 6 glucose units could not be branched, whereas branching invariably occurred when such chains contained 11–21 glucose units.

The mechanisms of action of various branching enzymes have been compared (*219, 220*) and certain differences noted. Whereas, for example, Larner (*220*), studying the branching enzyme from liver and various plants, reports no stimulation to branching of polysaccharides by the addition of various oligosaccharides, Barker *et al.* (*219*) report an acceleration with protozoan Q-enzyme and find incorporation of carbon-14 into the polysaccharide when Q-enzyme, polysaccharide, and maltose-C^{14} are incubated together. This finding suggests the possible occurrence of an intermolecular transglycosylation contributing to the synthesis and branching of polysaccharides.

The role of the branching enzyme in glycogen synthesis appears to be well established. The total synthesis of glycogen, like amylopectin in the plant kingdom, results from the combined action of two enzymes. The one, generating α-1,4 glucosidic linkages to form a polysaccharide chain from glucose-1-phosphate or UDPG, and the second generating the branch points. It is probable that some reactions originally assigned to phosphorylase may, in the light of present evidence, be attributed to UDPG-glycogen transferase.

5. Transglycosylation Reactions

Though enzymes that can synthesize oligosaccharides from maltose are known to be present in molds and bacteria, no such enzymes were reported in animal tissues. In 1955 an enzyme was reported from rat liver and brain homogenates (221) which synthesized maltotriose and maltotetraose when incubated with maltose. Beloff-Chain et al. (222) reported evidence for the existence of the series of malto-oligosaccharides in rat diaphragm at least up to maltoheptaose. The production of these oligosaccharides from glucose-C^{14} was enhanced by addition of insulin. Fishman and Sie (223) proved the existence in an aqueous homogenate of fresh rat liver of maltose, maltotriose, maltotetraose, and a number of higher glucosyl homologs.

The mechanism of action of a rat liver enzyme, termed transglucosylase, has been investigated by Stetten (224). It was found that glucose-C^{14} is introduced by the enzyme into only the terminal reducing sugar of the oligosaccharides. It was shown that, whereas the transfer of glucosyl residues from one sugar to another is reversible, the delivery of glucosyl residues to water is irreversible. The steps involved in the enzymatic reactions (the asterisk denotes radioactivity) may be represented as

$$\text{Glucosylglucose* + Enzyme} \rightleftharpoons \text{Glucosyl enzyme + Glucose*} \qquad (20)$$

$$\text{Glucosyl enzyme + Glucosylglucose*} \rightleftharpoons \text{Glucosylglucosylglucose* + Enzyme} \qquad (21)$$

$$\text{Glucosyl enzyme + H}_2\text{O} \rightarrow \text{Glucose + Enzyme} \qquad (22)$$

The reversibility of these steps was indicated by incubation of isotopic maltotriose, obtained by the above mechanism (Eq. 21), with the enzyme. Maltose-C^{14} and subsequently glucose-C^{14} appeared among the products. In addition to maltose and maltotriose, glycogen was found to be an active glucosyl donor, while glucose, maltose, and presumably higher oligosaccharides served as glucosyl acceptors. Glucose-1-phosphate was totally inactive either as a donor or acceptor of glucosyl residues, and the absence of inorganic phosphate did not alter the rate of transglucosylation. Thus a mammalian enzyme exists which is capable of a slow, simple transfer of glucosyl groups from maltose, malto-oligosaccharides, and possibly glycogen to glucose, maltose, and higher homologs, with the possible formation of seeds for a new polysaccharide. Neither phosphate nor phosphorylated intermediates are involved in these reactions.

Miller and Copeland (225–227) have studied a transglucosylase in serum which may prove to be identical with the heptatic enzyme. This enzyme reacted with amylosaccharides, such as maltose, amylose, and glycogen, to produce glucose. With maltose as substrate, oligosaccharides were synthesized, indicating that maltose and the oligosaccharides themselves acted as both glucosyl acceptors and donors. This enzyme had no effect upon isomaltose, cellobiose, gentiobiose, trehalose, glucose-1-phosphate, α- or β-methylglucosides, or cyclic Schardinger dextrins. The similarity between these enzymes and the D-enzyme isolated from potato juice (98) is apparent. But whereas the heptatic enzymes can utilize maltose as a donor substrate, D-enzyme appears to be without action on maltose. A presumably similar activity has been studied in rabbit liver by Petrova (228–230); for reaction to proceed, both dextrins, such as salivary amylase α-dextrins, and glucose are required. Maltose itself will not serve, in contrast to the substrate requirements of the enzyme of other workers (221, 224).

The importance of transglycosylation reactions in glycogen metabolism has been recently commented upon by Stetten and Stetten (231). These workers have pointed out that four enzymes, phosphorylase, UDPG-glycogen transferase, branching and debranching enzymes, acting together or separately, can account for changes in the structural pattern or for increases or decreases in the quantity of glycogen but fail to account for any process wherein the number of glycogen molecules increases. This stems from the fact that glycogen itself is a reagent in each of these four processes. If the number of glycogen molecules is to increase, additional seed must be supplied. New seeds might arise from an α-amylase type degradation of glycogen, and evidence suggesting the existence of α-amylases in blood-free skeletal muscle (232–234) and liver (235) has been reported. Alternatively, extra seed might arise by synthesis from maltose or other oligosaccharides by transglycosylations of the type discussed above. Since such transfer reactions cannot increase the net quantity of glucosidic bonds, as do reaction sequences via UDPG, it would appear unlikely that transglycosylation reactions as such result in the formation of appreciable quantities of glycogen. Transglycosylation, involving polysaccharide molecules, may effect changes in distribution of molecular sizes and branching patterns.

B. ENZYMATIC DEGRADATION OF GLYCOGEN

Hestrin (236) demonstrated that recrystallized muscle phosphorylase could degrade glycogen only to about 4%; from the limit dextrin produced, approximately one mole of maltose per end unit could be further removed with β-amylase. The β-amylase limit dextrin was likewise not degraded by purified phosphorylase. Cori and Larner (237) clearly showed that the complete degradation of branched polysaccharides in animal tissues required two enzymes: phosphorylase for the phosphorolysis of the α-1,4-linkages; and a special type of enzyme, termed amylo-1,6-glucosidase, for the hydrolysis of the α-1,6-linkages at the branch points. Glucose was the only free sugar detected in the digests by the combined action of these enzymes. The glucosidase alone, acting in a phosphate-free medium did not liberate glucose from glycogen. The formation of glucose requires that the glucose unit in α-1,6-linkage be exposed by preceding action of phosphorylase. The maltose liberated from phosphorylase limit dextrin by β-amylase digestion was therefore assigned to the main, or unbranched, arm of each terminal branch point, thus suggesting that in the phosphorylase limit dextrin this arm was five or six glucose units in length. Cori and Larner (237) also pointed out that the ratio of free glucose to glucose-1-phosphate in a digest of polysaccharide by the combined action of phosphorylase and glucosidase was a measure of the degree of branching.

Walker and Whelan (238), in a subsequent review of this topic, have suggested that glucose could be formed in the above reaction if the glucosidase were contaminated with an α-1,4-glucosyl transferase, known to be present in animal tissue. Such a transferase has been found in amylo-1,6-glucosidase preparations (238). A possible interpretation of this finding, together with other factors, may be that the branch chains of the phosphorylase limit dextrin of glycogen are longer than one glucose unit bound in α-1,6-linkage to the polysaccharide. Under these circumstances linear oligosaccharides removed by the "debranching enzyme" would be degraded to glucose by subsequent transfer of glucosyl residues. This revision of structure necessitates a reinvestigation of the action of amylo-1,6-glucosidase.

References

1. S. A. Barker and E. J. Bourne, Quart. Revs. (London) 7, 56–83 (1953).
2. T. K. Walker and H. B. Wright, Arch. Biochem. Biophys. 69, 362–371 (1957).
3. J. A. Gascoigne and M. M. Gascoigne, "Biological Degradation of Cellulose." Butterworths, London, 1960.
4. A. J. Brown, J. Chem. Soc. 49, 172–187, 432–439 (1886).
5. A. J. Brown, J. Chem. Soc. 51, 643 (1887).
6. R. Kaushral and T. K. Walker, Biochem. J. 48, 618–621 (1951).
7. K. S. Barclay, E. J. Bourne, M. Stacey, and M. Webb, J. Chem. Soc. pp. 1501–1505 (1954).
8. H. L. A. Tarr and H. Hibbert, Can. J. Research 4, 372–388 (1931).
9. H. Hibbert and J. Barsha, Can. J. Research 5, 580–591 (1931).
10. H. Hibbert and J. Barsha, Can. J. Research 10, 170–179 (1934).
11. J. Eggert and F. Luft, Z. physik. Chem. B7, 468–470 (1930).

12. S. A. Barker, E. J. Bourne, M. Stacey, and D. H. Whiffen, *Chem. & Ind.* (*London*) p. 196 (1953).
13. S. A. Barker, E. J. Bourne, M. Stacey, and D. H. Whiffen, *J. Chem. Soc.* pp. 171–176 (1954).
14. S. Hestrin and M. Schramm, *Biochem. J.* **58**, 345–352 (1954).
15. E. J. Bourne and H. Weigel, *Chem. & Ind.* (*London*) p. 132 (1954).
16. G. A. Greathouse, *J. Am. Chem. Soc.* **79**, 4503–4507 (1957).
17. M. Schramm, Z. Gromet, and S. Hestrin, *Nature* **179**, 28–29 (1957).
18. L. Glaser, *Biochim. et Biophys. Acta* **25**, 436 (1957).
19. J. R. Colvin, *Nature* **183**, 1135–1136 (1959).
20. B. Helferich, *Ergeb. Enzymforsch.* **2**, 74–89 (1933).
21. E. M. Crook and B. A. Stone, *Biochem. J.* **55**, xxv (1953).
22. S. A. Barker, E. J. Bourne, G. C. Hewitt, and M. Stacey, *J. Chem. Soc.* pp. 3734–3740 (1955).
23. K. Nishizawa and K. Wakabayashi, *Symposia on Enzyme Chem.* (*Japan*) **6**, 26–27 (1951); **7**, 97–98 (1952).
24. J. Honeyman, *in* "Recent Advances in the Chemistry of Cellulose and Starch," Heywood, London, 1959.
25. H. G. Ingersoll, *J. Appl. Phys.* **17**, 924–939 (1946).
26. J. A. Howsmon, *Textile Research J.* **19**, 152–162 (1949).
27. D. R. Whitaker, *in* "Friday Harbour Symposium on Marine Boring and Fouling Organisms." Univ. of Washington Press, Seattle, 1959.
28. K. Nishizawa, H. Matsuzaki, and A. Higuchi, *Research Repts., Fac. Textile Sericult. Shinschu Univ.* **3**, 69–71 (1953).
29. C. S. Walseth, "Enzymatic Hydrolysis of Cellulose." Inst. Paper Chemistry, Appleton, Wisconsin, 1948.
30. W. Gilligan and E. T. Reese, *Can. J. Microbiol.* **1**, 90–107 (1954).
31. D. R. Whitaker, *Can. J. Biochem. and Physiol.* **34**, *488–494* (1956).
32. P. Kooiman, P. A. Roelofsen, and S. Sweeris, *Enzymologia* **16**, 237–246 (1953).
33. J. H. Hash and K. W. King, *Science* **120**, 1033–1035 (1954).
34. E. T. Reese, E. Smakula, and A. S. Perlin, *Arch. Biochem. Biophys.* **85**, 171–175 (1959).
35. B. A. Stone, Ph.D. Thesis, University of London, 1954.
36. M. A. Jermyn, *Australian J. Sci. Research* **B5**, 409–432 (1952).
37. G. N. Festenstein, *Biochem. J.* **72**, 75–79 (1959).
38. H. S. Levinson, G. R. Mandels, and E T. Reese, *Arch. Biochem. Biophys.* **31**, 351–365 (1951).
39. D. R. Whitaker, *Arch. Biochem. Biophys.* **43**, 253–268 (1953).
40. K. Nishizawa and T. Kobayashi, *J. Agr. Chem. Soc. Japan* **27**, 239–242 (1953).
41. C. Matthijssen, *Dissertation Abstr.* **17**, 2141 (1957).
42. D. R. Whitaker, *Can. J. Biochem. and Physiol.* **34**, 102–115 (1956).
43. D. R. Whitaker and E. Meler, *Can. J. Biochem. and Physiol.* **34**, 83–89 (1956).
44. D. R. Whitaker, *Arch. Biochem. Biophys.* **53**, 436–439 (1954).
45. D. H. F Clayson, *Chem. & Ind.* (*London*) pp. 49–51 (1943).
46. K. Nishizawa, *J. Biochem.* (*Tokyo*) **42**, 825–835 (1955).
47. E. T. Reese, R. G. H. Siu, and H. S. Levinson, *J. Bacteriol.* **59**, 485–497 (1950)
48. E. T. Reese and H. S. Levinson, *Physiol. Plantarum* **5**, 345–366 (1952).

49. P. Kooiman, *Enzymologia* **18**, 371–384 (1957).
50. P. B. Marsh, K. Bollenbacher, M. L. Butler, and L. R. Guthrie, *Textile Research J.* **23**, 878–888 (1953).
51. E. T. Reese and W. Gilligan, *Textile Research J.* **24**, 663–669 (1954).
52. E. T. Reese and W. Gilligan, *Arch. Biochem. Biophys.* **45**, 74–82 (1953).
53. E. T. Reese, in "Friday Harbour Symposium on Marine Boring and Fouling Organisms." Univ. of Washington Press, Seattle, 1959.
54. E. J. Bourne, *Chem. & Ind. (London)* 1047–1052 (1951).
55. M. L. Wolfrom and A. Thompson, *J. Am. Chem. Soc.* **78**, 4116–4117 (1956).
56. S. Peat, J. R. Turvey, and J. M. Evans, *J. Chem. Soc.* 3223–3227, 3341–3344 (1959).
57. G. T. Cori and C. F. Cori, *J. Biol. Chem.* **131**, 397–398 (1939).
58. C. S. Hanes, *Nature* **145**, 348–349 (1940).
59. C. S. Hanes, *Proc. Roy. Soc.* **B128**, 421–450; **B129**, 174–208 (1940).
60. J. Monod and A. M. Torriani, *Compt. rend. acad. sci.* **227**, 240–243 (1948).
61. E. J. Hehre and D. M. Hamilton, *J. Biol. Chem.* **166**, 777–778 (1946).
62. S. Peat, W. J. Whelan, and W. R. Rees, *Nature* **172**, 158 (1953).
63. M. Doudoroff, H. A. Barker, and W. Z. Hassid, *J. Biol. Chem.* **168**, 725–732 (1947).
64. C. F. Cori, S. P. Colowick, and G. T. Cori, *J. Biol. Chem.* **121**, 465–477 (1937).
65. C. F. Cori, S. P. Colowick, and G. T. Cori, *J. Biol. Chem.* **123**, 375–389 (1938).
66. C. F. Cori, G. Schmidt, and G. T. Cori, *Science* **89**, 464–465 (1939).
67. A. Schäffner and H. Specht, *Naturwissenschaften* **26**, 494–495 (1938).
68. W. Kiessling, *Naturwissenschaften* **27**, 129–130 (1949).
69. P. Ostern, D. Herbert, and E. Holmes, *Biochem. J.* **33**, 1858–1878 (1939).
70. P. Ostern and E. Holmes, *Nature* **144**, 34 (1939).
71. W. E. Trevelyan, P. F. E. Mann, and J. S. Harrison, *Arch. Biochem. Biophys.* **39**, 419–449 (1952).
72. W. Z. Hassid and R. M. McCready, *J. Am. Chem. Soc.* **63**, 2171–2173 (1941).
73. W. N. Haworth, R. L. Heath, and S. Peat, *J. Chem. Soc.* pp. 55–58 (1942).
74. W. Z. Hassid, G. T. Cori, and R. M. McCready, *J. Biol. Chem.* **148**, 89–96 (1943).
75. S. A. Barker, E. J. Bourne and I. A. Wilkinson, *J. Chem. Soc.* pp. 3027–3030 (1950).
76. M. L. Wolfrom, C. S. Smith, D. E. Pletcher, and A. E. Brown, *J. Am. Chem. Soc.* **64**, 23–26 (1942).
77. M. L. Wolfrom, C. S. Smith, and A. E. Brown, *J. Am. Chem. Soc.* **65**, 255–259 (1943).
78. W. R. Meagher and W. Z. Hassid, *J. Am. Chem. Soc.* **68**, 2135–2137 (1946).
79. G. T. Cori and C. F. Cori, *J. Biol. Chem.* **131**, 397–398 (1939).
80. C. Weibull and A. Tiselius, *Arkiv Kemi, Mineral Geol.* **A19**, No. 19 (1945).
81. J. M. Bailey, W. J. Whelan, and S. Peat, *J. Chem. Soc.* pp. 3692–3694 (1950).
82. D. E. Green and P. K. Stumpf, *J. Biol. Chem.* **142**, 355–366 (1942).
83. E. J. Bourne, D. A. Stitch, and S. Peat, *J. Chem. Soc.* pp. 1448–1457 (1949).
84. E. C. Proehl and H. G. Day, *J. Biol. Chem.* **163**, 667–674 (1946).
85. C. F. Cori and G. T. Cori, *Ann. Rev. Biochem.* **10**, 152–180 (1941).

86. C. F. Cori, G. T. Cori, and A. A. Green, *J. Biol. Chem.* **151**, 39–55 (1943).
87. G. T. Cori, M. A. Swanson, and C. F. Cori, *Federation Proc.* **4**, 234–241 (1945).
88. M. A. Swanson and C. F. Cori, *J. Biol. Chem.* **172**, 815–824 (1948).
89. A. A. Green, G. T. Cori, and C. F. Cori, *J. Biol. Chem.* **142**, 447–448 (1942).
90. N. H. Creasey and C. H. Gray, *Biochem. J.* **50**, 74–81 (1951).
91. J. B. Sumner, T. C. Clou, and A. T. Bever, *Arch. Biochem.* **26**, 1–5 (1950).
92. W. J. Whelan and J. M. Bailey, *Biochem. J.* **58**, 560–569 (1954).
93. J. Monod and A. M. Torriani, *Compt. rend. acad. sci.* **228**, 718–720 (1949).
94. J. Monod and A. M. Torriani, *Ann. inst. Pasteur* **78**, 65–77 (1950).
95. J. Monod, *Biochem. Soc. Symposia (Cambridge, Engl.)* **4**, 51 (1950).
96. M. Doudoroff, W. Z. Hassid, E. W. Putman, A. L. Potter, and J. Lederberg, *J. Biol. Chem.* **179**, 921–934 (1949).
97. S. A. Barker and E. J. Bourne, *J. Chem. Soc.* pp. 209–215 (1952).
98. S. Peat, W. J. Whelan, and W. R. Rees, *J. Chem. Soc.* pp. 44–53 (1956).
99. S. Peat, W. J. Whelan, and G. Jones, *J. Chem. Soc.* pp. 2490–2495 (1957).
100. P. N. Hobson, S. Peat, and W. J. Whelan, *J. Chem. Soc.* pp. 1451–1459 (1951).
101. S. Peat, J. R. Turvey, and G. Jones, *J. Chem. Soc.* pp. 1540–1544 (1959).
102. G. J. Walker and W. J. Whelan, *Biochem. J.* **67**, 548–551 (1957).
103. G. J. Walker and W. J. Whelan, *Nature* **183**, 46 (1959).
104. W. N. Haworth, S. Peat, and E. J. Bourne, *Nature* **154**, 236 (1944).
105. S. A. Barker, E. J. Bourne, and S. Peat, *J. Chem. Soc.* pp. 1705–1711 (1949).
106. G. A. Gilbert and A. D. Patrick, *Nature* **165**, 573 (1950).
107. G. A. Gilbert and A. D. Patrick, *Biochem. J.* **51**, 181–186 (1952).
108. S. A. Barker, E. J. Bourne, S. Peat, and I. A. Wilkinson, *J. Chem. Soc.* pp. 3022–3027 (1950).
109. E. J. Bourne, and S. Peat, *J. Chem. Soc.* pp. 877–882 (1945).
110. P. N. Hobson, W. J. Whelan and S. Peat, *J. Chem. Soc.* pp. 3566–3573 (1950).
111. J. S. Ram and K. V. Giri, *Arch. Biochem. Biophys.* **38**, 231–236 (1952).
112. E. J. Hehre, D. M. Hamilton, and A. S. Carlson, *J. Biol. Chem.* **177**, 267–279 (1949).
113. A. Bebbington, E. J. Bourne, M. Stacey, and I. A. Wilkinson, *J. Chem. Soc.* pp. 240–245 (1952).
114. A. Bebbington, E. J. Bourne, and I. A. Wilkinson, *J. Chem. Soc.* pp. 246–253 (1952).
115. S. Nessenbaum and W. Z. Hassid, *J. Biol. Chem.* **190**, 673–683 (1951).
116. E. J. Bourne, A. Macey, and S. Peat, *J. Chem. Soc.* pp. 882–888 (1945).
117. S. Peat, E. J. Bourne, and S. A. Barker, *Nature* **161**, 127–128 (1948).
118. S. A. Barker, E. J. Bourne, I. A. Wilkinson, and S. Peat, *J. Chem. Soc.* pp. 93–99 (1950).
119. G. A. Gilbert and A. J. Swallow, *J. Chem. Soc.* pp. 2849–2852 (1949).
120. S. A. Barker, E. J. Bourne, and S. Peat, *J. Chem. Soc.* pp. 1712–1717 (1949).
121. P. N. Hobson, W. J. Whelan, and S. Peat, *J. Chem. Soc.* pp. 596–598 (1951).
122. J. M. Bailey, S. Peat, and W. J. Whelan, *Biochem. J.* **51**, xxxiv (1952).
123. S. Nessenbaum and W. Z. Hassid, *J. Biol. Chem.* **196**, 785–792 (1952).
124. M. Abdullah and W. J. Whelan, *Biochem. J.* **75**, 12P (1960).
125. S. C. Pan, L. W. Nicholson, and P. Kolachov, *J. Am. Chem. Soc.* **73**, 2547–2550 (1951).
126. J. H. Pazur and D. French, *J. Biol. Chem.* **196**, 265–272 (1952).

127. S. A. Barker and T. R. Carrington, *J. Chem. Soc.* pp. 3588–3593 (1953).
128. K. Saroja, R. Venkataraman, and K. V. Giri, *Biochem. J.* **60**, 399–403 (1955).
129. W. A. M. Duncan and D. J. Manners, *Biochem. J.* **69**, 343–348 (1958).
130. A. R. Archibald and D. J. Manners, *Biochem. J.* **73**, 292–295 (1959).
131. E. J. Hehre and D. M. Hamilton, *J. Bacteriol.* **55**, 197–208 (1948).
132. E. J. Hehre, D. M. Hamilton, and A. S. Carlson, *J. Biol. Chem.* **177**, 267–279 (1949).
133. S. A. Barker, E. J. Bourne, and M. Stacey, *J. Chem. Soc.* pp. 2884–2887 (1950).
134. D. J. Manners, *Ann. Repts. on Progr. Chem. (Chem. Soc., London)* **50**, 288–301 (1953).
135. K. H. Meyer, *Experientia* **8**, 405–420 (1952).
136. K. H. Meyer, *Angew. Chem.* **63**, 153–158 (1951).
137. K. Takaoka, H. Fuwa, and J. Nikani, *Mem. Inst. Sci. and Ind. Research, Osaka Univ.* **10**, 199–204 (1953).
138. A. Markovitz, H. P. Klein, and E. H. Fischer, *Biochim. et Biophys. Acta* **19**, 267–273 (1956).
139. W. J. Whelan, *Stärke* **12**, 358–364 (1960).
140. G. J. Walker and W. J. Whelan, *Biochem. J.* **76**, 257–263 (1960).
141. K. Myrbäck, *Arch. Biochem.* **14**, 53–56 (1947).
142. W. J. Whelan and P. J. P. Roberts, *Nature* **170**, 748–749 (1952).
143. P. J. P. Roberts and W. J. Whelan, *Biochem. J.* **76**, 246–253 (1960).
144. B. J. Bines and W. J. Whelan, *Biochem. J.* **76**, 253–257 (1960).
145. C. T. Greenwood, *Advances in Carbohydrate Chem.* **11**, 335–393 (1956).
146. S. Peat, G. J. Thomas, and W. J. Whelan, *J. Chem. Soc.* pp. 722–733 (1952).
147. E. T. Neufeld and W. Z. Hassid, *Arch. Biochem. Biophys.* **59**, 405–419 (1955).
148. W. Banks, C. T. Greenwood, and I. G. Jones, *J. Chem. Soc.* pp. 150–155 (1960).
149. W. L. Cunningham, D. J. Manners, A. Wright, and I. D. Fleming, *J. Chem. Soc.* pp. 2602–2613 (1960).
150. H. Baum, G. A. Gilbert, and N. D. Scott, *Nature* **177**, 889 (1956).
151. J. M. G. Cowie, I. D. Fleming, C. T. Greenwood, and D. J. Manners, *J. Chem. Soc.* pp. 697–707 (1958)
152. R. Bird and R. H. Hopkins, *Biochem. J.* **56**, 140–146 (1954).
153. J. M. Bailey and D. French, *J. Biol. Chem.* **226**, 1–14 (1957).
153a. D. French, *Nature* **190**, 445–456 (1961).
153b. P. J. Flory, "Principles of Polymer Chemistry," p. 318. Cornell Univ. Press, Ithaca, New York, 1953.
153c. F. R. Santi and G. E. Babcock, *Abstr. Papers Am. Chem. Soc.*, **138**, 16D (1960).
154. L. L. Phillips and M. L. Caldwell, *J. Am. Chem. Soc.*, **73**, 3559–3568 (1951).
155. Y. Tsujisaka, J. Fukumoto, and Y. Yamamuta, *Nature* **181**, 770–771 (1958).
156. S. A. Barker and J. G. Fleetwood, *J. Chem. Soc.* pp. 4857–4864 (1957).
157. S. A. Barker, E. J. Bourne, and J. G. Fleetwood, *J. Chem. Soc.* pp. 4865–4871 (1957).
158. D. French and D. W. Knapp, *J. Biol. Chem.* **187**, 463–471 (1950).
159. S. Peat, W. J. Whelan, P. N. Hobson, and G. J. Thomas, *J. Chem. Soc.* pp. 4440–4445 (1954).
160. W. J. Whelan and P. J. P. Roberts, *J. Chem. Soc.* pp. 1298–1304 (1953).
161. I. D. Fleming and D. J. Manners, *Chem. & Ind. (London)* 831–832 (1958).

162. B. Maruo and T. Kobayashi, *Nature* **167**, 606–607 (1951).
163. T. Kobayashi, *Nippon Nôgei-kagaku Kaishi* **31**, 865–867 (1957).
164. G. T. Cori and J. Larner, *J. Biol. Chem.* **188**, 17–29 (1951).
165. S. Peat, W. J. Whelan, and G. J. Thomas, *J. Chem. Soc.* pp. 3025–3030 (1956).
166. W. N. Haworth and E. G. V. Percival, *J. Chem. Soc.* pp. 1342–1349 (1931).
167. W. N. Haworth and E. G. V. Percival, *J. Chem. Soc.* 2277–2282 (1932).
168. D. J. Bell, *Biochem. J.* **30**, 1612–1616 (1936).
169. W. N. Haworth, E. L. Hirst, and F. Smith, *J. Chem. Soc.* pp. 1914–1922 (1939).
170. M. L. Wolfrom, E. N. Lassettre, and A. N. O'Neill, *J. Am. Chem. Soc.* **73**, 595–599 (1951).
171. M. L. Wolfrom and A. Thompson, *J. Am. Chem. Soc.* **79**, 4212–4215 (1957).
172. T. G. Halsall, E. L. Hirst, and J. K. N. Jones, *J. Chem. Soc.* pp. 1399–1403 (1947).
173. E. L. Hirst, J. K. N. Jones, and A. J. Roudier, *J. Chem. Soc.* pp. 1779–1783 (1948).
174. G. C. Gibbons and R. A. Boissonnas, *Helv. Chim. Acta* **33**, 1477–1481 (1950).
175. D. J. Bell and D. J. Manners, *J. Chem. Soc.* pp. 1891–1893 (1954).
176. M. Abdel-Akher, J. K. Hamilton, R. Montgomery, and F. Smith, *J. Am. Chem. Soc.* **74**, 4970–4971 (1952).
177. K. H. Meyer and J. Press, *Helv. Chim. Acta* **24**, 58–62 (1941).
178. D. L. Morris, *J. Biol. Chem.* **154**, 503 (1944).
179. D. J. Bell and D. J. Manners, *J. Chem. Soc.* pp. 3641–3645 (1952).
180. A. M. Liddle and D. J. Manners, *J. Chem. Soc.* pp. 3432–3436, 4708–4711 (1957).
181. J. Larner, B. Illingworth, G. T. Cori, and C. F. Cori, *J. Biol. Chem.* **199**, 641–651 (1952).
182. K. H. Meyer and P. Bernfeld, *Helv. Chim. Acta* **23**, 875–885 (1940).
183. G. T. Cori, *J. Biol. Chem.* **158**, 333–339 (1945).
184. G. T. Cori and C. F. Cori, *J. Biol. Chem.* **158**, 321–332 (1945).
185. G. T. Cori and A. A. Green, *J. Biol. Chem.* **151**, 31–38 (1943).
186. A. A. Green, *J. Biol. Chem.* **158**, 315–319 (1945).
187. A. A. Green and G. T. Cori, *J. Biol. Chem.* **151**, 21–29 (1943).
188. G. T. Cori, B. Illingworth, and P. J. Keller, *in* "Methods in Enzymology" (S. P. Colowick and N. O. Kaplan, eds.), Vol. I, p. 200. Academic Press, New York, 1955.
189. E. H. Fischer and E. G. Krebs, *J. Biol. Chem.* **216**, 121–132 (1955).
190. C. F. Cori and G. T. Cori, *J. Biol. Chem.* **158**, 341–345 (1945).
191. E. H. Fischer and E. G. Krebs, *J. Biol. Chem.* **231**, 65–71 (1958).
192. N. B. Madsen and C. F. Cori, *J. Biol. Chem.* **223**, 1055–1065 (1956).
193. N. B. Madsen and C. F. Cori, *J. Biol. Chem.* **224**, 899–908 (1957).
194. T. Baranowski, B. Illingworth, D. H. Brown, and C. F. Cori, *Biochim. et Biophys. Acta* **25**, 16–21 (1957).
195. E. G. Krebs, A. B. Kent, and E. H. Fischer, *J. Biol. Chem.* **231**, 65–71, 73–83 (1958).
196. E. G. Krebs and E. H. Fischer, *Biochim. et Biophys. Acta* **20**, 150–157 (1956).
197. E. G. Krebs, A. B. Kent, D. J. Graves, and E. H. Fischer, *Proc. Intern. Symposium on Enzyme Chem., Tokyo and Kyoto* **2**, 41–43 (1957).
198. J. Larner, *J. Biol. Chem.* **212**, 9–24 (1955).

199. J. Larner, B. R. Ray, and H. F. Crandall, *J. Am. Chem. Soc.* **78,** 5890–5898 (1956).
200. M. R. Stetten and D. Stetten, *J. Biol. Chem.* **232,** 489–504 (1958).
201. E. W. Sutherland, *in* "Phosphorus Metabolism" (W. D. McElroy and B. Glass, eds.), Vol. I, p. 54; Vol. II, p. 577. Johns Hopkins, Baltimore, 1951; 1952.
202. E. W. Sutherland and W. D. Wosilait, *J. Biol. Chem.* **218,** 459–468 (1956).
203. W. D. Wosilait and E. W. Sutherland, *J. Biol. Chem.* **218,** 469–481 (1956).
204. P. J. Keller and G. T. Cori, *J. Biol. Chem.* **214,** 127–134 (1955).
205. T. W. Rall, E. W. Sutherland, and W. D. Wosilait, *J. Biol. Chem.* **218,** 483–495 (1956).
206. T. W. Rall, E. W. Sutherland, and J. Berthet, *J. Biol. Chem.* **224,** 463–475 (1957).
207. E. W. Sutherland and T. W. Rall, *J. Am. Chem. Soc.* **79,** 3608 (1957).
208. L. F. Leloir and C. E. Cardini, *J. Am. Chem. Soc.* **79,** 6340–6341 (1957).
209. L. F. Leloir, J. M. Olavarriá, S. H. Goldemberg, and H. Carminatti, *Arch. Biochem. Biophys.* **81,** 508–520 (1959).
210. C. Villar-Palasi and J. Larner, *Biochim. et Biophys. Acta* **30,** 449 (1958).
211. R. Hauk and D. H. Brown, *Biochim. et Biophys. Acta* **33,** 536–539 (1959).
212. R. S. Bear and C. F. Cori, *J. Biol. Chem.* **140,** 111–118 (1941).
213. G. T. Cori and C. F. Cori, *J. Biol. Chem.* **151,** 57–63 (1943).
214. A. N. Petrova, *Biokhimiya* **13,** 244–252 (1948).
215. A. N. Petrova, *Biokhimiya* **14,** 155–166 (1949).
216. P. Bernfeld, *Advances in Enzymol.* **12,** 379–428 (1957).
217. S. Peat, *Advances in Enzymol.* **11,** 339–375 (1951).
218. J. Larner, *J. Biol. Chem.* **202,** 491–503 (1953).
219. S. A. Barker, A. Bebbington, and E. J. Bourne, *J. Chem. Soc.* pp. 4051–4058 (1953).
220. J. Larner and D. N. Uwah, *J. Am. Chem. Soc.* **78,** 3647–3648 (1956).
221. K. V. Giri, A. Nagabhushanam, V. N. Nigam, and B. Belavadi, *Science* **121,** 898–899 (1955).
222. A. Beloff-Chain, R. Catanzaro, E. B. Chain, I. Masi, F. Pocchiari, and C. Rossi, *Proc. Roy. Soc.* **B143,** 481–503 (1955).
223. W. H. Fishman and H. G. Sie, *J. Am. Chem. Soc.* **80,** 121–123 (1958).
224. M. R. Stetten, *J. Am. Chem. Soc.* **81,** 1437–1441 (1959).
225. K. D. Miller, *J. Biol. Chem.* **231,** 987–995 (1958).
226. K. D. Miller and W. H. Copeland, *Biochim. et Biophys. Acta* **22,** 193–194 (1956).
227. K. D. Miller and W. H. Copeland, *J. Biol. Chem.* **231,** 997–1008 (1958).
228. A. N. Petrova, *Biokhimiya* **23,** 30–36 (1958).
229. A. N. Petrova, *Biokhimiya* **24,** 228–233 (1959).
230. A. N. Petrova, *Doklady Akad. Nauk S.S.S.R.* **111,** 1054–1057 (1956).
231. D. Stetten and M. R. Stetten, *Physiol. Rev.* **40,** 505–537.
232. N. S. Drozdov and N. K. Zhuravaskaya, *Biokhimiya* **21,** 182–185 (1956).
233. E. M. Mystkowski, *Enzymologia* **2,** 152–160 (1937).
234. A. N. Petrova, *Biokhimiya* **11,** 119–131 (1946).
235. G. E. Glock, *Biochem. J.* **32,** 235 (1938).
236. S. Hestrin, *J. Biol. Chem.* **179,** 943–955 (1949).
237. G. T. Cori and J. Larner, *J. Biol. Chem.* **188,** 17–29 (1957).
238. G. J. Walker and W. J. Whelan, *Biochem. J.* **73,** 20P (1959).

CHAPTER 3

The Biochemistry of Lignin Formation*

F. F. Nord and Walter J. Schubert

Fordham University, New York

I. Introduction

During the growth of woody plant tissues, the carbohydrate constituents are formed first. Then the formation of another component, lignin, begins; the process is called "lignification." As a result of this chemical change, the spaces previously existing between the polysaccharide fibers gradually become filled in with lignin, or perhaps a part of the carbohydrate already present is somehow converted into lignin (1).

* Contribution No. 378 from the Laboratory of Organic Chemistry and Enzymology, Fordham University, New York. The experimental results from this laboratory were obtained with the aid of grants or fellowships of the Office of Naval Research, the National Science Foundation, the U. S. Public Health Service, the U. S. Atomic Energy Commission, the Research Corporation, and the Procter & Gamble Company. Parts of this report were discussed at the Fifth World Forestry Congress, held in Seattle, Washington, 1960.

The purpose of lignification appears to be twofold. It cements and anchors the cellulose fibers together, and, simultaneously, it stiffens them and protects them from physical and chemical damage. As a result, the completely lignified fiber no longer plays an active role in the life of the plant, but rather, it serves principally as a supporting structure.*

Although over one hundred years have passed since the discovery of lignin, and despite the tremendous amount of research which has been performed on it, the complete elucidation of its structure has not yet been achieved. Because of this still incomplete knowledge of the chemistry of lignin,† it is difficult even to define it. Indeed, the term "lignin" is not to be considered the designation of a chemically marked off compound, but it is rather a collective term for a group of high molecular weight molecules which are chemically related to one another in much the same way as are several other natural polymeric materials, such as cellulose, the hemicelluloses, and starch. Based upon earlier knowledge of its chemistry, lignin has been defined (3a) as: "that incrusting material of the plant which is built up mainly, if not entirely, of phenylpropane building stones; it carries the major part of the methoxyl content of the wood; it is unhydrolyzable by acids, readily oxidizable, soluble in hot alkali and bisulfite, and readily condenses with phenols and thio compounds." On the basis of more recent results, the definition of lignin can now be somewhat amplified. Thus, since lignin yields aldehydes when it is treated with nitrobenzene in alkali at 160°, it may be further stipulated as "that wood constituent which, when oxidized with nitrobenzene, yields vanillin in the case of coniferous woods, vanillin and syringaldehyde in the case of deciduous woods, and p-hydroxybenzaldehyde, vanillin, and syringaldehyde in the case of monocotyledons" (3d). In addition, lignin may be considered as "that plant component which, when refluxed with ethanol in the presence of catalytic amounts of hydrogen chloride, gives a mixture of ethanolysis products—'Hibbert's monomers'—such as α-ethoxypropioguaiacone, vanillin, and vanilloyl methyl ketone from coniferous woods and, in addition, the corresponding syringyl derivatives from deciduous woods" (3d).

---

* The spontaneous inhibition of lignin synthesis in "tension wood" cells has been found (1a) to be connected with the rate of growth, and was found to occur at the very beginning of lignin synthesis. This finding could conceivably be of importance in forestry genetics research, since it might permit the control (at least partially) of the chemical composition of growing wood.

† Progress in the chemistry of lignin has been reviewed by Nord and de Stevens (2), and by Brauns and Brauns (3d).

Lignin does not occur alone in nature, but rather it coexists with cellulose or some other polysaccharide. Although it is physically associated with these carbohydrates, this does not imply that lignin forms a chemical compound in the plant with the carbohydrates; in fact, the opposite is believed to be the case (1, 2). Indeed, much of the difficulty involved in studying the chemistry of lignin is attributable to the fact that, until relatively recently, no method was known by which it could be separated in an unchanged form from the coexisting carbohydrates. Whatever method was employed, a preparation was obtained which was no longer identical with lignin as it exists in nature.

Accordingly, it is quite premature at the present time to suggest a structural formula for lignin. However, on the basis of experimental results, it is possible to indicate certain structural features which any formula for lignin must accomodate (3b).

Thus, there is little doubt that lignin is a high polymer which is formed to a great extent (perhaps entirely) of phenylpropane building stones. How these building stones are joined to each other, whether they are combined according to a single pattern or in a variety of ways, are still unanswered questions. Hence, before a reliable structural formula for lignin can be proposed, one must first know the structures of all the lignin building stones, and then one must learn the mode of combination of the building stones, one to another, in order to establish how the sum total forms the lignin polymer.

Goring, too, believes that lignin is a polymeric material made up largely of phenylpropane building stones. He thinks that the configuration of the molecule is not that of a compact sphere (4). The polyelectrolyte expansion of selected fractions of sodium lignin sulfonate was measured viscometrically and by light scattering, and isoionic dilution techniques were applied. The results supported a microgel model for the macromolecule and a new theory was developed in which the molecule was assumed tc have free charges only on the surface. Furthermore, an idealized spherical model of the spruce lignin sulfonate macromolecule was presented (5).

The mechanism of the biogenesis of lignin has also intrigued lignin chemists ever since the discovery of this complex material. Simply stated, the process of lignification is the transformation which occurs in certain plants whereby the aromatic polymer lignin is synthesized, ultimately from CO_2, probably by way of intermediates of a carbohydrate nature. Accordingly then, lignification is but one illustration of the more general phenomenon of aromatization, i.e., the conversion by living cells of nonaromatic precursors into compounds containing benzenoid-type rings. In this connection, it may be noted that significant advances have been made in the elucidation of the biogenesis of the benzene rings of the aromatic amino acids tyrosine, phenylalanine, and tryptophan (6).

Fundamentally, the problem of the biogenesis of lignin is this: by what enzymic pathway is this aromatic compound of high degree of polymerization formed from substances pre-existing in the plant?

A comprehensive answer to this question requires the consideration of two fundamental assumptions. First, this complex material must have its ultimate origin in certain relatively simpler compounds. Second, the biogenesis of lignin must involve the functioning of not one enzyme system, but, rather, of several different systems, each exerting its influence on its substrate in a systematized and integrated sequence, with the sum total of the reactions giving rise to a product, lignin, which is required for the existence of the mature plant. Thus, in such a biosynthetic study, both the precursors of the final product and the energetics of the reactions involved must be considered. Too often, these concepts are neglected, with the result that suggested hypotheses frequently are unfounded.

Although knowledge of the total scheme of biogenesis of lignin is still incomplete,* there can be little doubt that it originates ultimately from the carbohydrates which are formed from atmospheric carbon dioxide by the process of photosynthesis. The "lignification problem" may then be considered to include the elucidation of the identity of the ultimate carbohydrate precursor of lignin, together with the enzymic mechanisms operative, and intermediate compounds formed, whereby this carbohydrate precursor is eventually transformed into the aromatic polymer lignin. Obviously, this transformation does not occur by a direct conversion, but must proceed by way of the polymerization of some simpler, monomeric unit (or units), referred to as the "primary building stones." However, the almost complete disparity of chemical nature between a carbohydrate on the one hand, and an aromatic polymer on the other, clearly implies an extended series of far-reaching enzyme reactions in order to effect this profound transformation.

Furthermore, the complexity of the structure of lignin precludes the possibility of the existence of but one simple building unit for lignin in the sense in which glucose or cellobiose are considered the building units of cellulose. Accordingly, for lignin formation, it is necessary to postulate the existence of dimeric "secondary building stones." The formation of lignin itself finally may involve either the direct polymerization of the secondary building stones as such, or else there may con-

* Older theories on the origin and mode of formation of lignin are reviewed by Brauns (3c,d).

ceivably occur additional modifications before the final polymerization results in the formation of the complex polymer we call lignin. The over-all picture of the lignification process may therefore be presented schematically (Reaction sequence 1).

$$
\begin{aligned}
\text{Carbon dioxide} &\xrightarrow{\text{photosynthesis}} \text{Carbohydrates} \\[4pt]
&\xrightarrow{\text{aromatization}} \text{Primary building stones} \\[4pt]
&\xrightarrow{\text{dimerization}} \text{Secondary building stones} \\[4pt]
&\xrightarrow{\text{polymerization}} \text{Lignin}
\end{aligned}
\tag{1}
$$

II. The Microbiological Degradation of Cellulose

As indicated above, lignin does not occur alone in nature, but rather, it always coexists with cellulose, or some other polysaccharide. Cellulose is generally regarded as the most abundant organic compound existing in nature. It comprises the skeletal framework of all higher plants, whether in the free state, as in the seed hairs of cotton, or in association with other polymers, as is the case in wood, where it exists together with lignin. Considering the abundance of cellulose in nature, it is inevitable that man should have attempted, with considerable success, to exploit this raw material.

But, while man utilizes this material which exists so abundantly in plant life, nature too has provided for the continuous removal of cellulose, and this is accomplished almost entirely by the action of microorganisms. The following groups are included in the organisms capable of decomposing cellulose in nature: aerobic bacteria, anaerobic bacteria, many types of higher fungi, filamentous fungi, certain actinomycetes, various protozoa, certain types of insects, and a variety of other invertebrate animals, including worms and snails (7).

Depending on the type of organism effecting the degradation of cellulose, a wide variety of end products may be obtained. But, regardless of the nature of the organism causing the degradation, it is generally agreed that an exoenzyme is required to bring about the hydrolysis of the polymeric cellulose molecules to give rise to water-soluble sugars which then enter the cell before dissimilation.

A. THE MECHANISM OF CELLULOSE DISINTEGRATION

All the details of the preliminary hydrolysis of cellulose are not yet completely understood. If one assumes that the cellulose molecules consist only of long chains of glucose units linked by β-1,4-glycosidic bonds, the hydrolysis might then consist merely of the cleavage of these linkages, with a gradual shortening of the chain. However, if one were to consider the possibility of cross-linkages binding the chains together, it is conceivable that two disinct processes might take place: (a) a reaction involving the rupture of the cross-linkages which hold the chains together, and (b) a reaction effecting the liberation of glucose units (7).

A prevalent theory for the enzymic hydrolysis of cellulose involves at least two enzymes, cellulase and cellobiase. Cellulase hydrolyzes cellulose to cellobiose and probably other oligosaccharides (containing three or more anhydroglucose units), whereas cellobiase hydrolyzes these products to glucose. On the one hand, it has been maintained (8) that the process is unienzymic, with the breakdown occurring via a random scission of the cellulose molecule. While many investigations have supported this view, it has also been contended (9) that the process is multienzymic, including a multicomponent cellulase in addition to a β-glucosidase, cellobiase.

It was Pringsheim (10), studying cellulolytic bacteria, who first postulated a two-step degradation of cellulose to glucose by the two enzymes cellulase and cellobiase. He was supported in this concept by Simola (11), who also studied cellulolytic bacteria. Grassmann et al. (12) came to the same conclusion as a result of their investigations of the cellulolytic enzyme system of Aspergillus oryzae.

However, Jermyn et al. (13) have since reported that cellulolytic enzyme preparations from A. oryzae consist of at least eight components. Further, Reese and Gilligan (14) have demonstrated that metabolic filtrates of certain organisms contain up to three cellulolytic components. They postulated (15) that the process of cellulose degradation is "multienzymic," including a multicomponent cellulase in addition to the β-glucosidase cellobiase.

Greathouse (16), studying polyhomologous hydrocelluloses with varying degrees of polymerization, concluded that the cellulose molecule is attacked in a random fashion. This view has been upheld by Whitaker (17), who investigated a purified enzyme preparation from metabolic filtrates of Myrothecium verrucaria. Kooiman (18), studying the same organism, supported this view, but in addition he showed the presence of the β-glucosidase cellobiase, as well as of a heat-stable component (probably cellulase) in his purified enzyme preparation.

On the other hand, Clayson (19) has hypothesized that an endwise attack on the cellulose molecule takes place during enzymic hydrolysis. This view has been supported by Nishizawa and Kobayashi (20), who studied the cellulolytic enzyme from the wood-destroying mold Irpex lacteus.

The cellulolytic enzyme system of the "brown rot" wood-destroying fungus *Poria vaillantii* has been isolated (*21*) and studied, and it appears to be relatively simple, consisting of two enzymes, the cellulolytic enzyme cellulase and the β-glucosidase cellobiase. The cellulase hydrolyzes cellulose to cellobiose (and perhaps to other less simple oligosaccharides), and the cellobiase further hydrolyzes these oligosaccharides to glucose (*22*). Accordingly, the mechanism of cellulose decomposition by the enzyme system of this organism has been represented (*23*) as shown in Reaction sequence 2.

$$\text{Cellulose} \xrightarrow{\text{cellulase}} \text{Cellobiose} \xrightarrow{\text{cellobiase}} \text{Glucose} \qquad (2)$$

The possibility that one or more other enzymes, intermediate in function between cellulase and cellobiase, may operate in this system was noted (*22*), but is still undetermined. At any rate, the *Poria vaillantii* cellobiase appears to function differently from several other fungal cellobiase preparations which have been demonstrated to have transglycosylase activity (*24*).

It is certainly difficult to correlate these widely divergent concepts of enzymic cellulose decomposition, especially when one considers the varied organisms which have been studied. It has been suggested that each organism may operate according to its own unique mechanism, even depending on its momentary environmental conditions (*23*).

It is thus evident that all the details of the precise mechanism of the enzymic degradation of cellulose are still not completely understood. Halliwell (*25*) has suggested that much of the difficulty arises from the insoluble nature of cellulose. A further problem, he feels, is the wide divergence of properties reported for the cellulases produced by different organisms, or by the same organism, but isolated in different laboratories. He concludes that the cultural conditions for the growth of organisms on different forms of cellulose merit further study and, presumably, require greater standardization.

B. THE DISSIMILATION OF GLUCOSE

Regardless of the type of organism causing the decay of wood, part of the cellulose portion of the wood is invariably destroyed. Although the decay of wood and its prevention are matters of great economic importance, relatively little was known about the mechanism of this decay caused by the activity of microorganisms. Perhaps the main reason for the lack of knowledge of the mechanism of this destruction was the inability to isolate intermediate breakdown products which would have helped to indicate the sequence of the degradation reactions and, further, to assist in clarifying the fate of the decaying cellulose when wood is attacked by fungi. The interest of this Laboratory was therefore earlier centered on an elucidation of the mechanism of destruction of the cellulose fraction of wood during its decay by fungi (7).

A direct approach to the problem would have consisted in the isolation and identification of intermediate breakdown products, but the objections to such an approach were soon obvious. Not only is the action of a microorganism slow in bringing about the decay of wood, but it would also be difficult to prove that any isolated product had arisen specifically from one of the several constituents of wood, and not from another. It was therefore decided to study the action of wood-destroying fungi on cellulose itself and on several simple sugars.

With some knowledge available on the terminal breakdown products of the action of this class of organisms on wood, it appeared that a correlation of the existing data with the results obtained from a study of the dissimilation of glucose and other simple sugars might afford a means of deducing a reaction sequence for the degradation of the cellulose constituent of wood during the process of decay.

The results of these investigations indicated that wood-destroying molds of the "brown rot" type degraded glucose to oxalic acid via acetic acid (26). These molds selectively decay the cellulose of wood in a similar way (leaving the lignin unaffected). Thus, it was anticipated that additional knowledge concerning the intermediate steps of carbohydrate breakdown by these organisms might provide information on the metabolic relationship between the cellulose and lignin components of living plant tissues.

Accordingly the mechanism of formation of oxalic acid by wood-destroying molds was established (27, 28) as proceeding via a two-pronged pathway (Reaction sequence 3).

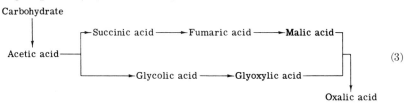

(3)

It was subsequently found that α-ketoglutaric acid (29) also gives rise to oxalic acid (Reaction sequence 4).

$$\alpha\text{-Ketoglutaric acid} \longrightarrow \text{Succinic acid} \longrightarrow \text{Oxalic acid} \qquad (4)$$

The biochemical relationship of α-ketoglutaric acid to glutamic acid then prompted a study of the possible functions of the dicarboxylic amino acids, aspartic and glutamic acids, to this process (30). The wood-destroying molds used in these experiments were *Trametes cinnabarina* and *Lentinus lepideus.*

It was observed that glutamic and aspartic acids were largely diverted to the synthesis of cellular material, rather than to the formation of oxalic acid. It was not unexpected therefore to find α-ketoglutarate being formed from glutamate; furthermore, no oxaloacetic acid was detected in the medium containing the aspartate; but oxaloacetate is known to be extremely unstable (*31*). The relatively low yields of oxalic acid derived from glutamic and aspartic acids were therefore attributed to the fact that these substrates also serve as source material for the synthesis of protoplasm and, in addition, are utilized in other metabolic activities of the molds as well.

These investigations indicated a cyclic mechanism to be operative in the formation of oxalic acid, wherein oxaloacetate yields either oxalate and acetate (which may be reoxidized), or pyruvate, which would in turn yield acetate. These concepts are illustrated in Reaction sequence 5 (*32*) for the formation of oxalic acid by wood-destroying microorganisms.

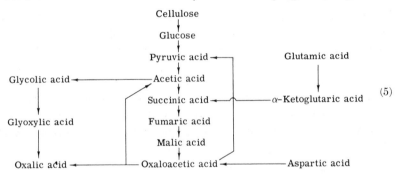

$$(5)$$

Since the same metabolic products were obtained from cellulose and from glucose by the enzymic activities of the wood-destroying fungi studied, an over-all mechanism for the degradation of the cellulosic fraction of wood by the action of these organisms can be derived. Accordingly, on the basis of these findings, Reaction sequence 6 was presented (*33, 34*) for the fate of the cellulose of wood when it is degraded by these organisms:

Cellulose ⟶ Cellobiose ⟶ Glucose ⟶ Pyruvic acid

⟶ Acetic acid ⟶ Oxalic acid

$$(6)$$

III. The Aromatization Process in Microorganisms

Biochemists had long speculated about the mechanism by which plants and microorganisms are able to achieve the synthesis of benzenoid compounds from nonaromatic precursors. The investigation of the biogenesis of the aromatic lignin building stones, and of lignin itself, in higher plants had earlier met with experimental difficulty. However, the opportunity for a biochemical approach to the general problem of "aromatization" arose from the isolation of aromatic polyauxotrophs of the microorganisms *Escherichia coli* (*35*) and *Neurospora crassa* (*36*), i.e., mutants of these microorganisms that require supplementary mixtures of aromatic compounds for their normal metabolic activities.

A. AROMATIC AMINO ACID BIOSYNTHESIS IN BACTERIA

The researches of Davis (*6, 37*), Sprinson, and their collaborators on the above mutants of *E. coli* have established a partial pathway for the biosynthesis of the aromatic amino acids from carbohydrate precursors. This work has been reviewed (*37, 38, 39, 39a*), and the presently considered pathway for the biogenesis of phenylalanine and tyrosine is presented in Fig. 1.

Thus, the carbon atoms of the two aromatic amino acids are derived from one mole of D-erythrose-4-phosphate (II) and two moles of phosphoenol pyruvate (I). The second mole of phosphoenol pyruvate is incorporated by a reaction with 5-phosphoshikimic acid (III) to give compound Z_1 or its phosphate (*40*) which then rearranges to form prephenic acid (IV). Prephenic acid then serves as a "branching point"; thus, it may be converted either to phenylpyruvic acid (V), or to *p*-hydroxyphenylpyruvic acid (VII), and these compounds give phenylalanine (VI) and tyrosine (VIII), respectively, by transamination reactions.

B. AROMATIC AMINO ACID BIOSYNTHESIS IN FUNGI

The mold *Neurospora crassa* also appears to utilize the shikimic acid pathway for the biosynthesis of its aromatic amino acids. Thus, Tatum *et al.* (*36*) obtained a mutant of this organism which demonstrated a multiple nutritional requirement for aromatic amino acids, and this requirement could be satisfied by added shikimic acid.

Thus, it would seem that *N. crassa* also synthesizes its aromatic amino acids by a pathway similar to that found in *E. coli*, although it has not yet been proved that the two pathways are identical in all respects (*38*). Other fungi have not yet been investigated to any great extent, although added shikimic acid has been found (*41*) to cause an increased yield of 6-methylsalicylic acid in experiments with *Penicillium patulum*.

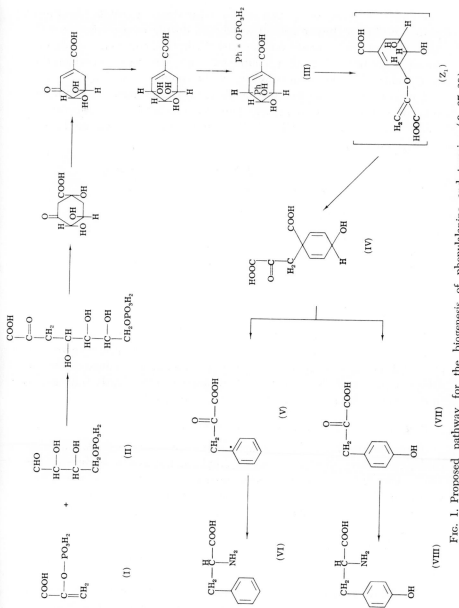

Fig. 1. Proposed pathway for the biogenesis of phenylalanine and tyrosine (6, 37–39).

C. METHYL p-METHOXYCINNAMATE METABOLISM IN *Lentinus lepideus*

Among the several species of wood-destroying fungi, *Lentinus lepideus* produces "brown rot" in wood; i.e., during its growth on wood, preferential attack is made on the carbohydrate components, with the lignin remaining unaffected, as contrasted with "white rot," in which the lignin seems to be the main substrate of the fungus.

It was observed (42) that the metabolic processes associated with the decay of wood by this organism give rise to certain aromatic esters, namely, methyl anisate (IX), methyl cinnamate (X), and methyl p-methoxycinnamate (XI).

Furthermore, it has long been realized (43) that if growing cultures of *Lentinus lepideus* are allowed to incubate in the presence of the produced crystalline deposit of methyl p-methoxycinnamate, after a sufficient period of time, the crystals disappear. This clearly indicates a further metabolism of the ester by the fungus (44).

1. *Biogenesis of Methyl p-Methoxycinnamate*

Investigations have shown that it is possible to grow *L. lepideus* on media containing glucose, xylose, or ethyl alcohol as sole carbon source (43), whereby methyl p-methoxycinnamate appears as a crystalline deposit in the culture medium after several weeks of growth. From this observation, it was concluded that the ester is not a product of the degradation of lignin, which might conceivably have been effected by the organism during its growth on wood, for the fungus is capable of synthesizing the aromatic ester either from carbohydrates or ethyl alcohol.

Results obtained from experiments on the biogenesis of methyl p-methoxycinnamate by *L. lepideus* have importance in theorizing on the formation of lignin, if one assumes the existence of similar pathways in the formation of the ester and of the lignin building stones

(7). The assumption of the similarity of the biogenesis of the ester and of the building stones is based upon the structural relationship of methyl p-methoxycinnamate and p-hydroxycinnamyl alcohol, which is one of the three fundamental building stones of lignin (1).

The following experiments were therefore undertaken as part of an investigation of the problem of the biogenesis of lignin. As a result of these studies, a number of products of the metabolism of *L. lepideus* was detected (45). Specifically, these were: pyruvic acid, acetoacetic acid, oxaloacetic acid, α-ketoglutaric acid, ribose, glucose, p-hydroxyphenylpyruvic acid (XII), sedoheptulose (XIII), and 5-phosphoshikimic acid (XIV).

(XII)   (XIII)   (XIV)

The origin of methyl p-methoxycinnamate ultimately from glucose was indicated by the fact that the organism, when grown on ethanol as substrate, synthesized glucose, and also by the results of certain competition experiments. In these experiments, ribose, sodium acetate, and shikimic acid were tested for their ability to serve as competitors in the biogenesis of methyl p-methoxycinnamate. In each case, the ester derived from the competition experiment did not show any dilution of activity when compared with the activity of the product of a control experiment (46).

The detection of the keto acids implied the functioning of the citric acid cycle. Acetic acid can be introduced into this cycle. However, the result of an experiment employing methyl-C^{14}-labeled sodium acetate, in addition to unlabeled glucose, did not show any significant incorporation of C^{14} into methyl p-methoxycinnamate. This result was interpreted as indicating that neither the keto acids nor acetic acid are directly involved in the formation of methyl p-methoxycinnamate (46).

Thus, the experiments indicated the origin of methyl p-methoxycinnamate from glucose. This conversion accordingly prompted a comparison with the biogenesis of the aromatic amino acids. Davis (6) had shown that the synthesis of tyrosine takes place via glucose and shikimic acid. Sedoheptulose, to which some importance had been attributed in the biogenesis of shikimic acid, appeared among the metabolic products of L. lepideus. Furthermore, p-hydroxyphenylpyruvic acid was considered to be an intermediate in the biogenesis of tyrosine (6). This compound was also identified in the medium of L. lepideus cultures, and could be considered a precursor of p-hydroxycinnamic acid (46).

These findings then indicated the possibility of a relationship between the formation of methyl p-methoxycinnamate by L. lepideus and the biogenesis of the aromatic amino acids by bacteria (47, 48).

Lentinus lepideus was also grown in media containing D-glucose-1-C^{14} and D-glucose-6-C^{14}. The activities of both tagged sugars were significantly incorporated into methyl p-methoxycinnamate. The comparative distributions of activity in the ester derived from the two differently labeled forms of D-glucose were determined (49) by specific degradation reactions which permitted the selective isolation of several of the individual carbon atoms of methyl p-methoxycinnamate (XV).

$$\underset{11}{\overset{9\quad 10}{\text{COOCH}_3}}$$

8 CH

7 CH

(ring: 1, 2, 3, 4, 5, 6)

$\underset{11}{\text{OCH}_3}$

(XV)

The relative distributions of activity of C^{14} from the two experiments are summarized in Table I.

The percentage distributions in each carbon of the side chain were found to be nearly identical when the esters obtained from the 1-C^{14} and 6-C^{14}-labeled D-glucose were compared; the observed absolute differences were attributable to a uniformly greater dilution of C-1. In the ester produced from D-glucose-6-C^{14}, significant activity was incorporated into carbons 7 and 2 or 6 of the phenylpropane moiety of the ester. In general, these results were quite similar to those obtained for tyrosine (6) and shikimic acid (50) biosyntheses from glucose.

Relating the results of the ester biosynthesis from D-glucose-6-C^{14} to those of the tyrosine biosynthesis, the probability that methyl p-methoxycinnamate is synthesized by L. lepideus from glucose via the shikimic acid pathway was apparent. However, in the ester biogenesis, the specific activity of carbon 1 underwent a greater dilution, as compared with carbon 6. This can be accounted for by an alternate oxidative decarboxylation of carbon 1 of glucose (49).

It was also observed that carbon 6 of glucose was significantly incorporated into the methoxyl carbon and the ester methyl carbon of the product. The nonequivalent incorporation of carbons 1 and 6 of glucose into these positions gave support to the occurrence in *L. lepideus* of a pathway other than glycolysis (49).

TABLE I

DISTRIBUTIONS OF ACTIVITY IN METHYL p-METHOXYCINNAMATE FORMED FROM D-GLUCOSE-1-C^{14} AND D-GLUCOSE-6-C^{14} (49)

Positions in methyl p-methoxycinnamate (Carbon No.)	Percentage of total activity of ester from	
	Glucose-1-C^{14}	Glucose-6-C^{14}
1	—	3.2
2 + 6	—	39.1
3 + 5	—	4.9
4	—	4.2
7	14.1	17.6
8 + 9	5.4	5.0
10	14.5	13.4
11	13.2	12.6

These findings then confirmed the existence of a relationship between the formation of methyl p-methoxycinnamate by *Lentinus lepideus* and the biogenesis of aromatic amino acids by bacteria and fungi. The structural relationship existing between methyl p-methoxycinnamate and the lignin building stones has already been discussed. Hence, it seemed possible that the lignin building stones might also be synthesized by a similar pathway (1).

2. *Metabolism of Methyl p-Methoxycinnamate*

As described above, *Lentinus lepideus* produces large amounts of crystalline methyl p-methoxycinnamate in its medium. It has since been observed (51) that if the cultures in which the deposit had accumulated were shaken, the amount of deposit in the medium diminished rapidly, and, after a few days, had almost completely disappeared. Simultaneously, the color of the medium turned brown. When, after one or two days of shaking the flasks, the medium was extracted with ether, the presence of a small amount of a previously undetected phenolic compound was established. This compound was isolated and identified (51) as methyl p-coumarate (XVI).

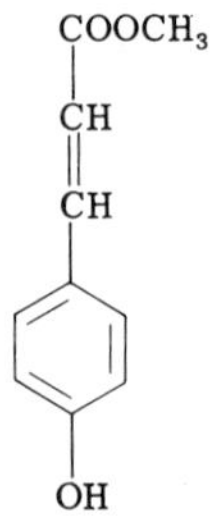

$$COOCH_3$$
$$CH$$
$$CH$$

OH

(XVI)

This methyl p-coumarate was easily oxidizable by a mycelial extract of the mold (51). It was therefore suggested that methyl p-coumarate might function as an intermediate in the metabolism of methyl p-methoxycinnamate by *Lentinus lepideus*, and possibly also in the biosynthesis of that compound. It was further considered that, in the first step of its metabolism, methyl p-methoxycinnamate may be demethylated to methyl p-coumarate, and then the latter may be oxidized by a phenolase, possibly tyrosinase (51).

In a subsequent study (52), the occurrence in the medium of the phenolic ester, methyl isoferulate (XVII), was established, together

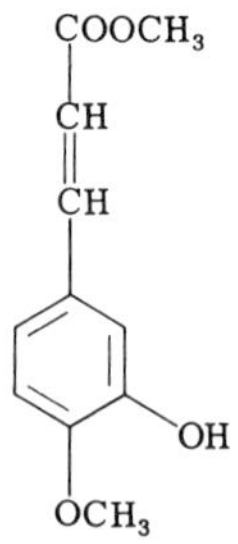

$$COOCH_3$$
$$CH$$
$$CH$$

OH

$$OCH_3$$

(XVII)

with methyl p-coumarate and methyl p-methoxycinnamate. It was further noted that methyl p-coumarate was accumulated only in small amounts and under certain special conditions, since this compound was rapidly oxidized by the phenolase present in the mold mycelium to a colored material. Accordingly, methyl p-coumarate is to be regarded as an intermediate in the biosynthesis of methyl p-methoxycinnamate by *Lentinus lepideus*.

When methyl p-coumarate-carboxyl-C^{14} was added to the culture medium, about 60% of the total isotopic activity was recovered in the methyl p-methoxycinnamate subsequently isolated. The isotopic activity of the carbon in the original carboxyl position of methyl p-coumarate did not migrate to the other carbons of methyl p-methoxycinnamate. The loss of about 40% of the original isotopic activity was accounted for on the basis of: (a) mechanical loss during the isolation and purification of the ester; (b) oxidation of some of the ester added to the medium by the phenolase enzyme present in the mycelium of the mold; and (c), dilution of the labeled ester added to the medium with that synthesized by the mold. Nevertheless, the significant recovery of the isotopic activity demonstrated that methyl p-coumarate was a direct precursor of methyl p-methoxycinnamate in the biosynthesis of the latter compound (52).

In another experiment, 20% of the total activity of added DL-methionine-methyl-C^{14} was recovered from the methyl p-methoxycinnamate subsequently isolated. Here, the isotopic activity was found principally in the ethereal methoxyl carbon, and (to the same extent) in the ester methyl carbon, indicating the absence of migration to other positions. This significant incorporation of the methionine-methyl carbon into the two methyl carbons of the ester demonstrates the possibility that methionine (or some related compound) may be the methyl donor for the ethereal and ester methyl groups of this compound (52).

Accordingly, in the biosynthesis of methyl p-methoxycinnamate by *Lentinus lepideus*, it is believed that methyl p-coumarate is methylated to methyl p-methoxycinnamate by methionine (or related compound). However, the reverse of this reaction might occur under different cultural conditions. Thus, although methyl p-coumarate does not accumulate in the medium (except under special conditions), small amounts of methyl isoferulate do accumulate, along with methyl p-methoxycinnamate.

Two possibilities for the formation of methyl isoferulate were considered. One is the O-methylation of methyl caffeate, which could be formed from methyl p-coumarate by the action of a phenolase. The other is the hydroxylation of methyl p-methoxycinnamate by some enzyme other than a phenolase.

In the metabolism of the p-methoxyaromatic esters methyl p-methoxycinnamate and methyl isoferulate, it is believed that these esters are first demethylated to the free phenolic compounds. This would correspond to the reverse of their biosynthesis. Then, the free phenols formed would be subject to the action of the phenolase present in the mold mycelium, and thereupon the colored oxidation products would be formed. These transformations are summarized in Fig. 2.

It is of interest to note that the three phenolic compounds identified were all accumulated in the medium of *Lentinus lepideus* in the form of their methyl esters—not as free acids. The accumulation of such compounds in the medium is not frequently encountered in studies of microorganisms. Accordingly, the mechanism of the O-methylation of phenols in microbial metabolism cannot yet be fully explained (52).

In a related investigation (53), the transformations of anisic acid and of methyl anisate by another wood-destroying fungus, *Polystictus*

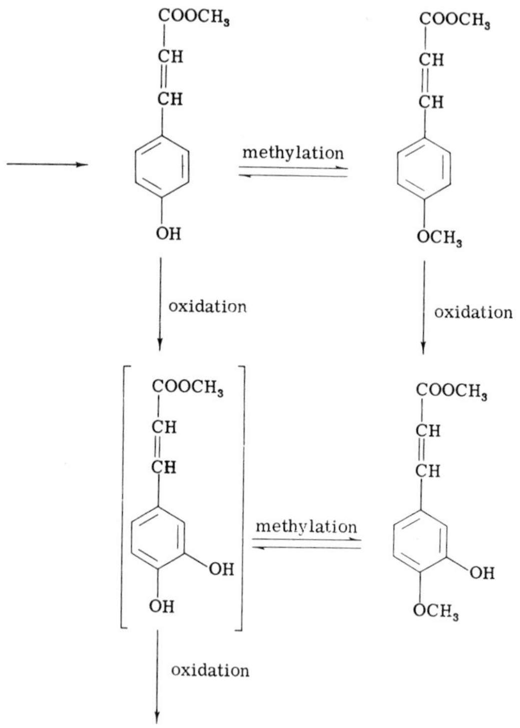

FIG. 2. Transformations occurring during the metabolism by *L. lepideus* of *p*-methoxyaromatic esters.

(*Polyporus*) *versicolor*, were studied. As contrasted with *Lentinus lepideus*, this organism does not accumulate significant amounts of aromatic compounds in its culture medium. However, when methyl anisate was added to its medium, transformations analogous to those undergone in the methyl *p*-methoxycinnamate metabolism of *Lentinus lepideus* were observed.

Thus, when methyl anisate was added to the medium of *P. versicolor*, demethylation and (simultaneously) hydroxylation were observed, and the color of the medium gradually turned brown. However, if the cultures were first heated, and then methyl anisate was added to the medium and shaken, no hydroxylated compounds could be detected. On the other hand, the conversion of methyl anisate to hydroxylated compounds was observed when an ascorbic acid system was employed (53). Accordingly, it was assumed that these transformations were achieved by a similar system inherently present in these molds.

However, significantly, if free anisic acid, rather than methyl anisate, was added to the medium of this fungus, no hydroxylated derivatives of anisic acid could be detected, nor did the color of the medium turn brown. Instead, the anisic acid was rapidly converted into anisaldehyde and anisyl alcohol, both identified in the medium. Thus, changes in the ultraviolet absorption patterns showed that anisic acid was converted to anisaldehyde and that the major portion of the aldehyde produced was reduced to anisyl alcohol (53).

The observed differences between the transformations of methyl anisate and of anisic acid by *P. versicolor* indicated that added methyl anisate was not significantly saponified; hence, the ester accumulates. However, a slow demethylation and hydroxylation of methyl anisate were achieved by the fungus, and these were followed by the reduction of a portion of the resultant products. The hydroxylated derivatives of methyl anisate are believed to be partially transformed by the general oxidizing processes of the organism, during which the color of the medium becomes brown (53).

When *p*-hydroxybenzoic acid was added to the medium of *P. versicolor*, *p*-hydroxybenzaldehyde was isolated (as its 2,4-dinitrophenylhydrazone). Hence, it is believed probable that *p*-hydroxybenzoic acid, possibly originating from methyl anisate, is likewise reduced to *p*-hydroxybenzaldehyde and to the corresponding alcohol (53).

W. C. Evans (54) also believes that the microbiological degradation of benzenoid compounds involves the formation of phenolic compounds at some stage. For example, when soil pseudomonads were grown in a liquid medium containing *trans*-cinnamic acid as sole carbon source, a mixture of phenols was obtained. In this mixture, two phenols were detected; the major constituent was an acidic catechol, the minor one a phenolic acid. These were identified as melilotic acid (*o*-hydroxyphenylpropionic acid) and 2,3-dihydroxyphenylpropionic acid (55). Hence, it was concluded that these two compounds represented the principal products of the pseudomonads' degradation of *trans*-cinnamic acid, prior to ring fission.

Finally, the structural relationships existing among the products of the metabolism of *Lentinus lepideus*, namely, methyl *p*-methoxycinnamate, methyl *p*-coumarate, and methyl isoferulate, and the lignin building stones, i.e., coniferyl alcohol, sinapyl alcohol, and *p*-hydroxycinnamyl alcohol, are apparent. Hence, it has long been considered possible (7) that lignin building stones are synthesized by a pathway similar to that of the biogenesis of the aromatic esters by L. lepideus. Thus, results obtained in studies of the metabolism of certain wood-destroying fungi, such as L. lepideus and P. versicolor, do offer a means of investigating the problem of the biogenesis of the lignin building stones. In particular, studies on the mechanism of the methylation of phenolic hydroxyl groups by L. lepideus (51, 52) could be of significance in relation to the origin of the guaiacyl and syringyl moieties of lignin.

IV. Lignification in Higher Plants

It would seem appropriate to consider the process of lignification as it occurs in higher plants first from the viewpoint of the sequence of events which occur in the lignifying plant. The development of mature wood-fiber has been divided (56) into four phases: cell division, cell enlargement, cell wall thickening, and lignification. However, these stages are not strictly consecutive and are not to be considered as separate and distinct phases.

Many suggestions have been made regarding the origin of lignin in plants (3c), but in general, these suggestions fall into three groups (56): (a) Lignin might arise in situ in the cell wall by the transformation of other cell wall constituents already present. (b) The lignin precursor(s) might be formed in the cambial zone, diffuse away, and then be incorporated into the differentiating cells of the xylem and phloem. (c) Lignin, or its precursor(s) might originate within the differentiating cell wall, and subsequently be incorporated into the cell wall.

Wardrop (56) has rejected the idea of molecular transformations within the cell wall itself, and he believes that the lignin precursor(s) diffuse outward from the interior of the cell.

The biochemical pathway of lignin formation in plant tissues has been divided (57) into two distinct phases: (a) the formation of the primary lignin building stones, such as p-coumaryl alcohol, coniferyl alcohol, and sinapyl alcohol, and (b) the conversion of these building stones into lignin itself. We may then ask, with Adler (57), how does nature synthesize molecules of the structural types of these lignin building stones?

Albeit a large number of plant constituents have been postulated as lignin precursors, in most cases, the evidence supporting these hypotheses has been meager. On the basis of recent observations, the most tenable theory would appear to be that lignin is a polymer of some compound or compounds with a phenylpropane skeleton, as for example, one or more of the above three lignin building stones (1, 2).

Although some information on isolated stages of lignin formation has appeared, the total, continuous, integrated series of biochemical reactions leading ultimately from carbon dioxide, via carbohydrate intermediates, to the primary lignin building stones long remained obscure. Accordingly, the following studies are described in an effort to help elucidate the pathway by which lignin is synthesized in growing plants.

A. LIGNIN FORMATION FROM CARBON DIOXIDE

After the exposure of sugar cane plants to radioactive carbon dioxide in the dark, the lignin fraction of these plants was found to contain radioactivity (58).

In a study of lignin biosynthesis in wheat plants, Stone et al. (59) had found that the greatest increase in the production of lignin, syringaldehyde, and vanillin was evidenced 45–70 days after seeding. The methoxyl content of the plants was also found to increase as the plants matured. Stone (60) then subjected the wheat plants to $C^{14}O_2$ in a "long-term" experiment. The $C^{14}O_2$ was fed at a stage of growth corresponding to rapid lignification. The plants were harvested every few days until maturity and were then oxidized with alkaline nitrobenzene; the resulting vanillin, syringaldehyde, and p-hydroxybenzaldehyde were separated by paper chromatography. The results indicated that all the $C^{14}O_2$ which was incorporated into the lignin was included within 24 hours after administration. The total activity originally acquired by the syringaldehyde portion of the lignin remained constant throughout the growth of the plant. From the results, Stone concluded that lignin is an end product of plant growth, and not a part of the respiratory system.

In "short-term" experiments (61), wheat plants, again at a stage of rapid lignification, were exposed for just 20 minutes to $C^{14}O_2$ in a closed chamber and were then grown for 1–24 hours in a normal atmosphere before harvesting. The results indicated that the synthesis of lignin was most rapid from 4 to 6 hours after $C^{14}O_2$ administration. Syringyl residues appeared to be formed more slowly than were guaiacyl residues. After 24 hours, C^{14} appeared in the lignin to the extent of about 1.5–2.0% of that administered.

B. CARBOHYDRATE PRECURSORS

The problem of the mechanism of lignification includes the elucidation of the identity of the carbohydrate precursor from which lignin is ultimately derived, together with the nature of the enzymic reactions operative during the process. As a result of these transformations, the carbohydrate precursor, photosynthetically derived from atmospheric carbon dioxide, is eventually converted into lignin (1).

Many suggestions have been advanced relative to the identity of this carbohydrate precursor, but these suggestions have been justly referred to as either purely speculative or else as based on evidence of an indirect or fragmentary character (7).

1. *The Role of* D-*Glucose*

In a preliminary investigation (62), uniformly labeled D-glucose-C^{14} was fed to a Norway spruce tree, and, after a suitable period of metabolism, radioactivity was detected in the cambium layer of the tree. The lignin of this layer was isolated and found to be radioactive (Table II).

TABLE II

DISTRIBUTION OF ACTIVITY IN NORWAY SPRUCE TREE
AFTER FEEDING UNIFORMLY LABELED D-GLUCOSE-C^{14} (62)

Plant material	Activity (counts/min./mg. C)
Stem	460
Lignin	240

From the data of Table II, it was obvious that the radioactivity of the labeled D-glucose fed to the tree was incorporated to a considerable extent into the lignin. Thus, it was apparent that the tree was able to convert glucose into lignin. Considering the central place that D-glucose occupies in plant biochemistry, both as a product of photosynthesis and as the monomeric unit of cellulose, it was considered significant that the tree also possessed the enzymic equipment necessary to convert this monosaccharide into lignin (62). Obviously, however, in the case of lignin, an aromatization process is also required. This will be considered in a later section.

In an extended investigation (63), the fate in lignification of glucose preparations which were labeled with C^{14} specifically in their number 1 or 6 positions (XVIII) was studied.

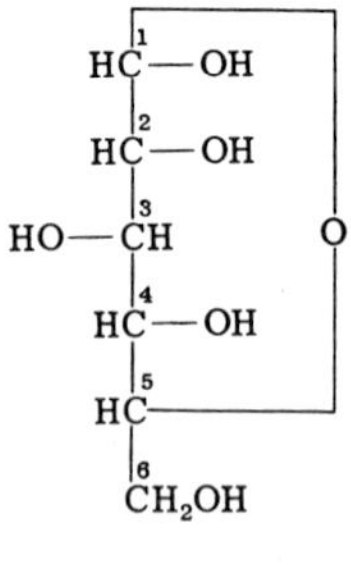

$$\begin{array}{c}
H\overset{1}{C}\!-\!OH \\
H\overset{2}{C}\!-\!OH \\
HO\!-\!\overset{3}{C}H \qquad O \\
H\overset{4}{C}\!-\!OH \\
H\overset{5}{C}\!-\! \\
\overset{6}{C}H_2OH
\end{array}$$

(XVIII)

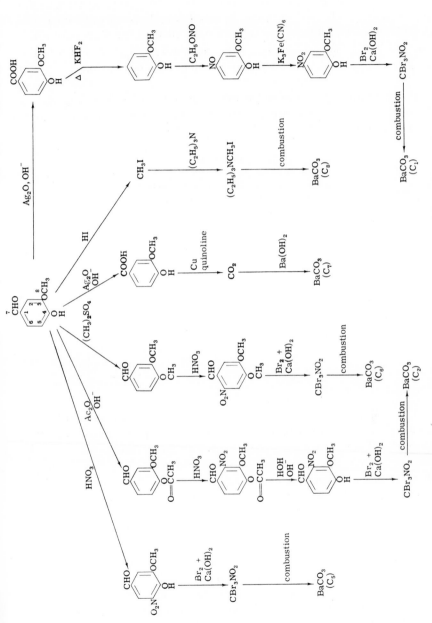

FIG. 3. Reactions employed in the chemical degradation of vanillin.

In these experiments, D-glucose-1-C^{14} and D-glucose-6-C^{14} were fed separately to individual Norway spruce trees. The method of feeding the tagged compounds and of isolating the lignin have already been described (64). The lignin was subjected to alkaline nitrobenzene oxidation (65), and vanillin was isolated. Carbons 1, 2, 5, 6, 7, and 8 of the vanillin were isolated by means of the degradation reactions shown in Fig. 3.

The activities of the several compounds obtained in the degradation of the lignins from the two specifically labeled D-glucose experiments are given in Table III.

TABLE III

PERCENTAGE DISTRIBUTION OF ACTIVITY IN VARIOUS POSITIONS OF
VANILLIN OBTAINED FROM D-GLUCOSE-1-C^{14} AND
D-GLUCOSE-6-C^{14} EXPERIMENTS (63)

	Percentage of total activity in vanillin	
Positions in vanillin	D-Glucose-1-C^{14} experiment	D-Glucose-6-C^{14} experiment
Total molecule	100.0	100.0
C-1	2.6	4.5
C-2	18.2	16.1
C-5	3.1	3.9
C-6	11.4	18.1
C-7	28.5	22.0
C-8	31.1	24.7
C-3, 4[a]	5.1	10.7

[a] Calculated values.

The comparative distribution of activity in the various positions of vanillin from the two experiments shows that appreciable activity was incorporated into carbons 2, 6, 7, and 8 of the vanillin, whereas considerably lesser amounts were incorporated into the other positions. These results are therefore similar to those obtained for the biosynthesis of shikimic acid (50) and of methyl p-methoxycinnamate (49) from glucose and have since been amply confirmed (66, 67).

Previously, it had been asserted (1, 2, 7) that both fungal and plant biosyntheses of phenylpropane moieties probably follow similar pathways. The similarity of C^{14} distribution from D-glucose-1-C^{14} and D-glucose-6-C^{14} in the aromatic rings of the methyl p-methoxycinnamate formed by Lentinus lepideus and of the vanillin derived from lignin oxidation shows that a marked similarity in metabolic pathways does indeed exist in the two apparently unrelated systems. This is obvious when we compare the percentage distributions of C^{14} from D-glucose-6-

C^{14} in the ester (XIX) derived from *L. lepideus* and the vanillin (XX) derived from the lignin of Norway spruce, using corresponding position designations, as in (XIX) and (XX).

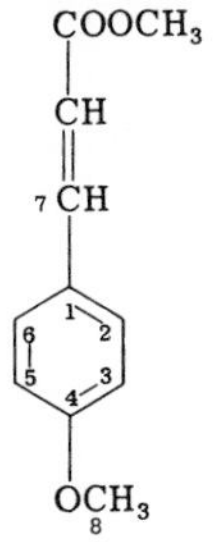

(XIX) 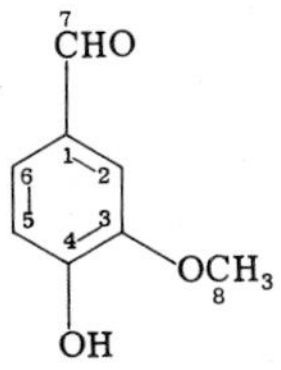   (XX)

The comparison in Table IV reveals a remarkable agreement in the distributions of radioactivity. From the data, it is apparent that both

TABLE IV

COMPARISON OF RELATIVE DISTRIBUTIONS OF ACTIVITY
IN CORRESPONDING POSITIONS OF METHYL *p*-METHOXYCINNAMATE AND VANILLIN

Positions in ester and vanillin	Percentage distribution of C^{14}	
	In ester (49)	In vanillin (63)
C-1	3.2	4.5
C-2	19.5[a]	16.1
C-3	3.5[a]	5.4[a]
C-4	4.2[a]	5.4[a]
C-5	3.5[a]	3.9
C-6	19.5[a]	18.1
C-7	17.6	22.0
C-8	12.6	24.7

[a] Calculated values.

the ester and the vanillin incorporated most of the activity in carbons 2, 6, 7, and 8.

2. The Cyclization Step

The mode of formation of shikimic acid from glucose (50) indicates that the latter is converted into this acid by the condensation of a triose derived via glycolysis, with a tetrose derived via the pentose phosphate pathway (39). Significantly, there is evidence that phosphoenol pyruvate and D-erythrose-4-phosphate, implicated in the synthesis of shikimic acid, are formed in higher plants (38). It may be noted that the

Embden-Meyerhof pathway produces phosphoenol pyruvate, whereas
D-erythrose-4-phosphate can be derived from the pentose phosphate
pathway.

Evidence for the formation of D-erythrose-4-phosphate in plants rests
mainly on its function as a substrate for the enzymes transketolase and
transaldolase. These enzymes are believed to form D-erythrose-4-phos-
phate as a transitory intermediate during respiration by the pentose
phosphate pathway (68) and also during photosynthesis (69). It is
necessary to postulate the formation of D-erythrose-4-phosphate in order
to explain the cyclic nature of these two processes (38). Furthermore,
there exists direct evidence (70) for the formation of D-erythrose-4-
phosphate during photosynthesis by *Chlorella*.

These considerations then provide an explanation for the observed
activity in positions 2 and 6 of the rings of shikimic acid (50) derived
from glucose, and of vanillin (63) obtained as described above, as
shown in Reactions 7–9.

$$\text{Glucose} \xrightarrow{\text{glycolysis}} \begin{array}{c} CH_2 \\ \parallel \\ C-O-PO_3H_2 \\ \mid \\ COOH \end{array} \quad \begin{array}{c} \text{2-Phosphoenol pyruvic} \\ \text{acid} \end{array} \qquad (7)$$

$$\text{Glucose} \xrightarrow[\text{pathway}]{\substack{\text{pentose} \\ \text{phosphate}}} \begin{array}{c} CHO \\ \mid \\ HC-OH \\ \mid \\ HC-OH \\ \mid \\ CH_2OPO_3H_2 \end{array} \quad \text{D-Erythrose-4-phosphate} \qquad (8)$$

$$\begin{array}{c} C \\ \mid \\ C \\ \diagup \diagdown \\ {}^*C \qquad C^* \\ \mid \qquad \mid \\ C \diagdown \diagup C \\ C \end{array} \xrightarrow[\text{Fig. 1}]{\text{as in}} \begin{array}{c} COOH \\ \mid \\ {}^*HC \diagup C \diagdown {}^*CH_2 \\ H \diagdown C \diagup \diagdown C \diagup H \\ HO \diagup H \diagdown O \diagup OH \\ H \end{array} \quad \text{Shikimic acid} \qquad (9)$$

Thus, the ultimate organic source of lignin is the carbohydrate
photosynthetically formed by the plant from atmospheric carbon dioxide.
Phosphoenol pyruvate and D-erythrose-4-phosphate may possibly serve
as the proximate precursors of the aromatic rings of lignin, while
D-glucose has been demonstrated (63) to be the ultimate carbohydrate
source.

C. THE SHIKIMIC ACID PATHWAY

As described above, the studies of Davis (6), and of Katagiri (71, 72)
confirmed the fact that shikimic acid plays an important role in bacterial
and fungal metabolism as a precursor of aromatic amino acids and that

the enzyme systems which bring about the transformation of glucose, via shikimic acid and other intermediates, into these aromatic acids are to be found in microorganisms. Furthermore, the presence of the enzyme system responsible for the synthesis of shikimic acid was confirmed not only in microorganisms, but also in higher plants, such as spinach and pea (73). These investigations then suggested the possibility that other aromatic products—such as lignin, which also is very widely distributed in higher plants—may also be formed via a sequence similar to the shikimic acid pathway.

Accordingly, in connection with the biosynthesis of lignin, it is of importance to consider the distribution of shikimic acid in higher plants, and particularly in woody plants. Hasegawa et al. (74) investigated the distribution of shikimic acid in the leaves of 164 plant species and found shikimic acid in 82 of these species. Further, Higuchi (75) investigated the distribution of shikimic acid in the leaves and cross sections of the young stems of 96 species of woody plants; shikimic acid was detected in 70 of these species. Hence, there can be little doubt that the shikimic acid pathway does indeed function in higher plants (38, 75).

Experiments with Sugar Cane Plants

The following results prove that shikimic acid, without any rearrangement of the carbon atoms of its six-membered ring, is to be considered a precursor of the aromatic rings of the lignin building stones, and accordingly, that their formation parallels the mechanism of formation of the aromatic amino acids by microorganisms.

Specifically labeled shikimic acid was prepared by fermentation of D-glucose-6-C^{14} by *Escherichia coli* mutant 83-24. As shown in Table V, such shikimic acid contains 44% of its total activity in position 2, and 52% in position 6 (50).

TABLE V

DISTRIBUTION OF THE C-6 CARBON ATOM OF GLUCOSE IN SHIKIMIC ACID (50)

Position of label in glucose	S-1	S-2	S-3	S-4	S-5	S-6	S-7
C-6	0	51	0	0	0	60	7

An aqueous solution of this specifically labeled shikimic acid was incorporated into a growing sugar cane plant. After several days of metabolism, the leaves were removed; the stem of the plant was cut, dried, and pulverized; the resulting powder was thoroughly extracted with water.

TABLE VI

DISTRIBUTION OF SHIKIMIC ACID ACTIVITY IN THE SUGAR CANE PLANT

Plant Material	Activity (counts/min.)
Stem (ground and water-extracted)	6
Klason lignin (10% of weight of stem)	42
Vanillin	58

Activity measurements of the plant materials (Table VI) indicated that, upon introduction of the specifically labeled shikimic acid into the ·sugar cane plant, the radioactive material was incorporated into non-water-extractable components of the stem. Examination of the isolated Klason lignin indicated that the radioactivity, to its greatest extent, was located in the lignin.

The pulverized plant material was submitted to treatment with Schweizer's reagent to remove the cellulose, and then to alkaline nitrobenzene oxidation; the resulting vanillin was isolated (65).

The distribution of radioactivity in the ring carbons of the vanillin was determined according to reactions analogous to those shown in Fig. 3. The activities in positions 2, 5, and 6 of the ring, determined according to such degradations, are shown in Table VII.

TABLE VII

DISTRIBUTION OF ACTIVITY IN SELECTED POSITIONS OF VANILLIN

Vanillin	Activity (counts/min.)	Percentage distribution of total activity
Total molecule	58	100
C-2	190	41
C-5	0	0
C-6	204	44

From these data, it is apparent that there was a distribution of activity in the aromatic ring of vanillin which agreed well with the original distribution of C^{14} in the cyclohexene ring of the incorporated shikimic acid (76).

No attempt was made to equate carbon-2 of vanillin with the corresponding position in shikimic acid, or carbon-6 of vanillin with this position in the acid, since one cannot distinguish these two positions, and since the two positions may be interconvertible.

Thus, after the absorption of specifically labeled shikimic acid into a sugar cane plant, it was established that this compound was metabolized by the plant and was incorporated to a great extent into its lignin.

The degradation of the lignin, via vanillin, revealed that the distribution of activity in the aromatic rings of the product was comparable to the distribution of activity in the incorporated shikimic acid. From these results, it was concluded that shikimic acid is an intermediate on the pathway from carbohydrate, formed from atmospheric CO_2 by photosynthesis, to the aromatic rings of the lignin building stones (77).

D. GENESIS OF THE LIGNIN BUILDING STONES

The use of the term "primary lignin building stone" is based upon the general assumption that lignin, like cellulose and starch, has a chainlike structure composed of simple "building stones" which, in turn, are linked in some way (or perhaps in several ways) to form a "lignin building unit" (1, 2, 3). This would correspond to the concept of "glucose anhydride" as the building stone for cellulose and starch.

The building stones of lignin, however, possess a phenylpropane carbon structure, and at least four of these must be linked together to form a "lignin building unit." A series of lignin building units then makes up the total lignin molecule. But, unlike the uniform building stones of cellulose and starch, lignin building stones, although they all have the same basic phenylpropane carbon structure, may be of the vanillyl (XXI), syringyl (XXII), or p-hydroxyphenylmethyl (XXIII) type (1, 2, 3).

(XXI)   (XXII)   (XXIII)

The phenolic cinnamic acids have come to be regarded as potential precursors of lignin, since they have the required phenylpropane carbon structure, they are known to be widely distributed in plants (78), and since they are highly ionized under physiological conditions (37).

Much recent speculation about lignification has centered on coniferyl alcohol as the key intermediate in a process of oxidation-polymerization. Historically, this idea developed from three circumstances: (*a*) the isolation of the glucoside coniferin from certain conifers; (*b*) the similarity in elementary analysis of isolated Klason lignins and coniferyl alcohol; and (*c*) the tendency of coniferyl alcohol to polymerize (79).

However, since coniferyl alcohol (XXIV) itself has not been found in plants, this hypothesis is really based on the natural occurrence of coniferin (XXV), the glucoside of coniferyl alcohol. Similarly, syringin (XXVI), the glucoside of sinapyl alcohol (XXVII), is regarded as a precursor of lignin in hardwoods. A survey (80) of the recorded occurrences of coniferin revealed that the presence of this glucoside has been established predominantly in coniferous wood species, with six families and fifteen species being represented. Regarding the reported occurrences of syringin, except for one finding of its presence in black locust, this glucoside has been isolated only from five genera of the olive family (80).

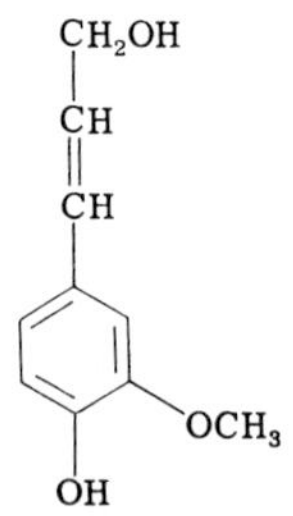

(XXIV) 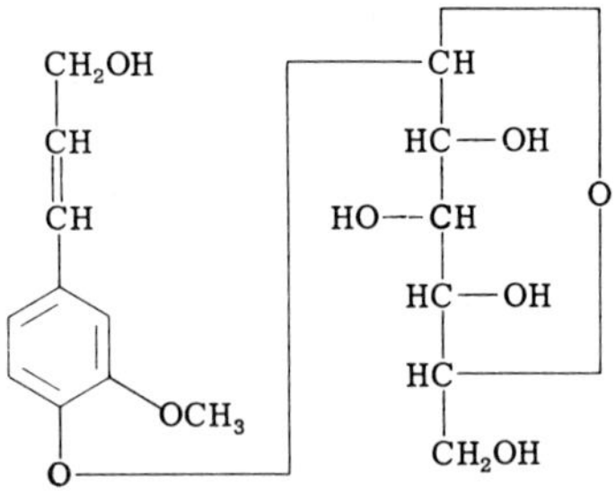   (XXV)

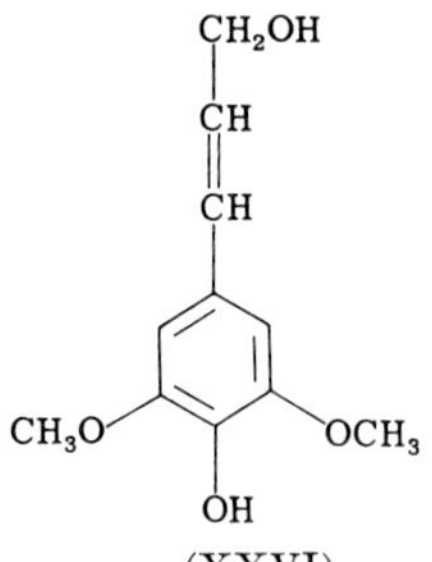

(XXVI) 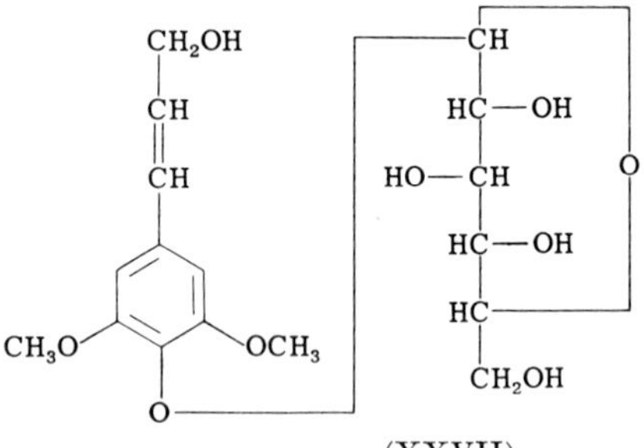   (XXVII)

The results of tracer studies in several laboratories have supported the concept that phenolic cinnamic alcohols and acids are precursors in the formation of lignin. For example, coniferyl alcohol has been synthesized with radioactive carbon in known positions of the mole-cule (*81, 82, 83*) and then fed to growing plants. Of equal signifi-cance has been the elaboration of degradation procedures to recover the radioactivity from the isolated lignin, or more particularly from the

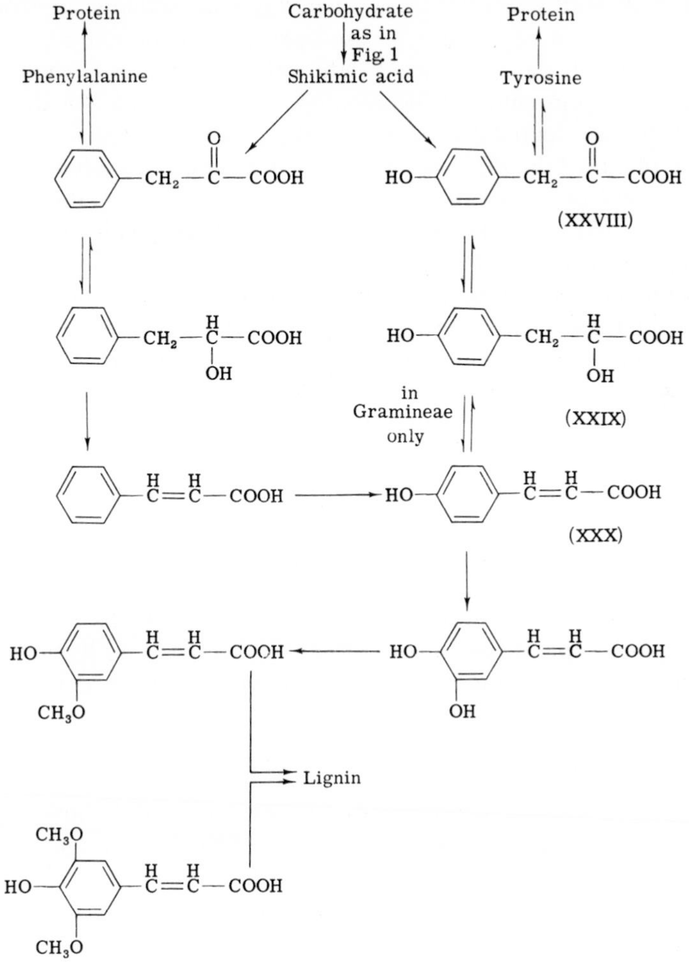

FIG. 4. Biogenetic reactions leading to the formation of lignin (*38*).

vanillin obtained by the oxidation of lignin (*63, 76*), or from the "Hib-bert ketones" obtained upon ethanolysis (*81*).

The synthesized radioactive compounds have been administered to growing plants in various ways: they may be fed directly to the plant or to excised shoots (*38*) or solutions of them may be absorbed through the ends of freshly cut stems, branches, leaves, or needles (*63,*

76). The localization of the introduced radioactive material may then be followed, if desired, by radioautography. The plant is allowed a certain time for metabolism; it is then worked up, and the specific activity of the lignin is measured.

The fact that the radioactive material was actually incorporated into the lignin can be assured by pre-extraction of the plant tissue with solvents in which the synthesized radioactive compound is known to be soluble. The lignin can then be isolated by some conventional method, followed by the degradative recovery of its radioactivity.

Data obtained in this way have been accepted as proof that suspected precursors, such as coniferyl alcohol, do mediate in lignin biosynthesis (57). Similar studies have also been made with sinapyl and p-hydroxycinnamyl alcohols.

A large number of other related C^{14}-labeled compounds have also been studied for their efficiency as precursors of lignin (38). Experiments of this kind have produced the scheme shown in Fig. 4.

The compounds shown as intermediates in Fig. 4 were fed by Neish et al. to excised shoots of wheat and maple plants and were found to be readily converted to lignin (84, 85). In these investigations, certain taxonomic differences were noted. For example, out of 11 species representing 10 plant families, only two converted tyrosine to lignin, although all utilized phenylalanine as a lignin precursor. The two species utilizing tyrosine were both members of the Gramineae (Poaceae) family. In this connection, it was suggested (85) that the failure of the non-Gramineae species to utilize tyrosine for synthesizing lignin was due to their enzymic inability to dehydrate p-hydroxyphenyllactic acid (XXIX).

The Role of p-Hydroxyphenylpyruvic Acid

It has already been mentioned that in the course of the investigations on the biogenesis of methyl p-methoxycinnamate by *Lentinus lepideus,* p-hydroxyphenylpyruvic acid was detected in the culture medium (45). The structural relationship of this acid to the suggested building stones of lignin prompted an investigation of the possible role of this acid in the biogenesis of lignin by the sugar cane plant.

p-Hydroxyphenylpyruvic acid-$C^{14}OOH$ was incorporated into a growing sugar cane plant by employing essentially the same technique as has been described for the D-glucose and shikimic acid experiments (86). A comparison of the radioactivity measurements of the introduced p-hydroxyphenylpyruvic acid, of the isolated lignin, and of the barium carbonate obtained on combustion of the latter revealed that most of the activity of the introduced acid was incorporated into the lignin (87).

The radioactive lignin obtained was subjected to alkaline nitrobenzene oxidation; the vanillin formed was isolated and, in this instance, was found to be nonradioactive. However, subjection of this lignin to alkaline fusion produced oxalic acid which was isolated and found to contain the radioactivity (88). It was concluded that the three-carbon side chain of the introduced p-hydroxyphenylpyruvic acid, which contained the radioactivity, was retained as a unit, possibly serving as a connecting link between the aromatic rings of the lignin polymer (47, 48). Accordingly, it appeared that p-hydroxyphenylpyruvic acid was an intermediate on the pathway between shikimic acid, derived from carbohydrates, and the lignin building stones, in the biogenesis of lignin by the sugar cane plant (77).

On the other hand, Billek (89) has reported that p-hydroxyphenylpyruvic acid was not converted into lignin by spruce trees. This apparent discrepancy has been resolved by Neish (90), who noted that p-hydroxyphenylpyruvic acid-3-C^{14} can be converted to guaiacyl or syringyl lignin in wheat, but not in buckwheat or sage. This difference in biosynthetic abilities among various species was later interpreted (85) as follows: Neither p-hydroxyphenylpyruvic acid (XXVIII) nor p-hydroxyphenyllactic acid (XXIX) is a *general* intermediate in lignification, and certain differences noted (as here) between grasses and nongrasses probably result from the unique ability of grasses to convert p-hydroxyphenyllactic acid (XXIX) to p-hydroxycinnamic acid (XXX). Since the sugar cane plants employed in the experiments described above are classed as grasses, they *are* able to utilize p-hydroxyphenylpyruvic acid (XXVIII) for lignin biosynthesis, as has been emphasized (91).

Thus, these results would seem to lend support to the scheme of Fig. 4 for the interconversions of phenylpropanoid compounds in the biogenesis of lignin (38).

E. CONVERSIONS OF THE LIGNIN BUILDING STONES

The hypothesis that lignin is biogenetically derived from coniferyl alcohol is suggested by the presence of the glucoside coniferin in precambial tissue (92).

The structure of coniferin was elucidated by Tiemann in 1875. Shortly thereafter, Tiemann and Mendelsohn (93) suggested that coniferyl alcohol, the aglucon of coniferin, bore some structural relationship to lignin. Then, in 1899, Klason (94) expressed the opinion that lignin was a condensation or polymerization product of coniferyl alcohol. Later, he suggested (95) that coniferyl aldehyde might be the fundamental building stone of lignin.

But the chemical nature of the polymerization of such monomers remained obscure until Cousin and Hérissey (96) in 1908 observed that isoeugenol underwent dimerization in the presence of air and under the influence of the oxidase enzymes present in a glycerol extract of the mushroom *Russula delica*. The product of the dimerization, dehydrodiisoeugenol, was found by Erdtman (97) to possess the structure of a phenylcoumaran derivative.

This discovery led Erdtman to an explanation of the mechanism for the polymerization of monomers into lignin. He postulated (98) that *p*-hydroxyphenylpropane compounds with unsaturated side chains, on oxidation, would initiate coupling reactions not only in the position *ortho* to the phenolic hydroxyl group, but also at the β-carbon atom of the side chain. Lignin might then originate from guaiacylpropane units which are first oxidized in the side chain and then dehydrogenated. Erdtman concluded that lignin is probably derived from precursors of structure similar to coniferyl alcohol (98). Subsequent to these hypotheses, it is now considered (99) that lignin is formed by the dehydrogenation of such compounds, with coniferous lignin probably being derived principally from coniferyl alcohol.

In her studies of the enzymic oxidations of phenolic compounds in living cells, Manskaja (100) investigated the chemical reactions taking place in cambial tissue. Her results have led her also to believe that lignification in plants takes place by oxidation-reduction reactions accompanying the enzymic changes that occur during the course of the metabolic conversions of coniferyl alcohol, which is thereby oxidized, and is eventually converted into the polymerized lignin (101).

About ten years after the original suggestions of Erdtman (98), these concepts were adopted by K. Freudenberg, who found that D-coniferin, labeled with C^{14} in its side chain, when incorporated into a spruce twig, was deposited in the stem in the form of a high-molecular material (102). Ethanolysis of this product yielded radioactive Hibbert ketones. In a similar experiment, L-coniferin remained unchanged (103). This indicated that D-coniferin was hydrolyzed by a β-glucosidase; the liberated coniferyl alcohol then polymerized. Accordingly, Freudenberg suggested an over-all scheme (Reaction 10) for the formation of lignin:

$$\text{Coniferin} \xrightarrow{\text{β-glucosidase}} \text{Coniferyl alcohol} \xrightarrow{\text{phenoldehydrogenase}} \text{Lignin} \quad (10)$$

Freudenberg then attempted to obtain polymeric products with lignin-like properties by the *in vitro* treatment of "primary lignin building stones" with air in the presence of a mushroom oxidase (104). Of the compounds tested, the dehydrogenation product of coniferyl alcohol (so-called DHP) showed the greatest similarity to lignin (82).

According to Freudenberg then, spruce lignin is a dehydrogenation polymer of coniferyl alcohol. By the action of enzymes, coniferyl alcohol is first dehydrogenated, forming highly reactive quinone methide radicals (82) (Sequence 11).

(11)

These radicals could then combine in various ways, forming a variety of carbon-carbon and carbon-oxygen-carbon linkages, which would seem to be characteristic of lignin.

Freudenberg then reported the isolation from the reaction mixture, at an intermediary stage, of three "secondary lignin building stones": dehydrodiconiferyl alcohol (XXXI), DL-pinoresinol (XXXII), and guaiacylglycerol-β-coniferyl ether (XXXIII).

These "secondary lignin building stones" (105) were condensed to the DHP polymer by treatment with dehydrogenating enzymes. In addition, they were reported to be present in cambial sap (106). Accordingly, Freudenberg seems to feel that the final phases of lignin formation are explainable (107) on the basis of the oxidation and condensation of coniferyl alcohol by plant enzymes.

However, many reservations and objections to this theory have been raised. For example, Nord and deStevens found that the oxidation products of certain native and enzymically liberated lignins contain p-hydroxybenzaldehyde (2, 108). Accordingly, they concluded that

(XXXI)   (XXXII)   (XXXIII)

coniferyl alcohol cannot be the *only* lignin precursor, or else, that it may be preceded in the scheme of lignification by some simpler, less-substituted aromatic monomer.

In addition, Erdtman (*109*) has pointed out that although in some respects Freudenberg's DHP's are similar to lignin, in other respects, they are quite different. Aulin-Erdtman considers the ill-defined (*110*) DHP's to be "stabilization products" of quinone methides. She also indicates that it has not been demonstrated that the DHP's are really formed by the further dehydrogenation of the dimeric dehydrogenation products of coniferyl alcohol. And although Freudenberg claims that these dimers are present in cambial sap, it must be borne in mind that the sap had already been drawn from the tree, and consequently, these compounds may actually be nonphysiological dehydrogenation products (*109*) or artifacts.

Further, Kremers (*79*) has rightly asked why, if coniferyl alcohol is the essential monomer of lignin, has it not been detected in woody plants? In this connection, it must be noted that numerous other substances, such as eugenol, ferulic acid, and several related compounds, which may be lignin precursors but are at least in part structurally different from lignin itself, have been tested as lignin progenitors with success (*111*).

Also, Baylis (*112*) has correctly pointed out that while Freudenberg has obtained some evidence for the transitory existence of quino-methide type compounds, he has not obtained direct evidence for the existence of his postulated free radical intermediates.

Finally, Goldschmid and Hergert (113) conducted a comprehensive examination of Western hemlock cambial constituents in an attempt to detect compounds that have been suggested as intermediates in the formation of lignin. The following substances were identified in the cambium: quinic acid, shikimic acid, coniferin, sucrose, fructose, glucose, leucocyanidin, catechin, epicatechin, and four depsides. In addition, glucosides were detected of several α-hydroxy guaiacyl compounds. However, significantly, compounds proposed by Freudenberg as lignin intermediates, e.g., coniferyl alcohol, dehydrodiconiferyl alcohol, and guaiacyl glycerol-β-coniferyl ether, were *not* found in the cambial zone.

Obviously, much still remains to be done in this area. Thus, for example, some of the more recent speculations of Freudenberg et al. (114) regarding the mode of adduct formation were later retracted and revised (115).

F. THE ENZYMES INVOLVED

Parallel with the question of the chemical structures of the precursors of lignin is the biochemical problem of the nature of the enzymes that convert these precursors into lignin. It must be noted that thus far there have been very few direct observations.

As mentioned above, Freudenberg (116) has observed that coniferyl alcohol may be dehydrogenated by either a mushroom or a cambial sap oxidoreductase, or by peroxidase with dilute hydrogen peroxide, to a polymer which has lignin-like properties.

Higuchi (117, 118) investigated the properties of a phenol oxidase responsible for lignification in the tissue of bamboo shoots and found that the enzyme had a substrate specificity similar to that of a laccase. Accordingly, he suggested that Freudenberg's enzyme may be a laccase.

The oxidation of coniferyl alcohol by crude mushroom extracts has been confirmed (119), but, when a purified mushroom polyphenol oxidase (tyrosinase) was employed, the oxygen consumption was negligible. Accordingly, it was concluded that, although there is present in crude mushroom extracts a heat-labile system which does catalyze the consumption of oxygen by coniferyl alcohol, it is not "polyphenol oxidase" which does this. Higuchi (75) has suggested that the preparation obtained from mushroom according to the procedure used by Freudenberg is a mixture of both laccase and tyrosinase.

Accordingly, it is now believed (75) that the enzyme acting on coniferyl alcohol is actually a laccase. However, the known distribution of laccase in higher plants is limited. On the other hand, the system, peroxidase-hydrogen peroxide, oxidizes the same types of compounds as does laccase. Thus, Freudenberg (104) found that the yield of a polymer, obtained by the action of a crude enzyme from *Araucaria excelsa* on coniferyl alcohol, could be increased severalfold by the addition of hydrogen peroxide.

S. M. Siegel (*120*) found that eugenol could be converted into a lignin-like product by embryonic root tips of the kidney bean in the presence of hydrogen peroxide; accordingly, he has attached importance to the role of peroxidase in the formation of lignin.

The chemical nature of the dehydrogenative-polymerization products of coniferyl alcohol, obtained by the action of mushroom phenol oxidase, *Rhus* laccase, and radish peroxidase, have been investigated (*121*). These studies indicated a close similarity among the three enzyme-formed DHP's and some resemblance to coniferous lignin. Thus, considering the wide distribution of peroxidase in higher plants, Higuchi (*75, 121*) has suggested that peroxidase may play an even more important role than does laccase in lignin biosynthesis.

V. Conclusion

There can be no doubt that lignin is a product of the shikimic acid pathway. The probable intervention of prephenic acid in this scheme provides an intermediate from which either phenylpyruvic or *p*-hydroxyphenylpyruvic acid might result. These may be converted to other intermediates, such as ferulic acid, and the latter in turn may be reduced to primary building stones of the type of coniferyl alcohol. An enzymic dehydrogenation-polymerization of this alcohol or of some related structure could then result in the formation of lignin.

To be sure, this oversimplification leaves many questions unanswered. For example, what moiety of the lignin structure is the source of the unmethoxylated *p*-hydroxyphenyl moieties that have frequently been detected in lignin oxidations (*2, 108*)? Furthermore, hardwood lignins yield significant amounts of syringyl derivatives. What is their source? It has been suggested (*122*) that the implicit methylation of guaiacyl nuclei can occur through the intervention of methionine, but this is certainly not the only possible explanation.

Finally, it must not be overlooked that the exact number and chemical nature of the primary building stones of lignin are still uncertain, and this regrettably is also true of the structure of the final product itself.

References

1. W. J. Schubert and F. F. Nord, *Advances in Enzymol.* **18,** 349 (1957).

1a. E. Correns, *Paperi ja Puu* **2,** 47 (1961).

2. F. F. Nord and G. deStevens, in "Handbuch der Pflanzenphysiologie" (W. Ruhland, ed.) Vol. 10, p. 389, Springer, Berlin, 1958.

3. F. E. Brauns, "The Chemistry of Lignin," Academic Press, New York, 1952; (a) p. 15; (b) p. 669; (c) p. 694; (d) F. E. Brauns and D. A. Brauns, "The Chemistry of Lignin: Supplement Volume." Academic Press, New York, 1960.

4. D. A. I. Goring, Pulp Paper Mag. Can. 58, No. 3, 165 (1957).

5. A. Rezanowich and D. A. I. Goring, Polyelectrolyte Expansion of a Lignin Sulfonate Microgel, Tech. Report No. 162, Pulp and Paper Research Inst. of Canada, Montreal, 1960.

6. B. D. Davis, Advances in Enzymol. 16, 247 (1955).

7. F. F. Nord and J. C. Vitucci, Advances in Enzymol. 8, 253 (1948).

8. D. R. Whitaker, Can. J. Biochem. and Physiol. 34, 488 (1956).

9. E. T. Reese, Appl. Microbiol. 4, 39 (1956).

10. H. Pringsheim, Z. physiol. Chem. 78, 266 (1912).

11. P. E. Simola, Ann. Acad. Sci. Fennicae, Ser. A, II 34, No. 6 (1931).

12. W. Grassmann et al., Ann. 502, 20 (1933); 503, 167 (1933).

13. M. A. Jermyn, J. M. Gillespie, and E. F. Woods, Nature 169, 487 (1952).

14. E. T. Reese and W. Gilligan, Can. J. Microbiol. 1, 90 (1954).

15. E. T. Reese, R. G. H. Siu, and H. S. Levinson, J. Bacteriol. 59, 485 (1950).

16. G. A. Greathouse, Textile Research J. 20, 227 (1950).

17. D. R. Whitaker, Arch. Biochem. Biophys. 43, 253 (1953).

18. P. Kooiman, Enzymologia 18, 371 (1957).

19. D. H. F. Clayson, J. Soc. Chem. Ind. (London) 62, 49 (1943).

20. K. Nishizawa and T. Kobayashi, J. Agr. Chem. Soc. Japan 27, 239 (1953).

21. B. C. Sison, W. J. Schubert, and F. F. Nord, Arch. Biochem. Biophys. 68, 502 (1957).

22. B. C. Sison, W. J. Schubert, and F. F. Nord, Arch. Biochem. Biophys. 75, 260 (1958).

23. B. C. Sison and W. J. Schubert, Arch. Biochem. Biophys. 78, 563 (1958).

24. S. A. Barker, E. J. Bourne, G. C. Hewitt, and M. Stacey, J. Chem. Soc. p. 3734 (1955).

25. G. Halliwell, Nutrition Abstr. & Revs. 29, 747 (1959).

26. F. F. Nord and L. J. Sciarini, Arch. Biochem. 9, 419 (1946).

27. F. F. Nord and J. C. Vitucci, Arch. Biochem. 14, 229 (1947).

28. F. F. Nord and W. J. Schubert, Holzforschung 5, 1 (1951).

29. R. M. DeBaun, S. F. Kudzin, and W. J. Schubert, Arch. Biochem. 26, 375 (1950).

30. G. deStevens, R. M. DeBaun, and F. F. Nord, Arch. Biochem. Biophys. 33, 304 (1951).

31. F. F. Nord and G. deStevens, Trans. N. Y. Acad. Sci. [2] 14, 97 (1951).

32. G. deStevens and F. F. Nord, Fortschr. chem. Forsch. 3, 70 (1954).

33. F. F. Nord and W. J. Schubert, Abstr. Fifth World Forestry Congr., Seattle, Washington, 1960.

34. F. F. Nord and W. J. Schubert, Holzforschung 15, 1 (1961).

35. B. D. Davis, Experientia 6, 41 (1950).

36. E. L. Tatum, S. R. Gross, G. Ehrensvaerd, and L. Garnjobst, Proc. Natl. Acad. Sci. U. S. 40, 271 (1954).

37. B. D. Davis, Arch. Biochem. Biophys. 78, 497 (1958).

38. A. C. Neish, Ann. Rev. Plant Physiol. 11, 55 (1960).

39. D. B. Sprinson, Advances in Carbohydrate Chem. 15, 235 (1960).

39a. M. I. Chudakov, Uspekhi Khim. 30, 184 (1961).

40. J. G. Levin and D. B. Sprinson, *Biochem. Biophys. Research Communs.* **3,** 157 (1960).
41. E. W. Bassett and S. W. Tanenbaum, *Biochim. et Biophys. Acta* **28,** 247 (1958).
42. J. H. Birkinshaw and W. P. K. Findlay, *Biochem. J.* **34,** 82 (1940).
43. F. F. Nord and J. C. Vitucci, *Arch. Biochem.* **14,** 243 (1947).
44. F. F. Nord and J. C. Vitucci, *Arch. Biochem.* **15,** 465 (1947).
45. G. Eberhardt and F. F. Nord, *Arch. Biochem. Biophys.* **55,** 578 (1955).
46. G. Eberhardt, *J. Am. Chem. Soc.* **78,** 2832 (1956).
47. F. F. Nord and W. J. Schubert, *TAPPI* **40,** 285 (1957).
48. W. J. Schubert and F. F. Nord, *Ind. Eng. Chem.* **49,** 1387 (1957).
49. H. Shimazono, W. J. Schubert, and F. F. Nord, *J. Am. Chem. Soc.* **80,** 1992 (1958).
50. P. R. Srinivasan, M. T. Shigeura, M. Sprecher, D. B. Sprinson, and B. D. Davis, *J. Biol. Chem.* **220,** 477 (1956).
51. H. Shimazono and F. F. Nord, *Arch. Biochem. Biophys.* **78,** 263 (1958).
52. H. Shimazono, *Arch. Biochem. Biophys.* **83,** 206 (1959).
53. H. Shimazono and F. F. Nord, *Arch. Biochem. Biophys.* **87,** 140 (1960).
54. W. C. Evans, in "Handbuch der Pflanzenphysiologie" (W. Ruhland, ed.), p. 454. Springer, Berlin, 1958.
55. C. B. Coulson and W. C. Evans, *Chem. & Ind. (London)* p. 543 (1959).
56. A. B. Wardrop, *TAPPI* **40,** 225 (1957).
57. E. Adler, *TAPPI* **40,** 294 (1957).
58. C. E. Hartt and G. O. Burr, *Proc. Intern. Botan. Congr., Stockholm, 1950* **7,** 748 (1953).
59. J. E. Stone, M. J. Blundell, and K. G. Tanner, *Can. J. Chem.* **29,** 734 (1951).
60. J. E. Stone, *Can. J. Chem.* **31,** 207 (1953).
61. S. A. Brown, K. G. Tanner, and J. E. Stone, *Can. J. Chem.* **31,** 755 (1953).
62. W. J. Schubert and S. N. Acerbo, *Arch. Biochem. Biophys.* **83,** 178 (1959).
63. S. N. Acerbo, W. J. Schubert, and F. F. Nord, *J. Am. Chem. Soc.* **82,** 735 (1960).
64. F. F. Nord and W. J. Schubert, *Experientia* **15,** 245 (1959).
65. Schimmel & Co., German Patent No. 693,350 (1940).
66. K. Kratzl and H. Faigle, *Monatsh. Chem.* **90,** 768 (1959).
67. K. Kratzl and H. Faigle, *Z. Naturforsch.* **15b,** 4 (1960).
68. P. A. Srere, J. R. Cooper, V. Klybas, and E. Racker, *Arch. Biochem. Biophys.* **59,** 535 (1955).
69. M. Calvin, *J. Chem. Soc.* p. 1895 (1956).
70. V. Moses and M. Calvin, *Arch. Biochem. Biophys.* **78,** 598 (1958).
71. M. Katagiri and R. Sato, *Science* **118,** 250 (1953).
72. M. Katagiri, *J. Biochem. (Tokyo)* **40,** 629 (1953).
73. S. Mitsuhashi and B. D. Davis, *Biochim. et Biophys. Acta* **15,** 54 (1954).
74. M. Hasegawa, T. Nakagawa, and S. Yoshida, *J. Japan. Forestry Soc.* **39,** 159 (1957).
75. T. Higuchi, *Proc. 4th Intern. Congr. Biochem., Vienna, 1958* **2,** 161 (1959).
76. G. Eberhardt and W. J. Schubert, *J. Am. Chem. Soc.* **78,** 2835 (1956).
77. F. F. Nord and W. J. Schubert, *Proc. 4th Intern. Congr. Biochem., Vienna 1958* **2,** 189 (1959).
78. E. C. Bate-Smith, *Sci. Proc. Roy. Soc. Dublin* **27,** 165 (1956).
79. R. E. Kremers, *Ann. Rev. Plant Physiol.* **10,** 185 (1959).

80. R. E. Kremers, *TAPPI* **40**, 262 (1957).
81. K. Kratzl, and G. Billek, *TAPPI* **40**, 269 (1957).
82. K. Freudenberg, *Fortschr. Chem. org. Naturstoffe* **11**, 43 (1954).
83. K. Freudenberg, *Proc. 4th Intern. Congr. Biochem.*, Vienna, *1958* **2**, 121 (1959).
84. S. A. Brown and A. C. Neish, *Can. J. Biochem. and Physiol.* **33**, 948 (1955).
85. S. A. Brown, D. Wright, and A. C. Neish, *Can. J. Biochem. and Physiol.* **37**, 25 (1959).
86. F. F. Nord, W. J. Schubert, and S. N. Acerbo, *Naturwissenschaften* **44**, 35 (1957).
87. W. J. Schubert, S. N. Acerbo, and F. F. Nord, *J. Am. Chem. Soc.* **79**, 251 (1957).
88. S. N. Acerbo, W. J. Schubert, and F. F. Nord, *J. Am. Chem. Soc.* **80**, 1990 (1958).
89. G. Billek, *Proc. 4th Intern. Congr. Biochem.*, Vienna, *1958* **2**, 207 (1959).
90. A. C. Neish, in Discussion of the paper of G. Billek, *Proc. 4th Intern Congr. Biochem.*, Vienna, *1958* **2**, 213 (1959).
91. C. J. Coscia, *Experientia* **16**, 81 (1960).
92. A. von Wacek, O. Härtel, and S. Meralla, *Holzforschung* **7**, 58 (1953); **8**, 65 (1954).
93. F. Tiemann and B. Mendelsohn, *Ber.* **8**, 1127, 1136, 1139 (1875).
94. P. Klason, *Svensk Kem. Tidskr.* **9**, 133 (1899).
95. P. Klason, *Ber.* **B53**, 706 (1920).
96. H. Cousin and H. Hérissey, *Compt. rend. acad. sci.* **147**, 247 (1908); *J. pharm. chim.* [6] **28**, 193 (1908).
97. H. Erdtman, *Biochem. Z.* **258**, 172 (1933); *Ann.* **503**, 283 (1933).
98. H. Erdtman, *Svensk Papperstidn.* **42**, 115 (1939); **44**, 249 (1941); *Research* **3**, 63 (1950); H. Erdtman and C. A. Wachtmeister, in "Festschrift A. Stoll," p. 145. Birkhäuser, Basel, 1957.
99. H. Erdtman, *Proc. 4th Intern. Congr. Biochem.*, Vienna, *1958* **2**, 10 (1959).
100. S. M. Manskaja, *Doklady Akad. Nauk S.S.S.R.* **62**, 369 (1948).
101. S. M. Manskaja, *Proc. 4th Intern. Congr. Biochem.*, Vienna, *1958* **2**, 215 (1959).
102. K. Freudenberg, *Holz Roh- u. Werkstoff* **11**, 267 (1953).
103. K. Freudenberg and F. Bittner, *Ber.* **86**, 155 (1953).
104. K. Freudenberg, R. Kraft, and W. Heimberger, *Ber.* **84**, 472 (1951); K. Freudenberg, H. Reznik, H. Boesenberg, and D. Rasenack, **85**, 641 (1952).
105. K. Freudenberg, *J. Polymer Sci.* **16**, 155 (1955).
106. K. Freudenberg, *Angew. Chem.* **68**, 84 (1956).
107. K. Freudenberg, *Ind. Eng. Chem.* **49**, 1384 (1957).
108. G. deStevens and F. F. Nord, *Proc. Natl. Acad. Sci. U. S.* **39**, 80 (1953).
109. H. Erdtman, *Ind. Eng. Chem.* **49**, 1385 (1957).
110. G. Aulin-Erdtman and L. Hegbom, *Svensk Papperstidn.* **59**, 363 (1956).
111. H. A. Stafford, *Plant Physiol.* **35**, 108, 612 (1960).
112. P. E. T. Baylis, *Sci. Progr.* **48**, 409 (1960).
113. O. Goldschmid and H. L. Hergert, *Tappi* **44**, 858 (1961).
114. K. Freudenberg, B. Lehmann, and A. Sakakibara, *Chem. Ber.* **93**, 1354 (1960); *Ann.* **623**, 129 (1959).
115. K. Freudenberg and M. Friedmann, *Chem. Ber.* **93**, 2138 (1960).
116. K. Freudenberg, *Angew. Chem.* **68**, 508 (1956).

117. T. Higuchi, I. Kawamura, and H. Ishikawa, *J. Japan. Forestry Soc.* **35,** 258 (1953); T. Higuchi, I. Kawamura, and I. Morimoto, **37,** 446 (1955).
118. T. Higuchi, *Plant Physiol.* **10,** 364 (1957).
119. H. S. Mason and M. Cronyn, *J. Am. Chem. Soc.* **77,** 491 (1955).
120. S. M. Siegel, *Physiol. Plantarum* **6,** 134 (1953); **7,** 41 (1954); **8,** 20 (1955); *J. Am. Chem. Soc.* **78,** 1753 (1956); *Quart. Rev. Biol.* **31,** 1 (1956).
121. T. Higuchi, *J. Biochem. (Tokyo)* **45,** 575 (1958).
122. R. U. Byerrum, J. M. Flokstra, L. J. Dewey, and C. D. Ball, *J. Biol. Chem.* **210,** 633 (1954).

CHAPTER 4

Nucleic Acids

GEORGE BRAWERMAN and HERMAN S. SHAPIRO

Cell Chemistry Laboratory, Department of Biochemistry,
College of Physicians and Surgeons, Columbia University, New York

I. Introduction

The recent developments in our knowledge of the nucleic acids have made their identification with the hereditary determinants of the cell increasingly evident. Both Feulgen staining of fixed cells and chemical analysis of isolated structures have demonstrated the localization of deoxyribonucleic acid (DNA) in the chromosomes. A direct experimental demonstration of the biological role of this substance was provided by the discovery of bacterial transformations. A further indication of the identity of DNA with the genetic material was provided by the finding that the amount present in the nucleus is constant within a species and that the quantity in sperm cells is one-half that of the diploid somatic cells. The nucleotide composition of DNA was also found to be constant and characteristic for a given species. In deoxyribonucleic acids from different species exhibiting similar nucleotide compositions, partial sequence analyses have revealed differences in the nucleotide distribution along the polynucleotide chains. A double-stranded helical structure was ascribed to DNA on the basis of X-ray crystallography data, and the pairing principles established as a result of the nucleotide composition studies have led to the suggestion that the two strands are complementary. This has provided a reasonable model for the self-duplication of the nucleotide sequence during DNA synthesis. Finally, an enzyme has been isolated that promotes the synthesis of the DNA polymer in the presence of some DNA added as a primer. The composition of the synthesized material is essentially that of the "primer" DNA, thus suggesting that a replicating mechanism is involved.

The evidence with respect to ribonucleic acid (RNA) is more complex and confusing. This substance was found to be localized mainly in the cytoplasm and to be more abundant in tissues where intense protein synthesis occurs. The cytoplasmic ribonucleoprotein particles, which appear to constitute the primary site of protein synthesis, were found to contain the bulk of the cellular RNA. A connection between the ribonucleoprotein particles and viruses is indicated by their similar RNA content. The fact that the turnover of nuclear RNA is considerably higher than that of cytoplasmic RNA has led some workers to suggest that RNA might be synthesized in the nucleus and then transferred to the cytoplasm. The isolation of infective RNA from viruses indicates that this substance can, like DNA, act as a primary carrier of hereditary information. Perhaps the most significant development in the biochemistry of ribonucleic acid is the finding that the cell contains two types of RNA: one of relatively low molecular weight, involved in the transport of activated amino acids to the microsomes; the other one of high molecular weight, connected primarily with the cytoplasmic ribonucleoprotein particles.

II. Cellular Localization of the Nucleic Acids

A. Distribution within the Cells

1. DNA

Much of the work on the distribution of the nucleic acids has been performed with the use of cytochemical techniques (1). The specific Feulgen reaction has been used extensively to demonstrate the localization of the DNA in the nuclear chromatin. Basic dyes in combination with ribonuclease have also contributed much to the study of RNA. However, direct chemical studies on isolated cell structures have proved far more informative, and whenever possible, greater emphasis will be placed on them.

a. DNA in the Nucleus. The localization of DNA in the nucleus has been demonstrated cytochemically in a large number of cells and tissues. The Feulgen staining material has in general been found to coincide with the chromosome structures (*2*). Furthermore, the exact correspondence in the position of DNA and basic proteins in the chromosomes (*3*) suggests that the nucleohistones isolated from mammalian tissues are genuine biological complexes rather than isolation artifacts.

Chemical analyses of centrifugal fractions of disrupted cells have failed to demonstrate the presence of DNA in any but the nuclear fraction, thus confirming the results obtained by cytochemical techniques. The DNA has been further localized through the isolation of chromosome-like structures (*2*). These structures have been identified as the interphase chromosomes. Their main constituents are DNA and histone, both of which are readily extracted with 1 M NaCl.

b. DNA in Bacteria. Although bacteria do not seem to contain nuclear structures similar to the ones in animal and plant cells, the existence in these organisms of chromatin bodies that contain Feulgen-positive material is now generally accepted (*4*). In the case of *Bacillus megatherium*, nuclear bodies that appear to contain all the DNA of the cells have been isolated from lysed protoplasts (*5*).

c. Presence of DNA in the Cytoplasm. Although the conclusion that cellular DNA is present in the nucleus exclusively is generally accepted, it has been disputed by some workers. Chayen has remarked that the Feulgen procedure involves a drastic acid treatment which could disrupt the organization of the cell, thus providing a distorted picture of the DNA distribution (*6*). As an example, he cites the case of the meristematic cells of the broad bean root. Ultraviolet absorption of the nuclei in the isolated living cells yields a DNA value much lower than normal; but after a treatment similar to the one involved in the Feulgen reaction, normal DNA values are obtained. These cells normally contain small basophilic particles, and this basophilia is lost after deoxyribonuclease treatment. Various agents, such as acids, fat solvents, and drastic homogenization procedures cause the loss of these particles and a corresponding increase in the basophilia and ultraviolet absorption of the nucleus. After gentle disruption of the cells, the nuclear fraction isolated by differential centrifugation contains very little DNA. The elongated cells of the root do not show this effect; all their DNA is found in the nucleus even in the absence of drastic treatment. These experiments suggest that in certain types of cells the standard techniques might bring about a diffusion into the nucleus of DNA originally present in the cytoplasm (*6*).

d. DNA in Chloroplasts. The presumed hereditary continuity of chloroplasts gives special importance to the possibility of the presence of DNA in these bodies. There exists evidence, both cytochemical and chemical, to this effect (7). However, many workers have failed to detect any DNA in the chloroplasts, or have cast doubt on the positive evidence on the grounds that it is difficult to obtain chloroplasts devoid of any contamination by nuclear fragments. Chiba and Sugahara have prepared from spinach and tobacco leaves chloroplasts essentially free of nuclear contaminants (7). Treatment of these preparations with hot perchloric acid under conditions normally used for the extraction of DNA failed to yield any of this substance. However, when higher concentrations of acid were used, material giving both the characteristic diphenylamine color and ultraviolet absorption of DNA was obtained in substantial amount. This unusual resistance of "chloroplastic" DNA to acid treatment is quite unprecedented, and this material will require further identification.

e. DNA in Eggs. Chemical analyses of the eggs of sea urchin and frog have yielded DNA values much higher than those in the corresponding sperm cells (8). In the case of the frog, a 5000-fold excess was obtained. This excess DNA must be present in the cytoplasm, where it is perhaps utilized in subsequent mitoses. Although the presence of DNA has been demonstrated in the egg cytoplasm, the latter is in general Feulgen negative. This lack of stainability could be due to the extra DNA being either spread throughout the whole cytoplasm in a very dilute form, or in a precursor state nonstainable by the Feulgen reaction (8). High DNA values have also been found in nematode, insect, and bird eggs (9).

It has been suggested by the Marshaks that the excess DNA in Arbacia eggs originates in material released into the cytoplasm during meiotic divisions, and in contaminating ovarian cells (10, 11). These authors estimate that the amount of DNA from these sources can account for all the DNA found in the egg. Furthermore, they find the nuclei of ripe eggs to be Feulgen negative. They therefore conclude that the nucleus of ripe unfertilized sea urchin eggs does not contain any DNA. This conclusion has been disputed by other workers, who have found Feulgen-positive material in these nuclei (12). This problem does not appear to be resolved yet (13).

2. RNA

a. Distribution of RNA in Centrifugal Fractions. The cellular constituents can be fractionated by centrifugation of disrupted cells at varying speeds (14). Four major fractions can thus be obtained: nuclei, mitochondria, microsomes, and cell sap or supernatant. RNA is present in all fractions. The greatest portion of the cellular RNA is generally present in the microsomal fraction. In liver, which has been the tissue most extensively studied in this respect, about 50% of the total RNA of the cell is present in this fraction. This is also the only fraction where the RNA concentration is higher than that of the whole tissue. The status of mitochondrial RNA is somewhat doubtful. The relatively small amount of RNA in the mitochondrial preparations could possibly originate from microsomal contaminants. However, careful purification of the mitochondria has failed to eliminate the RNA entirely. Table I shows

TABLE I

DISTRIBUTION OF RNA IN CELLULAR FRACTIONS OF MOUSE LIVER AND
ETIOLATED *Euglena gracilis*

Mouse liver (15)		*Euglena gracilis* (etiolated) (16)	
Fraction[a]	RNA (% of total)	Fraction[a]	RNA (% of total)
Nuclear fraction (1600 g, 10 min.)	11.0	"Chloroplast" fraction (1000 g, 20 min.)	11
Mitochondria (29,000 g, 10 min.)	16.8	Mitochondria (15,000 g, 15 min.)	12
Microsomes (130,000 g, 60 min.)	52.4	Microsomes (105,000 g, 60 min.)	55
Soluble fraction	16.5	Supernatant	22

[a] Values in parentheses indicate the centrifugal field and duration of centrifugation for each fraction.

the distribution of cellular RNA in mouse liver and in etiolated *Euglena gracilis*. It can be seen that this distribution is surprisingly similar in these two very different species.

Turnover studies have revealed deep metabolic differences among the ribonucleic acids of the various fractions (17). The incorporation of radioactive precursors into the nuclear RNA is much higher than in any cytoplasmic nucleic acid (see Fig. 1). Nuclear RNA also shows the highest initial rate of incorporation. Within the cytoplasm, the activity of the soluble fraction is higher than that of the particulate fractions. Microsomal and mitochondrial ribonucleic acids have in general similar turnover rates.

b. RNA in the Nucleus. There exists much confusion concerning the localization of RNA in the nucleus. Cytochemical studies have generally indicated that the nuclear RNA is concentrated in the nucleolus (18). However, very little systematic work has been done on the quantitative

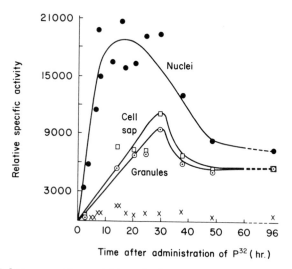

FIG. 1. Relative specific activities of the cytidylic acids of nuclear, mitochondrial, and microsomal RNA separated from rabbit liver at various times after the administration of P³². The points for mitochondrial and microsomal RNA were coincident, and the resultant curve has been termed "granules." Reproduced from R. M. S. Smellie (17).

distribution of RNA in the nucleus. It has been suggested that the RNA concentration in the nucleolus might be lower than that of the nucleus as a whole (19). In two amphibians, considerably higher RNA values were found in the whole nucleus than in the nucleolus: 4.7 to 1 in the case of liver cells of the larva *Ambystoma tigrinus;* 6.2 to 1 in liver cells of the adult salamander *Triturus viridescens,* and 3.8 to 1 in pancreas cells of the same animal (20). The RNA of the whole nucleus also showed a considerably higher incorporation of precursors than that of the nucleolus.

The isolation of chromosome-like material and of intact nucleoli has permitted the direct chemical study of the RNA in these structures. The RNA of the isolated chromosomes was found to be firmly bound to the insoluble "residual" portion left after extraction of the nucleohistones with strong salt solutions (2). The RNA content of these residual chromosomes varied with the type of tissues: liver, 12%; thymus, 3%; trout sperm, 0.15%. The RNA concentration in isolated chromosomes was also found to be about twice as high in leukemic mouse spleen as in the normal tissue (21). Isolated nucleoli were found to contain up to 4 or 5% RNA (19). The nucleoli of starfish oocytes have been investigated most extensively (22). They appear to contain all the RNA of the nucleus. A portion of their RNA is readily extracted with distilled water and is apparently metabolically different from the residual RNA, as evidenced by a much higher turnover.

Studies on whole nuclei provide additional evidence for the heterogeneity of nuclear RNA. In calf thymus nuclei, one-third of the RNA is readily extracted with phosphate buffer (fraction I), and one-third remains insoluble after extraction of the residue with 1 M NaCl (fraction II) (23). The incorporation of adenine into RNA was found to be more rapid and much higher in II than in I (24). However, in rabbit thymus nuclei, with phosphorus as the precursor, the turnover in fraction I appeared to be slightly higher than in fraction II (25).

Comparative studies of the total amount of RNA in the nuclei of different tissues have been made by several workers. In many cases, however, the nuclei were isolated in media containing citric acid. It has been shown that this method entails the loss of RNA from the nuclei (26). The RNA extracted in this manner is apparently different from the residual RNA, since it exhibits a lower turnover (25, 26). The use of nonaqueous media for the isolation of nuclei seems to prevent this loss of RNA. Some values for the RNA content of nuclei are listed in Table II. The higher value in wheat germ than in mature mammalian

TABLE II
RNA CONTENT OF NUCLEI

Tissue	RNA-P / DNA-P
Mammalian livers[a] (27)	0.10
Wheat germ[a] (28)	0.89
Rabbit[a] (26)	
Appendix	0.48
Intestinal mucosa	0.71
Thymus	0.21
Bone marrow	0.45
Lung	0.60
Embryo liver	0.975
Salamander liver[b] (20)	0.70

[a] Chemical analyses on nuclei isolated with the use of nonaqueous media.
[b] Cytochemical value.

tissues such as liver has been ascribed to the capacity for rapid growth of the wheat embryo (28).

c. RNA in the Small Cytoplasmic Particles and in Viruses. Palade made a systematic study by electron microscopy of the small cytoplasmic granules of rat and chicken tissues (29). The size of most particles ranged from 10 to 15 mμ; some varied between 8 and 10 mμ and others between 15 and 30 mμ. Only adult erythrocytes failed to show the presence of the granules. The number of particles was relatively constant for any given type of cell; it was lowest in granulocytes and seminal epithelia; highest in embryonic cells, rapidly proliferating adult cells, and certain glandular cells (from endocrine pancreas, salivary glands, mammary glands). The particles were associated with the membranes of the endoplasmic reticulum in cells with a high degree of differentiation and were freely distributed in the cytoplasm of cells characterized by rapid proliferation.

The particles associated with the endoplasmic reticulum probably correspond to those present in the microsomal fraction isolated by differential centrifugation; and the free particles, equivalent to the "post microsomal" particles of Palade and Siekevitz (30, 31). Both the microsomal and postmicrosomal particles have a size of about 15 mμ. The ratio of postmicrosomal to microsomal RNA is perhaps a measure of the relative amounts of free and bound particles. This ratio was 0.3 in rat liver and 1.3 to 1.8 in guinea pig pancreas (30, 31). The greater lability of pancreatic microsomes (31) could contribute to this difference.

Treatment of rat liver and guinea pig microsomes with deoxycholate liberates ribonucleoprotein particles (31, 32) which apparently correspond to the small cytoplasmic granules. In other organisms similar ribonucleoprotein particles can be isolated without preliminary deoxycholate treatment. The properties of the particles from pea seedlings, yeast, rat liver, and *Escherichia coli* are summarized in Table III. The striking similarities between the particles from these different sources

TABLE III

PROPERTIES OF RIBONUCLEOPROTEIN PARTICLES FROM VARIOUS SOURCES

Property	Pea seedlings (33)	Yeast (34)	Rat liver (36)	Escherichia coli (37)
Sedimentation constant	74 S	80 S	77.5 S	70 S
Size	28 mμ	21 mμ	18 mμ?	—
RNA content	34%	42%	40%	60–65%
RNA particle weight	1.7×10^6 [a]	1.7×10^6 [a]		1.7×10^6
Subunits, sedimentation constants	60, 40	60, 40 (35)		51, 32
Fraction of total cytoplasmic RNA present in particles	0.6–0.8	0.6		0.85–0.90

[a] Estimated by Tissières and Watson (37).

have been discussed by Tissières and Watson (37). Schachman and co-workers have studied the small particles of three microorganisms: *Escherichia coli, Pseudomonas fluorescens,* and *Rhodospirillum rubrum* (38). In all cases, the principal constituent had a sedimentation constant of 40 S. This was probably a degradation product of the 70 S compound of Tissières and Watson. The particles contained 30–40% RNA. In the case of *E. coli,* they comprised 86% of the total RNA of the cell, and in the case of *Pseudomonas,* 89%.

The estimated particle weight of 1.7×10^6 for the RNA of the ribonucleoprotein of pea root, yeast, and *E. coli* is of particular significance. RNA with a molecular weight of 1.8×10^6 has been isolated from both tobacco leaves and rat liver (39). This RNA presumably originated from the ribonucleoprotein particles. RNA isolated from tobacco mosaic virus also has a molecular weight of 1.7 to 2×10^6 (40, 41). The weight of the biologically active unit of tobacco mosaic virus was also estimated as 2×10^6 (41).

It has been noted that, although the size of a large variety of plant and animal viruses varies over a very wide range, the average weight of the RNA in these particles has a constant value of 2×10^6 (39, 42). This very close similarity between the size of the RNA of cytoplasmic particles and viruses has led Ping-Yao Cheng to postulate the existence of a fundamental unit of RNA with a molecular weight of 1.7×10^6 (43). This attractive generalization is, however, somewhat obscured by the existence of subunits both in viruses and cytoplasmic particles (42, 43).

d. Soluble RNA. In a study of the mechanism of incorporation of amino acids into protein in rat liver, Hoagland and co-workers discovered that the activated amino acids are first transferred to a ribonucleic acid present in the activating enzyme preparations (44). This RNA is apparently of low molecular weight. RNA from yeast, from liver microsomes, and degraded microsomal RNA could not serve as amino acid acceptors. These workers also found that the RNA-amino acid complex, isolated by a phenol method from the enzyme preparation, could transfer the bound leucine to microsomes. Thus it appeared that a specific RNA was acting as carrier of activated amino acids during their transfer from the supernatant fraction to the microsomes. Ribonucleic acids with similar properties were soon discovered in many different organisms. Evidence was also obtained to the effect that specific RNA molecules served as acceptors for different amino acids (45, 46, 47). It has been possible to achieve a partial separation of molecules specific for different amino acids (45, 48). While a specific RNA molecule seems to be required for each amino acid, there appears to exist a large degree of similarity between the soluble ribonucleic acids from different species. Thus RNA preparations from all mammalian tissues tested could serve as amino acid acceptors with guinea pig liver activating enzymes (49). RNA from *Escherichia coli* was also effective in this system, but at a slower rate. Similarly, RNA from *E. coli* was only 40% effective with the enzymes from yeast (46). It was also found that the supernatant fractions (containing RNA) from both *Tetrahymena* and rat liver could catalyze the incorporation of amino acids into each other's microsomes (50).

Berg and Ofengand have fractionated the total RNA of *E. coli* with 1.5 M NaCl (47). Over 50% of the RNA was precipitated in this manner, and active material was found only in the supernatant. This affords probably the best method for separating cellular ribonucleic acid into two functionally different classes: low molecular weight "carrier" RNA and high molecular weight "template" RNA. Low and high molecular weight fractions were also obtained from Ehrlich ascites tumor cells by chromatography (51). The low molecular weight component, which could not be precipitated by 1 M NaCl, comprised one-third of the total RNA and had a turnover higher than that of the other fraction. It apparently corresponds to the carrier RNA.

B. NUCLEIC ACID CONTENT OF CELLS

1. *DNA*

The study of the DNA content of cells has in general indicated a close connection between this material and the chromosomes. This subject has been extensively reviewed by R. Vendrely (8, 52).

a. *Constancy of DNA Content.* The concept that the DNA content of cells of a given species is constant was introduced by Boivin and co-workers. They established that nuclei from various calf tissues all contain about 6.5×10^{-6} μg. DNA. Furthermore, bull spermatozoa, containing the haploid amount of chromosomes, showed a value of 3.4×10^{-6} μg. DNA, approximately one-half the value of the diploid somatic cells (53). Mirsky and Ris essentially confirmed these findings, and by extending the study to many animal species they also found different DNA values for different species (54). The constancy of the DNA content per nucleus within a species and the haploid-diploid relation have subsequently been demonstrated in a large variety of species (8).

Several instances of irregularities in the DNA content of cells have been uncovered (8). In some plants the amounts of DNA in cells of various tissues are considerably different, although the number of chromosomes appears to be the same. These variations have been attributed to increases in the number of chromonemata threads within the chromosomes. A similar situation exists in the case of the giant chromosomes of the *Drosophila* salivary glands. DNA per nucleus values of 0.56 to 71.2 $\times$ 10^{-6} μg. are found in these cells as compared to an estimated normal diploid value of 0.17 $\times$ 10^{-6} μg. *Paramecium caudatum* and other ciliates have, in addition to the normal diploid nucleus, a macronucleus which contains up to forty times the normal DNA value. Irregularities have also been found in the process of pollen formation. In general, the relation between the number of chromosomes and the DNA content of the nucleus does not appear to be as strict in plants as in animals (8).

Another exception to the principle of constancy of DNA has been cited by Chayen (6). In certain plants grown at temperatures close to the freezing point ($+4°$ to $-7°$), or at elevated temperatures (37°), values for the DNA content 20% below normal were found. The values returned to normal when the plants were brought back to normal temperatures. A special role was suggested for this 20% portion of the total DNA.

b. Relation of DNA Content to Degree of Ploidy. The amount of DNA per nucleus was found to be higher in tissues containing polyploid cells (8). Measurements of the DNA content of single cells by microspectrophotometry have revealed the presence in rat liver of three classes of nuclei containing amounts of DNA in ratios of approximately 1:2:4. This relationship has been found in different organs and other species. A relation between the DNA content and the degree of ploidy was also found during the formation of gametes (8).

The use of Ehrlich ascites tumor cells has permitted a determination of the relation of DNA content to polyploidy by direct chemical anlyses. These cells are tetraploid and have twice the amount of DNA as that in the cells of normal rodent tissues (55) and in beef liver and lymphoma ascites tumor cells (56). A linear relation between DNA content of cells and number of chromosomes has been found in the course of a microspectrophotometric study of normal mouse tissue and ascites tumor cells (57). A similar relationship has been found in a comparison between original tumor cells and sublines with different chromosome numbers (58).

The relation between DNA content and degree of ploidy has also been demonstrated in diploid and haploid *Aspergillus* conidia (59, 60) and in a series of haploid, diploid, triploid, and tetraploid yeasts (61).

c. DNA in Rapidly Growing Cells. In proliferating cells, the constancy of DNA content cannot be expected to hold, since the DNA must double in amount at some point of the division cycle. Thus gross analysis of rapidly growing tissues yields values higher than those of resting cells (8).

The DNA content of individual cells of many growing tissues has been studied by microspectrophotometry. The conclusion from these studies is that DNA synthesis usually occurs during interphase (2, 12). In some cases, however, especially during egg cleavage, DNA synthesis may begin at telophase (12).

Some recent studies have provided more precise information on the timing and duration of DNA duplication. The uptake of radioactive DNA precursors in single cells has been measured by autoradiography. The results for bean root meristem, human bone marrow, and mouse Ehrlich ascites tumor (62) are summarized in Fig. 2. DNA synthesis

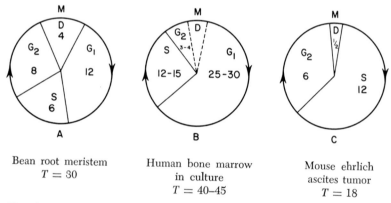

Bean root meristem
$T = 30$

Human bone marrow
in culture
$T = 40$–45

Mouse ehrlich
ascites tumor
$T = 18$

FIG. 2. Mitotic cycles deduced from autoradiography studies. Time in hours. M = metaphase; D = mitotic division; S = period of uptake of isotope into DNA; G_1 and G_2 = periods in early and late interphase during which DNA does not become labeled; T = total length of mitotic cycle. Reproduced from A. Howard (62).

appears to occur during a well-defined period of the interphase, but both the timing and the duration of the process are different in each case. Contradictory results were obtained by this technique and by Feulgen staining on ascites tumor cells. Autoradiography indicated a period of DNA synthesis starting soon after mitosis and lasting throughout the greater part of interphase (63). Feulgen staining, on the other hand, showed a rather steep curve for the same process, starting after six-tenths of the interphase time had elapsed (57). A similar curve was obtained with normal embryonic mouse cells (57). The same study revealed that the time required for the doubling of the DNA is about the same for mouse and chick embryonic cells, in spite of the fact that the latter have a shorter intermitotic time. In chick embryo tissue cultures partially synchronized by cold treatment, Feulgen measurements indicated a 1-hour lag between the completion of DNA synthesis and the beginning of mitosis. The duration of DNA duplication was estimated as slightly higher than 1 hour (64). Feulgen measurements on *Tetrahymena pyriformis* have also indicated that DNA synthesis starts some time after the beginning of interphase and is completed more than an hour before the cells begin to divide (65). This is remarkable in view of the short generation time of these cells (about 4 hours). DNA formation has been followed in synchronized cultures of *Escherichia coli* by chemical measurements. The DNA content of these cells was found to double before division (66). In another study, however, the curve for DNA synthesis failed to show the stepwise increase which should have been expected in a synchronized culture (67). A continuous synthesis of DNA in *Escherichia coli* and *Salmonella typhimurium* was also indicated by autoradiography measurements (68). The absence of a discontinuous synthesis of DNA can perhaps be attributed to the very short generation time of these organisms.

d. Quantity of Genetic Information in DNA. Several workers have attempted to estimate the size of a gene in terms of DNA nucleotide pairs. The principle of the method introduced by Benzer (69) is as follows: the total length of the genetic material is estimated in terms of units of recombination frequencies; the total amount of DNA in the chromosomes is calculated in terms of nucleotide pairs (taking into consideration the double-stranded configuration of the DNA chain); assuming that the total DNA is genetic material taking part in recombination, the number of nucleotide pairs per unit of recombination is calculated. The number of recombination units contained in a gene or in a functional segment as defined by the *cis-trans* test (69) can then be converted to a number of nucleotide pairs. The values obtained in this manner must, however, be considered as very crude estimates because of several shortcomings in the method (69, 70, 71).

Benzer (69) first estimated the number of nucleotide pairs per unit of recombination in phage T4 at 1×10^3. By modifying his assumptions (70), he reduced this value to 1×10^2. Pontecorvo and Roper (71), using a similar reasoning, obtained values of 8×10^4, 3×10^5, and 1×10^3 for *Aspergillus, Drosophila,* and phage T4, respectively. A value of 5×10^3 was obtained for *Escherichia coli* with the use of a more direct method: the comparison of the rate of transfer of DNA labeled with radioactive phosphorus and of genetic markers during mating (72). The number of nucleotide pairs contained in a "cistron" in phage was estimated (69) at 4×10^3, but subsequently revised (70) to 4×10^2.

A minimum value of 1 to 8×10^3 was obtained for the genes of *Aspergillus, Drosophila,* and phage (71). It is perhaps significant that the estimated values for the nucleotide content of a gene are of the same order of magnitude as the value for the number of nucleotides in an isolated DNA molecule (molecular weight: 6×10^6, 9×10^3 nucleotide pairs).

e. DNA Content of Cells. There already exists an impressive amount of information on the DNA content of cells of different species (8, 52, 73). Tables IV, V, and VI contain values for the vertebrates, invertebrates, and microorganisms and plants, respectively. Table VII represents a crude attempt at summarizing the values for the various classes investigated so far. Many more data will, however, be necessary before any clear-cut evolutionary pattern can be established. This task is also made more complicated by the frequent occurrence of polyploidy. Mirsky and Ris (73) have remarked that in invertebrates the most primitive animals show the lowest DNA values. These workers have determined the DNA content of a large variety of fish erythrocytes (8, 73) and have noticed in the teleosts a considerable uniformity within families. They have interpreted the values for snakes as indicating a tendency for the DNA content of recent reptiles to decline. A decrease was also apparent in the evolution of birds from reptiles. They recognized, however, that proper derivations of this kind would require the knowledge of the DNA content of the ancestors of present-day animals.

Among the vertebrates, mammals, birds, and reptiles have fairly constant values: 6 picograms (pg.) for the mammals; 2 pg. for birds; and 5 pg. for most reptiles. A large number of fish values lie around 2 pg.; the considerable variations can perhaps be ascribed to polyploidy (8). The amphibian values represent a remarkable, almost perfect, geometric progression ranging from 7 to 168 pg. DNA per cell. This suggests a very marked tendency for polyploidy in this class. The marsupials represent a somewhat special case among mammals (75). They contain fewer chromosomes than the other mammals, but have the same amount of DNA per nucleus. There also appears to be a tendency toward polyploidy in this group.

The data for the invertebrates are more scarce and therefore more difficult to interpret. The values appear to be constant in some classes, but in others very wide differences seem to occur: 0.2–6 pg. in the case of insects, and 0.6–4.5 pg. in the mollusks.

The values for bacteria and molds are very low. In bacteria, they range from 0.002 to 0.06 pg. In *Aspergillus* there appears to be polyploidy. The protozoan values are similar to those of cells of vertebrates. The high value for *Tetrahymena* is not unexpected since this organism

TABLE IV
DNA CONTENT OF SOMATIC CELLS OF VERTEBRATES[a]

Group	Organism	DNA[b]
Dipnoan	African lungfish (*Protopterus*)	100
Fishes	Carp (*Cyprinus carpio*)	3.49, 3.2
	Barbel (*Barbus barbus*)	3.4
	Roach (*Gardonus rutilus*)	1.9
	Tench (*Tinca tinca*)	1.7
	Perch (*Perca fluviatilis*)	1.9
	Pike (*Esox lucius*)	1.7
	Trout (*Salmo irideus*)	4.9
	Eel (*Anguilla anguilla*)	1.9
	Catfish (*Ameiurus nebulosus*)	1.89, 1.8
Amphibians	*Amphiuma*	168
	Salamander (*Triturus viridescens*) (*20*)	98
	Necturus	48.4
	Frog	15, 13 (*74*)
	Toad	7.33
Reptiles	Green turtle	5.27
	Wood turtle	4.92
	Snapping turtle	4.97
	Alligator	4.98
	Water snake	5.02
	Pilot snake	4.28
	Black racer snake	2.85
Birds	Domestic fowl	2.34, 2.2
	Guinea hen	2.27
	Goose	2.92, 1.9
	Duck	2.65, 2.2
	Pigeon	2.0
	Turkey	1.9
	Pheasant	1.7
	Sparrow	1.9
Mammals	Marsupials (*Trichosurus vulpecula*) (*75*)	6.0
	Ox	6.4, 6.9
	Pig	5.1, 6.8
	Guinea pig	5.9
	Dog	5.3, 6.7
	Man	6.0, 6.8
	Rabbit	5.3
	Horse	5.8
	Sheep	5.7, 6.8
	Rat	5.7
	Mouse	5.0

[a] Data reproduced from reviews by R. Vendrely (*8, 52*). A few values obtained from other sources have been included.

[b] Values are expressed in picograms (pg.; 10^{-12} gm.) DNA per cell.

TABLE V

DNA CONTENT OF CELLS OF INVERTEBRATES[a]

Group	Organism	Value	DNA[b]
Sponges	Tube sponge	Diploid	0.12
	Orange sponge (*Dysidea crawshagi*)	Diploid	0.11
Coelenterate	Jellyfish (*Cassiopeia*)	Sperm	0.33
Echinoderms	Sea urchin (*Echinometra*)	Sperm	0.98
	Sea urchin (*Lytechinus*)	Sperm	0.90
	Sea urchin (*Arbacia*)	Sperm	0.67 (*76*), 0.79 (*10*)
	Sea urchin (*Paracentrotus*) (*76*)	Sperm	0.70
	Sea cucumber (*Stichopus diabole*)	Sperm	0.99
Annelid	Nereid worm	Sperm	1.45
Mollusks	Limpet (*Fissurella barbadensis*)	Sperm	0.50
	Snail (*Tectarius muricatus*)	Sperm	0.67
	Chiton tuberculatus	Sperm	0.63
	Squid	Sperm	4.5
Crustaceans	Cliff crab (*Plagusia depressa*)	Sperm	1.49
	Goose barnacle	Sperm	1.46
Insects	Cricket (*Gryllus domesticus*) (*77*)	Sperm	6.0
	Drosophila (*78*)	Diploid	0.17
Tunicate	*Asidia atra*	Sperm	0.158

[a] Data reproduced from article by Mirsky and Ris (*73*). A few values from other sources have been included.

[b] Values are expressed in picograms (10^{-12} gm.) DNA per cell.

has a macronucleus. In higher plants, high values seem to prevail, probably the result of polyploidy.

The huge difference between the DNA content of bacteria and vertebrate cells (more than 100-fold) requires some comment. *Escherichia coli* and other bacterial cells are capable of growing in simple media and therefore possess a full complement of enzymes and other agents required for the processes of life. The degree of complexity of their genetic complement should therefore be of the same order of magnitude as that of higher organisms. In this context, the significance of the much greater DNA content of higher organisms is difficult to understand. It is not impossible that the latter contain many replicates of each genetic unit. This must certainly occur in the case of polyploidy. A possible clue to this problem is provided by the often observed parallelism between DNA content of nucleus and cell size (*52, 59–61, 73*). A larger cytoplasm would require a larger number of metabolic units, such as en-

TABLE VI
DNA CONTENT OF MICROORGANISMS AND PLANT CELLS

Organism	DNA[a]
Hemophilus influenzae (*79*)	0.002
Escherichia coli (*52*)	0.009
Salmonella typhimurium (*80*)	0.011
Bacillus lactis aerogenes (*81*)	0.021
Clostridium welchii (*82*)	0.024
Bacillus megatherium (*5, 83*)	0.07, 0.055
Yeast (bakers') (*84*)	0.065
Euglena gracilis (*85*)	2.9
Tetrahymena pyriformis (GL) (*86*)	13.6
Neurospora crassa (*87*) (per conidium)	0.017
Aspergillus nidulans (*60*) (haploid)	0.044
Aspergillus sojae (*59*) (per nucleus, haploid)	0.088
Tobacco (*88*) (diploid)	2.5
Broad bean (*Vicia faba*) (*89*) (diploid)	30
Onion (*Allium cepa*) (*89*) (diploid)	40

[a] Values are expressed in picograms (10^{-12} gm.) DNA per cell.

zymes, to perform a certain function, and if the genetic factors that control the formation of these units operate at a relatively slow rate, more of these factors would be required.

f. DNA in Viruses. While the plant viruses and some animal viruses contain ribonucleic acid, DNA is present in the insect polyhedral viruses, the adenoviruses, the poxviruses, in papilloma virus, and in the bacteriophages (*90*). The amount of phosphorus in the T phages has been estimated (*91*). Considering all the phosphorus in phage as part of DNA, one obtains DNA values of about 0.00024 pg. per particle for the even series and somewhat less for the odd series. A more precise determination based on measurements of the specific activity of P^{32}-labeled phages yielded the value of about 0.00008 pg. per infective unit for the odd series. A similar value was obtained for a virulent λ phage from *E. coli* and a temperate A_1 phage from *Salmonella typhimurium*. The particle weight of DNA in rabbit papilloma virus was estimated at 4×10^6. A still lower value, namely, 1.7×10^6, was obtained (*92*) for the DNA of the small bacteriophage φX174. This DNA was also found to be single stranded. It is probably highly significant that the size of this single-stranded DNA is the same as that of the RNA in viruses and nucleoprotein particles. The value for papilloma virus is about double that of φX172, and it should be of interest to know whether this virus contains one double-stranded DNA molecule.

TABLE VII
AMOUNTS OF DNA IN CELLS IN VARIOUS GROUPS OF
ANIMALS AND PLANTS AND IN VIRUSES

Group	DNA (pg.)[a]	Nucleotide pairs[b]
Fishes	2 (1-6)	2×10^9
Amphibians	7–168	6.5×10^9
Reptiles	5	4.5×10^9
Birds	2	2×10^9
Mammals	6	5.5×10^9
Sponges	0.1	0.1×10^9
Echinoderms	1.8	1.7×10^9
Mollusks	1.2	1.1×10^9
Crustaceans	3	2.8×10^9
Insects	0.17–12	0.16×10^9
Bacteria	0.002–0.06	0.002×10^9
Phytoflagellate	3	2.8×10^9
Fungi	0.02–0.17	0.02×10^9
Higher plants	2.5–40	2.3×10^9
T Bacteriophages (even)	0.00024	220×10^3
λ Bacteriophage	0.00008	70×10^3
Papilloma virus	—	6×10^3
Bacteriophage $\phi \times 174$	—	$5.1 \times 10^{3\,c}$

[a] Diploid values for all groups except microorganisms. Values that appear most frequently among representatives of each group are used; if none, range is indicated.

[b] Calculated on the basis of either the lowest or the most frequent value.

[c] Value expressed as single nucleotides because DNA is single stranded.

2. RNA

a. Relation of the RNA Content to the Physiological State of Cells and Tissues. In contrast to the behavior of DNA, the amount of RNA in cells can vary over wide ranges. The relation of RNA content of tissues to their physiological state has been the subject of numerous investigations (93, 94). In general, processes involving active protein synthesis are associated with rises in the RNA content of the tissues involved. In regenerating liver, both the amount of RNA per cell and the ratio of RNA to protein increases considerably during the period of most active growth (93). Similarly, the RNA per cell values increase during the period of most intensive cell division in tissue cultures. Neoplastic and embryonic tissues show in general lower values for the ratio of RNA to DNA or for the amount of RNA per cell. However, the cells in these tissues are smaller and their RNA concentration appears to be higher than that of the normal adult tissues. During the embryonic development of chicks and rats, the RNA content of the cells either increases or remains more or less constant, but the ratio of RNA to protein always decreases drastically (93).

b. *Relation between RNA Content and Rate of Growth of Microorganisms.* The RNA concentration and the ratio of RNA to DNA were found to increase in various microorganisms during rapid growth. Rises in the ratio of RNA to protein were also noted (93). Caldwell and

TABLE VIII

The RNA Content of Rat Tissues[a]

Tissue	RNA per cell (pg.)	RNA-P / DNA-P	RNA[b] / Protein
Liver	51	4.3	0.019
Regenerating liver (2 days)	68	4.8	—
Young liver (10 days)	12	1.8	0.019
Hepatoma	14	1.3	—
Pancreas	31	4.0	—
Brain	—	2.7	0.014
Skeletal muscle	—	2.7[c]	0.021
Testis	—	1.8	—
Kidney	12[c]	1.7[c]	0.017
Heart	7	0.9	—
Bone marrow	6[c]	0.8	—
Spleen	4[c]	0.7[c]	0.020
Small intestine	4	0.6	—
Lung	4	0.6	—
Thymus	1.3	0.2	—

[a] Values selected from data by Leslie (93).
[b] RNA nucleotides per amino acid residues in protein.
[c] Averages of widely scattered values.

co-workers have obtained cultures of *Bacterium lactis aerogenes* (*Aerobacter aerogenes*) with different generation times by either modifying the medium or using slow-growing mutants (95). They found a linear relation between the amount of RNA per cell and the reciprocal of the generation time. A similar linear relation was obtained by Price in the case of *Staphylococcus muscae* (96). Price also found that the amounts of protein and DNA per cell remained constant. Using a continuous-culture apparatus, Herbert also found that the RNA content of *Aerobacter aerogenes, Staphylococcus aureus* (*Micrococcus pyogenes* var. *aureus*), and *Bacillus megatherium* cells (expressed as percentage of RNA) increases linearly with the rate of growth (97). In the case of the rod-shaped organisms, the size of the cells increases considerably with the growth rate, and the variations in the absolute amounts of RNA per cell are therefore more complicated. Similar results were obtained in the case of *Salmonella typhimurium* (*98*). Jeener measured the RNA and protein contents of *Polytomella caeca* in continuous cultures with rates limited by the amounts of phosphate or carbon source (*99*). He obtained a strict linearity between the values for the ratio of RNA to protein and the rate of growth as indicated by protein synthesis. By extrapolating the curves to a rate of growth of zero, he obtained values for the "basal" amount of RNA in this organism. Wade and Morgan have compared the RNA contents of resting and actively growing cells in a large variety of microorganisms and found relative increases ranging from 1.3 to 16.5 (*100*). All the excess RNA in *E. coli* was found to be

TABLE IX

RNA in Homologous Tissues from Closely Related Species[a]

Tissue and organism	$\dfrac{\text{RNA-P}}{\text{DNA-P}}$	$\dfrac{\text{RNA}[b]}{\text{Protein}}$
Liver		
Rat	4.3	0.019
Mouse	3.5	0.016
Rabbit	3.1[c]	—
Cat	2.3	—
Guinea pig	2.3	—
Monkey	3.4	—
Man	2.5	0.012
Pullets	2.7	—
Cockerel	1.7	—
Kidney		
Rat	1.7[c]	0.017
Mouse	1.1	—
Rabbit	0.9[c]	—
Guinea pig	1.0	—
Man	1.4	0.015
Spleen		
Rat	0.7[c]	0.020
Mouse	0.3	—
Rabbit	0.6[c]	—
Guinea pig	0.8	—
Man	0.5	—

[a] Values selected from data by Leslie (*93*).
[b] RNA nucleotides per amino acid residues in protein.
[c] Averages of widely scattered values.

present in the fraction sedimenting at 100,000 g for 4 hours. The RNA content of the other fractions was essentially the same in resting and growing cells (*100*). The RNA connected with rapid multiplication is apparently similar to that of the ribonucleoprotein particles previously discussed.

c. RNA Content of Cells. In view of the marked variability of the RNA content of cells, it is difficult to produce a meaningful comparison of the amounts of RNA in cells of different species. The lack of any good standard method for the analysis of RNA does not make this problem any easier. This will perhaps explain the scarcity of data on the RNA content of cells, and also the wide variations in many results from different laboratories.

In Table VIII, the RNA contents of cells from rat tissues are listed. Tissues active in protein synthesis, such as liver and pancreas, have high RNA values, whereas tissues characterized by rapid cell proliferation show low values. Liver tissue from young rats and hepatoma have values close to those of the proliferating tissues. In spite of the wide differences in the amounts of RNA per cell, the ratio of RNA to protein remains remarkably constant. In homologous tissues from closely related species (Table IX), the ratio of RNA to DNA varies considerably, but the pattern of high values for tissues that synthesize proteins and low values for proliferating tissues remains. Again the ratio of RNA to protein stays roughly constant. The RNA values for a few widely different species are listed in Table X. Although both the amount of RNA per cell and

TABLE X
RNA CONTENT OF CELLS IN WIDELY DIFFERENT SPECIES

	RNA per cell (pg.)	$\dfrac{\text{RNA-P}}{\text{DNA-P}}$	$\dfrac{\text{RNA}[a]}{\text{Protein}}$
Rat liver (*93*)	51	4.5	0.019
Human liver (*93*)	26	2.5	0.012
Drosophila (whole larva) (*93*)	2.5[b]	14.4	0.030
Broad bean root (*89*)	290	3.6	0.080
Bacillus megatherium (protoplast) (*5*)	0.5	7.0	0.10
Escherichia coli (strain B)	0.04[b]	4.9[c]	0.071[c]
Yeast (*61*)	1.1	21	0.040[d]
Euglena gracilis (etiolated) (*85*)	20	7.0	0.030

[a] RNA nucleotides per amino acid residues in protein.
[b] Values estimated from ratio of RNA to DNA and separate data on amount of DNA per cell.
[c] Personal communication from Dr. J. Horowitz (of this laboratory).
[d] Calculated from data in (*101*).

the ratio of RNA to DNA vary widely, the ratio of RNA to protein appears to be a relatively stable value.

Of all the means of expressing the amount of RNA in cells, the ratio of RNA to protein appears to be the most meaningful one. It is remarkably similar for adult tissues of related species, but is higher in the corresponding embryonic tissues (93). It is also directly proportional to the rate of growth in cultures of microorganisms. Even among the widely different species in Table X, there appears to be a crude correlation between rate of growth and relative amounts of RNA and protein.

III. Comparative Structure of the Nucleic Acids

A. PROTEINS ASSOCIATED WITH NUCLEIC ACIDS

The use of the term proteins associated with nucleic acids as a cover for the following discussion is appropriate in view of the variation of cohesive forces between the nucleic acid and protein components. This term, unlike the use of the designation nucleoprotein, does not imply any particular characteristic of the type of bonding between the two which ranges from an apparently low order of bond strength in tobacco mosaic virus (102) and some bacteriophages (103) to the deoxyribonucleoprotein conjugates obtained from bacterial sources and cytoplasmic ribonucleoproteins, which are resistant to attempts to remove all the protein component (104–106). The historical background and some critical discussions concerning the preparation of nucleoproteins from diverse sources have been fully covered elsewhere (107–109).

1. Proteins Associated with DNA

a. Protamines. The nature of the protein component isolated by Miescher (110) from the nuclei of ripe salmon sperm was recognized by Kossel (111) to be a simple protein having a high proportion of basic amino acids, notably arginine, during his investigation of similar basic constituents from other fish sperm. These proteins, protamines, may be prepared directly from sperm heads or from the nucleoprotein obtained by strong saline extraction of the spermatozoa (112). Diffusion of protamines through cellophane in the presence of a high NaCl concentration or alcohol precipitation of the neutralized acid extracts of the nucleoprotein are common procedures for the purification of protamines. The success of these methods rests on the strongly basic properties of these proteins and their low molecular weight. The extreme ease of dissociation of the nucleoprotamines together with the analytical ratio of one phosphoric acid residue per one arginine guanidino group in the nucleoprotamines of trout, herring, and salmon have indicated to some investigators the existence of a true salt linkage between the nucleic acid and protamine units (113). In the case of nucleosturine from sturgeon, the inclusion of the appreciable lysine and histidine content maintains this unity relationship. Vendrely *et al.* (114) have confirmed these findings except in the cases of the spermatozoan nucleoprotein of carp and tench, which show an arginine:phosphorus ratio of 0.25, a value which is similar to that of the nucleohistone of the somatic nuclei from these sources. The arginine content of these fish sperm nucleoproteins is about 7.0% compared to a value of 30% for trout and salmon nucleoprotamines, indicating that these may not be protamines. It is known that the protein associated with the nucleic acid of cod sperm is not a protamine (115, 116), and the same may be true for the protein of ripe spermatozoa of carp and tench.

Examination by Daly *et al.* (117) of the amino acid composition of a protein prepared by the acid extraction of the nuclear material from fowl sperm has indicated the presence of a protamine in this source. The distribution of protamines is, therefore, not limited to fish spermatozoa. A comparison of amino acid composition of several protamines is made in Table XI. They are characterized by a simple amino acid composition and by the absence of aromatic and mercapto amino acids. The differences in composition of these protamines indicate a species specificity among these homologous proteins. These protamines appear only during the maturation of the testes (110). The presence of tyrosine, heretofore not encountered in protamines, in the gallin preparation of Mirsky from rooster sperm (117) is probably due to contamination by cytoplasmic proteins during the isolation of this protamine.

The protamines do not show marked heterogeneity, and fractionation by alcohol precipitation is accompanied by only slight changes in composition (130). Using filter paper chromatographic techniques, Goppold-Krekels and Lehmann have shown that clupeine hydrochloride, the protamine of herring sperm, may be separated into three major components (131). The inhomogeneity of clupeine methyl ester hydrochloride is demonstrable by electrophoretic and ultracentrifugal methods as well as by countercurrent distribution; these procedures show the protein to consist of six components (113). This heterogeneity appears to apply to other protamines. Iridine from the rainbow trout and clupeine from the Pacific herring were studied by Ando (132) by means of alumina chromatography and N-terminal amino acid analyses. Each preparation was separated into three peaks. While the total material and the fractions from iridine had only proline as the sole N-terminal group, the available data on the unfractionated clupeine showed only 40% of

TABLE XI

Amino Acid Composition of Some Protamines and Basic Proteins from Spermatozoan Sources[a]

Source	Reference	Arg	Pro	Ser	Gly	Val	Ileu	Ala	Lys	His	Thr	Glu	Leu
Salmine,[b] *Salmo salar*	(118–120)	21.6–	2.16–	2.70–	1.89–	1.56–	0.39–	0.55–	—	—	—	—	—
		22.7	3.33	3.64	1.97	1.92	0.40	0.75	—	—	—	—	—
Salmine, *Oncorhynchus keta*	(121)	22.5	2.70	3.12	1.80	1.40	0.44	0.45	—	—	—	—	—
Salmine, *O. tschawytscha*	(122)	22.3	3.24	3.14	2.03	1.46	0.39	0.58	—	—	—	—	—
Clupeine, *Clupea pallasii*	(118)	22.6	3.22	1.46	—	1.39	0.35	2.39	—	—	0.72	—	—
Clupeine, *Clupea harengus*	(123)	22.4	2.22	2.42	—	1.60	0.43	1.89	—	—	0.65	—	—
Sturine, *Acipenser sturio*	(124)	16.8	—	1.85	1.23	—	1.23	3.09	5.55	4.32	0.62	0.62	—
Scombrine, *Scomber scumbris*	(125)	23.6	1.50	0.80	—	0.64	0.21	1.94	—	—	0.35	—	—
Iridine,[c] *Salmo irideus*	(126)	22.9	2.29	1.37	0.92	1.83	0.46	0.92	0.92	—	—	—	—
Spheroidine, *Spheroides rubripes*	(125)	23.3	0.46	2.36	—	0.49	0.33	2.78	—	—	0.40	—	—
Gallin, *Gallus domesticus*	(127)	22.0	2.61	2.61	0.52	1.57	0.52	2.61	—	—	1.04	0.52	—
Patella vulgata	(128)	12.3	4.8	4.6	4.7	2.2	0.59	6.1	9.8	0.31	2.1	—	1.75
Arbacia lixula	(128)	6.95	6.1	4.3	10.8	1.45	2.0	14.8	14.3	0.51	1.39	—	2.4

[a] Results are expressed as grams amino nitrogen per 100 gm. amino acid nitrogen.

[b] These figures for salmine represent the range of values from the references cited. The identity of some of the salmon sources is uncertain and specimens of the genus *Oncorhynchus* may be included in this group.

[c] In the nucleoprotamines of rainbow trout (*Salmo irideus*), brook trout, and river trout, Felix et al. (129) have found aspartic and glutamine acids in addition to the amino acids usually encountered.

the N-terminal amino acid to be proline, the remainder probably alanine. Felix and Krekels (133), however, find that iridine, truttin (brook trout), fontanin (brook char), salmine, and clupeine have proline as the only end group and that alanine and glutamic acid appear as N-terminal amino acids from sturine (sturgeon), a preparation whose integrity these investigators question. Recent estimations of the molecular weight of salmine by end-group assay (122, 134) give a value near 4000 rather than the higher figures reaching 10,000 which were based on total amino acid composition and on the assumption that the preparations were homogeneous.

Basic proteins of a more complex nature have been obtained from echinoderms (sea urchins and gastropod mollusks) (128). These show a higher neutral amino acid content and a considerably higher lysine content than protamines, but tryptophan and the aromatic, acidic, and sulfur-containing amino acids are absent (Table XI).

b. Histones. The designation histone is applied to proteins with pronounced basic properties obtained from cell nuclei. The histones differ from protamines by having a higher molecular weight, a greater assortment of amino acids, and a considerable contribution of the acidic and aromatic amino acids. Ion exchange analyses and microbiological assays appear to exclude the presence of tryptophan and cystine from histone hydrolyzates. Histones have been found in the nuclei of all animal somatic cells investigated and are expected to be widely distributed among plants as well.

The nature of the association of histones to the nucleic acid component has been re-investigated by Crampton and Chargaff (107). In strong salt solutions they resemble nucleoprotamines: a separation of components occurs and then a reassociation (reconstitution) on dilution to isotonic concentration. The contribution of electrostatic interaction to the stability of the nucleohistone complex is recognized since similar properties are exhibited by a complex between deoxyribonucleic acid and the basic polyelectrolyte polylysine (135). Other factors may still influence the configuration and stability of the nucleoprotein since studies on artificial complexes between nucleic acids and proteins indicate that the increase of the number of guanidine groups in a protein does not alter its ability to bind DNA (136).

The properties of native nucleohistones, prepared by extraction with distilled water, and of reconstituted nucleohistones have been compared (137). When partially dissociated with moderate salt concentration, the two different preparations yielded histone fractions with dissimilar compositions. This suggests that the combination of DNA and histone is specific *in vivo.*

Investigations into the heterogeneity of histones from a wide variety of species and organs by Stedman and Stedman (130) resulted in the fractionation of these basic proteins by preferential alcohol precipitation into a main and a subsidiary component. The major component has been described as a fraction rich in arginine and tyrosine. This holds true for histones from cod sperm and wheat germ. The basicity of the subsidiary component is maintained by a relatively high lysine content. The results have been confirmed by studies involving different fractionation techniques (138–140).

Further investigations on calf thymocyte histone, by ultracentrifugal and electrophoretic techniques, indicate six components (141): 3-α, 1-β, and 2-γ components in descending order of mobility in an electrophoretic field at pH 7.4. Complete amino acid analyses of these components show characteristic compositions with the α_1 fraction being most unusual as it contains only 7 amino acids but is devoid of arginine. All have strongly basic properties. The same group of investigators have discussed the probability of cellular specificity of histones based on amino acid analyses of purified β components from fowl erythrocyte, spleen, and liver (142) and on ultracentrifugal resolution of the β fraction from ox thymus and liver histone (143). From these investigations physicochemical data are available showing species specificity of this component of the protein—a characteristic difficult to see from amino acid analyses.

The extraction of histones from mammalian sperm by the method of Mirsky and Pollister (144) is difficult. Only after the action of trypsin (107) or alkaline solvents (145) on defatted sperm is the nucleoprotein freely extractable with strong salt solution. The proteins from bull, boar, ram, dog, and human sperm, isolated by the use of $1 M$ NaCl – $1 M$ NaOH exhibit the solubility properties of histones, but only after they have been precipitated at pH 11. The arginine content of the histones from bull and ram sperm is 27.8% and 26.7%, respectively, corresponding to 10.9 and 12.6 gm. α-amino nitrogen per 100 gm. amino acid nitrogen (cf. Table XII).

Belozersky (147) has investigated the material obtained from cedar nut embryo, germinating haricot, and soybean by the method of Mirsky and Pollister (144). Although acid extraction dissolved about one-third of the protein so obtained, only the preparation from cedar nut resembled the histone of wheat germ and animal sources by its precipitability upon neutralization of the solution. The two others required addition of alcohol. The protein obtained from *Proteus vulgaris* behaved similarly. Since interest in the deoxyribonucleoprotein from microbial sources has usually centered upon the nucleic acid component, the

TABLE XII

AMINO ACID COMPOSITION OF SEVERAL TOTAL HISTONE PREPARATIONS[a]

Amino acid	Calf thymus (138)	Calf liver (138)	Rat liver (146)	Guinea pig testes (138)	Fowl erythro-cyte (117)
Alanine	8.7	8.2	7.41	7.6	7.30
Arginine	21.5	20.2	29.81	18.8	25.40
Aspartic acid	3.1	3.7	4.3	4.0	3.49
Cystine/2	<0.06	0.24	—[b]	0.20	—[b]
Glutamic acid	5.3	5.6	5.78	5.8	5.75
Glycine	5.4	5.4	6.31	5.7	5.79
Histidine	3.9	3.7	4.64	4.1	3.51
Isoleucine	2.8	2.9	3.54	2.6	3.68
Leucine	5.0	5.4	6.24	5.1	5.81
Lysine	19.1	16.4	12.20	15.2	12.58
Methionine	0.63	0.81	0.88	0.75	0
Phenylalanine	1.4	1.3	1.39	1.2	1.63
Proline	3.2	2.8	1.91	3.7	2.68
Serine	3.8	3.7	4.19	4.4	4.54
Threonine	3.7	3.7	4.42	3.5	3.39
Tyrosine	1.6	1.6	2.41	1.9	1.62
Valine	4.0	3.8	4.48	3.7	3.94
Amide NH$_3$	4.1	5.1	5.05	4.7	5.13
Recovery	97.3	94.5	104.9	93.0	96.2

[a] Results are expressed as gram-atoms nitrogen per 100 gm.-atoms of total protein nitrogen.
[b] Cystine absent (146) or not determined (117).

characterization of the protein moiety is not as extensive as those from mammalian sources where, it may be added, contamination from extraneous cytoplasmic proteins may be controlled.

c. *Nonhistone Proteins.* It appears strange that even in an organism as widely studied as *Escherichia coli* the characterization of the protein associated with the DNA rests on uncertain grounds. Analysis of a deoxyribonucleoprotein from *E. coli* prepared in the absence of deproteinizing agents, containing 50% protein and less than 5% RNA, suggests that there is no appreciable quantity of histone complexed with the bacterial DNA (148). The protein from this complex as well as the total cellular protein have amino acid compositions differing from the composition of calf thymus histone (see Table XII).

Initial studies of the character of bacterial nucleoproteins by Chargaff (104) had established the occurrence of a protein component in avian tubercle bacilli which, unlike protamines and histones, is not dissociated from the nucleic acid in the presence of high salt concentration and in which forces other than electrostatic ones may account for the association. Renewed interest in this protein prompted a detailed characterization of a purified DNA preparation from *Mycobacterium tuberculosis*, bovine type, containing 10% protein (*149*). Acid incubation of this material removed purines from the nucleic acid and extracted some of the protein present. Amino acid analysis of the extracted protein revealed only traces of arginine and lysine and a predominance of aspartic and glutamic acids. Detergent and phenol deproteinizing procedures were inferior to the action of crystalline trypsin in removing the protein.

The use of a variety of protein denaturing and precipitating agents, and of metal chelating agents effects only partial removal of the protein from microbial and mammalian deoxynucleoproteins, a finding that attests to the peculiar nature of this type of complex. The comprehensive amino acid analyses on the residually bound protein of rat liver DNA preparations carried out by Kirby (*150*) show that the number of aspartic and glutamic acid units is of the same order as the arginine and lysine content.

Analysis of a calf thymus DNA prepared by detergent deproteinization indicated that it contained 1% protein (*151*), not of a basic nature. From the changes apparent upon treatment of this preparation with chymotrypsin, but not trypsin, to yield a less polydisperse DNA, it has been suggested that this protein cross links intermolecularly with the DNA polymers and acts as a structural aid in the macromolecular configuration of the nucleoprotein in the cell. Some indirect evidence exists for the presence of nucleotide-amino acid compounds in a hydrolyzate obtained by serial action of trypsin, chymotrypsin, and DNase on a deoxynucleoprotein from rat liver; this evidence implies that such cross-linking occurs (*152*).

2. Proteins Associated with RNA

A discussion of ribonucleoproteins has been given in the section (I, A) dealing with the cytochemistry of RNA. Intense interest in recent years in the microsomal fraction of the cellular machinery with its direct implication in protein synthesis, and in the supernatant cytoplasmic nucleoprotein responsible for amino acid activation, justifies their consideration once more. According to Szafarz (*153*), all the cytoplasmic RNA exists in a form associated with protein; but only the proteins of the microsomes have received detailed study.

Amino acid analyses of several microsomal nucleoproteins having approximately the same protein content suggest that the homologous microsomal proteins from different cell sources may have a similar composition (Table XIII).

TABLE XIII

AMINO ACID COMPOSITION OF SEVERAL NON-HISTONE PROTEINS
ASSOCIATED WITH NUCLEIC ACIDS[a]

Amino acid	DNA-protein of E. coli (148)	Microsomal RNA-protein of		
		Rabbit reticulo-cyte (154)	Pea (154)	Guinea pig liver[b] (155)
Alanine	7.88	5.23	5.34	6.18
Arginine	19.0	23.3	18.6	16.0
Aspartic acid	7.81	5.72	6.35	8.05
Cystine/2	0.47	0.80	0.19	—[c]
Glutamic acid	8.98	6.70	6.41	9.20
Glycine	9.21	8.12	9.74	6.33
Histidine	3.98	4.67	4.97	5.46
Isoleucine	4.14	3.75	4.27	3.16
Leucine	6.71	5.72	5.53	7.12
Lysine	9.84	14.9	14.7	12.0
Methionine	1.25	1.17	1.19	1.29
Phenylalanine	2.42	2.28	2.58	3.81
Proline	3.28	3.51	3.96	5.75
Serine	3.36	1.48	2.07	4.31
Threonine	4.45	3.26	3.65	3.88
Tryptophan	—[c]	0.98	1.32	—[c]
Tyrosine	1.80	3.08	3.39	2.37
Valine	5.39	5.29	5.72	5.10

[a] Results are expressed as gram-atoms nitrogen per 100 gm.-atoms amino acid nitrogen recovered.

[b] Represents the average composition of fractions B and C obtained by Simkin and Work (155).

[c] Not determined or reported.

The methods applicable to the deproteinization of deoxyribonucleoproteins are equally useful for ribonucleoproteins (108), with the choice of procedure dictated by the interest in one or the other of the two components.

3. Proteins Associated with Viruses

That a protein was associated with the infectious agents responsible for viral diseases in plants had been recognized by many investigators. The first identification of both protein and nucleic acid as components of bacterial viruses (coliphage and staphylococcus phage) was made by Schlesinger in 1936 (156). Subsequent to the report in the same year by Stanley on the crystallization of tobacco mosaic virus, other plant viruses were purified and/or crystallized and characterized as ribonucleoproteins (109). Similar investigations on animal viruses were delayed, however, because of the extreme difficulty of purification from the host cell constituents. Except for the insect viruses (polyhedral and capsular) and vaccinia virus, which are deoxyribonucleoproteins, the animal viruses investigated contain ribonucleoprotein. Among the viruses a comprehensive investigation of the protein components has been initiated only on the coliphages and some of the plant viruses.

a. *Plant Viruses.* It has been noted from the analyses of the crystalline tobacco mosaic, tobacco necrosis, tobacco ring spots, tomato bushy stunt, and cucumber mosaic viruses that plant virus proteins do not contain large amounts of the basic amino acids and therefore differ from the protamines and histones (Table XIV). Unlike the residual

TABLE XIV

AMINO ACID COMPOSITION OF SEVERAL VIRUS PROTEINS[a,b]

Amino acid	TYMV (157)	BSV (158)	TMV (159)	HR (159)	T2 (160)	T3 (160)
Alanine	5.4	5.8	6.8	8.9	7.0	8.8
Arginine	2.2	7.0	10.0	9.3	4.6	5.6
Aspartic acid	6.3	11.2	14.5	15.8	10.6	10.8
Cystine/2	0[d]	0.7	—[c]	—[c]	<1	<1
Glutamic acid	8.0	6.0	13.0	17.2	10.8	10.6
Glycine	3.8	4.9	2.4	1.7	8.6	7.6
Histidine	1.6	1.5	0	0.7	0.8	1.6
Isoleucine	7.4	3.4	} 14.9	12.8	6.0	4.4
Leucine	8.6	10.8			5.4	8.8
Lysine	5.0	3.7	2.0	2.5	5.8	5.6
Methionine	2.1	1.1	0	2.1	2.0	1.8
Phenylalanine	3.6	4.5	7.6	5.6	5.0	3.2
Proline	11.8	3.3	5.3	5.3	3.6	4.2
Serine	6.7	6.6	9.5	8.5	4.8	3.8
Threonine	12.2	9.8	9.3	7.6	5.4	6.4
Tryptophan	—[c]	0.7	2.9	2.3	—[c]	—[c]
Tyrosine	2.2	3.9	4.3	6.6	5.8	4.8
Valine	6.2	8.6	10.1	6.2	5.4	6.0
Total	93.1	93.5	112.6	113.1	91.6	94.0
Protein in virus	65%	83%	95%	95%	50%	50%

[a] Results expressed as gm. amino acid per 100 gm. of protein.

[b] TYMV, turnip yellow mosaic virus; BSV, bushy stunt virus; TMV, tobacco mosaic virus; HR, Holmes ribgrass (strain of TMV); T2 and T3, bacteriophages.

[c] Not determined or reported.

[d] Analysis made for cystine only.

proteins associated with DNA, which they resemble by having a relatively large proportion of dicarboxylic amino acids, the proteins of most plant viruses are removed quite readily by the usual denaturation agents (108).

Some idea of the type of association between protein and nucleic acid in the TMV particle may be obtained from dye-binding studies. The isolated protein of TMV appears to have the same number of acidic groups as in the purified virus, but more basic groups (guanidine) in an amount equivalent to the acid groups of the nucleic acid. These data have allowed the interpretation that the binding force between the protein and nucleic acid is largely salt linkage accompanied certainly by H-bonding orientation (161).

In plant cells infected with virus, a protein constituent may accumulate which has the same immunological specificity as the virus, but lacks infectivity and contains no RNA. In TMV infections this constituent, variously called protein B, protein X, or soluble antigen, can be provoked to aggregate in vitro to form particles of a structure close to that of the virus but without infectivity (162). This behavior is similar to that of the protein subunits obtained from TMV by mild alkali, which reaggregate in the absence or presence of RNA upon lowering the pH (102, 163, 164). It has been suggested that the soluble antigen is the direct precursor of the protein portion of the virus (165).

Crystalline turnip mosaic virus obtained from infected plants is electrophoretically homogeneous, but examination in an ultracentrifugal field reveals two protein peaks with sedimentation constants of 106 S (75%) and 49 S (25%), which have been shown to be identical by the usual physicochemical characterizations and immunological tests. The fast component, however, contains all the RNA and is the infectious element (109). The slow component is probably homologous to the soluble antigen of TMV-infected plants. The electrophoretic identity of the turnip yellow mosaic (TYM) virus with the protein component (109) and the ineffectiveness of RNase on the intact virus particle (166) indicate that the RNA of the virus is located within the protein envelope; this is similar to the arrangement in TMV. The observation that the protein subunit from TMV has a lower mobility at pH 7 than the virus particle itself (167) seems at first to indicate that the nucleic acid does contribute to the surface potential of the particle. However, this phenomenon has been ascribed to a nonuniform distribution of surface charges on the subunits. When aggregation to a protein cylinder is effected at pH 7 by ultraviolet irradiation, the electrophoretic mobility of the protein is the same as that of the total virus particle (168).

The TMV rods are thought to contain 2800 protein units of 17,000 minimum molecular weight to account for a virus particle weight of 50 million. The only C-terminal amino acid is threonine (169). The inability to demonstrate a free N-terminal amino acid in TMV, as well as in tomato bushy stunt virus, cucumber virus 3 and 4, and potato X virus, suggests the possibility of a looped structure at this end of the protein units for the viruses cited (170). In the protein of TMV this is believed to be formed through an N-prolyl amide juncture with a β-carboxyl of aspartic acid (171). Other investigators dispute this interpretation of the structure of the viral protein, and Narita (172) has suggested instead that the N-terminal amino acid is masked by acetylation in the form of an N-acetyl seryltyrosine terminus for TMV and four of its strains.

The C-terminal amino acid of cucumber virus 3 and 4, potato X virus, and tomato bushy stunt virus proteins is alanine, proline, and leucine, respectively (172). In Table XIV are included the protein compositions of several plant viruses. Several strains of tobacco virus have been examined by Black and Knight (173) and were found to differ in amino acid composition from the typical strain of TMV from which they were derived. These fundamental changes in protein composition which accompany functional changes in the plant virus were not reflected by any compositional changes in the RNA.

b. Bacteriophages. Those bacteriophages which have been isolated and analyzed consist essentially of protein and DNA in nearly equal quantities. At times some lipid or carbohydrate material is found. The organization of the bacteriophage, as elicited by investigations on the T2 strain of coliphage, is of a much higher order than the plant viruses. In T2 for instance, at least three distinct structural proteins are integrated into the phage particle (174).

The binding forces between the DNA and protein appear to be different within related phages. Osmotic shock of T4r⁺ coliphage liberates the DNA in association with 25% of the total protein of the phage, the complex being ultracentrifugally homogeneous. The protein, moreover, is not easily removed by chloroform denaturation (175). In T2 such osmotic shock liberates into the supernatant all the DNA and no more than 3% of the phage protein (103).

Amino acid analyses of the total proteins of the T2 and T3 phages show that these bacteriophages have dissimilar protein components (Table XIV).

B. Nucleotide Distribution in DNA

1. Content of Nitrogenous Constituents

As a result of the work of Miescher (110), the first major cellular component containing phosphorus, since the isolation of lecithin, became available for study by organic chemists and physiologists: the nucleic acids. Much of the chemistry of the components of ribo- and deoxyribonucleic acids has been covered in excellent fashion by Levene and

Bass (*176*). A recent discussion by Brown and Todd (*177*) reviews the evidence for a polymeric structure involving the pentose carbons 3′ and 5′ in internucleoside phosphate linkage for both RNA and DNA. Only through the use of chromatographic and ultraviolet spectrophotometric techniques developed relatively recently have reliable data on the quantitative composition of the nucleic acids become available. In the deoxyribonucleic acids only four or five heterocyclic nitrogenous components in glycoside linkage to 2′-deoxyribose have been found in any single cellular preparation.

In view of the intention of referring subsequently to a physical model of the DNA macromolecule, the nitrogenous components are classified here as either 6-amino or 6-keto compounds. The purine adenine and the pyrimidines cytosine, 5-methylcytosine, and 5-hydroxymethylcytosine are the 6-amino units. The purine guanine and the pyrimidine thymine are the 6-keto units.

a. Unusual Nitrogenous Constituents of DNA. The first reliable identification of 5-methylcytosine as a bona fide component of DNA was made by Wyatt (*178*). From available analyses, the content of methylcytosine in DNA of diverse animal sources does not appear to exceed 2 nucleotide per cent (Table XV). Although methylcytosine was found in all animal DNA where specific search for its presence was made, there is no indication of its presence in either microbial or viral DNA. By far the highest content of methylcytosine occurs in DNA from some plant sources where it may account for nearly 6 mole per cent of the nucleotide composition (Table XVI).

Analyses of DNA prepared from bacteriophage show that of those preparations examined only T2, T4, and T6 contain the 5-hydroxy-methylcytosine in place of cytosine (Table XVII). Much of the hydroxy-methylcytosine in the DNA of bacteriophages T2, T4, and T6 is known to be present as glucosylated derivatives (*191, 192*).

6-Methylamino purine (N^6-methyladenine) has been reported to be a minor component of DNA from some microorganisms (*193*). In *E. coli* and *A. aerogenes* DNA, a content of approximately 0.4 and 0.5 nucleotide per cent, respectively, has been calculated. Its presence is also indicated in T2r⁺ and T2r phage DNA. It has not been detected in the DNA from yeast, wheat germ, and the several animal sources examined.

b. Compositional Regularities in DNA. The data on the composition of DNA illustrate several characteristics of this cellular constituent which have been cited previously by Chargaff (*194*).

The total DNA of an organism has been shown to have a constant and characteristic composition which is independent of the tissue source

TABLE XV

PURINE AND PYRIMIDINE CONTENTS OF DEOXYRIBONUCLEIC ACIDS FROM VARIOUS ANIMAL SOURCES[a]

Source	Adenine	Guanine	Cytosine	5-Methylcytosine[b]	Thymine	$\dfrac{A + T^c}{G + C + MC}$	Reference
Man[d]	30.4	19.6	19.9	0.7	30.1	1.53	107, 179
Pig[d]	29.8	20.4	20.7	—	29.1	1.43	107
Sheep[d]	29.3	21.1	20.9	1.0	28.7	1.38	107
Ox[d]	29.0	21.2	21.2	1.3	28.7	1.36	107
Rat, bone marrow	28.6	21.4	20.4	1.1	28.4	1.33	107
Hen, erythrocytes	28.0	22.0	21.6	—	28.4	1.29	107
Turtle, erythrocytes	28.7	22.0	21.3	—	27.9	1.31	107
Rainbow trout, sperm	29.7	22.2	20.5	—	27.5	1.34	180
Brook trout, sperm	29.8	21.9	21.0	—	27.2	1.33	180
Salmon, sperm	28.9	22.4	21.6	—	27.1	1.27	180
Salmon, sperm	29.7	20.8	20.4	—	29.1	1.43	107
Sturgeon, sperm	28.8	22.5	20.3	—	27.3	1.31	180
Herring, sperm	28.1	22.2	20.6	1.9	27.2	1.24	180
Herring, sperm	27.8	22.2	20.7	1.9	27.5	1.23	107
Locusta migratoria, whole	29.3	20.5	20.7	0.2	29.3	1.41	107
Arbacia punctulata, sperm	28.4	19.5	19.3	—	32.8	1.58	107
Arbacia lixula, sperm	31.2	19.1	19.2	—	30.5	1.61	107
Echinus esculentis, sperm	30.9	19.4	18.4	1.8	29.4	1.52	107
Echinocardium cordatum, sperm	32.9	17.0	17.9	—	32.2	1.86	107
Psammechinus miliaris, sperm	32.6	17.8	17.8	—	31.9	1.81	107
Paracentrotus lividus, sperm	32.8	17.7	16.2	1.1	32.1	1.85	107

[a] Proportions in moles of nitrogenous constituent per 100 gm.-atoms of phosphorus in hydrolyzate, corrected to 100% recovery.

[b] Where no methylcytosine values appear, no specific search for this component was made.

[c] A, adenine; T, thymine; G, guanine; C, cytosine; MC, methylcytosine.

[d] These data represent the average composition of at least two different organs.

TABLE XVI

PURINE AND PYRIMIDINE CONTENTS OF DEOXYRIBONUCLEIC ACIDS FROM SEVERAL PLANTS AND FUNGI[a]

Source	Adenine	Guanine	Cytosine	Methylcytosine	Thymine	$\dfrac{A + T^b}{G + C + MC}$	Reference
Wheat germ	28.1	21.8	16.8	5.9	27.4	1.25	181
Rye germ	27.8	22.7	16.2	5.9	27.5	1.24	182
Carrot[c]	26.7	23.1	17.3	5.9	26.9	1.16	183
Bracken fern	28.3	19.8	18.2	5.6	28.4	1.30	184
Clover	29.9	21.0	15.6	4.8	28.6	1.41	184
Kale	27.5	24.8	16.6	3.6	27.5	1.22	184
Neurospora crassa	23.0	27.1	26.6	—[d]	23.3	0.86	87
Saccharomyces cerevisiae	31.3	18.7	17.1	—[d]	32.9	1.79	107

[a] Proportions in moles of nitrogenous constituents per 100 gm.-atoms phosphorus in hydrolyzate, corrected for a 100% recovery.

[b] A, adenine; T, thymine; G, guanine; C, cytosine; MC, methylcytosine.

[c] No detectable differences in composition were observed among phloem, leaf, or crown gall tumor tissues.

[d] No specific search for methylcytosine was made in these analyses. Investigations of the DNA from several algae and diatoms (185) indicate the absence of methylcytosine in the lower plants studied.

TABLE XVII

Purine and Pyrimidine Contents of Deoxyribonucleic Acids from Several Coliphages and Insect Viruses[a]

Source	Adenine	Guanine	Cytosine	Hydroxymethylcytosine	Thymine	$\dfrac{A + T^b}{G + C(HMC)}$	Reference
Coliphage							
T2r+	32.0	18.0	—	16.8	33.3	1.88	186
T2r	32.3	17.6	—	16.7	33.4	1.91	186
T4r+	32.3	18.3	—	16.3	33.1	1.89	186
T4r	32.2	18.0	—	16.3	33.5	1.91	186
T6r+	30.9	18.4	—	17.4	33.3	1.79	107
T6r+	32.5	17.8	—	16.3	33.5	1.93	186
T6r	32.3	17.7	—	16.6	33.4	1.91	186
T1	27	23	25	—	25	1.08	187
T3	24.7	23.8	26.2	—	25.3	1.00	188
T5	30.3	19.5	19.5	—	30.8	1.57	186
T7	26.0	23.8	23.6	—	26.6	1.11	189
φX174	24.6	24.1	18.5	—	32.7	1.35	92
Polyhedral virus of:							
gypsy moth	21.2	30.5	28.3	—	20.1	0.70	190
Spruce budworm	24.8	26.7	24.5	—	24.0	0.95	190
Silkworm	29.3	22.5	20.2	—	28.0	1.34	190
Pine sawfly	32.3	19.5	17.9	—	30.3	1.67	190
Capsular virus of spruce budworm	32.8	18.4	16.4	—	32.4	1.87	190

[a] Proportions in moles of nitrogenous constituent per 100 gm.-atoms phosphorus in hydrolyzate, corrected for a 100% recovery.
[b] A, adenine; T, thymine; G, guanine; C, cytosine; HMC, 5-hydroxymethylcytosine.

or age of the organism (*107, 195*). No difference in composition can be shown for DNA of normal and tumorous tissue (*107, 183*). These observations indicate a species specificity for DNA.

Among the DNA preparations of diverse generic sources examined, distinct differences in composition may be detected. These differences are more readily noticed in terms of a dissymmetry ratio of the form $(A + T)/(G + C)$. Nucleic acids which have an adenine + thymine content greater than the guanine + cytosine content have been termed "AT type" (*194*). A DNA with a converse composition is termed "GC type." A much greater variation in composition is obvious among the preparations from microorganisms (Table XVIII) and viruses than among the animal and plant DNA examined.

A compositional dissimilarity between host and viral DNA is especially obvious in the T-even coliphage system and indirectly noticeable from the analyses of insect viruses (capsular and polyhedral viruses of the spruce budworm). Two alternatives present themselves to explain the compositional identity among the DNA's of closely related species exemplified by the data on fish DNA (Table XV) and bacterial DNA (Table XVIII): There may be some differences in nucleotide composition for a few DNA molecules, or identical composition with certain differences in nucleotide sequence characterizes the DNA from these sources. It is unlikely that the DNA of such related species are completely identical. Deviations from the expected compositional similarities among some of the microorganisms have been the basis of a suggestion for some modification of bacterial classification (*195, 196*).

Regardless of any variation of composition among these deoxyribonucleic acids, a basic simplicity and unity of structure must eventually be suggested to allow for a successful correlation between nucleic acid composition and its cellular function. An initial step in this direction was made by Chargaff (*194*) through the recognition that in the preparations examined some thread of regularity exists: the molar content of adenine is equal to the thymine content and the guanine content is equal to the cytosine plus methylcytosine, or hydroxymethylcytosine content. Consequently, the purine content equals the pyrimidine content, and the number of 6-amino constituents is equal to the number of 6-keto units.

c. A Proposed Structure for DNA. Integration of the compositional regularities (*194*) with a physical structure of DNA suggested by X-ray diffraction studies (*197*) has allowed Watson and Crick (*198*) to propose a structure for DNA which features a helix composed of two linear polymers of deoxyribonucleotides in such a fashion that adenylic (A), guanylic (G), thymidylic (T), and cytidylic (C) (methylcytidylic,

TABLE XVIII

PURINE AND PYRIMIDINE COMPOSITION OF DEOXYRIBONUCLEIC ACIDS
FROM BACTERIAL SOURCES[a]

Organism	Adenine	Guanine	Cytosine	Thymine	$\dfrac{A + T^b}{G + C}$	Reference
Welchia perfringens (Fred)	36.9	14.0	12.8	36.3	2.73	*196*
Clostridium perfringens	34.1	15.8	15.1	35.0	2.24	*195*
Clostridium valerianicum	35.1	16.2	15.6	33.1	2.14	*196*
Clostridium bifermentans	34.0	17.0	15.5	33.5	2.08	*196*
Micrococcus pyogenes (*145*)	34.4	16.2	15.2	34.2	2.18	*196*
Streptococcus pyogenes (group A)	33.4	16.6	17.0	33.0	1.98	*196*
Pasteurella tularensis	32.4	17.6	17.1	32.9	1.88	*193*
Pasteurella aviseptica	32.0	18.2	18.1	31.7	1.75	*192*
Pasteurella boviseptica	31.0	18.8	18.8	31.4	1.66	*192*
Bacillus cereus alesti	33.5	17.3	16.0	33.2	2.00	*192*
Bacillus thuringiensis amer.	32.2	18.1	17.8	31.9	1.79	*192*
Bacillus megatherium	31.8	19.1	18.5	30.6	1.66	*192*
Bacillus subtilis	28.9	21.0	21.4	28.7	1.36	*192*
Hemophilus influenzae type C	31.9	18.2	19.6	30.2	1.64	*107*
Proteus vulgaris[c]	31.1	19.2	19.3	30.5	1.60	*192, 193*
Vibrio cholerae	28.8	20.0	23.3	27.9	1.31	*192*
Escherichia coli	24.7	25.1	26.0	24.4	0.96	*107, 193*
Salmonella typhimurium	23.8	26.3	25.9	24.1	0.92	*192, 193*
Salmonella typhosa	23.5	26.7	26.4	23.4	0.88	*193*
Shigella dysenteriae	23.5	26.7	26.7	23.1	0.87	*193*
Azotobacter agile	21.4	28.3	26.5	23.8	0.82	*193*
Azotobacter vinelandii	22.1	27.4	28.9	21.7	0.78	*193*
Azotobacter chroöcoccum	20.5	28.7	28.5	22.2	0.75	*193*
Aerobacter aerogenes	20.9	29.1	27.9	22.2	0.76	*192, 193*
Brucella abortus	21.0	29.0	28.9	21.1	0.73	*193*
Serratia marcescens	20.9	28.1	30.5	20.5	0.71	*107, 192*
Bacillus schatz	19.9	29.1	32.3	18.6	0.63	*107*
Mycobacterium tuberculosis (bovine)	17.4	33.5	32.8	16.4	0.51	*149, 193*
Mycobacterium tuberculosis (avian)	15.1	34.9	35.4	14.6	0.42	*107*
Pseudomonas tabaci	16.2	33.7	33.7	16.4	0.48	*192*
Sarcina lutea	16.2	34.4	33.6	15.9	0.47	*192, 193*
Micrococcus lysodeikticus	14.4	37.3	34.6	13.7	0.39	*192*

[a] Proportions in moles of nitrogenous constituent per 100 gm.-atoms phosphorus in hydrolyzate, corrected for a 100% recovery.

[b] A, adenine; T, thymine; G, guanine; C, cytosine.

[c] Where two references are cited, the composition given is an average value of the data.

hydroxymethylcytidylic) acids situated on one of the DNA chains are hydrogen bonded through the heterocyclic ring systems to thymidylic, cytidylic (MC, HMC), adenylic, and guanylic acids, respectively, on the second chain.

A unique DNA obtained from the coliphage ϕX174 and having a molecular weight of 1.7×10^6 has been described by Sinsheimer (92). The physical and chemical properties of this DNA are distinctly compatible with a structure which does not involve a twin helix, namely, a single-stranded macromolecule independent of 6-amino to 6-keto hydrogen bonding. The unity relations involving the nitrogenous constituents are not evident, and this, perhaps, justifies the thought that these relations hold only because of an A $\cdots$ T and G $\cdots$ C complementariness between individual chains of the helix. The composition of this DNA is included in Table XVII.

2. Heterogeneity of Deoxyribonucleic Acids

The possibility that a DNA preparation from a given source might comprise many different molecules has been suggested by Chargaff (199) and Wyatt (200). Heterogeneity of the nucleic acids could result from a contribution of different molecular sizes, compositional differences among a series of molecular species, and variations of nucleotide sequence in polymers having similar composition. The first experimental evidence for heterogeneity was provided by the finding that two fractions of calf liver DNA with different solubilities in dilute NaCl solution showed unequal C^{14} incorporation (201).

Although DNA is not apparently separable into specimens of demonstrably different composition by fractional centrifugation (202) or absorption on charcoal (203) some preparative procedures which have been developed to fractionate DNA include (a) differential dissociation of nucleoprotein gels (204–206) or by a related chromatographic procedure applied to a nucleoprotein complex immobilized on an inert matrix (207, 208); (b) chromatographic elution from chemically modified cellulose behaving as a weakly anionic exchanger (209, 210).

a. Differential Dissociation of Deoxyribonucleoproteins. The contribution of electrostatic forces to the structure of nucleoprotamines and nucleohistones has been discussed in the section (III, A) concerned with the proteins associated with nucleic acids. The dissociating effect of strong electrolyte concentrations reflects upon the major contribution of salt linkages in these complexes. A recent comprehensive study of the influence of different salt environments on some of the properties of nucleoprotein complexes, initiated by Crampton et al. (211), has afforded a means of separating a DNA preparation into fractions having composi-

tions distinct from the total preparation (204, 205) by a procedure best
termed a differential dissociation of the nucleoprotein complex. From
nucleohistone gels formed in the presence of the protein denaturant
chloroform, DNA may be gradually released upon serial changes of the
aqueous phase from low ionic strength solutions to higher NaCl concentration. Successful fractionation of deoxyribonucleoprotein complexes
has been extended to material from several cell sources (107, 181).
One of the features of this procedure is that the stepwise extraction of
a nucleoprotein gel with salt solutions of increasing molarity results in
the release of DNA fractions exhibiting a diminishing content of guanine
and cytosine (methylcytosine) and concomitant increase of the adenine
and thymine contents. The variations in the composition of fractions
from calf thymus, pig liver, human spleen, and coliphage T6r⁺ are
represented graphically in Fig. 3. In all fractions, however, the com-

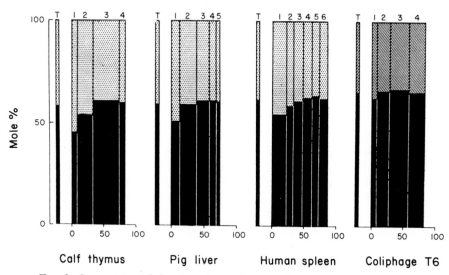

FIG. 3. Composition of fractions (in moles per 100 gm.-atoms of phosphorus)
prepared by the fractional dissociation of artificial histone complexes with the indicated sodium deoxypentose nucleate preparations. The abscissa indicates the proportion of original nucleic acid phosphorus recovered in each fraction. Solid bar, adenine
+ thymine; dotted, guanine + cytosine; crosshatched, guanine + hydroxymethylcytosine. Reproduced from E. Chargaff (107).

positional regularities discussed previously for the total DNA are maintained: adenine = thymine; guanine = cytosine; and purines = pyrimidines. A similar procedure for DNA fractionation has been successfully
applied to artificial complexes formed with globin (205) and with
polylysine (135). The results of these investigations indicate that

regardless of structural pecularities in nucleohistone complexes which may guide the dissociation, the electrostatic properties of the individual components of the conjugate are the basis on which the fractionation procedure rests. The separation of DNA into fractions of distinct composition has also been accomplished by successive extraction of a nucleohistone gel with a constant concentration of NaCl solution (206) in the presence of $CHCl_3$, indicating that time of contact of the extracting medium with the nucleoprotein is a factor which influences the dissociation of these complexes.

Brown and Watson have modified this differential dissociation method of fractionation into a column chromatographic technique (207). Histone immobilized on kieselguhr or diazobenzyl cellulose affords an insoluble protein site onto which DNA may be affixed. Elution with NaCl solutions in the same concentration range used for the fractional dissociation of nucleoprotein gels effected a fractionation of calf thymus DNA into material varying in composition in a regular fashion from an $(A + T)/(G + C)$ ratio of 0.9 to one of 2.0 (208). Similar results have been obtained with the DNA of avian tubercle bacilli, E. coli, human leukocytes, pneumococci, and Arbacia lixula. The chromatographic profile of T2r DNA appears to be a double peak reflecting the contribution of two major fractions in this DNA: A, 40% of the total, having a dissymmetry ratio $(A + T)/(G + HMC)$ of 1.9, and B, 60%, a $(A + T)/(G + HMC)$ ratio of 2.15. A fractionation of T6r⁺ DNA into species having an $(A + T)/G + HMC)$ ratio from 1.6 to 2.0 by fractional dissociation of a nucleoprotein gel has been reported by Crampton (205). Superimposed gradient elution patterns of the DNA from E. coli, calf thymus, and human leukocytes indicate a displacement from the column of the major portion of DNA in the same order as their A:G ratio increases (207); the elution pattern is characteristic of the composition of the specimen.

The use of heat-denatured histone or the requirement of the presence of a protein denaturant, $CHCl_3$, in these investigations suggests that an unfolding of the protein is essential for effective fractionation of the DNA (205, 206).

b. Chromatographic Fractionation on a Cellulose Anion Exchanger. The chromatographic elution of DNA by NaCl, NH_3, or NaOH, or with buffered eluents from ECTEOLA columns (a product of epichlorohydrin and triethanolamine action upon cellulose) affords recovery of the DNA in numerous fractions which, however, show no regular gradation of composition (209). The differences observed in the chromatographic profiles of DNA from different tissue sources of an organism are attributed to variations in the method of preparation of DNA (209, 212, 213).

Physical measurements have shown that the procedure of chloroform deproteinization used in the preparation of DNA leads to the removal of DNA material having a high sedimentation constant, which may be recovered with unchanged physical properties from the protein gel (212, 214). Loss of this material of high particle weight (sedimentation coefficient between 21 S and 54 S) results in an alteration of the elution pattern, especially in the terminal portion of the diagram. These results support the contention that the molecular size and shape of the DNA polymers are important factors in the fractionation on ECTEOLA, rather than compositional differences as in the studies already discussed. This polydispersity may arise to some extent from the effect of the residual nonhistone protein, a feature of these preparations which has been discussed in the section (III, A) dealing with protein associated with nucleic acid. Removal of this protein by digestion with chymotrypsin does not, however, entirely eliminate the spread of sedimentation values for the material (215). This size and shape heterogeneity may be further altered by heat (216) or the application of shear forces (217) to give a more paucidisperse material reflected by changes in the sedimentation coefficient and the chromatographic pattern on ECTEOLA.

Analyses of DNA preparations characterized by differences in their sedimentation constant show no significant compositional variations (209, 218), while fractionation into material showing compositional differences did not yield specimens of different sedimentation characteristics (219).

c. Physicochemical Demonstration of DNA Heterogeneity. Evidence for the heterogeneity of cellular DNA has also been obtained through studies on the denaturation of DNA by heat. The transition of DNA structure from a double helix configuration to that of a disordered coil, which occurs upon treatment with denaturing agents, is accompanied by an increase of the molecular extinction in the ultraviolet (220). This hyperchromic manifestation occurs within a relatively narrow temperature range during heating, and the point at which this change is half completed has been termed "melting temperature," T_m. A comparative study of DNA preparations of diverse total composition shows a direct relation between the melting temperature, T_m, and the G + C content of the specimens (221). These variations in T_m have been ascribed to differences in the stability between A $\cdots$ T and G $\cdots$ C hydrogen bonding; T_m should therefore be a reflection of the mean composition of the whole DNA molecules or of large segments in them (Fig. 4). The gradual slopes of the individual melting curves, as determined by the rise in ultraviolet absorption with increasing temperature, indicate that

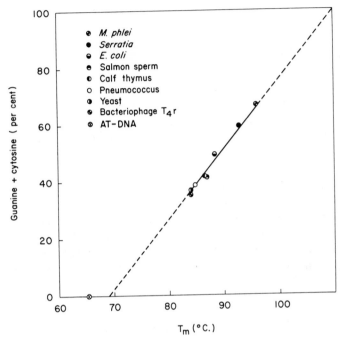

Fig. 4. Dependence of the denaturation temperature, T_m, on the guanine-cytosine content of various samples of deoxyribonucleic acid. Reproduced from J. Marmur and P. Doty (*221*).

the DNA samples contain a series of polymers having different T_m values. The synthetic AT polymer shows an abrupt melting profile. The steep profile of T4r bacteriophage DNA indicates a low degree of heterogeneity, whereas the broad melting curve of calf thymus DNA suggests extensive heterogeneity.

Similar conclusions have been derived from the broadness of bands obtained in the centrifugation of DNA preparations in a $CsCl_2$ concentration gradient (*222*). In these studies a direct relation has been observed between the $G + C$ content of the preparation and its mean density.

3. *Nucleotide Arrangement in DNA*

The compositional heterogeneity encountered in nucleic acid preparations and the limited variety of mononucleotide components contained therein are inherent features which prevent at the present time any means of sequential analysis of polynucleotides from leading to a unique sequence of nucleotides in DNA. An approach to this problem of sequence determination has been made through techniques which elicit information on the general nucleotide arrangement in the polymer population. This approach has given insight into some features of the structure of DNA obtained from several cell sources (*182, 223–230*).

The nonuniform distribution of nucleotides in DNA was initially suggested from examination of the nondialyzable portions of calf thymus and wheat germ DNA after extensive deoxyribonuclease digestion (*231, 232*). The composition of these residues differed markedly from that of the starting DNA; exhibiting a relatively greater ratio of adenine to guanine, thymine to cytosine, and purines to pyrimidines. These results were incompatible with a nucleotide arrangement of simple periodicity and a relatively even distribution of the component nucleotides.

Subsequent investigations into the distribution of the purine and pyrimidine nucleotides by chemical degradative techniques have involved initial hydrolysis of the labile purine deoxyriboside bonds (*223*). The resulting "apurinic acids" (APA) are nondialyzable and contain the total pyrimidine complement and phosphorus of the starting material (*233, 234*). Compounds of this type have been used for studies of the pyrimidine nucleotide distribution since their positions and sequential integrity have been maintained and each preparation is as unique in its nucleotide arrangement as the DNA from which it originated. Further degradation of APA by dilute alkali caused the loss of a considerable amount of deoxyribophosphate, but very little loss of pyrimidine nucleotide units. The interpretation made from these results, based on a preferential disposition to disintegration of the sugar phosphate units through a series of elimination reactions (*177*) or hydrolysis of an intermediate phosphoric acid triester (*223*), was that the APA, and consequently the DNA, contains stretches of nucleotides wherein pyrimidine nucleotides predominate, and consequently areas with a high density of purine nucleotides. These general conclusions have been extended to the structural features of fractions from calf thymus DNA and total human spleen DNA (*179*).

In other investigations (*224–227*), advantage was taken of the presence of reactive aldehydo groups in the deoxyribophosphate residues in APA to mark these former purine nucleotides by condensation reactions by forming the thioacetal derivative. This served to depress nonspecific decomposition of these sugar phosphate units and preferentially direct their decomposition via the transitory, alkali-labile phosphoric acid triester involving the available sugar hydroxyl at carbon 4 in a sequence of reactions similar to the alkaline depolymerization of RNA. Some of the fragments obtained upon alkaline degradation of the thioacetal of APA from calf thymus and *M. phlei* DNA have been characterized and estimated (227). The results of these investigations led to conclusions essentially similar to those reached by Tamm *et al.* (223), namely, that the nucleotide arrangement in the several DNA specimens studied included a higher proportion of pyrimidine polynucleotide regions than would have been expected from a random arrangement of nucleotides in a linear polymer.

Pyrimidine nucleoside 3′,5′-diphosphates had been early recognized to be products formed during moderate acid hydrolysis of DNA (235). If one dismisses the likelihood of large-scale random fission of internucleotide linkages, the formation of more than trace quantities of deoxycytidine and thymidine diphosphates, may be explained as being due to some mechanism operating at those positions in the polynucleotide where purine nucleotides flank a solitary pyrimidine nucleotide. According to Dekker *et al.* (236), an elimination reaction involving the phosphate group β to the aldehydo group plays a part in the process after the initial removal of purines. The yield of pyrimidine nucleoside diphosphates and analogous pyrimidine oligonucleotide units therefore reflects the number of such units which were flanked by purine nucleotides in the intact polymer. Standardized acid hydrolyses have been carried out on DNA from several sources in an attempt to correlate the yield of such fragments to the nucleotide arrangement in the polymers (182, 228, 229).

The results of this work may be briefly summarized as follows: (*a*) In no case is the nucleotide sequence of the deoxyribonucleic acid specimens investigated consistent with that expected from a random arrangement of monomers in a linear polymer. (*b*) At least 70% of the pyrimidines, and consequently 70% of the purine nucleotides, occur in tracts of at least three units. (*c*) Some analytically indistinguishable nucleic acid specimens from different cellular sources exhibit entirely different sequence characteristics (Table XIX). These observations have been extended to the DNA of rye germ and fractions derived from it (237). Of further interest were the results on the distribution of the minor nucleotide component, 5-methylcytidylic acid. Although methylcytosine behaves like cytosine in the complementariness rules previously discussed (Section III, B), this constituent appears to be involved in nucleotide sequences very different from those of its analog cytidylic acid. Experimentally, the relative contribution of M to sequences of a purine-pyrimidine-purine nature was nearly twice that of C. The dimer pyrimidine units flanked by purine nucleotides also show a relatively greater contribution of M than C. Enzymatic investigations on DNA have indicated a preferential association of methylcytidylic acid with guanylic acid (238). M does not therefore replace C randomly in the

TABLE XIX

PYRIMIDINE NUCLEOTIDE DISTRIBUTION IN THREE ANALYTICALLY INDISTINGUISHABLE DNA PREPARATIONS[a]

Preparation[b]	Total composition[c]					Nucleoside diphosphates[d]		
	A	G	C	T	T/C	pTp	pCp	pTp/pCp
Ox DNA, fraction at 0.75 M NaCl	31.1	19.0	20.0	29.9	1.50	15.9	9.2	2.58
Human DNA, fraction at 1.0 M NaCl	30.9	19.4	19.8	29.9	1.51	19.9	6.3	4.76
Arbacia lixula DNA, fraction at 2.6 M NaCl	31.0	18.5	19.6	30.9	1.58	16.0	14.0	1.80

[a] Data taken from Shapiro and Chargaff, (182).

[b] See reference (182) for the method of preparation and procedure of fractionation.

[c] Proportions in moles of nitrogenous constituents per 100 gm.-atoms of phosphorus in hydrolyzate, corrected to 100% recovery.

[d] Expressed as percentage of individual pyrimidine nucleotide released from the DNA as pyrimidine nucleoside 3′,5′-diphosphate, pTp, and pCp, during hydrolysis (0.1 M H$_2$SO$_4$, 30 minutes 100° C.). These conditions differentiate between nucleoside diphosphates originating from purine-pyrimidine-purine trinucleotide loci in the DNA and those originating at a slower rate from pyrimidine oligo-nucleotide tracts.

polymer, an observation which had earlier been arrived at from fractionation studies of wheat germ DNA (*181*).

A beginning in the correlation of DNA structure to specific function is predicated on the availability of material of far less heterogeneity than is afforded by present fractionation techniques.

C. NUCLEOTIDE DISTRIBUTION IN RNA

1. *Over-all Composition within Species*

Historically, the designation plant nucleic acid carried with it the implication that RNA was the characteristic cellular constituent of plant cells while DNA was an integral component only of animal cells. Extensive investigations involving histochemical, spectrophotometric, and cell fractionation techniques that are described elsewhere (*239, 240*), have indicated a more ubiquitous character of these nucleic acids. In the main, the cytoplasmic volume contains only pentose nucleic acid, most of which is associated with the microsomes. The nucleus is the repository of all the cellular deoxyribose nucleic acid and a portion of the RNA contained in the nucleolar apparatus (Section II, A).

RNA, like DNA, contains four major nitrogenous constituents in glycosidic linkage to the sugar component: adenine, guanine, cytosine, and uracil. The same type of 3′-5′ internucleoside phosphate linkages occur in RNA as those described for DNA. Reference should be made to several reviews on the chemistry of components of RNA and general structural features of the polymer (*176, 177, 241*).

To the several methods of isolation and purification of RNA which have been discussed by Magasanik (*108*) should be added the phenol procedure introduced by Gierer and Schramm for tobacco mosaic virus (*242*). Unfortunately, the ever present danger of ribonuclease activity during extraction procedures carried out in the absence of efficient protein denaturing agents (*243*) and the tenacious association observed between RNA and protein (*244*) undoubtedly lead to more than modest degradation and fractionation in most of the methods of isolation used. The consequences of such alterations of the composition of RNA upon the interpretation of the analytical data are obvious. For these reasons many investigators have preferred to analyze tissue nucleic acids contained in the cold-acid insoluble, defatted residues without prior isolation and purification of the nucleic acids. These difficulties do not arise when one deals with the plant viruses.

The analysis of RNA for the content of nitrogenous components may be carried out in one of three ways: (*a*) strong acid hydrolysis to purines and pyrimidines; (*b*) moderate acid hydrolysis to free purines and pyrimidine nucleotides; (c) dilute alkaline hydrolysis to constituent mononucleotides. The relative mildness of procedure c recommends it over the others. Methods that allow the separation of the four components of the hydrolyzate should be preferred to those relying on differential spectrophotometric estimation of mixtures of components when one realizes how many minor components of RNA may have gone unnoticed because of reliance on this technique.

a. RNA of Animal Sources. The available analyses of deoxyribonucleic acids have already permitted an affirmative answer for its species specificity. The narrower range of compositional variations among RNA's from animal tissues, and the use of preparations that may not have been representative samples of the cellular RNA, made elicitation of similar conclusions for ribonucleic acid initially difficult. One characteristic was, however, obvious. Whereas DNA from animal tissues showed a predominance of adenine and thymine over guanine and cytosine (AT type), the RNA's from these tissues were characterized by a content of guanylic and cytidylic acid relatively higher than that of adenylic and uridylic acid. The data cited in Table XX represent the composition of RNA obtained by analysis of cold-acid insoluble, lipid-free, tissue residues or analysis of tissue extracts where a recovery of at least 70% of the RNA is reported. The composition of unfertilized *Drosophila* eggs, characterized by a low guanylic and cytidylic acid content, resembles that of some plant viruses (Table XXII).

The species specificity of RNA from animal sources is less easily demonstrable than that of DNA. The work of Elson *et al.* (*253*) on sea urchin eggs and embryos and of Crosbie *et al.* (*247*) on the cytoplasmic RNA of pregnant and fetal rabbit livers indicate that no substantial change in the gross nucleotide composition occurs during the development of an organism. The emergence of a specific process in the cell, e.g., the photosynthetic apparatus in *Euglena gracilis*, has, however, been demonstrated to be accompanied by an alteration in the composition of the RNA (*248*).

In terms of the content of nitrogenous constituents, the one regularity which appears to be statistically evident among ribonucleic acids is that the molar sum of adenylic and cytidylic acid (6-amino nucleotides) equals that of guanylic plus uridylic acid (6-keto nucleotides) (*108, 246*). In many cases, the molar ratios A/U and G/C approximate unity. This would be a compositional prerequisite for any proposal of a complementary double-stranded RNA structure similar to that of DNA. Such associations have been observed to occur with synthetic polyribonucleotides (*254*). However, only limited intramolecular hydrogen bonding for RNA has been suggested (*246, 255*).

TABLE XX

NUCLEOTIDE COMPOSITION OF RNA FROM SEVERAL PLANT AND ANIMAL SOURCES[a]

Tissue	Adenylic acid	Guanylic acid	Cytidylic acid	Uridylic acid	$\dfrac{A + U^b}{G + C}$	$\dfrac{\text{6-Amino}^c}{\text{6-Keto}}$	References
Neurospora crassa	23.7	26.2	25.9	24.2	0.92	0.98	87
Penicillium stoloniferum	24.9	27.0	23.6	24.7	0.98	0.94	245
Saccharomyces cerevisiae	25.4	24.6	22.6	27.4	1.12	0.92	246
Saccharomyces cerevisiae	22.9	25.2	22.0	29.9	1.12	0.82	247
Euglena gracilis (green)	23.2	28.5	26.3	22.0	0.82	0.98	248
Euglena gracilis (etiolated)	21.8	29.9	27.5	20.9	0.74	0.97	248
Wheat germ	22.4	29.2	27.6	20.8	0.76	1.00	181
Paracentrotus lividus eggs and embryos	22.6	29.4	27.2	20.8	0.77	0.98	246
Drosophila eggs							
Type xxy[se8]	29.8	23.1	18.5	28.5	1.40	0.94	249
Type xx	25.2	24.4	20.5	30.0	1.23	0.84	249
Chicken embryo	21.2	30.6	28.0	20.3	0.71	0.97	245
Chicken liver	19.5	33.3	26.6	20.7	0.67	0.85	247
Mouse liver	21.0	31.2	28.3	19.5	0.68	0.97	245
Rat liver	20.2	31.1	27.1	21.6	0.72	0.90	250
Rat liver	19.0	33.4	27.2	20.5	0.65	0.86	247
Rat pancreas	20.5	31.3	26.9	21.3	0.72	0.90	250
Rat kidney	19.4	29.5	30.7	20.4	0.66	1.00	246
Rabbit liver	19.3	32.6	28.2	19.9	0.64	0.91	247
Cat brain	21.6	31.8	26.0	20.6	0.73	0.91	251
Calf liver	23.1	28.9	28.1	20.0	0.76	1.05	245
Calf liver	17.1	27.3	33.9	21.7	0.63	1.04	246
Calf kidney	19.7	26.7	33.4	20.2	0.66	1.13	246
Calf thymus	19.2	33.2	25.9	21.9	0.70	0.82	252

[a] Proportions in moles of ribonucleotide per 100 moles of total nucleotides recovered.
[b] A, adenylic acid; C, cytidylic acid; U, uridyhc acid; G, guanylic acid.
[c] 6-Amino, 6-Amino nucleotides; 6-keto, 6-keto nucleotides.

TABLE XXI
Nucleotide Composition of Bacterial RNA[a]

Organism	Adenylic acid	Guanylic acid	Cytidylic acid	Uridylic acid	$\dfrac{A + U^b}{G + C}$	$\dfrac{6\text{-Amino}^c}{6\text{-Keto}}$	References
Pasteurella tularensis	27.3	29.8	21.0	21.9	0.97	0.93	*256*
Micrococcus pyogenes var. *aureus*	26.9	28.7	22.4	22.0	0.96	0.97	*256*
Clostridium perfringens	28.1	29.5	22.0	20.4	0.94	1.00	*256*
Erwinia carotovora	26.5	29.5	23.7	20.3	0.88	1.01	*256*
Aerobacter aerogenes	26.0	30.3	24.1	19.6	0.84	1.00	*256*
Escherichia coli	25.3	28.8	24.7	21.2	0.87	1.00	*246*
Escherichia coli	26.0	30.7	24.1	19.2	0.82	1.00	*256*
Proteus morganii	26.0	31.1	23.7	19.2	0.82	0.99	*256*
Proteus vulgaris	26.3	31.0	24.0	18.7	0.82	1.01	*256*
Shigella dysenteriae	25.9	30.4	24.4	19.3	0.82	1.01	*256*
Salmonella typhosa	26.1	30.8	24.0	19.1	0.82	1.00	*256*
Salmonella typhimurium	26.1	31.0	23.8	19.1	0.82	1.00	*256*
Alcaligenes faecalis	25.7	30.9	24.1	19.3	0.82	0.99	*256*
Brucella abortus	25.4	30.2	24.9	19.5	0.81	1.01	*256*
Mycobacterium vadosum	23.8	31.7	23.5	21.0	0.81	0.90	*256*
Mycobacterium phlei	20.9	30.8	27.1	21.3	0.73	0.92	*246*
Pseudomonas aeruginosa	25.1	31.6	23.8	19.5	0.81	0.96	*256*
Corynebacterium diphtheriae	23.1	31.6	23.8	21.5	0.81	0.88	*256*
Serratia marcescens	20.3	31.2	24.3	24.1	0.80	0.81	*246*
Azotobacter vinelandii	24.2	30.6	25.7	19.5	0.78	1.00	*257*
Streptomyces griseus	23.8	31.1	25.2	19.9	0.78	0.96	*256*
Sarcina lutea	23.2	32.7	24.2	19.9	0.76	0.90	*256*
Mycobacterium tuberculosis BCG	20.1	31.3	29.4	19.2	0.65	0.98	*149*
Mycobacterium tuberculosis BCG	22.6	33.0	26.1	18.3	0.69	0.95	*256*

[a] Proportions in moles of ribonucleotide per 100 moles of total nucleotides recovered.

[b] A, adenylic acid; C, cytidylic acid; U, uridylic acid; G, guanylic acid.

[c] 6-Amino, 6-amino nucleotides; 6-Keto, 6-keto nucleotides.

TABLE XXII

Nucleotide Composition of Several Viruses[a]

Virus	Adenylic acid	Guanylic acid	Cytidylic acid	Uridylic acid	$\dfrac{A + U[b]}{G + C}$	$\dfrac{\text{6-Amino}[c]}{\text{6-Keto}}$	References
Turnip yellow mosaic	22.6	17.2	38.1	22.1	0.81	1.55	259
Southern bean mosaic	25.8	26.0	23.0	25.3	1.04	0.95	259
Tomato bushy stunt 3,9,10	25.8	28.1	20.5	25.6	1.06	0.86	260
Tomato bushy stunt	27.4	27.7	20.4	24.4	1.08	0.92	259
Tobacco necrosis	27.9	24.4	21.9	25.7	1.16	0.99	259
Ribgrass	29.3	27.1	17.3	26.3	1.25	0.87	261
Potato X	34.3	21.8	22.8	21.3	1.25	1.33	259
TMV	30.0	25.8	18.5	25.8	1.26	0.94	262
TMV and 15 strains	29.9	25.2	18.5	26.4	1.29	0.94	259
Cucumber virus 4	26.0	25.8	18.5	29.8	1.26	0.80	261
Cucumber virus 3,4	25.6	25.6	18.7	30.1	1.26	0.80	259
Tomato mosaic	29.5	26.0	18.3	26.3	1.26	0.91	261
Tomato aucuba mosaic	30.2	23.9	19.6	26.4	1.30	0.99	261
Influenza virus							
Strain WS	24.8	17.9	24.5	32.7	1.36	0.98	263
Strain MEL	24.6	17.7	24.4	33.3	1.38	0.96	263

[a] Proportions in moles of ribonucleotide per 100 moles of total nucleotides recovered.
[b] A, adenylic acid; C, cytidylic acid; U, uridylic acid; G, guanylic acid.
[c] 6-Amino, 6-amino nucleotides; 6-Keto, 6-keto nucleotides.

b. Bacterial RNA. Contrary to the difficulty encountered in demonstrating a species specificity of RNA in mammals, the ribonucleic acids from bacterial sources exhibit an obvious cellular specificity (Table XXI). Like the DNA of bacteria, the ribonucleic acids of microorganisms show a more diverse composition than any other group of related organisms. Some positive correlation of the composition of RNA and DNA in bacteria has been presented by Belozersky and Spirin (*256*). This is expressed as a tendency toward an increase in the ratio $(G + C)/(A + U)$ in RNA when passing from species of low $(G + C)/(A + T)$ ratio of the DNA to those with higher values. These results have suggested to these investigators that the composition of a portion of the RNA depends upon the composition of the DNA.

c. Viral RNA. The nucleic acid of tobacco mosaic virus (TMV) was described as a ribonucleic acid (*258*), and this identity has subsequently been established for all plant viruses investigated. The available nucleic acid analyses of the plant viruses (Table XXII) show, as do the bacterial ribonucleic acids, a greater variation of composition than the RNA of diverse animal sources. The nucleic acid composition of related virus strains are indistinguishable although they differentiate themselves by their infectious symptoms (*259*). Such alterations of biological character in TMV have been demonstrated by limited chemical deamination of the RNA (*264*).

The nucleotide composition of bushy stunt, southern bean mosaic, and potato X viruses are distinctly different from each other and from other unrelated viral nucleic acids. The protein components of some of these viruses may, however, be similar as suggested by serological cross reactivities (*261*). It has not yet been possible to establish a correlation between pathological symptoms due to the virus and its physical or chemical characteristics.

2. Composition of RNA in Subcellular Fractions

The heterogeneity of RNA has been established by the physical and chemical techniques that have already been applied to DNA (Section III, B). Ultracentrifugation studies of mammalian RNA indicate an effective separation of the material into two major fractions by this procedure (*265*). One characterized by a sedimentation constant less than 3 S and another of material between 15 and 32 S. The fractionation of RNA is also possible via column chromatography using methylated bovine serum albumin (*266*). This technique effects a separation between RNA components of low and high sedimentation values; the latter fraction apparently is similar to the RNA precipitated during the fractionation procedure involving $1 M$ NaCl (*265*). ECTEOLA has been used to fractionate RNA from microorganisms and from mammalian and viral sources (267). The chromatographic patterns obtained by this procedure reflect differences in the sedimentation coefficient of the constituent polymers. As in the investigations of DNA using this fractionation technique, the method of isolation and subsequent treatment of the RNA has a marked effect on the sedimentation characteristics of the polymer and consequently on the elution profile of the material. Some factors that influence the chromatography of RNA and DNA are discussed by Bradley and Rich (267).

The heterogeneity of RNA was also evident from the information that although the bulk of the cellular RNA is found in the microsomal particles, the metabolic activity of the nuclear RNA in both plant (268) and animal (17) systems is significantly higher than that of the RNA from the other cellular fractions (Section II, A).

The separation of ribonucleoproteins into distinctive fractions representative of a specific cellular structure is accomplished by use of the differential centrifugal techniques. Compositional differences among the RNA of the various fractions have aided in the elucidation of an intracellular specificity of RNA (Table XXIII). The species specificity of RNA is more apparent when comparison is made among the compositions of the several nuclear RNA preparations cited.

The compositional difference between nuclear and cytoplasmic RNA has been repeatedly confirmed (276). Some changes in RNA composition of cellular fractions have been observed to be induced by prolonged starvation of the organism (277, 278) or during active tissue regeneration (278). A change in total RNA composition during the development of a specific cellular apparatus has also been observed (248).

Suggestions of the nuclear origin of the cellular RNA and consequent nuclear control of all cellular processes have been based upon studies, covered in Section II, of the rate of isotope labeling in the various fractions and upon direct cytochemical autoradiographic studies (279, 280), which together imply a transfer of nuclear RNA into the cytoplasm. An objection to this hypothesis, which excludes a decomposition or alteration of the nuclear RNA prior to its transference to the cytoplasm, arises from the known difference in composition of nuclear and cytoplasmic RNA. Osawa et al. (252) have attempted to overcome this objection by determining the existence of a ribonucleic acid which has a composition common to the nucleolus and the cytoplasm. The nucleolar differentiation of ribonucleoprotein had been evident from histological investigations of Ehrlich ascites tumor cells which indicated the presence of two different ribonucleoproteins (281).

TABLE XXIII

NUCLEOTIDE COMPOSITION OF RNA FROM SUBCELLULAR FRACTIONS OF SEVERAL TISSUE SOURCES[a,b]

Source	Fraction	A	G	C	U	$\dfrac{A+U}{G+C}$	$\dfrac{\text{6-Amino}}{\text{6-Keto}}$	References
Lamium album	Chloroplasts	25.2	32.7	25.2	16.9	0.73	1.02	269
Lamium album	Cytoplasm	30.5	35.8	23.0	10.7	0.70	1.15	269
Symphytum officinale	Chloroplasts	27.2	34.3	20.7	17.7	0.82	0.92	269
Symphytum officinale	Cytoplasm	26.1	37.3	22.2	14.4	0.68	0.93	269
Turkish tobacco	Chloroplasts	22.7	31.2	24.7	21.5	0.79	0.90	270
Frog	Microsomes	20.1	27.9	32.2	19.8	0.66	1.10	271
	Cell sap	20.5	24.6	31.5	23.4	0.78	1.08	271
Rat	Nuclei	21.1	26.1	27.7	25.1	0.86	0.95	247, 271, 272
	Mitochondria	18.9	31.9	28.5	20.7	0.66	0.90	247
	Microsomes	18.1	32.9	29.1	19.9	0.61	0.89	247, 271, 273, 274
	Cell sap	18.5	31.3	29.3	20.8	0.65	0.92	247, 271
Rabbit	Nuclei	19.7	26.8	25.8	27.6	0.90	0.84	272
	Mitochondria	19.4	30.4	30.2	20.1	0.65	0.98	247
	Microsomes	18.9	31.9	29.4	19.8	0.63	0.93	247, 273
	Cell sap	19.7	30.4	30.2	19.7	0.65	1.00	247
Ox	Nuclei	20.3	27.5	28.6	23.6	0.78	0.96	252, 271
	Microsomes	19.1	33.6	27.9	19.3	0.62	0.89	252
	Cell sap	19.0	34.0	27.4	19.6	0.63	0.87	252
Human	Nuclei	19.9	35.8	21.1	23.1	0.76	0.70	275
	Mitochondria	18.7	30.2	38.2	12.8	0.46	1.32	275
	Microsomes	19.7	34.7	29.0	16.6	0.57	0.95	275
	Cell sap	25.7	36.0	26.2	12.1	0.61	1.08	275

[a] Proportions in moles of ribonucleotide per 100 moles of total nucleotides recovered.

[b] A, adenylic acid; C, cytidylic acid; U, uridylic acid; G, guanylic acid; 6-Amino, 6-amino nucleotides; 6-Keto, 6-keto nucleotides.

Calf thymus nuclei prepared by differential centrifugation in an aqueous medium has yielded three distinct ribonucleoproteins fractionated by differential solubility (252), one of which was similar to the composition of the cytoplasmic RNA and also showed physical properties similar to the microsomal nucleoprotein. On the basis of tracer experiments, however, this nuclear RNA did not totally satisfy the concept of its role as a precursor of cytoplasmic material. An interpretation of the data was offered which suggested that perhaps only a part of the microsomal RNA was derived from the nuclear source. Similar investigations have been directed to the nuclear RNA of rat and rabbit tissues (273).

A positive correlation of the composition of DNA and the nuclear RNA in several animal species based upon a close identity of the $(A + T)/(G + C)$ ratio of the former with the $(G + C)/(A + U)$ ratio of the latter suggested to Zubay that a portion of the cellular RNA is a product of gene action (282). The mechanism of such a control of composition would involve the formation of an intermediate triple-stranded helical polymer.

3. *Minor Nitrogenous Constituents of RNA*

The presence in ribonucleic acid of components which are structurally different from the four nucleotides usually found in RNA had been suspected by Cohn and Volkin upon examination of ion exchange chromatographic patterns of an alkaline digest of RNA (283).

Investigations into the composition of yeast RNA fractionated into a soluble and precipitable portion in $1 M$ NaCl solution have indicated a relatively high content of a fifth nucleotide component in the low molecular weight, soluble RNA. Chemical characterization together with the liberation of this component by RNase to the same extent as cytidylic and uridylic acids inferred a pyrimidine ribonucleotide character of this material (284). The composition of the material indicated that it was an isomer of uridylic acid (285, 286). Similarity of ultraviolet and nuclear magnetic resonance spectra between the nucleoside derived from this compound and synthetic 5-hydroxymethyluracil allowed the suggestion that a carbon-to-carbon linkage exists between C-1 of ribose and C-5 of the uracil ring rather than the normally encountered C-1 to N-3 glycoside bond (285, 286). In retrospect, this linkage explains the difficulty encountered in obtaining uracil through means by which the other nucleosides yielded their nitrogenous constituent. The content of this compound, for which the trivial name "ψ-uridine" has been suggested (286), in the $1 M$ NaCl soluble fraction and insoluble fraction of yeast RNA is 10.3 and 3.3 moles per 100 moles uridylic acid, respectively (287). It appears in the RNA of *Euglena gracilis* to the extent of approximately 5.7 moles per 100 moles uridylic acid (248).

The occurrence of a series of methylated purines in RNA has been confirmed by several laboratories (287–290). The presence of 6-methylaminopurine (N⁶-methyladenine) in yeast RNA to the extent of 0.1 mole % of the purine content was shown by Adler *et al.* (290). In addition to this component, Littlefield and Dunn (288) have shown the presence of 2-methyladenine and 6-dimethylaminopurine (N⁶-dimethyladenine) derived from nucleotides of an alkaline hydrolyzate of RNA. The sources of these components include RNA from several microorganisms, liver, and wheat germ (Table XXIV). Identification of these bases was made by chromatographic comparisons with synthetic compounds. The mode of isolation of these nitrogenous compounds obviates any suggestion that their sources were compounds extraneous to the RNA. Although 2-methyladenine and 6-dimethylaminopurine (N⁶-dimethyladenine) are normally found as constituents of pseudovitamin B_{12d} and puromycin, respectively, there appears to be no correlation between the occurrence of these natural products and the presence of the bases in the RNA of the cell sources (288).

Simultaneously with the isolation and characterization of methylated adenines, several methylated guanine compounds were detected as additional components of the same RNA sources (287, 289, 290); 1-methylguanine, 2-methylamino-6-hydroxypurine (N²-methylguanine), and 2-dimethyl-6-hydroxypurine (N²-dimethylguanine) in the form of ribonucleotides and ribonucleosides as well as the free bases. While 1-methylguanine and N²-methylguanine have been found in human urine, N²-dimethylguanine had not been previously reported to occur in nature. The distribution of the methylated guanine compounds in RNA shows a great similarity to that of the methylated adenines (Table XXIV). The 1 M NaCl soluble RNA of rat liver (and perhaps the soluble, low molecular weight fractions of other RNA specimens) differs from the precipitable fraction or total RNA by having an unusually high proportion of methylated guanines, N⁶-methyladenine, and the ψ-uridine components (289). None of these methylated purines have been detected in the RNA of TMV or TYM. N²-Dimethylguanine appears to be absent from the RNA of *Aerobacter aerogenes*.

5-Methylribocytidylic acid has been reported to be a minor nucleotide component of RNA from *E. coli* (291). The investigators suggest that deamination of methylribocytidylic acid during chemical hydrolytic procedures may be the origin of the thymine described as a component of several RNA preparations (287, 288). The identification of thymidine

TABLE XXIV

MOLAR PROPORTION OF METHYLATED BASES OF SEVERAL RNA PREPARATIONS[a,b]

Source	Thymine	2'CH₃ adenine	N⁶CH₃ adenine	N⁶(CH₃)₂ adenine	1'CH₃ guanine	N²CH₃ guanine	N²(CH₃)₂ guanine
Escherichia coli B/r	0.9	0.5	0.4	0.3	ND	ND	ND
Escherichia coli 15T⁻	1.0	0.3	ND	ND	ND	ND	ND
Aerobacter aerogenes	1.2	0.3	0.3	0.1	0.1	0.05	—
Staphylococcus aureus	0.9	0.05	0.2	—	ND	ND	ND
Yeast	0.6	0.1	0.2	0.05	0.02	0.02	ND
Wheat germ	3.7	0.1	3.7	0.06	0.6	0.2	0.5
Sugar beet	ND	ND	ND	ND	0.6	ND	0.1
Nicotiana glutinosa	ND	ND	ND	ND	0.2	ND	0.06
Whole rabbit liver	—	—	0.3	—	0.2	ND	ND
Rat liver, "soluble RNA" fraction	ND	ND	ND	ND	4.0	2.2	2.9
Rat liver, microsomes	—	—	0.5	0.1	0.09	0.08	0.09
Reference	(288)	(288)	(288)	(288)	(289)	(289)	(289)

[a] Results are expressed as moles of constituent per 100 moles of uracil.

[b] Dash indicates less than 0.05% content; ND, the preparation was not examined for the particular component. The RNA of TMV and TYM show less than 0.05 moles of each constituent per 100 moles of uracil.

from enzymatic hydrolyzates of *E. coli* RNA (*288*), however, does not indicate this explanation to be complete.

From the available data it appears unlikely that the occurrence of these compounds as minor constituents of RNA is a result of random incorporation due to a nonspecific utilization, but rather an indication of functional differentiation of a particular group of RNA units of the cell. In this regard the possible identity of the 1 *M* NaCl soluble RNA fraction, containing a high proportion of these minor components, with the RNA acting as a responsible agent for amino acid activation (*292*), must be cited.

In addition to these several satellite nitrogenous components, another sugar component obtained from dinucleotides resistant to further alkaline hydrolysis has been described (*293*). From chromatographic criteria, the sugar is believed to be 2′(or 3′)-*O*-methylribose.

The intensification of structural differences by virtue of this variety of components occurring in RNA will probably make the problem of RNA specificity more amenable to solution.

4. Nucleotide Arrangement in RNA

Pancreatic ribonuclease, RNase, hydrolyzes the phosphate ester bond distal to the 3′-phosphate ester linkage with pyrimidine nucleosides (*177*). Pyrimidine nucleoside 3′-phosphates and the original purine tracts terminated by pyrimidine nucleoside 3′-phosphate are the end products of the enzymatic digestions. The known specificity of pancreatic RNase, and the consequent realization that the end products of enzymatic action on RNA would be a relatively small group of compounds, has made possible investigations of the nucleotide arrangement in RNA similar to those performed on DNA by chemical methods (Section III, B). In the latter case, pyrimidine nucleotide tracts were obtained. In this instance, information on the arrangement of purine ribonucleotides is made directly available. An early attempt toward this end was made by Magasanik (*294*).

Initial investigations on the problem were made on the TCA-precipitable oligonucleotides after RNase digestion of RNA from TMV and strains YA, HR, M, and J14D1 (*295*). These oligonucleotide fractions were observed to have the same composition and indicated that some structural similarity among the nucleic acids of different strains of TMV existed: a common distribution of purine and pyrimidine nucleotides with potential variation of sequence in the polypurine and polypyrimidine nucleotide tracts.

Interesting results have been obtained from a study of the smaller fragments of such RNase digests (*296, 297*). The total RNA of TMV and strains HR, M, and YA are indistinguishable by their composition, but show significant differences in nucleotide arrangement when a comparison of the yields of pyrimidine mononucleotides (296), dinucleotides, and one trinucleotide (297) is made after RNase treatment. Analyses of this sort easily illustrate structural differences among the nucleic acids from closely related sources.

The application of this method of structural characterization to RNA of rat liver fractions (298)—nuclear, mitochondrial, microsomal, and supernatant—has again elicited differences in nucleotide arrangement among nucleic acids which have similar composition. From the data cited, it was concluded that the plan of structure in the mitochondrial RNA and microsomal RNA is quite similar, but differs significantly from the RNA of the cell sap. The nucleotide arrangement in the particulate cytoplasmic RNA fractions, as reflected in the proportions of several fragments present in the hydrolyzates, also differed from that of nuclear RNA.

The acceptor RNA involved in the formation of an aminoacyl RNA compound, assumed to mediate the synthesis of protein in the microsome, is a fraction of the cytoplasmic RNA having a relatively low molecular weight: 30,000–50,000 (299). Investigations concerned with the steps involved in the acceptor activity of this RNA have implicated a specific terminal sequence of nucleotides: RNA-pCpCpA (300–302). Different RNA molecules, apparently specific for different amino acids, have the same polymer termination. These conclusions were confirmed by isolation of an aminoacyl 2′(or 3′)-adenosine unit after RNase digestion of amino acyl RNA (300) and by the transfer of P^{32} from incorporated adenylic acid to the cytidylic acid in the RNA as shown by diesterase treatment of the RNA (302).

IV. Biological Specificity of the Nucleic Acids

A. BACTERIAL TRANSFORMATIONS

Avery and co-workers discovered that DNA preparations from encapsulated pneumococus cells could confer to nonencapsulated cells the ability to form a capsule (303). The modified cells retained this ability as an inheritable characteristic, and DNA prepared from these cells had the same transforming activity. Furthermore, the capsule of the transformed cells possessed the same antigenic characteristics as that of the donor cells. Thus, DNA behaved as an agent that could confer specific inheritable properties to certain cells. Numerous studies on the chemical and physical properties of the transforming preparations have confirmed the original conclusion that the active agent is

DNA (*304, 305*). Transformations for other characters have subsequently been obtained in pneumococcus strains (see Table XXV). Successful transformations have also been performed with different types

TABLE XXV
BACTERIAL TRANSFORMATIONS EFFECTED *in Vitro* WITH DNA PREPARATIONS[a]

Character transferred	Species[b]	Number of characters
Capsular antigens		
Type III	*D. pneumoniae*	1
Types II, VI, XIV	*D. pneumoniae*	4
Types I, VIII	*D. pneumoniae*	2
Intermediate type II	*D. pneumoniae*	1
Intermediate type III	*D. pneumoniae*	2
Reconstituted types III	*D. pneumoniae*	2 (to 4)
Deviant types III	*D. pneumoniae*	1 (to 3)
Types *a, b, c, d, e, f*	*H. influenzae*	6
Mixed type *ab*	*H. influenzae*	1
Types I, II	*N. meningitidis*	1
Antigen S_1	*E. coli*	1
Other surface factors		
Rough (nonfilamentous) antigen	*D. pneumoniae*	1
Extreme rough (filamentous)	*D. pneumoniae*	1
M-protein antigen	*D. pneumoniae*	1 (to 2)
Drug resistances		
Penicillin	*D. pneumoniae*	3
Streptomycin	*D. pneumoniae*	2
Streptomycin (high step)	*D. pneumoniae*	1
Streptomycin (high step)	*H. influenzae*	1
Sulfanilamide	*D. pneumoniae*	1
Enzymatic capacities		
Mannitol utilization	*D. pneumoniae*	1
Salicin	*D. pneumoniae*	1
Large colony (lactate?)	*D. pneumoniae*	1
Virulence in plant	*Agrobacterium*	1

[a] Table reproduced from article by Hotchkiss (*304*).
[b] *D.* = *Diplococcus; H.* = *Hemophilus; N.* = *Neisseria; E.* = *Escherichia.*

of bacterial cells (*304, 306*), such as meningococci, *Hemophilus influenzae*, and, more recently, *Bacillus subtilis* (*307*). Among the inheritable
characters transferred by DNA preparations are specific capsular antigens and other surface factors, drug resistance, ability to ferment certain
substances, and independence from certain nutritional requirements.
The transforming preparations must contain some DNA molecules

different from those of the recipient cells. Such differences are most likely much too subtle to be detected by our present chemical methods, and the transforming system thus provides a very useful tool for the comparative study of different DNA molecules originating from the same cells or from related organisms.

In *Hemophilus* and also in pneumococci, DNA preparations from cells containing two capsular antigens give rise both to single types of transformants and to cells containing both antigens (*305*). The frequency of the latter type is, however, higher than can be accounted for by independent transformations by two molecules. Moreover, a mixture of deoxyribonucleic acids from the two singly marked cell types does not yield this result. Such a link between different markers also exists in the case of mannitol utilization and streptomycin resistance in pneumococcus (*308*). The occurrence of these linked transformations strongly suggests that one molecule of transforming DNA can contain more than one genetic marker.

The investigation of DNA preparations containing several markers has also revealed differences in the stabilities of different transforming activities when exposed to various treatments. In *Hemophilus* the activity for streptomycin resistance proved considerably more resistant to ultraviolet irradiation than the activities for two capsular antigens (*305*). The streptomycin resistance markers from two different types of cells also showed a considerable difference in their stability. Treatments by heat, nitrogen mustards, and other agents revealed similar differences in stability. In pneumococcus, the activities for streptomycin resistance and optochin resistance also showed differences in their stability to ultraviolet irradiation (*309*).

The study of bacterial transformations has provided some information on the interesting problem of the degree of similarity among homologous genetic markers from different species. Schaeffer has studied the character for streptomycin resistance in three species of the genus *Hemophilus, H. influenzae, H. parainfluenzae,* and *H. suis* (*310*). *H. influenzae* cells could incorporate equally well DNA preparations from the three species, but the frequencies of transformation were considerably lower with the heterologous preparations. This indicates differences in the fine structure of the transforming DNA molecules from the three species. A similar, but more detailed study was performed by Leidy and co-workers (*311*). In addition to the three different species of *Hemophilus*, various strains of the same species were compared. Heterologous DNA preparations proved nearly as effective as the homologous DNA when recipient and donor strains were within the same species, and much less effective when they were from different species. Preparations from streptomycin-resistant pneumococci or menin-gococci were completely ineffective.

The use of transforming DNA labeled with P^{32} has permitted the measurement of the amount of material incorporated into the cells during the transformation. Both in pneumococcus (*312, 313*) and in *Hemophilus* (*314*) a correlation between the two events was demon-strated. Addition of DNA lacking transforming activity results in an inhibition of transformation. This is regarded as a competition of DNA molecules for surface receptors, with a resulting inhibition of incorpora-tion of the active agents (*310*). Deoxyribonucleic acids from the wild types of the three *Hemophilus* species were equally effective in inhibit-ing transformation (*310*). Preparations from calf thymus and from some other bacterial species, however, was less effective. Similar results were obtained in *Hemophilus* in the case of the capsular antigens (*306*). The addition of wild-type DNA to *Hemophilus* cells (*314*), and of calf thymus DNA to pneumococcus cells (*312*) resulted in an inhibi-tion of both the incorporation and the transformation. *Escherichia coli* and other microorganisms were found to incorporate much less DNA than the pneumococcus cells (*312*).

B. Enzymatic Synthesis of DNA

The partial purification of an enzyme system obtained from extracts of *E. coli* whose specific requirements strongly suggest its significance with regard to the biosynthesis of deoxyribonucleic acids has been described by Kornberg (*315*). The system is defined by a requirement for Mg^{2+} and the simultaneous presence of all four deoxyribonucleoside triphosphates (thymidine, deoxyadenosine, deoxyguanosine, and deoxy-cytidine triphosphates). The system is unique, however, because DNA, apparently acting as a primer, is essential to the reaction. The newly synthesized polymer, up to twenty times the amount of primer material, has been characterized by 3'-5' internucleoside phosphate linkages typical of the nucleic acids (*316*). In addition, the physical properties of the synthesized material are essentially identical to those of DNA isolated from cellular sources (*317*).

A polymerase from calf thymus has been described by Bollum (*318*) that has the same requirements as the *E. coli* system. Similar systems appear to have a wide distribution among mammalian tissues.

A simple, but critical, requirement which this product must satisfy in order to justify consideration of this enzymatic process as a synthesis of a specific DNA whose structure is predetermined by the primer DNA is that the composition of the product is the same as that of the primer material. The presence of a nuclease in the enzyme system makes a biological criterion for DNA synthesis difficult at present. In Table XXVI are compared the compositions of product and primer for a

TABLE XXVI

PURINE AND PYRIMIDINE COMPOSITION OF ENZYMATICALLY SYNTHESIZED DEOXYRIBONUCLEIC ACIDS AND OF THE DNA PRIMERS[a,b]

DNA	Number of analyses	A	T	G	C	$\dfrac{A + T}{G + C}$	$\dfrac{Pu}{Py}$
Mycobacterium phlei							
Primer	3	16.25	16.5	33.75	33.5	(0.48–0.49)	(0.98–1.04)
Product	3	16.5	20.0	29.25	33.5	(0.57–0.63)	(0.78–0.88)
Aerobacter aerogenes							
Primer	1	22.5	22.5	27.5	27.5	0.82	1.00
Product	3	25.5	25.0	24.25	25.25	(0.96–1.13)	(0.95–1.01)
Escherichia coli							
Primer	2	25.0	24.25	24.5	26.25	(0.96–0.99)	(0.97–0.99)
Product	2	26.0	25.0	24.25	24.5	(0.96–1.07)	(0.96–1.06)
Calf thymus							
Primer	2	28.5	26.25	22.5	21.25	(1.24–1.26)	(1.03–1.08)
Product	6	29.75	29.75	20.25	20.75	(1.22–1.67)	(0.82–1.04)
T2 coliphage							
Primer	2	32.75	33.0	16.75	17.5	(1.86–1.97)	(0.95–1.01)
Product	2	33.25	32.25	17.25	17.5	(1.82–1.98)	(1.01–1.03)
Synthetic A-T							
Copolymer	1	49.75	48.25	<1.3	<1.3	>40	1.05

[a] Data taken from a review by I. R. Lehman (*317*).

[b] Proportions in moles of nitrogenous constituent per 100 moles of total constituents recovered. A, T, G, and C refer to adenine, thymine, guanine, and cytosine, respectively, except that C in the case of T2 coliphage primer refers to hydroxymethylcytosine. Pu and Py refer to purines and pyrimidines. The values given represent averages of the number of analyses indicated. The figures in parentheses are the ranges of values obtained.

series of reactions using DNA from several natural sources. The compositions of the product polymers agree quite well with those of the primers regardless of the relative concentration of triphosphate precursors or length of time allowed for the synthesis. The likely participation of the primer DNA in determining the composition of the new DNA is an indication of its function as a matrix in a replication mechanism. The AT polymer cited in Table XXVI is produced in the system in the presence of thymidine and deoxyadenosine triphosphates after a long lag period. Once formed, however, this polymer acts as a primer material for additional AT polymer formation in the complete system.

Specific replacement of thymidine triphosphate by deoxyuridine and deoxybromouridine triphosphates, of deoxycytidine triphosphate by deoxymethylcytidine and deoxybromocytidine triphosphates, and of guanosine triphosphate by the inosine derivative has been demonstrated in this enzyme system (317). This incorporation of analogous 6-amino 6-keto components into the polymeric structure alludes to some flexibility in the specific hydrogen bond pairing among the nitrogenous constituents in this *in vitro* system.

An increased rate of synthesis occurs when the primer DNA is heat treated or when the single-stranded DNA from phage ϕX174 is used as a primer (317). This suggests that some physical modification of the primer, perhaps disruption of pre-existing H bonding between base pairs of the diad, must occur as the first step of the biosynthetic mechanism.

C. Role of RNA in Specific Cell Processes

The possible role of RNA in protein synthesis has been the subject of considerable speculation. The prevalent opinion is that RNA molecules serve as templates on which amino acid derivatives align themselves in an order somehow determined by the sequence of nucleotides along the polynucleotide chain, and polymerize to form specific proteins. Thus, for different types of protein in the cell there should exist specific RNA molecules with characteristic sequences of nucleotides. This problem can be approached experimentally by treating cells unable to form a certain protein with an RNA preparation from related cells which can make that protein. Cells capable of induced enzyme formation provide convenient systems for such experiments, and most attempts have consisted of adding to noninduced cells RNA preparations from the fully induced organisms or from related strains possessing the enzyme in a constitutive form. Perhaps the greatest difficulty in this kind of experiment resides in the preparation of undegraded RNA, and this may account for the fact that the observed effects are weak or erratic. Minagawa, using crude extracts and purified RNA preparations from yeast cells made more resistant to copper by growth in the presence of this substance, could induce the same degree of resistance in the normal cells (319). RNA from nonresistant cells was ineffective, and the active material was completely inactivated by ribonuclease. Gale and Folkes worked with *Staphylococcus aureus* cells disrupted by sonic oscillations and partially depleted of nucleic acids. These cell preparations were still capable of enzyme synthesis. The addition of RNA from the same strain produced a stimulation of catalase formation (320). RNA from ox liver was ineffective, and RNA from different strains of *Staphylococcus aureus* was only 10% as effective as that from the same strain. However, the results varied with the degree of nucleic acid depletion, and attempts to induce other enzymes were unsuccessful. Hunter and Butler produced a stimulation of β-galactosidase formation in noninduced *Bacillus megatherium* cells with purified RNA obtained from fully induced organisms (*321*). RNA from the noninduced cells showed a much smaller effect. The results were, however, not always reproducible. A much more impressive effect of RNA on enzyme formation was obtained by Kramer and Straub in the case of penicillinase induction in *Bacillus cereus* (*322*). Extracts from a strain containing a constitutive penicillinase were added to cells of a strain capable of forming the enzyme only after induction by penicillin. A considerable amount of enzyme was formed. Dialysis of the extract failed to decrease its activity, but ribonuclease abolished it completely. Extracts from the inducible strain were inactive. These results were corroborated in another laboratory, and effects of a magnitude one hundred times greater than those produced by induction with penicillin were obtained (*323*).

A less direct approach to the study of the biological specificity of RNA consists of the detection of new and different molecules of this substance in cellular systems undergoing certain metabolic changes, such as the appearance of new enzymes. Since such changes must involve only a very small portion of the total RNA of the cells, they should be well below the limit of detection by chemical analyses. With the use of radioactive isotopes, however, such small alterations in the cellular RNA could be detected. Chantrenne studied the turnover of RNA during the induced formation of catalase, cytochrome b, and cytochrome peroxidase in a resting suspension of yeast cells grown anaerobically and exposed to air (*324*). The incorporation of labeled adenine and uracil into RNA was stimulated during this process. Adenine was incorporated both into the adenylic and guanylic acids of RNA. The stimulation of incorporation into guanylic acid was considerably greater than in adenylic acid. Moreover, the incorporations into different RNA fractions were not equally stimulated. These facts suggest that only certain types of RNA molecules were involved in the turnover connected with the enzyme induction. Similar effects were obtained during the induction of chloroplast formation in resting *Euglena gracilis* cells grown in the dark and exposed to light (*16*). Both differential stimulation of incorporation into guanylic and adenylic acids, and an uneven stimulation in various RNA fractions were observed. Nucleotide analyses of the total RNA of the green and the colorless cells showed small but definite differences between the two types of cells (*248*). It appears therefore that a sufficiently large number of new RNA molecules are involved in the process of chloroplast formation, to produce measurable changes in the over-all composition of the cellular RNA. The formation of different RNA molecules was also detected during the infection of *Escherichia coli* by T2 phage (325). Although the infection brings about a complete cessation of net RNA synthesis, a rapid incorporation of P^{32} into the RNA takes place. The radioactivity was found to be unevenly distributed among the four RNA nucleotides. This was regarded as representing the synthesis of new RNA molecules prior to phage multiplication. The nucleotide composition of the newly formed RNA was deduced from the relative amounts of radioactivity in the four nucleotides. Some resemblance between the composition of this RNA and that of the phage DNA was noted.

D. RNA IN VIRUS INFECTION

The existence of plant and animal viruses containing RNA as the only type of nucleic acid suggests that, in some cases, RNA can be the carrier of hereditary information. This possibility received experimental support when both Fraenkel-Conrat and co-workers, and Gierer and Schramm succeeded in producing infections in plants with RNA preparations obtained from tobacco mosaic virus (TMV) (242, 326). The activity of the RNA was considerably lower than that of the intact virus. The infective preparations exhibited properties strikingly different from those of the virus particles. They were: (a) unstable; (b) inactivated by ribonuclease; (c) not affected by anti-TMV antibodies; (d) not sedimented in centrifugal fields that are used for the sedimentation of the virus particles. Therefore the activity of the RNA preparations could not be accounted for by the possible presence of some residual virus particle.

Subsequently, infectious preparations were obtained from many animal viruses by extracting infected tissues, and in some cases purified virus suspensions, with phenol (see Table XXVII). This is the method used by Gierer and Schramm to obtain infectious RNA from TMV. The active preparations exhibited properties similar to those of the RNA from TMV. Infectious RNA was also found to be precipitated in 1 M NaCl solution in the cold, while the viruses remained soluble under these conditions. This was used as an additional criterion to differentiate between RNA and intact virus, but Huppert and Sanders (332) found that when an excess of nonviral RNA is added to virus particles, some of them are carried down with the RNA during NaCl precipitation. The virus produced as a result of infection by RNA was usually identified by reaction with the corresponding antiserum. Most of the infec-

TABLE XXVII
INFECTIONS EFFECTED WITH VIRUS RNA

	Source of infectious RNA	Per cent of original activity[a]	References
Tobacco mosaic	Virus	0.1	242, 326
Mengo encephalitis	Infected ascites tumor cells	0.1	327
West Nile encephalitis	Infected ascites tumor cells	0.1	328
Poliomyelitis	Infected hamster brains	0.1	328
Poliomyelitis	Purified virus	—	329
Eastern equine encephalomyelitis	Infected mouse brains	—	330
Semliki forest	Infected mouse brains	0.1	331
Murine encephalomyocarditis	Infected ascites tumor cells	0.01–0.1	332
Foot-and-mouth disease	Infected tissue cultures	—	333
Foot-and-mouth disease	Infected cattle tongues	—	334
Influenza	Infected tissues	—	335
Murray Valley encephalitis	Infected mouse brains	1	336

[a] Per cent of total activity in starting material recovered in RNA preparation. Values represent maximum activities obtained.

tious RNA preparations were obtained from infected tissues, and the active material was presumed to originate from the virus particles present in these tissues. There is, however, some evidence that suggests that the source of the RNA may not always be the virus itself. In two instances, active extracts could not be obtained from purified virus suspensions, although the infected tissues yielded active material (332, 335). Huppert and Sanders sedimented culture fluids from infected cells at 105,000 g. This brought down all the virus activity, but active RNA extracts were obtained only from the supernatant (332). Incubation of the disrupted infected cells with ribonuclease prior to extraction with phenol did not reduce the activity of the extracts. This indicated that the nonviral material which yielded infectious RNA was more complex than RNA itself. Colter and co-workers also found that preincubation of disrupted cells with ribonuclease fails to affect the activity of the extracted RNA (328).

The many instances of infection by viral RNA indicate that the nucleic acid can carry all the information required for the multiplication of the virus. This must involve, in addition to the self-replication of the RNA, the control of the formation of the specific viral protein. The relationship between virus RNA and protein during infection has been studied with the help of "reconstituted" TMV. When native protein and RNA, isolated separately from TMV, are mixed under appropriate conditions, particles resembling the original virus are formed. This is accompanied by a considerable increase in the infectivity of the preparation (337, 338). Mixed reconstituted viruses were obtained by combining RNA and proteins from different strains of TMV. In all cases, the nature of the resulting lesions was determined by the type of RNA in the "hybrid" viruses. The protein of the HR strain of the virus has an amino acid composition markedly different from that of TMV. The protein of the virus produced by infection with the hybrid HR-RNA plus TMV protein had a composition very similar to that of the HR protein (159, 337). Thus, the RNA behaved as the sole repository of the virus specificity.

An additional indication of the determining role of the RNA in the specificity of the virus has been provided by an entirely different experimental approach. Gierer and Mundry obtained a considerable increase in the incidence of a mutation in TMV by treating either the virus or the isolated RNA with nitrous acid under controlled conditions (264). This treatment was known to convert adenine, guanine, and cytosine into hypoxanthine, xanthine, and uracil, respectively, while the RNA chain remains intact. Alteration of any one of about 3000 nucleotides in the RNA molecule by this treatment resulted in inactivation. By the time half the infectivity of the RNA had been lost, a twentyfold increase in the spontaneous mutation level was obtained. These experiments suggest that the mutation was caused by an alteration in one of the nucleotides in the RNA chain.

ACKNOWLEDGMENT

The authors wish to thank Professor E. Chargaff for the helpful suggestions which he has contributed during the preparation of this article.

References

1. H. Swift, in "The Nucleic Acids" (E. Chargaff and J. N. Davidson, eds.), Vol. II, p. 51. Academic Press, New York, 1955.
2. B. Thorell, in "The Nucleic Acids" (E. Chargaff and J. N. Davidson, eds.), Vol. II, p. 181. Academic Press, New York, 1955.
3. E. C. Horn and C. L. Ward, Proc. Natl. Acad. Sci. U. S. 43, 776 (1957).
4. C. F. Robinow, Bacteriol. Revs. 20, 207 (1956).
5. S. Spiegelman, A. I. Aronson and P. C. Fitz-James, J. Bacteriol. 75, 102 (1958).
6. J. Chayen, Exptl. Cell Research, Suppl. 6, 115 (1959).
7. Y. Chiba and K. Sugahara, Arch. Biochem. Biophys. 71, 367 (1957).
8. R. Vendrely, in "The Nucleic Acids" (E. Chargaff and J. N. Davidson, eds.), Vol. II, p. 155. Academic Press, New York, 1955.
9. V. Nigon and J. Daillie, Biochim. et Biophys. Acta 29, 246 (1958).
10. A. Marshak and C. Marshak, Exptl. Cell Research 5, 288 (1953).
11. A. Marshak and C. Marshak, Exptl. Cell Research 8, 126 (1955).

12. J. Brachet, "Biochemical Cytology." Academic Press, New York, 1957.
13. A. Marshak and C. Marshak, *Exptl. Cell Research* **10,** 246 (1956).
14. G. H. Hogeboom and W. C. Schneider, *in* "The Nucleic Acids" (E. Chargaff and J. N. Davidson, eds.), Vol. II, p. 199. Academic Press, New York, 1955.
15. W. C. Schneider, G. H. Hogeboom and H. E. Ross, *J. Natl. Cancer Inst.* **10,** 977 (1950).
16. G. Brawerman and E. Chargaff, *Biochim. et Biophys. Acta* **31,** 164 (1959).
17. R. M. S. Smellie, *in* "The Nucleic Acids" (E. Chargaff and J. N. Davidson, eds.), Vol. II, p. 393. Academic Press, New York, 1955.
18. A. L. Dounce, *in* "The Nucleic Acids" (E. Chargaff and J. N. Davidson, eds.), Vol. II, p. 93. Academic Press, New York, 1955.
19. W. Vincent, *Intern. Rev. Cytol.* **4,** 269 (1955).
20. H. Swift, *in* "The Chemical Basis of Development" (W. D. McElroy and B. Glass, eds.), p. 174. Johns Hopkins, Baltimore, 1958.
21. M. L. Petermann and E. J. Mason, *Proc. Soc. Exptl. Biol. Med.* **69,** 542 (1948).
22. W. Vincent, *in* "The Beginning of Embryonic Development," p. 1. Am. Assoc. Advancement Sci., Washington, D. C., 1957.
23. V. G. Allfrey, A. E. Mirsky, and S. Osawa, *Nature* **176,** 1042 (1955).
24. R. Logan, *Biochim. et Biophys. Acta* **26,** 227 (1957).
25. R. Logan and J. N. Davidson, *Biochim. et Biophys. Acta* **24,** 196 (1957).
26. E. R. M. Kay, R. M. S. Smellie, G. F. Humphrey, and J. N. Davidson, *Biochem. J.* **62,** 160 (1956).
27. V. Allfrey, H. Stern, A. E. Mirsky, and H. Saetren, *J. Gen. Physiol.* **35,** 529 (1952).
28. H. Stern and A. E. Mirsky, *J. Gen. Physiol.* **36,** 181 (1952).
29. G. E. Palade, *J. Biophys. Biochem. Cytol.* **1,** 59 (1956).
30. G. E. Palade and P. Siekevitz, *J. Biophys. Biochem. Cytol.* **2,** 171 (1956).
31. G. E. Palade and P. Siekevitz, *J. Biophys. Biochem. Cytol.* **2,** 671 (1956).
32. J. W. Littlefield, E. B. Keller, J. Gross, and P. C. Zamecnik, *J. Biol. Chem.* **217,** 111 (1955).
33. P. O. Ts'o, J. Bonner, and J. Vinograd, *J. Biophys. Biochem. Cytol.* **2,** 451 (1956).
34. F.-C. Chao and H. K. Schachman, *Arch. Biochem. Biophys.* **61,** 220 (1956).
35. F.-C. Chao, *Arch. Biochem. Biophys.* **70,** 426 (1957).
36. M. L. Petermann and M. G. Hamilton, *J. Biol. Chem.* **224,** 725 (1957).
37. A. Tissières and J. D. Watson, *Nature* **182,** 778 (1958).
38. H. K. Schachman, A. B. Pardee, and R. Y. Stanier, *Arch. Biochem. Biophys.* **38,** 245 (1952).
39. A. Gierer, *Z. Naturforsch.* **13b,** 788 (1958).
40. G. R. Hopkins and R. L. Sinsheimer, *Biochim. et Biophys. Acta* **17,** 476 (1955).
41. A. Gierer, *Z. Naturforsch.* **13b,** 477, 485 (1958).
42. W. Frisch-Niggemeyer, *Nature* **178,** 308 (1956).
43. P.-Y. Cheng, *Nature* **179,** 426 (1957).
44. M. B. Hoagland, P. C. Zamecnik, and M. L. Stephenson, *Biochim. et Biophys. Acta* **24,** 215 (1957).
45. R. S. Schweet, F. C. Bovard, E. H. Allen, and E. Glassman, *Proc. Natl. Acad. Sci. U. S.* **44,** 173 (1958).
46. F. H. Bergmann, P. Berg, J. Preiss, E. J. Ofengand, and M. Dieckmann, *Federation Proc.* **18,** 191 (1959).
47. P. Berg and E. J. Ofengand, *Proc. Natl. Acad. Sci. U. S.* **44,** 78 (1958).

48. R. W. Holley and S. H. Merrill, *Federation Proc.* **18,** 249 (1959).
49. J. Leahy, E. H. Allen, and R. Schweet, *Federation Proc.* **18,** 270 (1959).
50. J. Mager and F. Lipmann, *Proc. Natl. Acad. Sci. U. S.* **44,** 305 (1958).
51. R. A. Brown, M. C. Davies, J. S. Colter, J. B. Logan, and D. Kritchevsky, *Proc. Natl. Acad. Sci. U. S.* **43,** 857 (1957).
52. R. Vendrely, *Ann. inst. Pasteur* **94,** 143 (1958).
53. A. Boivin, R. Vendrely, and C. Vendrely, *Compt. rend. acad. sci.* **226,** 1061 (1948).
54. A. E. Mirsky and H. Ris, *Nature* **163,** 666 (1949).
55. C. Leuchtenberger, *Science* **120,** 1022 (1954).
56. C. Leuchtenberger, G. Klein, and E. Klein, *Cancer Research* **12,** 480 (1952).
57. B. M. Richards, P. M. B. Walker, and E. M. Deeley, *Ann. N. Y. Acad. Sci.* **63,** 831 (1956).
58. J. S. Colter, H. H. Bird, H. Koprowski, and H. B. Ritter, *Nature* **177,** 993 (1956).
59. G. Ishitani, K. Ochida, and Y. Ikeda, *Exptl. Cell Research* **10,** 737 (1956).
60. F. C. Heagy and J. A. Roper, *Nature* **170,** 713 (1952).
61. M. Ogur, S. Minckler, G. Lindegren, and C. L. Lindegren, *Arch. Biochem. Biophys.* **40,** 175 (1952).
62. A. Howard, *Ciba Found. Symposium on Ionizing Radiations and Cell Metabolism,* p. 196 (1956).
63. S. Hornsey and A. Howard, *Ann. N. Y. Acad. Sci.* **63,** 915 (1956).
64. H. Firket, *Compt. rend. soc. biol.* **150,** 1050 (1956).
65. B. B. McDonald, *Biol. Bull.* **114,** 71 (1958).
66. H. D. Barner and S. S. Cohen, *J. Bacteriol.* **72,** 115 (1956).
67. F. E. Abbo and A. B. Pardee, *Federation Proc.* **18,** 178 (1959).
68. M. Schaechter, M. W. Bentzon, and O. Maaløe, *Nature* **183,** 1207 (1959).
69. S. Benzer, *Proc. Natl. Acad. Sci. U. S.* **41,** 344 (1955).
70. S. Benzer, *in* "The Chemical Basis of Heredity" (W. D. McElroy and B. Glass, eds.), p. 70. Johns Hopkins, Baltimore, 1957.
71. G. Pontecorvo and J. A. Roper, *Nature* **178,** 83 (1956).
72. F. Jacob and E. L. Wollman, *Symposia Soc. Exptl. Biol.* **12,** 75 (1958).
73. A. E. Mirsky and H. Ris, *J. Gen. Physiol.* **34,** 451 (1951).
74. M. C. England and D. T. Mayer, *Exptl. Cell Research* **12,** 249 (1957).
75. J. M. Rendel, *Nature* **176,** 829 (1955).
76. R. Vendrely and C. Vendrely, *Experientia* **5,** 327 (1949).
77. M. C. Durand, *Compt. rend. acad. sci.* **241,** 1340 (1955).
78. N. B. Kurnick and I. H. Herskowitz, *J. Cellular Comp. Physiol.* **39,** 281 (1952).
79. S. Zamenhof, *in* "The Chemical Basis of Heredity" (W. D. McElroy and B. Glass, eds.), p. 351. Johns Hopkins, Baltimore, 1957.
80. K. G. Lark and O. Maaløe, *Biochim. et Biophys. Acta* **21,** 448 (1956).
81. P. C. Caldwell and C. Hinshelwood, *J. Chem. Soc.* p. 1415 (1950).
82. M. Webb, *Science* **118,** 607 (1953).
83. P. C. Fitz-James, *J. Bacteriol.* **75,** 369 (1958).
84. M. Ogur, S. Minckler, and D. D. McClary, *J. Bacteriol.* **66,** 642 (1953).
85. G. Brawerman, C. Rebman, and E. Chargaff, *Nature* **187,** 1037 (1960).
86. O. Scherbaum, *Exptl. Cell Research* **13,** 24 (1957).
87. T. Minagawa, B. Wagner, and B. Strauss, *Arch. Biochem. Biophys.* **80,** 442 (1959).
88. J. H. McClendon, *Am. J. Botany* **39,** 275 (1952).

89. W. A. Jensen, *Exptl. Cell Research* **14,** 575 (1958).
90. G. Schramm, *Ann. Rev. Biochem.* **27,** 101 (1958).
91. S. S. Cohen, *Advances in Virus Research* **3,** 1 (1955).
92. R. L. Sinsheimer, *J. Mol. Biol.* **1,** 43 (1959).
93. I. Leslie, *in* "The Nucleic Acids" (E. Chargaff and J. N. Davidson, eds.), Vol. II, p. 1. Academic Press, New York, 1955.
94. J. Brachet, *in* "The Nucleic Acids" (E. Chargaff and J. N. Davidson, eds.), Vol. II, p. 475. Academic Press, New York, 1955.
95. P. C. Caldwell, E. L. Mackor, and C. Hinshelwood, *J. Chem. Soc.* p. 3151 (1950).
96. W. H. Price, *J. Gen. Physiol.* **35,** 741 (1951).
97. D. Herbert, *Proc. 7th Intern. Congr. Microbiol., Stockholm, 1958* p. 381 (1959).
98. M. Schaechter, O. Maaløe, and N. O. Kjeldgaard, *J. Gen. Microbiol.* **19,** 592 (1958).
99. R. Jeener, *Arch. Biochem. Biophys.* **43,** 381 (1953).
100. H. E. Wade and D. M. Morgan, *Biochem. J.* **65,** 321 (1957).
101. M. Yčas and G. Brawerman, *Arch. Biochem. Biophys.* **68,** 118 (1957).
102. G. Schramm and W. Zillig, *Z. Naturforsch.* **10b,** 493 (1955).
103. A. D. Hershey, *Virology* **1,** 108 (1955).
104. E. Chargaff and H. F. Saidel, *J. Biol. Chem.* **177,** 417 (1949).
105. J. H. Phillips, W. Braun, and O. J. Plescia, *Nature* **181,** 573 (1958).
106. E. L. Grinnan and W. A. Mosher, *J. Biol. Chem.* **191,** 719 (1951).
107. E. Chargaff, *in* "The Nucleic Acids" (E. Chargaff and J. N. Davidson, eds.), Vol. I, p. 307. Academic Press, New York, 1955.
108. B. Magasanik, *in* "The Nucleic Acids" (E. Chargaff and J. N. Davidson, eds.), Vol. I, p. 373. Academic Press, New York, 1955.
109. R. Markham and J. D. Smith, *in* "The Proteins" (H. Neurath and K. Bailey, eds.), Vol. II, Part A, p. 1. Academic Press, New York, 1954.
110. F. Miescher, *in* "Die histochemischen und physiologischen Arbeiten von Friedrich Miescher. Gesammelt von seinen Freunden," 2 Vols. Vogel, Leipzig, 1897.
111. A. Kossel, *Z. physiol. Chem.* **25,** 165 (1898).
112. A. W. Pollister and A. E. Mirsky, *J. Gen. Physiol.* **30,** 101 (1946).
113. K. Felix, H. Fischer, and A. Krekels, *in* "Progress in Biophysics and Biophysical Chemistry" (J. A. V. Butler and B. Katz, eds.), Vol. 6, p. 2. Pergamon, New York, 1956.
114. C. Vendrely, A. Knobloch, and R. Vendrely, *Biochim. et Biophys. Acta* **19,** 472 (1956).
115. H. J. Cruft, C. M. Mauritzen, and Edgar Stedman, *Nature* **174,** 580 (1954).
116. A. Kossel and H. D. Dakin, *Z. physiol. Chem.* **40,** 565 (1904).
117. M. M. Daly, A. E. Mirsky, and H. Ris, *J. Gen. Physiol.* **34,** 439 (1951).
118. R. J. Block, D. Bolling, H. Gershon, and H. A. Sober, *Proc. Soc. Exptl. Biol. Med.* **70,** 494 (1949).
119. S. F. Velick and S. Udenfriend, *J. Biol. Chem.* **191,** 233 (1951).
120. G. L. Mills, *Biochem. J.* **50,** 707 (1952).
121. M. C. Corfield and A. Robson, *Biochem. J.* **55,** 517 (1953).
122. M. J. Callanan, W. R. Carroll, and E. R. Mitchell, *J. Biol. Chem.* **229,** 279 (1957).

123. K. Felix, H. Fischer, A. Krekels, and H. M. Rauen, Z. physiol. Chem. **286,** 67 (1950).

124. K. Felix, H. Fischer, and A. Krekels, Z. physiol. Chem. **289,** 127 (1952).

125. Y. Kuroda, J. Biochem. (Tokyo) **38,** 115 (1951).

126. K. Felix, H. Fischer, A. Krekels, and R. Mohr, Z. physiol. Chem. **287,** 224 (1951).

127. H. Fischer and L. Kreuzer, Z. physiol. Chem. **293,** 176 (1953).

128. T. Hultin and R. Herne, Arkiv Kemi Mineral. Geol. **26A,** No. 20 (1949).

129. K. Felix, A. Goppold-Krekels, O. Schiff, and T. Yamada, Z. physiol. Chem. **311,** 256 (1958).

130. Edgar Stedman and Ellen Stedman, Phil. Trans. Roy. Soc. **B235,** 565 (1951).

131. A. Goppold-Krekels and H. Lehmann, Z. physiol. Chem. **313,** 147 (1958).

132. T. Ando and F. Sawada, J. Biochem. (Tokyo) **46,** 517 (1959).

133. K. Felix and A. Krekels, Z. physiol. Chem. **295,** 107 (1953).

134. D. M. P. Phillips, Biochem. J. **60,** 403 (1955).

135. P. Spitnik, R. Lipshitz, and E. Chargaff, J. Biol. Chem. **215,** 765 (1955).

136. M. P. Znamenskaya, A. N. Belozersky, and L. P. Gavrilova, Biokhimiya **22,** 765 (1957).

137. C. F. Crampton, J. Biol. Chem. **227,** 495 (1957).

138. C. F. Crampton, W. H. Stein, and S. Moore, J. Biol. Chem. **225,** 363 (1957).

139. P. F. Davison and J. A. V. Butler, Biochim. et Biophys. Acta **15,** 439 (1954).

140. L. Hnilica, Experientia **15,** 139 (1959).

141. H. J. Cruft, J. Hindley, C. M. Mauritzen, and Ellen Stedman, Nature **180,** 1107 (1957).

142. C. M. Mauritzen and Edgar Stedman, Proc. Roy. Soc. **B150,** 299 (1959).

143. H. J. Cruft, C. M. Mauritzen, and Edgar Stedman, Phil. Trans. Roy. Soc. **B241,** 93 (1958).

144. A. E. Mirsky and A. W. Pollister, J. Gen. Physiol. **30,** 117 (1946).

145. R. D. Dallam and L. E. Thomas, Biochim. et Biophys. Acta **11,** 79 (1953).

146. R. Brunish, D. Fairley, and J. M. Luck, Nature **168,** 82 (1951).

147. A. N. Belozersky and S. O. Uryson, Biokhimiya **23,** 568 (1958).

148. G. Zubay and M. R. Watson, J. Biophys. Biochem. Cytol. **5,** 51 (1959).

149. T. Tsumita and E. Chargaff, Biochim. et Biophys. Acta **29,** 568 (1958).

150. K. S. Kirby, Biochem. J. **70,** 260 (1958).

151. J. A. V. Butler, D. M. P. Phillips, and K. V. Shooter, Arch. Biochem. Biophys. **71,** 423 (1957).

152. K. J. Monty and A. L. Dounce, J. Gen. Physiol. **41,** 595 (1958).

153. D. Szafarz, Biochim. et Biophys. Acta **6,** 562 (1951).

154. P. O. Ts'o, J. Bonner, and H. Dintzis, Arch. Biochem. Biophys. **76,** 225 (1958).

155. J. L. Simkin and T. S. Work, Biochem. J. **67,** 617 (1957).

156. M. Schlesinger, Nature **138,** 508 (1936).

157. D. Fraser and V. Cosentino, Virology **4,** 126 (1957).

158. D. de Fremery and C. A. Knight, J. Biol. Chem. **214,** 559 (1955).

159. H. Fraenkel-Conrat and B. Singer, Biochim. et Biophys. Acta **24,** 540 (1957).

160. D. Fraser, J. Biol. Chem. **227,** 711 (1957).

161. G. A. Kausche and F. Hahn, Z. Naturforsch. **3b,** 437 (1948).

162. B. Commoner, M. Yamada, S. D. Rodenberg, T. Y. Wang, and E. Basler, Jr., Science **118,** 529 (1953).

163. G. Schramm, *Advances in Enzymol.* **15**, 449 (1954).
164. H. Fraenkel-Conrat and R. C. Williams, *Proc. Natl. Acad. Sci. U. S.* **41**, 690 (1955).
165. C. Van Rysselberge and R. Jeener, *Biochim. et Biophys. Acta* **23**, 18 (1957).
166. H. S. Loring, *J. Gen. Physiol.* **25**, 497 (1942).
167. G. Schramm, G. Schumacher, and W. Zillig, *Z. Naturforsch.* **10b**, 481 (1955).
168. A. Kleczkowski, *Virology* **7**, 385 (1959).
169. R. E. Franklin, *Nature* **175**, 379 (1955).
170. C.-I. Niu, V. Shore, and C. A. Knight, *Virology* **6**, 226 (1958).
171. G. Braunitzer, *Biochim. et Biophys. Acta* **19**, 574 (1956).
172. K. Narita, *Biochim. et Biohpys. Acta* **30**, 352 (1958).
173. F. L. Black and C. A. Knight, *J. Biol. Chem.* **202**, 51 (1953).
174. E. A. Evans, Jr., *in* "The Viruses" (F. M. Burnet and W. M. Stanley, eds.), Vol. I, p. 459. Academic Press, New York, 1959.
175. E. Volkin, *Federation Proc.* **13**, 315 (1954).
176. P. A. Levene and L. W. Bass, "Nucleic Acids." Chem. Catalog Co., New York, 1931.
177. D. M. Brown and A. R. Todd, *in* "The Nucleic Acids" (E. Chargaff and J. N. Davidson, eds.), Vol. I, p. 409. Academic Press, New York, 1955.
178. G. R. Wyatt, *Biochem. J.* **48**, 584 (1951).
179. M. E. Hodes and E. Chargaff, *Biochim. et Biophys. Acta* **22**, 348 (1956).
180. K. Felix, I. Jilke, and R. K. Zahn, *Z. physiol. Chem.* **303**, 140 (1956).
181. R. Lipshitz and E. Chargaff, *Biochim. et Biophys. Acta* **19**, 256 (1956).
182. H. S. Shapiro and E. Chargaff, *Biochim. et Biophys. Acta* **26**, 608 (1957).
183. A. J. Thomas, *Arch. Biochem. Biophys.* **79**, 162 (1959).
184. A. J. Thomas and H. S. A. Sherratt, *Biochem. J.* **62**, 1 (1956).
185. E. M. Low, *Nature* **182**, 1096 (1958).
186. G. R. Wyatt and S. S. Cohen, *Biochem. J.* **55**, 774 (1953).
187. E. H. Creaser and A. Taussig, *Virology* **4**, 200 (1957).
188. H. S. Shapiro, K. Miura, and E. Chargaff, unpublished experiments (1959).
189. E. Volkin, L. Astrachan, and J. L. Countryman, *Virology* **6**, 545 (1958).
190. G. R. Wyatt, *J. Gen. Physiol.* **36**, 201 (1952).
191. R. L. Sinsheimer, *Proc. Natl. Acad. Sci. U. S.* **42**, 502 (1956).
192. M. R. Loeb and S. S. Cohen, *J. Biol. Chem.* **234**, 364 (1959).
193. D. B. Dunn and J. D. Smith, *Biochem. J.* **68**, 627 (1958).
194. E. Chargaff, *J. Cellular Comp. Physiol.* **38**, Suppl. 1, 41 (1951).
195. A. N. Belozersky, *in* "The Origin of Life on the Earth," Intern. Symposium, Moscow (A. I. Oparin *et al.*, eds.; Engl. transl., F. Clark and R. L. M. Synge, eds.), p. 194. Pergamon, New York, 1960.
196. K. Y. Lee, R. Wahl, and E. Barbu, *Ann. inst. Pasteur* **91**, 212 (1956).
197. M. H. F. Wilkens, A. R. Stokes, and H. R. Wilson, *Nature* **171**, 738 (1953).
198. J. D. Watson and F. H. C. Crick, *Nature* **171**, 737 (1953).
199. E. Chargaff, *Experientia* **6**, 201 (1950).
200. G. R. Wyatt, *Exptl. Cell Research* Suppl. 2, 201 (1952).
201. A. Bendich, *Exptl. Cell Res.* Suppl. 2, 181 (1952).
202. G. R. Wyatt, *Nature* **166**, 237 (1950).
203. S. Zamenhof and E. Chargaff, *Nature* **168**, 604 (1951).
204. E. Chargaff, C. F. Crampton, and R. Lipshitz, *Nature* **172**, 289 (1953).
205. C. F. Crampton, R. Lipshitz, and E. Chargaff, *J. Biol. Chem.* **211**, 125 (1954).
206. J. A. Lucy and J. A. V. Butler, *Nature* **174**, 32 (1954).

207. G. L. Brown and M. Watson, *Nature* **172**, 339 (1953).
208. G. L. Brown and A. V. Brown, *Symposia Soc. Exptl. Biol.* **12**, 6 (1958).
209. A. Bendich, H. B. Pahl, G. C. Corngold, H. S. Rosenkranz, and J. R. Fresco, *J. Am. Chem. Soc.* **80**, 3949 (1958).
210. A. Bendich, H. B. Pahl, H. S. Rosenkranz, and M. Rosoff, *Symposia Soc. Exptl. Biol.* **12**, 31 (1958).
211. C. F. Crampton, R. Lipshitz, and E. Chargaff, *J. Biol. Chem.* **206**, 499 (1954).
212. M. Rosoff, G. Di Mayorca, and A. Bendich, *Nature* **180**, 1355 (1957).
213. N. Kondo and S. Osawa, *Nature* **183**, 1602 (1959).
214. K. V. Shooter and J. A. V. Butler, *Nature* **177**, 1033 (1956).
215. J. A. V. Butler and P. F. Davison, *Advances in Enzymol.* **18**, 161 (1957).
216. S. Kitt, *Nature* **184**, 36 (1959).
217. L. F. Cavalieri, *J. Am. Chem. Soc.* **79**, 5319 (1957).
218. M. E. Reichmann, S. A. Rice, C. A. Thomas, and P. Doty, *J. Am. Chem. Soc.* **76**, 3047 (1954).
219. J. A. V. Butler and K. V. Shooter *in* "The Chemical Basis of Heredity" (W. D. McElroy and B. Glass, eds.), p. 540. Johns Hopkins, Baltimore, 1957.
220. G. H. Beaven, E. R. Holiday and E. A. Johnson, *in* "The Nucleic Acids" (E. Chargaff and J. N. Davidson, eds.), Vol. I, p. 493. Academic Press, New York, 1955.
221. J. Marmur and P. Doty, *Nature* **183**, 1427 (1959).
222. N. Sueoka, J. Marmur, and P. Doty, *Nature* **183**, 1429 (1959).
223. C. Tamm, H. S. Shapiro, R. Lipshitz, and E. Chargaff, *J. Biol. Chem.* **203**, 673 (1952).
224. A. S. Jones and D. S. Letham, *Biochim. et Biophys. Acta* **14**, 438 (1954).
225. P. W. Kent, J. A. Lucy, and P. F. V. Ward, *Biochem. J.* **61**, 529 (1955).
226. A. S. Jones, D. S. Letham, and M. Stacey, *J. Chem. Soc.* p. 2579 (1956).
227. A. S. Jones, M. Stacey, and B. E. Watson, *J. Chem. Soc.* p. 2454 (1957).
228. H. S. Shapiro and E. Chargaff, *Biochim. et Biophys. Acta* **23**, 451 (1957).
229. H. S. Shapiro and E. Chargaff, *Biochim. et Biophys. Acta* **26**, 596 (1957).
230. K. Burton and G. B. Petersen, *Biochim. et Biophys. Acta* **26**, 667 (1957).
231. S. Zamenhof and E. Chargaff, *J. Biol. Chem.* **187**, 1 (1950).
232. G. Brawerman and E. Chargaff, *J. Biol. Chem.* **210**, 445 (1954).
233. C. Tamm, M. E. Hodes, and E. Chargaff, *J. Biol. Chem.* **195**, 49 (1952).
234. C. Tamm and E. Chargaff, *J. Biol. Chem.* **203**, 689 (1953).
235. P. A. Levene, *J. Biol. Chem.* **48**, 119 (1921).
236. C. A. Dekker, A. M. Michelson, and A. R. Todd, *J. Chem. Soc.* p. 947 (1953).
237. H. S. Shapiro and E. Chargaff, *Biochim. et Biophys. Acta* **39**, 68 (1960).
238. R. L. Sinsheimer, *J. Biol. Chem.* **208**, 445 (1954).
239. J. N. Davidson, *in* "The Biochemistry of the Nucleic Acids" (R. A. Peters and F. G. Young, eds.), pp. 50–96. Wiley, New York, 1950.
240. J. N. Davidson and E. Chargaff, *in* "The Nucleic Acids" (E. Chargaff and J. N. Davidson, eds.), Vol. I, p. 1. Academic Press, New York, 1955.
241. A. Bendich, *in* "The Nucleic Acids" (E. Chargaff and J. N. Davidson, eds.), Vol. I, p. 81. Academic Press, New York, 1955.
242. A. Gierer and G. Schramm, *Nature* **177**, 702 (1956).
243. J. E. Bacher and F. W. Allen, *J. Biol. Chem.* **183**, 641 (1950).
244. E. Chargaff and E. Vischer, *Ann. Rev. Biochem.* **17**, 201 (1948).
245. W. J. Kleinschmidt and J. A. Manthley, *Arch. Biochem. Biophys.* **73**, 52 (1958).

246. D. Elson and E. Chargaff, *Biochim. et Biophys. Acta* **17**, 367 (1955).
247. G. W. Crosbie, R. M. S. Smellie, and J. N. Davidson, *Biochem. J.* **54**, 287 (1953).
248. G. Brawerman and E. Chargaff, *Biochim. et Biophys. Acta* **31**, 172 (1959).
249. L. Levenbook, E. C. Travaglini, and J. Schultz, *Exptl. Cell Research* **15**, 43 (1958).
250. J. P. Weil, M. Ledig, and P. Mandel, *Bull. soc. chim. biol.* **38**, 81 (1956).
251. H. A. Deluca, R. J. Rossiter, and K. D. Strickland, *Biochem. J.* **55**, 193 (1953).
252. S. Osawa, K. Takuta, and Y. Hotta, *Biochim. et Biophys. Acta* **28**, 271 (1958).
253. D. Elson, T. Gustafson, and E. Chargaff, *J. Biol. Chem.* **209**, 285 (1954).
254. A. Rich and D. R. Davies, *J. Am. Chem. Soc.* **78**, 3548 (1956).
255. P. Doty, H. Boedtker, J. R. Fresco, R. Haselkorn, and M. Litt, *Proc. Natl. Acad. Sci. U. S.* **45**, 482 (1959).
256. A. N. Belozersky and A. S. Spirin, *Nature* **182**, 111 (1958).
257. A. Lombard and E. Chargaff, *Biochim. et Biophys. Acta* **20**, 585 (1956).
258. F. C. Bawden and N. W. Pirie, *Proc. Roy. Soc.* **B123**, 274 (1937).
259. C. A. Knight, *Advances in Virus Research* **2**, 153 (1954).
260. C. A. Knight, *in* "The Viruses" (F. M. Burnet and W. M. Stanley, eds.), Vol. 2, p. 127. Academic Press, New York, 1959.
261. R. Markham and J. D. Smith, *Biochem. J.* **46**, 513 (1950).
262. B. Commoner and E. Basler, Jr., *Virology* **2**, 477 (1956).
263. D. C. Burke, A. Isaacs, and J. Walker, *Biochim. et Biophys. Acta* **26**, 576 (1957).
264. A. Gierer and K. W. Mundry, *Nature* **182**, 1457 (1958).
265. R. A. Brown, M. C. Davies, J. S. Colter, J. B. Logan, and D. Kritchevsky, *Proc. Natl. Acad. Sci. U. S.* **43**, 857 (1957).
266. L. S. Lerman, *Biochim. et Biophys. Acta* **18**, 132 (1955).
267. D. F. Bradley and A. Rich, *J. Am. Chem. Soc.* **78**, 5898 (1956).
268. P. O. Ts'o and C. S. Sato, *Exptl. Cell Research* **17**, 237 (1959).
269. H. Leyon, *Acta Chem. Scand.* **11**, 1599 (1957).
270. W. D. Cooper and H. S. Loring, *J. Biol. Chem.* **228**, 813 (1957).
271. D. Elson, L. W. Trent, and E. Chargaff, *Biochim. et Biophys. Acta* **17**, 362 (1955).
272. W. M. McIndoe and J. N. Davidson, *Brit. J. Cancer* **6**, 200 (1952).
273. Y. Hotta and S. Osawa, *Biochim. et Biophys. Acta* **28**, 642 (1958).
274. N. Frontali, *Acta Chem. Scand.* **13**, 390 (1959).
275. P. S. Olmsted and C. A. Villee, *J. Biol. Chem.* **212**, 179 (1955).
276. D. Elson and E. Chargaff, *in* "Phosphorus Metabolism" (W. D. McElroy and B. Glass, eds.), Vol. II, p. 329. Johns Hopkins, Baltimore, 1952.
277. J. D. Weil, M. Ledig, and P. Mandel, *Biochim. et Biophys. Acta* **20**, 430 (1956).
278. G. de Lamirande, C. Allard, and A. Cantero, *Biochim. et Biophys. Acta* **27**, 395 (1958).
279. M. Zalokar, *Nature* **183**, 1330 (1959).
280. L. Goldstein and W. Plaut, *Proc. Natl. Acad. Sci. U. S.* **41**, 874 (1955).
281. R. Love and T. P. Bharadwaj, *Nature* **183**, 1453 (1959).
282. G. Zubay, *Nature* **182**, 1290 (1958).
283. W. E. Cohn and E. Volkin, *Nature* **167**, 483 (1951).
284. F. F. Davis and F. W. Allen, *J. Biol. Chem.* **227**, 907 (1957).
285. C. T. Yu and F. W. Allen, *Biochim. et Biophys. Acta* **32**, 393 (1959).

286. W. E. Cohn, *Biochim. et Biophys. Acta* **32**, 569 (1959).

287. F. F. Davis, A. F. Carlucci, and I. F. Roubein, *J. Biol. Chem.* **234**, 1525 (1959).

288. J. W. Littlefield and D. B. Dunn, *Biochem. J.* **70**, 642 (1958).

289. J. D. Smith and D. B. Dunn, *Biochem. J.* **72**, 294 (1959).

290. M. Adler, B. Weissmann, and A. B. Gutman, *J. Biol. Chem.* **230**, 717 (1958).

291. H. Amos and M. Korn, *Biochim. et Biophys. Acta* **29**, 444 (1958).

292. P. Berg and E. J. Ofengand, *Proc. Natl. Acad. Sci. U. S.* **44**, 78 (1958).

293. J. D. Smith and D. B. Dunn, *Biochim. et Biophys. Acta* **31**, 573 (1959).

294. B. Magasanik and E. Chargaff, *Biochim. et Biophys. Acta* **7**, 396 (1951).

295. K. K. Reddi and C. A. Knight, *J. Biol. Chem.* **221**, 629 (1956).

296. K. K. Reddi, *Biochim. et Biophys. Acta* **25**, 528 (1957).

297. K. K. Reddi, *Biochim. et Biophys. Acta* **32**, 386 (1959).

298. C. Scholtissek, *Biochem. Z.* **331**, 138 (1959).

299. J. Preiss, P. Berg, E. J. Ofengand, F. H. Bergmann, and M. Dieckmann, *Proc. Natl. Acad. Sci. U. S.* **45**, 319 (1959).

300. L. I. Hecht, M. L. Stephenson, and P. C. Zamecnik, *Biochim. et Biophys. Acta* **29**, 460 (1958).

301. L. I. Hecht, M. L. Stephenson, and P. C. Zamecnik, *Proc. Natl. Acad. Sci. U. S.* **45**, 505 (1959).

302. L. I. Hecht, P. C. Zamecnik, M. L. Stephenson, and J. F. Scott, *J. Biol. Chem.* **233**, 954 (1958).

303. O. T. Avery, C. M. MacLeod, and M. McCarty, *J. Exptl. Med.* **79**, 137 (1944).

304. R. D. Hotchkiss, *in* "The Nucleic Acids" (E. Chargaff and J. N. Davidson, eds.), Vol. II, p. 435. Academic Press, New York, 1955.

305. S. Zamenhof, *in* "The Chemical Basis of Heredity" (W. D. McElroy and B. Glass, eds.), p. 351. Johns Hopkins, Baltimore, 1957.

306. S. Zamenhof, *in* "Progress in Biophysics and Biophysical Chemistry" (J. A. V. Butler and B. Katz, eds.), Vol. 6, p. 86. Pergamon, New York, 1956.

307. J. Spizizen, *Proc. Natl. Acad. Sci. U. S.* **44**, 1072 (1958).

308. R. D. Hotchkiss, *Symposia Soc. Exptl. Biol.* **12**, 49 (1958).

309. L. S. Lerman and L. J. Tolmach, *Biochim. et Biophys. Acta* **33**, 371 (1959).

310. P. Schaeffer, *Symposia Soc. Exptl. Biol.* **12**, 60 (1958).

311. G. Leidy, E. Hahn, and H. E. Alexander, *J. Exptl. Med.* **104**, 305 (1956).

312. L. S. Lerman and L. J. Tolmach, *Biochim. et Biophys. Acta* **26**, 68 (1957).

313. M. S. Fox, *Biochim. et Biophys. Acta* **26**, 83 (1957).

314. S. H. Goodgal and R. M. Herriott, *in* "The Chemical Basis of Heredity" (W. D. McElroy and B. Glass, eds.), p. 336. Johns Hopkins, Baltimore, 1957.

315. A. Kornberg, *in* "The Chemical Basis of Heredity" (W. D. McElroy and B. Glass, eds.), p. 579. Johns Hopkins, Baltimore, 1957.

316. I. R. Lehman, M. J. Bessman, E. S. Simms, and A. Kornberg, *J. Biol. Chem.* **233**, 171 (1958).

317. I. R. Lehman, *Ann. N. Y. Acad. Sci.* **81**, 745 (1959).

318. F. J. Bollum, *Ann. N. Y. Acad. Sci.* **81**, 792 (1959).

319. T. Minagawa, *Biochim. et Biophys. Acta* **16**, 539 (1955).

320. E. F. Gale and J. P. Folkes, *Biochem. J.* **59**, 675 (1955).

321. G. D. Hunter and J. A. V. Butler, *Biochim. et Biophys. Acta* **20**, 405 (1956).

322. M. Kramer and F. B. Straub, *Biochim. et Biophys. Acta* **21**, 401 (1956).

323. M. R. Pollock, *in* "The Enzymes" (P. D. Boyer, H. Lardy, and K. Myrbäck, eds.), Vol. I, p. 619. Academic Press, New York, 1959.

324. H. Chantrenne, *Arch. Biochem. Biophys.* **65,** 414 (1956).

325. E. Volkin and L. Astrachan, *in* "The Chemical Basis of Heredity" (W. D. McElroy and B. Glass, eds.), p. 686. Johns Hopkins, Baltimore, 1957.

326. H. Fraenkel-Conrat, B. Singer, and R. C. Williams, *Biochim. et Biophys. Acta* **25,** 87 (1957).

327. J. S. Colter, H. H. Bird, and R. A. Brown, *Nature* **179,** 859 (1957).

328. J. S. Colter, H. H. Bird, A. W. Moyer, and R. A. Brown, *Virology* **4,** 522 (1957).

329. H. E. Alexander, G. Koch, I. M. Mountain, and O. Van Damme, *J. Exptl. Med.* **108,** 493 (1958).

330. E. Wecker and W. Schäfer, *Z. Naturforsch.* **12b,** 415 (1957).

331. P.-Y. Cheng, *Nature* **181,** 1800 (1958).

332. J. Huppert and F. K. Sanders, *Nature* **182,** 515 (1958).

333. F. Brown, R. F. Sellers, and D. L. Stewart, *Nature* **182,** 535 (1958).

334. V. Spuhler, *Experientia* **15,** 155 (1959).

335. H. E. Maasab, *Proc. Natl. Acad. Sci. U. S.* **45,** 877 (1959).

336. G. L. Ada and S. G. Anderson, *Nature* **183,** 799 (1959).

337. H. Fraenkel-Conrat, *J. Am. Chem. Soc.* **78,** 882 (1956).

338. J. A. Lippincott and B. Commoner, *Biochim. et Biophys. Acta* **19,** 198 (1956).

CHAPTER 5

Protein Molecules: Intraspecific and Interspecific Variations

ALLEN VEGOTSKY and SIDNEY W. FOX

Oceanographic Institute, Florida State University, Tallahassee, Florida

I. Introduction

No other class of substance has permitted as sensitive an evaluation of many fine differences and of range of differences in structure as the protein macromolecule. As the molecular basis for the variety of living entities becomes more completely established, it becomes increasingly clear that great biological variety stems from much less variety in the chemical units of which life is comprised.

This relationship has been particularly evident from studies of variation in protein molecules. Such variation is the theme of this chapter. The criteria for evaluation of protein molecules and of gross protein make-up of organisms have developed first from qualitative knowledge of amino acids; nearly all proteins and virtually all organisms carefully studied have been found to be composed of the same eighteen or twenty amino acids (1). When methods of assay of amino acids were developed particularly through microbial estimation and through selective elution from sorbent columns, many inferences could be reliably drawn about the quantitative aspects.

The most sensitive and significant methodology for studying kinship of protein molecules is, however, widely believed to be that of determining and comparing sequences of amino acid residues. One of the authors reviewed in 1945 the previous accomplishments in this branch of chemistry and indicated future possibilities (2). The advances since then are both gratifying and surprising in their total volume. Also in 1945, Sanger first described the use of an N-terminal reagent in such analyses (3). After this, Sanger went on to elucidate the complete structure of insulin, and pioneers in this field have achieved many other triumphs of sequential investigations, which have been reviewed elsewhere (4–17).

Many data on differences within and between species are now available. It is time to catalog again the salient information of this kind and to ponder the meaning of what nature has written with her alphabet of some twenty amino acids.

II. Scope and Mechanics of the Review

The comparison of structures of protein molecules in this review is based predominantly on portions of sequences of amino acid residues. At one extreme this portion is the single terminal residue, usually N-terminal, of which many are recorded. At the other extreme, there are presented entire sequences, of which a few have been recorded in the literature.

The selections include both *homologous* (proteins of similar or identical function) and *heterologous* proteins. As will be brought out, although the distinction between homologous and heterologous is usually evident, a number of comparisons that leave the classification of relationship in doubt are at hand. Comparisons are alluded to also as intraspecific and interspecific. These adjectives are employed in the phylogenic sense.

The designation of type of amino acid residue is by the now popular three-letter prefix of the name of the amino acid except for isoleucine which is denoted as Ileu. If the residue is glutamine instead of glutamic acid or asparagine instead of aspartic acid, the abbreviation employed is Glu(NH$_2$) or Asp(NH$_2$);* the γ- or β-position for the amide is assumed. In all structures the amino terminus is placed on the left and the carboxyl terminus at the right. Ignorance, or lack of designation of subsequent positions, is indicated by unsatisfied bonds. For instance, -Phe-Val-Ala indicates a phenylalanylvalylalanyl tripeptide at the carboxyl terminus and Glu-Asp(NH$_2$)-Arg- indicates a glutamylasparaginylarginyl tripeptide at the amino terminus.

Residues or peptides at the amino terminus are denoted as N-terminal or in specific cases as N-aminoacyl or N-peptidyl, such as N-glycyl or N-Glu-Asp(NH$_2$)-Arg.

$$\text{NH}_2 \quad \text{NH}_2$$
$$| \qquad |$$
* Occasionally, Glu or Asp in tables.

Variations in structure in comparative tabulations are singled out in type, usually by italics.

Failure to cite some comparisons can be explained in one of the following ways. In a few cases the results are omitted because they appeared, in the judgment of the authors, to have little or no significance in *comparative* biochemistry. A designation of one N-terminus for a protein in a single species would, for example, be deemed to be improper for inclusion. In other cases, the designation was judged to be controversial and therefore deferred until it could be generally considered to be resolved. Evaluation of quantitative positional designations are much to be desired, but because of the special nature of the techniques employed these have not been more than mentioned except in those cases that have been independently verified. It is hoped that subsequent reviews by others will correct any errors of commission or omission for which the authors are responsible.

The authors have attempted to be exhaustive in their search until January, 1959. Subsequent to that time they have attempted to include major advances, with emphasis on the most recent; however, the temporal difficulties of modern abstracting, reading, and publication began to make themselves felt early in 1959.

III. Quantitative Comparisons of Amino Acid Compositions of Unfractionated Proteins

A logical way in which to begin a comparative study of proteins is to consider first the complement of amino acids that compose the proteins. Block and Weiss have provided extensive summary tables that describe the composition of amino acids in the proteins of whole organisms (*18*).

In Fig. 1, the proportions of amino acids in the proteins of bacteria, algae, protozoa, invertebrates, and mammals are compared. Before attempting to draw any inferences from this figure, one should note that the values shown are averages taken from analyses made in different laboratories and employing different methods. In some cases, the disagreement in values for some of the amino acids of proteins of the same organism analyzed in different laboratories is as great or greater than the average interspecies variation shown in Fig. 1. Furthermore, in many of these analyses, the completeness of removal of free amino acids and small peptides is subject to question. Thus, the values shown in Fig. 1 should be considered as only rough estimates of the true proportions of amino acids in the proteins of different species. In the light of these qualifications, perhaps the most notable feature is the

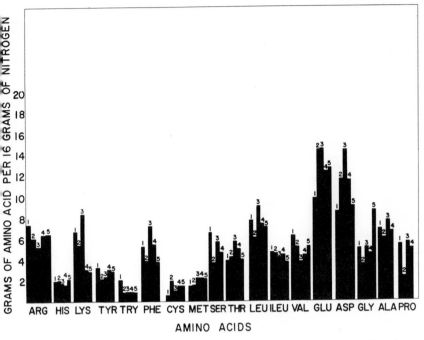

FIG. 1. Amino acid compositions in proteins of different organisms: (1) algae; (2) bacteria; (3) protozoa; (4) invertebrates; (5) mammals.

over-all similarity of the amino acid composition from the most simple to the most complex organisms (*18*) (cf. Section XI, C). We find throughout phylogeny a dominance of both dicarboxylic amino acids (including their amides) and relatively small proportions of amino acids like tryptophan, cystine (including cysteine), methionine, and histidine.

IV. Antibiotics

The antibiotics are of particular interest in studies of molecular variation in the polypeptides. Some of this interest derives from their definitional function as natural substances that inhibit the growth of organisms other than those that produce them. They are literally chemical weapons in the competitive struggle for existence among microbes. Many of the antibiotics for which sequences have been elucidated are among the smallest peptide structures to which comparative chemical and biological analyses might be applied. The systematic variations found are of particular interest because they could be considered as first clearly demonstrating that such differences were natural (*19*), rather than artifacts resulting from fractionation (*20*), a doubt which is not as clearly resolved with the larger molecules (*21*).

Thanks to the success of such investigators as Craig, Consden, Gordon, Martin, and Synge, structures of a number of the polypeptide antibiotics are known. Several of those that contribute to our understanding of comparative biochemistry are found in Fig. 2. These are

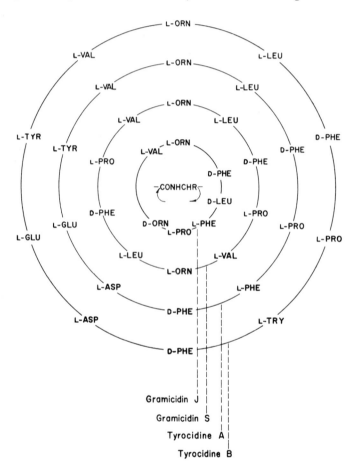

FIG. 2. Amino acid sequences in some bacterial antibiotics.

members of the gramicidin-tyrocidine family. Gramicidin J is a cyclo-heptapeptide; all the others are cyclodecapeptides. Without exception, each of the four antibiotics has an L-Val-L-Orn sequence. D-Phenylalanine follows L-ornithine in gramicidin J, but L-leucine intervenes between these two residues in the three other cases. This is an example of insertion of a residue, a type of relationship suggested elsewhere also (22). Gramicidin S is the most repetitious of the family inasmuch as the sequence L-Val-L-Orn-L-Leu-D-Phe-L-Pro is found twice in the same cyclodecapeptide. In fact, gramicidin S was first believed to be a cyclopentapeptide (23), until physical measurements revealed otherwise (24). In tyrocidine A and tyrocidine B, however, the minimal pentapeptide residue, although present, is not repeated. With the exceptions of protamines and silk fibroin, few, if any, intramolecular repetitions of sequences as large as tripeptide are otherwise known; the repetition of a pentapeptide residue is therefore unique. On the other hand, repetition within a cycle may require little more synthetic mechanism than production of multiple molecules of the same type.

In many ways molecules showing small differences between two large patterns are of major interest. Such an instance is found in the comparison between tyrocidine A and tyrocidine B. The only difference is that between phenylalanine and tryptophan, and even here the difference is that between two benzenoid amino acids.

In addition to this microvariation, the group of polypeptide antibiotics as a whole (25, 26) show several unique structural characteristics: (a) they usually contain D-amino acid residues such as D-phenylalanine and D-leucine; (b) they often contain unique amino acids differing but slightly from those found in protein, e.g., penicillamine (penicillin), methylvaline (actinomycin C_3), β-methyllanthionine (duramycin), and phenylsarcosine (etamycin) (25–28); (c) many are cyclic.

V. Hormones

A. OXYTOCINS AND VASOPRESSINS

Vasopressin and oxytocin provide a simple and definitive example of intraspecific and interspecific variation in both animal source and molecule. This example is a fully confirmed one since not only have the structures been assigned; these structures have been confirmed by synthesis, thanks to the persistent and comprehensive efforts of du Vigneaud and collaborators (29, 30). This accomplishment constitutes a landmark in that these were the first peptides of marked biological activity to be synthesized.

These two hormones of the posterior lobe of the pituitary gland have been historically thought of as distinct. Oxytocin induces contraction of smooth muscle whereas vasopressin raises blood pressure. It was possible, however, to demonstrate with the purified materials that each substance had a small degree of the activity of the other. This effect is not surprising when one recognizes that the two hormonal octapeptides

Oxytocin

Pig   CyS-Tyr-*Ileu*-Glu(NH₂)-Asp(NH₂)-CyS-Pro-*Leu*-GlyNH₂

Cow   CyS-Tyr-*Ileu*-Glu(NH₂)-Asp(NH₂)-CyS-Pro-*Leu*-GlyNH₂

Horse   CyS-Tyr-*Ileu*-Glu(NH₂)-Asp(NH₂)-CyS-Pro-*Leu*-GlyNH₂

Man   CyS-Tyr-*Ileu*-Glu(NH₂)-Asp(NH₂)-CyS-Pro-*Leu*-GlyNH₂

(I)

Vasopressin

Pig   CyS-Tyr-*Phe*-Glu(NH₂)-Asp(NH₂)-CyS-Pro-*Lys*-GlyNH₂

Cow   CyS-Tyr-*Phe*-Glu(NH₂)-Asp(NH₂)-CyS-Pro-*Arg*-GlyNH₂

Horse   CyS-Tyr-*Phe*-Glu(NH₂)-Asp(NH₂)-CyS-Pro-*Arg*-GlyNH₂

Man   CyS-Tyr-*Phe*-Glu(NH₂)-Asp(NH₂)-CyS-Pro-*Arg*-GlyNH₂

(II)

differ only in two residues (I, II). These are the isoleucine residue in the cystine loop for oxytocin and phenylalanine in the same position for vasopressin. In the "handle" of the molecule, leucine occupies the C-2 position whereas, in vasopressin, this position is occupied by lysine or arginine (29–36).

It is in this latter relationship that the interspecific variation is observed. In the pig, lysine is found, whereas in cow, horse, and man the same position is occupied by another basic amino acid, arginine. The stepwise variation is thus a minimal one. It is interesting to compare this small difference, which does not prevent any vasopressin from being medically useful to humans, with the difference of two residues in passing intermolecularly to oxytocin. In this instance, phenylalanine is replaced by isoleucine and the basic amino acid is replaced by leucine. The resultant biological difference is sufficiently great that these two hormones have by their action until recently been considered to be distinct, as stated above. From a higher perspective, what we regard as small chemical differences underlies apparently large biological differences.

Relative to such relationships it is of particular interest to note that du Vigneaud has with Bodánszky (37) synthesized the analog of oxytocin in which phenylalanine replaces tyrosine. The phenolic hydroxyl of oxytocin contributes to the biological activity of the hormone in tests on the rat, but it is not essential.

B. INTERMEDINS (MELANOTROPINS, MELANOPHORE-STIMULATING HORMONES, MSHs)

Examples of microvariation in structure are found in the phyletic comparisons of the intermedin molecule (Table I).* One of the pig

TABLE I
STRUCTURAL VARIATIONS IN INTERMEDINS

Species	Complete amino acid sequence
Pig-α	N-Acetyl-Ser-Tyr-Ser-Met-Glu-His-Phe-Arg-Try-Gly-Lys-Pro-ValNH₂
Pig-β	Asp-Glu-Gly-Pro-Tyr-Lys-Met-Glu-His-Phe-Arg-Try-Gly-Ser-Pro-Pro-Lys-Asp
Sheep-α	Asp-Glu-Gly-Pro-Tyr-Lys-Met-Glu-His-Phe-Arg-Try-Gly-Ser-Pro-Pro-Lys-Asp
Sheep	Asp-Ser-Gly-Pro-Tyr-Lys-Met-Glu-His-Phe-Arg-Try-Gly-Ser-Pro-Pro-Lys-Asp
Cow	Asp-Ser-Gly-Pro-Tyr-Lys-Met-Glu-His-Phe-Arg-Try-Gly-Ser-Pro-Pro-Lys-Asp

intermedins exhibits several suggestive differences from the others. The pig α-type is the only intermedin which has a substituted N-terminus. Thus far, N-acetylamino acids have been reported only in intermedin and tobacco mosaic virus (TMV) protein (38, 39). Interestingly enough, each of these proteins has N-acetyl-Ser-Tyr-Ser at the N-terminus. It should also be pointed out the α-MSH has a sequence of amino acids which is identical with the N-terminal tridecapeptide in another pituitary hormone, ACTH (see Section V, C). The great structural similarity of these two molecules dramatizes their biological differences. Corticotropin, which contains the entire sequence of amino acids that constitutes α-MSH, has only about 1% of the melanocyte-stimulating activity exhibited by α-MSH (38). The basis for such weak MSH activity in ACTH may be (a) difference in spatial relationships of amino acids in the common sequence (before or after isolation), (b) inhibitory activity due to part of the ACTH chain, or (c) the fact that the serine in ACTH is free. The latter possibility is suggested by studies of periodate-modified ACTH (40). The interpretation is obscured by the fact that the other MSHs do not contain serine at the same locus that pig α-MSH does (Table I).

Serine in the N-3 position of pig α-MSH differs from lysine in the other four types (Table I). It is of particular interest that in the N-11 position this relationship is inverted, pig-α intermedin having lysine whereas the others have serine at this locus. The pig-α peptide is also shorter by comparison and contains the unique valinamide (cf. glycin-

* See references 41–44.

amide in oxytocin and vasopressin). The other four intermedins are very much alike except that β-pig and α-sheep molecules have glutamic acid in the N-2 position whereas the other sheep and cow intermedins have serine in this position.

If one were to regard seriously the notion that a protein molecule is entirely species specific, he might be led to bizarre conclusions, e.g., that a sheep is a hybrid of a pig and a cow, inasmuch as the sheep intermedins are identical to cow and pig-β intermedins, respectively. The more plausible explanation is that, for each type of protein molecule, the animal or plant produces a familial variety and that the vagaries of evolution have been such that the spectrum of types can overlap from one species to another.

C. CORTICOTROPINS (ADRENOCORTICOTROPIC HORMONES, ACTHs)

These pituitary hormones influence the adrenal cortex, which secretes many steroid hormones. The structural and functional relationship of ACTHs and MSHs has already been noted (cf. Section V, B). The material usually obtained and studied, and which holds the hormonal activity, is a fragment of the parent protein of molecular weight 20,000 (11, 45).

The structures of the corticotropins vary slightly both within and between species. Four structures have been reported, two from pig, one from sheep, and one from cow (11, 45–52). The sequence is 39 residues long with a variant octapeptide. The aminoid 24-residue peptide (III) common to all these materials is:

Ser-Tyr-Ser-Met-Glu-His-Phe-Arg-Try-Gly-Lys-Pro-Val-Gly-Lys-Lys-Arg-Arg-Pro-
Val-Lys-Val-Tyr-Pro-

(III)

An invariant hexapeptide residue (IV) is found at the C-terminus.

-Ala-Phe-Pro-Leu-Glu-Phe
(IV)

In these two fragments one may note such salient features as a -Lys-Lys- sequence followed by an -Arg-Arg- sequence and such possibly coincidental repetitions as -Pro-Val- and -Gly-Lys-. The -Lys-Lys-Arg-Arg- sequence is reminiscent of Block's protein *anlage* (53).

The variant nonapeptide appears as shown in sequence (V) (11, 45–52).

In this region (V), only limited variability is found; in six of the nine positions, three of the four variants have the same amino acid. Furthermore, where variations do occur, there seems to be scrambling

$$
\begin{array}{ll}
 & \qquad\qquad\qquad\qquad\quad \overset{\displaystyle NH_2}{|} \\
\text{Cow} & \text{-Asp-Gly-Glu-Ala-Glu-Asp-Ser-Ala-Glu-} \\[1em]
 & \qquad\qquad\quad \overset{\displaystyle NH_2}{|}\quad\ \overset{\displaystyle NH_2}{|}\qquad\qquad \overset{\displaystyle NH_2}{|} \\
\text{Pig-}\beta & \text{-Asp-Gly-Ala-Glu-Asp-Glu-Leu-Ala-Glu-} \\[1em]
 & \qquad\qquad\qquad\qquad\qquad\qquad\qquad \overset{\displaystyle NH_2}{|} \\
\text{Pig-}\alpha & \text{-Gly-Ala-Glu-Asp-Asp-Glu-Leu-Ala-Glu-} \\[1em]
 & \qquad\qquad\quad \overset{\displaystyle NH_2}{|} \\
\text{Sheep-}\alpha & \text{-Ala-Gly-Glu-Asp-Asp-Glu-Ala-Ser-Glu-} \\
 & \qquad\qquad\qquad (\text{V})
\end{array}
$$

among positions. The cattle ACTHs are thus, notably, similar. Recent studies indicate that human ACTH is also similar in amino acid sequence to that of the other mammals reported (54).

The above comparisons provide two definite examples of pairs in which the compositions are the same but the sequences are different (cow vs. sheep-α and pig-β vs. pig-α).

D. Prolactins (Lactogenic Hormones, Luteotropins)

Prolactin is an anterior pituitary hormone that induces lactation. The physical and chemical properties of sheep and beef prolactin have been studied mainly by C. H. Li and colleagues (51, 55). Both hormones are the same size (mol. wt. 26,000), and have identical isoelectric points at 5.73 (51). In neither case has a C-terminal amino acid been found. A loop has been suggested for the C-terminus (56, 57). In both species, prolactin consists of a single chain, the N-terminal sequence being Thr-Pro-Val-Thr-Pro- (56, 58). Thus far, the only notable differences in the hormones are tyrosine content and partition coefficients (51).

E. Somatotropins (Pituitary Growth Hormones)

The somatotropins, from the anterior lobe of the pituitary gland, are large protein molecules. The information available on terminal sequences is summarized in Table II (59–64).

It is indeed of interest that nearly all of the termini, amino or carboxylic, are phenylalanine. The only exceptions are the N-termini of the cow and sheep in which N-phenylalanyl is found; in addition there is a second chain terminating in alanine. Incidentally, such disparities between the numbers of N-termini and of C-termini within the same molecule suggest that some protein molecules may be branched. Unquestionably, more data of this type, and more of quantitative data, are needed to assess the possibility of branching. When all the data now

TABLE II
VARIATIONS IN TERMINI OF SOMATOTROPINS

Species	N-Terminus	C-Terminus
Human	Phe-*Ser*-Thr-	-Ala-*Tyr-Leu*-Phe
Monkey	Phe-	-Phe
Pig	Phe-	-Phe
Whale	Phe-	-*Leu-Ala*-Phe
Cow	Phe-*Ala*-Thr- Ala-Phe-Ala-	-*Ala-Phe*-Phe
Sheep	Phe- Ala-	-*Ala-Leu*-Phe

available are reviewed, it can be seen that probably not many protein molecules are branched in the sense of having more than one N-terminus per C-terminus or vice versa and, quite certainly, few or no protein molecules which have been studied are extensively branched.

The double N-terminus thus far has been detected only in the ungulates.

F. HYPERTENSINS (ANGIOTONINS)

The sequence of residues in hypertensin has been determined both for the horse and the cow (VI). This extremely active renal vasopressor

Horse   Asp-Arg-Val-Tyr-*Ileu*-His-Pro-Phe
Cow   Asp-Arg-Val-Tyr-*Val*-His-Pro-Phe
(VI)

factor is an octapeptide of which seven residues and their arrangements are common to the two species (71–74).

The substitution is isoleucine for valine. This substitution represents a minimal alteration in view of the fact that the two amino acid residues occupy a similarly shaped volume. These two amino acids are distinguished from all the other common amino acids by virtue of the fact that in each of them the β-carbon atom is directly involved in branching. Such structure underlies steric hindrance in some of the behavior which they exhibit (75). It would be of interest to know whether these steric effects are related to the positioning of the residue in this case.

Hypertensinogen, the inactive precursor of hypertensin, is of the same sequence except that the C-terminus extends to -His-Leu as -Phe-His-Leu. This sequence is found in both the horse and cow hypertensinogens.

Isoleucine and valine residues are also found as alternative residues in insulins from different species (see Section V, G). The most striking aspect of this relationship is that in both insulin and hypertensin the bovine type has valine and the equine type has isoleucine. This relationship suggests that the cow is more characteristically valine-centered at loci which may be crucial in evolution, whereas the emphasis in the proteins of the horse is isoleucine. It will indeed be of interest to compare contents of these two amino acids in other homologous proteins from these two species.

G. Insulins

Our knowledge of the amino acid residue sequence of insulin has been pioneered by Sanger and others (4), first on beef insulin and then on sheep, pig, and horse (3, 70, 76–84). The first work on insulin by Sanger (3) called widespread attention to the possibilities (2) inherent in analysis of sequences of residues. The interesting comparisons on insulins from two species of whale, the sperm whale and the sei-whale, are by Ishihara and colleagues (85).

The differences in the glycyl chains of insulins from different species are summarized in Table III (3, 70, 76–85). No differences have yet been reported for the phenylalanyl chains of insulins in species which have been studied; they are therefore not presented here.

The alternations in the variant section of the glycyl chain are of a limited type. In position N-8 the alternation involves alanine and threonine. This alternation is found in the TMV and cucumber virus proteins (65–67), in two N-termini in prolamine in maize (68), and in the phyletic variation in serum albumins (69). In position N-9, the two amino acids are serine and glycine. In position N-10, the two residues are valine and isoleucine as in hypertensins (q.v.).

In comparisons such as these, the examination may be focused on the dominant components of each of the insulins by species. The structures assigned have been inferred from studies of insulins which have been recrystallized many times. Accordingly, the results may be biased in favor of major components. There is no good reason to exclude the likelihood that the insulins in nature are families of molecules like other proteins. In fact, Brown, Sanger, and Kitai reported that their recrystallized pig and sheep insulins contained smaller amounts of peptides that typify the molecular species known as "cattle insulin" (84).

It might be instructive if, at some future date, a yet more comprehensive comparison of species by types of insulin is made with the material as close in composition as possible to that which occurs in nature, i.e., without fractionation. When such a study becomes feasible,

TABLE III

STRUCTURES OF GLYCYL CHAINS OF INSULINS FROM VARIOUS SPECIES

Species	Sequence
Cow	Gly-Ileu-Val-Glu-Glu-CyS-CyS-Ala-Ser-Val-CyS-Ser-Leu-Tyr-Glu-Leu-Glu-Asp-Tyr-CyS-Asp (NH₂ groups): NH_2 (CyS-CyS), NH_2 (Glu-Glu), NH_2 (Glu-Leu-Glu)
Pig	Gly-Ileu-Val-Glu-Glu-CyS-CyS-CyS-Thr-Ser-Ileu-CyS-Ser-Leu-Tyr-Glu-Leu-Glu-Asp-Tyr-CyS-Asp
Sheep	Gly-Ileu-Val-Glu-Glu-CyS-CyS-Ala-Gly-Val-CyS-Ser-Leu-Tyr-Glu-Leu-Glu-Asp-Tyr-CyS-Asp
Horse	Gly-Ileu-Val-Glu-Glu-CyS-CyS-Thr-Gly-Ileu-CyS-Ser-Leu-Tyr-Glu-Leu-Glu-Asp-Tyr-CyS-Asp
Whale, sperm	Gly-Ileu-Val-Glu-Glu-CyS-CyS-Thr-Ser-Ileu-CyS-Ser-Leu-Tyr-Glu-Leu-Glu-Asp-Tyr-CyS-Asp
Whale, sei	Gly-Ileu-Val-Glu-Glu-CyS-CyS-Ala-Ser-Thr-CyS-Ser-Leu-Tyr-Glu-Leu-Glu-Asp-Tyr-CyS-Asp

individual differences or the range of intraspecific differences will become of interest. It is possible that the hemoglobin molecule would lend itself more easily to such comparative analyses (86).

VI. Enzymes

A. Active Sites

An impressive body of comparative knowledge about active sites has been accumulated (87). The assumption that relatively short sequences within a protein chain contribute strongly to the enzymatic activity of the whole molecule appears to be a safe one. However, it should not necessarily be inferred that the sequences of amino acids in the immediate vicinity of the so-called active site contain the entire catalytic activity of the protein.

In addition to the sequences depicted in Table IV (88–100), many data are at hand to implicate histidine residues and carboxylic groups also in the full three-dimensional active site (101), but such implication is not yet on a detailed structural basis.

The procedure, in simplified description, for isolation of the active sites involves "tagging" the site by an inhibitor such as diisopropyl fluorophosphate (DFP) or Sarin, or in one case by reaction with p-nitrophenyl acetate (NPA) as substrate. By using labeled inhibitor or substrate, the enzyme-inhibitor or enzyme-substrate complex could be partially hydrolyzed and the tracer-labeled fragments could be isolated. The amino acid residue sequence was then determined on the purified fragment (the inactivation site). One certification of the methodology is found in the fact that the heptapepide in which serine is N-3 is identical when determined with DFP or NPA. There is, however, some controversy about the amino acid residue sequences in chymotrypsin studied by different laboratories.

The fact that phosphoglucomutase has the same sequence as the "hydrolytic" enzymes has been commented on as applying to enzymes of different function. However, hydrolytic enzymes are truly transfer enzymes acting on water; as such they are functionally akin to an enzyme that transfers phosphate residue (102). It is notable that phosphorylase has a totally different sequence around phosphoserine at its active site (100).

The seryl or phosphoseryl residue is common to all the enzymes in Table IV. The sequences adjacent to this residue are, with the exception of those in phosphorylase (which is not further discussed here), either identical or very similar. The seryl or phosphoseryl residue is preceded by an aspartic acid residue in most cases, but in the aliesterase

TABLE IV

RESIDUE SEQUENCES AT ACTIVE SITES OF SOME ESTERASES

Enzyme	Sequence
Chymotrypsin-DFP[a]	-Gly-Asp-Ser-Gly-Gly-Pro-Leu-
Chymotrypsin-NPA[b]	-Gly-Asp-Ser-Gly-Gly-Pro-Leu
Chymotrypsin-Sarin[c]	-Gly-Asp-Ser-Gly-Glu-Ala-
Trypsin-DFP	-Asp(NH₂)-Ser-Cys-Glu-Gly-Gly-Asp-Ser-Gly-Pro-Val-Cys-Ser-Gly-Lys-
Liver-aliesterase-DFP	-Gly-Glu-Ser-Ala-Gly-Gly-
Pseudocholinesterase-DNP	-Phe-Gly-Glu-Ser-Ala-Gly-
Elastase	-Gly-Asp-Ser-Gly-
Thrombin-DFP	-Gly-Asp-Ser-Gly-
Phosphoglucomutase	$\overset{\text{P}}{\overset{\mid}{\text{-Asp-Ser-Gly-Glu-}}}$ [d]
Phosphorylase	$\overset{\text{NH}_2}{\overset{\mid}{\text{-Lys-Glu-Ileu-Ser-Val-Arg-}}}\ \text{P}$ [d]

[a] Diisopropyl fluorophosphate.
[b] p-Nitrophenyl acetate.
[c] Isopropyl methylphosphonylfluoridate.
[d] P = O-phosphate.

and cholinesterase, aspartic acid is replaced by the other dicarboxylic amino acid, glutamic acid. The adjacency of aspartic acid or glutamic acid to serine or phosphoserine recalls Perlmann's generalization on the α-relationship of phosphoserine and a dicarboxylic amino acid in phosphoproteins in general (103). On the other side of the central residue one finds mostly glycine, but in two cases alanine. It is remarkable that only in these latter two enzymes is the glutamic acid residue found on the other side of the serine; on each side of the serine the residue is enlarged by one methylene radical. It will be of interest to observe whether new data on other esterases are consistent with this tentative correlation. Glycine precedes the dicarboxylic amino acid in all instances.

The kind of sequential information made available by these studies seems to be particularly deserving of further contemplation and subsequent experimental action for the purpose of attempting to understand intimately the mechanism of enzyme action. Many other enzymes in addition to the esterases may be studied by the use of "irreversible" inhibitors.

B. CHYMOTRYPSIN AND TRYPSIN: STRUCTURE AND SPECIFICITY

Owing largely to the work of Sorm and colleagues (104), 127 sequences of 242 in chymotrypsinogen and 99 of 209 in trypsinogen had been assigned by 1959. More than half of a large number of peptides formed on tryptic digestion of the two enzymes were seen to be identical (105). A complete treatment of these structures is inconsistent with the dimensions of this review, but some of the dipeptides common to the two are presented below (VII). Comparison of the zymogens instead of the proteases in these investigations is valid inasmuch as the peptides that spell the difference between zymogen and protease are each small and well characterized (12).

Some examples may serve to describe the state of knowledge. Of ten cysteic acid-containing di- or tri-peptides isolated from partial acid hydrolyzates of trypsinogen, four were identical to ones isolated from chymotrypsinogen (cf. VII).

His-Cys
Thr-Cys
Phe-Cys
Cys-Gly
(VII)

Seven dipeptides containing arginine or histidine were isolated from trypsinogen. Four were identical to those from chymotrypsinogen (cf. VIII).

Ser-Arg
Val-Arg
Ala-His
His-Cys
(VIII)

The picture with lysine-containing peptides included nine dipeptides and one tripeptide from trypsinogen. Of these, six dipeptides were common to the two zymogens (cf. IX).

Gly-Lys
Ser-Lys
Thr-Lys
Lys-Leu
Lys-Cys
Lys-Glu
(IX)

Comparison of these two enzymes is of particular interest in the evaluation of differences and similarities in protein chemistry.

The similarities in structure match a re-evaluation of the concept of "specificity" such as became possible from study of proteolysis of large natural substrates by following quantitatively the exposure of N-termini and C-termini (106). This kind of study avoids the easy overemphasis on differences in proteolytic behavior when one uses synthetic peptides of small size (102). Both the proteolytic behavior and the structural information once again suggest that the similarities are greater than the differences (107).

Although chymotrypsin and trypsin seemed at one time to have markedly different functions, this pair poses what appears to be a yet not fully answered question of whether these enzymes are truly heterologous or indeed homologous in origin and function both.

C. RIBONUCLEASES

Ribonuclease, particularly the commercial crystalline bovine enzyme, has recently been the subject for concerted chemical structural studies which have culminated in the assignment of a total amino acid sequence (108–118), as shown in Fig. 3.

Comparative studies on the ovine and bovine enzyme have recently been reported and are of special interest in that in this molecule of 124 residues isolated from two different mammals, only three differences could be found (119–121). Two of the differences are replacement of threonine (bovine) by serine (ovine), and of lysine (bovine) by glutamic acid (ovine). The third difference which occurs nearest to the C-terminus has yet to be elucidated (120).

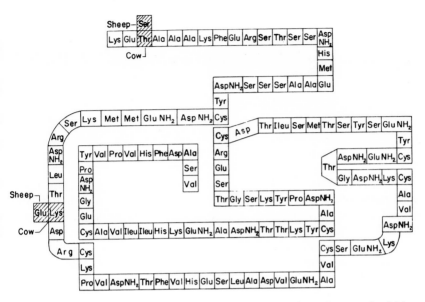

FIG. 3. Amino acid sequences of bovine and ovine ribonucleases. The folding shown is hypothetical.

Both commercial bovine ribonuclease and sheep crystalline enzyme have been shown to be heterogeneous (*119, 122–125*) and at least two of the bovine ribonucleases have different specificities (*124*). Further study should illuminate whether heterogeneity stems from sequential differences, from differences in tertiary structure (folding), from state of aggregation, or from changes in the molecules which may occur during purification (*21*).

D. LYSOZYMES

Another enzyme whose structure is being studied intensively by protein chemists is lysozyme, which acts on mucopolysaccharides. Currently, about 120 of the 130 residues in chicken egg lysozyme have been assigned to positions and the solution of the complete sequence appears imminent (*126–140*).

It is now possible to compare the amino acids at both ends of lysozymes isolated from dog spleen, rabbit spleen, and hen's egg (*134, 137, 139, 141*) (see Table V). The lysozymes isolated from vertebrates have identical terminal amino acid residues and are similar in composition (*137, 141*). Papaya latex lysozyme has *N*-glycyl in contrast to, but a composition similar to, that of the animal lysozymes (*135*). It may be noted that papaya latex lysozyme was discovered accidentally by Smith

TABLE V

TERMINAL AMINO ACID RESIDUES IN LYSOZYMES
ISOLATED FROM DIFFERENT ORGANISMS

Source	N-Terminus	C-Terminus
Chicken egg	Lys-	-Leu
Dog spleen	Lys-	-Leu
Rabbit spleen	Lys-	-Leu
Papaya latex	Gly-	

and colleagues (135) in the course of purification of papain. The amino acid composition and physical properties of an impurity in the latex suggested that this impurity was lysozyme. This inference was confirmed by studies of enzymatic activity.

Lysozyme or an enzyme resembling lysozyme in specificity and chromatographic behavior has recently been found in bacteriophage and appears to act as a bacterial cell wall-cleaving enzyme (142). However, nothing is known about the chemical nature of the viral enzyme. It is possible that future comparisons of the viral lysozyme with homologous enzymes from other organisms might help to elucidate the questionable position of the virus in evolution (143).

E. AMYLASES

Recent studies on amylase make possible a comparison of the N-terminal region (X) of these proteins of

$$\text{Ala-Gly-Asp*-Glu*-Ser-Ala-Leu-Thr-}$$
$$\text{(X)}$$

the mold *Aspergillus oryzae* and of the N-terminal region (XI) of the protein of the bacterium *Bacillus subtilis*. As can be seen in the diagram,

$$\text{Val-Asp*-Gly-Glu*-Ser-(Ala,Leu,Val)-}$$
$$\text{(XI)}$$

the two enzymes have different N-terminal amino acid residues (144, 145). The N-2 and N-3 amino acid residues, i.e., -Gly-Asp-, in the amylase of *Aspergillus* are reversed in the bacterial enzyme (146–149). The N-4 and N-5 amino acid residues, -Glu-Ser-, correspond exactly in the two microbes and, possibly, the correspondence between amino acid residues may extend to positions N-6 and N-7 (147–149).

* It is not yet known whether these amino acid residues are in the free or amide form.

F. GLYCERALDEHYDE-3-PHOSPHATE DEHYDROGENASES

Most comparative studies on proteins are limited to the animal kingdom. Accordingly, it is of interest to compare functionally identical (homologous) animal and plant proteins such as crystalline glyceraldehyde-3-phosphate dehydrogenase from rabbit muscle and yeast. The two enzymes have the same catalytic function with slightly different affinities for their substrate (150, 151). They have very similar amino acid compositions with detectable quantitative differences in glycine and glutamic acid and possibly histidine (152). Velick and Udenfriend reported N-valyl for both rabbit muscle and yeast glyceraldehyde-3-phosphate dehydrogenase (152, cf. 153).

G. CYTOCHROMES C

Interspecific variations have been found in a heme peptide which is resistant to peptic digestion and may therefore be isolated from enzymatic digests of cytochrome c. Cytochrome c, a protein that plays a key role in electron transport in organisms throughout phylogeny, has been studied by a variety of workers, notably Paleus, Tuppy, and Theorell and their colleagues. Glutamic acid or glutamine has been assigned as the C-terminus of cytochrome c in horse, whale, and yeast (154, 155). The N-termini of horse, cow, and yeast cytochrome c have also been studied, but there are conflicts in the literature that have yet to be resolved (155–157).

The molecular variations in the heme peptide from cytochrome c are summarized in Table VI (157–163).

Insofar as sequences have been assigned, the interior peptides are the same for cow, horse, pig, and salmon. The common structure is found for nine consecutive amino acid residues. Differences are found in chicken, silkworm, yeast, and the bacterium, *Rhodospirillum rubrum*. Instead of alanine, in one position chicken bears serine. The cytochrome c of silkworm has alanine, however, but arginine replaces the lysine found in that position in all the higher forms. In each case, the substitutions are structurally close, one 3-carbon amino acid for another and one basic amino acid for another. A large number of deviations are found in yeast and *R. rubrum*. Repetition of -Val-Glu- in most of the molecules is noteworthy.

Other indications of gross similarity in structure of cytochromes c of yeast, horse, and cow stem from comparative studies on amino acid composition in these species (164, 165a).

TABLE VI

Structural Variations in Amino Acid Residue Sequences
in Interior Peptides from Cytochromes c

Species	Amino acid residue sequences
Cow	$\overset{\displaystyle NH_2}{\overset{|}{}}$ $\overset{\displaystyle NH_2}{\overset{|}{}}$ -Val-Glu-*Lys*-CyS-*Ala*-Glu-CyS-His-Thr-*Val-Glu-Lys*
Horse	$\overset{\displaystyle NH_2}{\overset{|}{}}$ -*Lys*-CyS-*Ala*-Glu-CyS-His-Thr-*Val-Glu-Lys*
Pig	$\overset{\displaystyle NH_2}{\overset{|}{}}$ -*Lys*-CyS-*Ala*-Glu-CyS-His-Thr-*Val-Glu-Lys*-
Salmon	$\overset{\displaystyle NH_2}{\overset{|}{}}$ $\overset{\displaystyle NH_2}{\overset{|}{}}$ -Val-Glu-*Lys*-CyS-*Ala*-Glu-Cys-His-Thr-*Val-Glu*-
Chicken	$\overset{\displaystyle NH_2}{\overset{|}{}}$ $\overset{\displaystyle NH_2}{\overset{|}{}}$ -Val-Glu-*Lys*-CyS-*Ser*-Glu-CyS-His-Thr-*Val-Glu*-
Silkworm	$\overset{\displaystyle NH_2}{\overset{|}{}}$ $\overset{\displaystyle NH_2}{\overset{|}{}}$ -Val-Glu-*Arg*-CyS-*Ala*-Glu-CyS-His-Thr-*Val-Glu*-
Yeast	-*Arg*-CyS-*Glu-Leu*-CyS-His-Thr-*Val-Glu*-
Rhodospirillum rubrum	-CyS-*Leu-Ala*-CyS-His-Thr-*Phe-Asp-Glu*-

VII. Muscle Proteins

A. Myoglobins

The significance of the dark muscle heme protein, myoglobin, lies in its binding capacity for oxygen. Accordingly, it is not surprising to find that in aquatic diving mammals as much as 5–10% of the muscle press juice is composed of this protein. In mammals such as whales and seals, the skeletal muscles are found to be almost black in color (*165b*).

The N-terminal amino acid in myoglobin has been reported for several mammals [Table VII (*165b–169*)]. The two whale proteins have N-valyl; horse and seal have N-glycyl. It may be noted parenthet-

TABLE VII

N-Terminal Amino Acid Residues in Myoglobins of Different Species

Organism	N-Terminal amino acid
Whale (sperm)	Val-
Whale (finback)	Val-
Horse	Gly-
Seal	Gly-

ically, that the related blood protein, hemoglobin, generally contains N-valyl and in some cases contains N-glycyl (see Section VIII, D). There is also evidence for gross similarities in amino acid sequences in horse and beef myoglobin (*170*). These data are consistent with crystallographic and serological data on horse, seal, and whale (*165b*).

B. Tropomyosins (Paramyosins)

Tropomyosins are muscle fibril proteins; they have been studied both in vertebrates and in invertebrates. There are at least two kinds of tropomyosin; these are designated TM_A and TM_B (*171*). The former is identical to the globulin, paramyosin, which may function to hold muscles in a contracted state (*172*). TM_B is water soluble and is presumed to be related to the actomyosin contractile system (*171*).

The information on the N-terminus is such as to suggest that the small proportions which have been found by the DNFB (dinitrofluorobenzene) method are impurities (*172*).

The C-termini for tropomyosins in a number of species are presented in Table VIII (*172–176*). C-Isoleucine appears in five of the tissues, and

TABLE VIII
C-Terminal Amino Acid Residues in Tropomyosins

Animal and tissue	C-Terminus
Rabbit muscle	-Ser-Ileu
Pig heart	-Ileu-Ileu
Pig striated muscle	-Ileu
Pig bladder muscle	-Ser
Pig uterus muscle	-Leu
	-Asp (NH₂)
Duck gizzard	-Leu-Leu
Frog muscle	-Ileu
	-Ser (?)
Prawn muscle	-Ileu-Ileu
Sepia mantle	-Thr-Leu

C-leucine appears in three. Also, C-aspartic acid and C-serine have been recorded for two of the four pig muscles. The C-Ileu-Ileu dipeptide is found twice, once in the invertebrates and once in the vertebrates. Similarity of tropomyosins in vertebrates and invertebrates is further suggested by studies on amino acid composition (*172*).

VIII. Blood Proteins

A. Immunological Studies

Cross reactions have long been used by comparative serologists with frequent claims of success in applications to taxonomic problems. Nuttall performed 16,000 blood tests on more than 500 animal species, in pioneering work in this field (177). For an extensive review of research in comparative serology through about 1942, the classic book by Landsteiner (178) may be consulted. An illustration of the type of result obtained with cross reaction is shown in Table IX (179). Landsteiner

TABLE IX

VOLUMETRIC MEASUREMENTS OF PRECIPITATES SECURED WITH
CHICKEN OVALBUMIN IMMUNE SERA BY PRECIPITATION WITH
DIFFERENT EGG ALBUMINS[a]

Measurement	Egg albumin tested			
	Turkey	Guinea hen	Duck	Goose
Mean of 22 cross reactions and standard error	50 ± 2.4	42 ± 2.3	25 ± 1.7	19 ± 1.3

[a] The value for chicken ovalbumin is taken as 100.

concluded from studies of this sort that the quantitative responses paralleled the phylogenic placement as determined by the usual taxonomic criteria. In later attempts to assess the value of cross reactions in biological classification, the serological approach was tested on marsupials (180), carnivora (181), whales (182), birds (183, 184), fishes (185), insects (186), crustaceans (187), protozoans (188), plants (189), and other organisms (for example, see references 190 and 191). Where direct comparisons of serological and other studies on classification of animals are possible, the serological studies have frequently, but not always, been confirmatory (cf. 180).

In the realm of microorganisms, serological tests have proved to be very sensitive in detecting differences in cultures of morphologically similar bacteria. For example, two morphological groups of *Bacillus megatherium* were found to be composed of 38 distinct serological groups (192). Several other recent applications of immunological techniques to taxonomic problems in microbes might be cited here (193–196).

The fact that differences in proteins can be detected serologically and, furthermore, that such changes may be correlated with phylogenic kinship appears clear. The absolute meaning of comparative serological findings is, however, still nebulous. Whole-animal immunological experiments have been justly criticized by Hyman (197). This criticism would apply particularly to the bacterial studies already cited. When homogenates of whole organisms are used to induce antibodies, it is difficult to tell whether the response is to one, several, or thousands of proteins, although some of the more recent methods give some quantitative data about the number of antigens (198).

It is becoming increasingly clear that studies of unpurified serum proteins are subject to the same criticism as serological experiments with whole organisms. Free-flow and paper electrophoresis have shown that blood serum can be separated into four or five bands of proteins. Newer techniques have resulted in further separation of the serum into twenty bands (199) and the γ-globulins into four fractions (200). Ultimately, as preparative methods become more sensitive, it may be anticipated that still more fractions of protein will be distinguished.

The serological approach to classification of organisms is beset with yet other difficulties. The intensity of a precipitation band is not necessarily an index of the concentration of an antigen (201), nor is turbidity an accurate measure of the amount of precipitate in an antigen-antibody complex (202). Finally, it would be of interest to know the relationship of mutations or "mutant proteins" to immunological differences. Even if we could interpret results of cross reactions on the basis of number of mutations, our classification problems would not be solved inasmuch as a new species is determined not by a difference in a single gene or a few genes but by an entire genome (203).

Studies by comparative serologists have been both extensive and promising, yet the problems inherent in this approach to classification of organisms suggest a need for much more investigation, particularly in development and applications of the newer, more sensitive methods, such as, e.g., Ouchterlony plate techniques (204) and immunoelectrophoresis (205).

As Boyden (191) has written, "A whole generation of biologists must be prepared to attack the problems of evolution of proteins on the molecular level, and among these the serologists . . ."

B. ELECTROPHORESIS OF SERUM PROTEINS

The electrophoretic technique permits analysis of differences in sera by partial resolution of the mixtures of proteins into bands. For treatment of the theory of electrophoresis, books edited by Peeters (206) and by Bier (207) may be consulted. This method is sensitive to total charge of a protein molecule. Thus, the hemoglobin of patients with sickle-cell anemia and the normal hemoglobin may be separated electrophoretically in spite of the fact that the two proteins differ by only two amino acid residues per molecule of 600 (see Section VIII, D, 4). Although no attempt will be made to treat completely the extensive literature on electrophoresis of blood serum proteins, a few illustrative examples of application of this method to problems in taxonomy, genetics, and developmental biology follow. Engle and colleagues studied electrophoretic patterns of serum proteins in eighteen species of marine fish (208) and Zweig and Crenshaw demonstrated differences in four species of turtle (209). In a study of amphibians, Frieden and co-workers demonstrated marked changes during metamorphosis (210). The increasing applications of electrophoresis to detect abnormal proteins is also notable (211–214). A particularly fruitful area for electrophoretic study has been and continues to be in the research on mutant hemoglobins, which is discussed later. Several detailed reviews may be consulted for a more complete treatment of the literature and significance of electrophoresis of serum proteins (206, 215–218).

The idea that A:G (albumin:globulin) ratios may be a useful characteristic for taxonomists is a very old one.* In recent years, there has been a growing availability of data on concentrations of serum albumins and globulins in man because of the medical implications of abnormal serum patterns. Accordingly, the result of a random selection of eighteen reports on electrophoresis of blood serum from many different geographical regions were summarized (220–235). The mean A:G ratios were seen to vary from 0.42 to 2.36. The wide range of A:G ratios, which, incidentally, overlaps the A:G ratios of numerous other mammals, fishes, amphibians, and reptiles (102, 236–238), indicates that this quantitative approach, at its present state of development, has little taxonomic significance. The variability in the results stems largely from problems in methodology (215) as well as environmental and, possibly, racial effects on human sera. A partial breakdown of possible environmental or racial factors which affect serum protein concentrations might include diet or lack of diet (239, 240), age of organisms (241, 242), pregnancy (243, 244), exercise (245, 246), race (247, 248), storage of serum (249), pathological conditions (215, 250, 251), and many others (215). Clearly, a necessity for rigorous standardization of method and very careful comparisons of organisms has been demonstrated.

C. Serum Albumins

There is hope that the tremendous backlog of data in the relating of animals to each other by serological testing may be rationalized by in-

---

* Long before the technique of electrophoresis was originated, primitive studies of albumin:globulin ratios had been reported and forgotten. For example, one such study was made by Hammerstein in 1878. For a review of the "ancient history" of research on blood proteins, see *The Differentiation and Specificity of Corresponding Proteins and other Vital Substances in Relation to Biological Classification and Organic Evolution: The Crystallography of Hemoglobins*, by Reichert and Brown (219).

cisive *N*-terminal or other sequential information on serum albumins. This possibility was foreshadowed by the work of Landsteiner (*179*), who showed such relationships by coupling the peptides glycylglycine, glycylleucine, leucylglycine, and leucylleucine to proteins and inducing antisera to each of these (*252*). The antiserum to the leucylglycyl antigen reacted most strongly to the leucylglycyl test antigen but not at all to the glycylleucine antigen. The reaction to the glycylglycyl antigen was intermediate in strength. The possibility of a basis for such molecular relationships in natural antigens may be seen in Table X (*253–258*).

TABLE X
N-TERMINI AND *C*-TERMINI IN SERUM ALBUMINS

Animal	*N*-Terminus	*C*-Terminus
Human	Asp-Ala-	-Leu
Dog	Asp-·	-Leu
Rabbit	Asp-	-Leu
Horse	Asp-Ala-	-Ala
Donkey	Asp-	-Ala
Mule	Asp-	-Ala
Cow	Asp-Thr-	-Ala
Pig	Asp-	-Ala
Goat	Asp-	-Ala
Sheep	Asp-	-Ala
Chicken	Asp-	-Ala
Duck	Asp-	-Ala
Turkey	Asp-	-Val

Many of the termini have been identified by two or more students of the subject. It is, however, true that many of the designations have been made in one laboratory by Peters and co-workers (*258*). This fact lends assurance to the comparative value of the data. The data available are too scanty to permit conclusions. The fact that differences can be detected at the extreme ends, however, as well as elsewhere in the molecule, indicates that there may be found molecular differences to compare with phyletic positions (*259*).

D. HEMOGLOBINS

Hemoglobin is usually thought of as occurring in the erythrocytes of mammals. Closely related respiratory pigments have, however, been found in invertebrates, molds, yeasts, and symbiotic plants and bacteria (*260*). The invertebrate hemoglobins are sometimes called "erythrocruorins." Some polychete worms have related proteins of very high molecular weight known as "chlorocruorins."

1. N-Termini

One of the N-terminal amino acid residues in most hemoglobins thus far studied is valine, which has been reported for normal and abnormal human hemoglobins, for pig, horse, donkey, mule, cow, sheep, goat, rabbit, guinea pig, dog, hen, and snake (261–263). In addition to N-valyl chains, fetal hemoglobins contain N-glycyl chains (264) and the hemoglobins of cow, goat, and sheep contain N-methionyl chains (261). Yagi and co-workers found proline and glycine, but no valine, in the terminal position of lamellibranch erythrocruorin (265).

2. C-Termini

Although C-terminal amino acids are reported for different species, the results (263, 266–268) in the literature need to be reconciled. Some of the difficulty in this controversy probably has a methodological basis.

3. Internal Peptides

There is now an impressive amount of data provided by Czechoslovakian and Japanese workers on the sequences of amino acids in basic peptides isolated from horse, pig, and cow [Table XI (269–273)].

TABLE XI

SOME BASIC DIPEPTIDES IN HORSE, PIG, AND COW HEMOGLOBINS

Dipeptide	Presence of dipeptide in			Dipeptide	Presence of dipeptide in		
	Horse	Pig	Cow		Horse	Pig	Cow
Ala-Arg	+[a]	+	+[a]	Gly-Lys	+	+	+
Asp-Arg	+		+	His-Lys	+	+	+
Glu-Arg	+		+	Ser-Lys	+		
Gly-Arg	+		+	Thr-Lys	+	+	
His-Arg	+[a]		+	Lys-Ala	+	+	
Leu-Arg	+[a]		+	Lys-Leu	+	+	
Lys-Arg		+		Lys-Val	?[b]	+	
Phe-Arg	+	+					
Ser-Arg	?[b]	+		Ala-His	+	+	+
Tyr-Arg	+	+		Leu-His	+	+	
Val-Arg			+	Ser-His	+	+	
Arg-Glu	+		+	His-Ala	+	+	
Arg-Leu	+	+		His-His			+
Arg-Lys	+	?[b]					
Arg-Phe	+	+					

[a] Independently reported by two different laboratories. Blank spaces indicate no report as yet.

[b] A dipeptide containing these two amino acids was identified, but the order has not been established.

These data suggest that the basic regions of hemoglobin in these mammals have much similarity and some differences. Recent preliminary studies extend the similarity also to cat, rat, monkey, and man (274–276).

4. Human Hemoglobins and Genetic Control

An intriguing picture of a precise relationship between amino acid sequence and normal and abnormal human hemoglobins is rapidly being uncovered. The provocative aspect of these studies is that the abnormal hemoglobins have been shown in a number of cases to be characteristic of genetic diseases or "inborn errors of metabolism" (277). The hemoglobins in these diseases appear to be almost identical to normal adult hemoglobin but with very significant structurally minor differences in amino acid sequence. The genetic studies are too numerous to be recounted here; they are amply developed in several reviews (278, 279).

The technique of "fingerprinting," which is used for detecting differences between peptides in partial hydrolyzates of different proteins, highlights current research on hemoglobins. In the pioneering studies of Ingram and co-workers, a tryptic hydrolyzate of hemoglobin was subjected first to electrophoresis and then to partition chromatography, which separated numerous peptides. The patterns of peptides obtained by this technique characterizes a protein as "fingerprints" (280). By use of this technique, the structure of an octapeptide from partial hydrolyzates of several hemoglobins was determined, as shown in (XII).

Hb A (normal)	Val-His-Leu-Thr-Pro-*Glu*-*Glu*-Lys-
Hb S (sickle cell)	Val-His-Leu-Thr-Pro-*Val*-*Glu*-Lys-
Hb C (sickle-cell trait)	Val-His-Leu-Thr-Pro-*Lys*-*Glu*-Lys-
Hb G (abnormal hemoglobin)	Val-His-Leu-Thr-Pro-*Glu*-*Gly*-Lys-

(XII)

In each case, the abnormality occurs in two of four hemoglobin chains, the β-chains (280–283), and has now been shown to be near the N-terminus of these chains (284). The similarities in these octapeptides are striking. Furthermore, studies of other peptides in digests from the different hemoglobins indicate that the rest of the molecules are identical or very nearly so. Thus, for example, sickle-cell anemia appears to be a manifestation of a single mutation leading only to replacement of glutamic acid by valine in one position. The resultant decrease in solubility and change in electrophoretic behavior are consistent with the molecular change (285). It is also notable that the same gene is responsible for hemoglobins C and S (280) and that the difference in the proteins is at the same position (residue 6). On the other hand, hemoglobin G differs from hemoglobins A, C, and S at another position (residue 7), and hemoglobins G and S are believed to be products of genes that are not alleles (286). If these interpretations are all correct, it may be deduced that two different parts of one or more chromosomes in some way control placement of neighboring amino acids and further that two or more genes are controlling synthesis of one chain [cf. Beadle's one gene – one enzyme theory (287)].

There are new indications that other human hemoglobins are markedly similar to these already described. Hemoglobins F (fetal) and A (normal) have identical α-chains (288, 289). Hence, the differences between these two proteins must·be in the β-chains. Recent work indicates that the sequential differences in these two proteins are minor (290). Another abnormal hemoglobin, H, is composed of four identical chains of the β-type (291). Still another abnormal hemoglobin, I, apparently derives its uniqueness from replacement of one lysine residue by aspartic acid (292).

Most of the abnormal hemoglobins now known have been detected by their unusual behavior in electrophoresis. It is also possible to have in a protein mutational changes that do not measurably affect the mobility of the molecule. Such is the case with hemoglobin D. By fingerprinting techniques, Benzer and associates were able to demonstrate three chemically different varieties of this hemoglobin; they were designated hemoglobins Dα, Dβ, and Dγ (293).

5. Heterogeneity

Although it has been suggested that heterogeneity of hemoglobins is due to variations in tertiary structure (294), this explanation cannot satisfy all the data. For example, fetal blood is very rich in hemoglobin F and contains a small proportion of hemoglobin A. The mixture changes gradually to blood rich in adult hemoglobin A with very little hemoglobin F (fetal). [In this respect, the infant "matures" in 4 months (295).] Another example of heterogeneity in hemoglobins was given by Allen and others, who reported that human hemoglobin A contains 90% of a major component; the other 10% consists of three heme proteins and one nonheme protein (296). Hemoglobin A$_2$, one of the minor components, has recently been found to be very similar to hemoglobin A with one difference being substitution of alanine for glutamic acid in one peptide fragment (297).

E. FIBRINS

Mention of the enzymatic conversion of fibrinogen to fibrin during blood clotting has been in the literature for almost a hundred years, but only recently has the nature of the changes in these proteins been investigated (298–303). Blombäck and Yamashina have studied the limited proteolysis of fibrinogen in seven mammals (301). In all species surveyed, N-tyrosyl was found in both fibrin and fibrinogen (Fig. 4). In

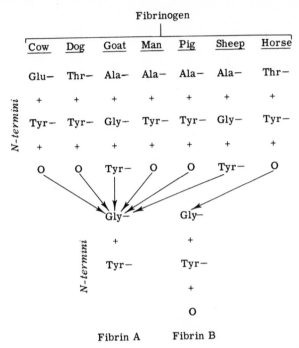

FIG. 4. Conversion of fibrinogen to fibrin in seven animals. Circles represent chains which have no N-terminal amino acid. Six of the fibrins are identical in N-termini and are designated A; horse fibrin, B, is unique.

addition to tyrosine, either one or two additional N-terminal amino acid residues were found in the fibrinogen, and in all cases, glycyl (as well as tyrosyl) was N-terminal in fibrins (301). Quantitative data indicate that both fibrinogen and fibrin have six chains although six N-terminal amino acids are not always found.

IX. Miscellaneous Proteins

A. PROTAMINES

Work on the protamines is among the earliest in the field of sequence determination. Felix and co-workers began to report on these in 1933, being preceded only by researchers from the laboratories of Fischer and

Abderhalden, who studied peptides from silk fibroin in the period 1902–1943 (*304, 305*). The protamines offer special difficulties in purification, and the compositional preponderance of arginine in the protamines poses some unique problems in ascertaining the arrangement. The data are shown in Table XII (*306–316*).

TABLE XII
TERMINI IN PROTAMINES

Species	N-Terminus	C-Terminus
Clupeine		
Clupea harengus	Pro-Ala-	-Arg
Clupea pallasii	Pro-Arg-, Ala-Arg-	-Arg
Salmine		
Salmo oncorhyncus	Pro-Val-	-Arg
Iridine		
Salmo irideus	Pro-Val-	-Arg
Truttine		
Salmo trutta	Pro-Val-	-Ala
Fontinine		
Salmo fontinalis	Pro-Val-	-Ala
Sturine		
Acipenser sturio	Ala-Glu-, Glu-	-Arg

The Pro-Val- sequence is dominant in the proteins from salmon whereas the Pro-Arg- and Pro-Ala- termini characterize clupeine in herring. On the other hand, the N-termini in sturine from sturgeon are alanine and glutamic acid. [These particular assignments are open to question because the sperm heads were aged (*317*).] If the information is correct, the salmon, herring, and sturgeon protamine each has its characteristic N-terminus (cf., however, *318, 319*).

The C-termini do not occur in a regular mode. Two of the salmon types are C-alanine whereas all others are C-arginine.

B. FLAGELLINS

The ability of some algae and bacteria to thrive at temperatures near that of boiling water is well known although the physiological basis for thermophilic organisms is still a mystery (*320*). One possible explanation for this phenomenon is heat stability due to molecular structure (*320–322*). Accordingly, comparative studies of proteins from thermophilic and mesophilic bacteria may be illuminating.

Flagellin is a structural protein which composes bacterial flagella; these flagella, in turn, are believed to function in bacterial locomotion.

This protein mirrors the thermal properties of the organism from which it is isolated. Thus, flagella from *Escherichia coli*, a mesophile, disintegrate at 50°; flagella of a thermophile (*Bacillus* sp. 11330) disintegrate at temperatures above 75° (*320*). Weibull (*323*) and Koffler *et al.* (*324*) found only N-alanine in the flagellins of three thermophilic and three mesophilic bacteria. Comparative studies of flagella from mesophiles (*Proteus vulgaris, Escherichia coli, Bacillus megatherium, Bacillus subtilis*) and thermophiles (*Bacillus stearothermophilus NCA 2184, Bacillus* sp. *Purdue CD, Texas 11330, Nebraska 39*) indicate that the latter are more resistant to denaturation by urea or acetamide (*325*).

C. Plant Virus Proteins

The tobacco mosaic and related virus strains, which have received so much attention at the Virus Laboratory of the University of California (*326*) and the Max Planck Institute at Tübingen (*327*), provide a very rich background of information. Fraenkel-Conrat and his associates and Schramm and his co-workers have particularly illuminated this field.* Also, C. A. Knight, whose extensive compositional studies of proteins and nucleic acids of viruses has provided much background, has reported, with Niu, Woody, and Shore, on some of the sequences.

The information available on the virus protein molecules has emphasized the C-termini rather than the N-termini. The N-terminus was for long a subject of contention, but the studies of Narita (*328*) revealed that the terminus was not simply a loop without a terminal amino group. Rather, the residue that would otherwise be N-terminal was substituted by acetyl. The N-terminal dipeptide of TMV protein is thus N-acetyl-Ser-Tyr-, the same as found in one of the pig intermedins (cf. Section V, B). With the question of the N-terminus resolved, further assignments of residues have proceeded rapidly (*329*). Narita has reported (*328*) for cucumber virus N-acetyl-Ala-Tyr-Asp(NH_2)-Pro-Ileu-Thr-Ser-, which is notable for its N-acetyl-Ala-Tyr- terminus as compared to the N-acetyl-Ser-Tyr- of TMV protein.

The C-terminal hexapeptide of four strains of TMV protein and the C-termini of four other virus proteins are given in Table XIII (*330–337*). All the terminal hexapeptides in the TMV proteins examined have the same sequence except for the HR strain. In the designation for the HR strain, all the sequentially placed residues also comport with those in the corresponding positions in the molecules of the other strains. As is conventional, the two residues in the unsettled unique C-4 and C-5 positions are indicated by brackets. It will be of interest to determine

* See the *Notes added in proof* at the end of this chapter.

TABLE XIII
C-TERMINAL AMINO ACID RESIDUE SEQUENCES IN SOME
VIRAL PROTEINS

Virus	C-Terminus of protein
TMV	-Thr-Ser-Gly-Pro-Ala-Thr
M-TMV	-Thr-Ser-Gly-Pro-Ala-Thr
YA-TMV	-Thr-Ser-Gly-Pro-Ala-Thr
HR-TMV	-Thr-(Thr,Ala)-Pro-Ala-Thr
Tomato bushy stunt	-Leu
Potato X	-Pro
Cucumber No. 3	-Ala
Cucumber No. 4	-Ala

whether this dipeptide sequence should prove to be -Thr-Ala- to parallel -Ser-Gly-.

It is clear from Table XIII that the C-terminus of the tomato virus protein differs from that of potato virus protein and each of these differs from that of the C-alanine common to both cucumber types.

Recent studies by Knight and Woody by "fingerprinting techniques" reveal some salient information about the interior of the viral proteins from different strains. They report that the peptides in the partial hydrolyzates of TMV and M-TMV proteins are identical, that these viral proteins differ slightly from proteins of $J_{14}D_1$-TMV and YA-TMV in this respect, and that all four viral proteins are very different from HR-TMV (338, 339).

X. Attempts to Govern the Structures of Protein Molecules

A. CONTROL THROUGH DIET OR MEDIUM

The student of evolution of protein molecules may at some time wonder how one might alter protein molecules or their evolution experimentally. In an earlier era, a number of attempts to do this by control of the proportions of amino acids in the diets of animals or the media of microbes were made. Many claims of alteration in this manner have been made, and many of these claims have been refuted. Confusion as to whether the proposed alteration affected genotype or phenotype is possible on reading some of the early papers. For instance, Steinberg and Thom (340) studied the effect of nitrous acid on aspergilli and explained mutants as due to chemical action of nitrous acid on ε-amino side chains of lysine residues. More modern work ascribes the mutagenicity of nitrous acid to reactions of amino groups in nucleotides (341; cf. reference 342). Most of the claims of alteration by governing the composition of the diet or medium are in question on the basis of two potential alternative explanations. One of these explanations is that only imprecise methods of amino acid assay were available at the time of the experiment. The other is that change in amino acid composition of an organism may be explained as a change in proportion of individual proteins rather than in composition of a single protein (343).

B. Alteration with Unnatural Amino Acids

Investigators have used unnatural amino acids in an attempt to overcome these difficulties. Dyer (344) first synthesized ethionine for such studies and found it to be antagonistic to methionine rather than a replacement for it. Atkinson and co-workers tested p-fluorophenylalanine, in this context, in 1951 (345). Tarver reported early studies on incorporation of ethionine (346). Evidence has accumulated for incorporation into biosynthesized protein of thienylalanine (347), azatryptophan (348), selenomethionine (349), and others (343–350). Quite conclusive evidence, on the basis of obtaining peptides containing such analogs from partial hydrolyzates, has been at hand since 1954 (351). Without such evidence, the experimental results with unnatural amino acids could be explained as some kind of incorporation not involving peptide bond formation.

The significance of such experiments is at least that protein biosynthesis is not rigidly restricted to the known natural amino acids. A field for fertile future investigation may now be open and the laboratories of Cohen, in particular, and of others have been engaged in such investigations. Cohen and co-workers have followed the balance between phenylalanine and the analog into the proteins of E. coli. For a fuller treatment of this topic, the review of Vaughan and Steinberg (350) may be consulted.

C. Control of Structure by Synthesis under Hypothetically Prebiological Conditions

Another kind of attempt to control the structure of proteins is that which involves trying to imitate the prebiotic evolution of the first protein. Such attempts have, by thermal polycondensation of free amino acids, yielded materials that are distinguishable with difficulty as a class from natural proteins by many of the criteria applied (1). The attempts to produce such primitive proteins, in this laboratory, were in fact an intellectual outgrowth of studies of bioevolution of protein molecules viewed from recent times and extrapolated to primitive periods. Whether or not, and the ways in which, such presumed prebiotic evolution can be related to bioevolution is under investigation. Parallelisms with comparative biochemistry that suggest an evolutionary relationship between such thermally controlled polymerizations and protein biosynthesis include: (a) large proportions of dicarboxylic amino acid are found in the products (1); (b) both kinds of synthesis are promoted by phosphate; and (c) syntheses involving peptide bonds between glutamic acid and proline, whether thermal (352) or enzyme controlled (353) are uniquely unproductive. This kind of relationship is, as stated, suggestive and should be regarded at least as an example of a kind of attempt to learn about evolution of protein molecules at the roots of that developmental process. Other approaches to primordial protein have also been considered (354).

D. Control by Alteration of Polynucleotides

The experiments of Tsugita and Fraenkel-Conrat on tobacco mosaic virus (TMV) are especially notable in the context of governing the structure of protein by control of the medium (342). These authors induced mutations in TMV by treatment of isolated RNA with nitrous acid. The proteins of the mutant were shown to differ from those of the parent strain in three residues (leucine, alanine, and serine replace proline, aspartic acid, and threonine). This approach to governing protein structure may lead to the discovery of clues to the mechanisms by which sequences of amino acids are coded by the gene, especially after the nucleic acid–protein code is broken.

XI. Comparisons among Heterologous Proteins

A. Definitions

It is convenient to consider homologous proteins and heterologous proteins separately from the vantage point of molecular evolution even though classification into these categories is difficult and at times arbitrary. In this paper, the term *heterologous* is used to refer to the functionally nonequivalent proteins and peptides. Thus, ACTH and oxytocin are each from the pituitary gland but are heterologous because they possess different functions. Likewise, trypsin and pepsin have similar functions in that each is a proteolytic enzyme, but their specificity is sufficiently different that they may be regarded as heterologous. The definition of heterologous proteins becomes cumbersome when applied to some proteins in which the functions are not clear cut, for example, the different serum proteins. In this paper, electrophoretically distinct blood proteins are arbitrarily listed as heterologous.

B. SIMILARITIES AMONG HETEROLOGOUS PROTEINS

On the basis of this definition, a number of cases of structurally related heterologous proteins can be cited. For example, oxytocin and vasopressin are each octapeptides with six amino acids in common and two differing amino acid residues, yet the hormones have quantitatively different functions.* Similarly, the polypeptides ACTH (corticotropin) and MSH (intermedin) have nine amino acids in common. Seven of these amino acids form a common heptapeptide core and the other two additional identical amino acids are separated by either lysine or serine in a crisscross arrangement. To cite another example, four proteolytic enzymes, trypsin, chymotrypsin, papain, and pepsin have N-terminal isoleucine. The picture is complicated by the finding of N-terminal alanine in a bacterial proteolytic enzyme, subtilisin. Furthermore, trypsin and chymotrypsin have an active site† and other dipeptides in common (see Section VI, B). There are many additional instances in which small peptide fragments contain two or three amino acid residues common to more than one protein. However, these cases should not be considered proof of an over-all relationship among heterologous proteins without statistical evaluation (cf. 9).

C. STATISTICAL COMPARISONS OF HETEROLOGOUS PROTEIN COMPOSITIONS

It is interesting to consider large groups of heterologous proteins inasmuch as statistical treatments may be applied (355, 356). Fox and Homeyer found that the *index of correlation* for ten amino acids in six seed globulins is 0.973 and is 0.625 for the same ten amino acids in twenty-four heterologous proteins (355). An index of 1.000 signifies that the amino acid composition of all the proteins is the same; an index of 0.000 indicates that the composition of amino acids in these proteins is unrelated. Thus, the value of 0.973 states that the six seed globulins studied are nearly identical in amino acid composition. The value of 0.625 means that the amino acid compositions of these proteins are related, but significantly less so than in the case of the seed proteins.

* Highly purified oxytocin has a slight amount of vasopressin activity, and vice versa. The small degrees of vasopressin activity in oxytocin and oxytocin activity in vasopressin are believed to be inherent in the similar structures (du Vigneaud, 29). It should be noted also that Bell (46) found a constant level of intermedin activity in purified corticotropin, an observation which might be explained by the similarity in structure of part of these two hormones.

† From studies of DFP-inhibited enzymes, it is possible to designate a similar peptide at the active site of trypsin, chymotrypsin, thrombin, phosphoglucomutase, and other esterases (see Section VI, A).

One might state also that 0.625 indicates that these proteins are more related than they are independent. Although applied to purified proteins, this interpretation of kinship in composition is consistent with Fig. 1.

Statistical treatments of sequences of amino acids in heterologous proteins are few inasmuch as the bulk of the literature on this subject is recent and not enough data have been accumulated for a rigorous treatment. Gamow *et al.* interpreted data from sequential assignments of twenty-two heterologous proteins as evidence for *randomness*. They found that the distribution of neighbors of amino acids in peptides followed a Poisson distribution. More recently, in an exhaustive analysis, Sorm and colleagues assembled data on dipeptide sequences in 68 proteins (9). These authors found qualitative suggestion of favored sequences (i.e., nonrandom arrangements). Such results could be at least partly explained by the fact that some amino acids, such as glycine or alanine, are found in proteins more frequently than are others, such as tryptophan or cysteine. Unfortunately, the data of Sorm and colleagues were not treated statistically and the significance of these data is therefore doubtful.

The state of the literature now permits preliminary comparison of reliable data on the frequency of occurrence of each of the common amino acids in total compositions and in N-termini. To the extent that these relative occurrences are the same, the comparison provides an index of randomness of arrangement of these residues within protein molecules, for the one position.

First, the literature of N-terminal amino acid residues was compiled [Table XIV (5, 6, 9, 72, 298, 358–380)]. Care was taken to include only proteins that were quite certainly heterologous. Thus, the termini of α-corticotropin, but not β-corticotropin, were recorded. In cases in which different authors were in discord over the correct N-terminal amino acid for a given protein, data were not recorded for either. Most proteins which have not been extensively purified are not included in this list (e.g., elastin), nor are N-terminal amino acids reported when present in trace quantities. An additional qualification in considering the data in this table is its tentative nature. The current status of methodology for purification and structural analysis of proteins is such that one cannot preclude the possibility of errors in the recorded literature. It is nevertheless believed that the number of errors in Table XIV are few inasmuch as the N-terminal amino acids of at least twenty-three of the fifty-seven proteins studied have been determined by two or more methods.

The data in Table XIV are summarized in Table XV. In Table XV,

TABLE XIV

A Listing of Proteins by N-Terminal Amino Acids

Amino acid	Protein or peptide in which amino acid is N-terminal[a]
Alanine	γ-Globulin, *chymotrypsin*, flagellin, α-glycoprotein, somatotropin ovomucoid, conalbumin, avidin, parotin, ribonucleoprotein, taka-amylase, ferritin, subtilisin, prothrombin, zein, collagen, fibroin
Arginine	Parotin, ferritin, casein
Aspartic acid or asparagine	α-Glycoprotein, *serum albumin*, carboxypeptidase, dentin,[b] *hypertensin*, cryoglobulin, *intermedin*, *lipoprotein*, trypsin inhibitor, sericin, hypertensinogen
Half-cystine	*Serum albumin*, chymotrypsinogen, oxytocin, vasopressin
Glutamic acid or glutamine	Fibrinogen, dentin, β₂-globulin, *lipoprotein*, cryoglobulin, α-crystallin
Glycine	*Fibrin*, ribonucleoprotein, ferritin, *silk fibroin*, *insulin*, *myoglobin*, sericin, collagen
Histidine	Parotin, ferritin, glucagon
Isoleucine or leucine	Chymotrypsin, bacitracin, β-lactoglobulin, *papain*, *pepsin*, pepsinogen, pepsin inhibitor, trypsin, neurotoxin, collagen
Lysine	Ferritin, *casein*, *lysozyme*, ribonuclease
Methionine	Ferritin
Phenylalanine	Somatotropin, gliadin, *insulin*, phosphoglucomutase
Proline	*Salmine*, aldolase
Serine	Ribonucleoprotein, ACTH, silk fibroin, lipoprotein, sericin
Threonine	Prolactin, lipoprotein, zein
Tryptophan	None
Tyrosine	*Fibrin*, fibrinogen
Valine	Triosephosphate dehydrogenase, β₁-globulin, *hemoglobin*, *trypsinogen*

[a] The N-terminal amino acids of proteins which are in italics have been determined by two or more methods.
[b] After treatment with acid.

the frequency of occurrence of the different amino acids in the N-terminal position is found to range from seventeen times for alanine to zero for tryptophan.

For suitable comparison, knowledge of the frequency of amino acids

TABLE XV

N-Terminal Amino Acids in Order of Their Decreasing
Frequency in Proteins and Peptides[a]

Amino acids	Number of times found in N-terminal position
Alanine	17
Aspartic acid[b]	11
Glycine	8
Glutamic acid[c]	6
Serine, (leucine + isoleucine)/2[d]	5
Valine, phenylalanine, half-cystine, lysine	4
Arginine, threonine, histidine	3
Tyrosine, proline	2
Methionine	1
Tryptophan	0

[a] This table summarizes the data in Table XIV

[b] Includes asparagine.

[c] Includes glutamine.

[d] The value for leucine and isoleucine was obtained by dividing the total number of occurrences of either leucine or isoleucine by 2.

in an *average* protein is needed. Choice of such a protein is somewhat arbitrary. In this study, therefore, a composite "average" protein was computed in two different ways and compared [Table XVI (*18, 320, 381–387*)]. One procedure employed was to take whole plant and animal proteins from which were calculated the "type I average." A weighted average, animals: plants (3:1), was used to give a population of types like those in Table XIV, in which animal proteins are predominant. An alternate approach constituting the "type II average," was to take the average of the amino acid concentrations in 53 of the 57 proteins in Table XVI. The 53 proteins used for the calculation are those proteins for which compositional information is available. The rank order correlation coefficient of the two so-called "average proteins" was found to be 0.95; this coefficient signifies that the two methods lead to a similar "average protein" and lends support to this approach (*388*).

It is also possible to use rank order correlation coefficients to compare N-terminal frequency ranks and compositional frequency ranks for an indication of the randomness or nonrandomness of sequential arrangements. Complete randomness would be indicated by a coefficient of 1.00; complete nonrandomness would be indicated by a coefficient of −1.00. The actual results were coefficients of 0.80 and 0.87 when the N-terminal ranks were compared to compositional ranks for the "type I average" and "type II average" protein, respectively. Each of these

TABLE XVI

N-Terminal Frequency Ranks Compared to Compositional Ranks
of an "Average Protein"

Amino acid	"Average protein" type I[a] molar ratios	Rank for type I "average protein"	"Average protein" type II[b] molar ratios	Rank for type II "average protein"	N-Terminal frequency rank[c]
Glu[d,e]	9.26	1	8.20	2	4
Asp[f]	7.13	3	8.27	1	2
Gly	9.19	2	7.21	3	3
Arg	3.62	11	3.76	12	13
Lys	4.30	9	4.46	10	9.5
Ala	6.96	4	6.40	5	1
(Leu + Ileu)/2[g]	4.42	6.5	5.11	6.5	6
Pro	4.51	5	5.10	8	15.5
Val	4.26	10	4.68	9	9.5
Ser	4.38	8	7.19	4	6
Phe	2.72	13	3.35	14	9.5
Thr	3.53	12	4.35	11	13
Tyr	1.71	14	3.29	15	15.5
His	1.29	16	1.78	16	13
Met	1.27	17	1.13	18	17
Cys	1.33	15	3.39	13	9.5
Try	0.49	18	1.15	17	18

[a] The proteins in this study are primarily of animal origin although a smaller number are derived from plants. For comparison of the ranking of N-terminal amino acid residues with the ranking of residues in over-all compositional frequency, a protein typical of the proteins in Table XIV was sought. The type I average was obtained by taking a weighted average of whole animal and plant proteins of 3:1. These data were obtained from Block and Weiss (18).

[b] From average composition of 53 of the 57 proteins of Table XIV.

[c] Taken from Table XV.

[d] The first three letters of the amino acid are used as an abbreviation; Ileu signifies isoleucine.

[e] Includes glutamine.

[f] Includes asparagine.

[g] The sum of leucine and isoleucine values were taken and then divided by 2.

values indicates a high degree of randomness in N-terminal amino acids. Thus, within the sensitivity of this statistical approach, the amino acids in heterologous proteins appear to be N-terminal in proportion close to their compositional frequency in nature.

These results were rechecked by a second statistical method, which was proposed by Kendall (389). Kendall's method gave a coefficient of 0.64, which indicates significance at the 1% level for the hypothesis that amino acids in heterologous proteins are N-terminal in proportions close to their frequency in nature.

The relatively high randomness of amino acid residues in the N-terminal position of heterologous proteins does not of course indicate randomness in the interior or C-terminal residues. When the data on homologous proteins and the controversial data on C-termini were eliminated, the remaining information was insufficient for statistical treatment and consequently is not reported.

D. Quantitative Comparisons of Unfractionated Proteins for Specific Positions in the Chains

Quantitative sequential analyses afford comparisons of unfractionated proteins at a specific position in a protein, such as the N-terminus. In an attempt to evaluate the effect of hybridization on amino acid composition, the total, N-terminal and N-penultimate content of leucine and lysine in wheat, rye, and wheat-rye hybrid proteins were studied by a modified Edman procedure (390).

The results suggest that there is no relationship between the genotype and the leucine, N-terminal leucine, or N-penultimate leucine contents. On the other hand, the contents of lysine, N-terminal lysine, and N-penultimate lysine in the hybrid is intermediate between the two corresponding values in each case. More such data are needed to reveal whether some amino acids or some amino acids in some positions are most characteristic of the hereditary endowment.

Some interesting studies on unfractionated proteins of E. coli by Morowitz and co-workers compare the proportion of a given amino acid at the N-terminus with the proportion of that amino acid which follows Lys or Arg residues in the interior (391–393). Such studies suggest a convenient means for assaying the amino acid content of a protein at some particular position, which is made available to terminal assay methods by hydrolysis with proteases.

XII. Perspectives

This chapter and related reviews and books have surveyed protein systematics from a variety of perspectives (4–6, 8, 10–18, 55, 102, 104, 107, 178, 191, 278, 355, 394). In what follows, an attempt is made to evaluate critically some of the perspectives and principles that appear to be ready for such review.

A. Darwinian Considerations

A rudimentary, yet fundamental, premise in this field is based on the view that Darwinian evolution can be understood at the molecular level (*107*). Since protein molecules comprise the direct enzymatic control of metabolism in the cell, this is taken to mean that the molecule is fundamentally subject to variation and selection, as is the organism. Simply represented, this appears as shown in the accompanying scheme (XIII).

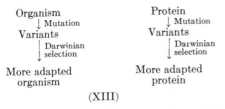

(XIII)

It is understood that mutation of molecular synthesis is under genic control, but the protein phenotypes are as yet much more suitable for structural study than DNA, which presumably orders the synthesis. Although there may be other departures from the normal in protein synthesis (Section X, B), only those which involve an alteration in genic control need be considered here. Any such mutation which confers a selective advantage upon the organism in which it occurs will be selected because it will survive in the lineal descendants of that organism. This mutual dependency thus involves an interweaving of evolution at the molecular and organismic levels.

B. MICROHETEROGENEITY

When we study protein molecules we are struck with the frequent familial clustering of types. Although this variation has been vexatious, it may well be that such variation is a crucial component in the evolutionary process which resulted in the existence and individuality of the protein chemist whose annoyance with this phenomenon has been a powerful stimulus to research in this field.

On this point rest several outlooks. Colvin and associates have reviewed the evidence and have concluded that many variations in protein molecules are inherent (*20*), rather than artifacts of purification, as has sometimes been suggested. One can add to their reasoning the fact that similar molecules which are however too small to be proteins, i.e., polypeptide antibiotics, also occur in families in which differences are obviously due to single variations in amino acid sequences (*19*). These cannot be ascribed to the processes of purification used. Likewise, it has been shown more recently that sibling hemoglobin molecules have few residue differences (*297*).

Despite these facts, there persists the notion that the conclusion of

Colvin and co-workers should be tempered because of the finding of instances of variations which occur during purification (21).

Some of the objection to the concept of natural heterogeneity of protein is raised in relation to statements defending the uniqueness of sequential arrangements as they have been determined in proteins. Analysis of the situation reveals that the two types of concept are not incompatible and that an assigned sequence need not be considered incorrect if the source material is not entirely homogeneous. At the biosynthetic level, families of protein molecules may be produced. By the time the protein is purified it is almost homogeneous, or at any rate much closer to homogeneity. Such relative homogeneity can be close enough to purity to permit determination of the dominant sequence without discordances being introduced in significant proportion. The obtaining of a relatively unique structure does not vitiate the likelihood of some heterogeneity in the purified or unpurified material, and likewise the evolutionary interpretation is not impaired by this kind of result.

C. Randomness

Quantitative evaluation of amino acid compositions of proteins by a special statistical device (355) has indicated a high degree of kinship by this criterion. On the other hand, the sequences of adjacent residues in proteins have been evaluated as indicating a high degree of randomness (15). A similar evaluation of the latter sort is presented in Table XVI, in which frequency of N-terminal type is compared with frequency of composition.

The tabulations of Yčas (15) and the proteins of Table XIV were deliberately selected on the basis of what is believed to be heterology. The many obvious stepwise differences in structure emphasized by this review are predominantly for homologous proteins. Evaluations of this sort very much depend upon whether one is dealing with homologous or heterologous proteins. Establishment of a sure criterion for distinguishing homologous comparisons from heterologous comparisons is therefore a major problem to be solved in this field. At the same time there can be little doubt that proteins which are assuredly homologous are very much alike in both composition and sequence. Preliminary evaluations lead to the inference that heterologous proteins may also be much alike in composition, but that they differ markedly in the sequences of their individual residues.

If this last relationship is a true one, many explanations are possible. For example, evolution many have allowed much randomization in sequence from a single or a few types of primordial protein, but little randomization in the proportions of amino acids. The feeding from metabolic pools of amino acids into synthesis of proteins could be more highly fixed. Perhaps, however, proteins began as many heterologous lines of macromolecules out of the same prebiological mixture of a fixed proportion of amino acids. This problem is one that is perhaps awaiting final definition rather than solution. There can be little question that more data and subsequent refinement of interpretation are needed in order to test these and other explanations. Further development of conceptualization may be necessary before we can hope to answer the first and most fundamental question: is there in an evolutionary context a different starting point for what we think of as homologous proteins and heterologous proteins?

D. STEPWISE VARIATION IN HOMOLOGOUS LINES

The total survey reveals that the variation between homologous protein molecules typically involves one to a few residues in a large molecule. This realization may contribute to understanding the wide spectrum of biological variation on the organismic level which is constructed on a relatively narrow spectrum of types of protein molecule. This narrowness of spectrum is consistent with the general picture of the "unity of biochemistry" (395).

The limited degree of variation of protein molecules in several mammals is illustrated in Table XVII, which includes many of the

TABLE XVII

INDEX OF SIMILARITY OF HOMOLOGOUS PEPTIDES OR PROTEINS
IN SEVERAL MAMMALS

Comparison of cow and	Number of peptides or protein used for comparison[a]	Total residues compared	Identical residues	Index of similarity[b]
Horse	5	89	87	0.98
Pig	6	136	127	0.94
Sheep	5	142	131	0.92

[a] The total sequences of oxytocin, vasopressin, intermedin (MSH), corticotropin (ACTH), hypertensinogen, and insulin were used in this analysis. The first 39 residues of ribonuclease and the heme decapeptide of cytochrome c were also included.

[b] Index of similarity is defined as the number of identical residues divided by the total number of amino acid residues.

comparative data on amino acid sequences of Sections V and VI. In this table, *indexes of similarities* of homologous proteins of four pairs of mammals were obtained by dividing the number of identical residues by the total number of amino acid residues compared. An index of 1.00 would signify complete identity of the proteins compared in the two organisms; an index of 0.0 would indicate that the amino acid sequences of the proteins were totally unlike. The results which range from 0.92 to 0.98 indicate that the homologous proteins in horse, cow, pig, and sheep are markedly similar.

Insofar as it is possible to summarize in a single sentence the inferences from studies of interspecific variations in sequence, one may again emphasize that the similarities are much greater than the differences (107).

E. Structural Bases for Biological Activity

A salient revision in thought relative to the structural basis of biological activity is the abandonment of the generalization that structures permitting activity are sharply specific (102). Instead, we can now recognize that one molecule may have several kinds of activity, as in oxytocin, which has also vasopressin activity (Section V, A), and in instances in which a homogeneous enzyme can catalyze several kinds of reaction (396). Also, it is clear that many closely related structures can have different degrees of the same activity, as in synthetic MSH peptides (14) and in strepogenins (397). Closely related structures with many sequences (including much of the active site) in common may have what we recognize as different activities, as in the case of chymotrypsin and trypsin (Section VI, B).

These relationships are consistent with the fundamental Darwinian interpretation and the concept that a degree of "sloppiness" in synthetic mechanisms permits the effective spontaneous experiments of the evolutionary process. From this point of view, a so-called perfection in the molecular copying process would have served to halt evolution entirely (Section XII, A).

At first analysis, one may wonder how the vast variety of organisms can stem from this newly recognized narrow spectrum of types of protein molecule. The answer may well be that interactions of the structures within the range of variation of molecule permits an exponentially larger diversity.

Notes Added in Proof

A number of newer advances in knowledge of sequences in proteins have been recorded. Several publications of primary interest to comparative biochemistry are cited in this section.

ACTINOMYCINS (Sections IV and X, A)

The actinomycins as a family of decapeptide antibiotics produced by *Streptomyces* are growing in recognition. Such molecules vary solely in their amino acid constituents; two pentapeptide chains are bound by amide linkage to an invariable chromophore, a phenoxazinone derivative. The recent surge of interest in these antibiotics has led to the demonstration of some 35 members of this molecular family (*398, 399*). A single species of bacterium, such as *Streptomyces chrysomallus*, produces a mixture of actinomycins which vary at the "D-valine/D-alloisoleucine" site of the peptide. Addition of certain amino acids, such as sarcosine or isoleucine, to the culture medium results in biosynthesis of biologically active natural and unnatural actinomycins. Approximately ten unnatural actinomycins have been induced and characterized (*399*).

HORMONES (Sections V, A, B, and C)

In the course of chemical synthesis of peptide hormones, Katsoyannis and du Vigneaud prepared a chemical hybrid of oxytocin and vasopressin (*400*). This peptide, *arginine-vasotocin,* contains the rings of oxytocin and the side chain of vasopressin. More recently, Acher and colleagues characterized a pituitary hormone from the frog, *Rana esculenta,* with the amino acid composition and pharmacological activity of the synthetic vasotocin (*401*).

Two other milestones in research on pituitary hormones were the determination of the total sequence of bovine ACTH (*402*) and of equine intermedin (*403*). It is notable that the intermedin isolated from the posterior lobes of horse pituitary gland is identical to the homologous α-hormone of cow and pig.

ENZYMES (Sections VI, A and B)

Determination of amino acid sequences in the vicinity of active sites continues to be an intriguing area for research. An element of controversy regarding the active site of phosphoglucomutase has been introduced by Milstein and Sanger (*404;* cf. *91*). These authors present data from which the inference can be drawn that the sequence of amino acid residues surrounding the serine phosphate residue includes two unidentified neutral amino acids on the N-terminal side, and histidine followed by an acidic amino acid on the C-terminal side. The suggested proximity of serine and histidine is notable since for some time the latter amino acid has been implicated in esterase activity, but in a less pointed manner (*101*). Other recent studies on the sequences of amino acids at the active sites of enzymes involve the following: (*a*) an endopeptidase from *Bacillus subtilis* (*405*); (*b*) pseudocholinesterase (*406*); and (*c*) human muscle phosphorylase (*407*). The last mentioned peptide is identical in sequence to a hexapeptide similarly prepared from the homologous rabbit muscle enzyme (*407*).

Research on the structure of chymotrypsin and trypsin continues actively. Considerable portions of the primary structure of trypsin (*408–410*) and chymotrypsin (*411–413*) have now been elucidated; complete assignment of residues in these enzymes is now in sight.

HEMOGLOBINS (Sections VIII, D, and XII, A)

The hemoglobins continue to be a favorite topic for comparative biochemists. Recently, great strides have been made toward determination of the complete structure of normal adult hemoglobin (*414–419*). The application of X-ray crystallographic techniques (*417, 418*) promises to be of much value in analysis of the primary structure of proteins. One interesting observation is the notable similarity of parts of the α- and β-chains of hemoglobin (*416*); a second is the correspondence of sequences in hemoglobin and in the muscle protein, myoglobin (*417*). Such findings are subject to Darwinian interpretations (*416, 420, 421*).

Research on the abnormal human hemoglobins has also been prolific (*422–425*). New variants of hemoglobin such as hemoglobin A_2' (*423*), hemoglobin X (*424*), and Norfolk hemoglobin (*425*) show discrete simple differences from normal adult hemoglobin A. For example, there is a substitution of aspartic acid (Norfolk hemoglobin) for glycine (hemoglobin A) at position N-57 (*425*). As a result of further genetic analysis, Hill and co-workers reported that it is not necessary to assume that hemoglobins S and G are controlled by nonallelic genes (*422*).

TOBACCO MOSAIC VIRUS PROTEIN (Sections V, B; IX, C; and X, D)

The recent determination of the total amino acid sequence of tobacco mosaic virus protein (158 residues) stands out as a triumph in research on protein structure (*426–427*). Detailed knowledge of the primary structure of this protein permits definitive study of the relationship between stepwise mutation and protein structure and, indeed, such studies are underway (*426–428*). The N-acetyl terminus first discovered by Narita in TMV protein (Section IX, C) has since been found in pig-α intermedin, ovalbumin (*429, 430*), and fibrin (*431*); these are N-acetyl-Ser-Tyr-, N-acetyl-Gly-Ser-, and N-acetyl-Thr-, respectively.

PERSPECTIVES (Section XII)

Needleman *et al.* have statistically analyzed positional relationships of amino acid residue types in "biologically active" as distinct from "structural" proteins (*432*). One would like to see more of the primary data, including the selection of proteins. These authors however state that: "One may further conclude that a natural barrier appears to exist for the occurrence of certain amino acid sequences in peptides." This conclusion is in accord with the fundamental evolutionary concept of self-directing internal forces, here applied at the molecular level (*433*). Although Needleman *et al.* had more data available to them than was available to theoretical comparative biochemists who had published similar studies earlier, it will be of interest to observe the mathematically based techniques and conclusions yet to come. An accurate evaluation of the extent and precise nature of internal limitations which have existed on the evolutionary highway looms continually larger as a fundamental problem approachable by studies of sequence of units in biomacromolecules.

ACKNOWLEDGMENT

The library research necessary for this study was supported financially by Grant No. RG-4666 of the National Institutes of Health, United States Public Health Service for studies in Protein Genealogy, and by Grant No. B-5744 of the National Science Foundation. Aid in sifting and examining the literature in detail was provided by Mrs. Elizabeth Couey, Mrs. Gail Summers, Mrs. Mary Lou Kovacic, and Mrs. Patricia Malphurs, to whom the authors express their thanks.

References

1. S. W. Fox and K. Harada, *J. Am. Chem. Soc.* **82**, 3745 (1960).

2. S. W. Fox, *Advances in Protein Chem.* **2**, 155 (1945).

3. F. Sanger, *Biochem. J.* **39**, 507 (1945).

4. F. Sanger, *Advances in Protein Chem.* **7**, 1 (1952).

5. C. B. Anfinsen and R. R. Redfield, *Advances in Protein Chem.* **11**, 1 (1956).

6. H. Fraenkel-Conrat, *Ann. Rev. Biochem.* **25**, 291 (1956).

7. S. Brenner, *Proc. Natl. Acad. Sci. U. S.* **43**, 687 (1957).

8. C. H. Li, *Advances in Protein Chem.* **12**, 269 (1957).

9. F. Sorm, B. Keil, V. Holeysovsky, V. Knesslova, V. Kostka, P. Mäsiar, B. Meloun, O. Mikes, V. Tomasek, and J. Vanecek, *Chem. listy* **51**, 1171 (1957).

10. D. Steinberg and E. Mihalyi, *Ann. Rev. Biochem.* **26**, 373 (1957).

11. O. K. Behrens and W. W. Bromer, *Ann. Rev. Biochem.* **27**, 57 (1958).

12. G. H. Dixon, H. Neurath, and J. Pechere, *Ann. Rev. Biochem.* **27**, 489 (1958).

13. A. Neuberger, ed., "Symposium on Protein Structure." Wiley, New York, 1958.

14. R. Schwyzer, *Chimia* (*Switz.*) **12**, 53 (1958).

15. M. Yčas, *in* "Symposium on Information Theory in Biology" (H. P. Yockey *et al.*, eds.), p. 70. Pergamon, New York, 1958.

16. R. L. Hill, J. R. Kimmel, and E. L. Smith, *Ann. Rev. Biochem.* **28**, 97 (1959).

17. H. Tuppy, *Naturwissenschaften* **46**, 35 (1959).
18. R. J. Block and K. W. Weiss, "Amino Acid Handbook." Charles C Thomas, Springfield, Illinois, 1956.
19. S. W. Fox, *Am. Naturalist* **87**, 253 (1953).
20. J. R. Colvin, D. B. Smith, and W. H. Cook, *Chem. Revs.* **54**, 687 (1954).
21. M. Vaughan and D. Steinberg, *Advances in Protein Chem.* **14**, 115 (1959).
22. M. Brenner, *J. Cellular Comp. Physiol.* **54**, Suppl. 1, 221 (1959).
23. R. L. M. Synge, *Biochem. J.* **39**, 363 (1945).
24. A. R. Battersby and L. C. Craig, *J. Am. Chem. Soc.* **73**, 1887 (1951).
25. E. B. Chain, *Ann. Rev. Biochem.* **27**, 167 (1958).
26. E. P. Abraham, "Biochemistry of Some Peptide and Steroid Antibiotics." Wiley, New York, 1957.
27. H. Brockmann and P. Boldt, *Naturwissenschaften* **46**, 262 (1959).
28. O. L. Shotwell, F. H. Stodola, W. R. Michael, L. A. Lindenfelser, R. G. Dworschack, and T. G. Pridham, *J. Am. Chem. Soc.* **80**, 3912 (1958).
29. V. du Vigneaud, *Harvey Lectures, 1954–1955* **50**, 1 (1956).
30. P. G. Katsoyannis, D. T. Gish, and V. du Vigneaud, *J. Am. Chem. Soc.* **79**, 4516 (1957).
31. E. A. Popenoe, H. C. Lawler, and V. du Vigneaud, *J. Am. Chem. Soc.* **74**, 3713 (1952).
32. R. Acher, J. Chauvet, and C. Fromageot, *Biochim. et Biophys. Acta* **9**, 471 (1952).
33. J. G. Pierce, S. Gordon, and V. du Vigneaud, *J. Biol. Chem.* **199**, 929 (1952).
34. H. Tuppy and H. Michl, *Monatsh. Chem.* **84**, 1011 (1953).
35. A. Light and V. du Vigneaud, *Proc. Soc. Exptl. Biol. Med.* **98**, 692 (1958).
36. R. Acher, J. Chauvet, and M. T. Lenci, *Biochim. et Biophys. Acta* **31**, 545 (1959).
37. M. Bodánszky and V. du Vigneaud, *J. Am. Chem. Soc.* **81**, 1258 (1959).
38. J. I. Harris, *Biochem. J.* **71**, 451 (1959).
39. H. Fraenkel-Conrat and K. Narita, *in* "Symposium on Protein Structure" (A. Neuberger, ed.), p. 249. Wiley, New York, 1958.
40. H. B. F. Dixon, *Biochem. J.* **62**, 25P (1956).
41. I. I. Geschwind, C. H. Li, and L. Barnafi, *J. Am. Chem. Soc.* **78**, 4494 (1956).
42. J. I. Harris and A. B. Lerner, *Nature* **179**, 1346 (1957).
43. I. I. Geschwind, C. H. Li, and L. Barnafi, *J. Am. Chem. Soc.* **79**, 6394 (1957).
44. J. I. Harris and P. Roos, *Biochem. J.* **71**, 434 (1959).
45. C. H. Li, *Advances in Protein Chem.* **11**, 101 (1956).
46. P. H. Bell, *J. Am. Chem. Soc.* **76**, 5565 (1954).
47. C. H. Li, I. I. Geschwind, R. D. Cole, I. D. Raacke, J. I. Harris, and J. S. Dixon, *Nature* **176**, 687 (1955).
48. W. F. White and W. A. Landmann, *J. Am. Chem. Soc.* **77**, 1711 (1955).
49. R. G. Shepherd, S. D. Willson, K. S. Howard, P. H. Bell, D. S. Davies, S. B. Davis, E. A. Eigner, and N. E. Shakespeare, *J. Am. Chem. Soc.* **78**, 5067 (1956).
50. C. H. Li, J. S. Dixon, and D. Chung, *J. Am. Chem. Soc.* **80**, 2587 (1958).
51. C. H. Li, *in* "Symposium on Protein Structure" (A. Neuberger, ed.), p. 302. Wiley, New York, (1958).
52. J. Leonis, C. H. Li, and D. Chung, *J. Am. Chem. Soc.* **81**, 419 (1959).
53. R. J. Block, *Yale J. Biol. and Med.* **7**, 235 (1935).
54. T. H. Lee, A. B. Lerner, V. Buettner-Janusch, *J. Am. Chem. Soc.* **81**, 6084 (1959).
55. C. H. Li, *Advances in Protein Chem.* **12**, 269 (1957).

56. C. H. Li, *J. Biol. Chem.* **229,** 157 (1957).
57. C. H. Li and J. T. Cummins, *J. Biol. Chem.* **233,** 73 (1958).
58. R. D. Cole, I. I. Geschwind, and C. H. Li, *J. Biol. Chem.* **224,** 399 (1957).
59. C. H. Li, *Federation Proc.* **16,** 775 (1957).
60. F. Heijkenskvöld, *Acta Chem. Scand.* **12,** 132 (1958).
61. A. J. Parcells and C. H. Li, *J. Biol. Chem.* **233,** 1140 (1958).
62. C. H. Li, A. J. Parcells, and H. Papkoff, *J. Biol. Chem.* **233,** 1143 (1958).
63. H. Papkoff and C. H. Li, *Biochim. et Biophys. Acta* **29,** 145 (1958).
64. H. Papkoff, R. G. Moudgal, and C. H. Li, *Federation Proc.* **19,** 157 (1960).
65. G. Schramm, *Ann. Rev. Biochem.* **27,** 101 (1958).
66. H. Fraenkel-Conrat and L. K. Ramachandran, *Advances in Protein Chem.* **14,** 175 (1959).
67. K. Narita, *Chem. and Chem. Ind.* (*Japan*) **12,** 193 (1959).
68. T. Deutsch, *Magyar Kém. Folyóirat* **61,** 135 (1955); *Chem. Abstr.* **52,** 8251 (1958).
69. E. O. P. Thompson, *J. Biol. Chem.* **208,** 565 (1954).
70. J. I. Harris, F. Sanger, and M. A. Naughton, *Arch. Biochem. Biophys.* **65,** 427 (1956).
71. F. M. Bumpus and I. H. Page, *Science* **119,** 849 (1954).
72. K. E. Lentz, L. T. Skeggs, Jr., K. R. Woods, J. R. Kahn, and N. P. Shumway, *J. Exptl. Med.* **104,** 183 (1956).
73. D. F. Elliott and W. S. Peart, *Biochem. J.* **65,** 246 (1957).
74. L. T. Skeggs, Jr., J. R. Kahn, K. E. Lentz, N. P. Shumway, *J. Exptl. Med.* **106,** 439 (1957).
75. K. Harada and S. W. Fox, *J. Am. Chem. Soc.* **80,** 2694 (1958).
76. F. Sanger, *Biochem. J.* **45,** 563 (1949).
77. J. Lens, *Biochim. et Biophys. Acta* **3,** 367 (1949).
78. C. Fromageot, M. Jutisz, D. Meyer, and L. Penasse, *Biochim. et Biophys. Acta* **6,** 283 (1950).
79. F. Sanger and H. Tuppy, *Biochem. J.* **49,** 463, 481 (1951).
80. J. I. Harris, *J. Am. Chem. Soc.* **74,** 2944 (1952).
81. H. Tuppy, *Monatsh. Chem.* **84,** 996 (1953).
82. H. Fraenkel-Conrat, *J. Am. Chem. Soc.* **76,** 3606 (1954).
83. F. Sanger, E. O. P. Thompson, and R. Kitai, *Biochem. J.* **59,** 509 (1955).
84. H. Brown, F. Sanger, and R. Kitai, *Biochem. J.* **60,** 1955 (1956).
85. Y. Ishihara, T. Saito, Y. Ito, and M. Fujino, *Nature* **181,** 1468 (1958).
86. V. M. Ingram, *Natl. Acad. Sci.—Natl. Research Council Publ.* **557** (1958).
87. J. A. Cohen, R. A. Oosterbaan, H. S. Jansz, and F. Berends, *J. Cellular Comp. Physiol.* **54,** Suppl. 1, 231 (1959).
88a. N. K. Schaffer, S. Harshman, R. R. Engle, and R. W. Drisko, *Federation Proc.* **14,** 275 (1955).
88b. J. A. Cohen, R. A. Oosterbaan, M. G. P. J. Warringa, and H. S. Jansz, *Discussions Faraday Soc.* **20,** 114 (1955).
89. N. K. Schaffer, S. Harshman, and R. R. Engle, *J. Biol. Chem.* **214,** 799 (1955).
90. F. Turba and G. Grundlach, *Biochem. Z.* **327,** 186 (1955).
91. D. E. Koshland and M. J. Erwin, *J. Am. Chem. Soc.* **79,** 2657 (1957).
92. G. H. Dixon, D. L. Kauffman, and H. Neurath, *J. Biol. Chem.* **233,** 1373 (1958).
93. J. A. Gladner and K. Laki, *J. Am. Chem. Soc.* **80,** 1263 (1958).
94. R. A. Oosterbaan and M. E. van Adrichem, *Biochim. et Biophys. Acta* **27,** 423 (1958).

95. R. A. Oosterbaan, P. Kunst, J. van Rotterdam, and J. A. Cohen, *Biochim. et Biophys. Acta* **27**, 556 (1958).
96. N. K. Shaffer, R. P. Lang, L. Simet, and R. W. Drisko, *J. Biol. Chem.* **230**, 185 (1958).
97. B. S. Hartley, M. A. Naughton, and F. Sanger, *Biochim. et Biophys. Acta* **34**, 243 (1959).
98. H. S. Jansz, C. H. Posthumus, and J. A. Cohen, *Biochim. et Biophys. Acta* **33**, 387, 396 (1959).
99. H. S. Jansz, D. Brons, and M. G. P. J. Warringa, *Biochim. et Biophys. Acta* **34**, 573 (1959).
100. E. H. Fischer, D. J. Graves, E. R. S. Crittenden, and E. G. Krebs, *J. Biol. Chem.* **234**, 1698 (1959).
101. M. L. Bender, *Chem. Revs.* **60**, 53 (1960).
102. S. W. Fox and J. F. Foster, "Introduction to Protein Chemistry." Wiley, New York, 1957.
103. G. E. Perlmann, *Advances in Protein Chem.* **10**, 1 (1955).
104. B. Keil, F. Sorm, V. Holeysovsky, V. Kostka, B. Meloun, O. Mikes, V. Tomasek, and J. Vanecek, *Collection Czech. Chem. Communs.* **24**, 3491 (1959).
105. B. Keil, F. Sorm, B. Meloun, J. Vanecek, O. Mikes, and V. Holeysovsky, *Proc. 4th Intern. Congr. Biochem., Vienna*, **15**, 20 (1960).
106. T. L. Hurst and S. W. Fox, *Arch. Biochem. Biophys.* **63**, 352 (1956).
107. S. W. Fox, *Am. Scientist* **44**, 347 (1956).
108. G. Kalnitsky and E. E. Anderson, *Biochim. et Biophys. Acta* **16**, 302 (1955).
109. C. B. Anfinsen, *Biochim. et Biophys. Acta* **17**, 593 (1955).
110. C. H. W. Hirs, S. Moore, and W. H. Stein, *J. Biol. Chem.* **219**, 623 (1956).
111. R. R. Redfield and C. B. Anfinsen, *J. Biol. Chem.* **221**, 385 (1956).
112. C. H. W. Hirs, *Federation Proc.* **16**, 196 (1957).
113. C. B. Anfinsen, *Federation Proc.* **16**, 783 (1957).
114. C. H. W. Hirs, W. H. Stein, and S. Moore, *in* "Symposium on Protein Structure" (A. Neuberger, ed.), p. 211. Wiley, New York, 1958.
115. C. B. Anfinsen, *in* "Symposium on Protein Structure" (A. Neuberger, ed.), p. 223. Wiley, New York, 1958.
116. C. H. W. Hirs, *J. Biol. Chem.* **235**, 625 (1960).
117. C. H. W. Hirs, S. Moore, and W. H. Stein, *J. Biol. Chem.* **235**, 633 (1960).
118. D. H. Spackman, W. H. Stein, and S. Moore, *J. Biol. Chem.* **235**, 648 (1960).
119. S. E. G. Aqvist and C. B. Anfinsen, *J. Biol. Chem.* **234**, 1112 (1959).
120. C. B. Anfinsen, S. E. Aqvist, J. P. Cooke, and B. Jönsson, *J. Biol. Chem.* **234**, 1118 (1959).
121. C. B. Anfinsen, *J. Cellular Comp. Physiol.* **54**, Suppl. 1, 215 (1959).
122. A. J. P. Martin and R. R. Porter, *Biochem. J.* **49**, 215 (1951).
123. C. H. W. Hirs, S. Moore, and W. H. Stein, *J. Biol. Chem.* **200**, 493 (1953).
124. A. A. Hakim, *Arch. Biochem. Biophys.* **70**, 591 (1957).
125. N. Muić, A. Meniga, and M. Fleš, *Arch. Biochem. Biophys.* **77**, 20 (1958).
126. A. R. Thompson, *Nature* **169**, 495 (1952).
127. W. A. Schroeder, *J. Am. Chem. Soc.* **74**, 281, 5118 (1952).
128. J. I. Harris, *J. Am. Chem. Soc.* **74**, 2944 (1952).
129. F. C. Green and L. M. Kay, *Anal. Chem.* **24**, 726 (1952).
130. R. Acher, J. Thaureaux, C. Crocker, M. Jutisz, and C. Fromageot, *Biochim. et Biophys. Acta* **9**, 339 (1952).
131. W. A. Landmann, M. P. Drake, and J. Dillaha, *J. Am. Chem. Soc.* **75**, 3638 (1953).

132. H. Fraenkel-Conrat, *J. Am. Chem. Soc.* **76**, 3606 (1954).
133. D. De Fontaine and S. W. Fox, *J. Am. Chem. Soc.* **76**, 3701 (1954).
134. P. Jollès and C. Fromageot, *Biochim. et Biophys. Acta* **14**, 228 (1954).
135. E. L. Smith, J. R. Kimmel, D. M. Brown, and E. O. P. Thompson, *J. Biol. Chem.* **215**, 67 (1955).
136. A. R. Thompson, *Biochem. J.* **61**, 253 (1955).
137. P. Jollès, J. Jolles-Thaureaux, and C. Fromageot, *in* "Symposium on Protein Structure" (A. Neuberger ed.), p. 277. Wiley, New York, 1958.
138. T. Ando, H. Fujioka, and Y. Kawanishi, *Biochim. et Biophys. Acta* **31**, 553 (1959).
139. P. Jollès and M. Ledieu, *Biochim. et Biophys. Acta* **36**, 284 (1959).
140. F. Tietze, *Arch. Biochem. Biophys.* **87**, 73 (1960).
141. P. Jolles and M. Ledieu, *Biochim. et Biophys. Acta* **31**, 100 (1959).
142. G. Koch and W. J. Dreyer, *Virology* **6**, 291 (1958).
143. F. M. Burnet, "Principles of Animal Virology," p. 443. Academic Press, New York, 1955.
144. S. Akabori and T. Ikenaka, *J. Biochem. (Tokyo)* **42**, 603 (1955).
145. K. Sugae, *J. Biochem. (Tokyo)* **47**, 170 (1960).
146. K. Narita and S. Akabori, *J. Biochem. (Tokyo)* **46**, 91 (1959).
147. A. Tsugita, *J. Biochem. (Tokyo)* **46**, 583 (1959).
148. K. Sugae and Y. Honda, *J. Biochem. (Tokyo)* **47**, 307 (1960).
149. A. Yoshida and T. Tobita, *Biochim. et Biophys. Acta* **37**, 513 (1960).
150. G. T. Cori, M. W. Slein, and C. F. Cori, *J. Biol. Chem.* **173**, 605 (1948).
151. T. Bücher and K. H. Garbade, *Biochim. et Biophys. Acta* **8**, 220 (1952).
152. S. F. Velick and S. Udenfriend, *J. Biol. Chem.* **203**, 575 (1953).
153. T. Dévényi, B. Szorényi, and M. Sajgó, *Magyar Kém. Folyóirat* **62**, 377 (1956); *Chem. Abstr.* **52**, 8230 (1958).
154. K. Titani, H. Ishikura, and S. Minakami, *J. Biochem. (Tokyo)* **44**, 499 (1957).
155. K. Titani, H. Ishikura, and S. Minakami, *J. Biochem. (Tokyo)* **46**, 151 (1959).
156. E. Margoliash, *Nature* **175**, 293 (1955).
157. H. Matsubara, B. Hagihara, T. Horio, and K. Okunuki, *Nature* **179**, 250 (1957).
158. H. Tuppy and G. Bodo, *Monatsh. Chem.* **85**, 1182 (1954).
159. H. Tuppy and K. Dus, *Monatsh. Chem.* **89**, 407 (1958).
160. H. Tuppy, *Z. Naturforsch.* **12b**, 784 (1957).
161. H. Tuppy, *in* "Symposium on Protein Structure" (A. Neuberger, ed.), p. 66. Wiley, New York, 1958.
162. S. Paleus and H. Tuppy, *Acta Chem. Scand.* **13**, 641 (1959).
163. E. Margoliash, N. Frohwirt, and E. Wiener, *Biochem. J.* **71**, 559 (1959).
164. A. Ehrenberg and H. Theorell, *Acta Chem. Scand.* **9**, 1193 (1955).
165a. R. Nunnikhoven, *Biochim. et Biophys. Acta* **28**, 108 (1958).
165b. J. C. Kendrew, R. G. Parrish, J. R. Marrack, and E. S. Orlans, *Nature* **174**, 946 (1954).
166. R. R. Porter and F. Sanger, *Biochem. J.* **42**, 287 (1948).
167. K. Schmid, *Nature* **163**, 482 (1949).
168. J. R. Holleman and G. Biserte, *Biochim. et Biophys. Acta* **33**, 143 (1959).
169. N. M. Rumen, *Acta Chem. Scand.* **13**, 1542 (1959).
170. V. Tomasek, V. Knesslova, and F. Sorm, *Proc. 4th Intern. Congr. Biochem. Vienna* **15**, 21 (1960).
171. K. Bailey and J. C. Rüegg, *Biochim. et Biophys. Acta* **38**, 239 (1960).
172. Jen Mei-Hsuan and Tsao Tien-Chin, *Sci. Sinica (Peking)* **6**, 317 (1957).

173. R. H. Locker, *Biochim. et Biophys. Acta* **14**, 533 (1954).

174. D. R. Kominz, F. Saad, J. A. Gladner, and K. Laki, *Arch. Biochem. Biophys.* **70**, 16 (1958).

175. Jen Mei-Hsuan, Wen Hsiao-Yao, and Niu Ching-I, *Acta Biochim. Sinica (Peking)* **1**, 167 (1958).

176. F. Saad, D. R. Kominz, and K. Laki, *J. Biol. Chem.* **234**, 551 (1959).

177. G. H. Nuttall, "Blood Immunity and Blood Relationship." Cambridge Univ. Press, London and New York, 1904.

178. K. Landsteiner, "The Specificity of Serological Reactions," 2nd ed. Harvard Univ. Press, Cambridge, Mass., 1946.

179. K. Landsteiner and J. van der Sheer, *J. Exptl. Med.* **71**, 445 (1940).

180. C. T. Wemyss, Jr., *Zoologica* **38**, 173 (1953).

181. L. K. Pauly and H. R. Wolfe, *Zoologica* **42**, 159 (1957).

182. A. A. Boyden and D. G. Gemeroy, *Zoologica* **35**, 145 (1950).

183. R. J. De Falco, *Biol. Bull.* **83**, 205 (1942).

184. D. Mainardi, *Rend. ist. lombardo sci.*, Pt. I **92b**, 180 (1957); *Chem. Abstr.* **53**, 6381 (1959).

185. D. G. Gemeroy, *Zoologica* **28**, 109 (1943).

186. C. A. Leone, *Biol. Bull.* **93**, 64 (1947).

187. C. A. Leone, *Biol. Bull.* **98**, 122 (1950).

188. J. B. Loefer, R. D. Owen, and E. Christensen, *J. Protozool.* **5**, 209 (1958).

189. P. G. H. Gell, J. G. Hawkes, and S. T. C. Wright, *Proc. Roy. Soc.* **B151**, 364 (1960).

190. A. A. Boyden, *in* "Serological and Biochemical Comparisons of Proteins" (W. H. Cole, ed.), p. 3. Rutgers Univ. Press, New Brunswick, N. J., 1958.

191. A. A. Boyden, "The Measurement and Significance of Serological Correspondence among Proteins," p. 74. Rutgers Univ. Press, New Brunswick, N. J., 1954.

192. J. B. Baumann-Grace and J. Tomcsik, *J. Gen. Microbiol.* **17**, 227 (1957).

193. H. G. Aach, *Z. Naturforsch.* **12b**, 614 (1957).

194. M. J. Crumpton and D. A. L. Davies, *Nature* **180**, 863 (1957).

195. L. LeMinor and H. Darrasse, *Ann. inst. Pasteur* **95**, 112 (1958).

196. R. Sakuzaki and S. Mamioka, *J. Exptl. Med.* **28**, 85 (1958).

197. L. H. Hyman "The Invertebrates," Vol. II, p. 4. McGraw-Hill, New York, 1951.

198. H. E. Schultze, *Clin. Chim. Acta* **3**, 24 (1958).

199. M. D. Poulik and O. Smithies, *Biochem. J.* **68**, 636 (1958).

200. N. R. Hansl, *J. Am. Chem. Soc.* **79**, 1511 (1957).

201. W. G. Glenn, *in* "Serological and Biochemical Comparisons of Proteins" (W. H. Cole, ed.), p. 71. Rutgers Univ. Press, New Brunswick, N. J., 1958.

202. F. Haurowitz, *in* "Serological and Biochemical Comparisons of Proteins" (W. H. Cole, ed.), p. 113. Rutgers Univ. Press, New Brunswick, N. J., 1958.

203. J. A. Moore, *Publ. Am. Assoc. Advance. Sci.* **50** (1957).

204. J. E. Cushing and D. H. Campbell, "Principles of Immunology." McGraw-Hill, New York, 1957.

205. P. Grabar, *Advances in Protein Chem.* **13**, 1 (1958).

206. H. Peeters, ed., "Protides of the Biological Fluids." Elsevier, Amsterdam, 1959.

207. M. Bier, ed., "Electrophoresis: Theory, Methods and Applications." Academic Press, New York, 1959.

208. R. L. Engle, Jr., K. R. Woods, E. C. Paulsen, and J. H. Pert, *Proc. Soc. Exptl. Biol. Med.* **98**, 905 (1958).

209. G. Zweig and J. W. Crenshaw, *Science* **126**, 1065 (1957).

210. E. Frieden, A. E. Herner, L. Fish, and E. J. C. Lewis, *Science* **126,** 559 (1957).
211. H. E. Sutton, J. V. Neel, G. Binson, and W. W. Zuelzer, *Nature* **178,** 1287 (1956).
212. G. C. Ashton, *Nature* **180,** 917 (1957).
213. A. G. Bearn and E. C. Franklin, *Science* **128,** 596 (1958).
214. O. Smithies, *Nature* **181,** 1203 (1958).
215. E. L. Durrum, *Ann. Rev. Med.* **9,** 451 (1958).
216. R. A. Kekwick, *Advances in Protein Chem.* **14,** 231 (1959).
217. R. L. Engle, Jr., and K. R. Woods, *in* "The Plasma Proteins" (F. Putnam, ed.), Vol. II, p. 184. Academic Press, New York, 1960.
218. M. L. Johnson and M. J. Wicks, *Systematic Zool.* **8,** 88 (1959).
219. E. T. Reichert and A. P. Brown, *Carnegie Inst. Wash. Publ.* **116** (1909).
220. S. Kon, *Seibutsu Butsuri Kagaku* **2,** 199 (1955); *Chem. Abstr.* **52,** 12127 (1958).
221. M. Bloch and R. Gavidia, *Arch. col. méd. El Salvador* **9,** 19 (1956); *Chem. Abstr.* **51,** 10628 (1957).
222. W. Bielawski, *Acta Biochim. Polon.* **2,** 409 (1955); *Chem. Abstr.* **51,** 13984 (1957).
223. O. L. N. Montiel, *Acta Cien. Venezolana* **8,** 37 (1957); *Chem. Abstr.* **51,** 14059 (1957).
224. M. M. Pokhno, *Vrachebnoe Delo* No. 5, 531 (1957); *Chem. Abstr.* **51,** 15736 (1957).
225. M. V. Nunez, *Actas y trabajos congr. peruano quím 4th Congr.* p. 294 (1953); *Chem. Abstr.* **51,** 4527 (1957).
226. J. Radl, Z. Kraus, and M. Tousek, *Dermatol. Wochschr.* **135,** 609 (1957); *Chem. Abstr.* **52,** 11244 (1958).
227. L. P. Matias, *Bol. soc. quím. Peru* **22,** 103 (1956); *Chem. Abstr.* **51,** 2970 (1957).
228. T. Orlowski and B. Kleczkowski, *Pol. Arch. Med. Wewnet.* **24,** 63 (1954); *Chem. Abstr.* **51,** 5240 (1957).
229. F. A. Zubieta and J. M. C. Rio, *Anales fac. med. Univ. nacl. mayor San Marcos Lima* **37,** 243 (1954); *Chem. Abstr.* **51,** 16786 (1957).
230. A. M. Zerman and F. Franca, *Giorn. gerontol.* **4,** 519 (1956); *Chem. Abstr.* **51,** 12284 (1957).
231. W. Tangheroni and R. Bartalena, *Minerva pediat.* **7,** 606 (1955); *Chem. Abstr.* **50,** 2803 (1956).
232. M. Real and J. I. Routh, *Proc. Iowa Acad. Sci.* **64,** 252 (1957).
233. A. Cutroneo, D. Pustorino, and I. Liotta, *Lattante* **27,** 498; 554 (1956); *Chem. Abstr.* **51,** 3788 (1957).
234. G. Franco and E. Tapparelli, *Riv. ostet. e ginecol. pratica* **38,** 208 (1956); *Chem. Abstr.* **51,** 15743 (1957).
235. M. Maneschi, F. Rio, and D. Lucarelli, *Minerva ginecol.* **9,** 468, 508 (1957); *Chem. Abstr.* **51,** 16809 (1957).
236. C. L. Prosser, "Comparative Animal Physiology." Saunders, Philadelphia, 1950.
237. Y. Tokuzi, *Japan. J. Bacteriol.* **10,** 545 (1955).
238. B. L. Antonaci and G. Macagnino, *Monit. zool. ital.* **65,** 19 (1957); *Chem. Abstr.* **52,** 20541 (1958).
239. K. F. Sorvachev, *Biokhimiya* **22,** 872 (1957).
240. A. G. Mulgaonkar and A. Sreenivasan, *Proc. Soc. Exptl. Biol. Med.* **98,** 652 (1958).

241. J. Nöcker, *Experientia* **12**, Suppl. **4**, 188 (1956); *Chem. Abstr.* **51**, 13119 (1957).

242. C. Gyllenswärd and B. Josephson, *Scand. J. Clin. & Lab. Invest.* **9**, 29 (1957); *Chem. Abstr.* **52**, 3966 (1958).

243. W. Vocke, *Klin. Wochschr.* **34**, 591 (1956).

244. C. Orlandi, *Riv. ital. ginecol.* **40**, 110 (1957); *Chem. Abstr.* **51**, 15742 (1957).

245. F. A. Chirkin, *Trudy Buryat.-Mongol. Zoovet. Inst.* No. 10, 117 (1956); *Chem. Abstr.* **52**, 17455 (1958).

246. K. Sumiyoshi, *Nippon Naikagakkai Zasshi* **45**, 1315 (1957); *Chem. Abstr.* **52**, 1398 (1958).

247. H. M. Rawnsley, V. L. Yonan, and J. G. Reinhold, *Science* **123**, 991 (1956).

248. F. D. Schofield, *W. African J. Biol. Chem.* **1**, 44 (1957); *Chem. Abstr.* **52**, 3069 (1958).

249. R. J. Henry, O. J. Golub, and C. Sobel, *Clin. Chem.* **3**, 49 (1957).

250. F. W. Sunderman, Jr., and F. W. Sunderman, *Am. J. Clin. Pathol.* **27**, 125 (1957).

251. G. J. Thorbecke, H. A. Gordon, B. Wostman, M. Wagner, and J. A. Reyniers, *J. Infectious Diseases* **101**, 237 (1957).

252. K. Landsteiner and J. van der Scheer, *J. Exptl. Med.* **55**, 781 (1932).

253. P. Desnuelle, M. Rovery, and C. Fabre, *Compt. rend. acad. Sci.* **233**, 987 (1951).

254. E. O. P. Thompson, *J. Biol. Chem.* **208**, 565 (1954).

255. A. Caputo and R. Zito, *Bull. soc. chim. biol.* **37**, 1255 (1955).

256. W. F. White, J. Shields, and K. C. Robbins, *J. Am. Chem. Soc.* **77**, 1267 (1955).

257. K. Kusama, *J. Biochem.* (*Tokyo*) **44**, 375 (1957).

258. T. Peters, A. C. Logan, and C. A. Sanford, *Biochim. et Biophys. Acta* **30**, 88 (1958).

259. V. Knesslova, V. Kostka, B. Keil, and F. Sorm, *Collection Czech. Chem. Communs.* **20**, 1311 (1955).

260. J. S. Fruton and S. Simmonds, "General Biochemistry," 2nd ed., p. 164. Wiley, New York, 1958.

261. R. R. Porter and F. Sanger, *Biochem. J.* **42**, 287 (1948).

262. H. Ozawa and K. Satake, *J. Biochem.* (*Tokyo*) **42**, 641 (1955).

263. T. Dévényi, *Acta Physiol. Acad. Sci. Hung.* **9**, 321 (1956).

264. W. A. Schroeder and G. Matsuda, *J. Am. Chem. Soc.* **80**, 1521 (1958).

265. Y. Yagi, T. Tsujimura, and K. Sato, *J. Biochem.* (*Tokyo*) **44**, 11 (1957).

266. T. H. J. Huisman and A. Dozy, *Biochim. et Biophys. Acta* **20**, 400 (1956).

267. T. Kauffmann and F.-P. Boettcher, *Z. Naturforsch.* **13b**, 467 (1958).

268. T. Kauffmann and F.-P. Boettcher, *Chem. Ber.* **92**, 2707 (1959).

269. P. Mäsiar, B. Keil, and F. Sorm, *Collection Czech. Chem. Communs.* **22**, 1203 (1957).

270. S. Sasakawa and K. Satake, *J. Biochem.* (*Tokyo*) **45**, 867 (1958).

271. P. Mäsiar, B. Keil, and F. Sorm, *Collection Czech. Chem. Communs.* **23**, 734 (1958).

272. F. Sorm, *in* "Symposium on Protein Structure" (A. Neuberger, ed.), p. 88. Wiley, New York, 1958.

273. H. Ozawa, K. Tamai, and K. Satake, *J. Biochem.* (*Tokyo*) **47**, 244 (1960).

274. P. Mäsiar, M. Jurovcik, and T. Smolnicky, *Proc. 4th Intern. Congr. Biochem.*, Vienna **15**, 17 (1960).

275. P. Mäsiar and M. Jurovcik, *Chem. zvesti* **13**, 58 (1959).

276. P. Mäsiar and T. Smolnicky, *Collection Czech. Chem. Communs.* **24**, 2790 (1959).

277. A. E. Garrod, "Inborn Errors of Metabolism," 2nd ed. Oxford Univ. Press, London and New York, 1923.
278. J. T. Edsall, ed., *Natl. Acad. Sci.—Natl. Research Council Publ.* **557** (1958).
279. H. A. Itano, *Advances in Protein Chem.* **12**, 216 (1957).
280. V. M. Ingram, *Nature* **180**, 326 (1957).
281. V. M. Ingram, *Biochim. et Biophys. Acta* **28**, 539 (1958).
282. J. A. Hunt and V. M. Ingram, *Biochim. et Biophys. Acta* **28**, 546 (1958).
283. V. M. Ingram, *Biochim. et Biophys. Acta* **36**, 402 (1959).
284. N. Hilschmann and G. Braunitzer, *Z. physiol. Chem.* **317**, 285 (1959).
285. J. A. Hunt and V. M. Ingram, *in* "Symposium on Protein Structure" (A. Neuberger, ed.), p. 148. Wiley, New York, 1958.
286. R. L. Hill and H. C. Schwartz, *Nature* **184**, 641 (1959).
287. G. W. Beadle, *Science* **129**, 1715 (1959).
288. J. A. Hunt, *Nature* **183**, 1373 (1959).
289. R. T. Jones, W. A. Schroeder, and J. R. Vinograd, *J. Am. Chem. Soc.* **81**, 4749 (1959).
290. A. M. Katz and A. I. Chernoff, *Science* **130**, 1574 (1959).
291. R. T. Jones, W. A. Schroeder, J. E. Balog, and J. R. Vinograd, *J. Am. Chem. Soc.* **81**, 3161 (1959).
292. M. Murayama, *Federation Proc.* **19**, 78 (1960).
293. S. Benzer, V. M. Ingram, and H. Lehmann, *Nature* **182**, 852 (1958).
294. W. H. Stein, *Natl. Acad. Sci.—Natl. Research Council Publ.* **557** (1958).
295. G. H. Beaven, H. Hoch, and E. R. Holiday, *Biochem. J.* **49**, 374 (1951).
296. D. W. Allen, W. A. Schroeder, and J. Balog, *J. Am. Chem. Soc.* **80**, 1628 (1958).
297. A. O. W. Stretton and V. M. Ingram, *Federation Proc.* **19**, 343 (1960).
298. K. Bailey, F. R. Bettelheim, L. Lorand, and W. R. Middlebrook, *Nature* **167**, 233 (1951).
299. B. Blombäck and A. Vestermark, *Arkiv Kemi* **12**, 173 (1958).
300. B. Blombäck and T. C. Laurent, *Arkiv Kemi* **12**, 137 (1958).
301. B. Blombäck and I. Yamashina, *Arkiv Kemi* **12**, 299 (1958).
302. B. Blombäck, P. Wallen, and J. Sjoquist, *Acta Chem. Scand.* **13**, 819 (1959).
303. J. E. Folk, J. A. Gladner, and K. Laki, *J. Biol. Chem.* **234**, 67 (1959).
304. F. Lucas, J. T. B. Shaw, and S. G. Smith, *Advances in Protein Chem.* **13**, 107 (1958).
305. K. Felix, H. Fischer, and A. Krekels, *in* "Progress in Biophysics and Biophysical Chemistry" (J. A. V. Butler, ed.), Vol. 6, p. 9. Pergamon, New York, 1956.
306. G. R. Tristram, *Nature* **160**, 637 (1947).
307. S. F. Velick and S. Udenfriend, *J. Biol. Chem.* **191**, 233 (1951).
308. E. Waldschmidt-Leitz, K. Kühn, and F. Zinnert, *Experientia* **7**, 183 (1951).
309. D. M. P. Phillips, *Biochem. J.* **60**, 403 (1955).
310. K. Felix, *Am. Scientist* **43**, 431 (1955).
311. F. S. Scanes and B. T. Tozer, *Biochem. J.* **63**, 565 (1956).
312. V. Tomasek, *Chem. listy* **50**, 840 (1956).
313. T. Ando, Y. Nagai, and H. Fujioka, *J. Biochem. (Tokyo)* **44**, 779 (1957).
314. T. Ando, T. Tobita, and M. Yamasaki, *J. Biochem. (Tokyo)* **45**, 285 (1958).
315. T. Ando and C. Hashimoto, *J. Biochem. (Tokyo)* **45**, 453 (1958).
316. T. Ando, M. Yamasaki, and E. Abukumagawa, *J. Biochem. (Tokyo)* **47**, 82 (1960).
317. K. Felix and A. Krekels, *Z. physiol. Chem.* **295**, 107 (1953).
318. E. Waldschmidt-Leitz and K. Gauss, *Z. physiol. Chem.* **293**, 10 (1953).

319. R. Monier and M. Jutisz, *Biochim. et Biophys. Acta* **14**, 551 (1954).

320. H. Koffler, *Bacteriol. Revs.* **21**, 227 (1957).

321. E. R. L. Gaughran, *Bacteriol. Revs.* **11**, 189 (1947).

322. M. B. Allen, *Bacteriol. Revs.* **17**, 125 (1953).

323. C. Weibull, *Acta Chem. Scand.* **7**, 335 (1953).

324. H. Koffler, T. Kobayashi, and G. E. Mallett, *Arch. Biochem. Biophys.* **64**, 509 (1956).

325. G. E. Mallett and H. Koffler, *Arch. Biochem. Biophys.* **67**, 254 (1957).

326. H. Fraenkel-Conrat and L. K. Ramachandran, *Advances in Protein Chem.* **14**, 175 (1959).

327. G. Schramm, *Ann. Rev. Biochem.* **27**, 101 (1958).

328. K. Narita, *Biochim. et Biophys. Acta* **31**, 372 (1959).

329. F. A. Anderer, E. Weber, and H. Uhlig, *Z. Naturforsch.* **15b**, 79 (1960).

330. J. I. Harris and C. A. Knight, *J. Biol. Chem.* **214**, 215 (1955).

331. C. A. Knight, *J. Biol. Chem.* **214**, 231 (1955).

332. C.-I. Niu and H. Fraenkel-Conrat, *J. Am. Chem. Soc.* **77**, 5882 (1955).

333. C.-I. Niu and H. Fraenkel-Conrat, *Biochim. et Biophys. Acta* **16**, 597 (1955).

334. C.-I. Niu and H. Fraenkel-Conrat, *Arch. Biochem. Biophys.* **59**, 538 (1955).

335. G. Braunitzer, *Chem. Ber.* **88**, 2025 (1955).

336. H. Fraenkel-Conrat and K. Narita, *in* "Symposium on Protein Structure" (A. Neuberger, ed.), p. 249. Wiley, New York, 1958.

337. C.-I. Niu, V. Shore, and C. A. Knight, *Virology* **6**, 226 (1958).

338. C. A. Knight and B. R. Woody, *Federation Proc.* **18**, 263 (1959).

339. B. R. Woody and C. A. Knight, *Virology* **9**, 359 (1959).

340. R. A. Steinberg and C. Thom, *J. Agr. Research* **64**, 645 (1942).

341. F. Kaudewitz, *Nature* **183**, 1829 (1959).

342. A. Tsugita and H. Fraenkel-Conrat, *Proc. Natl. Acad. Sci. U. S.* **46**, 636 (1960).

343. R. S. Baker, J. E. Johnson, and S. W. Fox, *Biochim. et Biophys. Acta* **28**, 318 (1958).

344. H. M. Dyer, *J. Biol. Chem.* **124**, 519 (1938).

345. D. E. Atkinson, S. Melvin, and S. W. Fox, *Arch. Biochem. Biophys.* **31**, 205 (1951).

346. H. Tarver, *in* "The Proteins" (H. Neurath and K. Bailey, eds.), Vol. 2, Part B, p. 1295. Academic Press, New York, 1954.

347. R. Munier and G. N. Cohen, *Biochim. et Biophys. Acta* **31**, 378 (1959).

348. A. B. Pardee and L. S. Prestidge, *Biochim. et Biophys. Acta* **27**, 330 (1958).

349. D. B. Cowie and G. N. Cohen, *Biochim. et Biophys. Acta* **26**, 252 (1957).

350. M. Vaughan and D. Steinberg, *Advances in Protein Chem.* **14**, 115 (1959).

351. R. S. Baker, J. E. Johnson, and S. W. Fox, *Federation Proc.* **13**, 178 (1954).

352. A. Vegotsky, Ph.D. Dissertation, Florida State University, 1961.

353. C. S. Hanes, F. J. R. Hird, and F. A. Isherwood, *Biochem. J.* **51**, 25 (1952).

354. S. W. Fox, *Science* **132**, 200 (1960).

355. S. W. Fox and P. G. Homeyer, *Am. Naturalist* **89**, 163 (1955).

356. J. D. Perrone, D. Parreira, and E. Tomalsquim, *Proc. 3rd Intern. Congr. Biochem. Brussels, 1955* p. 14 (1956).

357. G. Gamow, A. Rich, and M. Yčas, *Advances in Biol. and Med. Phys.* **4**, 23 (1956).

358. S. Akabori, N. Sakota, H. Ono, Y. Okada, and H. Hanabusa, *Symposia on Enzyme Chem. (Japan)* **9**, 25 (1954); *Chem. Abstr.* **48**, 7082 (1954).

359. H. E. Schultze, I. Göllner, K. Heide, M. Schönenberger, and G. Schwick, *Z. Naturforsch.* **10b**, 463 (1955).

360. S. Aonuma, *J. Pharm. Soc. Japan* **76**, 201 (1956).
361. K. Shimura, J. Sato, S. Suto, and A. Kikuchi, *J. Biochem. (Tokyo)* **43**, 217 (1956).
362. M. Kanamori and O. Tanaka, *J. Agr. Chem. Soc. Japan* **28**, 642 (1954); *Chem. Abstr.* **50**, 7902 (1956).
363. M. Ottesen and C. G. Schellman, *Compt. rend. trav. lab. Carlsberg, Ser. chim.* **30**, 157 (1957).
364. S. Magnusson, *Acta Chem. Scand.* **12**, 355 (1958).
365. T. Deutsch, *Magyar Kém. Folyóirat* **61**, 135 (1955); *Chem. Abstr.* **52**, 8251 (1958).
366. W. Grassmann and K. Kühn, *Z. physiol. Chem.* **301**, 1 (1955).
367. K. Hayashi, J. Oda, and K. Kobayashi, *Nippon Nogei-kagaku Kaishi* **30**, 538 (1956); *Chem. Abstr.* **52**, 7380 (1958).
368. E. F. Mellon, A. H. Corn, and S. R. Hoover, *J. Am. Chem. Soc.* **75**, 1675 (1953).
369. C. C. Solomons and J. T. Irving, *S. African J. Med. Sci.* **21**, 49 (1956); *Chem. Abstr.* **51**, 4455 (1957).
370. F. W. Putnam and A. Miyake, *Arch. Biochem. Biophys.* **65**, 39 (1956).
371. K. Titani, H. Yoshikawa, and K. Satake, *J. Biochem. (Tokyo)* **43**, 737 (1956).
372. G. Braunitzer, A. Hillmann-Elies, F. Lohs, and G. Hillmann, *Z. Naturforsch.* **9b**, 615 (1954).
373. M. Rodbell, *Science* **127**, 701 (1958).
374. H. Bloemendal and G. T. Cate, *Nature* **181**, 340 (1958).
375. W. R. Middlebrook, *Biochem. J.* **59**, 146 (1955).
376. V. K. Orekhovitch, L. A. Lokshina, V. A. Mant'ev, and O. V. Troitskaya, *Doklady Akad. Nauk S.S.S.R.* **110**, 1041 (1956).
377. H. Van Vunakis and R. M. Herriott, *Biochem. et Biophys. Acta* **22**, 537 (1956).
378. T. Sasaki, *J. Pharm. Soc. Japan* **77**, 845 (1957).
379. S. Udenfriend and S. F. Velick, *J. Biol. Chem.* **190**, 733 (1951).
380. H. Boser, *Z. physiol. Chem.* **307**, 240 (1957).
381. K. Shimura, J. Sato, S. Suto, and A. Kikuchi, *J. Biochem. (Tokyo)* **43**, 217 (1956).
382. A. J. Shaeffer and J. D. Murray, *A.M.A. Arch. Ophthalmol.* **43**, 1056 (1950).
383. W. W. Bromer, A. Staub, E. R. Diller, H. L. Bird, L. G. Sinn, and O. K. Behrens, *J. Am. Chem. Soc.* **79**, 2794 (1957).
384. H. Boser, *Z. physiol. Chem.* **300**, 1 (1955).
385. H. Van Vunakis and R. M. Herriott, *Biochim. et Biophys. Acta* **23**, 600 (1957).
386. S. F. Velick and E. Ronzoni, *J. Biol. Chem.* **173**, 627 (1948).
387. I. I. Geschwind, C. H. Li, and L. Barnafi, *J. Am. Chem. Soc.* **79**, 1003 (1957).
388. H. M. Walker and J. Lev, "Statistical Inference." Henry Holt, New York, 1953.
389. M. G. Kendall, "Rank Correlation Methods," 2nd ed. Charles Griffin, London, 1955.
390. S. W. Fox and D. De Fontaine, *Proc. Soc. Exptl. Biol. Med.* **92**, 503 (1956).
391. H. J. Morowitz and M. S. Spaulding, *Biochim. et Biophys. Acta* **29**, 514 (1958).
392. H. J. Morowitz, *Biochim. et Biophys. Acta* **33**, 494 (1959).
393. H. J. Morowitz and R. V. Barra, *Biochim. et Biophys. Acta* **33**, 505 (1959).
394. C. B. Anfinsen, "The Molecular Basis of Evolution." Wiley, New York, 1959.
395. A. J. Kluyver and C. B. Van Niel, "The Microbe's Contribution to Biology." Harvard Univ. Press, Cambridge, Mass., 1956.
396. D. E. Green, *in* "Chemical Pathways of Metabolism" (D. M. Greenberg, ed.), Vol. 1, p. 61. Academic Press, New York, 1954.
397. R. B. Merrifield and D. W. Woolley, *J. Am. Chem. Soc.* **80**, 6635 (1958).

398. H. Brockmann, *Fortschr. Chem. org. Naturstoffe* **18**, 1 (1960).
399. E. Katz and L. H. Pugh, *Appl. Microbiol.* **9**, 263 (1961).
400. P. G. Katsoyannis and V. du Vigneaud, *J. Biol. Chem.* **33**, 1352 (1958).
401. R. Acher, J. Chauvet, M. T. Lenci, F. Morel, and J. Maotz, *Biochim. et Biophys. Acta* **42**, 379 (1960).
402. C. H. Li, J. S. Dixon, and D. Chung, *Biochim. et Biophys. Acta* **46**, 324 (1961).
403. J. S. Dixon and C. H. Li, *J. Am. Chem. Soc.* **82**, 4568 (1960).
404. C. Milstein and F. Sanger, *Biochim. et Biophys. Acta* **42**, 173 (1960).
405. F. Sanger and D. C. Shaw, *Nature* **187**, 872 (1960).
406. H. S. Jansz, F. Berends, and R. A. Oosterbaan, *Rec. trav. chim.* **78**, 876 (1959).
407. R. C. Hughes, A. A. Yunis, E. H. Fisher, and E. G. Krebs, *Federation Proc.* **20**, 386 (1961).
408. P. Desnuelle, in "The Enzymes" (P. D. Boyer, H. Lardy, and K. Myrbäck, eds.), Vol. IV, p. 119. Academic Press, New York, 1960.
409. O. Mikes, I. Kakol, A. J. Zbrozyna, and F. Sorm, *Collection Czechoslov. Chem. Communs.* **25**, 1946 (1960).
410. K. A. Walsh, D. L. Kauffman, and H. Neurath, *Federation Proc.* **20**, 385 (1961).
411. P. Desnuelle, in "The Enzymes" (P. D. Boyer, H. Lardy, and K. Myrbäck, eds.), Vol. IV, p. 93. Academic Press, New York, 1960.
412. B. S. Hartley, *J. Cellular Comp. Physiol.* **54**, Suppl. No. 1, 203 (1959).
413. B. Meloun, J. Vanacek, Z. Pruski, B. Keil, and F. Sorm, *Collection Czechoslov. Chem. Communs.* **25**, 571 (1960).
414. R. L. Hill and W. Konigsberg, *J. Biol. Chem.* **235**, PC21 (1960).
415. J. R. Shelton and W. A. Schroeder, *J. Am. Chem. Soc.* **82**, 3342 (1960).
416. G. Braunitzer, N. Hilschmann, V. Rudloff, K. Hilse, B. Liebold, and R. Müller, *Nature* **190**, 480 (1961).
417. H. C. Watson and J. C. Kendrew, *Nature* **190**, 670 (1961).
418. J. C. Kendrew, H. C. Watson, B. E. Strondberg, R. E. Dickerson, D. C. Phillips, and V. C. Shore, *Nature* **190**, 666 (1961).
419. A. B. Edmundson and C. H. W. Hirs, *Nature* **190**, 663 (1961).
420. E. Zuckerkandl, R. T. Jones, and L. Pauling, *Proc. Natl. Acad. Sci. U. S.* **46**, 1349 (1960).
421. V. M. Ingram, *Nature* **189**, 704 (1961).
422. R. L. Hill, R. T. Swenson, and H. C. Schwartz, *J. Biol. Chem.* **235**, 3182 (1960).
423. T. H. J. Huisman, B. Horton, and T. B. Sevena, *Nature* **190**, 357 (1961).
424. C. Baglioni and V. M. Ingram, *Biochim. et Biophys. Acta* **48**, 253 (1961).
425. C. Baglioni, *Federation Proc.* **20**, 254 (1961).
426. F. A. Anderer, H. Uhlig, E. Weber, and G. Schramm, *Nature* **186**, 922 (1960).
427. A. Tsugita, D. T. Gish, J. Young, H. Fraenkel-Conrat, C. A. Knight, and W. M. Stanley, *Proc. Natl. Acad. Sci. U. S.* **46**, 1463 (1960).
428. A. Tsugita and H. Fraenkel-Conrat, *Federation Proc.* **20**, 254 (1961).
429. K. Narita, *Biochem. Biophys. Research Communs.* **5**, 160 (1961).
430. R. D. Marshall and A. Neuberger, *Biochem. J.* **78**, 31P (1961).
431. J. E. Folk and J. A. Gladner, *Biochim. et Biophys. Acta* **44**, 383 (1960).
432. S. B. Needleman, R. Q. Blackwell, and L. S. Fosdick, *Can. J. Chem.* **38**, 477 (1960).
433. S. W. Fox, *Soc. Gen. Systems Research Yearbook* p. 57 (1960).

CHAPTER 6

Metabolism of Aromatic Amino Acids

L. M. Henderson and R. K. Gholson

Department of Biochemistry, Oklahoma State University, Stillwater, Oklahoma

and

C. E. Dalgliesh

Miles Laboratories, Ltd., London

I. Introduction

The aromatic amino acids to be considered (phenylalanine, tyrosine, and tryptophan) are formulated in Fig. 1. Unless otherwise noted the discussion will concern the naturally occurring L-isomer.

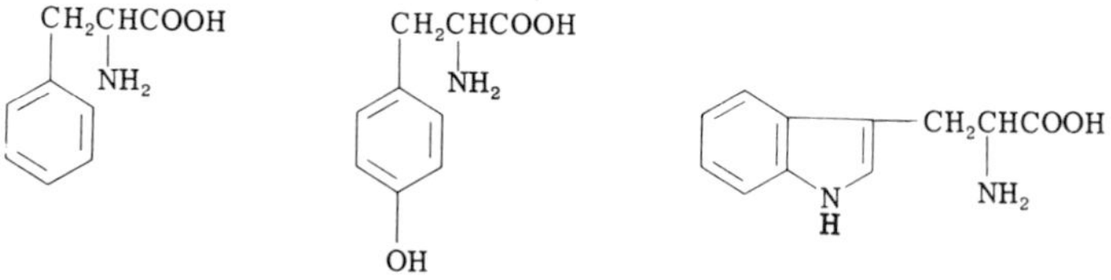

FIG. 1. The aromatic amino acids commonly occurring in proteins.

In the protein molecule the aromatic amino acids probably play a fundamental structural role. Their large size, relative to most other amino acid residues, suggests that they might be important in determining the over-all conformation of the protein molecule. The peculiar properties of the aromatic system allow a protein molecule with a suitable proportion of constituent aromatic amino acids to take part in resonance transfer of electrons (1) and this may be of particular importance both in enzyme catalysis and in muscle contraction.

The amounts of the aromatic amino acids in proteins vary considerably. Tryptophan is one of the rarer of the amino acids and usually does not exceed 1.5% of a protein, but the amounts of phenylalanine and tyrosine are frequently appreciably higher, up to 5–10% of each. The incorporation of the aromatic amino acids into proteins probably follows a course similar to that of other amino acids. Activating systems for tryptophan and tyrosine have been partially purified (2). Besides their role as protein constituents, the aromatic amino acids are precursors of biologically important substances. Phenylalanine and tyrosine are precursors of the thyroid hormones and catechol amines; tryptophan is the precursor of the animal hormone 5-hydroxytryptamine and the plant hormone indoleacetic acid, as well as of the B vitamin nicotinic acid.

Errors in the metabolism of the aromatic amino acids occur in natural mutants in man, and much information in this area has been obtained from studies of such cases. It is probable that much more information could be obtained from natural mutants in animals, but such mutants are rarely detected because of the still very limited application of clinical biochemistry in the veterinary field. More recently mutants of microorganisms have been extensively studied. Knowledge of the reactions of the aromatic amino acids in plants has been slow to develop. Recently investigations of the metabolism of these amino acids in all living forms has been facilitated by the development of adsorption techniques for the isolation of metabolites (3), chromatographic methods for their examination (4), and fluorometric methods for their determination (5).

The history of the discovery of the aromatic amino acids has been reviewed carefully by Vickery and Schmidt (6). Tyrosine, largely because of its relative insolubility, was isolated rather early—by Liebig in 1846 (7). Phenylalanine was first isolated in 1879 (8) and tryptophan as recently as 1902 (9).

The solubilities per 100 gm. water at 25° are phenylalanine 2.97 gm., tyrosine 0.048 gm., and tryptophan 1.14 gm. These values may be compared with those for glycine, 25.3 gm., valine 8.85 gm., and cystine 0.011 gm. The ultraviolet absorption maxima in $N/10$ alkali are for phenylalanine 258 mμ ($\epsilon_{mol} = 206$); tyrosine 293 mμ ($\epsilon_{mol} = 2330$) and 240 mμ ($\epsilon_{mol} = 11,050$); tryptophan 280 mμ ($\epsilon_{mol} = 5430$) and 222 mμ ($\epsilon_{mol} = 34,600$) with a minimum at 244 mμ (10). Maximum excitation of fluorescence occurs at the ultraviolet absorption maxima. The maxima for the fluorescence emission lie at 282 mμ for phenylalanine, 303 mμ for tyrosine, and 348 mμ for tryptophan, the quantum yield being approximately 4, 21, and 20%, respectively (11).

In this chapter the major pathways for biosynthesis and degradation of the aromatic acids will be described. For more detailed references to work up to 1927 the review by Neubauer (12) should be consulted and for work up to 1954, the review by Dalgliesh (13).

II. Biosynthesis

Mammals, including man, have lost the ability to synthesize the aromatic ring. The aromatic amino acids phenylalanine and tryptophan are essential for the life of many species and, therefore, have to be derived from exogenous sources. The greater part, in higher animals, comes from the diet, but in ruminants the synthetic activities of the microflora are important. Tyrosine is not an essential amino acid for higher organisms as it is formed in mammalian tissues by the hydroxylation of phenylalanine (14).

The most important ultimate source of the aromatic amino acids is plant material. As we shall see later, biosynthesis of the aromatic amino acids is intimately associated with the biosynthesis of lignin, and thus has enormous quantitative importance. As a matter of experimental convenience investigation of the biosynthetic pathways has been carried out mainly on microorganisms, but the available evidence suggests that similar routes are used by higher plants (see Section II, C).

A. Mutants of Microorganisms

The use of mutants, whether naturally occurring or artificially produced, in the elucidation of metabolic pathways depends on the fact that if a precursor (A) is converted via intermediates to a substance (E) necessary for growth of the organism,

$$A \rightarrow B \rightarrow C \left.\begin{matrix} \, \\ \downarrow \end{matrix}\right| \rightarrow D \rightarrow E$$
$$C' \text{ Excreted}$$

and if the conversion of (C) to (D) is blocked, then the mutant will require an external source of (D) or (E) for growth. If (A) is supplied, the substrate (C) of the blocked reaction, or perhaps a simple derivative (C'), is likely to be formed in large amounts. Hence, mutants can accumulate intermediates in metabolic pathways, the normal small pool sizes of which would make their detection by other means difficult.

1. Common Precursors

Davis, using the penicillin technique (15), isolated several mutants of *Escherichia coli* requiring two or more aromatic amino acids for growth (16). He then tested a wide variety of substances to see whether any would support growth. Shikimic acid (Fig. 2) proved to be such a substance, indicating that it was either a precursor of these amino acids or could be converted into a precursor. Since some mutants accumulate shikimic acid (16) this substance appears to be a true precursor. Davis found that not all mutants responding to shikimic acid would respond to a mixture of phenylalanine, tyrosine, and tryptophan, and that, therefore, shikimic acid must be a precursor of other substances essential for growth of these mutants. The other substances were identified as *p*-aminobenzoic acid and *p*-hydroxybenzoic acid (17).

The precursors of shikimic acid were detected by testing mutants for syntrophism, i.e., for the ability of one mutant to provide a substance necessary for the growth of a second mutant. Two precursors were thus detected, isolated, and identified as 5-dehydroshikimic and 5-dehydroquinic acids (18, 19, 20) (see Fig. 2). The enzymes 5-dehydroquinase (21) (Reaction 1, Fig. 2) and 5-dehydroshikimic reductase (22) (Reaction 2, Fig. 2), have been partially purified (23).

Aerobacter aerogenes (24) and *Neurospora* (25) possess an enzyme, quinic dehydrogenase, which converts quinic acid to dehydroquinic

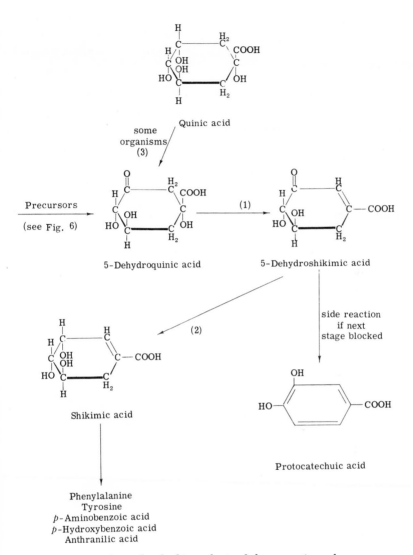

FIG. 2. Scheme for the biosynthesis of the aromatic nucleus.

acid (Reaction 3, Fig. 2). However quinic acid appears not to be a true aromatic precursor (26). The results of experiments with mutants (27, 28) suggest that two metabolites arising from shikimic acid are 5-phosphoshikimic acid (Fig. 3) and a cyclic acetal of shikimic acid and pyruvic acid. The point of divergence of the pathways to the various aromatic substances is not known but is likely to be at least one step removed from shikimic acid, as mutants are known which require all five aromatic substances, yet secrete shikimic acid into the medium.

2. Immediate Precursors of Phenylalanine and Tyrosine

Mutants are known which excrete a labile substance, prephenic acid (29), which is readily converted into phenylpyruvic acid. The structure of prephenic acid (30) is shown in Figs. 3 and 4. Phenylpyruvic acid

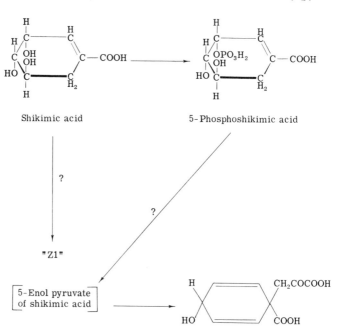

FIG. 3. Possible synthesis of prephenic acid.

is the immediate precursor of phenylalanine. Some microorganisms resemble animals in forming tyrosine directly from phenylalanine (31). In other cases direct hydroxylation is not involved and tyrosine is formed by a vitamin B_6-dependent transamination of p-hydroxyphenyl pyruvate (32). Isotopic evidence (Section II, B) shows that the carbon atoms of the side chains of phenylalanine and tyrosine have a similar origin, and it is likely that p-hydroxyphenylpyruvic acid is also derived from prephenic acid (Fig. 4). A mutant blocked in the conversion of prephenic acid to phenylpyruvic acid can accumulate either p-hydroxy-phenyllactic acid or tyrosine (33) (Fig. 4).

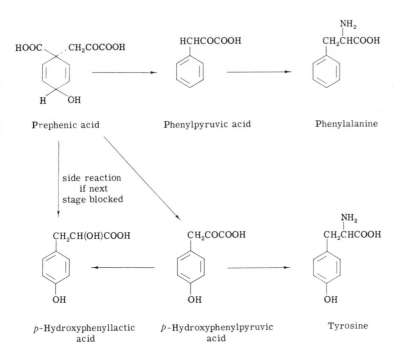

FIG. 4. Scheme for the conversion of prephenic acid to phenylalanine and tyrosine.

3. Immediate Precursors of Tryptophan

A cell-free preparation from a tryptophanless mutant of *E. coli* catalyzes the formation of anthranilic acid from 5-phosphoshikimic acid and L-glutamine in the presence of oxidized pyridine nucleotides (*34*). Evidence from mutants (*35, 36*) has established that indolylglycerol phosphate is an intermediate between anthranilic acid and tryptophan. That indole can serve as a substrate for tryptophan synthetase (tryptophan desmolase) has been known for several years. The pyridoxal phosphate-dependent condensation of the indole with serine made indole appear to be an obligatory intermediate (*37*). It now appears that this condensation of indole and serine is only one manifestation of the catalytic activity of tryptophan synthetase. A protein, immunologically related to tryptophan synthetase, is formed in certain *E. coli* mutants which lack tryptophan synthetase (*35*). This protein catalyzes the conversion of indolylglycerol phosphate to indole, but cannot convert indole to tryptophan. Some *Neurospora* mutants accumulate indolylglycerol phosphate and cannot use indole. Tryptophan synthetase catalyzes Reactions 4, 5, and 6 (Fig. 5). Free indole is not involved in

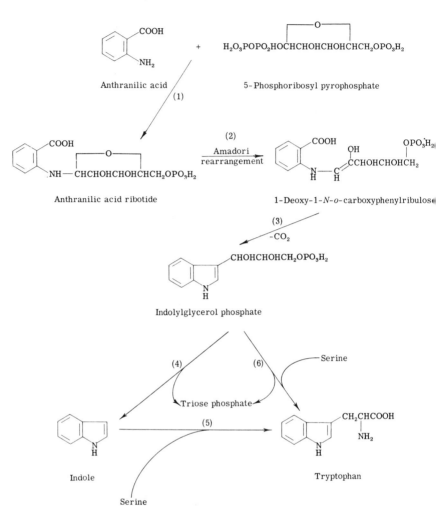

FIG. 5. The synthesis of tryptophan from anthranilic acid.

Reaction 6. It appears that Reactions 4 and 5 are partial reactions and that Reaction 6 represents the usual route of tryptophan synthesis (35).

The conversion of anthranilic acid to the indole nucleus involves loss of the carboxyl group (38). The two carbons necessary for formation of the pyrrole ring are derived from 5-phosphoribosyl pyrophosphate (39) (Fig. 5) which is transferred to the amino group of anthranilic acid to give a ribotide. This undergoes the Amadori rearrangement to 1-deoxy-1-N-o-carboxyphenylribulose (40) which undergoes decarboxylative cyclization, the 5-phospho group of the 5-phosphoribosyl pyrophosphate becoming the phosphate group of indolylglycerol phosphate. As 4-methylanthranilic acid is converted solely to 6-methylindole, cyclization must occur at the ring position vacated by the anthranilic acid carboxyl group (41). In a yeast (Saccharomyces) there is evidence that biosynthesis may go through an anthranilic acid fructoside and indoletetrose phosphate (42). Chemical analogies are available for the cyclization step. For example, N-methylanthranilic acid and glycolic aldehyde readily give N-methylindole (43).

At various times it has been suggested, mainly because of evidence derived from the use of competitive inhibitors of aromatic amino acids, or the sparing action of one aromatic amino acid for another, that in some microorganisms the aromatic amino acids are interconvertible. Apart from the conversion of phenylalanine to tyrosine, isotopic evidence does not support such suggestions (44).

B. Isotopic Evidence

The ultimate origin of all the carbon of the aromatic amino acids is atmospheric carbon dioxide, which is incorporated by photosynthesis into reactive compounds of low molecular weight. Aromatic compounds can be derived from acetate or from carbohydrate (e.g., glucose). Gilvarg and Bloch, using the yeast Saccharomyces cerevisiae (45), showed that if the organism had the choice of acetate or glucose as a carbon source, the aromatic amino acids were derived from glucose. Baddiley and co-workers (46), using Torulopsis utilis and doubly labeled acetate (C^{14} and C^{13}) as a sole carbon source, showed that the labeling pattern of the derived aromatic amino acids excluded the formation of the aromatic ring by condensation of 2-carbon units, or of 3-carbon units. The labeling pattern could best be explained by the participation of a C_7 sugar formed from a triose and a tetrose (47), a route that would conform with the participation of shikimic acid, a C_7 compound. The 3-carbon side chain of phenylalanine and tyrosine was shown by the results of tracer studies to arise by addition of a 3-carbon glycolysis fragment to the C_7 intermediate, followed by loss of one carbon (48).

$$C_6 - \genfrac{}{}{0pt}{}{C_1}{C_3} \rightarrow C_6 \genfrac{}{}{0pt}{}{C_3}{C_1} \rightarrow C_6 - C_3 + C_1$$

This is in agreement with the participation of prephenic acid.

Isotopic evidence on the carbohydrate intermediates has been obtained, particularly by Sprinson and collaborators (49). Preliminary evidence suggested that the C_7 sugar derivative involved was sedoheptulose-1,7-diphosphate. However, this acted as an aromatic precursor only in the presence of diphosphopyridine nucleotide (DPN), and isotopic evidence showed that when sedoheptulose diphosphate was converted to shikimic acid, the order of carbons 1, 2 and 3 of the sugar was reversed, indicating that cyclization could not be direct. Moreover, the configuration of C-4 of sedoheptulose is opposite to that of the corresponding carbon in shikimic acid. The probable pathway which emerged is shown in Fig. 6. The 3- and 4-carbon precursors are phosphoenol pyruvate and erythrose-4-phosphate, which condense to give 2-keto-3-deoxy-7-phospho-D-araboheptonic acid (50), which then cyclizes. Sedoheptulose diphosphate can act as an aromatic precursor in the presence of DPN as it can split to erythrose-4-phosphate and dihydroxyacetone phosphate, and the latter in the presence of DPN can give phosphenol pyruvate. Both erythrose-4-phosphate and phosphoenol pyruvate are readily available from the photosynthetic cycle. The above interpretation is compatible with the large amount of isotopic evidence of Rafelson and colleagues (51) and has been confirmed by studies of the purified enzyme which catalyzes the condensation of D-erythrose-4-phosphate and phosphoenol pyruvate to 5-dehydroquinic acid (52).

There is always considerable difficulty in interpreting isotopic data from experiments with labeled glucose because of the variation possible in its metabolism and the rapidity of isotopic equilibration in compounds of low molecular weight. Yanofsky, studying 1- and 2-labeled glucose as a source of the additional carbons needed for conversion of anthranilic acid to indole, has shown (53) that two pathways of incorporation are involved. One pathway corresponds to the main route of formation of C_5 from C_6 sugars involving the reaction of fructose-6-phosphate and 3-phosphoglyceraldehyde to give ribulose-5-phosphate, in which C-1 and C-2 of the hexose correspond to C-1 and C-2 of the pentose. The alternative route is by the hexose monophosphate pathway in which C-1 of the pentose is derived from C-2 of the hexose.

The routes for biosynthesis of the aromatic amino acids as now known are summarized in Fig. 7.

C. Biosynthesis in Plants

Dehydroshikimic acid and shikimic acid occur in plants (54). This strongly suggests that the same routes are used for aromatic biosynthesis in these species as in bacteria. Plants can carry out many reactions not found in higher organisms, and the additional occurrence of dihydroshikimic acid and quinic acid is not surprising. Possible pathways from intermediates in aromatic biosynthesis, e.g., shikimic acid, to such typical plant products as gallic acid (3,4,5-trihydroxybenzoic acid) can readily be formulated. In a survey of the distribution of shikimic acid in plants,

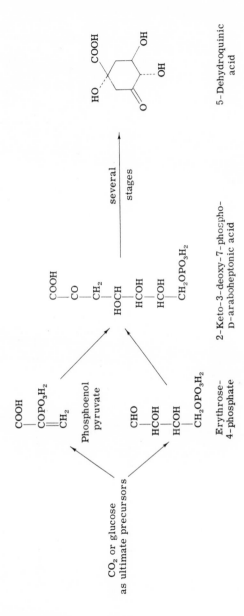

FIG. 6. Probable synthesis of aromatic compounds from simple molecules.

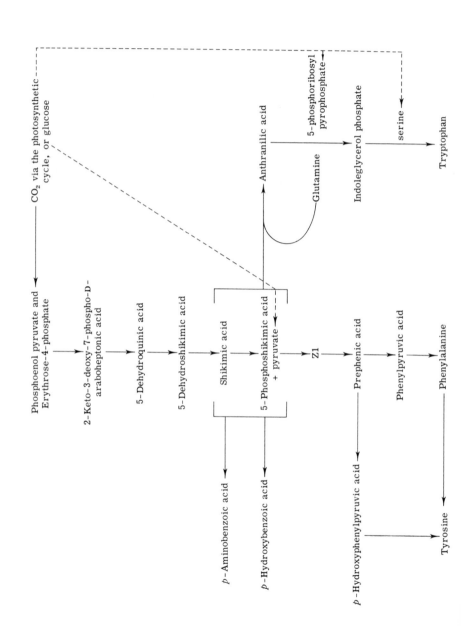

Hasegawa *et al.* (*55*) found this compound in the leaves of 82 of 164 species included in the survey.

III. Metabolism of Phenylalanine and Tyrosine

A. DEGRADATION TO ACETOACETATE AND FUMARATE

Phenylalanine is an essential amino acid for higher organisms, i.e., it cannot be synthesized in the animal's own tissues and therefore must be derived from an exogenous source (*14*). Tyrosine is not an essential amino acid as it is derived from phenylalanine. However, in phenyl-ketonuria, in which this conversion is inhibited, tyrosine can become essential (*56*). In many species, i.e., rat, mouse, and man, D-phenyl-alanine or phenylpyruvic acid can replace L-phenylalanine (13). The interconversion of these compounds to L-phenylalanine is vitamin B_6 dependent.

Embden and co-workers in 1906 first showed that phenylalanine and tyrosine are ketogenic, i.e., that they give rise to acetoacetic acid (*57*). This has been confirmed many times by classic methods and more recently by isotopic techniques (*58, 59*). Both phenylalanine and tyrosine have also been shown to be glycogenic (*60*), and this also has been confirmed isotopically (*61*). The glycogen and ketone bodies are derived from different parts of the molecule.

Indications of the nature of intermediates in phenylalanine and tyrosine metabolism came first from humans suffering from a congenital biochemical disorder, one of Garrod's "inborn errors of metabolism" (*62*) (Fig. 8). Such individuals have a congenital inability to carry out

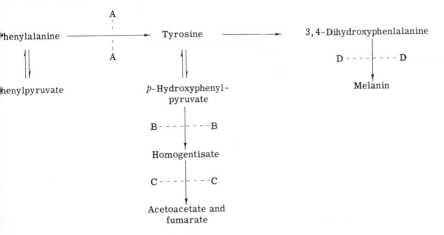

FIG. 8. Inborn errors of the metabolism of phenylalanine and tyrosine.

a normal metabolic reaction, i.e., they are natural mutants. The particular disorder was alcaptonuria, in which the patient's urine turns black on exposure to air. The colorless precursor responsible for the color change was isolated in 1891 by Wolkow and Baumann (63) and characterized as homogentisic acid (V, Fig. 9). These authors considered it to be a bacterial metabolite, but it was soon shown to arise in mammalian tissues from either phenylalanine or tyrosine (64). It was postulated that a side-chain migration is involved in its formation (65). Homogentisic acid was found to be excreted by the alcaptonuric after giving tyrosine or p-hydroxyphenylpyruvic acid (66). Homogentisic acid gives rise to acetoacetic acid when perfused through the liver (57), as does p-hydroxyphenylpyruvic acid, but not phenylpyruvic acid (67). A probable metabolic pathway is. therefore, phenylalanine → tyrosine → p-hydroxyphenylpyruvic acid → homogentisic acid → acetoacetic acid. 2,5-Dihydroxyphenylalanine (68) was shown not to be an intermediate in homogentisate formation.

Several other inborn errors of metabolism in the reaction sequence by which phenylalanine and tyrosine are degraded have been observed in man. These are summarized in Fig. 8. They will be discussed when the appropriate conversions are considered.

1. Conversion of Phenylalanine to Tyrosine: Phenylketonuria

The first stage in phenylalanine metabolism, hydroxylation in the *para* position to give tyrosine, was also first studied because of its relation to an inborn error of metabolism. In 1934 Fölling (69) described a syndrome characterized clinically by a mental defect and biochemically by the presence in the urine of large amounts of phenylpyruvic acid. The incidence is rather high for a metabolic error, about one in 25,000 in Great Britain, where approximately one in 200 are carriers of the involved gene. In addition to phenylpyruvic acid, phenylalanine (70), phenyllactic acid (71), and phenylacetylglutamine (72) are excreted in increased amounts. The latter two substances might be expected to arise from phenylpyruvic acid. Jervis (73) showed that normal individuals given phenylalanine had increased levels of blood phenols, whereas phenylketonurics did not. The metabolic failure in phenylketonuria was thus shown likely to be a failure to carry out a hydroxylation reaction. It was not at first clear whether the normal hydroxylation reaction was conversion of phenylalanine to tyrosine, or of phenylpyruvic acid to p-hydroxyphenylpyruvic acid.

Moss and Schoenheimer (74) showed that in the rat deuterium-labeled phenylalanine is converted to tyrosine by a process not affected by the amount of tyrosine already available. A specific enzyme system

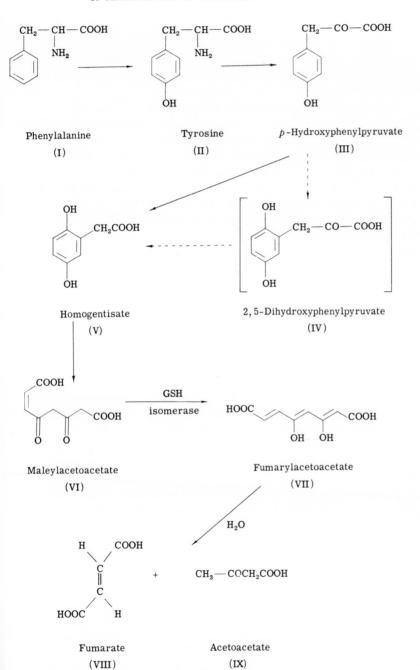

FIG. 9. Pathway of degradation of phenylalanine and tyrosine in animals.

of rat liver which converts phenylalanine to tyrosine was described by Udenfriend and Cooper (75). A similar enzyme system was shown by Jervis to be present in the liver of the normal human, but not the phenylketonuric (76), thus establishing the enzymatic basis for the metabolic defect.

Phenylalanine hydroxylase has been studied in a number of laboratories and many conflicting observations have been reported. Mitoma (77) described an enzyme from liver which required DPNH and an unstable protein present in other tissues. The enzyme from liver appears to be the missing factor in phenylketonuria (78). Kaufman and coworkers (79) have shown that only one enzyme from rat liver and an organic cofactor are required for the hydroxylation of phenylalanine. The cofactor appears to be a tetrahydropteridine derivative, which during the hydroxylation is oxidized to an intermediate that is rapidly converted to a dihydropteridine. A second enzyme found in sheep liver catalyzes the reduction of the cofactor to the active form at the expense of TPNH. Tetrahydrofolic acid was much less active as a cofactor than 2-amino-4-hydroxy-6-methyltetrahydropteridine. Folic acid antagonists, aminopterin and amethopterin, inhibit the formation of tyrosine both *in vitro* and *in vivo*.

The phenylalanine hydroxylase system is absent from the fetal liver, but rapidly appears after birth (80). In the rat full activity has appeared by the fourth day of age. The factor missing at birth is the same as that missing in phenylketonuria (80). Conversion of phenylalanine to tyrosine can occur also in muscle (81). Carriers of the recessive gene of phenylketonuria can be distinguished by their reduced capacity to metabolize phenylalanine in a load test (82). No conversion of tyrosine to phenylalanine occurs in mammals, even if phenylalanine deficient (83).

It is generally assumed that abnormal metabolites which accumulate as a result of the metabolic block are responsible for the mental symptoms in phenylketonuria. Besides the metabolites mentioned above, there is excretion of *o*-hydroxylation products, such as *o*-hydroxyphenylacetic acid (84). These probably arise from the abnormally accumulated metabolites by the nonspecific "detoxicating" hydroxylation systems of the body (85). Excretion of indolic metabolites such as indolelactic acid (86) also occurs in phenylketonuria. The latter is probably derived from indolepyruvic acid formed from tryptophan, because the excess phenylalanine competitively inhibits the usual pathways for tryptophan degradation. Phenylalanine is also a competitive inhibitor of normal L-tyrosine breakdown (87) as well as of the tyrosinase reaction (88).

2. Conversion of Tyrosine to p-Hydroxyphenyl Pyruvate

This conversion could conceivably take place either by transamination or by oxidative deamination. It is generally considered that only transamination occurs, since tyrosine oxidation does not give rise to ammonia. If the p-hydroxyphenylpyruvic acid formation is made rate limiting in vitro, tyrosine oxidation shows a pyridoxal phosphate dependence (89) indicating that transamination is involved. As livers of some species, including the rat, contain a powerful tyrosine deaminase (90), it is possible that oxidative deamination of tyrosine can provide an alternative route.

Tyrosine-α-ketoglutarate transaminase has been partially purified (91). It is pyridoxal phosphate-dependent and α-ketoglutarate cannot be replaced by pyruvate or oxalacetate. Among animal species tested, the dog has the highest activity, followed by the rabbit, pigeon, rat, and cow. The enzyme occurs in many other tissues, but liver is most active. Several animal tissues also contain an enzyme, keto-enol tautomerase, which catalyzes the interconversion of the keto and enol forms of p-hydroxyphenylpyruvic acid (and phenylpyruvic acid), but the physiological function of this enzyme is not known (92).

In the fetal mammal the tyrosine-oxidizing ability of the liver is only one-tenth to one-thirtieth that of the adult liver (93), and this appears to be due to lack of an apoenzyme, not of cofactors. Tyrosine transaminase may be the enzyme involved since this enzyme is low in the fetal liver of the rat, but reaches very high values shortly after birth (94). In the adult animal tyrosine transaminase is formed adaptively (95), the amount increasing up to tenfold after administration of tyrosine or of hydrocortisone.

3. Conversion of p-Hydroxyphenyl Pyruvate to Homogentisate

a. Tyrosinosis. Tyrosinosis (Fig. 8) is the name given to a metabolic defect in which large amounts of p-hydroxyphenylpyruvic acid are excreted. The defect is exceedingly rare, only one case having been studied in detail (96). Lesser degrees of p-hydroxyphenylpyruvic acid excretion occur in many pathological conditions (97). Abnormal excretion can also result from feeding large amounts of phenylalanine or tyrosine to normal animals (98); from scurvy, whether natural or artificial (99); in artificial alcaptonuria induced by a diet deficient in sulfur-containing amino acids (100); and in premature infants. In these cases abnormal excretion in general ceases on giving ascorbic acid.

The conversion of p-hydroxyphenyl pyruvate to homogentisate involves three reactions, ring hydroxylation, oxidative decarboxylation, and migration of the side chain, all of which appear to be catalyzed by a single enzyme (*101*). It was once supposed that 2,5-dihydroxyphenyl-pyruvic acid (IV, Fig. 9) was an intermediate in this transformation (*13*). Neubauer (*12*) found that this compound was converted to homogentisic acid in the alcaptonuric and Knox (*89*) showed that it was converted to acetoacetate by the same crude liver enzyme preparations which oxidize tyrosine. The alternate possible intermediates, *p*-hydroxyphenylacetic acid and 2,5-dihydroxyphenylalanine were not metabolized by this system. In addition, Uchida *et al.* (*102*) reported that a soluble system from rabbit liver which produced homogentisate (V) from *p*-hydroxyphenyl pyruvate (III) could be resolved into two fractions, one of which converted (III) to (IV), which was identified by paper chromatography; the other converted (IV) to (V). More recent studies have shown that this supposed intermediate (IV) is not significantly oxidized by an *in vitro* system from dog liver which converts *p*-hydroxyphenyl pyruvate to homogentisate (*103*). Hager *et al.* (*101*) reported that a single enzyme, *p*-hydroxyphenyl pyruvate oxidase prepared from beef or pork liver, converts (III) to (V) and that (IV) is not an intermediate.

A number of contradictory reports on the identity and role of the cofactors involved in this conversion have also appeared. Ascorbic acid was implicated when it was found that *p*-hydroxyphenyl pyruvate was excreted by scorbutic guinea pigs (*104*), human adults (*105*), infants (*106*), and monkeys (*107*). This excretion can be eliminated by vitamin C and reduced by pteroylglutamic acid administration (*108*). This "hydroxyphenyluria," which is distinct from tyrosinosis (*109*), is also observed in certain anemias, some cases of which are relieved by folic acid or vitamin B_{12}, as well as by ascorbate (*13*). *In vitro* evidence has indicated that ascorbic acid (*89, 110, 111*), glutathione (*110*), vitamin B_{12} (*102*), and 2,6-dichlorophenolindolphenol (*112*) are required for the conversion of *p*-hydroxyphenyl pyruvate to homogentisate. However, studies with the purified enzyme system have shown that catalase, ascorbic acid or dichlorophenolindolphenol, and glutathione are required under certain assay conditions only to avoid inhibition of the enzyme (*101*).

It appears (*113, 114*) that the defect in scurvy is not lack of *p*-hydroxyphenyl pyruvate oxidase, but the accumulation of the substrate which inhibits the oxidase. Ascorbic acid, or other reducing substances reverse the substrate inhibition readily demonstrable with the purified enzyme. It seems likely (*114*) that an inhibitory product is formed from the excess substrate during the course of the reaction. Identification of such a product might shed light on the nature of this complex reaction and on the manner by which reducing substances nullify such an inhibition.

The side-chain migration involved in the formation of homogentisate was so novel as to prevent the early acceptance of Neubauer's original scheme (12), and the mechanism by which this occurs is still unresolved. The formation of an intermediate quinol derivative has a precedent in organic chemistry in the conversion of p-cresol to methylhydroquinone (115).

Witkop has synthesized the p-hydroxyphenyl acetate quinol and found it inactive in a liver system which oxidizes tyrosine (116). It, therefore, appears that migration must occur before conversion of the side chain from a pyruvate to an acetate moiety (115).

4. Homogentisate to Fumarate and Acetoacetate

a. Alcaptonuria. Alcaptonuria was the first of Garrod's (62) "inborn errors in metabolism" to be recognized (see Fig. 8) (see review, 117). It is characterized by the excretion of large amounts (up to 500 mg. per day) of homogentisic acid, "alcaptone," in the urine. Alcaptonuria is caused by an inability further to metabolize homogentisate. This metabolic defect was shown to be due to the absence of homogentisic acid oxidase activity in the affected individual (118). This same study also provided enzymatic evidence that the sequence of reactions in tyrosine oxidation is the same in human liver as in the other mammalian species. The genetic defect responsible for the missing enzyme is inherited as a single recessive Mendelian character (117). Unlike phenylketonuria, alcaptonuria is not accompanied by mental symptoms, but it appears to be associated almost invariably with ochronosis and crippling arthritis in later life (117).

The occurrence of this disease provided a valuable aid in the early elucidation of the degradative pathway of phenylalanine metabolism in man. Normal humans rapidly metabolize homogentisic acid, but alcaptonurics excrete all of a test dose of this substance in the urine. They also excrete excessive homogentisate after administration of phenylalanine, p-tyrosine, p-hydroxyphenyl pyruvate, 2,5-dihydroxyphenyl pyruvate, phenyl pyruvate, and phenyl acetate, but not of o-tyrosine, m-tyrosine, or the corresponding keto acids (12, 119, 120). These findings led Neubauer (12) to the early postulation of the main pathway of phenylalanine metabolism (Fig. 9), which more recent evidence has shown to be substantially correct.

Artificial "alcaptonuria" can be induced in experimental animals by very large doses of phenylalanine or tyrosine (121, 122, 123) by feeding diets deficient in sulfur-containing amino acids (*100*) or by administration of α,α′-dipyridyl (*124*). In one set of experiments (*104*) homogentisate excretion in guinea pigs was related to ascorbic acid deficiency.

b. Oxidative Fission of Homogentisate. The reactions leading from homogentisate to acetoacetate are among the best-understood aspects of tyrosine metabolism. Ravdin and Crandall (*125*) demonstrated that an enzyme system in rat liver converts homogentisate to fumarylacetoacetate (VII, Fig. 9). Suda and Takeda (*126*) showed that this conversion also occurs in a cell-free preparation of *Pseudomonas*. They also studied the reaction in rabbit liver (*127*) and found that the enzyme required ferrous iron. Ascorbic acid also had some effect in restoring activity to the resolved enzyme. Knox (*115*) views the action of ascorbate and glutathione in this reaction as being due only to a reduction of the sulfhydryl groups on the enzyme. The belief that ascorbate has a direct function in homogentisate metabolism is based on a single authenticated case of homogentisate excretion in scorbutic guinea pigs fed tyrosine (*104*), which could have been due to the high level of tyrosine employed. The best present evidence seems to indicate that ascorbate has no specific cofactor role in this pathway of phenylalanine metabolism (*101, 115*).

Mammalian homogentisic acid oxidase appears to be very similar in its mode of action and many of its other properties to several other "phenolytic oxygenases" (*128*) from mammals and microorganisms (see Section IV, C).

c. Isomerization and Hydrolysis. Direct formation of a *trans* compound, fumarylacetoacetate from a benzenoid ring would be surprising. Knox and co-workers (*115, 129*) have demonstrated that the more probable maleylacetoacetate (VI) is the primary product of homogentisate oxidase. An isomerase requiring glutathione as co-factor converts this *cis* compound to fumarylacetoacetate (VII) (*130*).

Fumarylacetoacetate, but not its *cis* isomer (*115*), is hydrolyzed to fumarate and acetoacetate by a soluble rat liver enzyme (*125*). It seems to be identical with a previously described enzyme (*131*) which hydrolyzes many diketo acids, but apparently fumarylacetoacetate is its natural substrate.

B. Catechol Pathways

1. Epinephrine and Norepinephrine

The formation of these compounds, although probably a quantitatively minor pathway of tyrosine metabolism, is of great physiological importance since epinephrine and norepinephrine are the chemical mediators of sympathetic nervous transmission in mammals. Norepinephrine now appears to be the primary adrenergic compound. For recent reviews of the metabolism of catechol hormones in mammalian systems see Hagan and Welch (132), von Euler (133), and Senoh et al. (134). Epinephrine has also been found together with tryptamine derivatives in the toxic skin secretions of many species of *Bufo* (toads) (e.g., 135, 136). In invertebrates, epinephrine has been reported in the paramecia (137, 138), and it is found in the annelids (139), particularly in leeches (*Hirudo*) (138). Several pressor substances related to epinephrine have been found in the salivary glands of cephalopods (140) e.g., *Octopus vulgaris* (141).

The most probable pathway for epinephrine (adrenaline) biosynthesis is shown in Fig. 10. It is based chiefly on experiments on mam-

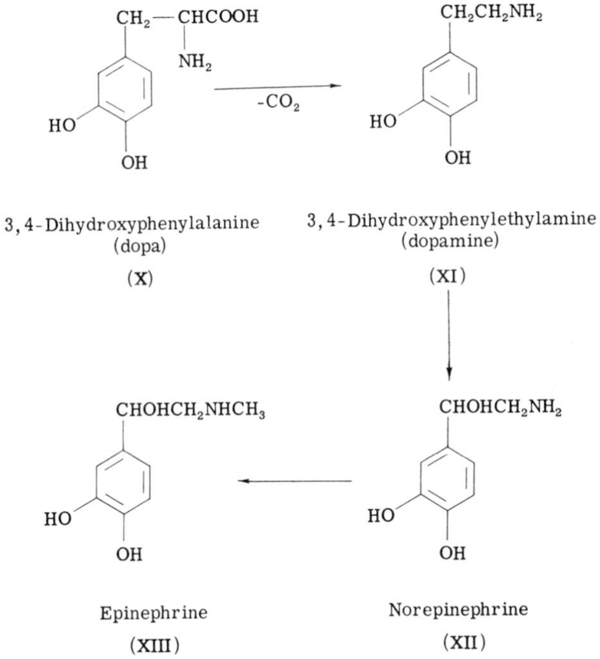

3,4-Dihydroxyphenylalanine
(dopa)

(X)

3,4-Dihydroxyphenylethylamine
(dopamine)

(XI)

Epinephrine

(XIII)

Norepinephrine

(XII)

FIG. 10. Route of biosynthesis of epinephrine and norepinephrine.

malian adrenal systems, but this route probably also functions in most epinephrine-forming organisms. The assumption of early workers (142) that epinephrine is derived from phenylalanine and tyrosine was conclusively demonstrated when phenylalanine-α-C^{14} was shown to be converted to epinephrine in the rat *in vivo* (143). Tyrosine-α-C^{14} was subsequently shown to yield correspondingly labeled epinephrine in rats (144). In similar isotopic experiments, phenylalanine, tyrosine, and dihydroxyphenylalanine, but not tyramine or phenylethylamine were shown to be precursors of epinephrine (145). Homogenates of chicken adrenal glands were reported to form hydroxytyramine and norepinephrine when incubated with dihydroxyphenyalanine (146). The pathway shown in Fig. 10 was confirmed *in vitro* with bovine adrenal slices and with C^{14}-labeled substrates (147). An adrenal particulate fraction was shown to convert hydroxytyramine-C^{14} to norepinephrine. Dihydroxyphenylserine was ruled out as an intermediate in the formation of norepinephrine in this system (148). A soluble system from the adrenal medulla completes the synthesis by methylating norepinephrine to form epinephrine (149).

The conversion of tyrosine to dihydroxyphenylalanine is catalyzed by tyrosinase, an enzyme which is found in tissues of many animal species (150, 151) and in such plants as potatoes (152) and mushrooms (153). A specific mammalian decarboxylase converts dihydroxyphenylalanine to hydroxytyramine (154). Mammals also have a tyrosine decarboxylase (155) distinct from dihydroxyphenylalanine decarboxylase (156), and both require pyridoxal phosphate (157).

An interesting species difference in the pharmacological effect of dihydroxyphenylalanine has been reported (142). This compound causes an increase in blood pressure in the cat, but a decrease in rabbits and guinea pigs. The latter two species have a high level of kidney monoamine oxidase which converts the hydroxytyramine produced from dihydroxyphenylalanine into dihydroxyphenylacetaldehyde, a depressor substance. The cat has little monoamine oxidase so the pressor compounds formed from dihydroxyphenylalanine accumulate more in this species.

The formation of norepinephrine from hydroxytyramine by side-chain hydroxylation has been demonstrated with isotopes (148), but the enzyme responsible has not been characterized. A similar side-chain hydroxylation occurs in the biosynthesis of ephedrine in plants (see Section III, E, 2).

Tyramine (141) and p-hydroxyphenylethanolamine (octopamine) (158) have been found in the octopus. Two possible sequences for the biosynthesis of norepinephrine in this species have been suggested (13):

Tyrosine → Tyramine → Octopamine → Norepinephrine

or

p-Hydroxyphenylserine → Octopamine → Norepinephrine

No experimental evidence for either scheme has been reported. Mammals can produce tyramine from tyrosine, especially in the pancreas (*158*), but any tyramine formed appears to be metabolized by amine oxidase to form ultimately *p*-hydroxyphenylacetic acid (*159*). Isoprenaline, the isopropyl analog of epinephrine has recently been reported to occur in the adrenals of the monkey, cat, and man (*160*).

The degradation of epinephrine and norepinephrine in rats was studied by Schayer (*161, 162*) using these compounds variously labeled with C^{14}. He concluded that at physiological doses they are almost entirely degraded in the rat by amine oxidase to urinary compounds retaining both side-chain carbon atoms. Subsequently 3-methoxy-4-hydroxymandelic acid was identified as a major product of norepinephrine metabolism in man (*163*). Axelrod *et al.* (*164*) have recently proposed the scheme shown in Fig. 11 for the metabolism of epineph-

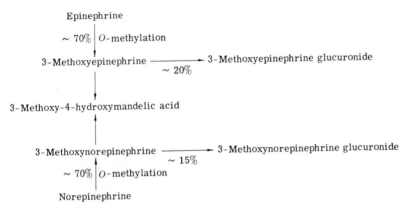

FIG. 11. Probable fate of epinephrine and norepinephrine in the rat.

rine and norepinephrine on the basis of their experiments in the rat. They concluded that little epinephrine or norepinephrine is degraded by amine oxidase. It has recently been shown that exogenous 3-hydroxytyramine, the direct precursor of norepinephrine, is largely degraded via amine oxidase and methylation to form 3-methoxy-4-hydroxyphenylacetic acid (*165*).

2. *Melanin*

Melanin is an inhomogenous, polymeric, protein-bound pigment found in mammalian skin and hair and in the pigmented tissues of other vertebrates and invertebrates, for example in the eyes of fish and the cuticle of orthopods. In vertebrates melanin granules are localized in specialized cells, the melanocytes. The "ink" of cephalopods is a melanoprotein. In plants "browning" of seed coats and of injured tissues is due to the formation of melanin-like pigments by the enzymatic oxidation of phenols (166).

Melanin-like material can be formed from the oxidation of adrenochrome (Fig. 12), which is formed from epinephrine enzymatically with

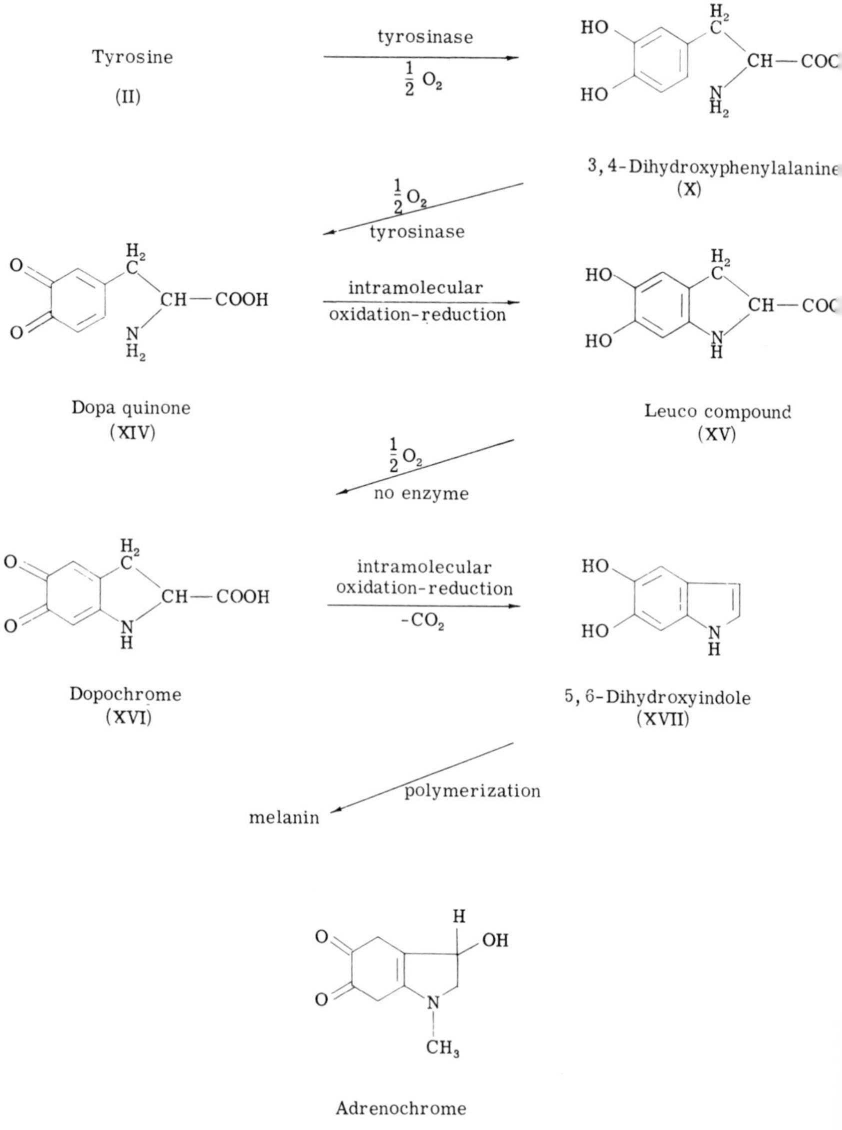

FIG. 12. Proposed pathway for melanin formation.

the polyphenol oxidase of the mushroom *Agricus campestris,* or non-enzymatically with various oxidizing agents (*167*). Adrenochrome was formerly thought to be an important natural product of epinephrine; many physiological functions have been suggested (*142*) for this compound. However, recent evidence shows that it is not a normal metabolite of epinephrine in the mammal (*168*).

The pathway of melanogenesis from tyrosine shown in Fig. 12 (see reviews, *169, 170*) was elucidated by Raper (*171*) and has been confirmed spectrophotometrically by Mason (*172*). Tyrosine is oxidized to dihydroxyphenylalanine by a copper-containing enzyme system which has been variously named tyrosinase, phenol- or polyphenol oxidase and the phenolase complex (see reviews, *166, 173*). This enzymatic activity appears to be almost ubiquitously distributed among living things (e.g., *174, 175*). Mason (*166*) has developed this system as an example of the "heterotypic expression" of a single enzymatic activity by the various phyla. In plants it may catalyze the formation of intermediates in the biosynthesis of tannins, melanins, lignins, flavonoids, etc. In other phyla this same enzymatic activity appears to be involved in the formation of the cuticle of orthopods, the pigmentation of the epithelial structures in the chordates, and probably in the biosynthesis of epinephrine.

Dihydroxyphenylalanine is further oxidized by tyrosinase to the quinone (XIV) which by an internal oxidation-reduction reaction, cyclizes to form (XV). Apparently (XV) undergoes spontaneous oxidation to dopochrome (XVI), which by a further intramolecular oxidation-reduction and loss of CO_2 forms 5,6-dihydroxyindole (XVII), the probable precursor of melanin. The nonenzymatic polymerization of (XVII) has been studied and possible mechanisms suggested (*176*).

Although this series of reactions can undoubtedly take place *in vitro,* Knox (*177*) has pointed out that there is little direct evidence that melanin is formed from tyrosine and dihydroxyphenylalanine in man. Recent experiments have also cast doubt on the role of this pathway in melanization in insects and *Neurospora.* Catechol, but not dihydroxyphenylalanine, can cause melanization in the albino locust (*Schistocerca gregaria*) (*178*). Similar results have been obtained in the silkworm (*Bombyx mori*) in which protocatechuic acid rather than tyrosine appears to be concerned with melanization (*179*). An albino mutant of *Neurospora crassa* was shown to form dopochrome from tyrosine (*180*).

The catechol pathway of tyrosine metabolism appears to be important in the formation and hardening of insect cuticle. The cuticle of the cockroach (*Blatta orientalis*) ootheca is formed by the interaction of a water-soluble protein and 3,4-dihydroxybenzoic acid, secreted by separate glands (*181*). The phenol probably "tans" the protein by oxidation to the quinone, which reacts with free amino groups on the protein (*166*). Insect cuticle has also been shown to contain 3,4-dihydroxyphenylacetic acid, 3,4-dihydroxyphenyllactic acid, and dihydroxyphenylalanine (*13*); this suggests biogenesis from the latter compound. Dihydroxyphenylalanine and 3,4-dihydroxybenzoic acid have been shown to be involved in the sclerotinization, but not melanization, of the locust cuticle (*178*).

C. HALOGENATED DERIVATIVES

1. *Thyroid Hormones*

Tyrosine is the precursor of thyroxine and the other iodinated phenol derivatives produced by the thyroid gland. Thyroxine does not appear to be of metabolic importance in the invertebrates, but functional thyroid tissue is found in all vertebrates (see reviews, *182, 183*). The thyroid hormones have a profound influence on the metabolism of mammals. The striking effect of thyroxine on tadpole metamorphosis (*184*) is a well-known example of the importance of this compound for growth and differentiation in the lower vertebrates (*185*).

a. Biosynthesis. The pathway of thyroxine biosynthesis has not been rigorously demonstrated, but the route shown in Fig. 13 has been postulated (*186, 187*). Tyrosine is iodinated to monoiodotyrosine (XVIII) and then to 3,5-diiodotyrosine (XIX). Two molecules of (XIX) then condense with loss of one of the side chains to form thyroxine (XX).

Some experimental support for this scheme is available. Soluble and mitochondrial enzymes which catalyze the iodination of tyrosine to monoiodotyrosine have been prepared from rat and sheep thyroid (*188*). 3,5-Diiodotyrosine is present in considerable amounts in thyroid tissue, and simple peptide derivatives of this compound have been shown to condense nonenzymatically under physiological conditions to produce thyroxine derivatives in high yield (*187*). The condensation of many analogs of diiodotyrosine to thyroxine analogs has been studied in model systems (*189*).

Relatively recently, 3,5,3'-triiodothyronine has been discovered in the thyroid and plasma (*190*). This substance is several times as active as thyroxine under certain conditions, and it has been proposed as the true thyroid hormone. More recently, 3,3'-diiodothyronine (*191*) and 3,3',5'-triiodothyronine (*192*) have been found in the thyroid gland and shown to have thyroid activity. Triiodothyronine could be formed by deiodination of thyroxine, a hypothesis favored by English workers (*193*). Roche

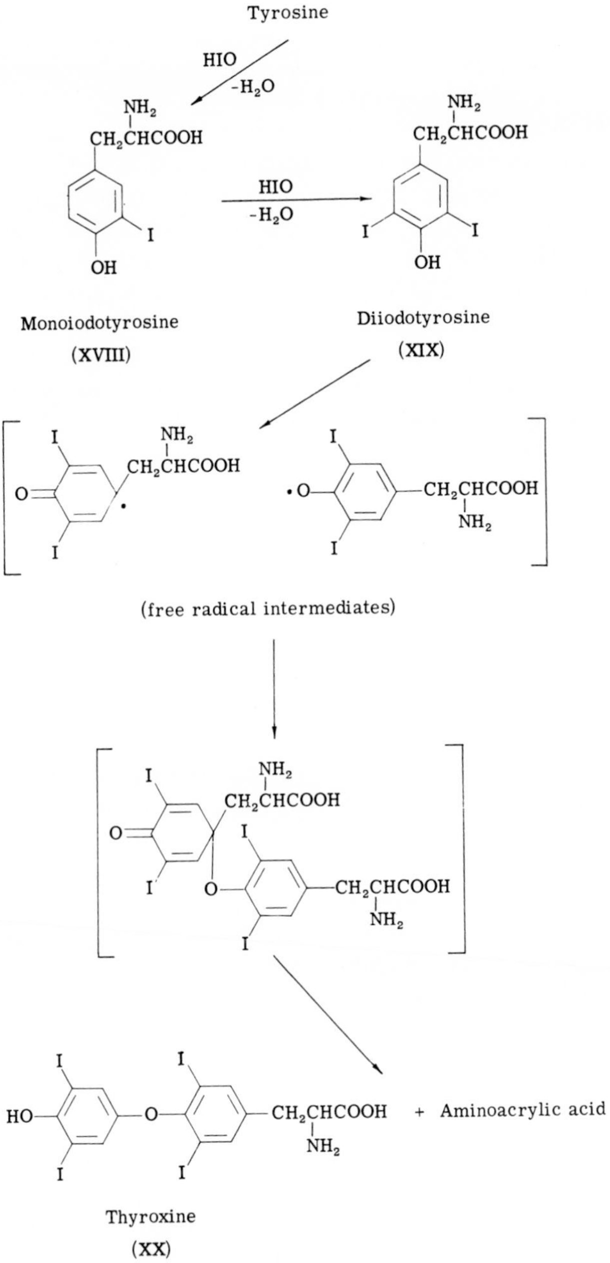

FIG. 13. Thyroxine biosynthesis.

and co-workers (*192, 194*) believe it is formed by condensation of mono-and diiodotyrosine or by incomplete iodination of preformed thyronine(s).

b. Metabolism of Thyroid Hormones. In mammals, both thyroxine and triiodothyronine are excreted unchanged and as their glucuronides in the bile, but the greater part of these compounds probably undergoes deiodination (*13*). Cell-free enzyme systems which deiodinate mono-iodotyrosine (*195*) and diiodotyrosine (*196*) have been prepared from sheep thyroid, liver, and kidney tissues. Liver and kidney slices convert diiodotyrosine to the corresponding lactic and pyruvic acids, but no deamination of diiodotyrosine was observed in thyroid slices (*197*). Triiodothyronine and thyroxine give the corresponding pyruvic acids when incubated with liver and kidney tissues (*198*). These α-keto analogs may then be decarboxylated. The acetic acid analogs of thyroxine and 3,5,3'-triiodothyronine are formed upon prolonged incubation of thyroxine with rat kidney cortex (*199*). This finding is of interest since these analogs have recently been postulated as the active forms of the thyroid hormone because they show no lag in biological assays as do the other thyroid-active compounds (*200*).

2. Other Halogenated Derivatives

Drechsel (*201*) in 1896 reported the isolation from the coral *Gorgonia cavolinii* of an iodine-containing amino acid which he named diiodo-gorgoic acid. This compound was later identified as 2,3-diiodotyrosine, and it has since been found that halogenated tyrosines are widely distributed in marine organisms, especially in the corneous skeleton of various Anthozoa and sponges. Besides diiodotyrosine there occurs monoiodotyrosine, thyroxine, monobromotyrosine, and dibromotyrosine. Their distribution has been used for biological classification. Such organisms concentrate considerable amounts of halogens from sea water, the amount fixed as halogenated tyrosine depending upon the organism's tyrosine content. This field has been comprehensively reviewed by Roche (*202*).

D. OTHER PATHWAYS IN MAMMALS

Although tyrosine is an intermediate in the major routes of phenyl-alanine metabolism in mammals, it appears that the latter amino acid can also be degraded by pathways not involving tyrosine. Transamination to form phenyl pyruvate is a quantitatively major pathway of phenylalanine metabolism in phenylketonuria and also occurs to a lesser degree in normal individuals. It has been known for some time that phenylacetylglutamine is excreted by man after ingestion of phenylacetic acid. Phenylacetylglutamine has also been reported as the detoxication product of phenylacetic acid in the chimpanzee (203). In other species (see Meister, 204, for references), including the rat, rabbit, cat, dog, sheep, horse, and monkey, ingested phenylacetic acid is excreted as phenylacetylglycine. Recently phenylacetylglutamine has been shown to be a normal constituent of human urine (205). These findings suggest the pathways for phenylalanine degradation shown in Fig. 14. Some phenylalanine is also converted to benzoic acid in mammals. Several lines of evidence support this. Hippuric acid, the glycine conjugate of benzoate, is found in the urine of fasted humans (205). C^{14}-Labeled benzoate is diluted in going to urinary hippurate in fasted rats (206), indicating the formation of endogenous benzoate. Labeled phenylalanine produces radioactive urinary hippurate (207) (Fig. 14). Bruns and Fiedler (208) have shown that β-phenylserine as well as phenylalanine is converted to benzoate in humans and rats, and they have prepared from rat liver and kidney a phenylserine aldolase which specifically cleaves L-threo-β-phenylserine to benzaldehyde and glycine. Thus, the side-chain hydroxylation of phenylalanine, which probably occurs in the biosynthesis of the alkaloid ephedrine (Section III, E, 3) also appears to take place in mammals.

Armstrong et al. (4) have detected more than forty phenolic compounds in human urine. During the feeding of purified diets, or even during starvation, phenolic compounds occur in rat urine and presumably arise from the aromatic amino acids. Booth and co-workers (209) have shown that tyrosine ingestion leads to increased excretion of phloretic (p-hydroxyphenylpropionic) acid, p-hydroxyphenyllactic, p-hydroxyphenylacetic, p-hydroxyphenylacrylic (p-coumaric), and p-hydroxybenzoic acids by rats. They suggested that these compounds arise from p-hydroxyphenylpuruvic acid by the following reactions (see Fig. 14):

p-hydroxyphenyl pyruvate → p-hydroxyphenyl lactate → p-coumarate → phloretate

p-Hydroxyphenyl acetate might arise from p-hydroxyphenyl pyruvate and p-hydroxybenzoate from p-coumarate. In the rat as much as 5% of a test dose of tyrosine might be excreted as these phenols or their conjugates. That the side chains of ortho- and meta-substituted phenols undergo similar reactions is indicated by the urinary excretion products detected by paper chromatography. β-m-Hydroxyphenylhydracrylic and m-hydroxyhippuric acids are major phenolic constituents of human urine. They appear to arise from substances present in the diet (210).

Another metabolic fate of tyrosine is the formation of the O-sulfate derivative which is found in normal human urine (211). The formation

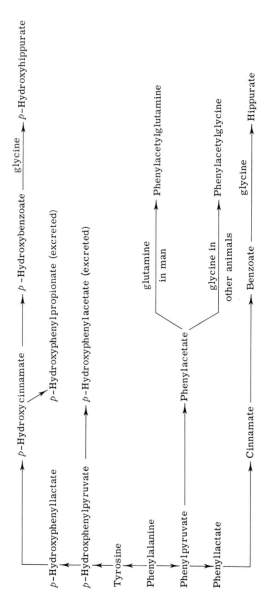

FIG. 14. Formation of excretory products of phenylalanine and tyrosine.

of this sulfate may have greater metabolic significance than a detoxication of excess tyrosine since this form of tyrosine is also found in the protein fibrinogen (*212*).

E. PATHWAYS IN HIGHER PLANTS AND FUNGI

Until recently the metabolism of phenylalanine and tyrosine in plants had not received as much study as it had in animals. As a consequence the metabolic pathways of the aromatic amino acids are, in general, known in greater detail in mammals than in plants. However, the evidence which has already become available indicates that these compounds are metabolized by many more diverse routes in the plant than in the animal kingdom. The introduction of isotopes has provided a powerful tool which has enabled the plant biochemist to demonstrate that the structural similarities between many nautral products and the aromatic amino acids are in fact based upon biogenetic relationships.

1. *Flavonoids and Lignins*

A vast number of these derivatives of flavone are found throughout the plant kingdom. The early suggestion (*213*) that these compounds are formed by the condensation of hexoses and trioses has been shown to be erroneous. The latest evidence indicates that the A ring is synthesized from acetate units whereas the B ring and C_2, C_3, and C_4 (Fig. 15) are formed from a precursor(s) very closely related to phenylalanine and tyrosine (*214*).

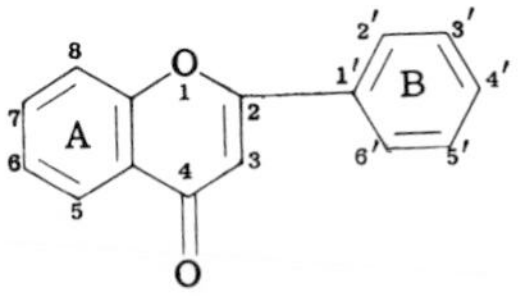

Flavone

FIG. 15. Structure of the parent flavone.

In 1953 Birch *et al.* (*215*) reported that the green alga *Chlamydomonas eugametos* synthesized isorhamnetin by the pathway shown in Fig. 16. This compound was reported to function as the female sex hormone for the dioecious form of the alga. Mutants of this organism were obtained in which the synthesis of (XXIII) was blocked at various stages and which therefore required exogenous (XXIII) or its precursors to effect copulation. The pathway in Fig. 16 was developed using these mutants and a copulation assay. The validity of these results have been

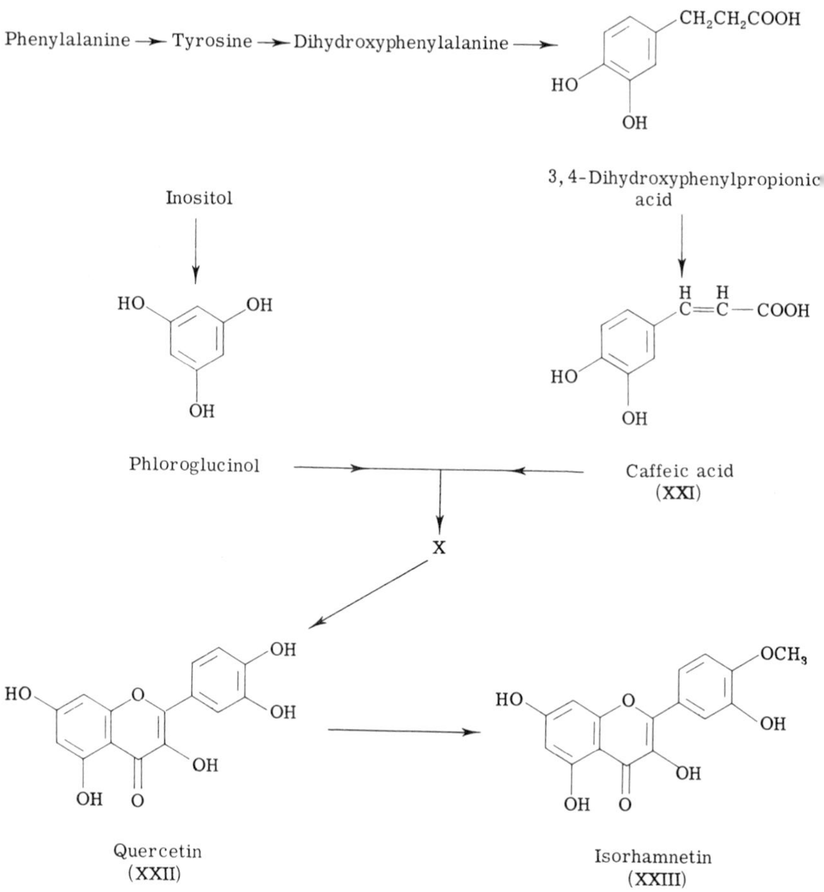

Fig. 16. Proposed scheme for isorhamnetin biosynthesis in *Chlamydomonas* (green algae).

placed in doubt by the subsequent failure to repeat some of the biological experiments with *C. eugametos* (*216*); the C¹⁴-labeled inositol and phloroglucinol are not incorporated into flavonoids by other species (*217*).

The synthesis of quercetin in *Fagopyrum tataricum* (buckwheat) has been studied (*217*) using shikimic acid, phenylalanine, and cinnamic, caffeic, sinapic, and ferulic acids (Fig. 16), all labeled with C¹⁴. These compounds were incorporated into the B ring of quercetin, and their efficiency as precursors decreased in the order listed. These findings led to the conclusion that phenylpyruvic acid, which is an intermediate in the biosynthesis of phenylalanine, is the key (C_6-C_3) intermediate in flavonoid biosynthesis. Other evidence that phenylalanine is involved in quercetin biosynthesis was provided by the finding that when $C^{14}O_2$ and phenylalanine were supplied to buckwheat the A ring of quercetin contained almost all the radioactivity, thus showing that the unlabeled atoms of phenylalanine were producing the B ring (*218*). Geissman and Swain (*219*) confirmed the conversion of phenylalanine-2-C^{14} to quercetin in *F. esculentum.* This species and *Nicotiana tabacum* also formed caffeic acid-2-C^{14} (XXI, Fig. 16) from phenylalanine-2-C^{14}. Since the closely related ferulic acid-3-C^{14} (XXIV, Fig. 17) is converted to

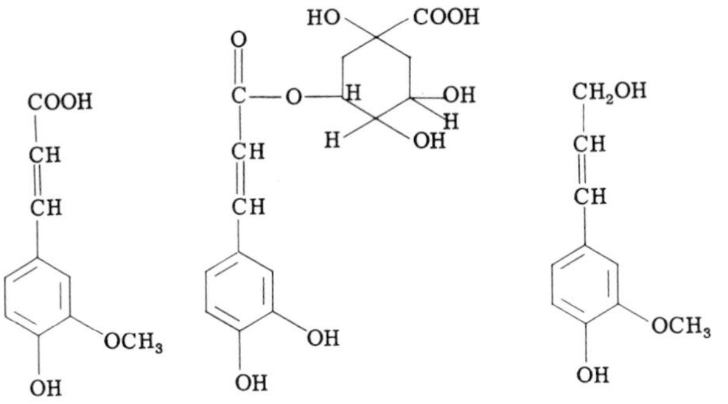

Ferulic acid (XXIV) — Chlorogenic acid (XXV) — Coniferyl alcohol (XXVI)

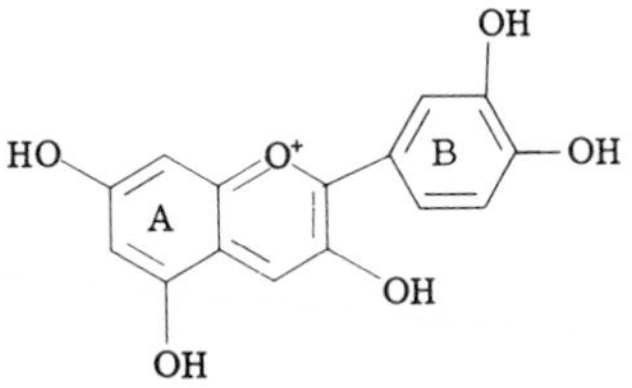

Cyanidin (XXVII)

FIG. 17. Some plant products related to the aromatic amino acids.

chlorogenic acid (XXV) and cyanidin (XXVII) in wheat, it appears probable that these compounds are also derived from phenylalanine or its aromatic precursors. Recently all nine carbon atoms of phenylalanine have been shown to be utilized in forming cyanidin in red cabbage plants (*220*).

The A ring of flavonoids has been shown by isotopic experiments to be derived from acetate (*221*). The labeling pattern in the A ring of cyanidin produced from acetate-1-C^{14} in red cabbage seedlings (222) shows that this ring is probably formed by the head-to-tail condensation of three acetate units, as was postulated earlier by Birch and Donovan (223). The biosynthesis of flavonoid compounds has been recently reviewed by Bogorad (214).

Lignin is a polymeric plant constituent of uncertain and probably variable composition. Spruce lignin, one of the most widely studied, appears to be a polymer derived by dehydrogenative polymerization of coniferyl alcohol (XXVI, Fig. 17) (for reviews see also Higuchi, 224). Enzymatic dehydrogenation of coniferyl alcohol in the presence of mushroom laccase or horse-radish peroxidase and hydrogen peroxide gives rise to products which appear to be identical with natural lignin (225). Brown and Neish (226) reported that C^{14}-labeled phenylpropanes including phenylalanine, tyrosine, phenylpyruvic, cinnamic, and ferulic acids were incorporated into the precursors of lignin. Though the C_6–C_3 carbon skeleton is used, the C_6–C_1 compounds of the benzoic acid type were not incorporated. The distribution of C^{14} in vanillic acid obtained by degradation of the lignin of sugar cane grown on labeled shikimic acid shows that the pattern of incorporation into the benzene rings of lignin is the same as that found in phenylalanine and tyrosine (227). The keto acids, phenylpyruvic and p-hydroxyphenylpyruvic acids are more likely to be direct intermediates than the amino acids, though the keto acids and amino acids are probably in equilibrium. Further studies (228) suggest that aromatization occurs before introduction of substituents in the benzene ring, which in turn occurs before polymerization. Each type of lignin has its own monomers, e.g., one has the series:

Precursors   Unsubstituted   Ring-substituted
(shikimic acid →   aromatic C_6 – C_3 →   aromatic C_6 – C_3 → Lignin
   etc.)   compounds   compounds

The work of Freudenberg and co-workers (225) suggests that the glucoside coniferin is formed and that a β-glucosidase releases the free alcohol, which is then oxidatively polymerized by laccase and peroxidase.

2. Alkaloids and Related Compounds

The structural similarity of the aromatic amino acids to many of the simpler alkaloids is obvious. The complex structures of some of the higher molecular weight alkaloids have led many organic chemists, notably Robinson (229) to postulate ingenious schemes for their biosynthesis in plants, often starting from the aromatic amino acids. Before the advent of isotopic tracers the only method available to test a postulated biogenetic pathway was to administer a suspected precursor to the plant and measure the amount of alkaloid subsequently produced.

This method cannot yield unequivocal results, since an increased alkaloid production following administration of a postulated precursor compound might be due to side effects and, conversely, a true precursor might not cause an increase in alkaloid production. The extensive experimentation which has been done by this technique has been reviewed by Dawson (230) and James (231).

Only in recent years, using isotopes, has it been possible to test critically some of the many postulated schemes for alkaloid synthesis by definitive experiments in the alkaloid producing plants. The contributions of isotopes to the problems of alkaloid biosynthesis have been reviewed recently by Leete (232).

a. *Phenylethylamine Alkaloids.* Several members of this group of alkaloids, all of which have an obvious structural relationship to phenylalanine, have been shown to be derived from the aromatic amino acids. Considerable evidence is available to show that hordenine (XXX), the chief alkaloid of barley (*Panicum*) is formed from phenylalanine by the pathway shown in Fig. 18. Leete et al. (233)

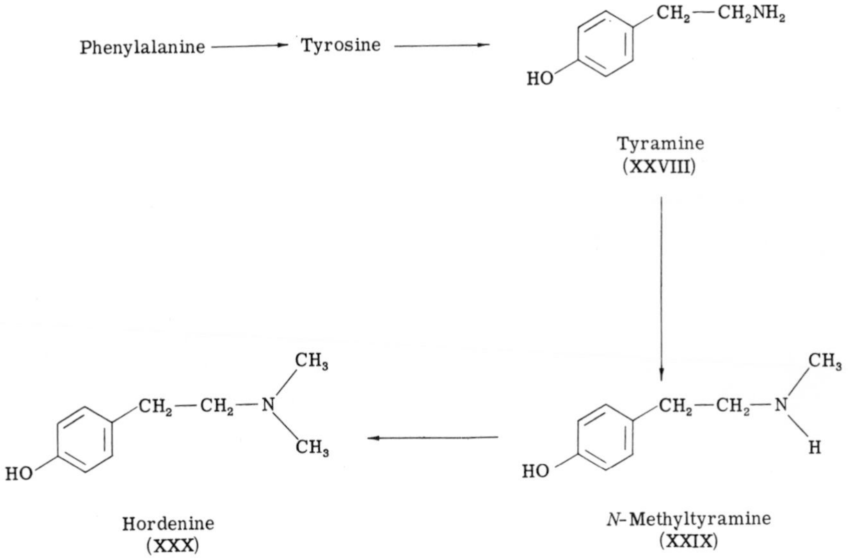

Fig. 18. Scheme for hordenine biosynthesis (232).

found that tyramine-2-C^{14} (XXVIII) added to the nutrient solution of sprouting barley was converted to N-methyltyramine (XXIX) and hordenine (XXX). The higher specific activity of (XXIX) was interpreted as evidence for the product-precursor relationship shown. Degradation studies showed that the C^{14} was in C-2 of the alkaloid, indicating direct conversion without rearrangement. Similar experiments with tyrosine-2-C^{14} (*234*) and phenylalanine-2-C^{14} (*235*) established the pathway illustrated. Partial confirmation of this scheme has been obtained in experiments with excised barley embryos (*236*), in which tyramine, but not tyrosine, was found to be converted to (XXIX) and (XXX). The synthesis of (XXX) in excised barley roots has also been reported (*232*).

Mescaline, one of the chief alkaloids of *Echinocactus williamsii*, the peyote cactus, is also derived from tyrosine. This alkaloid was shown to be formed from tyrosine-2-C^{14} without randomization of the isotope (*237*) (Fig. 19). However, phenylalanine-3-C^{14} failed to yield labeled

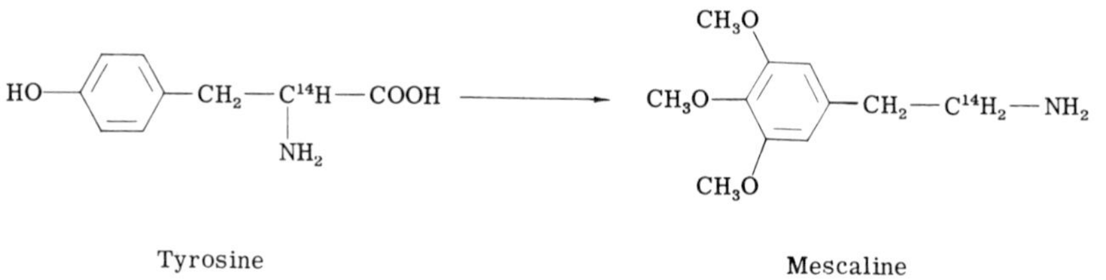

Tyrosine   Mescaline

FIG. 19. Synthesis of mescaline from tyrosine (*232*).

mescaline (*232*), thus suggesting that this species, unlike barley, does not convert phenylalanine to tyrosine.

Another route of alkaloid biosynthesis from phenylalanine involves hydroxylation of the side chain rather than the benzene ring. This reaction appears to be the initial step in the formation of ephedrine in *Ephedra distachya* and d-norpseudoephedrine in *Catha edulis* (Fig. 20). It has been shown (*238*) that l-ephedrine-N^{15} is formed from phenyl-alanine-N^{15} in both the intact plant and excised root of the former species. The closely related alkaloid d-norpseudoephedrine has been shown to be derived from phenylalanine-3-C^{14} in an excised shoot of *C. edulis* (*239*). In further studies on ephedrine biosynthesis it was found that the N-methyl, but not the C-methyl, group could arise from methionine (*240*). However, formate is a precursor of both these methyl groups (*241*). It was also shown that α-amino-β-ketophenylpropanol-C^{14} (XXXIV) is converted to ephedrine (*242*). A biosynthetic scheme consistent with these data is presented in Fig. 20.

A similar side-chain hydroxylation of tyrosine appears to be the first step in the biosynthesis of amygdalin (*p*-hydroxymandelonitrile-β-glyco-side). This compound was labeled with C^{14} in the nitrile group (Fig. 21)

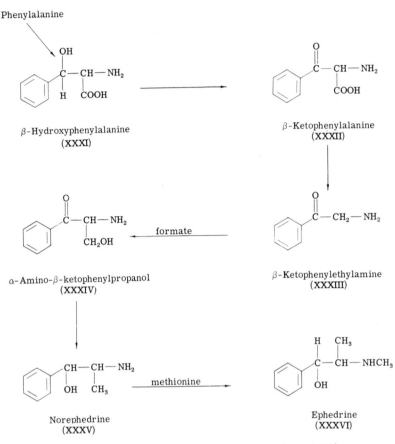

FIG. 20. Postulated route of ephedrine biosynthesis (232).

when tyrosine-2-C^{14} was fed to *Sorghum vulgare* plants (243). There is evidence that *p*-hydroxyphenylserine (XXXVII) is an intermediate in this conversion.

b. Morphine. The biosynthesis of this important alkaloid has been shown to proceed essentially by the route suggested in 1925 by Robinson, who proposed that morphine is formed from two molecules of 3,4-dihydroxyphenylalanine (X, Fig. 22). Transamination and decarboxylation of (X) would form 3,4-dihydroxyphenylacetaldehyde (XXXIX) which, upon condensation with another molecule of (X) by a Mannich reaction, accompanied by decarboxylation, would produce norlaudanosine (XL). Cyclization of (XL), followed by N-methylation, would yield morphine. More than thirty years later this scheme was

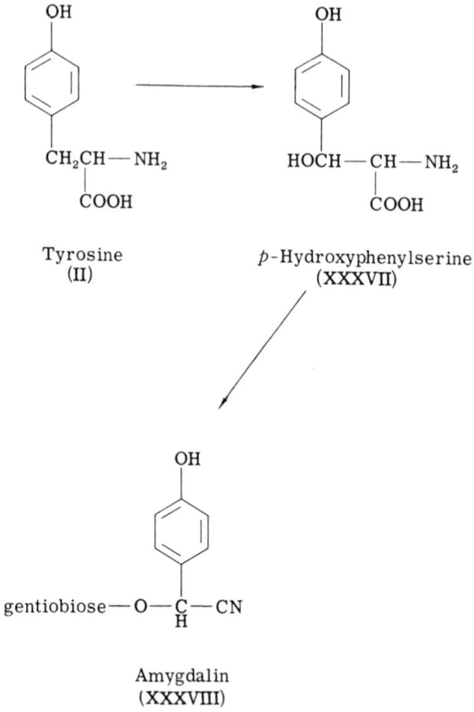

FIG. 21. Biosynthesis of amygdalin (232).

tested when DL-tyrosine-2-C¹⁴ was fed to intact plants of *Papaver somnif-erum* by addition to the nutrient medium bathing the roots. Morphine isolated from the poppies was radioactive (244), and degradation showed that one-half this activity was located in C-16. Subsequent degradations (245) demonstrated that the remaining C¹⁴ was located at C-9 or C-12 or both. If, as seems most logical, this C¹⁴ is in C-9, the hypothesis of Robinson is confirmed. Phenylalanine-2-C¹⁴ was also found to be incorporated into morphine by *Papaver* (246), showing that this plant probably converts phenylalanine to tyrosine.

c. *Indole Alkaloids.* Tryptophan is an obvious potential precursor for this group of compounds. Although the remainder of tryptophan metabolism will be discussed in a later section, the formation of gramine and lysergic acid will be treated here. Gramine is an alkaloid produced in young barley plants. Gramine labeled with C¹⁴ in the methylene group was formed when tryptophan-β-C¹⁴ was fed to germinating barley seedlings (247). The conversion of the intact tryptophan molecule to gramine was studied with tryptophan labeled with C¹⁴ in the β-carbon

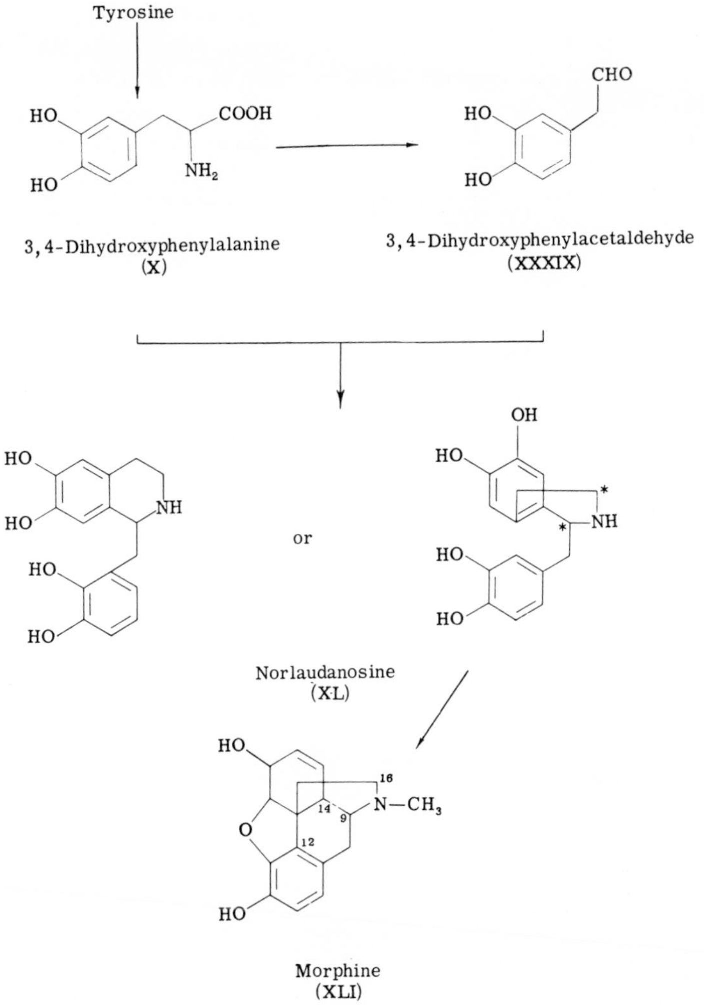

FIG. 22. Biosynthesis of morphine from two molecules of tyrosine (*232*).

and in carbon-2 of the indole nucleus (*248*). An attractive hypothesis at this stage was that gramine is formed from tryptophan via indole-acetic acid (see Section IV, G). Thus formation of gramine might have the physiological function of regulating indoleacetic acid concentration in young barley plants. However, it was shown that neither indoleacetic acid-α-C^{14} (*249, 250*) nor indole-3-aldehyde-C^{14} (*249*) were incorporated into gramine. Henry and Leete (*250*) concluded, on the basis of experiments with tryptophan, that gramine must be formed as a result of a direct cleavage between the α- and β-carbon atoms under a nucleo-philic attack by ammonia; the primary products are glycine and 3-aminomethylindole. Since Breccia and Marion (249) found the indole-3-pyruvic acid-β-C[14] and indole-3-acrylic acid-β-C[14] produced methylene-labeled gramine, the scheme shown in Fig. 23 was postulated

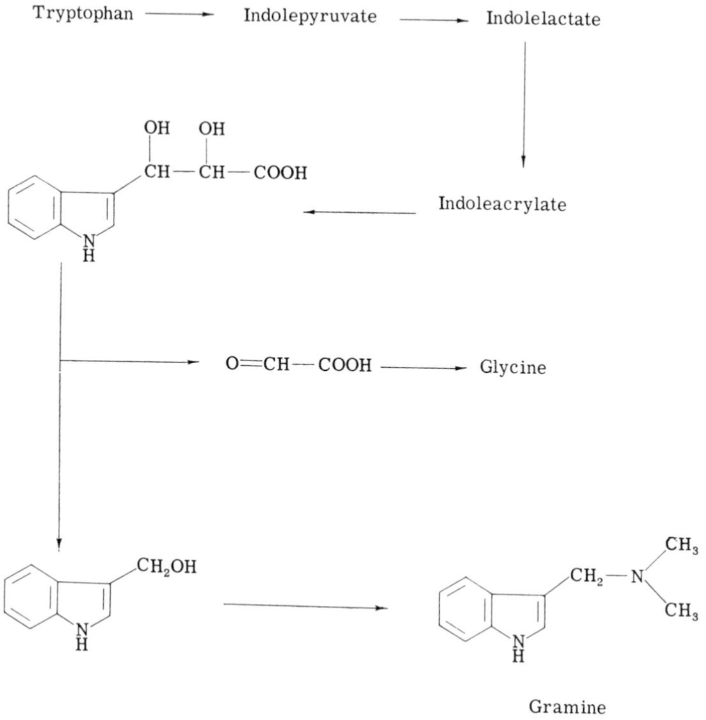

FIG. 23. Biosynthesis of gramine from tryptophan (232).

to account for the labeling of glycine from α-labeled tryptophan in bar-ley (232).

Several hypothetical schemes for the biosynthesis of the lysergic acid moiety of the ergot alkaloids have been proposed, all of them starting from tryptophan. Suhadolnik et al. (251) injected tryptophan-7a-C[14] into the stem of rye infected with the ergot-producing fungus Claviceps purpurea. The incorporation of C[14] into the isolated ergot alkaloids was so slight (0.003–0.019%) that these workers considered tryptophan not to be an ergot precursor. However, Mothes et al. (252) reported in-corporation of tryptophan-β-C[14] into the lysergic acid moiety of three ergot alkaloids and considered tryptophan to be a lysergic acid pre-

cursor. The production of the related alkaloids elymoclavin and agro-
clavin in saprophytic cultures of certain strains of mold, from labeled
tryptophan, is more convincing evidence that tryptophan is converted
to lysergic acid-like compounds (253). The incorporation of phenyl-
alanine-C^{14} into ergotamine, presumably as a portion of the cyclic
peptide side chain, has been reported to occur in homogenates or
ergot sclerotia (254).

   d. Gliotoxin. Although it is an indole derivative this substance produced by the fungus *Trichoderma viride* is not generally classified as
an alkaloid. Despite its obvious structural relationship to tryptophan
this amino acid is not incorporated (255). The biosynthesis of the complete carbon skeleton of gliotoxin has been elucidated by Suhadolnik
and co-workers (255, 256, 257) (Fig. 24). Phenylalanine-1-C^{14} or -2-C^{14},
when added to the culture medium of *T. viride* was incorporated into
gliotoxin with little dilution. Most of the activity incorporated from

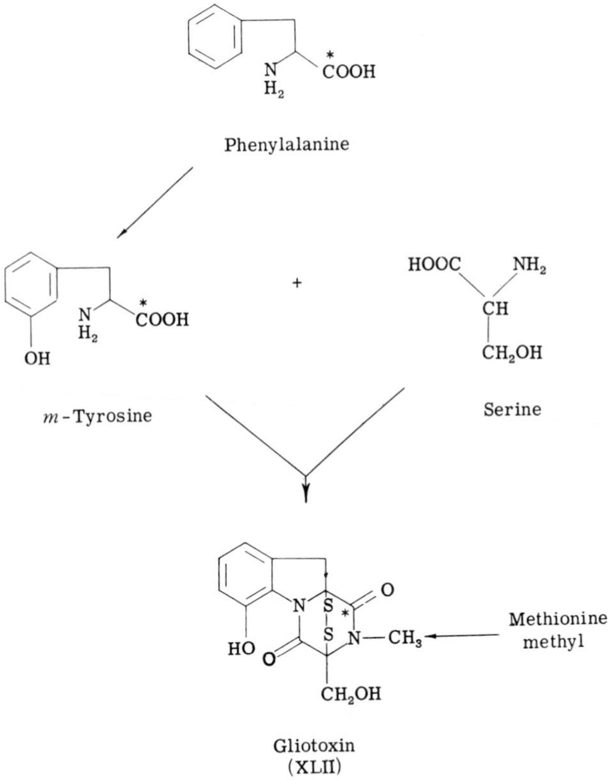

Fig. 24. Gliotoxin biosynthesis.

phenylalanine-1-C^{14} was found in the expected carbonyl group. The remainder of the carbon skeleton is derived from serine (256, 257) with methionine providing the N-methyl carbon. m-Hydroxyphenylalanine is an even better precursor of gliotoxin than is phenylalanine (256), thus indicating that hydroxylation probably precedes ring closure. This hydroxylation of phenylalanine in the *meta* rather than the *para* position represents a novel route for its metabolism. The dietary sources of compounds leading to urinary m-hydroxy acids referred to in Section III, D may arise in plants by similar reactions.

3. Other Pathways in Plants

Very little work appears to have been done in this area. Enzyme systems which catalyze transamination between α-ketoglutarate and phenylalanine and tyrosine have been prepared from lupine and barley seedlings (258). It has been reported (259) that lupine mitochondria oxidize phenylpyruvate to benzaldehyde and CO_2. The presence of 3,4-dihydroxyphenylalanine in plants (260), as well as an active tyrosinase in many species (166), indicates that melanin formation may occur by a route similar to that in mammals.

There is some indirect evidence that a pathway of degradation of phenylalanine similar to the homogentisic acid pathway of mammals may exist in plants. For example, it was found that an unsaturated fatty acid became heavily labeled with C^{14} from phenylalanine-2-C^{14} in barley (248), and the lipid fraction of *Trichoderma viride* (255) was heavily labeled with C^{14} after phenylalanine-C^{14} administration.

F. Pathways in Microorganisms

Phenylalanine and tyrosine are metabolized by a large number of pathways by this chemically versatile group of organisms. Among the wide variety of microorganisms that can utilize phenylalanine or tyrosine as carbon and/or energy sources, some appear to degrade these amino acids by routes similar to the homogentisic acid pathway used in mammals. Some strains of *Vibrio* and *Pseudomonas* convert tyrosine to p-hydroxyphenyl pyruvate and homogentisate (261). The enzymes which convert homogentisate to acetoacetate are found in pseudomonads (126), and *Aspergillus niger* converts phenylalanine and phenylacetic acid to homogentisate (262).

Decarboxylation of the aromatic amino acids to form the corresponding amines, a reaction which can occur also in mammals, at least in the case of tyrosine, is carried out by a large variety of bacteria. The phenylalanine decarboxylase of *Streptococcus faecalis* can be used to assay phenylalanine (263). Bacterial tyrosine decarboxylase has been studied in detail, especially by Gale and co-workers, who investigated tyrosine decarboxylation in over 1000 strains of bacteria (see review, 264). This bacterial enzyme requires pyridoxal phosphate as a cofactor, and, unlike mammalian tyrosine decarboxylase, it also attacks dihydroxyphenylalanine. Decarboxylation usually occurs only in acid media and is probably a protective mechanism tending to restore pH to neutrality. Under alkaline conditions the splitting of tyrosine to form phenol (see below) is usually favored. The amine resulting from decarboxylase action can be further metabolized by oxidative deamination to the aldehyde or, more often, by further oxidation to the corresponding acid:

$$R—CH_2NH_2 \rightarrow RCHO \rightarrow RCOOH$$

Another common bacterial route of phenylalanine and tyrosine metabolism involves the formation of the corresponding keto acids by oxidative deamination or transamination. For example, an L-amino acid oxidase of *Proteus vulgaris* readily deaminates phenylalanine and tyrosine (as well as some other amino acids) to the keto acids (265). Unlike the amino acid oxidase of rat kidney, this enzyme does not produce H_2O_2. *Mycobacterium lacticola* deaminates and oxidizes tyrosine, but not phenylalanine (266). Phenylalanine and tyrosine are transaminated by *Escherichia coli* (267) and *Bacillus subtilis*. The keto acids formed by transamination and deamination can be oxidatively decarboxylated to the acetic acid derivatives in some organisms. The pathways shown in Fig. 25 have been demonstrated in a *Vibrio* species (31).

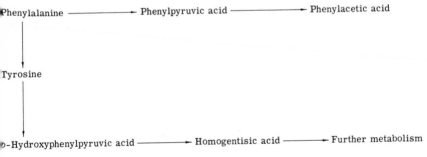

FIG. 25. Pathways of degradation of phenylalanine and tyrosine by *Vibrio* (31).

An even more complicated set of reactions has been ascribed to a strain of *Pseudomonas fluorescens* which, on the basis of sequential induction data, was reported to carry out the transformations (268) shown in Fig. 26. This organism can carry out many of the reactions of

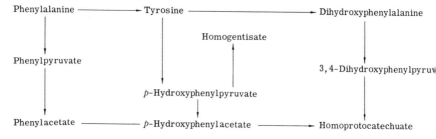

Fig. 26. Pathways of degradation of phenylalanine and tyrosine demonstrated with *Pseudomonas flourescens* (*268*).

the aromatic amino acids which occur in mammals.

A variation in this keto acid type pathway has been observed in *Saccharomyces cerevisiae* (*269*). In this organism tyrosine is transaminated with α-ketoglutarate to form *p*-hydroxyphenyl pyruvate, which is then decarboxylated to *p*-hydroxyphenylacetaldehyde. The aldehyde is reduced by DPNH and alcohol dehydrogenase to form tyrosol.

Reduction of the pyruvic acid side chains of the transamination products of phenylalanine and tyrosine would give the corresponding phenyllactic acids (*270*), and dehydration of the lactic acids would yield the corresponding acrylic acids, *p*-coumaric from tyrosine (*271*) and cinnamic from phenylalanine. The arylpropionic acids which have been observed in microorganisms (*272*) could be derived by reduction of the acrylic acid side chains. The degradation of the phenylalanine and tyrosine side chains can proceed all the way to the formation of benzoic acid and *p*-hydroxybenzoic acid in some pseudomonads (*273*). Several groups of microorganisms including many bacteria, *Actinomycetes*, and *Neurospora* possess the almost universally distributed ability to form melanin from tyrosine (*274*).

A reaction of tyrosine which seems to be found only in bacteria is the cleavage by β-tyrosinase of *E. coli* to form phenol (*275*) and alanine. This reaction is analogous to the bacterial formation of indole from tryptophan (Section IV, H).

IV. Metabolism of Tryptophan

Since the discovery of tryptophan by Hopkins and Cole (*9*) in 1902, the study of its metabolism has been a challenge to those who are interested in the comparative aspects of biochemistry. While the known metabolites of this amino acid are numerous, some of the intermediates through which the indole nucleus passes in its dissimilation to carbon dioxide have not yet been identified. The recognition of indican, kynurenic acid, kynurenine, xanthurenic acid, indoleacetic acid, and other excretory products placed the state of knowledge of the fate of tryptophan in a relatively advanced position at one time. However, because of the complexity of the pathways involved, even in a single species, progress in the elucidation of the individual reactions in the oxidation of tryptophan has lagged behind that of other amino acids. Of considerable interest is the fact that this compound, which is required in relatively small amounts, preformed in the diet of many species, is the precursor of such diverse and biochemically important compounds as a vitamin (niacin), a neurohormone (serotonin), a phytohormone (indoleacetic acid), and an eye pigment in *Drosophila* (ommochrome).

The key experiment of Krehl *et al.* (*276*) which showed that tryptophan would replace niacin in the diet of the rat, provided new approaches to the study of the metabolism of this amino acid. The hypothesis that tryptophan is a direct precursor of niacin was supported by much experimental work and then established unequivocally by experiments with isotopic tryptophan (*277*). This recognition of its niacin-precursor role made possible the application of the biochemical genetics method which has been so effectively used to elucidate the route of biosynthesis of other vitamins and amino acids. Niacin-requiring mutants of *Neurospora* played a major role in bringing to light the individual reactions in this sequence. The discussion which follows will be concerned largely with the conversion of tryptophan to niacin and related reactions with emphasis on the species variations which have been detected.

At least four reactions of tryptophan play a part in its metabolism: (*a*) oxidation to formylkynurenine; (*b*) hydroxylation to 5-hydroxytryptophan; (*c*) conversion to indole-3-acetic acid; (*d*) fission to indole, pyruvic acid, and ammonia. Although none of these reactions, with the possible exception of the conversion to indole-3-acetic acid, fit the usual pattern of initial transamination, this amino acid can undergo transamination *in vitro* under the influence of enzymes found in animals, plants, and bacteria (*278*) and *in vivo* as shown by the ability of indole pyruvate (*279*) and D-tryptophan (*280*) to support the growth of rats on tryptophan-deficient diets (*279*). The evidence that indole pyruvate is involved in indole acetate formation will be considered later. The role of transamination in the complete degradation of tryptophan is difficult to evaluate *in vivo* since the alanine arising from the side chain through kynurenine would label indicator compounds such as glutamate or glycogen in the same way as would pyruvate arising in a trytophanase-type reaction with tryptophan or indole pyruvate.

Reaction (*a*) above appears to lead to the important routes of degradation in the rat (*281*), *Pseudomonas fluorescens* (*282*), and per-

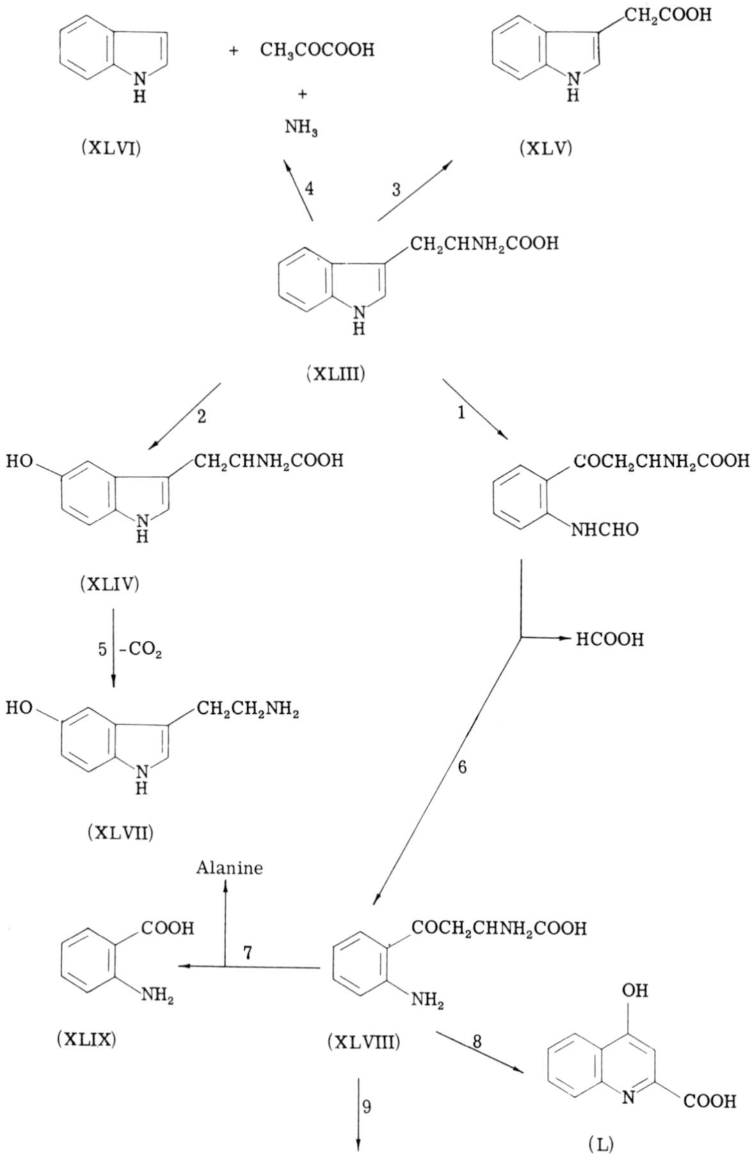

(Continued)
Fig. 27. Kynurenine-3-hydroxyanthranilate pathway of tryptophan metabolism and related reactions.

haps other species. The same initial reaction is involved in niacin synthesis in animals, *Neurospora*, and possibly other forms. This pathway, illustrated in Fig. 27 has been formulated largely from results obtained with niacin-requiring mutants of *Neurospora crassa*, with animal growth, excretion, and isotope experiments and with *in vitro* studies of *Neurospora* and various animal tissues. This development has been extensively reviewed (*13, 283–286*) and will be considered in more detail as individual reactions are discussed.

Before proceeding to specific reactions some attention will be given to the experimental approaches which led to the scheme outlined in Fig. 27. The evidence for the participation of kynurenine (XLVIII) in *Neurospora crassa* was based on the accumulation N^a-acetylkynurenine by one mutant (287) and utilization of kynurenine for growth by other mutants (288). 3-Hydroxyanthranilate (LII) was first recognized as an intermediate when it was isolated from the culture filtrates of one niacin-dependent strain (289, 290) and was found to replace niacin (LVIII) for other mutants. At this stage it was evident that 3-hydroxy-kynurenine (LI) was also an intermediate, since anthranilic acid (XLIX) was not a niacin precursor as would be anticipated if Reaction 7 (Fig. 27) were followed by hydroxylation of anthranilic acid. This means that Reactions 9 and 10 are involved in 3-hydroxyanthranilate formation. This was verified when hydroxykynurenine was isolated from pupae of *Calliphora erythrocephala* (291, 292) synthesized (293), and shown to replace niacin in a *Neurospora* mutant which accumulates N^a-acetyl-kynurenine (287, 294). This compound, an intermediate (cn⁺ substance), in the conversion of kynurenine to ommochrome, an eye pigment in *Drosophila*, was also isolated from silkworm larvae (295). Quinolinic acid (LVI), first identified as an excretion product of tryptophan in rats (296), accumulates in the medium of one mutant and supports the growth of a niacin-dependent mutant of *Neurospora* (297, 298).

The results of growth experiments and analysis of excretory products suggested that the scheme also operates in mammals. This was subsequently established by isotopic studies. Kynurenine, which is recognized as an excretory product (299) of trpytophan, will substitute for niacin for rat growth (300, 301) as will hydroxykynurenine (301). Administration of both compounds enhances the excretion of quinolinic acid, niacin, and xanthurenic acid (LIII) (302). 3-Hydroxyanthranilate likewise supports growth (303) and increases the excretion of pyridinecarboxylic acids and their metabolites (302, 304) in niacin-deficient rats.

Isotopic experiments showed that C^{14}-labeled kynurenine and kynurenic acid (L) arise from tryptophan-β-C^{14} (305) and N^1-methylnicotinamide (LIX) (277) from tryptophan-3-C^{14}. The retention of N^{15} from the indole ring of tryptophan in kynurenine, kynurenic, xanthurenic (306), and quinolinic acids (307) was consistent with the reaction sequence shown in Fig. 27. Likewise when tryptophan and 3-hydroxy-anthranilate labeled with C^{14} were given to rats, the labeling patterns in quinolinic acid (308) and N^1-methylnicotinamide (309) were consistent with this scheme.

In addition to all this evidence, individual reactions of this pathway have been studied *in vitro* using a variety of enzyme sources. The following sections deal with these individual reactions and the enzymes and coenzymes involved.

A. KYNURENINE FORMATION

1. Cleavage of the Indole Nucleus

The conversion of L-tryptophan to kynurenine involves a 4-electron oxidation (addition of O_2) and hydrolysis of the resulting formylkynurenine to kynurenine and formate (Reaction 6, Fig. 27). These reactions were first observed in vitro by Kotake and Masayama (310), who named the enzyme system responsible "tryptophan pyrrolase." The liver system was partially purified (311) and shown to consist of what appeared to be a coupled peroxidase-oxidase which formed formylkynurenine and a formamidase (312) which hydrolyzed the initial product to kynurenine and formate.

$$\text{L-Tryptophan} \xrightarrow{O_2} \text{Formyl-L-kynurenine}$$

$$\text{Formyl-L-kynurenine} \xrightarrow{H_2O} \text{L-Kynurenine} + \text{formate}$$

The enzyme which catalyzes the first of these reactions was found (311) to be inhibited by cyanide, carbon monoxide, and catalase. The catalase inhibition and its reversal by enzymatically generated hydrogen peroxide, suggested that the oxygen-requiring reaction formed H_2O_2 which was needed in the next step of a two-step process catalyzed by a single enzyme. The sensitivity to both cyanide and carbon monoxide suggested that the enzyme was an iron porphyrin compound whose action depended upon the reversible oxidation of the iron. The enzyme was named tryptophan peroxidase-oxidase.

More recently (313) the rat liver enzyme and a similar one from *Pseudomonas* sp. (282) have been purified and found not to require peroxide for catalysis. The peroxide is required in the presence of substrate to reduce the inactive ferriporphyrin protein to the active ferro form which catalyzes the addition of molecular oxygen to the substrate.

The use of O_2^{18} and H_2O^{18} has demonstrated (314) that both oxygen atoms introduced in the conversion of tryptophan to formylkynurenine arise from molecular oxygen. This finding and the failure of 2-oxindoly-alanine (315, 316) or α,β-dihydroxytryptophan (314) to react in this system indicate that oxidation and cleavage of the indole ring both occur in a single step. This and similar reactions catalyzed by "oxygenases" were discussed by Hayaishi et al. (314).

Tryptophan pyrrolase is found in relatively small amounts, though it is sufficiently active in the liver to account for all the tryptophan which is metabolized. Although other organisms including *Neurospora* must contain a similar system, tryptophan pyrrolase does not appear to have been studied except in liver and pseudomonads. As expected, the enzymes from these two sources are different, but both are rather specific for L-tryptophan and act slowly, if at all, on 5- or 7-hydroxy-tryptophan (*317*), D-tryptophan, or α-methyltryptophan (*313*).

a. *Adaptive Formation of Tryptophan Pyrrolase.* While adaptive formation of bacterial enzymes in response to exposure to the substrate is commonplace, adaptive formation in animal systems seems to have been first observed with liver tryptophan pyrrolase (*318*). The administration of tryptophan by the oral, intravenous, or intraperitoneal route to rabbits or rats caused five- to tenfold increase in the liver concentration of the enzyme in 4–10 hours. Ethionine inhibits adaptation in rats (*319*) and in perfused rabbit liver (*320*), suggesting that the adaptation involves *de novo* synthesis of the enzyme. Methionine reverses the ethionine effect in the isolated perfused liver. Liver slices retain their ability to adapt (*321*), and it has been reported (*322*) that preincubation of liver homogenates with L-tryptophan for 30 minutes increased the pyrrolase activity by 46%. The lack of correlation between the capacity of tryptophan analogs to stabilize the enzyme *in vitro* and to induce enzyme formation *in vivo* suggests (*323*) that the induction is more than stabilization of enzyme already formed. Whether the "induction" is stimulation of protein synthesis or release of latent enzyme has not been determined.

The induction of pyrrolase by adrenocorticotropic hormone or glucocorticoids appears to occur by a mechanism distinct from that involved in substrate induction (*324*). Substrate is effective in adrenalectomized rats and hydrocortisone did not elevate the free tryptophan in liver or the tryptophan metabolites in the urine. The hormone mechanism may account for the nonspecific response to a number of aromatic compounds, and to certain stress conditions.

The adaptive formation of this enzyme led to investigations of its occurrence in fetal liver (*94, 325*). It first appears in the liver of the rat about the twelfth day after birth, in the guinea pig late in gestation, and in the rabbit at birth (*326*). Premature and postmature rabbit fetuses developed the enzyme within a few hours of delivery. In all cases the adaptive response to tryptophan did not appear until normal adult levels of the enzyme had been attained.

2. Hydrolysis of Formylkynurenine

The accumulation of N-formylkynurenine when L-tryptophan is incubated with a partially purified tryptophan pyrrolase from liver (*311*), but not in the whole animal or in an unfractionated liver extract, suggests that a potent formylase normally hydrolyzes this amide as fast as it is formed. Such an enzyme has been observed in liver (311), in bacteria (282), and Neurospora (327). These enzymes are relatively specific, although the Neurospora enzyme will hydrolyze formamides of other aromatic amines at slower rates. Rabinowitz and Tabor (328) reported the increased excretion of formate by normal rats given L-tryptophan. In folic acid-deficient rats the extra formate excretion represented about 40% of the tryptophan administered. This indicates that the deficient and probably normal rats metabolize tryptophan via formylkynurenine.

B. REACTIONS OF KYNURENINE

1. Hydroxylation

This pathway appears to be the major one for some organisms while in some bacteria, discussed below, this reaction is not involved in the dissimilation of the indole nucleus. The role of hydroxykynurenine as a precursor of the eye pigments of insects has been referred to above, and its role as a precursor of hydroxyanthranilic acid will be discussed in Section IV, B, 2.

Many investigators attempted to obtain hydroxylation in vitro before it was accomplished by de Castro, Price, and Brown (329). They demonstrated a TPNH-dependent, oxygen-requiring enzyme in liver mitochondria which catalyzes the reaction shown in Fig. 28. This system has also been described by Saito et al. (330) and by Kotake et al. (331).

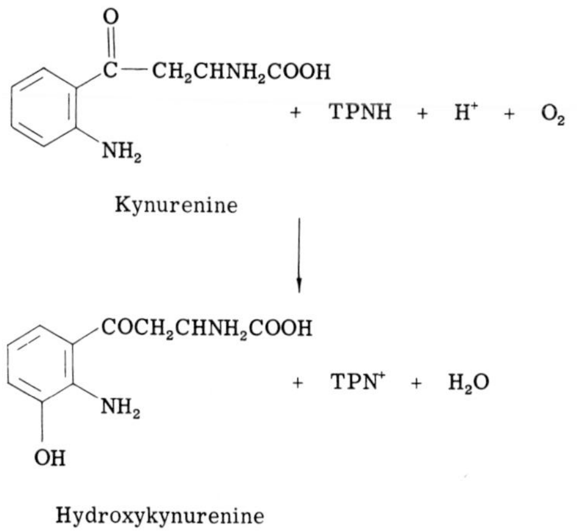

FIG. 28. Hydroxylation of kynurenine.

The enzyme has been partially purified (332) and thoroughly studied. It was released by disrupting the mitochondria with sonic oscillation or by cholate or digitonin treatment. This oxygenase is specific for reduced triphosphopyridine nucleotide and for the L-isomer of kynurenine. Replacement of the amino group in the 2-position with a hydroxyl or nitro group gives substrates which are hydroxylated at reduced rates, but other compounds tested, including the N-formyl and N-acetyl derivatives, were completely inactive. The oxygenase activity was enhanced three- to tenfold by the addition of any of a number of monovalent anions. The oxygen of the hydroxyl group arises not from water, but from molecular oxygen which seems to be characteristic of this type of reaction (332).

In addition to the TPNH and monovalent anion requirement, it has been suggested on the basis of excretion studies in rats that riboflavin might be involved in the hydroxylation of kynurenine (333). The increased kynurenic acid excretion (334) by riboflavin-deficient rats given tryptophan (see Fig. 27) is in keeping with this proposed role of riboflavin. Likewise, increased excretion of anthranilic acid and its derivatives (335, 336) and decreased excretion of niacin metabolites (337) and quinolinic acid (333) in deficient animals was not at variance with this proposed site of the function of riboflavin in this system. Further evidence was provided by the observation (302) that quinolinic acid excretion in response to tryptophan and kynurenine was reduced in riboflavin-deficient animals, while the response to hydroxykynurenine and 3-hydroxyanthranilate, metabolites beyond the suggested impaired step, gave rise to normal amounts of quinolinic acid. The observed increase in the percentage of tryptophan which appears as urinary xanthurenic acid in riboflavin-deficient rats (302, 335) could be interpreted as indicating that hydroxylation of kynurenine is not the reaction in which riboflavin is involved. However, the excretion of xanthurenic acid following kynurenine administration is not elevated (302) above normal levels and approximates the amount observed from tryptophan in normal rats.

In vitro evidence on this matter has not been conclusive (286, 338). Cholate extracts of the mitochondria from the livers of riboflavin-deficient animals contain 30–50% as much kynurenine hydroxylase as like preparations from inanition control animals. Addition of known flavin coenzymes did not increase the hydroxylase activity, but known flavoproteins are not restored to normal activity by the addition of the coenzymes to tissues of deficient animals (339). More direct evidence on this point must await the purification of kynurenine hydroxylase. The partially purified enzyme (338) required no readily dialyzable cofactors other than those mentioned above, in contrast to the liver system which catalyzes a similar hydroxylation of phenylalanine (79).

The early developments of the information on tryptophan metabolism resulted from studies of substances excreted by animals fed this amino acid under various dietary conditions. Kynurenic acid, known since 1858, was shown in 1904 to arise from tryptophan (340). Kynurenine (341), another excretory product of tryptophan (299) was recognized much later and its correct structure established in 1942 (342, 343). Musajo (344, 345) isolated xanthurenic acid (LIII, Fig. 27) from the urine of rats fed large amounts of tryptophan and then established the structure as 8-hydroxykynurenic acid. A green, iron complex of this metabolite was observed in the urine of vitamin B_6-deficient rats (346, 347).

In addition to the above-named metabolites, many others have been detected in the urine of vitamin B_6-deficient animals (348, 349). In all cases the urinary products which predominate retain the carbon skeleton of the kynurenine side chain. Nicotinic acid (350, 351) and other products (333) formed by side-chain removal are excreted in lesser amounts by vitamin B_6-deficient animals. A partial explanation for the excretion patterns in deficient animals is provided by the now established roles of pyridoxal phosphate in kynureninase and kynurenine trans-aminase action discussed in the paragraphs which follow.

2. Kynureninase

Kynureninase catalyzes the removal of the side chain from ky-nurenine to form anthranilic acid or from hydroxykynurenine to form 3-hydroxyanthranilic acid as illustrated in Fig. 29. These reactions form

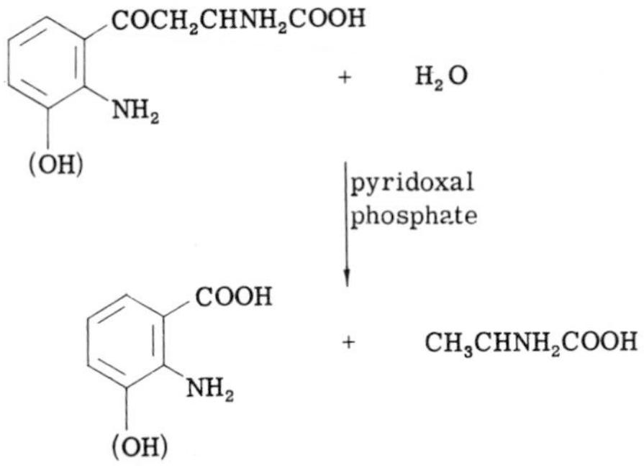

FIG. 29. Action of kynureninase on kynurenine and hydroxykynurenine.

key intermediates in two divergent pathways of degrading the indole nucleus. Anthranilic acid is involved in the aromatic pathway in

Pseudomonas fluorescens and 3-hydroxyanthranilic acid is important in the oxidative pathway and in niacin synthesis in mammals and *Neurospora*.

Kynureninases are found in animal tissues (*352, 353*), bacteria (*354*), and *Neurospora* (*355, 356*). The products are anthranilic or hydroxyanthranilic acid and alanine, not pyruvate (*354*). A pyridoxal phosphate requirement for the enzyme from each source has been reported. The relative affinities of the enzymes from various sources for kynurenine and hydroxykynurenine have been studied (*357*). Formylkynurenine is a substrate for *Neurospora* kynureninase, but not for kynureninase from *Pseudomonas*. The *Neurospora* enzyme does not split N^a-acetyl-L-kynurenine or D-kynurenine (*356*).

3. *Kynurenine Transaminase*

The formation of kynurenic acid (Fig. 30) occurs by transamination,

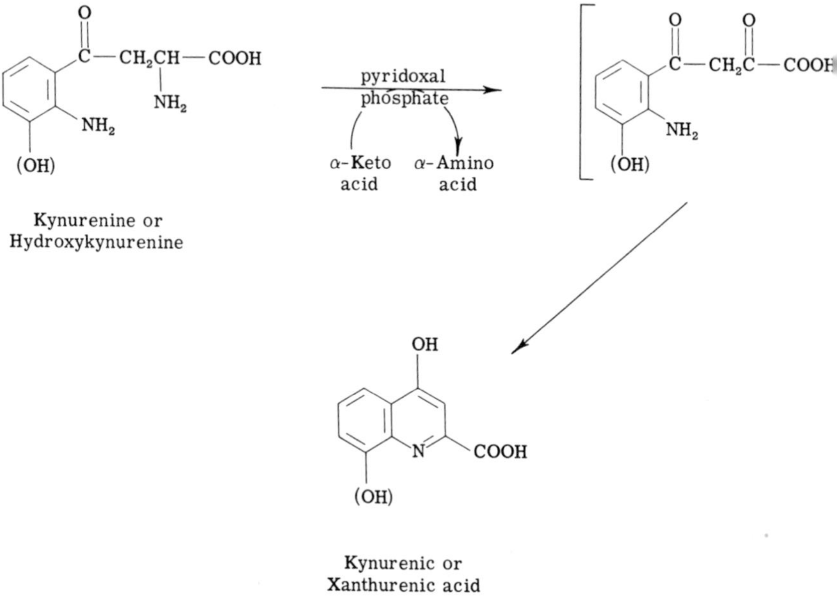

FIG. 30. Action of kynurenine transaminase on kynurenine and hydroxykynurenine.

followed by ring closure (*358, 359*). Evidence that the ring closure can occur without an enzyme was provided by the demonstration that L-amino acid oxidase acts on kynurenine to form only kynurenic acid. No *o*-aminobenzoylpyruvic acid, accumulates (*360*). Although kynurenic acid is not readily metabolized by most species, the enzyme which forms it is widely distributed. It occurs in animal tissues (*361, 362*), especially kidney, and in *Pseudomonas fluorescens* (*363, 364*), *E. coli* (*364*), and *Neurospora* (*365*). Both kynurenine and hydroxykynurenine serve as substrates (*359, 365*). The α-keto acid most effective for the pork liver enzyme is α-ketoglutarate (*359*); for the rat kidney enzyme α-ketoglutarate and oxalacetate are about equally effective (*366*) and more active than other amino group acceptors. For the *Neurospora* enzyme (*365*) a number of α-keto acids are about equally active. The coenzyme pyridoxal phosphate is readily dissociable at pH 6.3 (*365, 366*), but the dissociation can be prevented by adding the coenzyme or α-ketoglutarate (*366*). Kynureninase is found in higher concentrations in the liver whereas kynurenine transaminase is more concentrated in the kidney than in the liver (*358*).

That kynureninase is distinct from the vitamin B_6-dependent transaminase for kynurenine and hydroxykynurenine was established by separation of the two enzymes from pork liver (*359*). This distinction in bacteria was made evident by the isolation of strains of *Pseudomonas fluorescens*, some of which metabolize tryptophan via anthranilic acid and some via kynurenic acid. An interesting species difference which supports the distinction between these enzymes has been observed in mammals. The dog excretes chiefly kynurenic acid (*340*) whereas the cat excretes essentially none of this and the other common metabolites (*367*) but does excrete anthranilic acid (*368*), presumably because kynureninase is very active in cat liver and kidney (*369*) so that it acts on kynurenine more rapidly than the competing transaminase. The kynureninase from pork liver has been prepared in electrophoretically pure form (*370*) and it still contains pyridoxal phosphate.

To explain the disproportionately large amount of tryptophan which is excreted as xanthurenic acid during a vitamin B_6 deficiency, it has been necessary to assume that kynureninase and kynurenine transaminase are more sensitive to the lack of vitamin B_6 in the diet than is hydroxykynurenine transaminase; thus Reactions 7, 8, and 10 in Fig. 27 are slowed, causing Reactions 9 and 11 to dominate in the disposal of kynurenine, which is formed readily by vitamin B_6-deficient animals. Comparison of kynureninase and hydroxykynurenine transaminase levels in the liver of rats during the development of a vitamin B_6 deficiency reveals that the former is reduced three times as fast as the latter (*371*).

In a vitamin B_6-deficient rat, kynurenine accumulates as shown by its increased urinary excretion. It should be transaminated and form kynurenic acid presumably under the influence of the same enzyme which catalyzes the transamination of hydroxykynurenine. Yet kynurenic acid excretion is not elevated as is the case with kynurenine and xanthurenic acid. Thus it appears that the explanation for the excretion pattern observed must entail some distinction between the manner or site of transamination of kynurenine and hydroxykynurenine.

4. Other Reactions of Kynurenine and Its Metabolites

A large number of products have been observed to result from the action of biological systems on tryptophan, kynurenine, and hydroxykynurenine. Most of these have been detected in the urine of various species after ingestion of the recognized metabolites, sometimes during a period of vitamin in B_6 deprivation. Most of these compounds are minor components and many are metabolically inert, representing detoxication products. Renewed interest in studies of this kind has resulted from the development of new methods of isolating and detecting these minor excretory products and from the recognition of a broader biochemical significance of tryptophan. In general, the observations have been restricted to a few species, though a number of interesting species variations have been noted. It seems likely that as more is known about the reactions and the levels of enzymes which catalyze the reactions of tryptophan, still other biochemically important compounds having their origin in this amino acid will be detected.

Table I lists the compounds recognized as products of tryptophan metabolism. Each is listed under the major, recognized metabolite from which it is thought to arise. The "major" metabolites include three products of kynurenine already discussed and the two primary products of 3-hydroxykynurenine.

In addition to the three reactions of kynurenine already discussed, others have been reported. A report (372) that o-aminoacetophenone (formed from kynurenine by the action of alkali) is also a very minor metabolite of tryptophan in humans, has not been confirmed. Silkworm pupae contain kynurine or 4-hydroxyquinoline (373, 374). This compound might arise from kynurenic acid by decarboxylation, but it seems more likely that it arises by the action of amine oxidase on the decarboxylation product of kynurenine, kynurenamine. The corresponding compound from hydroxykynurenine, 4,8-dihydroxyquinoline was reported to be formed when 3-hydroxykynurenine was incubated with mouse liver (375).

Paper chromatography of the urine from vitamin B_6-deficient rats demonstrated the presence of many tryptophan metabolites, especially after overloading doses of tryptophan (348). Two of these were identified as the N-acetyl derivatives of kynurenine and hydroxykynurenine. The former accumulates in the medium of a Neurospora mutant (287) which lacks the capacity to utilize kynurenine. Many other metabolites can be separated on paper chromatograms and detected by color tests. Two of these are the sulfuric acid and glucuronic acid conjugates of 3-hydroxykynurenine.

The use of ion exchange chromatography has permitted the detection and separation of other urinary products shown in Table I. Of those presumed to be formed from 3-hydroxykynurenine, mention should be made of the 8-methyl ether of xanthurenic acid. This compound, which occurs in small amounts in normal human urine (376), represents the first known case of a methyl ether being formed in animals from a normal nutrient. The failure of xanthurenic acid to give rise to this product both *in vivo* and *in vitro* (377) and the ability of 3-methoxy-DL-kynurenine to form this metabolite both in fortified rat tissue and in the intact rat and human provides strong support for the view that methylation precedes transamination. The excretion of this compound increases in man in response to tryptophan.

Mention has already been made of the early recognition of kynurenic acid as an excretory product of tryptophan and its mode of formation from kynurenine. This compound, like kynurenine, is a major urinary product in the dog, rat, and man, but not in the cat (367). Xanthurenic acid is an important excretory product of tryptophan in man and the rat (367) as well as other species. Human subjects treated with deoxypyridoxine excrete very large amounts of kynurenic acid and xanthurenic acid in response to tryptophan while isoniazid treatment reduces the kynurenic acid excretion slightly and allows only a moderate increase in xanthurenic acid excretion (378). Since subjects receiving either of these vitamin B_6 antagonists excrete large amounts of kynurenine and hydroxykynurenine, it appears that isoniazid suppresses transamination of these two substances more effectively *in vivo* than does deoxypyridoxine. In humans (379) kynurenic acid and N-methyl-2-pyridone-5-carboxamide are the major excretory products detected following a test dose of 2 gm. of L-tryptophan. All urinary products account for only about 2% of the administered tryptophan in normal human subjects (379) whereas in those treated with isoniazid or deoxypyridoxine as much as 40% of the test dose of tryptophan appears as recognizable urinary metabolites. Since the compounds excreted are products of what is thought to be the major route of tryptophan degradation in the rat (380, 281), it is suggested that they are accumulating because of suppression of the action of kynureninase on 3-hydroxykynurenine. This reaction is severely limited by lack of vitamin B_6 *in vivo* in the rat, as indicated by the levels of urinary quinolinic acid (302). The fact that the percentage of the C^{14} from 7a-labeled tryptophan which appears in the CO_2 expired is reduced from about 27–35% in normal rats to 16% in a

TABLE I

PRODUCTS FORMED FROM MAJOR TRYPTOPHAN METABOLITES
IN VARIOUS LIVING SYSTEMS

Product	Source or conditions of formation	Reference
	Kynurenine	
o-Aminoacetophenone	Human urine	372
N-Acetylkynurenine	Rat and human urine	348, 375
	Accumulated by Neurospora	287
Kynurenamine	Silkworm pupa	373
Kynurine (4-hydroxyquinoline)	Silkworm pupae	373, 374
3-Hydroxykynurenine	Rat liver mitochondria	374
Anthranilic Acid	Kynureninase (liver)	329
Kynurenic Acid	Kynurenine transaminase (kidney)	See text
	3-Hydroxykynurenine	
3-Hydroxyanthranilic acid	Kynureninase (liver)	See text
4,8-Dihydroxyquinoline	Mouse liver	375
O-Glucuronide	B_6-Deficient rat urine	348
O-Sulfate	B_6-Deficient rat urine	348
N-acetylhydroxykynurenine	B_6-Deficient rat urine	348
Xanthurenic acid	Kynurenine transaminase (kidney)	See text
8-Methyl ether of xanthurenic acid	Normal human urine Increased by tryptophan	376
	Kynurenic acid	
Quinaldic acid	Human and rat urine	382
Quinaldyl glycine	Rabbit urine	383
6-Hydroxykynurenic acid	Pig urine	383
	Xanthurenic acid	
4,8-Disulfate ester	Rabbit urine	384
8-Glucuronide-serine	Rat urine	384
4,8-Diglucuronide-serine	Rat urine	384
8-Methyl ether	See 3-hydroxykynurenine	376
8-Hydroxyquinaldic acid	Rabbit urine and vitamin B_6-deficient rat urine	383
	Anthranilic acid	
o-Aminohippuric acid	Urine, especially dog	367, 535
Glucuronide	Urine, especially dog	367
3-Hydroxyanthranilic acid	Slight in rats	536
β-Glucoside	Plants or bacteria	385
Catechol	Pseudomonas fluorescens	537

TABLE I (*Continued*)

Product	Source or conditions of formation	Reference
	3-Hydroxyanthranilic acid	
Unstable intermediate	Liver preparations	*407*
Pyridine nucleotides	*Neurospora* and animals	*289, 303*
Quinolinic acid	Rat urine and liver and *Neurospora*	*398, 402*
Glutaric acid	Rats	*429*
Glycine conjugate		*535*
	Indolepyruvic acid	
Indoleacetic acid	*Rhizopus*, plants, animals, bacteria	*448, 453, 454*
Indoleaceturic acid	Urine	*454*
Indoleacetaldehyde	Plants	*456, 449*
Tryptophenol	*Agrobacterium tumefaciens*	*455*
	5-Hydroxytryptophan	
5-Hydroxytryptamine (serotonin)	Serum	*493*
N,*N*-dimethyl-5-hydroxy-	Toad venom	*136*
tryptamine (bufotenine)	Plants	*538*
	Toxic mushrooms	*508*
5-Hydroxyindoleacetic acid	Urine	*539*
Violacein	*Chromobacterium violaceum*	*516*
5-Hydroxytryptamine-*O*-sulfate	Serotonin in liver homogenate	*531*
	Tryptamine	
Indoleacetic acid	Urine	*454, 540*
Indoleacetaldehyde	Formed by plant amine oxidase	*529*

vitamin B_6-deficient animal (*381*), provides additional evidence that the kynurenine-hydroxyanthranilate pathway is the major route of tryptophan catabolism. The urinary excretion of C^{14} products increased from about 10% to 55% of the test dose as a result of pyridoxine deficiency.

Man, rats, and possibly other species convert kynurenic acid to the dehydroxylated product, quinaldic acid (*382*). In man as much as 29% of an oral dose of kynurenic acid appears in the urine as quinaldic acid. The report of isotopic evidence for this transformation establishes the first known biological dehydroxylation of an aromatic compound. Quinaldic acid is excreted by normal rabbits both in the free form and conjugated with glycine (*383*) as another presumed product of kynurenic acid.

Xanthurenic acid likewise has a number of fates in the animal body. The 8-methyl ether, already discussed, appears to arise from the ether of hydroxykynurenine. When isotopically labeled xanthurenic acid was given to rabbits, the 4,8-diethereal sulfate was detected in the urine whereas in rats two new conjugates containing glucuronic acid plus serine were found and tentatively identified (384). Still another urinary product excreted by rabbits and vitamin B_6-deficient rats is 8-hydroxy-quinaldic acid (384), presumably formed by dehydroxylation in the 4-position (384a).

C. Anthranilic Acid Metabolism

Anthranilic acid, another compound arising from tryptophan via kynurenine, will be considered separately because it is a compound of little apparent consequence to mammals. However, it is an intermediate on the major metabolic route for tryptophan degradation by certain bacteria. Its role in tryptophan synthesis has already been considered. While the structural similarity to 3-hydroxyanthranilic acid suggests that hydroxylation would be a logical first step, animal tissues appear to lack the enzyme for catalyzing this process at a significant rate. The compound is detoxified as the glycine and glucuronic acid conjugates (Table I) and has been reported to form the β-glucoside in plants and bacteria (385). Mutants of Aspergillus appear to make niacin by direct oxidation of anthranilic acid to 3-hydroxyanthranilic acid (386).

The most interesting fate of anthranilic acid is its conversion to catechol. This pathway of dissimilation of tryptophan by Pseudomonas was very effectively elucidated by Stanier, Hayaishi, and co-workers by the sequential induction technique. The strains of Pseudomonas examined developed enzymes for forming kynurenine from tryptophan. Most of these strains then split kynurenine with a kynureninase to yield anthranilic acid (aromatic pathway), but a few strains form kynurenic acid (quinoline pathway) (387). The quinoline pathway is not completely understood, though a preliminary report (388) indicated that a Pseudomonas strain forms glutamic acid from the carbons and nitrogen in the heterocyclic ring of kynurenic acid. More recent evidence (389) demonstrated that the degradation of kynurenic acid proceeds by (a) hydroxylation in positions 7 and 8; (b) rupture of the benzene ring between C-8 and C-9; (c) reduction of the double bond of the side chain with TPNH; (d) loss of CO_2 from the carboxyl group arising from C-8; and (e) further degradation of the resulting pyridone to alanine, acetate, CO_2, etc.

More extensive studies of the aromatic pathway, using sequential induction of pseudomonads, indicated that catechol, cis,cis-muconic acid, its γ-lactone, and β-ketoadipic acid are involved in the utilization of anthranilic acid arising from kynurenine. Little is known about the conversion of anthranilic acid to catechol since cell-free systems which catalyze this reaction have not been described. Many other aromatic compounds are oxidized adaptively by bacteria via catechol. This compound is also the last aromatic substance formed in the oxidation of phenol and benzoic acid. Its oxidative splitting to form *cis,cis*-muconic acid is catalyzed by pyrocatechase from anthranilate-adapted *Pseudomonas*. This enzyme is typical of the "phenolytic oxygenases" which have been found to oxidize protocatechuic acid, homogentisic acid, gentisic acid, homoprotocatechuic acid, and 3-hydroxyanthranilic acid (*390*). It introduces two atoms of oxygen across the double bond, as shown in Fig. 31.

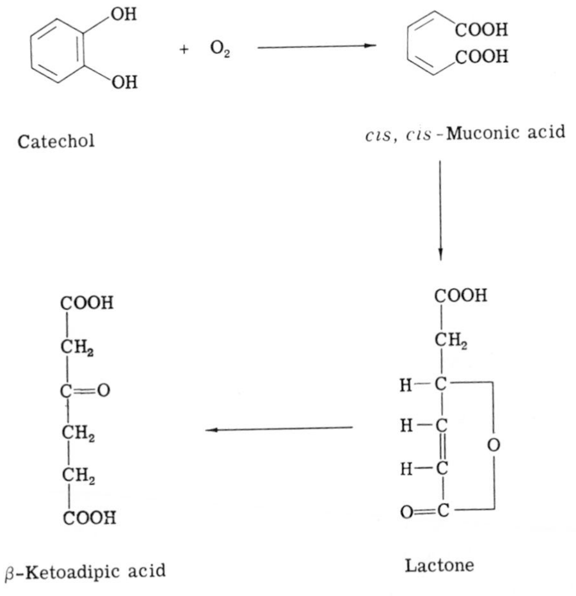

FIG. 31. Oxidative fission of catechol to aliphatic products.

Experiments with O^{18} and H_2O^{18} have shown that molecular oxygen appears in the product (*390*). The requirement for ferrous iron (*391*) and other cofactors (*392*) has been reported. The purified enzyme (*390*) is specific for catechol, contains two atoms of ferrous iron per mole, and is inhibited by several sulfhydryl reagents. Two enzymes involved in this sequence have been partially purified from mandelate-adapted cells of *Pseudomonas fluorescens* (*393*). The first catalyzes the formation of (+)-γ-carboxymethyl-Δ^{α}-butenolide while the delactonizing enzyme converts the lactone to β-ketoadipic acid, presumably by a shift of the double bond and hydrolysis of the lactone to give the enol form of β-ketoadipate. A similar series of reactions, catalyzed by enzymes formed adaptively by *Neurospora crassa*, converts protocatechuic acid through a β-carboxymuconolactone to β-ketoadipate by decarboxylation during the shifting of the double bond and delactonization.

The fate of the β-ketoadipic acid has been studied in a cell-free system prepared from *Pseudomonas fluorescens* grown on tryptophan (*394*). The system converts β-ketoadipate to succinate and acetyl coenzyme A in the presence of coenzyme A and succinyl coenzyme A. The first step is catalyzed by a specific thiophorase which transfers coenzyme A from succinate to β-ketoadipate. In the second or thiolase step, the β-ketoadipoyl coenzyme A is cleaved in the presence of coenzyme A to form succinyl coenzyme A and acetyl coenzyme A. The succinyl coenzyme A is then used for the thiophorase step. Thus, the over-all reaction is:

$$\text{β-Ketoadipate} + \text{Coenzyme A} \rightarrow \text{Succinate} + \text{Acetyl coenzyme A}$$

These products readily enter into the citric acid cycle for complete oxidation.

D. 3-HYDROXYANTHRANILIC ACID

Reference has already been made to the discovery of the role of 3-hydroxyanthranilic acid as an intermediate in the biosynthesis of nicotinic acid from tryptophan in *Neurospora* (*289, 290*). That the synthesis of niacin in the rat also involves this route was shown by the niacin-replacing activity (*395*) of 3-hydroxyanthranilic acid and its effect on the level of niacin metabolites excreted in the urine (*304*). Results with isotopes have since confirmed this view (*396*). The first report that liver preparations convert 3-hydroxyanthranilate to nicotinic acid (*397*) was later shown to reflect the formation of quinolinic acid, not nicotinic acid (*398, 399*). There appear to be no well-documented reports of the *in vitro* conversion of 3-hydroxyanthranilic acid or its precursors to nicotinic acid or one of its derivatives, though it serves a number of species as a source of niacin (*400*).

The appearance of quinolinic acid in the urine in response to both tryptophan and 3-hydroxyanthranilic acid (*401, 402*) and the nearly quantitative conversion of the latter to quinolinic acid by liver preparations (*397, 398*) suggested that 3-hydroxyanthranilic acid is metabolized by oxidative fission in the 3,4-position followed by formation of a new ring between the amino group and carbon 4 (*401*).

Further *in vitro* studies showed that liver and kidney, but none of the other tissues examined (403), contain a soluble enzyme which catalyzes the oxidation of 3-hydroxyanthranilate with the uptake of one mole of oxygen (404–406). The primary product of this oxidation was detected (407) by its intense absorption at 360 mμ. This unstable intermediate is converted nonenzymatically and almost quantitatively to quinolinic acid, slowly at room temperature or quickly at elevated temperatures. Approximately 10% of a test dose of tryptophan or 3-hydroxyanthranilic acid is converted to urinary quinolinate by the intact rat. It has been assumed that in vivo the unstable intermediate is in part converted enzymatically to niacin or its equivalent and, as will be seen below, the major part is degraded via aliphatic intermediates to CO_2. The pyridine carboxylic acids arising from the intermediate will be considered in more detail later.

3-Hydroxyanthranilic acid oxidase is a typical "phenolytic oxygenase" (390). It requires ferrous iron (408), and other metals will not replace divalent iron (405, 409). Ferrous sulfate (410) at $5 \times 10^{-5} M$ is sufficient if reduced glutathione ($10^{-5} M$) is also added to the aged, dialyzed enzyme and preincubation is carried out at pH 3.3. The usual sulfhydryl reagents (409, 410) are effective inhibitors. The enzyme is dependent upon ionic strength for full activity (411), as is bacterial pyrocatechase (390).

The product of the oxygenase appears to be largely the unstable substance (LIV, Figs. 27, 32) absorbing at 360 mμ. The oxidation state, the absorption spectrum, and the nature of its chief product (quinolinic acid, LVI) indicated that the intermediate was 1-amino-4-formyl-1,3-butadiene-1,2-dicarboxylic acid (LIV, Fig. 32). Wiss and co-workers (406, 412) presented more data supporting this structure. More rigorous identification has been difficult because of the unstable nature of (LIV). Others (404, 405) have reported that acid, even at low temperatures, quickly converts (LIV) to another compound (LX) with the loss of ammonia (286, 404) and the carboxyl carbon (413). The presence of a reactive carbonyl group in (LIV) has been questioned (405) on the basis of the failure of the usual carbonyl reagents to react. On the other hand, the intense absorption band of (LX) at 375 mμ ($\epsilon =$ 20,000) disappears immediately when hydroxylamine or bisulfite is added.

That most of the substrate oxidized can be accounted for as the unstable compound (LIV) after a few minutes of incubation with an active enzyme is indicated by studies of the stoichiometry of the reaction as measured by oxygen uptake, substrate disappearance, and the appearance of (LIV) (405). This compound in ethanol solution exhibits two maxima at 340 mμ and 290 mμ. In aqueous buffer at pH 7.5 the

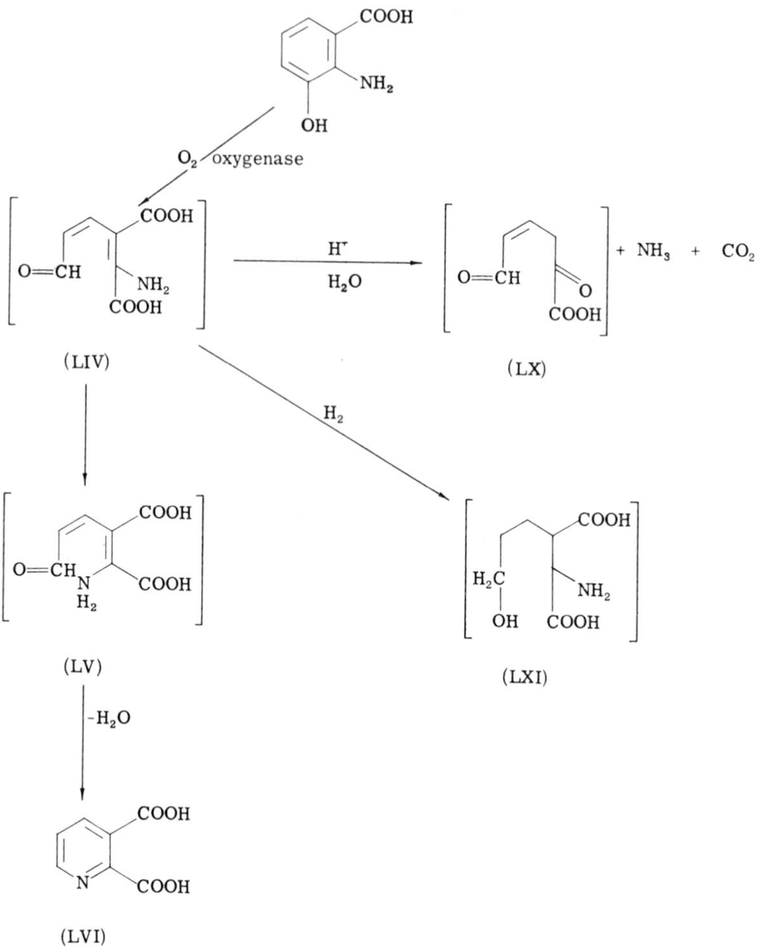

FIG. 32. Postulated reactions of the unstable intermediate formed by the action of the phenolytic oxygenase of rat liver on 3-hydroxyanthranilate.

major absorption band is at 360 mμ (405). Wiss et al. reported two absorption maxima for the primary oxidation product of 3-hydroxyanthranilate, at 275 mμ ($\epsilon = 6000$) and at 360 mμ ($\epsilon = 47,000$). That the products observed are the same compounds is indicated by the agreement that it is converted spontaneously to quinolinate.

E. PYRIDINE CARBOXYLIC ACIDS

An examination of Fig. 32 shows that quinolinic acid might arise by Schiff's base formation from the cis-form of the aldehyde amine (LV).

No evidence has been presented for an enzyme which catalyzes the isomerization at the double bond (Reaction 13, Fig. 27). Such a reaction is needed to bring the amino group near the carbonyl carbon. Removal of one of the carboxyl groups before isomerization and ring closure would cause the formation of nicotinic (LVIII) or picolinic acid (LXIII, Fig. 33). Likewise, removal of one or the other

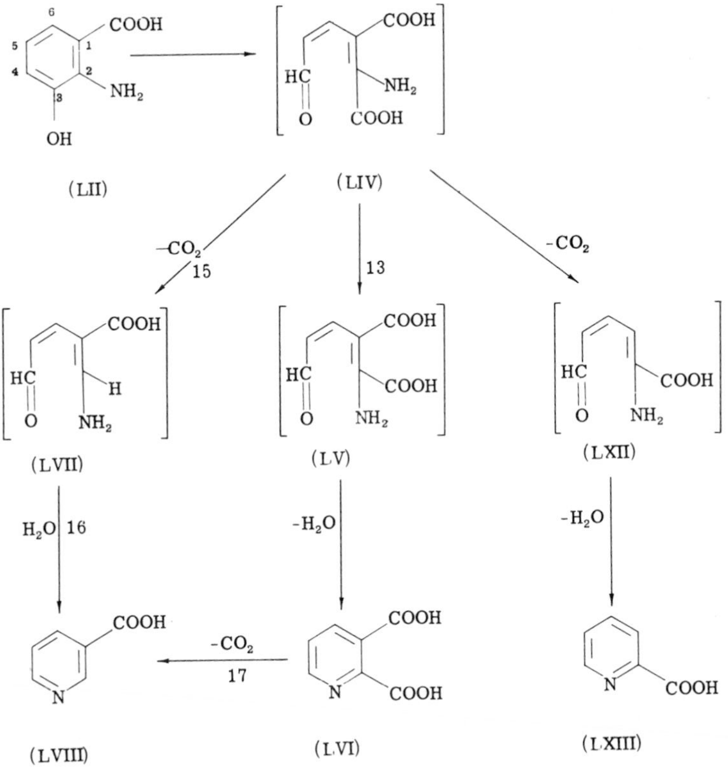

FIG. 33. Possible scheme for the formation of pyridine carboxylic acids from 3-hydroxyanthranilate.

of the carboxyl groups from quinolinic acid would give rise to nicotinic or picolinic acid. Both these monocarboxylic acids are formed under certain conditions. *In vivo* in the rat tryptophan, 3-hydroxyanthranilate, and all compounds on the metabolic pathway between these two are converted to nicotinic acid in some degree (286). Liver extracts (414), particularly from the cat, form picolinic acid *in vitro* from the primary oxidation product (LIV) of 3-hydroxyanthranilate.

The formation of nicotinic acid may occur primarily by decarboxylation followed by ring closure (Reactions 15 and 16, Fig. 33), but there is substantial evidence that the decarboxylation of quinolinic acid does occur *in vivo* (Reaction 17, Fig. 33). Quinolinic acid accumulates in the medium of some *Neurospora* mutants and is utilized, though rather poorly, by other mutants as a source of niacin (*298, 402*). It serves as a niacin source for rats as evidenced by both growth (*402*) and isotope data (*415*) and is converted to niacin in developing chick embryos (*416*). In evaluating the evidence for the direct participation of quinolinate in niacin synthesis, two facts should be kept in mind. In growth experiments with *Neurospora*, assimilation of quinolinic acid is poor because of the low pK_A values (*298, 402*) of this acid. In animals, perhaps for the same reason, excretion is rapid. Approximately 80% of what might be considered a physiological dose is excreted in the urine (*402*). In both cases the exogenously administered compound may not be reaching the site of the enzymes which catalyze the decarboxylation; whereas when 3-hydroxyanthranilic acid or its precursors are given, they may be metabolized at or near the site of quinolinate decarboxylation. It is pertinent to note that tryptophan and particularly kynurenine and hydroxykynurenine are also rather inefficiently utilized for niacin synthesis in animals (*286*).

Picolinic acid (LXIII) was identified (*414*) as the product of enzymatic decarboxylation of the primary oxidation product (LIV) of 3-hydroxyanthranilate. Sources of this enzyme fail to decarboxylate quinolinic acid (*417*). Picolinic acid formation is of doubtful biochemical significance since two species examined by isotopic methods failed to form urinary picolinic acid or its glycine conjugate from tryptophan (*418*). Only a small amount of tritium from 3-hydroxyanthranilate appeared in picolinic acid in cat or rat urine, though the cat liver extract converted the major part of labeled 3-hydroxyanthranilate to picolinic acid. Evidence that picolinic acid formation *in vitro* is catalyzed by acid, and not an enzyme, has been presented (*419*), though this view does not explain many experimental observations (*420*).

F. Scope of the Kynurenine Pathway

1. *Mammals*

Thus far little attention has been given to the quantitative aspects of the various routes of metabolism. In normal animals no more than a small percentage of a test dose of tryptophan appears in the urinary excretion products considered. A balance study on tryptophan in the rat reveals that, as with other amino acids, a major part of the tryptophan ingested does not appear in the tissues or the excreta. While the conversion of tryptophan to a number of excretory products, including kynurenine (305, 306), kynurenic acid (305, 306), xanthurenic acid (306), N-methylnicotinamide (277), and quinolinic acid (307), was shown with isotopes, until rather recently few experiments have cast light on the major fate of this amino acid. Dalgliesh and Tabechian (380) found that 25% of the C^{14} from uniformly labeled tryptophan was expired as $C^{14}O_2$ within 4 hours after giving a 4-mg. dose. A similar experiment with DL-tryptophan-3a,7a,7-C^{14} gave similar yields of $C^{14}O_2$, while one-third of the C^{14} from position 7a of tryptophan appeared as CO_2 within a few hours (421). These results clearly demonstrate the capacity of the rat to degrade completely the indole nucleus, but they shed no light on the manner in which this degradation takes place.

If, as has been assumed, the primary metabolic lesion of vitamin B_6 deficiency, so far as tryptophan is concerned, is in the action of kynureninase on 3-hydroxykynurenine, the urinary excretion data point to this pathway as the chief route of tryptophan degradation. However, the possibility exists that some other vitamin B_6-dependent reaction is stopped, diverting tryptophan to the kynurenine pathway. Another route of tryptophan metabolism in animals was suggested by Sanadi and Greenberg (422), who interpreted their *in vivo* experiments with tryptophan-β-C^{14} as indicating that the side chain of tryptophan is removed as CO_2 and acetate, not as alanine. These conclusions were based chiefly on the labeling pattern in urinary glucose from phlorizinized rats given β-labeled tryptophan. Examinations of the results in the light of present day knowledge shows that they are not inconsistent with the kynurenine pathway. Experiments with tryptophan-α-C^{14} clearly demonstrated (281) by the C^{14}-labeling pattern in serine, alanine, aspartic acid, and glutamic acid, that the side chain of the tryptophan is removed as pyruvate or alanine-2-C^{14}. This finding is consistent with the kynurenine-3-hydroxyanthranilic acid pathway already discussed.

The availability (423) of tryptophan labeled in the 7a-position with C^{14} has made possible studies which have shed light on the mode of degradation of the indole nucleus. The distribution of the C^{14} in several nonessential amino acids of the carcass and liver protein of the rat indicated that C-7a might be metabolized via the carboxyl carbon of acetate (421). The deviation of the ratio of specific activities of C-5 to C-1 in glutamate from the theoretical value of 2 (424) to values of 5 for liver and 3 for carcass suggested that a route to glutamate, more direct than through acetate, may be functioning. This possibility prompted the use of the acetate trapping technique using chiefly cyclohexylalanine as a foreign amine. In these experiments the trapped acetate was labeled to about the extent expected from the size of the acetate pool (425), assuming that 27% of the 7a-carbon of tryptophan is converted directly to acetate. Essentially all of the C^{14} was present in the carboxyl carbon. A similar experiment with tryptophan 3a,7a,7-C^{14} yielded trapped acetate with a specific activity ratio in the two carbon atoms which would be expected if C-3a and C-7a gave rise to the methyl and carboxyl carbons, respectively, of acetate.

The relatively high incorporation (6%) of C-7a of tryptophan into lipid (421) of the carcass and liver and the extensive labeling in cholesterol (426) is in keeping with the proposed metabolism via acetate.

Support for the view that the major route of tryptophan degradation is through 3-hydroxyanthranilic acid and acetate was provided by whole animal experiments using isotopically labeled 3-hydroxyanthranilic acid. While approximately 60% of the carboxyl carbon of this compound is expired as CO_2 by the rat within 3 hours (309), C-1 is released even less rapidly than C-7a of tryptophan (427). If the degradation occurs in a manner similar to that illustrated in Fig. 34, C-1 would give rise to C-2 of acetate, which is slowly oxidized in the whole animal (428). More than 50% of this carbon atom appeared in the carcass; this is in keeping with the known behavior of acetate. Furthermore, trapped acetate from C-1-labeled 3-hydroxyanthranilate was labeled largely in the methyl group (427). 3-Hydroxyanthranilate labeled in both the C-1 and the carboxyl group yielded trapped acetate labeled chiefly in C-2, indicating that C-2 or C-6 of 3-hydroxyanthranilate is the source of the carboxyl carbon of acetate. The former seems a more logical source in view of the known formation from tryptophan, whose corresponding carbon atom has been established as a source of C-1 of acetate (Fig. 34).

The sequence of reactions shown in Fig. 34 would account for the results thus far discussed. The very active enzyme (Reaction 12) which converts 3-hydroxyanthranilic acid to the unstable intermediate (LIV) should lead to very high levels of excretion of quinolinic acid in animals if there were not another enzyme(s) to prevent this nonenzymatic closure of the ring. That the degradation does not proceed via pyridine carboxylic acids is suggested by the relative metabolic inertness of these compounds. It seems likely that aliphatic compounds arise by a series of reactions involving deamination, loss of the carboxyl carbon of 3-hydroxyanthranilate as CO_2, oxidation of C-4, oxidative decarboxylation to lose C-3, and fission of the 5-carbon acid to give acetate.

Evidence has been obtained which implicates glutaric acid in this sequence (429). Using the metabolite overloading technique with labeled tryptophan or 3-hydroxyanthranilate and a massive dose of unlabeled glutarate, it was found that the urinary glutarate was radio-

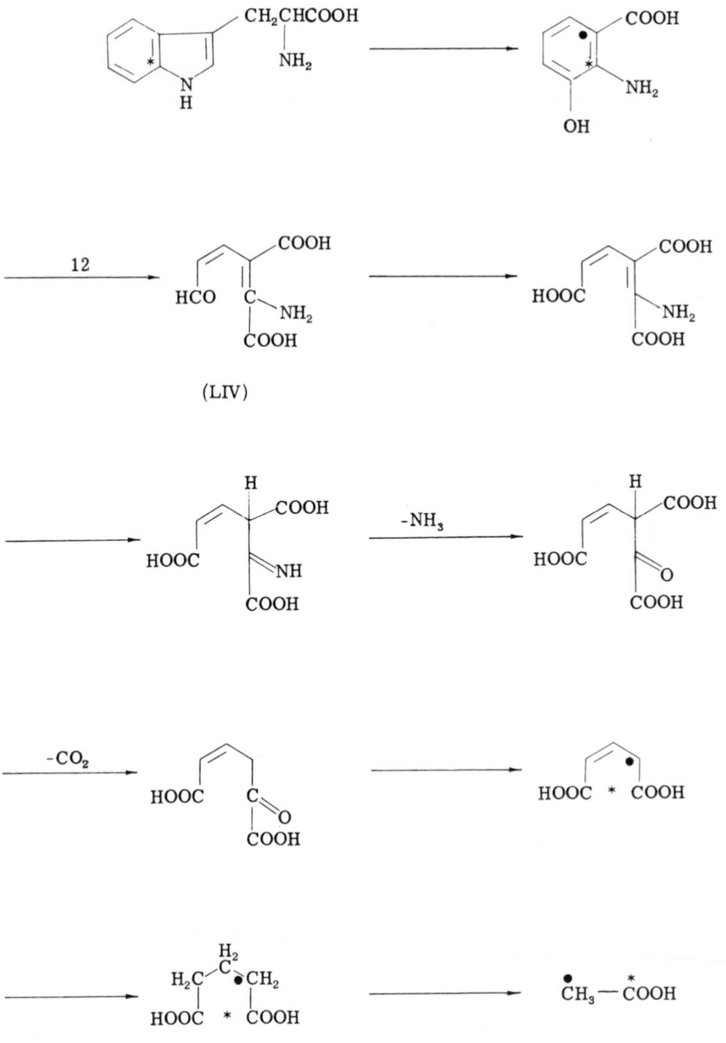

Fig. 34. Possible scheme to explain the labeling of glutarate and acetate arising from tryptophan and hydroxyanthranilate.

active. The details of glutarate metabolism have not yet been established. On the basis of the labeling pattern in acetate, acetoacetate, and glucose, Rothstein and Miller (430) concluded that decarboxylation to butyrate or oxidation of C-3 to give β-ketoglutaric acid, followed by decarboxylation to acetoacetate, were the most likely routes of catabolism of glutarate in the rat. On the basis of metabolite overloading experiments the same authors suggested that α-ketoglutarate and acetate were the products of glutarate arising from lysine (431). Hobbs and Koeppe (432) on the other hand, obtained amino acid-labeling data from glutaric acid-3-C^{14} which indicates that the major metabolic route is through acetate rather than conversion of the carbon chain directly to α-ketoglutarate. They suggest glutaconate, β-hydroxyglutarate, and β-ketoglutarate as intermediates. The latter could then give acetoacetate plus CO_2, or malonate plus acetate. Further experiments will be needed to determine the sequence of events by which the individual carbon atoms of the indole nucleus reach acetate, glutamate, and other aliphatic products en route to CO_2.

2. Plants

The evaluation of the kynurenine pathway in plants has been made on the basis of the capacity of tryptophan to serve as a niacin precursor. Most of the experiments in this area have involved the administration of exogenous tryptophan and related compounds to growing or germinating plants already forming nicotinic acid. Observed small increases in the niacin content as a result of these additions have been interpreted as evidence for a tryptophan-niacin relationship (433, 434, 435).

Among the most extensive studies of this kind were those of Nason (436, 437), who used germinating corn or growing, excised embryos of corn under sterile conditions. The niacin synthesis in both types of preparation was enhanced by tryptophan and 3-hydroxyanthranilate. Similar experiments (438) with whole kernels of the same strain of corn failed to show a consistent or marked increase in the niacin content of each embryo, though niacin was being formed during the germination. Isotopically labeled tryptophan or 3-hydroxyanthranilate failed to cause labeling in the niacin or trigonelline isolated from 7–9-day corn embryos.

Tobacco, likewise, forms niacin by a route distinct from that used by *Neurospora* and animals. The pyridine ring of nicotine arises from nicotinic acid (439), but the carbon of tryptophan and some of its metabolites fails to become incorporated into nicotine (438, 440, 441, 442). Ricinine, a pyridine alkaloid formed by the castor bean, also from nicotinic acid (443), can serve as an indicator of the precursors of nicotinic acid in this plant.

3. Bacteria

Comparatively little is known about the extent to which bacteria degrade tryptophan via kynurenine and 3-hydroxyanthranilate. In a previous section, the quinoline and aromatic pathways by which pseudomonads metabolize tryptophan were considered. Hydroxylation of kynurenine was not observed in these studies.

A plant pathogen, *Xanthomonas pruni*, which requires niacin or tryptophan for growth, can use the compounds between tryptophan and niacin in the scheme (*444*) (Fig. 27). This suggests that this organism resembles *Neurospora* and animals with respect to niacin synthesis, though the unexpected activity of anthranilic acid might indicate a short circuit, by direct hydroxylation. Although it has been proposed (*445*) that *Escherichia coli* synthesizes niacin from tryptophan, conclusive evidence has appeared to the contrary for this organism as well as for *Bacillus subtilis* (*446*).

G. Indoleacetic Acid Pathway

1. *Synthesis of Indoleacetic Acid*

Interest in the formation of indoleacetic acid centers around its pronounced effect as a plant growth substance. Kögl and co-workers (*447*) isolated "heteroauxin" from human urine and in 1934 identified it as indole-3-acetic acid (XLV, Fig. 35). Its formation in plants established it as a substance of great metabolic consequence. The first indication of its origin was reported by Thimann (*448*), who found that tryptophan was needed in the medium of *Rhizopus* for auxin production. The existence in plants (*449, 450, 451*) of enzymes which form indole acetate from tryptophan has also been reported. More recent experiments have amply confirmed the view that tryptophan is the source of indoleacetic acid in plants (*452, 453*), in animals (*454*), and in bacteria (*454, 455*).

Two reaction sequences from tryptophan to indoleacetic acid seem plausible (Fig. 35). One involves the transamination or oxidative deamination to indolepyruvic acid (LXIV) followed by decarboxylation or oxidative decarboxylation. The other proceeds by decarboxylation to form tryptamine (LXV) then oxidative deamination with monoamine oxidase to give indoleacetaldehyde (LXVI). The latter could participate (*456*) in either of these pathways, and this compound is oxidized by leaf tissue preparations (*449*). Before data were presented to allow a choice between these two routes other compounds were discovered which make still other reactions possible. Among these should be mentioned indoleacetonitrile (LXVII) which was detected (*457*) and shown to be converted to indoleacetic acid (*458*). It was proposed that the nitrile and the amide (LXVIII) are involved in auxin formation, but the amide is not biologically active (*457*). Paper chromatography of plant materials (*458*) showed the presence of indolepyruvic acid and two other indole compounds that promote plant growth.

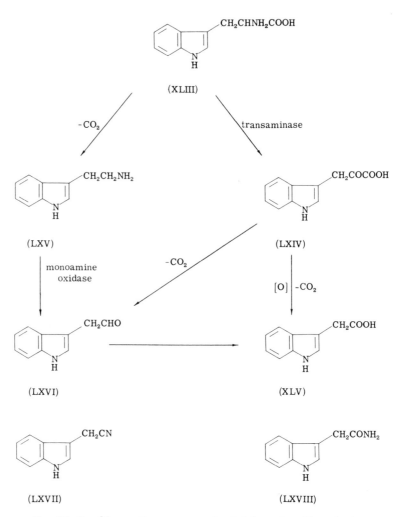

FIG. 35. Possible reaction sequences for indoleacetic acid synthesis.

Watermelon slices convert C^{14}-labeled tryptophan to a number of indole derivatives including compounds tentatively identified as indole-pyruvic acid, indoleacetic acid, indolealdehyde, tryptamine, and indole acetonitrile (453). The major route for auxin synthesis in this tissue appears to be through indole pyruvate, though other routes might be important as well (459). In a paper describing a very thorough study of this in *Agrobacterium tumefaciens*, Kaper and Veldstra (455) question some of the work in which indole pyruvate was identified. They stressed the lability of this compound. Tryptamine is apparently not a product of tryptophan in this organism. During the first 23 hours indoleacetic acid was the main product, but during the subsequent 15 hours, indolepyruvic, indoleacetic, and tryptophol were formed. Many other products detected appear to result from subsequent reactions of the compounds mentioned.

The assumption that the intestinal flora is solely responsible for the indoleacetic acid which appears in urine has been made untenable by the demonstration that animal tissues can convert tryptophan to indoleacetic acid (454). The process, catalyzed by enzymes present in the supernatant fraction from several tissues, is stimulated by pyridoxal phosphate and α-ketoglutarate, thus suggesting that the primary reaction is transamination. Mixed cultures of fecal bacteria also form indoleacetic acid from tryptophan and, like the animal tissue, primarily via the transamination route. An alternate route through tryptamine appears to operate in the animal tissues and the bacteria.

2. Degradation

Some of the indole compounds found in plant materials are undoubtedly arising from indoleacetic acid. If this compound is to control processes related to growth, some provision must be made for its disposal. Photooxidation is one means of destroying the hormonal properties of indoleacetic acid (460, 461). In beans and peas the destruction of the hormone is accelerated by light whereas for corn, destruction is entirely dependent upon light (461). A detailed discussion of the enzymatic destruction of indoleacetic acid and related compounds is beyond the scope of this chapter. This subject was reviewed in 1958 (460). Among the products arising from the action of various systems on indoleacetic acid are indole-3-carboxaldehyde (462, 463), indole-3-carboxylic acid (464), an unidentified aliphatic acid (463), and other unidentified compounds that retain the 2-carbon side chain of indoleacetic acid (465).

The enzyme responsible for the oxidation has been found in a number of higher plants (462, 466, 467) and fungi (468). In most cases Mn^{2+} is a cofactor, and in some cases a phenolic compound stimulates oxidation. The nature of the enzymatic process is not clear (see Ray, 460), but the indoleacetic acid oxidase activity may be a special aspect of peroxidase activity. The soluble enzyme from *Omphalia flavida* or horse-radish peroxidase oxidize indoleacetic acid with the uptake of one molecule of oxygen and release one molecule of CO_2 to give a neutral compound (465). This intermediate reacts with bisulfite, absorbs like an indole derivative, and is converted spontaneously into at least two products, which are not indole-like. Ray (460) suggested that the intermediate might contain the skatole nucleus oxidized in the 1- or 2-position or both. Stutz (463), using a system from lupine, obtained evidence that the primary oxidative attack occurs on the ring. He observed the formation of indolecarboxaldehyde when a cytochrome-cytochrome oxidase system was added, and he presented evidence for other reactions, one of which gives an aliphatic product containing C-2 of the indole nucleus.

H. INDOLE FORMATION

Indole formation during putrefaction has been recognized for over eighty years (469). Its formation from tryptophan by E. coli under aerobic conditions was noted (470) shortly after tryptophan was discovered. Until relatively recently it was assumed that the side-chain removal was a several-step process, but in 1935 (471, 472) it became clear that "tryptophanase" catalyzes the direct removal of the side chain. The products of the enzyme are indole, pyruvate and ammonia, and pyridoxal phosphate is a cofactor. The similarity of this fission to a reversal of the synthesis of tryptophan from indole and serine, already considered, is striking, but the two reactions are distinct. No serine is formed in the reaction, and neither serine nor alanine is deaminated by tryptophanase preparations. The reaction appears to be of little consequence in most living forms. Fermentable carbohydrate in the medium prevents indole formation in E. coli. The literature in this field, most of which appeared before 1950, has been carefully reviewed (473).

Further metabolism of indole has been observed in bacteria. Sequential induction studies (474) have indicated that isatin, formylanthranilic acid, anthranilic acid, salicylic acid, and catechol are formed in turn from indole. An extract of rabbit liver decomposes indole and skatole, and the reaction is enhanced by vitamins C and B_{12} (475). Isatin is converted to anthranilic acid by a partially purified rabbit liver enzyme.

Another fate of indole in mammals is detoxication and excretion in the urine as the salt of the O-sulfate of indoxyl, known as indican. Indole produces nausea, headache, and other unpleasant symptoms whereas indican is harmless (476) and is a normal constituent of urine (6). About 30–50% of ingested indole is absorbed by man (477); the remainder is excreted in the feces. The horse excretes particularly large amounts of indican. Skatole is also formed in the tract and absorbed. It also is detoxified by hydroxylation and conjugation with sulfate. The early report (478) and commonly accepted idea that skatoxyl is formed and excreted as the O-sulfate conjugate is erroneous. The major product from skatole is formed by hydroxylation in the 5-position followed by conjugation with sulfate (479).

I. INSECT PIGMENTS

The substances that are involved in "tanning" of the cuticle of insects have already been discussed. Melanin is also the name which had been applied to certain yellow, red, or brown pigments whose true chemical nature has come to light rather recently. These pigments are found particularly in the orthopods, but their occurrence is not restricted to these organisms. Since they were recognized as the pigments of the ommatidia of insect eyes the name ommochrome (480) was suggested. These pigments are also found in the epidermis and in the outer covering or the organs in many orthopods, particularly mites, caterpillars, and in adult forms, e.g., butterfly wings. Large amounts are present in the eyes and epidermis of cephalopods (481).

The ommochrome pigments were recognized as distinct substances when biochemical genetics was applied to the origin of the pigments in the eyes of *Ephestia kuhniella* and *Drosophila melanogaster*. Testing the inheritance factors which determine the shade of the eyes of various mutants led to the conclusion that these ommochromes are derived from tryptophan (see review, 482). The nature of the process of pigment formation was brought to light by the now familiar technique of showing the accumulation of the substrate of the enzyme missing from a given mutant and the utilization of that substrate by mutants lacking an enzyme involved earlier in the sequence.

A partial scheme for the reactions by which ommochromes are formed is shown in Fig. 36. It will be noted that when the cn⁺ gene is

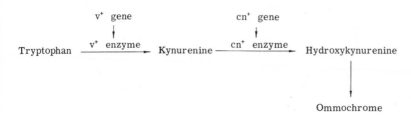

FIG. 36. Scheme showing the relationship between the genes and the enzymes involved in the formation of ommochromes from tryptophan.

missing, enzyme cn⁺ is not formed, and its substrate, kynurenine, accumulates. 3-Hydroxykynurenine was shown to be the product of cn⁺ enzyme. Hydroxykynurenine is a precursor of the ommochromes which are formed by oxidative processes.

Much attention has been given to the mechanism by which hydroxy-kynurenine leads to these pigments. It is evident from the variety of colors they exhibit that ommochromes are multiple in nature. Ommo-chromes formed in the retinal and secondary pigment cells of the *Ephestia* eye are dark brown. In the corneal cells the pigment is yellow, and in the larval epidermis the ommochrome is red. Though these pigments arise from a common precursor, they have not been charac-terized nor have the divergent pathways beyond hydroxykynurenine been elucidated. Two approaches to the chemistry of the ommochrome pigments have been used (*482*). One involves the study of variation in the composition, functional groups, etc., of the isolated pigments; the other is the use of model systems for oxidizing hydroxykynurenine to compounds that resemble the natural pigments. The latter approach has led to the synthesis of various phenoxazines from *o*-aminophenols by oxidation with air, HgO, or ferricyanide in weakly alkaline or alcoholic solutions (*483*). Many of the products obtained resemble insect pig-ments, and it has been concluded that the natural ommochromes are phenoxazine derivatives (*484*).

Starting with the molting secretion (*Schlupfsekret*) of 5000 butter-fly larvae, Butenandt and co-workers (*484*) isolated pure ommatins. Xanthommatin was crystallized, and rhodommatin, ommatin C, and om-matin D were obtained in chromatographically pure form (*482*). These pigments are similar in physicochemical behavior to the pigments of the eye of *Ephestia* and *Drosophila*. Pigments from the eye of *Calliphora erythrocephala* and the molting secretion of *Vanessa* originate from tryptophan as demonstrated with isotopes (*485, 486*).

Degradation studies established the structure of xanthommatin as the phenoxazine shown in Fig. 37 (*487*). It is readily reduced to hydro-xanthommatin (LXXI), a bright red pigment, which is reoxidized by air to yellow-brown xanthommatin. The presence of the alanine side chain was proved by its removal from xanthommatin with kynureninase (*488*). It has been suggested that xanthommatin and related pigments arise from hydroxykynurenine by oxidative condensation in a manner similar to the chemical oxidation. Tyrosinase in the presence of dihydroxy-phenylalanine produces dopaquinone which might be the oxidant for *in vitro* production of xanthommatin (*489*). Xanthommatin is thus a prototype of pigments known for many years in the laboratory, but only by the genetic approach identified in nature.

In addition to the low molecular weight, dialyzable ommatins dis-cussed above, high molecular weight ommines occur in many animal species (*480*). Because of the problems of working with these poly-meric pigments it has not been possible to determine whether there is one ommine or a family of these pigments corresponding to the om-

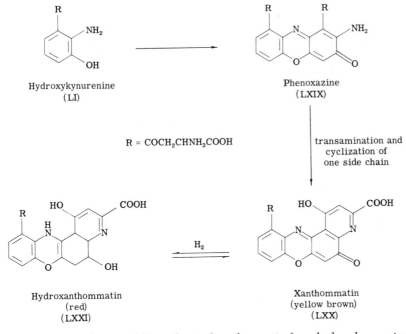

R = COCH$_2$CHNH$_2$COOH

FIG. 37. Proposed route of biosynthesis of xanthommatin from hydroxykynurenine.

matins. They yield, on acid and alkaline degradation, hydroxykynurenine, xanthurenic acid, and 2-amino-3-hydroxyacetophenone, as do ommatins.

J. THE 5-HYDROXYTRYPTAMINE PATHWAY

5-Hydroxytryptamine (XLVII, Fig. 38) is a hormone generally considered to be of great importance though the exact nature of its functions are still somewhat obscure (490). It is of comparatively recent discovery, and interest in it arose from three directions (491). Erspamer, from a detailed study of the enterochromaffin cell system, deduced that this system produced a substance of high physiological activity. Enterochromaffin cells which give characteristic histological reactions occur in mammals principally in the gastrointestinal tract. In other species these cells can be more widespread, e.g., enterochromaffin cells occur extensively in the skin of the toad among the cells secreting the cutaneous venom. Erspamer established by 1948 that the physiologically active substance was a basic phenolic derivative of indole (492). Meanwhile Page, Rapport and their colleagues had been studying the vasoconstrictor substance in serum, which in 1948 was isolated and

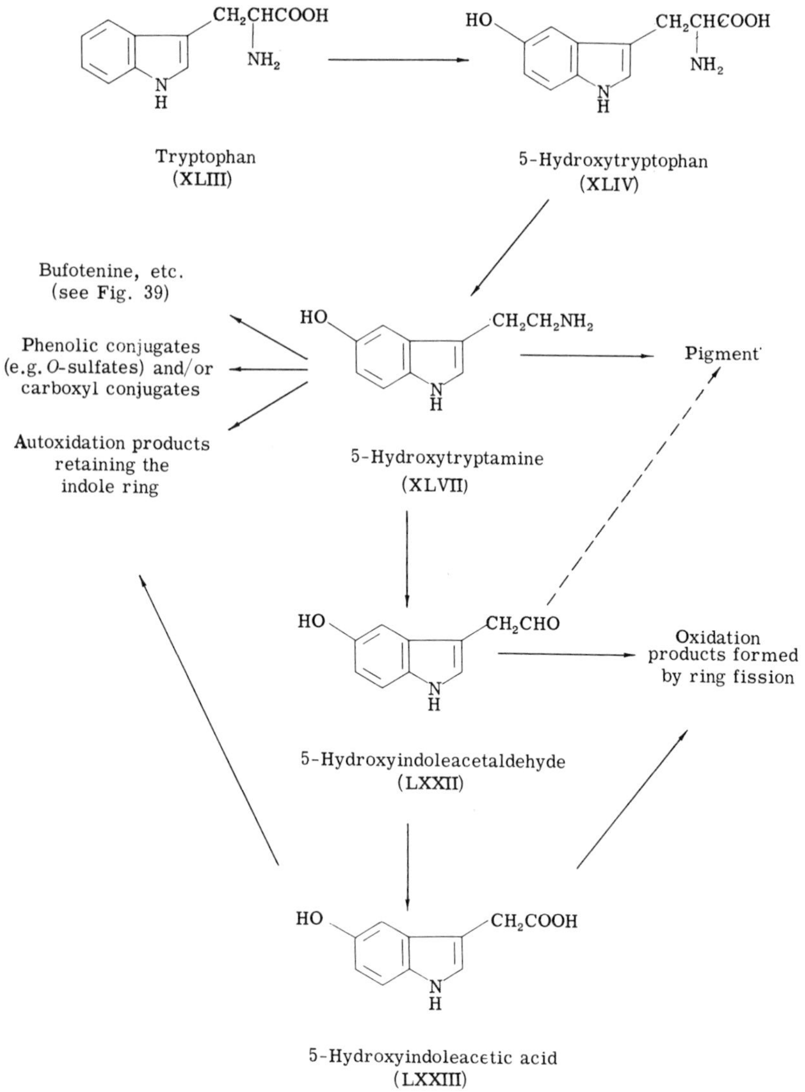

FIG. 38. Route of formation and degradation of serotonin.

shortly afterward identified as 5-hydroxytryptamine (*493*). Erspamer's material was also found to be 5-hydroxytryptamine (*494*). The third line of evidence came from studies of human patients with carcinoid (tumors of the enterochromaffin argentaffin cells), which were shown by Thorson *et al.* (*495*) to form large amounts of 5-hydroxytryptamine (*491*).

Although an origin from tyrosine is theoretically possible (*496*), in all cases investigated 5-hydroxyindoles are derived from tryptophan. Two routes from tryptophan to 5-hydroxytryptamine can be envisaged:

(*a*)   tryptophan → 5-hydroxytryptophan → 5-hydroxytryptamine

or

(*b*)   tryptophan → tryptamine → 5-hydroxytryptamine

Evidence for pathway (*a*) was first provided by the work of Udenfriend and colleagues (*497*), who found an enzyme in mammalian kidney which decarboxylates 5-hydroxytryptophan but not tryptophan, 7-hydroxytryptophan, or tyrosine. Moreover, venom glands of the toad were found to contain 5-hydroxytryptophan, 5-hydroxytryptamine, *N*-methylated derivatives of 5-hydroxytryptamine, but no tryptamine. The evidence for pathway (*a*) is very convincing. It includes the results of both *in vitro* and *in vivo* experiments employing isotopes and has been reviewed (*498, 499*).

1. *Distribution of 5-Hydroxyindoles*

In mammals 5-hydroxytryptamine occurs principally in the intestinal tract. It has been found in the gastrointestinal mucosa of all mammals, birds, reptiles, and amphibians examined (*500*). It occurs also in lung and spleen and in blood platelets. It occurs in nerve tissue and in the brain, in which it is confined to the gray matter. It also occurs in mast cells of the skin in a few species, e.g., rat and mouse. 5-Hydroxytryptamine is liberated from cells in which it is stored by several substances, notably reserpine. This release is due to inhibition of an active transport system (*501*), which otherwise keeps it concentrated within the cells.

5-Hydroxytryptamine is a common constituent of venoms, e.g., it occurs in toad venom (*502*), wasp venom (*503*), scorpion venom (*504*), and nettle stings (*505*). In invertebrates and amphibians 5-hydroxytryptamine sometimes occurs in large amounts, for example in the posterior salivary glands of octopods and the hypobranchial body of *Muricidae*. Very large amounts can occur in the skin of amphibia, and 5-hydroxytryptamine here is usually accompanied by related substances such as the *N*-methyl derivatives bufotenine, bufotenidine, dehydrobufotenine, and bufothionine (*136, 506*), the structures of which are shown in Fig. 39.

5-Hydroxyindoles also occur in bacteria (*507*), fungi (*508*), and plants (*509*), a particularly interesting case being the comparatively large amount of 5-hydroxytryptamine (and of catechol amines) in the banana (*510*). Melatonin, a constituent of the pineal gland which

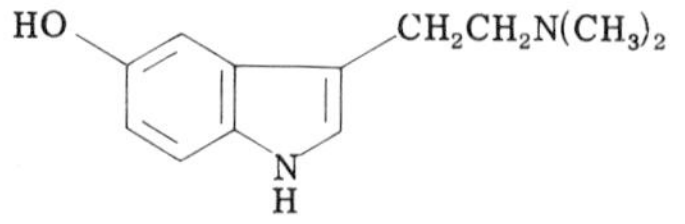

FIG. 39. Some 5-hydroxyindoles occurring particularly in amphibian skin.

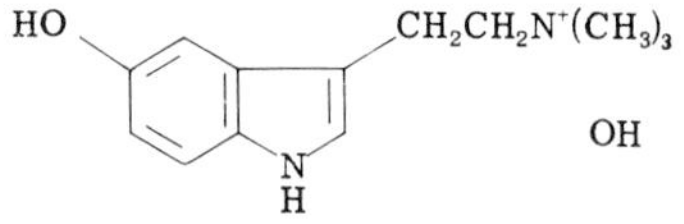

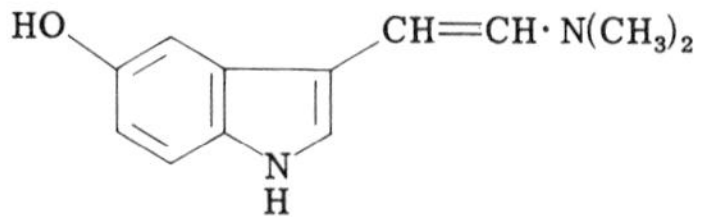

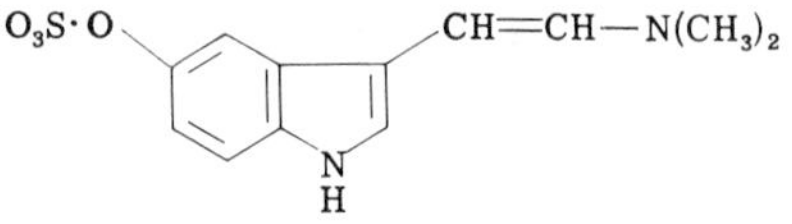

reverses the effect of melanocyte-stimulating hormone, may be a related substance (*511*).

2. Conversion of Tryptophan to 5-Hydroxytryptophan

Tryptophan 5-hydroxylase has not been prepared in the cell-free state. Conversion of tryptophan to 5-hydroxytryptophan has been shown in *Chromobacterium violaceum* (*407*) and in the toad (*512*). 5-Hydroxy-tryptophan can be excreted by man in certain unusual types of carcinoid (*513*). There is strongly suggestive evidence that in mammals the formation of 5-hydroxytryptophan does not occur to more than a minor extent in the liver, the usual site for aromatic hydroxylation reactions. There are indications that this reaction occurs in the enterochromaffin cell system, and that it is the rate-limiting step in 5-hydroxytryptamine formation (*491, 514*).

Resting cells of *Chromobacterium violaceum* form large amounts of 5-hydroxyindole compounds, most of which is 5-hydroxytryptophan (*507*). 5-Hydroxyindoleacetic and 5-hydroxyindolepyruvic acids are also formed. The purple pigment violacein contains the 5-hydroxyindole moiety (*515*), and tryptophan is needed for pigment formation (*516*). 5-Hydroxytryptamine is not formed by this organism, and most of the 5-hydroxytryptophan formed is used for pigment formation.

3. Conversion of 5-Hydroxytryptophan to 5-Hydroxytryptamine

Since the initial report (*497*) much has been learned about 5-hydroxytryptophan decarboxylase, the enzyme responsible for this reaction. It occurs in the kidney and liver of all animal species tested, as well as in stomach and lung (517). It is highly specific, attacking L- but not D-5-hydroxytryptophan. The enzyme and substrate have high affinity, and vitamin B_6 is a cofactor for the reaction (518). The effect of chelating agents suggests that a metal cofactor may be involved (519). The optimum pH is 8.1. The enzyme is quite distinct from dopa decarboxylase and it occurs in the soluble fraction of the cell. Besides the liver, kidney, and the gastrointestinal tract the nervous system contains this enzyme. Since no appreciable amount of the decarboxylase is found in spleen, blood platelets, or bone marrow, these tissues are probably not important in 5-hydroxytryptamine synthesis (520). 5-Hydroxytryptophan-C^{14} is rapidly decarboxylated to give labeled serotonin in the tissue depots (521). This finding makes it possible to increase the 5-hydroxytryptamine level in tissues including the brain, since 5-hydroxytryptophan readily penetrates and is rapidly decarboxylated. The half-life of serotonin in several tissues is 10–20 hours whereas in blood platelets the half-life is 33 hours, very close to the half-life of the platelets themselves (499). In the gastrointestinal tract the occurrence of the enzyme is roughly parallel to the occurrence of 5-hydroxytryptamine, but this is not the case in the brain where the enzyme is located chiefly in the sympathetic ganglia (522). The enzyme in brain tissue differs from that from other sources in being inhibited by excess substrate. This enzyme as well as tryptophan decarboxylase is inhibited by various metabolites of phenylalanine, e.g., phenylpyruvic, phenyllactic, phenylacetic, and p-hydroxyphenylpyruvic acids (523). This may correlate with the low rate or formation of 5-hydroxytryptamine by phenylketonurics (524). The distribution of the enzyme in tumor and related tissues in man has also been studied (525).

4. Conversion of 5-Hydroxytryptamine to 5-Hydroxyindoleacetic Acid

5-Hydroxytryptamine is readily attacked by the widespread enzyme, amine oxidase (526, and review, 527). The same enzyme catalyzes the oxidation of adrenaline (epinephrine), noradrenaline (norepinephrine), and dopamine (see Section III, B). Destruction by amine oxidase is the major route for normal degradation of 5-hydroxytryptamine (528). Inhibitors of amine oxidase, such as isoniazid (isonicotinic acid hydrazide) and iproniazid (Marsalid, N-isopropyl-N'-isonicotinoylhydrazine) inhibit breakdown of 5-hydroxytryptamine.

5-Hydroxyindoleacetaldehyde is oxidized to 5-hydroxyindoleacetic acid by an aldehyde dehydrogenase, about which little is known. Under normal circumstances in mammalian tissues the conditions are such that the intermediate aldehyde is further oxidized as fast as it is formed.

Plant amine oxidase can be freed from aldehyde dehydrogenase (529), and then the reaction can be stopped at the aldehyde stage. Mammalian amine oxidase occurs both in the mitochondria and in the soluble fraction of the cell. The soluble enzyme has also been freed of aldehyde dehydrogenase (530).

5. Other Reactions of 5-Hydroxyindoles

In mammals 5-hydroxyindoles behave like other phenols in undergoing conjugation reactions. Chromatograms of the urine of human patients with carcinoid show several 5-hydroxyindole conjugates (7). 5-Hydroxytryptamine forms the O-sulfate (531) and O-glucuronide, and 5-hydroxyindoleacetic acid forms the O-sulfate (532) though, unlike indoleacetic acid, it does not appear to undergo glycine or glutamine conjugation to any marked extent.

N-Methylation probably does not occur to an appreciable extent in the mammal (e.g., 533), but it does in lower organisms, such as the toad, in which bufotenine and related compounds (cf. Fig. 39) are produced. Nothing appears to be known of the details of these reactions. Similarly, very little is known of the types of reactions in plants in which 5-hydroxyindoles are involved in alkaloid biosynthesis. 5-Hydroxytryptamine in plants presumably arises by a pathway similar to that in mammals, but there is at present no direct evidence for this.

5-Hydroxyindoles can also give rise to pigments of unknown structure. This is not surprising since these substances are potential quinones. If 5-hydroxytryptamine and 5-hydroxyindoleacetaldehyde are present together, as is likely to be the case when amine oxidase functions, condensation to polycyclic compounds may occur, and this could be a stage in the biosynthesis of certain alkaloids. Oxidations of 5-hydroxyindoles may occur nonenzymatically. 5-Hydroxytryptophan may also be converted to 5-hydroxyindoleacetic acid by way of the corresponding pyruvic acid. Oxidative deamination of 5-hydroxytryptophan is brought about by the digestive gland of Mytilus edulis (534).

References

1. G. Karreman, R. H. Steele, and A. Szent-Györgyi, Proc. Natl. Acad. Sci. U. S. 44, 140–143 (1958); I. Isenberg and A. Szent-Györgyi, ibid., pp. 519–521.
2. E. W. Davie, V. V. Koningsberger, and F. Lipmann, Arch. Biochem. Biophys. 65, 21–38 (1956); R. S. Schweet, R. W. Holley, and E. H. Allen, ibid. 71, 311–325 (1957); A. M. Van de Ven, V. V. Koningsberger, and J. T. G. Overbeek, Biochim. et Biophys. Acta 28, 134–143 (1958); M. Karasek, P. Castelfranco, P. R. Krishnaswamy, and A. Meister, J. Am. Chem. Soc. 80, 2335–2336 (1958).
3. C. E. Dalgliesh, J. Clin. Pathol. 8, 73–78 (1955); A. Asatoor and C. E.

Dalgliesh, *J. Chem. Soc.* pp. 2291–2299 (1956); pp. 1498–1501 (1958); R. R. Brown and J. M. Price, *J. Biol. Chem.* **219**, 985–997 (1956).

4. M. D. Armstrong, K. N. F. Shaw, and P. E. Wall, *J. Biol. Chem.* **218**, 293–303 (1956); C. E. Dalgliesh, *Biochem. J.* **64**, 481–485 (1956).

5. D. E. Duggan, R. L. Bowman, B. B. Brodie, and S. Udenfriend, *Arch. Biochem. Biophys.* **68**, 1–14 (1957).

6. H. B. Vickery and C. L. A. Schmidt, *Chem. Revs.* **9**, 169–318 (1931).

7. J. Liebig, *Ann.* **57**, 127 (1846).

8. E. Schulze and J. Barbieri, *Ber.* **12**, 1924–1925 (1879).

9. F. G. Hopkins and S. W. Cole, *J. Physiol.* **27**, 418–428 (1902).

10. G. H. Beaven and E. R. Holiday, *Advances in Protein Chem.* **7**, 319–386 (1952).

11. F. W. J. Teale and G. Weber, *Biochem. J.* **65**, 476–482 (1957).

12. O. Neubauer, *in* "Handbuch der normalen und pathologischen Physiologie" (A. Bethe, G. von Bergmann, *et al.*, eds.), Vol. 5. Springer, Berlin, 1928.

13. C. E. Dalgliesh, *Advances in Protein Chem.* **10**, 31–150 (1955).

14. M. Womack and W. C. Rose, *J. Biol. Chem.* **166**, 429–434 (1946).

15. B. D. Davis, *Experientia* **6**, 41–50 (1950).

16. B. D. Davis, *J. Biol. Chem.* **191**, 315–325 (1951).

17. B. D. Davis, *Nature* **166**, 1120–1121 (1950).

18. I. I. Salamon and B. D. Davis, *J. Am. Chem. Soc.* **75**, 5567–5571 (1953).

19. B. D. Davis, *J. Bacteriol.* **64**, 729–763 (1952).

20. U. Weiss, B. D. Davis, and E. S. Mingioli, *J. Am. Chem. Soc.* **75**, 5572–5576 (1953).

21. S. Mitsuhashi and B. D. Davis, *Biochim. et Biophys. Acta* **15**, 54–56 (1954).

22. H. Yaniv and C. Gilvarg, *J. Biol. Chem.* **213**, 787–795 (1955).

23. B. D. Davis, *Advances in Enzymol.* **16**, 247–312 (1955).

24. B. D. Davis and U. Weiss, *Arch. exptl. Pathol. Pharmakol.* **220**, 1–15 (1953).

25. M. Gordon, F. A. Haskins, and H. K. Mitchell, *Proc. Natl. Acad. Sci. U. S.* **36**, 427–430 (1950).

26. S. Mitsuhashi and B. D. Davis, *Biochim. et Biophys. Acta* **15**, 268–280 (1954).

27. B. D. Davis and E. S. Mingioli, *J. Bacteriol.* **66**, 129–136 (1953).

28. U. Weiss and E. S. Mingioli, *J. Am. Chem. Soc.* **78**, 2894–2898 (1956).

29. B. D. Davis, *Science* **118**, 251–252 (1953); M. Katagiri and R. Sato, *ibid.* pp. 250–251.

30. U. Weiss, C. Gilvarg, E. S. Mingioli, and B. D. Davis, *Science* **119**, 774–775 (1954).

31. S. Dagley, M. E. Fewster, and F. C. Happold, *J. Gen. Microbiol.* **8**, 1–7 (1953).

32. D. E. Atkinson, S. Melvin, and S. W. Fox, *Arch. Biochem. Biophys.* **31**, 205–211 (1951); J. T. Holden, *ibid.* **61**, 128–136 (1954).

33. J. J. Ghosh, E. Adams, and B. D. Davis, *Federation Proc.* **15**, 261 (1956).

34. P. R. Srinivasan, *J. Am. Chem. Soc.* **81**, 1772–1773 (1959).

35. C. Yanofsky and M. Rachmeler, *Biochim. et Biophys. Acta* **28**, 640–641 (1958).

36. C. Yanofsky, *Biochim. et Biophys. Acta* **31**, 408–416 (1959).

37. C. Yanofsky, *Proc. Natl. Acad. Sci. U. S.* **38**, 215–226 (1952).

38. J. F. Nyc, H. K. Mitchell, E. Leifer, and W. H. Langham, *J. Biol. Chem.* **179**, 783–787 (1949).

39. C. Yanofsky, *Biochim. et Biophys. Acta* **16**, 594–595 (1955).

40. F. W. E. Gibson, C. H. Doy, and S. B. Segall, *Nature* **181**, 549–550 (1958).

41. C. Yanofsky, *Science* **121**, 138–139 (1955).

42. D. W. Parks and H. C. Douglas, *Biochim. et Biophys. Acta* **23**, 207–208 (1957).
43. J. Harley-Mason, *Chem. & Ind.* p. 355 (1955).
44. W. B. Jakoby, *Biochim. et Biophys. Acta* **21**, 390 (1956); D. A. Miller and S. Simmonds, *Science* **126**, 445–446 (1957).
45. C. Gilvarg and K. Bloch, *J. Am. Chem. Soc.* **72**, 5791–5792 (1950).
46. J. Baddiley, G. Ehrensvärd, E. Klein, L. Reio, and E. Saluste, *J. Biol. Chem.* **183**, 777–788 (1950).
47. G. Ehrensvärd, *Svensk. Kem. Tidskr.* **66**, 249–268 (1954); C. E. Dalgliesh, in "Chemical Biogenesis" (A. J. Birch, ed.). Butterworths, London, 1960.
48. G. Ehrensvärd and L. Reio, *Arkiv Kemi* **5**, 229–234 (1953); P. R. Srinivasan, M. Sprecher, and D. B. Sprinson, *Federation Proc.* **13**, 302–303 (1954).
49. E. B. Kalan, B. D. Davis, P. R. Srinivasan, and D. B. Sprinson, *J. Biol. Chem.* **223**, 907–912 (1956); P. R. Srinivasan, D. B. Sprinson, E. B. Kalan, and B. D. Davis, *ibid.* pp. 913–920; P. R. Srinivasan, M. Katagiri, and D. B. Sprinson, *J. Am. Chem. Soc.* **77**, 4943–4944 (1955); P. R. Srinivasan, H. T. Shiguera, M. Sprecher, D. B. Sprinson, and B. D. Davis, *J. Biol. Chem.* **220**, 477–497 (1956).
50. J. Rothschild, *Federation Proc.* **16**, 239 (1957); P. R. Srinivason and D. B. Sprinson, *ibid.* p. 253.
51. M. E. Rafelson, G. Ehrensvärd, and L. Reio, *Exptl. Cell Research* Suppl. 3, 281–286 (1955); M. E. Rafelson, G. Ehrensvärd, M. Bashford, E. Saluste, and C. G. Heden, *J. Biol. Chem.* **211**, 725–735 (1954); M. E. Rafelson, *ibid.* **212**, 953–962; **213**, 479–486 (1955).
52. P. R. Srinivasan, M. Katagiri, and D. B. Sprinson, *J. Biol. Chem.* **234**, 713–722 (1959).
53. C. Yanofsky, *J. Biol. Chem.* **217**, 345–354 (1955).
54. D. E. Hathway, *Biochem. J.* **63**, 380–387 (1956).
55. M. Hasegawa, T. Nakagawa, and S. Yoshida, *J. Japan. Forestry Soc.* **39**, 159–163 (1957).
56. H. Bickel, J. Gerrard, and E. M. Hickmans, *Acta Paediat.* **43**, 64–77 (1954).
57. G. Embden, H. Salomon, and F. Schmidt, *Beitr. chem. Physiol. u. Pathol.* **8**, 129–155 (1906).
58. S. Weinhouse and R. H. Millington, *J. Biol. Chem.* **175**, 995–996 (1948).
59. T. Winnick, F. Friedberg, and D. M. Greenberg, *J. Biol. Chem.* **173**, 189–197 (1948).
60. J. S. Butts, M. S. Dunn, and L. F. Hallman, *J. Biol. Chem.* **123**, 711–718 (1938); J. S. Butts, R. D. Sinnhuber, and M. S. Dunn, *Proc. Soc. Exptl. Biol. Med.* **46**, 671–673 (1941).
61. A. B. Lerner, *J. Biol. Chem.* **181**, 281–296 (1949).
62. A. E. Garrod, in "Inborn Errors of Metabolism" (H. Frowde, ed.), 2nd ed. Hodder & Houghton, London, 1923.
63. M. Wolkow and E. Baumann, *Z. physiol. Chem.* **15**, 228–285 (1891); O. Neubauer and W. Falta, *ibid.* **42**, 81–101 (1904).
64. E. Abderhalden, B. Bloch, and P. Rona, *Z. physiol Chem.* **52**, 435–447 (1907); W. Falta and L. Langstein, *ibid.* **37**, 513–517 (1903).
65. F. Meyer, *Deut. Arch. klin. Med.* **70**, 443 (1901); E. Friedmann, *Beitr. chem. Physiol. u. Pathol.* **11**, 304–307 (1908).
66. O. Neubauer, *Deut. Arch. klin. Med.* **95**, 211–256 (1909).
67. G. Embden and K. Baldes, *Biochem. Z.* **55**, 301–322 (1913).
68. A. Neuberger, C. Rimington, and J. M. G. Wilson, *Biochem. J.* **41**, 438–449 (1947); A. Neuberger, *ibid.* **43**, 599–605 (1948).

69. A. Fölling, Z. physiol. Chem. **227**, 169–176 (1934).
70. A. Fölling, K. Closs, and T. Gamnes, Z. physiol. Chem. **256**, 1–14 (1938); M. Dann, E. Marples, and S. Z. Levine, J. Clin. Invest. **22**, 87–93 (1943).
71. K. Closs and A. Fölling, Z. physiol. Chem. **254**, 250–255 (1938); K. Closs and K. Braaten, ibid. **271**, 221–245 (1941).
72. W. H. Stein, A. C. Paladini, C. H. W. Hirs, and S. Moore, J. Am. Chem. Soc. **76**, 2848–2849 (1954).
73. G. A. Jervis, J. Biol. Chem. **169**, 651–656 (1947).
74. A. R. Moss and R. Schoenheimer, J. Biol. Chem. **135**, 415–429 (1940).
75. S. Udenfriend and J. R. Cooper, J. Biol. Chem. **194**, 503–511 (1952).
76. G. A. Jervis, Proc. Soc. Exptl. Biol. Med. **82**, 514–515 (1953).
77. C. Mitoma, Arch. Biochem. Biophys. **60**, 476–484 (1956).
78. H. W. Wallace, K. Moldave, and A. Meister, Proc. Soc. Exptl. Biol. Med. **94**, 632–633 (1957); C. Mitoma, R. M. Auld, and S. Udenfriend, ibid. **95**, 634–635 (1957).
79. S. Kaufman, J. Biol. Chem. **234**, 2677–2682 (1959); S. Kaufman and B. Levenberg, ibid. pp. 2683–2688 (1959).
80. G. H. Reem and N. Kretchmer, Proc. Soc. Exptl. Biol. Med. **96**, 458–460 (1957); F. T. Kenney, G. H. Reem, and N. Kretchmer, Science **127**, 86 (1958).
81. O. G. Lien and D. M. Greenberg, J. Biol. Chem. **195**, 637–644 (1952).
82. D. Y. Y. Hsia, K. W. Driscoll, W. Troll, and W. E. Knox, Nature **178**, 1239–1240 (1956).
83. M. Womack and W. C. Rose, J. Biol. Chem. **107**, 449–458 (1934).
84. R. J. Boscott and H. Bickel, Scand. J. Clin. & Lab. Invest. **5**, 380–382 (1953).
85. C. E. Dalgliesh, Arch. Biochem. Biophys. **58**, 214–226 (1955); C. Mitoma, H. S. Posner, H. C. Reitz, and S. Udenfriend, ibid. **61**, 431–441 (1956).
86. M. D. Armstrong and K. S. Robinson, Arch. Biochem. Biophys. **52**, 287–288 (1954).
87. T. J. Bickis, J. P. Kennedy, and J. H. Quastel, Nature **179**, 1124–1126 (1957).
88. M. Miyamoto and T. B. Fitzpatrick, Nature **179**, 199–200 (1957).
89. W. E. Knox and M. LeMay-Knox, Biochem. J. **49**, 686–693 (1951).
90. P. S. Cammarata and P. P. Cohen, J. Biol. Chem. **193**, 45–52 (1951).
91. Z. N. Canellakis and P. P. Cohen, J. Biol. Chem. **222**, 53–62, 63–71 (1956).
92. W. E. Knox and B. M. Pitt, J. Biol. Chem. **225**, 675–688 (1957).
93. N. Kretchmer, S. Z. Levine, H. McNamara, and H. L. Barnett, J. Clin. Invest. **35**, 236–244 (1956); N. Kretchmer and H. McNamara, ibid. pp. 1089–1093 (1956).
94. V. H. Auerbach and H. A. Waisman, J. Biol. Chem. **234**, 304–306 (1959); F. Sereni, F. T. Kenney, and N. Kretchmer, ibid. pp. 609–612 (1959).
95. E. C. C. Lin and W. E. Knox, Biochim. et Biophys. Acta **26**, 85–88 (1957).
96. G. Medes, Biochim. J. **26**, 917–940 (1932).
97. H. Gros and E. J. Kirnberger, Klin. Wochschr. **32**, 115–118, 645–646 (1954).
98. Y. Kotake, Y. Masai, and Y. Mori, Z. physiol. Chem. **122**, 195–200 (1922).
99. R. R. Sealock, J. D. Perkinson, and D. H. Basinski, J. Biol. Chem. **140**, 153–160 (1941); R. R. Sealock and H. E. Silberstein, ibid. **135**, 251–258 (1940).
100. L. E. Glynn, H. P. Himsworth, and A. Neuberger, Brit. J. Exptl. Pathol. **26**, 326–337 (1945); A. Neuberger and T. A. Webster, Biochem. J. **41**, 449–457 (1947).
101. S. E. Hager, R. I. Gregerman, and W. E. Knox, J. Biol. Chem. **225**, 935–947 (1957).

102. M. Uchida, S. Suzuki, and K. Ichihara, *J. Biochem. (Tokyo)* **41**, 41–65 (1954).
103. B. N. La Du and V. G. Zannoni, *J. Biol. Chem.* **217**, 777–787 (1955).
104. R. R. Sealock and H. E. Silberstein, *J. Biol. Chem.* **135**, 251–258 (1940).
105. W. F. Rogers and F. Gardner, *J. Clin. Invest.* **28**, 806–807 (1949).
106. J. E. Morris, E. R. Harper, and A. Goldbloom, *J. Clin. Invest.* **29**, 325–335 (1950).
107. R. J. Salmon and C. D. May, *J. Lab. Clin. Med.* **36**, 591–598 (1950).
108. C. W. Woodruff, M. E. Cherrington, A. K. Stockell, and W. J. Darby, *J. Biol. Chem.* **178**, 861–868 (1949).
109. K. Felix, G. Leonhardi, and I. Glosenopp, *Z. physiol. Chem.* **287**, 141–147 (1951).
110. J. N. Williams, Jr., and A. Sreenivasan, *J. Biol. Chem.* **203**, 613–623 (1953).
111. R. R. Sealock and R. L. Goodland, *Science* **114**, 645–646 (1951).
112. B. N. La Du and V. G. Zannoni, *J. Biol. Chem.* **219**, 273–281 (1956).
113. W. E. Knox, *Proc. 4th Intern. Congr. Biochem, Vienna, 1958* **11**, 307–312 (1959).
114. V. G. Zannoni and B. M. La Du, *J. Biol. Chem.* **234**, 2925–2931 (1959).
115. W. E. Knox, in "Amino Acid Metabolism" (W. D. McElroy and B. Glass, eds.), p. 836. Johns Hopkins, Baltimore, 1955.
116. B. Witkop and S. Goodwin, *Experientia* **8**, 377–379 (1952).
117. W. E. Knox, *Am. J. Human Genet.* **10**, 95–124 (1958).
118. B. N. La Du, V. G. Zannoni, L. Laster, and J. E. Seegmiller, *J. Biol. Chem.* **230**, 251–260 (1958).
119. A. Neuberger, C. Rimington, and J. M. G. Wilson, *Biochem. J.* **41**, 438–449 (1947).
120. K. Fromherz and L. Hermanns, *Z. physiol. Chem.* **91**, 194–229 (1914).
121. E. Abderhalden, *Z. physiol. Chem.* **77**, 454–461 (1912).
122. E. Papageorge and H. B. Lewis, *J. Biol. Chem.* **123**, 211–220 (1938).
123. A. Fölling and K. Closs, *Z. physiol. Chem.* **254**, 256–265 (1938).
124. M. Suda, Y. Takeda, K. Sujishi, and T. Tanaka, *J. Biochem. (Tokyo)* **38**, 297–302 (1951).
125. R. G. Ravdin and D. I. Crandall, *J. Biol. Chem.* **189**, 137–149 (1951).
126. M. Suda and Y. Takeda, *Med. J. Osaka Univ.* **2**, 37–40 (1950).
127. M. Suda and Y. Takeda, *Med. J. Osaka Univ.* **2**, 41–44 (1950).
128. D. I. Crandall, in "Amino Acid Metabolism" (W. D. McElroy and B. Glass, eds.), p. 867. Johns Hopkins, Baltimore, 1955.
129. W. E. Knox and S. W. Edwards, *J. Biol. Chem.* **216**, 489–498 (1955).
130. S. W. Edwards and W. E. Knox, *J. Biol. Chem.* **220**, 79–91 (1956).
131. A. Meister, *J. Biol. Chem.* **178**, 577–589 (1949).
132. P. Hagan and A. D. Welch, *Recent Progr. in Hormone Research* **12**, 27–41 (1956).
133. U. S. von Euler, *Recent Progr. in Hormone Research* **14**, 483–507 (1958).
134. S. Senoh, B. Witkop, C. R. Creveling, and S. Udenfriend, *Proc. 4th Intern. Congr. Biochem., Vienna, 1958* **13**, 176–188 (1959).
135. J. J. Abel and D. I. Macht, *J. Pharmacol. Exptl. Therap.* **3**, 319–377 (1911).
136. V. Deulofeu and E. Duprat, *J. Biol. Chem.* **153**, 459–463 (1944).
137. G. Bayer and T. Wense, *Pflügers. Arch. ges. Physiol.* **237**, 651–654 (1936).
138. Z. M. Bacq, *Biol. Revs. Cambridge Phil. Soc.* **22**, 73–91 (1947).
139. J. F. Gaskell, *J. Gen. Physiol.* **2**, 73–85 (1919).
140. M. Henze, *Z. physiol. Chem.* **87**, 51–58 (1913).

141. V. Erspamer, *Experientia* **5,** 79 (1949).
142. M. Guggenheim, "Die biogenen Amine." S. Karger, Basel, 1951.
143. S. Gurin and A. M. Delluva, *J. Biol. Chem.* **170,** 545–550 (1947).
144. S. Udenfriend, J. R. Cooper, C. T. Clark, and J. E. Baer, *Science* **117,** 663–665 (1953).
145. S. Udenfriend and J. B. Wyngaarden, *Biochim. et Biophys. Acta* **20,** 48–52 (1956).
146. P. Hagen, *J. Pharmacol. Exptl. Therap.* **116,** 26 (1956).
147. McC. Goodall and N. Kirshner, *J. Biol. Chem.* **226,** 213–221 (1947).
148. N. Kirshner, *J. Biol. Chem.* **226,** 821–825 (1957).
149. N. Kirshner and McC. Goodall, *Biochim. et Biophys. Acta* **24,** 658–659 (1957).
150. W. L. Duliere and H. S. Raper, *Biochem. J.* **24,** 239–249 (1930).
151. A. B. Lerner, T. B. Fitzpatrick, E. Calkins, and W. H. Summerson, *J. Biol. Chem.* **178,** 185–195 (1949).
152. P. Kubowitz, *Biochem. Z.* **299,** 32–57 (1938).
153. D. Kertesz and R. Zito, *Nature* **179,** 1017–1018 (1957).
154. P. Holtz, R. Heise, and K. Luidtke, *Arch. exptl. Pathol. Pharmakol.* **191,** 87–118 (1938).
155. P. Holtz, *Z. physiol. Chem.* **251,** 226–232 (1938).
156. P. Holtz, K. Credner, and H. Walter, *Z. physiol. Chem.* **262,** 111–119 (1939).
157. H. Blaschko, *Advances in Enzymol.* **5,** 67–85 (1945).
158. H. A. Heinsen, *Z. physiol. Chem.* **245,** 1–10 (1937).
159. R. W. Schayer, *Proc. Soc. Exptl. Biol. Med.* **84,** 60–63 (1953).
160. M. F. Lockett, *Brit. J. Pharmacol.* **9,** 498–505 (1954).
161. R. W. Schayer, *J. Biol. Chem.* **189,** 301–306 (1951).
162. R. W. Schayer, *J. Biol. Chem.* **192,** 875–881 (1951).
163. M. D. Armstrong and A. McMillan, *Federation Proc.* **16,** 146 (1957).
164. J. Axelrod, J. K. Inscoe, S. Senoh, and B. Witkop, *Biochim. et Biophys. Acta* **27,** 210–211 (1958).
165. M. Goldstein, A. J. Friedhoff, and C. Simmons, *Biochim. et Biophys. Acta* **33,** 572–574 (1959).
166. H. S. Mason, *Advances in Enzymol.* **16,** 105–184 (1955).
167. D. E. Green and O. Richter, *Biochem. J.* **31,** 596–616 (1937).
168. R. W. Schayer and R. L. Smiley, *J. Biol. Chem.* **202,** 425–430 (1953).
169. H. S. Mason, *in* "Pigment Cell Growth" (M. Gordon, ed.), p. 277. Academic Press, New York, 1953.
170. A. B. Lerner, *Advances in Enzymol.* **14,** 73–128 (1953).
171. H. S. Raper, *Biochem. J.* **20,** 735–742 (1926); **21,** 89–96 (1927); **26,** 2000–2004 (1932); *J. Chem. Soc.* pp. 125–130 (1938).
172. H. S. Mason, *J. Biol. Chem.* **168,** 433–438 (1947); **172,** 83–99 (1948); **181,** 803–812 (1949).
173. I. W. Sizer, *Advances in Enzymol.* **14,** 129–161 (1953).
174. H. Gest and N. H. Horowitz, *J. Gen. Microbiol.* **18,** 64–70 (1958).
175. N. H. Horowitz and M. Fling, *in* "Amino Acid Metabolism" (W. D. McElroy and B. Glass, eds.), pp. 207–218. Johns Hopkins, Baltimore, 1955; H. Hoagland, *Ann. N. Y. Acad. Sci.* **66,** 445 (1958).
176. J. M. Bruce, *J. Appl. Chem. (London)* **4,** 469–473 (1954).
177. W. E. Knox, *Am. J. Human Genet.* **10,** 249 (1958).
178. B. M. Jones and W. Sinclair, *Nature* **181,** 926–927 (1958).
179. S. Kawase, *Nature* **181,** 1350–1351 (1958).

180. A. S. Fox and J. B. Burnett, *Proc. Soc. Exptl. Biol. Med.* **98**, 110–114 (1958).
181. M. G. M. Pryor, P. B. Russell, and A. R. Todd, *Biochem. J.* **40**, 627–632 (1946).
182. W. Fleischmann, *Quart. Rev. Biol.* **22**, 119–140 (1947).
183. J. Roche and R. Michel, *Recent Progr. in Hormone Research* **12**, 1–22 (1956).
184. J. F. Gudernatsch, *Arch. Entwicklungsmech. Organ.* **35**, 457–483 (1913).
185. W. J. Leach, *Physiol. Zool.* **19**, 365–374 (1946).
186. C. R. Harington, *J. Chem. Soc.* pp. 193–201 (1944).
187. R. Pitt-Rivers, *Biochem. J.* **43**, 223–231 (1948).
188. G. S. Serif and S. Kirkwood, *J. Biol. Chem.* **233**, 109–115 (1958).
189. T. Matsuura and H. J. Cahnmann, *J. Am. Chem. Soc.* **81**, 871–878 (1959).
190. J. Gross and R. Pitt-Rivers, *Biochem. J.* **53**, 645–657 (1953).
191. J. Roche, R. Michel, W. Wolf, and J. Nunez, *Compt. rend. acad. sci.* **240**, 921–923 (1955).
192. J. Roche, R. Michel, and W. Wolf, *Compt. rend. acad. sci.* **240**, 251–253 (1955).
193. J. H. Wilkinson and N. F. MacLagan, *Biochem. J.* **58**, 87–90 (1954).
194. J. Roche, M. Pavlovic, and R. Michel, *Biochim. et Biophys. Acta* **24**, 489–495 (1957).
195. J. B. Stanbury, *J. Biol. Chem.* **228**, 801–811 (1957).
196. J. B. Stanbury and M. L. Morris, *J. Biol. Chem.* **233**, 106–108 (1958).
197. W. Tong, A. Taurog, and I. L. Chaikoff, *J. Biol. Chem.* **207**, 59–76 (1954).
198. J. Roche, R. Michel, and J. Tata, *Biochim. et Biophys. Acta* **15**, 500–507 (1954).
199. S. B. Barker and N. Etling, *Federation Proc.* **17**, 9 (1958).
200. O. Thibault and R. Pitt-Rivers, *Lancet* **268**, 285 (1955).
201. E. Drechsel, *Z. Biol.* **33**, 85 (1896).
202. J. Roche, *Experientia* **8**, 45–54 (1952).
203. F. W. Power, *Proc. Soc. Exptl. Biol. Med.* **33**, 598–600 (1935).
204. A. Meister, "Biochemistry of the Amino Acids," p. 354. Academic Press, New York, 1957.
205. W. H. Stein, A. C. Paladini, C. H. W. Hirs, and S. Moore, *J. Am. Chem. Soc.* **76**, 2848–2849 (1954).
206. K. Schreier, K. I. Altman, and L. H. Hempelmann, *Proc. Soc. Exptl. Biol. Med.* **87**, 61–63 (1954).
207. M. D. Armstrong, F. C. Chao, V. J. Parker, and P. E. Wall, *Proc. Soc. Exptl. Biol. Med.* **90**, 675–679 (1955).
208. F. H. Bruns and L. Fiedler, *Biochem. Z.* **330**, 324–341 (1958).
209. A. N. Booth, M. S. Masri, D. J. Robbins, O. H. Emerson, F. T. Jones, and F. DeEds, *J. Biol. Chem.* **235**, 2649–2652 (1960).
210. M. D. Armstrong and K. N. F. Shaw, *J. Biol. Chem.* **225**, 269–278 (1957).
211. H. Tallan, S. T. Bella, W. H. Stein, and S. Moore, *J. Biol. Chem.* **217**, 703–708 (1955).
212. F. R. Bettelheim, *J. Am. Chem. Soc.* **76**, 2838–2839 (1954).
213. R. Robinson, *Nature* **137**, 172–173 (1936).
214. L. Bogorad, *Ann. Rev. Plant Physiol.* **9**, 417–448 (1958).
215. A. J. Birch, F. W. Donovan, and F. Moewus, *Nature* **72**, 902–904 (1953).
216. F. J. Ryan, *Science* **122**, 470 (1955).
217. E. W. Underhill, J. E. Watkin, and A. C. Neish, *Can. J. Biochem. Physiol.* **35**, 219–228 (1957).

218. H. Reznik and R. Urban, *Naturwissenschaften* **44**, 592–593 (1957).

219. T. A. Geissman and T. Swain, *Chem. & Ind.* p. 984 (1957).

220. H. Grisebach, Z. *Naturfosch.* **13b**, 335–336 (1958).

221. J. E. Watkin, E. W. Underhill, and A. C. Neish, *Can. J. Biochem. Physiol.* **35**, 229–237 (1957).

222. H. Grisebach, Z. *Naturforsch.* **12b**, 227–231, 597–598 (1957).

223. A. J. Birch and F. W. Donovan, *Australian J. Chem.* **6**, 360–368 (1953).

224. R. E. Kremers, *Ann. Rev. Plant Physiol.* **10**, 185–186 (1959); K. Kratzl and G. Billek, eds., *Proc. 4th Intern. Congr. Biochem., Vienna, 1958* **2**, 161–187 (1959).

225. K. Freudenberg, *Nature* **183**, 1152–1155 (1959).

226. S. A. Brown and A. C. Neish, *Nature* **175**, 688–689 (1955); *Can. J. Biochem. Physiol.* **33**, 948–962 (1955); *J. Am. Chem. Soc.* **81**, 2419–2424 (1959).

227. G. Eberhardt and W. J. Schubert, *J. Am. Chem. Soc.* **78**, 2835–2837 (1956).

228. S. A. Brown and A. C. Neish, *Can. J. Biochem. Physiol.* **34**, 769–778 (1956).

229. R. Robinson, "The Structural Relations of Natural Products." Oxford Univ. Press, London and New York, 1955.

230. R. F. Dawson, *Advances in Enzymol.* **8**, 203–251 (1948).

231. W. O. James, in "The Alkaloids" (R. H. F. Manske and H. L. Holmes, eds.), Vol. I, p. 15. Academic Press, New York, 1950.

232. E. Leete, in "The Biogenesis of Natural Substances" (M. Gates, ed.). Interscience, New York, in press.

233. E. Leete, S. Kirkwood, and L. Marion, *Can. J. Chem.* **30**, 749–760 (1952).

234. E. Leete and L. Marion, *Can. J. Chem.* **31**, 126–128 (1953).

235. J. Massicot and L. Marion, *Can. J. Chem.* **35**, 1–4 (1957).

236. W. O. James and C. S. Butt, "Biochemie und Physiologie der Alkaloide," p. 182. Academie-Verlag, Berlin, 1957.

237. E. Leete, *Chem. & Ind.* p. 604 (1959).

238. S. Shibata and I. Imaseki, *Pharm. Bull. (Japan)* **4**, 277–280 (1956).

239. E. Leete, *Chem. & Ind.* pp. 1088–1089 (1958).

240. S. Shibata, I. Imaseki, and M. Yamazaki, *Pharm. Bull, (Japan)* **5**, 71–73 (1957).

241. S. Shibata, I. Imaseki, and M. Yamazaki, *Pharm. Bull. (Japan)* **5**, 594 (1957).

242. I. Imaseki, S. Shibata, and M. Yamazaki, *Chem. & Ind.* p. 1625 (1958).

243. J. E. Gander, *Federation Proc.* **18**, 232 (1959).

244. A. R. Battersby and B. J. T. Harper, *Chem. & Ind.* p. 364 (1958).

245. E. Leete, *J. Am. Chem. Soc.* **81**, 3948–3951 (1959).

246. E. Leete, *Chem. & Ind.* pp. 977–978 (1958).

247. K. Bowden and L. Marion, *Can. J. Chem.* **29**, 1037–1042 (1951).

248. E. Leete and L. Marion, *Can. J. Chem.* **31**, 1195–1202 (1953).

249. A. Breccia and L. Marion, *Can. J. Chem.* **37**, 1066–1070 (1959).

250. D. W. Henry and E. Leete, *Abst. 134th Meeting Am. Chem. Soc. Chicago 1958* P43C.

251. R. J. Suhadolnik, L. M. Henderson, J. B. Hanson, and Y. H. Loo, *J. Am. Chem. Soc.* **80**, 3153–3154 (1958).

252. K. Mothes, F. Weygand, D. Gröger, and H. Grisebach, Z. *Naturforsch.* **13b**, 41–44 (1958).

253. D. Gröger, H. J. Wendt, K. Mothes, and F. Weygand, Z. *Naturforsch.* **14b**, 355–358 (1959).

254. A. G. Paul, Ph.D. Dissertation, University of Connecticut (1957).

255. R. J. Suhadolnik and R. G. Chenoweth, *J. Am. Chem. Soc.* **80**, 4391–4392 (1958).
256. J. A. Winstead and R. J. Suhadolnik, *J. Am. Chem. Soc.* **82**, 1644–1647 (1960).
257. R. J. Suhadolnik, A. Fischer, and J. Wilson, *Federation Proc.* **19**, 8 (1960).
258. D. G. Wilson, K. W. King, and R. H. Burris, *J. Biol. Chem.* **208**, 863–874 (1954).
259. E. E. Conn and S. L. Seki, *Federation Proc.* **16**, 167 (1957).
260. M. Guggenheim, *Z. physiol. Chem.* **88**, 276–284 (1913).
261. J. D. Jones, B. S. W. Smith, and W. C. Evans, *Biochem. J.* **51**, xi (1952).
262. A. J. Kluyver and J. C. M. Van Zifp, *Antonie van Leeuwenhoek J. Microbiol. Serol.* **17**, 315–324 (1951).
263. S. Udenfriend and J. R. Cooper, *J. Biol. Chem.* **203**, 953–960 (1953).
264. E. F. Gale, *Advances in Enzymol.* **6**, 1–32 (1946).
265. P. K. Stumpf and D. E. Green, *J. Biol. Chem.* **153**, 387–399 (1944).
266. F. Bernheim, *J. Biol. Chem.* **143**, 383–389 (1942).
267. D. Rudman and A. Meister, *J. Biol. Chem.* **200**, 591–604 (1953).
268. N. Kunita, *Med. J. Osaka Univ.* **7**, 203 (1956).
269. S. Sentheshanmuganathan and S. K. Elsden, *Biochem. J.* **69**, 210–218 (1958).
270. Y. Kotake, M. Chikono, and K. Ichihara, *Z. physiol. Chem.* **143**, 218–228 (1925).
271. K. Hirai, *Biochem. Z.* **114**, 71–80 (1921).
272. R. J. Boscott and S. Greenberg, *Biochem. J.* **55**, xviii (1953).
273. F. C. Happold, *Biochem. Soc. Symposia (Cambridge, Engl.)* **5**, 85–96 (1950).
274. K. V. Thimann, "The Life of Bacteria." Macmillan, New York, 1955.
275. M. Uchida, Y. Takemoto, Y. Kikihara, and K. Ichihara, *Med. J. Osaka Univ.* **3**, 509–519 (1953).
276. W. A. Krehl, L. J. Teply, P. S. Sarma, and C. A. Elvehjem, *Science* **101**, 489–490 (1945).
277. C. Heidelberger, E. P. Abraham, and S. Lepkovsky, *J. Biol. Chem.* **179**, 151–155 (1949).
278. A. Meister, *Advances in Enzymol.* **16**, 185–246 (1955).
279. R. W. Jackson, *J. Biol. Chem.* **84**, 1–22 (1929).
280. V. du Vigneaud, R. R. Sealock, and C. Van Etten, *J. Biol. Chem.* **98**, 565–575 (1932).
281. R. K. Gholson, L. M. Henderson, G. A. Mourkides, R. J. Hill, and R. E. Koeppe, *J. Biol. Chem.* **234**, 96–98 (1959).
282. O. Hayaishi and R. Y. Stanier, *J. Bacteriol.* **62**, 691–701 (1951).
283. D. M. Bonner and C. Yanofsky, *J. Nutrition* **44**, 603–616 (1951).
284. C. E. Dalgliesh, *Quart. Revs. (London)* **5**, 227–244 (1951).
285. A. H. Mehler, *in* "Amino Acid Metabolism" (W. D. McElroy and B. Glass, eds.), pp. 882–908. Johns Hopkins, Baltimore, 1955.
286. L. M. Henderson, *in* "Symposium on Vitamin Metabolism," Nutrition Symposia Series No. 13 (E. E. Snell, chairman), pp. 1–18. Natl. Vitamin Foundation, New York, 1956.
287. C. Yanofsky and D. M. Bonner, *Proc. Natl. Acad. Sci. U. S.* **36**, 167–176 (1950).
288. G. W. Beadle, H. K. Mitchell, and J. F. Nyc, *Proc. Natl. Acad. Sci. U. S.* **33**, 155–158 (1947).
289. H. K. Mitchell and J. F. Nyc, *Proc. Natl. Acad. Sci. U. S.* **34**, 1–4 (1948).
290. D. M. Bonner, *Proc. Natl. Acad. Sci. U. S.* **34**, 5–9 (1948).

291. A. Butenandt, *Angew. Chem.* **61**, 262–263 (1949).
292. L. Musajo, A. Spada, and E. Cassini, *Gazz. chim ital.* **80**, 171–176 (1950).
293. A. Butenandt, W. Weidel, and H. G. Schlossberger, *Z. Naturforsch.* **4b**, 242–244 (1949).
294. F. A. Haskins and H. K. Mitchell, *Proc. Natl. Acad. Sci. U. S.* **35**, 500–506 (1949).
295. Y. Hirata, K. Nakanishi, and H. Kikkawa, *Science* **112**, 307–308 (1950).
296. L. M. Henderson, *J. Biol. Chem.* **178**, 1005–1006 (1949).
297. L. M. Henderson, *J. Biol. Chem.* **181**, 677–685 (1949).
298. D. M. Bonner and C. Yanofsky, *Proc. Natl. Acad. Sci. U. S.* **35**, 576–581 (1949).
299. Y. Kotake and J. Iwaoh, *Z. physiol. Chem.* **195**, 139–158 (1931).
300. O. Wiss, G. Viollier, and M. Muller, *Helv. Chim. Acta* **33**, 771–775 (1950).
301. L. M. Henderson, R. E. Koski, and F. D'Angeli, *J. Biol. Chem.* **223**, 479–484 (1956).
302. L. M. Henderson, R. E. Koski, and F. D'Angeli, *J. Biol. Chem.* **215**, 369–376 (1955).
303. H. K. Mitchell, J. F. Nyc, and R. D. Owen, *J. Biol. Chem.* **175**, 433–438 (1948).
304. P. W. Albert, B. T. Scheer, and H. J. Deuel, Jr., *J. Biol. Chem.* **175**, 479–480 (1948).
305. C. Heidelberger, M. E. Gullberg, A. F. Morgan, and S. Lepkovsky, *J. Biol. Chem.* **179**, 143–150 (1949).
306. R. W. Schayer, *J. Biol. Chem.* **187**, 777–786 (1950).
307. R. W. Schayer and L. M. Henderson, *J. Biol. Chem.* **195**, 657–661 (1952).
308. L. M. Henderson and L. V. Hankes, *J. Biol. Chem.* **222**, 1069–1077 (1956).
309. L. V. Hankes and L. M. Henderson, *J. Biol. Chem.* **225**, 349–354 (1957).
310. Y. Kotake and T. Masayama, *Z. physiol. Chem.* **243**, 237–244 (1936).
311. W. E. Knox and A. H. Mehler, *J. Biol. Chem.* **187**, 419–430 (1950).
312. A. H. Mehler and W. E. Knox, *J. Biol. Chem.* **187**, 431–438 (1950).
313. T. Tanaka and W. E. Knox, *J. Biol. Chem.* **234**, 1162–1170 (1959).
314. O. Hayaishi, S. Rothberg, A. H. Mehler, and Y. Saito, *J. Biol. Chem.* **229**, 889–896 (1947).
315. T. Sakan and O. Hayaishi, *J. Biol. Chem.* **186**, 177–180 (1950).
316. M. Mason and C. P. Berg, *J. Biol. Chem.* **188**, 783–788 (1951).
317. A. Ek and B. Witkop, *J. Am. Chem. Soc.* **75**, 500–501 (1953).
318. W. E. Knox and A. H. Mehler, *J. Biol. Chem.* **187**, 419–430 (1950).
319. N. D. Lee and R. H. Williams, *Biochim. et Biophys. Acta* **9**, 698 (1952).
320. J. B. Price and L. S. Dietrich, *J. Biol. Chem.* **227**, 633–636 (1957).
321. E. F. Efimohkina, *Biokhimiya* **19**, 68–79 (1954).
322. T. Dashman and P. Feigelson, *Abstr. 136th Meeting, Am. Chem. Soc., Atlantic City, 1959,* p. 41c (1960).
323. P. Feigelson and T. Dashman, *Abstr. 136th Meeting, Am. Chem. Soc., Atlantic City, 1959,* p. 41c (1960).
324. M. Civen and W. E. Knox, *J. Biol. Chem.* **234**, 1787–1790 (1959).
325. A. M. Nemeth and V. T. Nachmias, *Science* **128**, 1085–1086 (1958).
326. A. M. Nemeth, *J. Biol. Chem.* **234**, 2921–2924 (1959).
327. W. B. Jakoby, *J. Biol. Chem.* **207**, 657–663 (1954).
328. J. C. Rabinowitz and H. Tabor, *J. Biol. Chem.* **233**, 252–255 (1958).

329. F. T. de Castro, J. M. Price, and R. R. Brown, *J. Am. Chem. Soc.* **78,** 2904–2905 (1956).
330. Y. Saito, O. Hayaishi, S. Rothberg, and S. Senoh, *Federation Proc.* **16,** 240 (1957).
331. Y. Kotake, A. Toratani, K. Miyamoto, and Y. Shibata, Seikagaku **28,** 105 (1957).
332. Y. Saito, O. Hayaishi, and S. Rothberg, *J. Biol. Chem.* **229,** 921–934 (1957).
333. L. M. Henderson, I. M. Weinstock, and G. B. Ramasarma, *J. Biol. Chem.* **189,** 19–29 (1951).
334. C. C. Porter, I. Clark, and R. H. Silber, *Arch. Biochem. Biophys.* **18,** 339–343 (1948).
335. H. F. Charconnet, C. E. Dalgliesh, and A. Neuberger, *Biochem. J.* **53,** 513–521 (1953).
336. M. Mason, *J. Biol. Chem.* **201,** 513–518 (1953).
337. P. B. Junqueira and B. S. Schweigert, *J. Biol. Chem.* **175,** 535–546 (1948).
338. C. O. Stevens and L. M. Henderson, *J. Biol. Chem.* **234,** 1191–1194 (1959).
339. H. B. Burch, O. H. Lowry, A. M. Padilla, and A. M. Combs, *J. Biol. Chem.* **223,** 29–45 (1956).
340. A. Ellinger, *Z. physiol. Chem.* **43,** 325–337 (1904).
341. Z. Matsuoka and N. Yoshimatsu, *Z. physiol. Chem.* **143,** 206–210 (1925).
342. A. Butenandt, W. Weidel, and H. Schlossberger, *Naturwissenschaften* **30,** 51 (1942).
343. A. Butenandt, W. Weidel, R. Weichert, and W. von Derjuigin, *Z. physiol. Chem.* **279,** 27–43 (1943).
344. L. Musajo, *Atti. accad. Lincei.* **21,** 368–371 (1935).
345. L. Musajo, *Gas. chim. ital.* **67,** 165–171, 171–178, 179–188 (1937).
346. S. Lepkovsky and E. Nielson, *J. Biol. Chem.* **144,** 135–138 (1942).
347. S. Lepkovsky, E. Roboz, and A. J. Haagen-Smit, *J. Biol. Chem.* **149,** 195–201 (1943).
348. C. E. Dalgliesh, *Biochem. J.* **52,** 3–14 (1952).
349. C. E. Dalgliesh, W. E. Knox, and A. Neuberger, *Nature* **168,** 20–22 (1951).
350. F. Rosen, J. W. Huff, and W. A. Perlzweig, *J. Nutrition* **33,** 561–567 (1947).
351. B. S. Schweigert and P. B. Pearson, *J. Biol. Chem.* **168,** 555–561 (1947).
352. A. E. Braunshtein, E. V. Goryachenkova, and T. S. Pashkina, *Biokhimiya* **14,** 163–179 (1949).
353. O. Wiss and F. Hatz, *Helv. Chim. Acta* **32,** 532–537 (1949).
354. I. L. Miller and E. A. Adelberg, *J. Biol. Chem.* **205,** 691–698 (1953).
355. W. B. Jakoby and D. M. Bonner, *J. Biol. Chem.* **205,** 699–708 (1953).
356. W. B. Jakoby and D. M. Bonner, *J. Biol. Chem.* **205,** 709–715 (1953).
357. O. Hayaishi, in "Amino Acid Metabolism" (W. D. McElroy and B. Glass, eds.), pp. 914–929. Johns Hopkins, Baltimore, 1955.
358. M. Mason and C. P. Berg, *J. Biol. Chem.* **195,** 515–524 (1952).
359. O. Wiss, *Z. physiol. Chem.* **293,** 106–121 (1953).
360. A. Meister, *J. Biol. Chem.* **206,** 577–585 (1954).
361. O. Wiss, *Z. Naturforsch.* **7b,** 133–136 (1952).
362. M. Mason, *J. Biol. Chem.* **211,** 839–844 (1954).
363. I. L. Miller, M. Tsuchida, and E. A. Adelberg, *J. Biol. Chem.* **203,** 205–211 (1953).
364. C. Yanofsky, in "Amino Acid Metabolism" (W. D. McElroy and B. Glass, eds.), pp. 930–939. Johns Hopkins, Baltimore, 1955.

365. W. B. Jakoby and D. M. Bonner, *J. Biol. Chem.* **221,** 689–695 (1956).

366. M. Mason, *J. Biol. Chem.* **227,** 61–68 (1947).

367. R. R. Brown and J. M. Price, *J. Biol. Chem.* **219,** 985–997 (1956).

368. Y. Kotake and S. Otani, *Z. physiol. Chem.* **214,** 1–13 (1933).

369. F. T. deCastro, R. R. Brown, and J. M. Price, *J. Biol. Chem.* **228,** 777–784 (1957).

370. O. Wiss and F. Weber, *Z. physiol. Chem.* **304,** 232–240 (1956).

371. O. Wiss and F. Weber, *Med. J. Osaka Univ.* **8,** 41–46 (1958).

372. M. Spacek, *Nature* **172,** 204 (1953).

373. A. Butenandt, P. Karlson, and W. Zillig, *Z. physiol. Chem.* **288,** 125–129 (1951).

374. A. Butenandt and U. Renner, *Z. Naturforsch.* **8b,** 454–462 (1953).

375. K. Makino and K. Arai, *Science* **121,** 143–144 (1955).

376. J. M. Price and L. W. Dodge, *J. Biol. Chem.* **223,** 699–704 (1956).

377. J. K. Roy, J. M. Price, and R. R. Brown, *Federation Proc.* **17,** 300 (1958).

378. J. M. Price, R. R. Brown, and T. C. Larson, *J. Clin. Invest.* **36,** 1600–1607 (1957).

379. J. M. Price, R. R. Brown, and M. E. Ellis, *J. Nutrition* **60,** 323–333 (1956).

380. C. E. Dalgliesh and H. Tabechian, *Biochem. J.* **62,** 625–633 (1956).

381. R. K. Gholson and L. M. Henderson, *in* "Symposium Tryptophan Metabolism" (J. M. Price, ed.), pp. 38–51. Div. Med. Chem., Am. Chem. Soc., Washington, D. C., 1959.

382. H. Takahashi, M. Kaihara, and J. M. Price, *J. Biol. Chem.* **223,** 705–708 (1956).

383. J. K. Roy, and J. M. Price, *Federation Proc.* **18,** 313 (1959).

384. M. Rothstein and D. M. Greenberg, *Arch. Biochem. and Biophys.* **68,** 206–214 (1957).

384a. H. Takahashi and J. M. Price, *J. Biol. Chem.* **233,** 150–153 (1958).

385. J. Tabone, D. Tabone, and S. Thomassey, *Bull. soc. chim. biol.* **36,** 565–566 (1954).

386. G. Ponecorvo, *Biochem. Soc. Symposia (Cambridge, Engl.)* **4,** 40 (1950).

387. R. Y. Stanier and O. Hayaishi, *Science* **114,** 326–330 (1951).

388. E. J. Behrman and T. Tanaka, *Federation Proc.* **18,** 189 (1959).

389. O. Hayaishi, H. Taniuchi, M. Tashero, H. Yamada, and S. Kuno, *J. Am. Chem. Soc.* **81,** 3483–3484 (1959); and personal communication.

390. O. Hayaishi, M. Katagiri, and S. Rothberg, *J. Biol. Chem.* **229,** 905–920 (1957).

391. M. Suda, K. Hashimoto, H. Matsuoka, and T. Kamahora, *J. Biochem. (Tokyo)* **38,** 289–296 (1951).

392. M. Uchida and K. Matsuda, *Symposia on Enzyme Chem. (Japan)* **10,** 57–67 (1954).

393. W. R. Sistrom and R. Y. Stanier, *J. Biol. Chem.* **210,** 821–836 (1954).

394. M. Katagiri and O. Hayaishi, *J. Biol. Chem.* **226,** 439–448 (1957).

395. O. Wiss, G. Viollier, and M. Müller, *Helv. Physiol. Pharmacol. Acta* **7,** C64 (1949).

396. L. V. Hankes and M. Urivetsky, *Arch. Biochem. Biophys.* **52,** 484–485 (1954).

397. B. S. Schweigert, *J. Biol. Chem.* **178,** 707–708 (1949).

398. L. M. Henderson and G. B. Ramasarma, *J. Biol. Chem.* **181,** 687–692 (1949).

399. B. S. Schweigert and M. M. Marquette, *J. Biol. Chem.* **181,** 199–205 (1949).

400. R. H. Decker and L. M. Henderson, *J. Nutrition* **68,** 17–24 (1959).

401. L. M. Henderson and H. M. Hirsch, *J. Biol. Chem.* **181**, 667–675 (1949).

402. L. M. Henderson, *J. Biol. Chem.* **181**, 677–685 (1949).

403. R. E. Priest, A. H. Bokman, and B. S. Schweigert, *Proc. Soc. Exptl. Biol. Med.* **78**, 477–479 (1951).

404. A. Miyake, A. H. Bokman, and B. S. Schweigert, *J. Biol. Chem.* **211**, 391–404 (1954).

405. C. L. Long, H. N. Hill, I. M. Weinstock, and L. M. Henderson, *J. Biol. Chem.* **211**, 405–417 (1954).

406. O. Wiss, H. Simmer, and H. Peters, *Z. physiol. Chem.* **304**, 221–231 (1956).

407. A. H. Bokman and B. S. Schweigert, *Arch. Biochem. Biophys.* **33**, 270–276 (1951).

408. L. M. Henderson, *Abstr. 121st Meeting Am. Chem. Soc., Milwaukee*, p. 23c (1952).

409. O. Wiss, *Proc. Intern. Symposium on Enzyme Chem.*, Tokyo and Kyoto, 1957, *I.U.B. Symposia Ser.* **2**, 200–203.

410. C. O. Stevens and L. M. Henderson, *J. Biol. Chem.* **234**, 1188–1190 (1959).

411. R. H. Decker, and F. R. Leach, *Federation Proc.* **19**, 8 (1960).

412. O. Wiss and G. Bettendorf, *Z. physiol. Chem.* **306**, 145–153 (1957).

413. A. H. Mehler, *Proc. 4th Intern. Congr. Biochem., Vienna, 1958* **13**, 164–171 (1959).

414. A. H. Mehler, *J. Biol. Chem.* **218**, 241–254 (1956).

415. L. V. Hankes and I. H. Segal, *Proc. Soc. Exptl. Biol. Med.* **94**, 447–449 (1957).

416. R. G. Wilson and L. M. Henderson, *J. Biol. Chem.* **235**, 2099–2102 (1960).

417. C. O. Stevens and L. M. Henderson, unpublished work (1957).

418. R. J. Suhadolnik, C. O. Stevens, R. H. Decker, L. M. Henderson, and L. V. Hankes, *J. Biol. Chem.* **228**, 973–982 (1957).

419. O. Wiss and F. Weber, *Proc. 4th Intern. Congr. Biochem. Vienna, 1958* **13**, 172–175 (1959).

420. L. M. Henderson, *Proc. 4th Intern. Congr. Biochem. Vienna, 1958* **13**, 175 (1959).

421. R. K. Gholson, D. R. Rao, L. M. Henderson, R. J. Hill, and R. E. Koeppe, *J. Biol. Chem.* **230**, 179–184 (1958).

422. D. R. Sanadi and D. M. Greenberg, *Arch. Biochem.* **25**, 323–334 (1950).

423. L. M. Henderson, D. R. Rao, and R. F. Nystrom, *Biochem. Preparations* **6**, 90–95 (1958).

424. G. Hogstrom, *Acta Chem. Scand.* **7**, 45–50 (1953).

425. K. Bloch and D. Rittenberg, *J. Biol. Chem.* **159**, 45–58 (1945).

426. R. K. Gholson and L. M. Henderson, unpublished work (1958).

427. R. K. Gholson, L. V. Hankes, and L. M. Henderson, *J. Biol. Chem.* **235**, 132–135 (1960).

428. M. Kleiber, A. H. Smith, A. L. Black, M. A. Brown, and B. M. Tolbert, *J. Biol. Chem.* **197**, 371–379 (1952).

429. R. K. Gholson, D. C. Sanders, and L. M. Henderson, *Biochem. Biophys. Research Communs.* **1**, 98–100 (1959).

430. M. Rothstein and L. L. Miller, *J. Biol. Chem.* **199**, 199–205 (1952).

431. M. Rothstein and L. L. Miller, *J. Biol. Chem.* **206**, 243–253 (1954).

432. D. C. Hobbs and R. E. Koeppe, *J. Biol. Chem.* **230**, 655–660 (1958).

433. B. J. Klatzkin, *Biochem. J.* **60**, viii–ix (1955).

434. R. G. Chitre, D. B. Desai, and V. S. Raut, *Indian J. Med. Research* **44**, 217–226 (1956).

435. F. G. Gustafson, *Science* **110**, 279–280 (1949).
436. A. Nason, *Science* **109**, 170–171 (1949).
437. A. Nason, *Am. J. Botany* **37**, 612–623 (1950).
438. L. M. Henderson, J. F. Someroski, D. R. Rao, P. L. Wu, T. Griffith, and R. U. Byerrum, *J. Biol. Chem.* **234**, 93–95 (1959).
439. R. F. Dawson, D. R. Christman, R. C. Anderson, M. L. Solt, A. F. D'Adamo, and U. Weiss, *J. Am. Chem. Soc.* **78**, 2645–2646 (1956).
440. R. F. Dawson, A. Bothner-By, L. M. Henderson, D. R. Christman, and R. C. Anderson, *Abstr. 2nd Ann. Meeting Plant Chem. and Biochem.*, Rutgers Univ., 1955.
441. E. Leete, *Chem. & Ind.* p. 1270 (1957).
442. J. Grimshaw and L. Marion, *Nature* **181**, 112 (1958).
443. E. Leete and F. H. B. Leitz, *Chem. & Ind.* 1572 (1957).
444. D. Davis, L. M. Henderson, and D. Powell, *J. Biol. Chem.* **189**, 543–549 (1951).
445. C. Marnay, *Bull. soc. chim. biol.* **33**, 174–178 (1951).
446. C. Yanofsky, *J. Bacteriol.* **68**, 577–584 (1954).
447. F. Kögl, A. J. Haagen-Smit, and H. Erxleben, *Z. physiol. Chem.* **228**, 90–103 (1934).
448. K. V. Thimann, *J. Biol. Chem.* **109**, 279–291 (1935).
449. S. A. Gordon and F. Sánchez Nieva, *Arch. Biochem. Biophys.* **20**, 356–366 and 367–385 (1948).
450. S. G. Wildman, M. G. Ferri, and J. Bonner, *Arch. Biochem.* **13**, 131–144 (1947).
451. S. G. Wildman and R. M. Muir, *Plant Physiol.* **24**, 84–92 (1949).
452. P. Larsen, *Ann. Rev. Plant Physiol.* **2**, 169–198 (1951).
453. W. N. Dannenburg and J. L. Liverman, *Plant Physiol.* **32**, 263–269 (1957).
454. H. Weissbach, W. King, A. Sjoerdsma, and S. Udenfriend, *J. Biol. Chem.* **234**, 81–86 (1959).
455. J. M. Kaper and H. Veldstra, *Biochim. et Biophys. Acta* **30**, 401–420 (1958).
456. P. Larsen, *Danske Botan. Ark.* **11**, 11 (1944).
457. E. R. H. Jones, H. B. Henbest, G. F. Smith, and J. A. Bentley, *Nature* **169**, 485–487 (1952).
458. B. B. Stowe and K. V. Thimann, *Arch. Biochem. Biophys.* **51**, 499–516 (1954).
459. J. B. Greenberg, A. W. Galston, K. N. F. Shaw, and M. D. Armstrong, *Science* **125**, 992–993 (1957).
460. P. M. Ray, *Ann. Rev. Plant Physiol.* **9**, 81–118 (1958).
461. S. C. Fang and J. S. Butts, *Plant Physiol.* **32**, 253–259 (1957).
462. Y. U. Tang and J. Bonner, *Arch. Biochem.* **13**, 11–25 (1947).
463. R. E. Stutz, *Plant Physiol.* **33**, 207–212 (1958).
464. E. R. H. Jones and W. C. Taylor, *Nature* **179**, 1138 (1957).
465. P. M. Ray and K. V. Thimann, *Arch. Biochem. Biophys.* **64**, 175–192 (1956).
466. R. E. Stutz, *Plant Physiol.* **32**, 31–39 (1957).
467. A. C. Wagenknecht and R. H. Burris, *Arch. Biochem.* **25**, 30–53 (1950).
468. L. Sequeira and T. A. Steeves, *Plant Physiol.* **29**, 11–16 (1954).
469. M. Nencki, *Ber.* **8**, 336 (1875).
470. F. G. Hopkins, and S. W. Cole, *J. Physiol.* (*London*) **29**, 451 (1903).
471. F. C. Happold and L. Hoyle, *Biochem. J.* **29**, 1918–1926 (1935).
472. D. D. Woods, *Biochem. J.* **29**, 640–648 and 649–655 (1935).
473. F. C. Happold, *Advances in Enzymol.* **10**, 51–82 (1950).

474. Y. Sakamoto, M. Uchida, and K. Ichihara, *Med. J. Osaka Univ.* **3,** 477 (1953).
475. K. Ichihara, Y. Sakamoto, K. Kometani, F. Inoeu, and M. Kotake, *Symposia on Enzyme Chem.* (*Japan*) **11,** 241–252 (1956).
476. J. A. Izquierdo and A. O. M. Stoppani, *Brit. J. Pharmacol.* **8,** 389–394 (1953).
477. F. Bohm, *Biochem. Z.* **290,** 137–171 (1937); N. J. Novello, W. Wolf, and C. P. Sherwin, *Am. J. Med. Sci.* **170,** 888 (1925).
478. L. Brieger, *Z. physiol. Chem.* **4,** 414–418 (1880).
479. E. C. Horning, C. C. Sweeley, C. E. Dalgliesh, and W. Kelly, *Biochim. et Biophys. Acta* **32,** 566–567 (1959).
480. E. Becker, *Biol. Zentr.* **59,** 597–627 (1939); *Naturwissenschaften* **48,** 237–238 (1941); *Z. indukt. Abstamm.- u. Vererbungsl.* **80,** 157 (1942).
481. I. Schwinck, *Naturwissenschaften* **40,** 365 (1953).
482. A. Butenandt, *Angew. Chem.* **69,** 16–23 (1957).
483. K. von Auwers, E. Borsche, and R. Weller, *Ber.* **54B,** 1291–1316 (1921).
484. A. Butenandt, J. Keck, and G. Neubert, *Ann. Chem., Liebigs* **602,** 61–72 (1957).
485. A. Butenandt and R. Beckmann, *Z. physiol. Chem.* **301,** 115–117 (1955).
486. A. Butenandt and G. Neubert, *Z. physiol. Chem.* **301,** 109–114 (1955).
487. A. Butenandt, U. Schiedt, E. Biekert, and R. J. T. Cromartie, *Ann. Chem. Liebigs* **590,** 75–90 (1954).
488. A. Butenandt, U. Schiedt, and E. Biekert, *Ann. Chem., Liebigs* **586,** 229–239 (1954).
489. A. Butenandt, E. Biekert, and B. Linzen, *Z. physiol. Chem.* **305,** 284–289 (1956).
490. V. Erspamer, *Pharmacol. Revs.* **6,** 425–487 (1954); H. Langemann, *Schweiz. med. Wochschr.* **85,** 541–544 (1955); I. H. Page, *Physiol. Revs.* **34,** 563–588 (1954); **38,** 277–335 (1958).
491. C. E. Dalgliesh, *Advances in Clin. Chem.* **1,** 193–235 (1958).
492. V. Erspamer, *Rend. sci. farmitalia* **1,** 1–193 (1954).
493. M. M. Rapport, A. A. Green, and I. H. Page, *Science* **108,** 329–330 (1948); *J. Biol. Chem.* **174,** 735–741 (1948); **176,** 1237–1241 and 1243–1251 (1948); M. M. Rapport, *ibid.* **180,** 961–969 (1949).
494. V. Erspamer and B. Asero, *Nature* **169,** 800–801 (1952); *J. Biol. Chem.* **200,** 311–318 (1953).
495. A. Thorson, G. Biörck, G. Björkman, and J. Waldenstrom, *Am. Heart J.* **47,** 795–817 (1954).
496. J. Harley-Mason, *Chem. & Ind.* p. 173 (1952).
497. S. Udenfriend, C. T. Clark, and E. Titus, *J. Am. Chem. Soc.* **75,** 501–502 (1953).
498. S. Udenfriend, C. R. Creveling, H. S. Posner, B. G. Redfield, J. Daly, and B. Witkop, *Arch. Biochem. Biophys.* **83,** 501–507 (1959).
499. H. Weissbach, in "Symposium on Tryptophan Metabolism" (J. M. Price, ed.), pp. 13–23. Div. Med. Chem., Am. Chem. Soc., Washington, D. C., 1959.
500. V. Erspamer, *Naturwissenschaften* **40,** 318 (1953).
501. F. B. Hughes, P. A. Shore, and B. B. Brodie, *Experientia* **14,** 178–180 (1958).
502. S. Udenfriend, C. T. Clark, and E. Titus, *Experientia* **8,** 379–380 (1952).
503. R. Jaques and M. Schachter, *Brit. J. Pharmacol.* **9,** 53–88 (1954).
504. K. R. Adam and C. Weiss, *Nature* **178,** 421–422 (1956).
505. H. O. J. Collier and G. B. Chesher, *Brit. J. Pharmacol.* **11,** 186–189 (1956).
506. H. Jensen, *J. Am. Chem. Soc.* **57,** 1765–1768 (1935); H. Jensen and K. K.

Chen, *J. Biol. Chem.* **116**, 87–91 (1936); H. Wieland, W. Konz, and H. Mittasch, *Ann. Chem. Liebigs* **513**, 1–25 (1934); H. Wieland and T. Wieland, *ibid.* **528**, 234–246 (1937).

507. C. Mitoma, H. Weissbach, and S. Udenfriend, *Arch. Biochem. Biophys.* **63**, 122–130 (1956).

508. T. Wieland and W. Motzel, *Ann. Chem. Liebigs* **581**, 10–16 (1953).

509. K. Bowden, B. G. Brown, and J. E. Batty, *Nature* **174**, 925–926 (1954); M. S. Fish, N. M. Johnson, and E. C. Horning, *J. Am. Chem. Soc.* **77**, 5892–5895 (1955).

510. T. P. Waalkes, A. Sjoerdsma, C. R. Creveling, H. Weissbach, and S. Udenfriend, *Science* **127**, 648–650 (1958).

511. A. B. Lerner, J. D. Case, Y. Takahashi, T. H. Lee and W. Mori, *J. Am. Chem. Soc.* **80**, 2587 (1958).

512. S. Udenfriend, E. Titus, H. Weissbach, and R. E. Peterson, *J. Biol. Chem.* **219**, 335–344 (1956).

513. A. N. Smith, L. M. Nyhus, C. E. Dalgliesh, R. W. Dutton, B. Lennox, and P. S. Macfarlane, *Scott. Med. J.* **2**, 24–38 (1957); M. Sandler and P. J. D. Snow, *Lancet* **i**, 137–140 (1958).

514. C. E. Dalgliesh and R. W. Dutton, *Brit. J. Cancer* **11**, 296–309 (1957).

515. R. J. S. Beer, B. E. Jennings, and A. Robertson, *J. Chem. Soc.* pp. 2679–2685 (1954).

516. R. D. DeMoss and M. E. Happel, *Bacteriol. Proc.* (*Soc. Am. Bacteriologists*) **55**, 138 (1955).

517. C. T. Clark, H. Weissbach, and S. Udenfriend, *J. Biol. Chem.* **210**, 139–148 (1954).

518. J. Buxton and H. M. Sinclair, *Biochem. J.* **62**, 27P (1956); J. A. Buzard and P. D. Nytch, *J. Biol. Chem.* **227**, 225–230 (1957); **229**, 409–413 (1957); H. Weissbach, D. F. Bogdanski, B. G. Redfield, and S. Udenfriend, *ibid.* **227**, 617–624 (1957).

519. J. M. Beiler and G. J. Martin, *J. Biol. Chem.* **211**, 39–41 (1954).

520. J. H. Gaddum and N. J. Giarman, *Brit. J. Pharmacol.* **11**, 88–92 (1956).

521. S. Udenfriend and H. Weissbach, *Proc. Soc. Exptl. Biol. Med.* **97**, 748–751 (1958).

522. D. F. Bogdanski, H. Weissbach, and S. Udenfriend, *J. Neurochem.* **1**, 272–278 (1957).

523. R. E. Tashian, *Proc. Soc. Exptl. Biol. Med.* **103**, 407–410 (1960).

524. A. N. Davison and M. Sandler, *Nature* **181**, 186–187 (1958).

525. H. Langemann and J. Kägi, *Klin. Wochschr.* **34**, 237–241 (1956).

526. H. Blaschko and F. J. Philpot, *J. Physiol.* (*London*) **122**, 403–408 (1953).

527. H. Blaschko, *Pharmacol. Revs.* **4**, 415–458 (1952).

528. A. Sjoerdsma, T. E. Smith, T. D. Stevenson, and S. Udenfriend, *Proc. Soc. Exptl. Biol. Med.* **89**, 36–38 (1955); J. Corne and J. D. P. Graham, *J. Physiol.* (*London*) **135**, 339–349 (1957).

529. A. J. Clark and P. J. G. Mann, *Biochem. J.* **65**, 763–774 (1957).

530. H. Weissbach, B. G. Redfield, and S. Udenfriend, *J. Biol. Chem.* **229**, 953–963 (1957).

531. B. T. Chadwick and J. H. Wilkinson, *Biochem. J.* **68**, 1P (1958).

532. G. Curzon, *Arch. Biochem. Biophys.* **66**, 497–499 (1957).

533. R. Rodnight, *Biochem. J.* **64**, 621–626 (1956).

534. H. Blaschko and D. B. Hope, *J. Physiol.* **128**, 11P (1955).

535. S. Senoh, T. Seki and H. Kikkawa, *J. Inst. Polytech. Osaka City Univ.* **C3,** 59 (1952).

536. F. D'Angeli, R. E. Koski, and L. M. Henderson, *J. Biol. Chem.* **214,** 781–787 (1955).

537. R. Y. Stanier, O. Hayaishi, and M. Tsuchida, *J. Bacteriol.* **62,** 355–366 (1951).

538. V. L. Stromberg, *J. Am. Chem. Soc.* **76,** 1707 (1954).

539. S. Udenfriend, E. Titus, and H. Weissbach, *J. Biol. Chem.* **216,** 499–505 (1955).

540. R. W. Schayer, K. Y. T. Ulu, R. L. Smiley, and Y. Katayashi, *J. Biol. Chem.* **210,** 259–267 (1954).

CHAPTER 7

Structural and Chemical Properties of
Keratin-Forming Tissues*

A. Gedeon Matoltsy

*Department of Dermatology, Boston University, School of Medicine,
Boston, Massachusetts*

I. Introduction

Keratin is a highly resistant protein formed in the cytoplasm and retained by the cell throughout its life. Keratin-forming cells are all of ectodermal origin; they form the outer covering as well as the various appendages of the vertebrate skin. The keratinizing epithelia are closely interrelated with one another and with the adjacent dermal tissue, and functionally unite into a single highly integrated system (*1, 2*). To our present knowledge keratin-forming tissues occur only in vertebrates; below this level the organisms produce chitinous or collagenous cuticles, cellulose mantles, etc.

In the sections to follow, different keratinizing tissues of vertebrates will be discussed separately, but by that it is not implied that any of

* The experimental work described in this paper was started in the Dermatological Research Laboratories, Harvard Medical School, and Massachusetts General Hospital, and continued in The Rockefeller Institute and University of Miami, and was aided by grants from the National Institutes of Health (RG-3921, C-4036, 2G-224, A-5924).

these would function as an independent system. The term "keratinizing tissue" will be used to designate an epithelial tissue consisting of both a keratinized and a nonkeratinized fraction. The keratinized part, consisting of keratin-containing horny cells, will be called *horny tissue*.

II. Biological Properties of Keratinizing Tissues

Keratinizing tissues occur in various regions of the vertebrate body and form essential parts of different physiologic systems. The epidermis, hair, wool, quill, feather, nail, claw, and horn may be regarded as parts of the protective system. Hoof and feather form essential parts of the locomotion system of certain animals, and beak and keratinized tooth may be considered as part of the alimentary system. Although keratin-forming tissues serve different purposes and also greatly differ in macroscopic anatomy, it is common that each consists of a reproductive and a nonreproductive part (3).

The reproductive part of keratinizing tissues contains undifferentiated germinative cells. They maintain the reproductive part and also yield specialized cells that are engaged in production of the keratinized part of the tissue. The germinative cells are remarkable because they possess the property of being "indifferent" cells. This inherent mark distinguishes them from the other cellular constituents of the tissue. They not only have the capacity to give rise to the keratin-forming cell of the particular tissue, but are also capable of producing cells (on specific induction) able to form another kind of keratin, or sebum, or even mucus. Deviations from the normal course of cell specialization regularly occur during skin regeneration and disease processes and may be produced experimentally by excess vitamin A or hormones (1, 2, 4–7).

The germinative cells of some keratinizing tissues give rise to only a single line of specialized cells. In this instance the horny portion of the tissue will consist of a single type of cornified cell. In other tissues, different cell lines develop from the same germinative layer and these form a horny tissue of heterogeneous cell-type composition. Consequently, the different keratinizing tissues may be grouped into two main classes, designated simple and complex. The *simple* keratinizing tissues are the epidermis, nail, claw, horn, hoof, and beak; the *complex* ones are the hair, wool, quill, and feather.

Specialization of cells in the keratinizing tissues is a most complex process. Its main characteristics are the loss of capacity of the cells to divide and an increase in metabolism related to the beginning of new and specialized activities, such as formation of differentiation products. It is also highly significant that some of the existing activities of the cell become de-emphasized and certain constituents, such as mitochondria, decrease in quantity. Others, such as the nuclear substances, become partially or fully decomposed and eliminated from the cell (8). Keratinization, therefore, may be considered as a specific form of cell differentiation, a process best characterized by Grobstein (9) as "relatively stable, maturational changes of cellular properties which progressively concentrate the activities and the structure of the cell, or portions of it, in particular directions at the expense of others."

Although specialized cells of each keratinizing tissue reveal the above phenomena, differences occur in the actual mechanism of keratinization. This is indicated by the appearance of various differentiation products in the specialized cells and by the structurally and chemically different horny content of the terminal cells. This is schematically illustrated in Table I. The first and second columns show various cell types of the

TABLE I

Schematic Illustration of Structural and Chemical Properties
of Various Keratinizing Epithelial Cell-Lines

Characteristics of terminal horny cell: Sulfur: Molecular str.: Macromol str.:	Simple keratinizing tissue		Complex keratinizing tissue		
	Epidermis		Hair		
	Aves low α- or β-keratin fibrous	Mammals low α - keratin fibrous	Cuticle high amorphous amorphous	Cortex high α-keratin fibrous	Medulla in traces amorphous amorphous
Terminal horny cell					
Specialized cell					
Differentiation products:	Tonofibrils	Keratohyalin granules + tonofibrils	Cytoplasmic droplets	Tonofibrils	Cytoplasmic droplets
Germinative cell					
Column	I	II	III	IV	V

epidermis in two different species. The first column refers to the avian epidermis. Both germinative and specialized cells manufacture cytoplasmic fibrils (5), which are called tonofibrils and considered as the precursors of keratin (10). The terminal horny cells have relatively low sulfur content, and in most regions of the avian skin the horny cells contain an α-keratin type (in a few regions, however, β-keratin may also occur). The second column shows cellular members of the mammalian epidermis. The specialized cells, in addition to tonofibrils, also produce an amorphous prekeratin in the form of cytoplasmic droplets, which are called keratohyalin granules (11). The terminal horny cell has a relatively low sulfur content and contains α-keratin (12, 13, 14). Columns 3, 4, and 5 illustrate cell lines which form the hair, each cell line originating from the same germinative layer of the matrix. Members of both cuticular and medullary lines are engaged in the production of cytoplasmic droplets, whereas those of the cortical line form cytoplasmic filaments. The terminal cuticular cells are known to contain an amorphous keratin (15, 16) with a high sulfur content (17, 18, 19). Cortical cells form a fibrous keratin of high sulfur content; medullary keratin is amorphous and contains very little or no sulfur (16, 20–25). These few examples thus clearly indicate that different cell lines within one tissue, or even the same cell line in different species may form keratin by different mechanisms. It is also evident that generalization (26, 27) with regard to the mechanism of keratinization, is confronted with difficulties, and it is more appropriate to consider keratinization in each epithelial cell line as a separate mechanism (8).

Horny tissues, such as the hair, wool fiber, feather, or quill, are lost in their entirety and are renewed in cycles. Keratinizing tissues, such as the epidermis, nail, hoof, horn, lose their outermost exposed horny cells continuously by means of spontaneous shedding, wear and tear, disintegration, etc., and are replaced in most vertebrates by a continuous renewal system. The different horny tissues produced by various vertebrates are the subject of this paper, and their structural and chemical properties are discussed.

III. Structural Properties of Horny Tissues

Horny tissues are built up of single dry horny cells which are tightly packed and interdigitate and interlock at several points. A cementing substance is present between the horny cells (28, 29), but its chemical nature is not known. Specific attachments between cell membranes, such as the desmosomes of keratinized epidermal cells, also may contribute to the physical strength and coherence (30–35).

Horny cells appear under the light microscope as translucent and light-refractile bodies. Structural details are difficult to recognize because the components are coalesced. Most horny cells show double refraction in polarized light, mainly due to oriented molecules of fibrous keratin (36–39). The magnitude of birefringence is relatively high in hair and wool; it ranges from 0.011 to 0.013 (40). Double refraction of some horny substances is low; horny cells of the human skin gave values ranging from 0.002 to 0.003 (39–41). The birefringent substance is usually oriented to some characteristic axis of the cell or the tissue. In the hair, it is oriented in the direction of the growth and is parallel to the long axis of the fiber (40), whereas in the nail it is perpendicular to the direction of growth and parallel to the surface plane of the nail plate (13). Orientation of keratin in the thin horny layer of the epidermis is parallel to the skin surface (1, 13, 41) whereas in the thickened horny layer of the palm and sole orientation is complex (37, 38).

The macromolecular units of keratin were identified with the electron microscope; two types were distinguished, fibrous and amorphous keratin. Fibrous keratin was seen as filaments several microns long, varying in width from 50 to 100 Å., in the uppermost epidermal cells of amphibians, birds, and mammals and in cortical cells of the hair, or wool or quill (2, 30–34, 42–50). A fine substructure was also noted in amphibian material; shadowed preparations reveal nodes spaced in a distance of about 100 Å. along the length of the filament (30). Amorphous keratin was noted in cuticular and medullary cells of the hair, or wool, or quill (15, 16). A fine, granular substructure is suspected but has not yet been adequately resolved to measure its dimensions (15).

Significant data were obtained on the molecular structure of crystalline regions of the horny tissues mainly by wide-angle X-ray diffraction studies (12–14, 27, 40, 51–67).* Two types of keratin structures were distinguished; one was called α-keratin, the other β-keratin. The structure of α-keratin was studied mainly in the hair and wool fibers, and was characterized by a very strong meridional spot at 5.15 Å. and an equatorial spacing at 9.8 Å. When hair or wool was stretched more than 50%, another type of diagram was obtained, showing two prominent equatorial spots at 9.7 Å. and 4.65 Å., respectively, and a meridional arc with spacing at 3.33 Å. This type of diagram was named β-keratin pattern. The α-keratin pattern was identified, with a few exceptions, in most horny substances of vertebrates and also in muscle proteins and fibrinogen (K-M-F class). A β-keratin-like pattern was found to occur normally in the horny shield of tortoise (64), snake scales, skin and

---

* Significant data were obtained also by application of polarized infrared radiation. For review see Elliott (67a) and Rudall (14).

feather of birds (12, 52) and in the medulla of the porcupine quill (62, 63). A prominent β-keratin diagram is given by the silk fiber.

Astbury and his co-workers (51–56) related the X-ray data to main chains and amino acid residues of polypeptides.* The α-keratin diagram was assumed to be reflected by parallel layers of folded polypeptide chains. The folds were considered to be repeated at a distance of 5.1 Å., three residues occupying the length of 5.1 Å. along the axis. The β-keratin pattern was regarded to be reflected by a parallel assemblage of extended polypeptide chains. The spacings of 3.33 Å. show a repeating distance along the axis, corresponding to the length of one residue.

Pauling and Corey (68) determined the interatomic distances and the length of hydrogen bonds in polypeptides but could not correlate their data with those of Astbury. They propose a helical structure instead of the folded chain with amino acid residues occurring at 1.5 Å. intervals along the axis. Evidence in favor of such helixes in keratin was presented by Perutz (65), who resolved in hair a repeating unit at 1.5 Å. Pauling (69) assumed that α-keratin consists of seven tightly packed helixes forming α-cables. Single α-helixes are assumed to occur in the interstices of the cables.

The amino acids occurring in horny substances all belong to the L-configurational series. They couple by peptide bonds in a manner common to all proteins. Detailed informations on amino acid sequences in polypeptide chains are not known. The best-characterized peptide isolated from wool was found to consist of glycine, alanine, valine, leucine, cystine, glutamic acid, and aspartic acid (70).

Analyses of free amino groups of residues occurring at the end groups of polypeptide chains show that there are 6–9 glycine, 2 alanine, 4–8 valine, 6–8 threonine, 1 aspartic acid, 2 glutamic acid per million grams of hair or wool keratin (71, 72). These different N-terminal amino acids would indicate that there are at least seven different kinds of polypeptide chains in keratin (71).

The side chains of the amino acids play an important role in the stabilization of the structure of the horny substances, especially those having thiol or polar groups. Cysteine is assumed to be oxidized to cystine during keratinization and with one-half of its molecule built into adjacent polypeptide chains forming the strongest covalent bond (53, 73). The disulfide bonds are considered highly significant in keratins and are held responsible for their high structural stability, insoluble character, and high degree of resistance toward proteolytic enzyme

---

* For interpretation of supercontraction see Astbury and Woods (53), and for cross β-keratin structure, Rudall (14).

action. Disulfide linkages are numerous in the hair or wool cortex, nail, horn; they are less abundant in the horny layer of the epidermis, medulla of the hair, wool, or quill. Cleavage of these disulfide bonds does not result in the dissociation of keratins because they are stabilized by other types of bonds, too. Charged polar groups of acidic and basic character are abundant in keratins and form salt linkages. At these sites hydrogen bonds may also be formed (74). Hydrogen bonds regularly occur between adjacent NH and CO groups of neighboring polypeptide chains (75–78). Atoms in a close distance exert mutual attraction, and therefore the van der Walls' forces may also play some role in the stabilization of the structure of the horny substances. These forces are very weak and rapidly decrease with increasing distance. After reduction of disulfide bonds and breaking the hydrogen bonds and salt linkages, horny substances readily pass into solution, a fact indicating that these three kinds of bonds are primarily involved in the stabilization of their structure.

IV. Chemical Composition of Horny Tissues

Horny tissues are highly dehydrated and usually contain less than 20% water. Horny tissues are of heterogeneous composition. With regard to heterogeneity it is first recalled that the complex keratinizing tissues produce different cell lines, which form different keratins. Heterogeneity exists at the single cell level, too, because horny cells, in addition to keratin, also contain a variety of other substances. Nonkeratin includes such components as the cell membrane which envelops the horny material. Some remnants of nuclear and various cytoplasmic constituents also occur in the horny cell. The ratio of keratin to nonkeratin varies greatly; it is primarily dependent on the degree of synthetic and resorptive activities of the keratinizing tissue. Those which produce keratin in a large quantity and effectively eliminate nonkeratin substances yield a horny cell with a keratin:nonkeratin ratio of approximately 9:1. This ratio is found in nail, horn, and cortical cells of the hair, or wool, or quill. Keratin is produced at a lower rate in some other keratin-forming cells, and elimination of nonkeratin substances is poor. Consequently, the terminal cells reveal a keratin:nonkeratin ratio which may range from 7:3 to 5:5. Values in this range were found in horny layers derived from the human epidermis (8, 39, 79).

The amino acid composition of various keratins is shown in Tables II and III. Data for epidermal keratin are not shown, because the values released by different laboratories show extreme differences (71, 80–89) and none of these analyses were yet confirmed by some other laboratory. (Values for cystine, for instance, range from 0.6 to 11.5%.) In the strict

TABLE II

COMPOSITION OF REPRESENTATIVE HORNY TISSUES[a]

	Wool, sheep	Hair, human	Horn, cattle	Quill, porcupine	Feather, chicken
Glycine	5.2–6.5	4.1–4.2	9.6	5.7	7.2
Alanine	3.4–4.4	2.8	2.5	—	5.4
Valine	5.0–5.9	5.5–(5.9)	5.3–5.5	—	8.3–8.8
Leucine	7.6–8.1	6.4–(8.3)	7.6–8.3	—	7.4–8.0
Isoleucine	3.1–4.5	(4.7)–4.8	4.3–4.8	—	5.3–6.0
Phenylalanine	3.4–4.0	2.4–3.6	3.2–4.0	3.6	4.7–5.3
Proline	5.3–8.1	4.3–(9.6)	8.2	—	8.8–10.0
Serine	7.2–9.5	7.4–10.6	6.8	6.1–6.2	10.2–14
Threonine	6.6–6.7	7.0–8.5	6.1	3.9–5.4	4.4–4.8
Tyrosine	4.0–6.4	2.2–3.0	3.7–5.6	3.3	2.0–2.2
Aspartic acid	6.4–7.3	3.9–7.7	7.7–7.9	8.7	5.8–7.5
Glutamic acid	13.1–16.0	13.6–14.2	13.8	17.6	9.0–9.7
Arginine	9.2–10.6	8.9–10.8	6.8–10.7	7.6–8.0	6.5–7.5
Lysine	2.8–3.3	1.9–3.1	2.4–3.6	2.6	1.0–1.7
Hydroxylysine	0.2	0	—	—	—
Histidine	0.7–1.1	0.6–1.2	0.6–1.0	0.6	0.3–0.7
Tryptophan	1.8–2.1	0.4–1.3	0.7–1.4	0.9	0.7
Cystine	11.0–13.7	16.6–18.0	10.5–15.7	8.0–9.5	6.8–8.2
Methionine	0.5–0.7	0.7–1.0	0.5–2.2	0.8	0.4–0.5

[a] Compiled by Ward and Lundgren (71).

sense, the figures shown in Tables II and III give values of purified horny tissues and not that of a homogeneous protein. The analyzed substances may be regarded as heterogeneous, because in addition to keratin they contain the membrane material of the horny cell (some other contaminant may also be present). The cell membranes cannot be separated from keratin by the usual purification techniques used, because they are more resistant than keratin. The cell membranes can be separated only by the use of keratolytic agents, which solubilize keratin and leave the empty cell envelop behind (39, 43).

The amino acid analyses shown in Tables II and III indicate that cystine is present in keratin in a much higher quantity than in any other protein. Serine and arginine are also high (71). Since methionine is present only in a very small quantity (less than 1%), it may be concluded that most of the sulfur of keratins is in the cystine. Epidermal keratin is believed to be exceptional, containing less cystine than most other keratins. Data on sulfur analyses favor this concept, because sulfur in most keratins ranges from 3 to 5% (84) whereas values range from 1.4 to 1.7% for epidermal keratin (13, 14).

It was assumed by Block and Vickery (90) that the basic amino acids, such as histidine, lysine, and arginine occur in the molecular ratio of 1:4:12 in most of the horny substances (see Table III). Con-

TABLE III
AMINO ACIDS OF REPRESENTATIVE HORNY TISSUES[a]

	Histidine	Lysine	Arginine	Cystine	Tyrosine	Tryptophan	Phenylalanine	Glycine
Human hair	0.6	2.5	8.0	15.5	3.0	0.7	2.6	4.3
Chimpanzee hair	0.6	2.0	8.1	15.5	3.3	1.4	—	—
Goat hair	0.7	3.2	8.1	8.9	3.0	0.9	4.6	6.3
Cow hair	0.7	2.0	7.5·	13.4	3.3	1.4	3.9	10.3
Lamb wool	0.7	2.5	8.7	13.1	4.5	0.7	4.0	6.5
Camel wool	0.6	2.7	8.6	11.0	3.1	0.8	4.1	9..2
Cattle horn	0.6	2.4	8.6	8.2	3.7	0.7	4.0	9.8
Rhinoceros horn	0.6	2.6	8.2	8.7	8.6	1.7	5.0	7.4
Fingernails	0.5	2.6	8.5	12.0	3.0	1.1	2.5	—
Porcupine quills	0.6	2.6	7.6	9.4	3.3	0.9	3.6	5.7
Echinus quills	0.5	1.8	6.8	11.9	9.1	2.2	6.8	—
Hen feathers	0.3	1.6	6.0	6.8	2.2	0.7	5.3	9.5

[a] Data from Block (84).

sequently, they attempted to define and group keratins on this basis. Horny substances, such as hair, wool, nail, etc., revealing the ratio of 1:4:12 for histidine, lysine, and arginine, respectively, were called eukeratins, and all those that do not show this ratio were designated as pseudokeratins (85). Since Ward and Lundgren (71) provided evidence for large variations in basic amino acid composition among keratins (see Table II), the terms *eu-* or *pseudokeratin* lost their significance.

Nonkeratin components were studied mainly in human material, such as the horny layer of the skin (39, 79, 91, 92) the hair (93, 94), and the nail plate (95). A few data are also available on the hair of different mammals, horny layer of the skin and feather of birds, and the horny part of snake skin (96). Some of the water-soluble components were identified as free amino acids, urea, uric acid, carbohydrates, and various salts. Free amino acids are extractable in the largest quantity from the horny cells scraped from the back of humans. In such extracts the following free amino acids were identified: aspartic acid, glutamic acid, serine, glycine, threonine, alanine, tyrosine, valine, leucine, phenylalanine, citrulline, lysine, histidine, arginine, tryptophan and proline (79). Serine and citrulline occur in the largest percentage. In extracts of human hair the following free amino acids were identified in small quantities: aspartic acid, glutamic acid, glycine, alanine, tyrosine, and leucine (94). It is remarkable that neither the horny layer of the epidermis, nor the hair contains cystine or methionine in the free form.

Estimating the lipid content in horny tissues, it is difficult to distinguish between lipids of endogenous or exogenous origin. The lipid content of the horny layer derived from human epidermis was found to range from 2.4 to 9.0% (39, 97), and the components were identified as phospholipids, cholesterol, and fatty acids (98, 99).

The exact composition of cell membranes is not known. Cell membranes isolated from the thick horny layer of the human skin (callus) by the use of 0.1 N sodium hydroxide, indicate the presence of glycine, valine, leucine, isoleucine, serine, threonine, aspartic acid, glutamic acid, arginine, lysine, histidine, and methionine (87).

V. Epidermal Keratin

The structure of epidermal keratin was studied in great detail by Rudall (12, 14) in a wide variety of vertebrates. Rudall found in X-ray diffraction studies that crystalline regions of epidermal keratin reveal the structure of α-keratin in cyclostomes, teleosts, amphibians, reptiles, birds, and mammals. In some reptiles and birds regions of α-keratin were combined with ill-defined β-keratin. On the basis of this study, Rudall concluded that α-keratin is a specific product of the vertebrate epidermis to be considered as "a mark of affinity of all these creatures" (12). Rudall's observations are confirmed and extended by the work of other investigators, who identified α-keratin in the horny layer of the human skin (9), cow's nose (13, 57, 66), and horse burr (27, 60).

Rudall made another important observation, too, finding that although α-keratin is dominant in the vertebrate epidermis, the stability of the structure is different (12, 14). Evidence for this was presented by demonstrating that the isolated horny layer of triturus contracts in the range of 65 to 75° C., whereas that of the human leg contracts in the range of 80 to 90° C. Stabilization of the structure is largely dependent on the frequency of —S—S— bonds between adjacent polypeptide chains. Since —S—S— bonds were found to be less abundant in the horny layer of lower vertebrates, it may be postulated that the weak stability of their epidermal keratin is related to the absence or less frequent occurrence of —S—S— bonds. This is indicated by histochemical studies showing an intense reaction for free —SH groups and none or a very weak reaction for —S—S— bonds in the outermost epidermal cells of triturus (14), frog, toad (100), and chick (10). The reaction is weak for —SH and strong for —S—S— in the horny layer of mammals (101, 102, 103).

The macromolecular structure of epidermal keratin was studied in mammals by low-angle X-ray diffraction and with the electron micro-scope. Low-angle X-ray diffraction studies of Swanbeck (67) indicate fibrous macromolecules with a diameter of 250 Å. in the horny layer of the human skin (callus). Electron microscopic studies of such material reveal a coalesced amorphous structure in most of the horny cells (45, 48, 50). However, in the lower portions of the horny layer and also scattered at higher levels, fine filaments may be clearly resolved (2), having a diameter of about 100 Å. (Plate I).* Filaments, wider than 100 Å. are rare; accordingly, electron microscopic observation does not support the 250-Å. thick filament, derived from calculations of data obtained by low-angle X-ray diffraction. Brody (46, 47) noted in the lower portion of the horny layer of the guinea pig skin regular arrays of about 100 Å.-thick filaments placed in a distance of about 30 Å. He assumed that the epidermal keratin consists of a fibrous and an amor-phous phase. The amorphous phase residing in the 30-Å. wide inter-fibrillary spaces was regarded to contain material of dispersed kerato-hyalin granules. The ratio of fibrous: amorphous material was calculated as 2:3.

Chemical properties of epidermal keratin have been studied in more detail only in material derived from humans. Although the horny layer of the human skin is homogeneous at the cellular level and consists of one type of horny cell, fractionation studies point to extreme degrees of complexity (39). Fractionation of the native dry stratum corneum of the human skin, derived from soles and palms, shows that it consists of about 65% epidermal keratin, 5% resistant cell membrane material, 7–9% ethanol-extractable lipids, and 20% soluble material. The latter may be further fractionated into dialyzable and nondialyzable fractions. The dialyzable fraction consists mainly of small peptides and free amino acids. The nondialyzable fraction consists of an electrophoretically homogeneous soluble protein, having an isoelectric point of pH 4.1, called keratin A (Fig. 2). These data, thus, clearly demonstrate that analyses of native or ill-purified materials are misleading and are of little value for understanding the properties of epidermal keratin.

A convenient method for fractionation of horny material derived from the human sole is schematically outlined in Fig. 2.† The residue obtained by this method is quite satisfactory for study of the properties of epidermal keratin because estimates indicate that about 92% consists of keratin and the rest constitutes resistant cell membrane material (8, 87). Information was obtained on the stability of the structure of epi-

* Plates I–V follow page 360.

† Phosphate buffer of pH 7.1 is recommended for adequate extraction and separation of the soluble component from the insoluble one (39).

354 A. GEDEON MATOLTSY

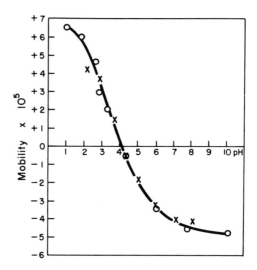

Fig. 1. Electrophoretic mobility of keratin A and keratin B is plotted as a function of pH. The preparations were derived from horny cells of the human epidermis. Keratin A, ×; keratin B, ○. From Matoltsy and Balsamo (39); reproduced by permission of the Press of The Rockefeller Institute.

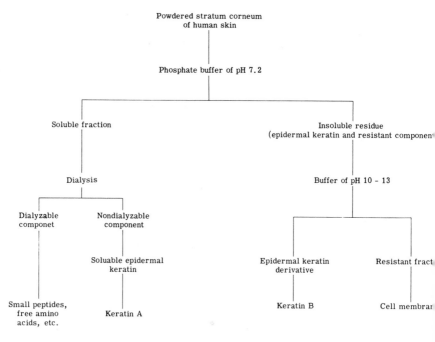

Fig. 2. Scheme of fractionation of the stratum corneum of human skin. From Matoltsy and Balsamo (39).

dermal keratin by exposing this residue to buffers of different pH, or urea solutions of different concentrations, or various reducing substances (39). The results of such studies show that the "stability zone" of epidermal keratin is in the range of pH 4–8. Acid swelling occurs between pH 1 and 4 and alkaline swelling between pH 8 and 10. In alkaline solutions higher than pH 10, epidermal keratin irreversibly swells and gradually passes into solution. Neutral solutions of urea, in concentrations from 10 to 50%, do not solubilize keratin, whereas weakly alkaline urea solutions readily disperse it. Reducing substances, such as sodium sulfite, dissociate it in 0.05 N concentration, whereas potassium cyanide is effective only in 0.4 M solution. Since the above chemicals specifically attack either —S—S— cross linkages, or hydrogen bonds or salt linkages and dispersion occurs only after cleavage of —S—S— linkages and not by opening the salt linkages or breaking the hydrogen bonds, it can be concluded that the disulfide bonds play a primary role in stabilization of the structure of epidermal keratin, as they do in other keratins. The relatively low concentrations of alkali or reducing substances needed to cleave disulfide bonds in epidermal keratin favor the concept that it has less —S—S— bonds than most other keratin.

Information was also obtained on the nature of dispersed epidermal keratin (39). Quantitative studies dealing with this problem are shown in Fig. 3. The results indicate that after treatment for 24 hours with weak alkali or sodium sulfite or potassium cyanide or thioglycolate or urea in weakly alkaline medium, most of the solubilized material can be recovered as a nondialyzable substance and that not more than about 20% is dialyzable. This shows that the main process consists of dispersion of the epidermal keratin into a high molecular weight derivative and hydrolytic decomposition is only of secondary importance.

The epidermal keratin derivative, obtained by solubilization with 0.02 N sodium hydroxide was called keratin B (39). Keratin B reveals a single peak in electrophoresis in buffers ranging from pH 1.5 to 10.0 Its isoelectric point was determined as pH 4.1, coinciding with that of the naturally occurring soluble keratin A (Fig. 1). Ultracentrifugation studies of keratin B reveal two components. About 35% sediments rapidly and shows a sedimentation constant of 3.8. Approximately 56% sediments slowly and shows a sedimentation constant of 2.2 (104).

The precursor of epidermal keratin resides in the metabolically active cells of the epidermis. X-ray diffraction studies indicate that it has an α-keratin structure (12, 13, 14, 27). The macromolecular preunits of fibrous epidermal keratin are long cytoplasmic filaments showing the same range of diameter/of 50–100 Å. in the various vertebrates (30–34, 42–46, 48–50). The filaments first appear singly, later they associate

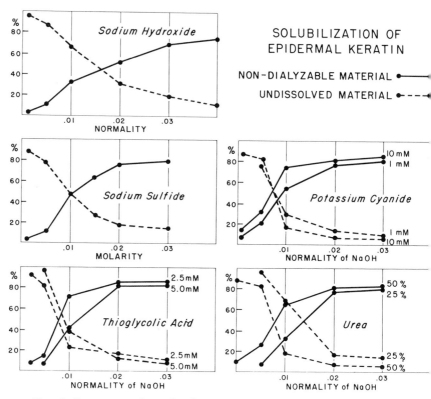

FIG. 3. Percentage of powdered and extracted cornified epithelium found as nondialyzable and undissolved fractions after treatment of the cornified epithelium for 24 hours with alkali, reducing substance, mixtures of reducing substances with alkali and alkaline urea. Cornified epithelium was derived from the human skin. From Matoltsy and Balsamo (39); reproduced by permission of the Press of The Rockefeller Institute.

laterally and form fibrils. At places, where desmosomes occur, the filaments are more numerous and tightly attach to the cell membrane. Thermal contraction studies of isolated strips of the thick epidermis of the cow's nose show that the fibrous precursor of epidermal keratin is weakly stabilized. Rudall (14) noted that strips, derived from the lower layer of the epidermis, contract at 70–80° C., whereas the isolated horny layer contracts at 80–90° C. Histochemical studies show that the cytoplasmic filaments are rich in free —SH groups and —S—S— bonds do not occur (10, 100–103).

The chemical nature of prekeratin was studied by Rudall (14), who found that dissolution of epidermal proteins in the cow's nose may be readily achieved by urea. Some dispersal takes place in 1 M urea solution, but really effective solution is obtained only in concentrations up to 6 M. By the use of 6 M urea solution, Rudall extracted two kinds of proteins. One was identified as a fibrous protein and called epidermin. Epidermin reveals a molecular weight of about 60,000 and a frictional ratio of 3.5, indicating a very asymmetric particle (105). Films of epidermin show an α-keratin diagram (14). Thermal contraction of the film was found identical to that of strips isolated from the lower layer of the cow's nose epidermis. Chemical analyses reveal 0.8–1.08% sulfur. The other protein is nonfibrous and has the remarkable property of containing sulfur in a higher quantity than epidermin, ranging from 1.12 to 2.86%. Both these proteins are present in the lower and middle portion of the cow's nose epidermis. An epiderminlike protein has not been isolated from the human epidermis. Soluble proteins are extractable with neutral or slightly alkaline buffers from metabolically active portions of the human epidermis. These have not yet been sufficiently characterized to decide whether they originate from fibrous preunits of keratin or from other cell constituents (106–110).

A nonfibrous prekeratin called keratohyalin is formed by specialized cells of the mammalian epidermis. The small granules, about 0.2 μ in diameter, grow to several microns during maturation of the cell (Plate II). Their macromolecules consist of fine particles, measuring 100 to 250 Å. in diameter (46). Histochemical studies indicate neither —SH groups nor —S—S— bonds (1, 101, 102). The granules, however, resist weak acid and alkaline solutions in the pH range 2.9–8.6, quite close to that of epidermal keratin. They resist trypsin, and effective dispersion occurs only in 4–6 M urea solutions (111).

VI. Hair Keratin

Hair is formed exclusively by mammals (pilifera) (112). The only exception to this rule, so far found, is the fossil aquatic reptile *Ramphorynchus*, which has skin follicles capable of developing hair (113).

The term "hair keratin" defines a group of different proteins produced by different cell lines of the hair follicle. Three kinds of hair keratins are generally distinguished; cuticular, cortical, and medullary keratin. They differ from each other in some structural or chemical aspect. Human hair and finer wool fibers consist mainly of cortical keratin and contain about 10% cuticular keratin. Medullary keratin occurs in negligible amounts. The hair of some primates, coarse sheep wool ("kemp" wool), goat hair and that of most rodents are examples containing all three keratins in considerable quantities. Variations in the distribution of these keratins depend largely on the development of cuticle, cortex, or medulla of the particular hair. In "kemp" wool, medullary keratin is estimated to form about 15% of the fiber (114).

There is considerable information on the structural properties of different hair keratins. Their chemical properties have not yet been adequately characterized. Most techniques so far used for the isolation of the different cell types of the hair shaft or wool fiber yield heterogeneous material, and the agents applied for dispersion usually cause some chemical modification in the isolated material.

The most characteristic property of cuticular keratin is its amorphous structure (115). It is originally formed of small droplets (300 Å.) which grow in size and finally coalesce into an amorphous material in the mature cuticular cell (Fig. 6) (15, 16). Analyses of isolated cuticular cells reveal 4.83% sulfur and 18.1% cystine in contrast to 3.5% sulfur and 12.2% cystine of the total wool fiber (18, 19). Accordingly it appears that cortical keratin is richer in sulfur than the other keratins of the wool fiber. Considerable evidence also exists (116–120) that cuticular keratin is heterogeneous and consists of two main fractions, a trypsin-resistant and a trypsin-digestible one. The outer portion of the cuticular cell, facing the outer surface of the wool, is the site of the trypsin-resistant fraction (Plate III), while the nonresistant fraction is located at the inner side of the cell. The resistant fraction has been named k_1 phase or keratin of the exocuticle; the nonresistant, k_2 phase, or the keratin of the endocuticle.

Cortical keratin is distinguished from cuticular keratin by its highly fibrous character. Films of isolated cortical cells have the same α-keratin diagram and reveal identical physical properties as the whole non-medullated wool fiber or hair shaft (121). The macromolecular units of cortical keratin consist of filaments 60–80 Å. thick, embedded in an interfibrillary cement (16, 43) (Plate IV). The most prominent property of cortical keratin is its high cystine content facilitating abundant cross linking of polypeptide chains by —S—S— bonds. The closest estimate of amino acid composition of cortical keratin may be given by the amino acid composition of nonmedullated wool fibers, 90% of which consist of cortical cells. The most probable amino acid composition of such fibers, as calculated by Harris et al. (122) is shown in Table IV.

Medullary keratin is an amorphous protein (25). Medulla cells appear isotropic in polarized light, indicating the lack of an oriented submicroscopic structure (24). The most significant property of medullary keratin is its very low sulfur content (20, 21, 22, 23). Sulfur determinations of medullary keratin, isolated from the goat hair, reveal only 0.23% sulfur (22). Medullary keratin of rabbit hair gives cystine values as low as 0.28% (24). Citrulline, which is absent from cortical keratin,

TABLE IV
AMINO ACID COMPOSITION OF WOOL[a]

Amino acid	%	Amino acid	%
Glycine	6.50	Aspartic acid	7.27
Alanine	4.40	Glutamic acid	15.27
Valine	4.72	Arginine	10.40
Leucine	11.30	Lysine	3.30
Phenylalanine	3.75	Histidine	0.70
Proline	6.75	Tryptophan	0.70
Serine	9.41	Cystine	12.20
Threonine	6.76	Methionine	0.71
Tyrosine	5.80	Amide nitrogen	1.40

[a] From Harris and Brown (122).

has been identified in medullary keratin. Lysine and arginine occur in very large quantities, indicating that medullary keratin is a highly charged protein (25).

For chemical studies of hair keratin, nonmedullated wool fibers are most suitable because nearly 90% of them consist of cortical keratin. Many attempts were made to solubilize wool fibers with keratolytic agents and isolate the basic keratin "molecule" which forms the bulk of the wool. The main building block of wool fiber has not yet been isolated in a form acceptable as a basic "molecule." The various split products are of considerable interest for understanding the structure and various building units of keratin. Some of these studies are briefly described here.

It has been long observed that moderately strong alkalies readily attack wool fibers and cause rapid solubilization. Concentrated solutions of sodium hydroxide (14%), however, are ineffective in this respect, because it forms a hydrate which has very few free hydroxyl ions. Very low concentrations of sodium hydroxide capable of solubilizing epidermal keratin do not cause appreciable solution of wool keratin. For instance, 0.065 N sodium hydroxide solution heated to 65° C. solubilizes only about 30% of the wool within 24 hours (123, 124). Alkalies hydrolyze wool in moderately strong solutions and lead to formation of small peptides. Amino acids, such as cystine, arginine, histidine, and serine, may be destroyed (125). It has been long observed that alkali is capable of cleaving —S—S— bonds of keratin and that a new type of C—S—C bond may be formed, characteristic for lanthionine (126, 127).

Reducing substances, such as sodium sulfite, or potassium cyanide, or thioglycolate in alkaline medium (pH 12), completely solubilize wool at room temperature. The soluble wool preparations contain practically the same amounts of sulfur, nitrogen, and cystine as the original material (128). The isoelectric point of such preparations was estimated to be between pH 4.0 and 4.7. Sedimentation and diffusion studies of preparations obtained with sodium sulfite showed polydispersity. The average molecular weight was calculated to be 9000, the average length of the molecules was estimated 170 Å. and the width 11 Å. (129). Preparations obtained by sodium bisulfite-urea mixture adjusted to pH 8 revealed particles of a molecular weight of 84,000. The approximate

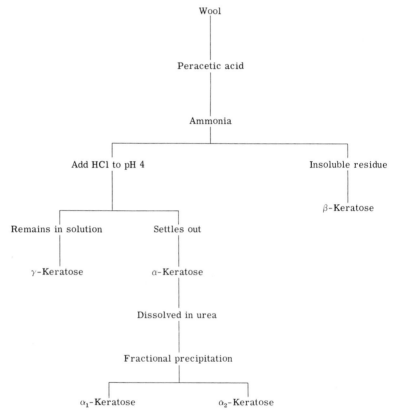

Fig. 4. Scheme of wool fractionation. From Alexander and Hudson (114).

length of the macromolecules was calculated at 1150 Å. and the width 12.8 Å. (130). Wool solubilized in alkaline thioglycolate proved to be of complex composition containing at least 4 components, distinguishable by their different mobility values, 6.3, 7.2, 9.3, 10.5, respectively (131). A severe breakdown of wool fibers may be achieved by oxidation

PLATE I. Electron micrograph of filaments of horny cells of the human epidermis. [From Matoltsy (2).]

Plates I–V face page 360.

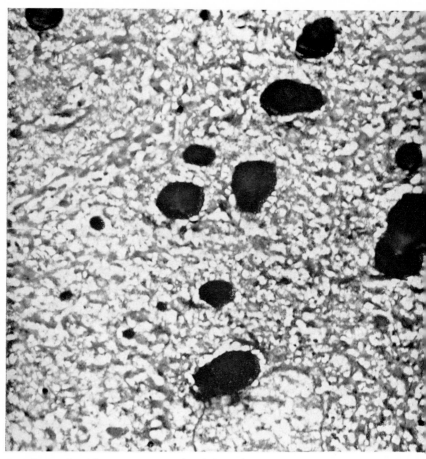

PLATE II. Electron micrograph of keratohyalin granules (dense bodies) and fibrous cytoplasm of epidermal cells of the newborn rat skin.

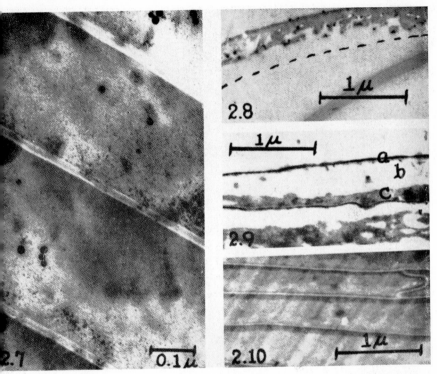

PLATE III. Electron micrographs of cuticular cells of the hair. Cells are filled with amorphous keratin (2.7). Inner portion of a cell is removed by trypsin treatment. Dotted lines indicate presumed position of the inner cell membrane (2.8). The outer, trypsin-resistant fraction is removed by peracetic acid treatment followed by extraction with ammonia (2.9). Lighter and darker regions correspond to the trypsin-resistant and trypsin-digestible fractions (2.10). Reproduced by permission of Drs. M. S. C. Birbeck and E. H. Mercer and the Press of The Rockefeller Institute (15).

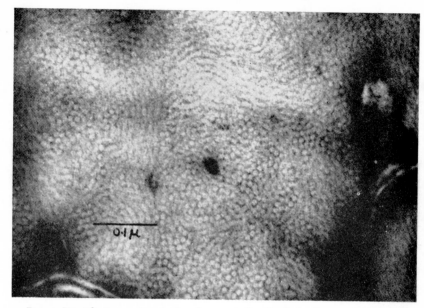

PLATE IV. Electron micrograph of a cortical cell of the human hair revealing cross sections of filaments (white dots) and interfibrillary cement (dark areas). Reproduced by permission of Dr. G. E. Rogers and the Press of The New York Academy of Sciences (16).

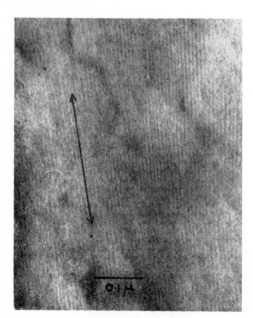

PLATE V. Electron micrograph of a longitudinal section of the porcupine quill tip. The light lines correspond to filaments, the dark ones to the interfibrillary cement. Reproduced by permission of Dr. G. E. Rogers and the Press of The New York Academy of Sciences (16).

with aqueous chlorine dioxide, when about half of the material passes into solution as small peptides or polypeptides ranging in molecular weight from 2000 to 12,000 (132, 133). Wool oxidized with peracetic acid and subsequently solubilized with ammonia may be separated into three major fractions (Fig. 4) (114, 134, 135). The largest fraction, called α-keratose, gives an α-keratin diagram in powder form or when spun into fibers. Its sulfur content is 2.4%, being relatively low when compared with the 6.1% sulfur of γ-keratose. Electrophoresis studies revealed two components of α-keratose, called α_1- and α_2-keratose. Isolated α_1-keratose gives an X-ray diagram identical to that of the whole wool fiber, indicating that it is derived from the cortical region of the wool. Physicochemical studies revealed a sedimentation constant of 2.00 and diffusion constant of 3.12. The molecular weight of α_1-keratose was calculated as 67,000. This component most probably represents a main building unit of cortical keratin. α_2-Keratose shows an ill-defined β-keratin structure and is a heterogeneous substance of low molecular weight. β-Keratose forms the smallest fraction of the wool. It is assumed to be derived from the subcuticle, a membranelike region of the wool extending between cuticle and cortex. β-Keratose gives an ill-defined β-keratin pattern and reveals heterogeneity in the ultracentrifuge. Its sulfur content is 2.2%. γ-Keratose is also a heterogeneous fraction and most probably consists of smaller and larger peptides. As mentioned above, it has a high sulfur content of 6.1%.

Partial solubilization of the wool was also achieved by agents known to break specifically the hydrogen bonds and leave the disulfide bonds intact (136). Formamide solubilizes about 40% of the wool; the amino acid composition of the solubilized material was found similar to the residue, particularly in the cystine content.

Of the precursors of hair keratin, cortical keratin received the most attention. Cytoplasmic fibrillation occurs early in the presumptive cortical cell. The first filaments are 60–80 Å. in diameter, corresponding to the dimension of filaments observable in mature cortical cells (16). Histochemical studies show that these filaments are rich in free —SH groups and contain no —S—S— bonds (101, 102). While the presumptive cortical cells ascend in the hair bulb, the number of filaments greatly increases and they start to assemble into microscopic fibrils. At the neck of the hair bulb, the parallel oriented fibrils show an α-keratin structure (40). This α-prekeratin, however, is not yet fully stabilized. If a plucked hair is heated to 90–95° C., the keratogenous zone collapses without contraction. If it is suspended in urea, which breaks the hydrogen bonds of prekeratin, the keratogenous zone readily disperses. Histochemical studies also show that —S—S— bonds are not yet formed. The prekeratin contains only free —SH groups in large quantities (*101, 102*). At a higher level the —SH groups are oxidized to —S—S— bonds and a highly resistant and stable cortical keratin is formed.

Information was obtained on the source which yields the hair keratins by analyzing isolated wool roots. It was found that all amino acids are present in a free form, necessary for synthesis of wool keratins, including small quantities of free cystine and methionine (*25, 137*). In wool root extracts, obtained with 8 *M* urea solutions, Rogers (*25*) identified 5 proteins by electrophoresis studies, each revealing different mobility. Two of these proteins precipitate at pH 5.2 and the rest at pH 3.5. The material precipitating at pH 5.2 reveals the α-keratin diagram. Its sulfur content is 1.6–1.79%. This material was considered by Rogers (*25*) to contain fibrous macromolecular preunits of cortical keratin. Its molecular weight was estimated as 100,000. The other fraction precipitating at pH 3.5 shows a sulfur content of 4.00 to 4.13% and it is assumed to contain the cementing material which will be deposited in the interfibrillary spaces of fibrous keratin in the wool fiber.

VII. Quill, Feather, and Horn Keratin

Very little work has been done on keratins other than hair and epidermis. Quill, feather, and horn received some attention, but our knowledge is fragmentary on nail, claw, hoof, or beak keratin.

Information on quill keratin was obtained by studies on the South African and North American porcupine quills. The amino acid composition of quill is shown in Tables II and III. The quill of the North American porcupine (*Erithizon*) has been found more satisfactory for studies of component keratins than quill of the other porcupines, because this lacks the radial septa and therefore its medulla can be readily dissected from the cortex (*138*). X-ray investigations show that the cortical keratin of quill is an α-type of keratin. The macromolecular units were seen in the electron microscope as filaments, 60 Å. thick and several microns long, embedded in an amorphous matrix (Plate V). Analyses revealed 2.3% sulfur in cortical keratin. Medullary keratin was identified as a β-type keratin, its macromolecular units forming an amorphous structure in the medulla cells. The sulfur content of medullary keratin is 0.3%, much less than that of cortical keratin (*12, 16, 62, 138, 139*). These data reveal that quill keratins, in both structural and chemical aspects, are quite similar to those of medullated hair fibers.

Feathers differ from most keratins by revealing a β-keratin pattern, also called the "feather keratin pattern" (*12, 52, 64*). Analyses of constituent layers, however, show that the differently specialized cells of the feather follicle produce structurally different keratins. The outermost cells of the stratum intermedium synthetize β-keratin. In the outermost stratum corneum and in the stratum lucidum mainly an α-keratin is formed (12). The amino acid composition of the whole feather is shown in Tables II and III. The data given by Ward and Lundgren indicate (Table II) that feather differs from hair, wool, horn, or quill by a lower content of lysine and higher quantities of valine and phenylalanine. Explanation for these differences has not yet been offered. Solubilization of feathers with a mixture of bisulfite and urea at pH 6.0–8.5 revealed a homogeneous feather keratin derivative with a molecular weight of 10,000 (140, 141). Larger particles were obtained by dispersion in bisulfite and alkyl benzenesulfonate, showing an average molecular weight in the range 34,000–40,000 (142).

Cattle horn is built up of a single type of horny cell. Horn keratin is known to give an α-keratin pattern and its amino acid composition is similar to that of wool, hair, and quill (Table II), with the exception of glycine which seems to be somewhat higher. The precursor of horn keratin was found to be extractable with urea solution, and sulfur determination of the prekeratin derived from different levels of the reproductive layer are of significance for understanding the mechanism of keratin formation. Rudall (138) found that at an early stage the pre-keratin of the horn contains 0.71% sulfur. At a later stage the sulfur content was 1.51%. The sulfur content of the horn containing the final keratin was estimated 3.15%, thus revealing that, immediately before formation of the final keratin, large quantities of sulfur are incorporated into the prekeratin.

VIII. One-Component and Two-Component Theories of Keratin

A most puzzling problem for the biochemist is whether keratin is a single protein or a mixture of different substances. The N-terminal amino acid analyses and the work with keratolytic agents made this question even more pressing. The theories dealing with this subject are very stimulating; a few of them are briefly outlined here.

The one-component theory assumes that the precursor of keratin is the tonofibril with an α-keratin structure (27). In the early stages of cell differentiation the tonofibril contains no cystine, only cysteine with free —SH groups. At a later stage, most probably more cysteine is incorporated into the tonofibril, which at the final stage will be oxidized and the —S—S— bonds of cystine formed. As a result, the formerly "fragile" tonofibril changes into a coherent and resistant keratin, with polypeptide chains frequently cross-linked by disulfide bonds. Giroud and Leblond (27) believe that "this is at least one of the mechanisms by which the strength and chemical inertness of keratin may be explained."

The two-component theory of keratin actually finds its origin in a three-phase model of Astbury and Woods (53). This model was developed purely on the basis of mechanical studies to explain the elastic properties of wool fibers. It consists of small compartments having a wall (K_2). In the compartments, micelles (K_3) are assumed to be embedded in a cement (K_1). Alexander and Hudson (114) related their chemical studies to this model and assumed that α-keratose, the wool fraction which reveals an α-keratin structure and contains relatively small quantities of sulfur, corresponds to the micelles. γ-Keratose, the fraction with amorphous structure and a high sulfur content, was regarded as the cementing substance of the micelles. β-Keratose was taken not as a wall (K_2), but as a membrane material, extending throughout the entire length of the wool fiber between cortex and cuticle. Hence, a physical model was translated into a chemical system. Alexander (77) also assumed that the structure of "micelles" is stabilized by hydrogen bonds, whereas the disulfide bonds connect the "micelles" to the cement. Birbeck and Mercer correlated the results of their electron microscopic studies (43) with Alexander and Hudson's keratose fractions. They noted in osmium tetroxide-fixed preparations that the 60–80 Å.-thick filaments of cortical cells of the hair are embedded in a highly electron-dense cement. Since Bahr (143) emphasized that cystine and cysteine react with osmium tetroxide, the high electron density of the cement was interpreted as the reaction of a sulfur-rich substance. On account of this, Birbeck and Mercer assumed that the amorphous cement may be identical with Alexander and Hudson's γ-keratose. The filaments were considered as α-keratin of low sulfur content and correlated to α-keratose. Hence, Birbeck and Mercer's two-component theory assumes that keratin "consists of two proteins in close association, one of which is fibrous and the other amorphous" (43).

The two-component theory may be regarded as an extension of the one-component theory, since its α-keratin component is essentially identical with the tonofibril. The weak point of the one-component theory is that it does not explain satisfactorily the sudden increase of sulfur at the stage (keratogenous zone) immediately before formation of the final keratin (27). The two-component theory does not have this difficulty because its γ-keratose component of high sulfur content is noted to be deposited between the filaments, immediately before formation of the final keratin (43). The weak point of the two-component theory is that it is based purely on a histochemical reaction, the exact mechanism of which requires further exploration. Furthermore, γ-keratose, the substance assumed to react with osmium tetroxide, has not yet been fully characterized. Alexander and Hudson (114) refer to it as a heterodispersed protein which reveals a high degree of heterogeneity in both electrophoresis and ultracentrifugation studies. At the present time it is very difficult to judge whether γ-keratose originates from filaments, interfibrillary cement, remnants of nuclear or cytoplasmic components or perhaps is a mixture of these. If γ-keratose were better characterized, the two-component theory would receive substantial support.

The two-component theory of keratin is supported by Brody's (46, 47) observation finding a similar α-keratin filament – γ-keratin cement system in the epidermis of the guinea pig. Rogers' studies (16) on cortical cells of the porcupine quill also favor a filament-matrix theory for keratin. It is noteworthy to recall that Rudall's work on the cow's nose epidermis (14) also is chemical evidence to suggest the possibility of a two-component system for keratin, with epidermin of low sulfur content and a nonfibrous prekeratin of high sulfur content.

IX. Concluding Remarks

The study of keratinizing tissues has contributed a great deal to the development of our concepts on molecular and macromolecular structure of proteins, on their fibrogenesis and stabilization. For the biologist, the keratinizing tissues yield a remarkable material to study in a single tissue the phenomena of proliferation, differentiation, senescence, and death. The study of keratinizing tissues is of great importance for medicine because the cause of many skin diseases lies in the malfunction of germinative or specialized cells, resulting skin tumors, production of abnormally scaling horny layers with anomalous keratin, etc. Better knowledge of animal fibers is of importance for the wool industry.

ACKNOWLEDGMENT

The author acknowledges the valuable help of Mrs. Margit Matoltsy in preparation of the manuscript.

References

1. W. Montagna, "The Structure and Function of Skin." Academic Press, New York, 1956.
2. A. G. Matoltsy, Intern. Rev. Cytol. 10, 315 (1961).
3. C. P. Leblond, in "Dynamics of Proliferating Tissues" (D. Price, ed.), p. 1. Univ. of Chicago Press, Chicago, 1958.
4. H. B. Fell and E. Mellanby, J. Physiol. (London) 119, 470 (1953).
5. H. B. Fell, Proc. Roy. Soc. B146, 242 (1957).
6. P. Weiss and R. James, Exptl. Cell Research Suppl. 3, 381 (1955).
7. I. Lasnitzki, Intern. Rev. Cytol. 7, 79 (1958).
8. A. G. Matoltsy, in "The Biology of Hair Growth" (W. Montagna and R. A. Ellis, eds.), Chapter 7, p. 135. Academic Press, New York, 1958.

9. C. Grobstein, in "The Cell" (J. Brachet and A. E. Mirsky, eds.), Vol. I, p. 437. Academic Press, New York, 1959.
10. A. G. Matoltsy, *J. Invest. Dermatol.* **31**, 343 (1958).
11. J. Hanson, *J. Anat.* **81**, 174 (1947).
12. K. M. Rudall, *Biochim. et Biophys. Acta* **1**, 549 (1947).
13. J. C. Derksen, G. C. Heringa and A. Weidinger, *Acta. Neerl. Morphol.* **1**, 31 (1937).
14. K. M. Rudall, *Advances in Protein Chem.* **7**, 253 (1952).
15. M. S. C. Birbeck and E. H. Mercer, *J. Biophys. Biochem. Cytol.* **3**, 215 (1957).
16. G. E. Rogers, *Ann. N.Y. Acad. Sci.* **83**, 378 (1959).
17. E. Elöd and H. Zahn, *Naturwissenschaften* **33**, 158 (1946).
18. W. B. Geiger, *Textile Research J.* **14**, 82 (1944).
19. W. B. Geiger, *J. Research Natl. Bur. Standards* **32**, 127 (1944).
20. J. Barrit and A. T. King, *Biochem. J.* **25**, 1075 (1931).
21. J. G. Bekker and A. T. King, *Biochem. J.* **25**, 1077 (1931).
22. D. J. Lloyd and R. H. Marriott, *Biochem. J.* **27**, 911 (1933).
23. S. Blackburn, *Biochem. J.* **43**, 114 (1948).
24. A. G. Matoltsy, *Exptl. Cell Research* **3**, 98 (1953).
25. G. E. Rogers, *Ann. N.Y. Acad. Sci.* **83**, 408 (1959).
26. C. P. Leblond, *Ann. N.Y. Acad. Sci.* **53**, 464 (1951).
27. A. Giroud and C. P. Leblond, *Ann. N.Y. Acad. Sci.* **53**, 624 (1951).
28. M. S. C. Birbeck and E. H. Mercer, *Nature* **178**, 985 (1956).
29. M. S. C. Birbeck and E. H. Mercer, *Proc. Conf. on Electron Microscopy, Stockholm, 1956* p. 156 (1957).
30. K. R. Porter, *Proc. 3rd Intern. Conf. Electron Microscopy, London, 1954* p. 539 (1956).
31. P. Weiss and W. Ferris, *Exptl. Cell Research* **6**, 546 (1954).
32. C. C. Selby, *J. Biophys. Biochem. Cytol.* **1**, 429 (1955).
33. E. Horstmann and A. Knoop, *Z. Zellforsch.* **47**, 348 (1958).
34. G. F. Odland, *J. Biophys. Biochem. Cytol.* **4**, 529 (1958).
35. R. G. Hibbs and W. Clark, *J. Biophys. Biochem. Cytol.* **6**, 71 (1959).
36. W. J. Schmidt, *Protoplasma* **29**, 300 (1937).
37. A. G. Matoltsy and G. F. Odland, *J. Biophys. Biochem. Cytol.* **1**, 191 (1955).
38. A. G. Matoltsy and G. F. Odland, *J. Invest. Dermatol.* **26**, 121 (1956).
39. A. G. Matoltsy and C. A. Balsamo, *J. Biophys. Biochem. Cytol.* **1**, 339 (1955).
40. E. H. Mercer, *Biochim. et Biophys. Acta* **3**, 161 (1949).
41. G. Swanbeck, *J. Ultrastruct. Research* **3**, 51 (1959).
42. E. H. Mercer, in "Biology of Hair Growth" (W. Montagna and R. A. Ellis, eds.), Chapter 5, p. 91. Academic Press, New York, 1958.
43. M. S. C. Birbeck and E. H. Mercer, *J. Biophys. Biochem. Cytol.* **3**, 203 (1957).
44. K. R. Porter, *Anat. Record* **118**, 433 (1954).
45. C. C. Selby, *J. Invest. Dermatol.* **29**, 131 (1957).
46. I. Brody, *J. Ultrastruct. Research* **3**, 84 (1959).
47. I. Brody, *J. Ultrastruct. Research* **2**, 482 (1959).
48. C. C. Selby, *J. Soc. Cosmetic Chem.* **7**, 584 (1956).
49. A. Charles and F. G. Smiddy, *J. Invest. Dermatol.* **29**, 327 (1957).
50. A. Charles, *J. Invest. Dermatol.* **33**, 65 (1959).
51. W. T. Astbury and A. Street, *Phil. Trans. Roy. Soc.* **A230**, 75 (1931).
52. W. T. Astbury and T. C. Marwick, *Nature* **130**, 309 (1932).

53. W. T. Astbury and H. J. Woods, *Phil. Trans. Roy. Soc.* **A232,** 333 (1933).
54. W. T. Astbury, *Trans. Faraday Soc.* **29,** 193 (1933).
55. W. T. Astbury, *Chem. & Ind.* (*London*)**60,** 491 (1941).
56. W. T. Astbury and F. O. Bell, *Nature* **147,** 696 (1941).
57. J. C. Derksen and G. C. Heringa, *Polska Gaz. lekarska* **15,** 532 (1936).
58. A. Giroud, H. Bulliard, and C. P. Leblond, *Bull. histol. appl. physiol. et pathol. et tech. microscop.* **11,** 129 (1934).
59. A. Giroud and H. Bulliard, *Arch. anat. microscop.* **31,** 271 (1935).
60. A. Giroud and C. Champetier, *Bull. soc. chim. biol.* **18,** 656 (1936).
61. A. R. Lang, *Acta Cryst.* **9,** 436 (1956).
62. A. R. Lang, *Acta Cryst.* **9,** 446 (1956).
63. I. MacArthur, *Nature* **152,** 38 (1943).
64. T. C. Marwick, *J. Textile Sci.* (*Leeds*) **4,** 31 (1931).
65. M. F. Perutz, *Nature* **167,** 1053 (1951).
66. K. M. Rudall, *J. Soc. Dyers Colourists* **62,** 15 (1946).
67. G. Swanbeck, *Acta Dermato-Venereol.* **39,** Suppl. 43 (1959).
67a. A. Elliott, *Research* **7,** 210 (1954); A. Elliott and E. J. Ambrose, *Nature* **166,** 194 (1950).
68. L. Pauling and R. B. Corey, *Nature* **171,** 59 (1953).
69. L. Pauling, *Inst. intern. chim. Solvay, 9ᵉ Conseil chim.,* Brussels p. 63 (1953).
70. S. Blackburn, *Biochem. J.* **47,** 443 (1950).
71. W. H. Ward and H. P. Lundgren, *Advances in Protein Chem.* **9,** 243 (1954).
72. W. R. Middlebrook, *Biochim. et Biophys. Acta* **7,** 547 (1951).
73. O. Mark and K. Philip, *Naturwissenschaften* **25,** 119 (1937).
74. M. Laskowski and H. A. Scheraga, *J. Am. Chem. Soc.* **76,** 6305 (1954).
75. A. Nowothny and H. Zahn, *Z. physik. Chem.* **B51,** 265 (1942).
76. E. Elöd and H. Zahn, *Melliand Textilber.* **30,** 17 (1949).
77. P. Alexander, *Ann. N.Y. Acad. Sci.* **53,** 653 (1951).
78. L. Pauling and R. B. Corey, *Proc. Natl. Acad. Sci. U. S.* **37,** 251 (1951).
79. H. W. Spier and G. Pascher, *In* "Aktuelle Probleme der Dermatologie" (R. Schuppli, ed.), Vol. I, pp. 3–11. S. Karger, Basel, 1959.
80. V. A. Wilkerson, *J. Biol. Chem.* **107,** 377 (1934).
81. H. C. Eckstein, *Proc. Soc. Exptl. Biol. Med.* **32,** 1573 (1935).
82. V. A. Wilkerson and V. J. Tulane, *J. Biol. Chem.* **129,** 477 (1939).
83. R. J. Block, *Proc. Soc. Exptl. Biol. Med.* **32,** 1574 (1935).
84. R. J. Block, *J. Biol. Chem.* **128,** 181 (1939).
85. R. J. Block, *Ann. N. Y. Acad. Sci.* **53,** 608 (1951).
86. D. Mütting, H. Langhof, and V. Wortmann, *Z. klin. Med.* **152,** 495 (1955).
87. A. G. Matoltsy, *Proc. 11th Intern. Congr. Dermatol.* (1957) **3,** 422 (1959).
88. B. Lustig, B. Katchen, and F. Reiss, *J. Invest. Dermatol.* **30,** 159 (1958).
89. G. Pascher, *In* "Aktuelle Probleme der Dermatologie" (R. Schuppli, ed.), Vol. I, p. 5. S. Karger, Basel 1959.
90. R. J. Block and H. B. Vickery, *J. Biol. Chem.* **93,** 113 (1931).
91. G. Pascher, G. Steinrück, and H. W. Spier, *Arch. klin. u. exptl. Dermatol.* **204,** 140 (1957).
92. S. Rothman, A. M. Smiljanic, and J. C. Murphy, *J. Invest. Dermatol.* **13,** 317 (1949).
93. A. Bollinger, *J. Invest. Dermatol.* **17,** 79 (1951).
94. N. A. Barnicot, *Brit. J. Dermatol.* **71,** 303 (1959).
95. A. Bollinger and R. Gross, *Australian J. Exptl. Biol. Med. Sci.* **31,** 127 (1953).

368 A. GEDEON MATOLTSY

96. A. Bollinger and R. Gross, *Australian J. Exptl. Biol. Med. Sci.* **30,** 399 (1952).
97. A. Szakall, *Arch. klin. u. exptl. Dermatol.* **201,** 331 (1955).
98. D. J. Kooyman, *Proc. Soc. Exptl. Biol. Med.* **29,** 485 (1931–32).
99. D. J. Kooyman, *Arch. Dermatol. and Syphilol.* **25,** 444 (1932).
100. A. G. Matoltsy, unpublished observations (1955).
101. R. J. Barrnett and A. M. Seligman, *J. Natl. Cancer Inst.* **13,** 905 (1953).
102. A. Z. Eisen, W. Montagna, and H. B. Chase, *J. Natl. Cancer Inst.* **14,** 341 (1953).
103. A. G. Matoltsy and J. S. Sinesi, *Anat. Record* **128,** 55 (1957).
104. A. G. Matoltsy, *J. Biophys. Biochem. Cytol.* **2,** 361 (1956).
105. E. H. Mercer and B. Oloffson, *J. Polymer Sci.* **6,** 261 (1951).
106. H. W. Spier, H. Röckl, and G. Pascher, *Klin. Wochschr.* **32,** 795 (1954).
107. A. G. Matoltsy and F. S. M. Herbst, *Invest. Dermatol.* **27,** 263 (1956).
108. A. G. Matoltsy and F. S. M. Herbst, *J. Invest. Dermatol.* **26,** 339 (1956).
109. D. A. Roe, *J. Invest. Dermatol.* **27,** 1 (1956).
110. D. A. Roe, *J. Invest. Dermatol.* **27,** 319 (1956).
111. A. G. Matoltsy and M. Matoltsy, *J. Invest. Dermatol.* in press (1962).
112. R. Bonnet, *Anat. Hefte* **1,** 233 (1892).
113. F. Broili, *Bayer. Akad. Wiss. München Math.-Naturwiss.* **49,** (1927).
114. P. Alexander and R. F. Hudson, "Wool, Its Chemistry and Physics." Reinhold, New York, 1954.
115. K. M. Rudall, *Proc. Leeds Phil. Lit. Soc., Sci. Sect.* **4,** 13 (1941).
116. E. H. Mercer and A. L. G. Rees, *Nature* **157,** 589 (1946).
117. E. H. Mercer and A. L. G. Rees, *Australian J. Exptl. Biol. Med. Sci.* **24,** 147 (1946).
118. J. E. Lindberg, E. H. Mercer, B. Philip, and N. Gralen, *Textile Research J.* **19,** 673 (1949).
119. R. D. B. Fraser and G. E. Rogers, *Australian J. Biol. Sci.* **8,** 288 (1955).
120. N. Ramanathan, J. Sikorski, and H. J. Woods, *Biochim. et Biophys. Acta* **18,** 323 (1956).
121. H. J. Woods, *Proc. Roy. Soc.* **A166,** 76 (1938).
122. M. Harris and O. Brown, *J. Soc. Dyers and Colourists* **62,** 203 (1946).
123. H. Zahn, *Textil Praxis* **2,** 70 (1949).
124. M. Harris and K. Smith, *J. Research Natl. Bur. Standards* **25,** 451 (1940).
125. G. Warner and C. Cannan, *J. Biol. Chem.* **19,** 404 (1942).
126. J. B. Speakman and K. Whewell, *J. Soc. Dyers and Colourists* **52,** 380 (1936).
127. K. Horn, C. B. Jones and P. Ringel, *J. Biol. Chem.* **138,** 141 (1941).
128. D. R. Goddard and L. Michaelis, *J. Biol. Chem.* **106,** 605 (1934).
129. B. Oloffson and N. Gralen, *Proc. 11th Intern. Congr. Pure and Appl. Chem., London, 1947* **5,** 151 (1952).
130. E. H. Mercer and B. Oloffson, *J. Polymer Sci.* **6,** 671 (1951).
131. J. M. Gillespie and F. G. Lennox, *Biochim. et Biophys. Acta* **12,** 481 (1953).
132. J. B. Speakman, *Melliand Textilber.* **33,** 823 (1952).
133. J. B. Speakman, in "Fibre Science" (J. M. Preston, ed.), Chapter 16. The Textile Inst., Manchester, England, 1949.
134. P. Alexander and C. Earland, *Nature* **166,** 396 (1950).
135. P. Alexander, H. Zahn, and H. Haselmann, *Textile Research J.* **21,** 236 (1951).
136. E. Elöd and H. Zahn, *Kolloid-Z.* **108,** 6 (1944).
137. W. J. Ellis, J. M. Gillespie, and H. Lindley, *Nature* **165,** 545 (1950).

138. K. M. Rudall, *Proc. 1st Intern. Wool Textile Research Conf., Australia, 1955* **F**, 177 (1956).
139. W. T. Astbury, *Proc. 1st Intern. Wool Textile Research Conf., Australia, 1955* **B**, 202 (1956)
140. A. M. Woodin, *Nature* **173,** 823 (1954).
141. A. M. Woodin, *Biochem. J.* **57,** 99 (1954).
142. W. H. Ward, L. M. High, and H. P. Lundgren, *J. Polymer Research* **1,** 22 (1946).
143. G. F. Bahr, *Exptl. Cell Research* **7,** 457 (1954).

CHAPTER 8

Sclerotization

M. G. M. PRYOR

Department of Zoology, Cambridge University, England

I. Introduction

A. THE FUNCTIONAL REQUIREMENTS OF SKELETONS

Sclerotins, skeletal proteins that owe their stability to tanning by orthoquinones, are characteristic of the exoskeleton of arthropods; to understand their position in nature it is important to know something of the history of skeletal proteins in arthropods and in other phyla. The skeletons of primitive arthropods are essentially turgid tubes; tubes with inextensible walls filled with fluid. Any change of shape tends to decrease the internal volume and is resisted by tensile forces in the wall; the skeleton is never required to resist compression at all. In the higher arthropods mobility is increased by reducing the internal pressure, and this is made possible by introducing rigid plates at the muscle insertions; any movement of the plate causes a relatively large internal volume change and is the more easily resisted. From this beginning has been

371

evolved the fully articulated exoskeleton which does not rely on internal pressure at all.

The materials have evolved to suit their function. Chitin, using the word in a loose sense to mean a complex of polyacetylglucosamine and protein, is an economical material for a skeleton that depends on internal pressure. The long high-polymer chains are strong and have a high elastic modulus lengthwise. In flat cuticles they are usually aligned roughly parallel, arranged in thin lamellae, each with the direction of the "grain" at an angle to that of its neighbors, like the veneers in plywood. This arrangement gives a flexible but inextensible skin. It is flexible because the lateral bonds between molecular chains are weak, and the bonds between successive lamellae weaker still, so that when the cuticle is bent there is little resistance to shear between the sheets. To confer stiffness in bending the lamellae must be stuck together and the individual crystallites or molecules within the lamellae stabilized by embedding them in a continuous matrix. This is done by converting the protein part of the chitin-protein complex into sclerotin.

The skeletons of plants also started as turgid tubes, this time of cellulose; the skeletons of herbaceous plants are still essentially bundles of turgid tubes, and when the internal pressure is lost, they wilt. The massive skeletons of trees are built up from dead, empty tubes, and this is made possible by stabilizing the cellulose of the cell walls by impregnating it with lignin, a three-dimensional aromatic polymer based on condensed phenylpropane.

The vertebrates never operated on the turgid-tube principle. Primitive Chordata swam by propagating sinusoidal waves down their muscular tails; the tail being a solid mass of muscle hardly needs a skeleton at all, although it does usually possess a central rod, the notochord, which fixes the neutral axis of bending. The typical skeletal protein of vertebrates, keratin, seems to have been evolved in the first instance not as a structural material, but as a waterproof skin. For this, the requirement is for a protein that does not swell excessively when wet, or split and crack when dry. Any protein that fulfills this specification is likely to have good mechanical properties too, and these were developed and exploited later in claws and in beaks and feathers. In bird's beaks, or in tortoiseshell, or the scales of *Manis*, keratin provides, locally at any rate, an exoskeleton, and comes to fulfill a function comparable with that of sclerotin.

B. WAYS OF MEETING THE FUNCTIONAL REQUIREMENTS

To restrain swelling, the most effective method is to introduce primary valence cross linkages between protein chains. Keratin depends for its stability on disulfide bonds formed between cysteine side chains. Sclerotin depends on the formation of bridges between free amino groups by allowing them to react with an orthoquinone; the reaction involves the elimination of the strongly polar amino groups, so that the effect on swelling is a double one. Sclerotization resembles in its chemical mechanism the tanning of collagen by benzoquinone, and the essential conditions for effective tanning, which have been reviewed by Gustavson (1), apply. The most important of these affects the size of the tannin molecule. Quinone has two reactive sites and so is theoretically capable of reacting with two different side chains, but the most reactive sites are close together on the ring and their chance of making contact with two free amino groups from different side chains is small. Benzoquinone in fact is only effective as a tanning agent under conditions in which it is free to polymerize, and the same is probably true of the natural tanning agents in sclerotins; the greater the capacity of the tannin to polymerize and condense, the better its chances of reacting with several different side chains. Essentially similar steric difficulties must apply to the keratins; and it is probably an essential condition that the protein chains should be aligned more or less parallel, so that the distances to be bridged are decreased and the chances of a cysteine side chain finding a suitable neighbor within reach increased. It is a characteristic difference between the two types of protein that sclerotins are mostly disoriented and amorphous, whereas the keratins are oriented and partially crystalline.

Polymerization of tanning agents may lead to the introduction of a quite considerable bulk of condensed aromatic material, which fills the voids between protein or chitin crystallites, and so stabilizes them mechanically. Perhaps the whole of the tanned protein in an insect cuticle ought to be regarded from the mechanical point of view as a continuous matrix which stabilizes the chitin mechanically and so enables it to sustain compression. In the manufacture of synthetic plastics, phenol-formaldehyde resins are used in the same way to stabilize paper or fabric. The lignin of plant skeletons is an extreme example of this principle; polymerization and condensation of the aromatic component is extremely active, and the protein is left out altogether.

The relation of lignin to cellulose has been much studied and may be taken as a pattern of the relation of sclerotin to chitin. Like sclerotin, lignin is amorphous and isotropic; by filling the intermicellar spaces it abolishes the form birefringence of the cellulose, so that a highly lignified cell wall is isotropic in polarized light. If the lignin is removed, form birefringence is restored; if the cellulose is removed the resulting elongate voids in the isotropic lignin matrix also show form birefringence (2). Lignin and cellulose evidently form two independent but mutually interpenetrating three-dimensional networks. Heavily sclerotized chitin is isotropic; it becomes birefringent if the sclerotin is removed. The converse experiment of removing the chitin has not been performed; chitin is more stable than cellulose and would be difficult to remove. Both lignified cellulose and sclerotized chitin appear to be chemically inert and are difficult to stain; this is no doubt due partly to the fact that the complex is very impermeable to reagents, but it is also possible that the reactive groups of both components engage each other so that they are not free to react with stains. In lignified cellulose, characteristic properties of cellulose—for example, staining with chlor-zinc iodide—reappear in zones where slip planes due to incipient shear failure have appeared in the cell walls (3), but no such effect has been observed in sclerotized chitin. Foster and Hackman (4) have found that in calcified parts of the cuticle of the edible crab *Cancer pagurus* protein appears to be bound to the chitin by covalent bonds; if this were so in the sclerotized parts of the cuticle, it would mean that the chitin and the sclerotin networks were in fact continuous with one another.

From the mechanical point of view the stabilizing matrix need not be organic, and there are many examples of fibrous materials stabilized by impregnation with inorganic salts: the bones of vertebrates consist of protein stabilized with calcium phosphate; and the skeletons of the crustacean subclass Malacostraca, of chitin stabilized with calcium carbonate. The inorganic matrix has an elastic modulus at least ten times greater than that of sclerotin or lignin, but it is some two and a half times heavier and it is brittle, disadvantages which have restricted its use to applications where weight and brittleness are not important.

II. Sclerotization

A. General

Having considered the general principles involved, we shall go on to describe some examples of sclerotization, before proceeding to a more detailed study of the chemistry of the process. The first example to be described, and in many ways the simplest, is the sclerotization of the ootheca or egg case of the cockroach (5). The ootheca is about 8 mm. long, shaped like a carpet bag; the outer wall is composed of a typical reddish brown sclerotin in which are embedded crystals of calcium oxalate, the function of which is unknown. It is secreted over a period of from 24 to 36 hours by the female, who carries the incomplete ootheca about with her in a pouch formed from the ventral sternites of the terminal abdominal segments. If an incomplete ootheca is removed from the pouch it is seen that the edges of the newly secreted part are white and soft; next comes a pink zone, and then the translucent reddish brown part, which resembles the general external skeleton of the insect. The material is derived from the left and right colleterial glands, branching tubular glands which occupy a fair proportion of the hind part of the abdomen. The histology of the glands has been described by Brunet (6). The left gland secretes a milky protein, mixed with calcium oxalate crystals, and also the glucoside of protocatechuic acid (7). The right gland secretes a clear fluid which contains a glucosidase. When the secretions are mixed the glucoside is hydrolyzed, setting free protocatechuic acid (I) which is oxidized by a polyphenoloxidase contained in the secretion of the left gland. The products of oxidation of the protocatechuic acid then react with the protein to produce a resistant, reddish brown sclerotin.

The darkening and hardening of the cuticle of insects appears to be a similar process: the cuticle of a newly molted insect is white and soft; it hardens and darkens in much the same way as the ootheca. In many insects protocatechuic acid, or related substances such as homocatechuic acid (II) or dihydroxyphenyllactic acid (III) have been isolated (8, 9, 10), and there is present in most cuticles a tyrosinase capable of pro-

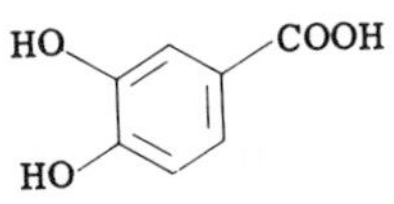

(I) 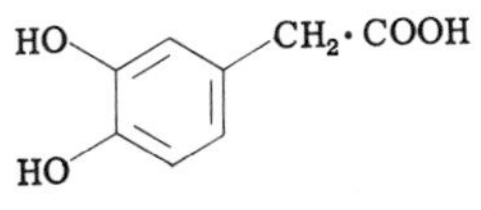   (II)

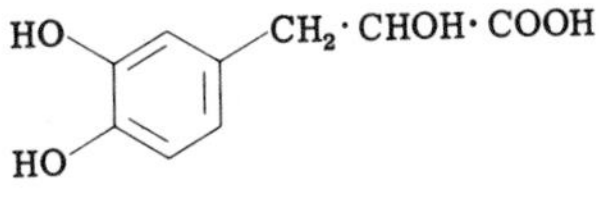

(III)

moting the oxidation of dihydroxyphenols to orthoquinones. Detailed investigation of the chemistry of cuticles is more difficult because we have to deal not with relatively large volumes of secretion separated from the glands that produced them, but with material present in very small quantities and still connected to the cells that secreted it. The situation is further complicated by the presence of chitin. Usually chitin and protein are secreted together by the same cells and darkening and hardening follow closely on secretion, but in the higher Diptera (Cyclorrhapha) the puparium is formed by the darkening and hardening of the last larval cuticle without any secretion of chitin, so that secretion of chitin and protein and the sclerotization of the cuticle are separated in time. For this reason blowfly puparia have been a favorite subject for the study of the chemistry of sclerotization.

B. Details of the Reaction

The chemistry of the reaction between proteins and quinones has been reviewed by Mason (11). To judge from their behavior *in vitro* one might expect that orthoquinones would react with amino groups first in the 4,5-positions, opposite to the quinone groups. Aniline, for example, first condenses with orthoquinone in these positions; if excess aniline is present it will react in the 3,6-positions as well and will also replace one oxygen, allowing five aniline residues in all to react with the ring. Amino acids react in a similar way. If catechol is oxidized in the presence of one equivalent of amino acid it takes up one atom of oxygen per molecule of catechol and the reaction goes no further. Excess amino acid is deaminated with the evolution of ammonia. The mechanism of the reaction has been discussed by Trautner and Roberts (12), who suggest that the orthoquinone with one amino acid attached to the ring reacts with a second amino acid to form an unstable quinonimine, which decomposes to yield ammonia, the corresponding keto acid, and the reduced dihydroxyphenol again. The substituted phenol is oxidized, and the cycle then repeats. The oxidation of the substituted phenol is spontaneous and will proceed in the presence of cyanide or other poisons of polyphenol oxidase. As long as excess amino acid remains the reaction is continuous, and when all the substrate is exhausted the aromatic components are left in the oxidized state and slowly take up more oxygen, eventually condensing and polymerizing to form an insoluble black precipitate.

In the oxidation of tyrosine (also reviewed by Mason) the first step is the introduction of a second hydroxyl to form 3,4-dihydroxyphenylalanine (dopa), which is then oxidized to the orthoquinone. The amino group of the side chain then reacts with the ring to form an indole ring, which eventually condenses and precipitates as "melanin." Amino acids do not have an appreciable tanning effect on proteins because their own amino groups react preferentially in this way, thus preventing the formation of any connections with the protein.

Sulfur might be expected to react in much the same way as nitrogen, and *in vitro* it does so. Reduced glutathione reacts with orthoquinone to form compounds containing two, three, or five molecules of glutathione according to the relative concentrations of the reactants. The sulfur compounds are more stable than the nitrogen compounds, and the reaction proceeds no further. This reaction does not seem to be of any wide significance in nature because the proteins of the cuticle of most arthropods are remarkable in containing practically no sulfur; it is worth noting that for any reaction to occur, the sulfhydryl groups of the protein would have to be in the reduced form; oxidized glutathione or cystine do not react (13).

C. DIFFICULTIES AND OBJECTIONS

Having considered the general nature of the reactions involved, we are now in a position to consider in detail the schemes which have been proposed to describe the process of sclerotization. The most widely accepted is that o-dihydroxyphenols are secreted into the cuticle and are there oxidized by the enzyme tyrosinase to the orthoquinones, which react with free amino groups of neighboring protein chains to form cross linkages. There is a fair amount of supporting evidence. Suitable dihydroxyphenols (8, 9, 10) have been isolated from various species of insect; the observed color changes suggest the formation of quinones; there is a decrease in free amino groups as sclerotization proceeds (14, 15, 16), and the proteins become insoluble at the same time (17). If radioactive tyrosine is injected into maggots at the time of puparium formation, 75% of it appears in the sclerotized puparium, and this does not happen for nonaromatic amino acids (18). There remain, however, some difficulties.

The first of these concerns the nature of the aromatic compounds isolated. The side chain of protocatechuic acid is readily displaced by amino groups, so that if there are two free amino groups within reach, a direct connection might be established with two protein chains (19). Homocatechuic and dihydroxyphenyllactic acid on the other hand do not easily lose their side chains, so that it is more difficult for them to establish bonds with more than one protein side chain. As Hackman (20) points out, on the analogy of their reaction with aniline they might still react with two or three amino groups, but it is not certain that they would react with an amino group attached to an aliphatic side chain as readily as they react with aniline. It is of course possible that some degree of polymerization and condensation take place and that only the condensation products are effective.

Another objection is that protocatechuic acid is not very reactive, and is very slowly oxidized by tyrosinase, compared to catechol; homocatechuic acid is even less reactive. These two are the phenols the presence of which is most easily demonstrated, but even they cannot be found in all the insects examined. In *Calliphora* puparia, for example, protocatechuic acid can be demonstrated (*10*), but in the related *Lucilia*, which has a very similar puparium, no ether- or alcohol-soluble dihydroxyphenols can be demonstrated without elaborate techniques of concentration (*21*). The fact that dihydroxyphenols can be extracted from mature cuticles at all has also been used as an argument that they are not the active agents for sclerotization; if they were they should be firmly linked to the proteins. When Brunet and Kent (*7*) showed that the protocatechuic acid responsible for the sclerotization of the cockroach ootheca was secreted as a glucoside, it seemed that this might offer an explanation of the apparent absence of extractable phenols in some cuticles. No such glucosides have been found, however, and incubation of blowfly homogenates with emulsin has no effect in increasing the yield of phenols (*22*); it seems that the formation of glucosides, which is the normal detoxification mechanism for phenols injected into the blood (*23*), is an adaptation peculiar to the cockroach, which enables it to store relatively large quantities of catechuic acid.

D. Alternative Schemes

1. *Nonenzymatic Hydroxylation*

Dennell (*24*) has sought to meet these difficulties by suggesting an entirely new pathway for the synthesis of the tannins. He suggests that there exists in the cuticle a nonspecific, nonenzymatic mechanism for the hydroxylation of aromatic amino acids, which is capable of introducing one, two, or three hydroxyl groups onto the benzene ring, at the same time splitting off the side chain. Such a mechanism has been described by Dalgliesh (*25*), who has made an artificial system consisting of ascorbic acid and a ferric salt which is capable of producing tyrosine from phenylalanine or dopa from tyrosine; catechol or pyrogallol are also produced from dopa by splitting off the side chain. It is characteristic of this system that it produces a mixture of *o*- and *p*-tyrosine from phenylalanine, and in support of his hypothesis, Dennell has shown that *o*-tyrosine is present in some insect cuticles, and that phenylalanine disappears from solution when incubated with cockroach epidermis in the process of darkening. He claims to have found *p*-aminophenols among the decomposition products of cuticle reduced by stannite.

Dennell's scheme does not seem to meet the original difficulty, that in some cuticles suitable polyphenols cannot easily be demonstrated. If the phenolic compounds responsible for tanning the cuticle were produced in the way Dennell suggests, one would expect to be able to isolate them in fair concentration, whereas in fact they can only be found after careful concentration on activated charcoal. The small concentrations of catechol and pyrogallol found might have arisen during the enzymatic oxidation of dopa; particularly if there is repeated oxidation and reduction some loss of side chains is likely to take place, and the enzymatic oxidation of catechol (which involves the uptake of two atoms of oxygen per catechol) probably involves the formation of trihydroxyphenols at some stage (26). In general, it seems unlikely that a nonenzymatic process could be controlled so as to synchronize exactly with the biological differentiation of the epidermis; there is, moreover, some evidence from the injection of tyrosine labeled in the side chain that the side chain is not broken off (27).

2. Enzymatic Deamination

It is easier to suppose that the active polyphenols concerned are derived from dopa by enzymatic deamination or transamination (or perhaps deamination by orthoquinones). This would yield as first product dihydroxyphenylpyruvic acid, which is a reactive compound, rapidly oxidized by tyrosinase. It is indeed, rapidly oxidized at pH 7 even without tyrosinase. Deaminases have a slow turnover, so that in the presence of an active tyrosinase, or at a pH above 7, no dihydroxyphenylpyruvic acid could be expected to accumulate.

The oxidation of synthetic dihydroxyphenylpyruvic acid has been studied at pH 8, without tyrosinase (22); after taking up approximately one oxygen atom per four molecules of dihydroxyphenylpyruvic acid, further oxidation proceeds at a steady but much slower rate, with the evolution of carbon dioxide. Dihydroxyphenylpyruvic acid disappears from the solution, and homocatechuic acid and catechol appear. If dopa is incubated in the presence of maggot homogenate in which tyrosinase has been inhibited by phenylthiourea or cyanide, and the products are treated with 2,4-dinitrophenylhydrazine, the dinitrophenylhydrazone of dihydroxyphenylpyruvic acid can easily be demonstrated by paper chromatography in the ether extract. After prolonged incubation, particularly in the presence of cyanide, all the ether-soluble aromatic constituents disappear, the last to go being traces of catechol. Controlled model experiments, with viper venom as a source of deaminase and dopa, showed that in the presence of catalase abundant dihydroxyphenylpyruvic acid is produced, and in the absence of catalase or after prolonged incubation, mixtures of dihydroxyphenylpyruvic acid, homocatechuic acid, and catechol are produced, the proportion of catechol increasing with increased time of incubation. A reaction of this kind would explain all the experimental findings on insect cuticle: the failure to isolate polyphenols from some material and the presence of catechuic acid or homocatechuic acid in others. The disappearance of phenyl-alanine observed by Dennell may perhaps be explained by its having been deaminated; the o-tyrosine may be a regular constituent of some insect cuticles. Hackman (28) finds only p-tyrosine in *Calliphora augur*.

3. Autotanning

The apparent absence of suitable polyphenols is a difficulty that is not confined to insects. Brown (29, 30) found the same situation in a mollusk and in some elasmobranch fishes, and she proposed a solution that would account for sclerotization in the complete absence of all free polyphenols. She suggests that aromatic side chains of proteins are oxidized without being detached and that the quinones thus formed react with amino groups in other side chains; for this process she suggests the name "autotanning."

Autotanning was first suggested to explain the sclerotization of the byssus of *Mytilus edulis* (Mollusca Lamellibranchiata). The byssus is the bundle of threads by which the mullusk anchors itself to the ground. The threads are secreted by a composite gland on the foot; when first secreted they are pale translucent brown, but on exposure to sea water rapidly darken to a dark purplish brown and become resistant to heat, reducing agents, and proteolytic enzymes. According to Brown's account the material of the byssus is secreted by two sets of glands, one of which secretes a colorless protein and the other a dark brown, granular protein; these two secretions are mixed together, and darkening and hardening follow. Smyth (31) distinguishes a further component, which secretes a polyphenoloxidase; he doubts whether Brown's colorless protein really exists at all, claiming that the brown granular protein is the sole constituent of the threads. Both authors agree, however, that the brown protein is rich in aromatic residues, although it does not yield any alcohol-soluble phenols; they both conclude that sclerotization is brought about by the oxidation of the aromatic side chains of the protein.

The sclerotization of the egg cases of skates and dogfish seems to be a similar process in that the material is a protein rich in aromatic residues, but not yielding any soluble polyphenols. Hardening seems to involve oxidation, and there is a similar color change from white to dark brown. Details of the process have not been described.

Blower (32) has suggested autotanning as an explanation for the sclerotization of the cuticle of Chilopoda. Here the facts to be explained are not very different from those found in some insects; there is a darkening and hardening after molting, the cuticle contains proteins rich in aromatic residues, but no phenols can be extracted.

Sizer (33) and Hackman (16) have shown that the reaction suggested by Brown is possible by demonstrating that tyrosine with both the amino and carboxy groups combined will oxidize in the manner required. Even if the oxidation of attached tyrosyl side chains is possible, however, there are still serious steric difficulties. The attached tyrosyl side chains cannot polymerize, so that their range of possible contacts is limited, and the most reactive positions in the oxidized molecule will be those next to the stalk, which are the least accessible. These objections are serious and raise doubts whether, if autotanning does indeed occur, its mechanism may not be different from that of tanning by free quinones. It is easier to imagine a linkage between two aromatic side chains of the kind found in quinhydrone. This would involve oxidizing only half the available dopa side chains, which might then form complexes of the quinhydrone type with unoxidized side chains. It is tempting to extend this idea to account for the stability of the structural proteins of the bath sponge and of the horny corals (Antipatharia). Spongin, the protein of the bath sponge, contains 4.7% of diiodotyrosine (34), and the proteins of Antipatharia contain an unknown but fairly high percentage of dibromotyrosine (35). The addition of electron-attracting atoms such as iodine or bromine in the 3,5-positions will, by promoting a positive charge on the phenolic hydroxyl tend to promote ionization or complex formation.

E. Relation between Keratinization and Sclerotization

Spongin contains a trace of cystine (34). The protein of the *Mytilus* byssus contains 0.76% of sulfur (36), and that of elasmobranch egg cases, 1.2–0.81% (37). Both proteins have on this account been classified as keratins, but it is not clear what part the sulfur plays in stabilizing the protein, although it is noticeable that skates' egg cases are much swollen and softened by alkaline sodium sulfide, while cockroach egg cases are scarcely affected. The occurrence of sulfur in sclerotins is very irregular; the cuticular proteins of most insects contain no sulfur, but it is found in the hard chorion of some insect egg shells. This is remarkable because the chorion is secreted by the maternal epithelium of the ovary and might be expected to resemble the maternal cuticle. The colorless chorion of the eggs of *Rhodnius prolixus* (Hemiptera) contains about 3% of sulfur, but the dark purplish black chorion of the eggs of *Aedes aegypti* (Diptera) contains none (22). Among the Arachnida, the occurrence of sulfur is much commoner, first having been reported by Lafon (38) from the cuticle of *Limulus*. The cuticle of *Limulus* contains 2.85%, and in cuticles of some scorpions sulfur can be demonstrated by color reactions. The cuticles of both *Limulus* and of scorpions look like typical sclerotins, but Lafon has suggested that the cuticular proteins of *Limulus* owe some at least of their stability to the presence of disulfide links as in typical keratins, because he finds that the cuticle will swell and disintegrate in alkaline solutions of sodium sulfide. If his interpretation is correct, this is the only recorded instance of the occurrence of this mechanism in an arthropod, and the only example of a keratin-like protein impregnating a chitinous skeleton. The cuticle of some scorpions swells in thioglycolate solutions (39), but that of other related species does not (40). Alcohol-soluble polyphenols have been extracted from the cuticles of several species of scorpion (38). In spiders, Sewell (41) found no signs of disintegration in the cuticle of *Tegenaria domestica* when immersed in sodium sulfide solution, nor could he confirm the presence of sulfur or of cystine or cysteine in acid hydrolyzates of *Limulus* cuticle.

These conflicting results suggest that there may be disulfide bonds in some arachnid cuticles, but that they are not very important functionally. An explanation of some of the discrepancies between the findings of different authors is perhaps provided by Krishnan (42) and Kennaugh (43), who suggest that in scorpions sulfur bonding is confined to the "hyaline exocuticle," a layer external to the sclerotized exocuticle, which is not found in insects. If the sulfur is confined to certain layers of the cuticle it is possible that disulfide bonding and aromatic tanning never occur together and that no quinone-sulfur linkages are formed.

III. Systematic Distribution of Sclerotin

It is difficult to make any wide general survey of the occurrence of sclerotin in the animal kingdom, because such exact chemical knowledge as we possess is confined to the arthropods and vertebrates; in attempting a review of the incidence of sclerotin, a much less definite criterion must be adopted. Brown (44) has described tests which serve to distinguish the main types of structural protein. If the material is not affected by LiCNS or by cuprethylenediamine it is probably held together by primary valence cross linkages; if it does not dissolve in hot alkaline sodium sulfide, these are probably not disulfide bonds, which would be reduced and would dissolve under these conditions. If the protein is colored brown or black, is bleached and dissolved by strong oxidizing agents, and will reduce an ammoniacal solution of silver oxide (Fontana's reagent), it is probably a sclerotin, with aromatic cross linkages. These tests are not specific, but they make possible a useful general distinction between structural proteins which are dissolved by hot alkaline reducing agents, which we may call keratins, using the term in a broad sense, and those which are not and which show some reducing power of their own, which we may call sclerotins, using the term in an even broader sense. Unless the original material before it becomes insoluble is available for test, it is not always easy to be sure that the finished product is a protein at all; one can imagine a ligninlike material which would be classified as a sclerotin under these tests, and some artificial products, such a phenol-formaldehyde or aniline-formaldehyde resins would probably be included if they occurred in nature. Bearing in mind these qualifications, it is interesting to review the occurrence of sclerotin from the systematic point of view.

In the Protozoa, the central capsule of the radiolarian *Thalassicola* is black and reduces Fontana's reagent (*30*). In the Nematoda, cysts of eelworms (Heterodera) are formed by the darkening and hardening of the maternal cuticle, a process which seems to be a typical sclerotization (*45*). Among Platyhelminthes the eggs of *Fasciola hepatica* (Trematoda) (*46*) and of *Dendrocelium* (Turbellaria) (*47*) appear to be sclerotized; and in Mollusca, the byssus of *Mytilus* and *Dreissensia* and the hinges of other lamellibranchs (*48, 49*). The radulae of gastropods contain chitin; and in the whelk *Buccinum*, changes have been described as the teeth age which suggest a process of sclerotization (*50*). In the Annulata there are examples of sclerotin in the chaetae of earthworms (Oligochaeta) (*51*) and Polychaeta (*30*). Among the Chordata sclerotization seems to be uncommon, but it would be rash to assume that it does not occur. As we have already seen, the hardening of the egg cases of elasmobranchs seems to involve a process very like sclerotization. Among the lower coelomate phyla, the tubes secreted by the Pterobranchiata, and in particular the stolon, look as if they were sclerotized, although they have not been investigated from this point of view.

The general conclusion that sclerotization is typical of the Mollusca and Annulata, and rare in the Chordata, Echinodermata, Prochordata, and Stomochordata, certainly seems justified, but it seems quite probable that exceptions to this may appear. It is best to regard sclerotization as a development of a mechanism latent in any protein which contains aromatic amino acids, a mechanism which was evolved very early and was probably possessed by groups ancestral to Annulata, Mollusca, and Chordata.

Within the Arthropoda [see reviews by Richards (*52, 53*)] the relative importance of sclerotization and calcification follows regular phylogenetic lines. Sclerotization seems to be common in the hard parts of Annelida, and we may suppose that the primitive Arthropoda were sclerotized; the hard parts of *Peripatus* are brown and hard, and in sections they reduce ammoniacal silver oxide like any insect sclerotin. The hard parts of all modern Arachnida appear to be sclerotized, although very little detailed work has been done except on *Limulus*, scorpions, and spiders. The lower Crustacea all seem to be sclerotized, notably the Branchiopoda. Calcification first appears in the higher Crustacea (Malacostraca), and in them sclerotization is still found in bristles and the tips of the legs, positions in which brittleness would be a disadvantage. In the line leading to the Insecta, sclerotization again seems to be primitive; the Chilopoda show typical sclerotization. In the Diplopoda, calcification seems to have been developed separately; the Pselaphognatha, which are bristly, are sclerotized, while the Chilognatha are calcified, although there is an outer layer which is apparently sclerotized. Within the Insecta, calcification has been developed sporadically, being found in the larval cuticles of many Stratiomyidae (Diptera: Brachycera) and in the puparial cuticles of some Trypetidae (Diptera: Cyclorrhapha, Acalyptrata). The distinction between those groups of Arthropoda which have adopted calcium carbonate as a stabilizing matrix and those which have retained sclerotin is well shown in the fauna of dark caves. The insects, chilopods, and the hard parts of arachnids, such as *Obysium spelaum* (Pseudoscorpionida), are all brown or black, whereas Crustacea (Isopoda, Amphipoda, Decapoda) are white. Vertebrates are mostly white.

IV. Enzymes

Tyrosinase is usually assumed to be the enzyme mainly concerned in sclerotization. The nature and properties of tyrosinase have been reviewed by Dawson and Tarpley (54). The enzyme has been prepared in highly concentrated form from mushrooms and from potatoes, and has been shown to be a protein containing copper. It acts on tyrosine and other monophenols, such as cresol, by introducing a second hydroxyl group onto the ring next to the first; it also promotes oxidation of the *o*-phenols so formed to the corresponding quinones. These two types of activity seem to belong to the same enzyme; it is easy to make a preparation with reduced monophenolase and full diphenolase activity, but it is not possible to make a concentrate in which monophenolase activity is increased and diphenolase activity reduced.

The tyrosinase which has been most studied has been isolated from mushrooms (*Psalliota campestris*). An enzyme with similar properties can be prepared from meal worms (larvae of *Tenebrio molitor*) or maggots, but has never been so thoroughly studied.

Early work on the properties of tyrosinase was much concerned with the question of whether the enzyme was a deaminase or not. Crude preparation of tyrosinase do deaminate amino acids, but it has now been shown that this effect is due to the action of quinones. The deaminating action of quinones is very like the action of an enzyme, in that it may be specific for certain amino acids; Kisch has shown that the specificity depends on the nature of the side chains (55). It is possible that de-amination by quinones may be an essential part of the process of sclerotization, but it does not seem likely that it is, because homogenates of blowfly larvae are still capable of deaminating dopa even if prepared in the presence of phenylthiourea, which completely prevents the action of tyrosinase in oxidizing phenols originally present.

Not only will orthoquinones act as an oxidative deaminase for amino acids, they will oxidize ascorbic acid. A simple model system, consisting of catechol, glycine, and tyrosinase will reduce toluidine blue, and a homogenate of *Calliphora* larvae in which both tyrosinase and dehydro-genases have been inhibited will reduce methylene blue (13). It is tempting to suppose that this system is part of the terminal oxidase system of the insects. Plant physiologists, with similar evidence before them, for long accepted that this was an important oxidase system. Szent-Györgyi in 1921 (56) described the properties of "tyrin," the quinonoid oxidation product formed in homogenates of many plants, and suggested that it played a part in cellular respiration. The idea fits in well with the occurrence of oxidative enzymes in plants, and for long held the field. The idea that the tyrosinase system of insects might func-tion in a similar way has been suggested by Karlson and Wecker (57).

If the tyrosinase system were part of the intracellular oxidase system of arthropods, it is easy to see how it might have become modified and adapted as a means of hardening epidermal proteins; the hypothesis brings the two systems together in a way that is very attractive. Evi-dence is accumulating, however, that the system is not important in uninjured tissue of either plants or animals. Increased oxygen uptake following the addition of aromatic substrates to tissue slices in plants may be due partly to tissue damage by the aromatic compound. A surer criterion is the proportion of the inhibition of respiration by carbon monoxide which is not reversed by light, since light reverses the effect of carbon monoxide on cytochrome oxidase but not on polyphenol oxidase (58). Judged by this criterion only a few instances of polyphenol oxidase acting as a cellular oxidase in plants can be substantiated. There remains a doubt introduced by the fact that although tyrosinase is inhibited by carbon monoxide, other polyphenol oxidases (the laccases) are not, and the occurrence of laccases is probably wide.

For insects, the respiratory function of the polyphenol oxidase sys-tem is even harder to substantiate. When an insect is killed the blood blackens; if the reaction is allowed to take place in blood collected into a glass capillary it will remove all the oxygen from an included bubble of air, with only slight blackening (13). If a bubble is introduced into the body of a living insect, however, there is no blackening, and the oxygen content of the bubble remains high. The total oxygen consumption of an insect increases by a factor of about five times when it dies, and the blood and tissues blacken, suggesting that the tyrosinase system was not active before and only became active as the tissues autolyzed after death. This increase in tyrosinase activity after death is found in both plants and insects; volatile anesthetics or freezing and thawing will bring about the blackening of either an insect or a potato. The respiration rate of whole, living insects is not much affected by injecting either tyrosinase poisons or suitable aromatic substrates (59). Very little work has been done to find out how much of the inhibitory effect of carbon monoxide on insect respiration is not reversed by light.

Dennell (60) has suggested that between molts tyrosinase is inhibited by the action of a glucose dehydrogenase. An active dehydrogenase would indeed prevent the blackening of blood by reducing colored oxidation products as they formed, but this is not a true inhibition of the enzyme and would involve a continuous high consumption of oxygen and substrate. It is not possible in vitro to inhibit the action of tyrosinase by the action of any reducing substance likely to be present in the living insect; ascorbic acid or reduced glutathione are ineffective even at very low concentrations of oxygen. Fuzeau-Braesch (61) finds that reducing agents will prevent darkening of the thorax of Gryllus bimaculatus if applied to the outside of the cuticle directly after a molt. At this stage the wax layer is not fully formed and reagents penetrate; hydroquinone, catechol, ascorbic acid, and sodium sulfite and hydrosulfite were all effective in preventing blackening, although they did not prevent hardening. Such substances would reduce the colored oxidation products and might prevent the formation of black pigments without having truly inhibited the action of tyrosinase.

The effect of chloroform or methanol in promoting the blackening of insect tissues (62) is probably due to their action in breaking down cell structure rather than to their effect in eliminating dehydrogenases. Both substances do in fact depress the rate of action of tyrosinase, but it is not very sensitive to their action, and as they penetrate into the cuticle there is presumably a period during which activation brought about by tissue damage is complete and yet the concentration is not high enough entirely to prevent tyrosinase from acting.

Activation by tissue damage seems to have some physiological function in promoting the hardening of blood clots in wounds. Blood clots in both insects and Crustacea blacken in a way that suggests that the most important reaction involved is the oxidation of free dopa, with the formation of dihydroxyindole compounds. *In vitro* this reaction is not effective in tanning proteins (*63*), but perhaps *in vivo* continual reduction of the quinones first formed promotes loss of the side chain, leading to the formation of simple orthoquinones which are more effective as tanning agents. The blackening of blood clots around internal parasites described by Salt (*64, 65*) appears to be a similar reaction. If a parasitic larva of a species not normally attacking that host is injected into the body cavity of an insect it is attacked by phagocytes, which start to form a cyst around it. The parasite eats the phagocytes, but as they die they blacken and contract, forming an insoluble plug blocking mouth and anus, and sometimes also a ring around the middle of the body which shrinks as it blackens until the parasite is miserably constricted in the middle. As against these instances in which the blackening of the blood appears to be performing a useful function should be set the observation of Williams (*66*) that mortality after experimental operations in insects is much decreased if blackening of the blood at the wound is prevented by implanting crystals of phenylthiourea or by the application of potassium cyanide in saline.

Activation by tissue damage will not explain the normal activation of tyrosinase (if indeed the enzyme concerned is tyrosinase) when the new cuticle is hardened after a molt. If the activation is conceived of as involving a series of reactions like those concerned in the clotting of mammalian blood, then it is possible to imagine that the epidermal cells at the proper time secrete the normal activating enzyme without having suffered any damage. Several authors (*18, 67, 68*) have recently produced evidence from kinetic studies that tyrosinase is produced in homogenates of insect tissue by an autocatalytic reaction, involving the combination of a proenzyme with an activator to yield the enzyme and more activator. Ohnishi (*69*) has had some success in separating proenzyme and activator.

The polyphenolase present in homogenates of whole insects seems to be a typical tyrosinase, very like the enzyme isolated from mushrooms; there may be other types of polyphenolase present as well, but most insect tissues can be made to yield tyrosinase. It may be misleading, however, to concentrate entirely on its polyphenolase activity, which is perhaps not its most important function. If the polyphenol directly concerned in the sclerotization of insect cuticle is indeed dihydroxyphenylpyruvic acid it hardly seems necessary to invoke a polyphenolase at all, because at physiological pH it oxidizes so rapidly without. The more important function of tyrosinase may well be that of acting as a monophenolase, which introduces a second hydroxyl into tyrosine.

Tyrosinase is not the only known type of polyphenol oxidase. Laccase from the latex of the tree *Rhus vernicifera* differs from tyrosinase in having no monophenolase activity, and it is not inhibited by carbon monoxide. Keilin and Hartree (70) have prepared a laccase from mammalian kidneys. Whitehead, Brunet and Kent (71) have prepared from the left colleterial gland of *Periplaneta* a laccase which has no action on tyrosine or dopa, but does oxidize protocatechuic acid. If protocatechuic acid is important in the sclerotization of insect cuticle, this rather than tyrosinase may be the enzyme concerned, a possibility which answers Dennell's objection that protocatechuic acid is too stable to act as an effective tanning agent. A study of the darkening of homogenates of whole insects or of cuticle caused to darken by treatment with methanol or ether suggests that tyrosinase is not concerned in typical sclerotization. A homogenate of whole maggots, for example, first turns a bright pink, then a dingy purple and finally black, and more or less the same series of changes can be observed in an intact cuticle treated with methanol. The normal cuticle, however, at puparium formation changes from white to a translucent amber, without passing through either a pink or a purple stage. The pink and purple colors of the homogenate are probably due to the formation of compounds of amino acids with quinones derived from free dihydroxyphenols present, as well as to dopaquinone and dihydroxyindole formed by the oxidation of dopa. If tyrosinase is poisoned by making the homogenate in the presence of phenylthiourea, and bacterial activity is prevented by adding a trace of penicillin, the homogenate slowly turns to a clear amber color very like that of the natural puparium.

There is very little evidence about the ultimate source of the aromatic compounds concerned in sclerotization; it is not even very clear whether insects or other arthropods can synthesize the benzene ring, although it would be surprising perhaps if they could not, at least with the aid of symbionts. Mosquito larvae fed on a diet deficient in aromatic amino acids fail to develop their characteristic dark pigment, although they appear to be normally sclerotized (72). There is evidence that some larvae derive their tyrosine from phenylalanine in the diet; phenylalanine labeled in the ring with C^{14} reappears as tyrosine (74). No enzyme system has been described from arthropods which will promote this reaction, although it would of course be brought about by the nonenzymatic system postulated by Dennell.

The metabolism of aromatic amino acids has been reviewed by Dalgliesh (75) and Lerner (76). Mammals have two alternative pathways for the metabolism of tyrosine; either it is converted by transamination into 2,5-dihydroxyphenylpyruvic acid, and so into homogentisic acid and eventually into acetoacetic acid, or it is oxidized to 3,4-

dihydroxyphenylalanine, which oxidizes and condenses to give dihydroxyindole. The pathway leading to homogentisic acid has never been found in arthropods, but there must be something analogous which leads to the formation of *para-* instead of *ortho*-quinones. Paraquinones are quite commonly found in the repugnatorial glands of insects and Diplopoda (77) where, being more volatile than the orthoquinones, they are presumably more effective; their unpleasant effect on enemies depends primarily on their tanning action on the victim's proteins. Even homogentisic acid, or presumably its oxidation products, seem to have some tanning effect, because in the pathological condition of alcaptonuria in man, in which homogentisic acid is present in the blood, the cartilages of the ears darken, and are said to become brittle.

V. Variety of Sclerotins

It cannot be assumed that all sclerotins are the same. A general survey of insect cuticles suggests that there are at least two kinds, the brown and the black, which are probably connected by intermediates. Brown sclerotin is found in its typical form in cuticle that is not normally exposed to view, as in the buried pupae of Lepidoptera, or in those parts of the adults which are covered with scales, or in ectoparasites such as fleas. It is also generally found in the condyles of joints, in mandibles, and in the tentorium. From the distribution of this kind of sclerotin it seems reasonable to conclude that it represents a condition in which the mechanical requirements alone are important, and that this clear amber is the "natural" color of sclerotin. In very hard, thick cuticles of this type, as for example in the elytra of *Tenebrio molitor*, the over-all effect may be nearly black, but a thin shaving or section will still appear brown. Typical black sclerotins are found only in exposed cuticles, often as part of a conspicuous pattern, for example on exposed lepidopterous pupae, or on the thorax and wings of locusts. The color is evenly dispersed through the exocuticle, without any discrete granules, but the dark layer is often very thin and does not always seem to fulfill any important mechanical function; the glossy black of the cuticle of meloid beetles for example is due to a very thin black layer in the exocuticle, which is intensely folded, so that the whole abdomen remains soft. Even thin sections of such material may be gray or black.

In *Drosophila*, body-color mutants show various combinations of these two types. Waddington (78) has described two processes in the sclerotization of *Drosophila* adults; the first in point of time he calls "browning," and it consists in the browning of the major bristles and other mechanically important parts to produce what seems to be a typical amber sclerotin. The second process, which he calls "blackening," follows later. Either may be exaggerated or suppressed by genetic factors: thus in "black," blackening is increased and browning diminished; in "straw," blackening is diminished; and in "ebony," both are increased. Nothing is known of the chemical basis of these differences, but it may be that they depend on relative differences in the intensity and time of action of deaminases and tyrosinase; early and complete deamination gives a pale amber sclerotin, and incomplete deamination followed rapidly by oxidation gives an intense black. In many instances, however, the difference between black sclerotin and brown is probably not so simple; the formation of some black sclerotins appears to involve tryptophan derivatives as well as simple aromatics derived from tyrosine. The black patches on the thorax of the nymphs of locusts (either *Locusta migratoria* or *Schistocerca gregaria*) are a case in point.

The exocuticle of parts of the thoracic terga of migratory nymphs of *Locusta migratoria* or *Schistocerca gregaria* is a dense black, homogeneous and without any separate granules of "melanin." At molting these black markings appear in the exuviae. So far, the distinction between the exocuticle of these black patches and a typical sclerotin might seem to be one of intensity of color only, but if the whole insect is boiled or treated with alcohol, the black stripes turn to a brilliant scarlet. The effective treatments are all such as would denature proteins, coupled with reducing conditions. This color change is like that shown by the pigment granules in the epidermal cells, which in life are foxy red in the gregarious phase but may be buff or brown in the solitaria phase. The epidermal pigment has been shown to be an ommochrome (79), and the conclusion seems to be that some black cuticles at least contain ommochromes. It is interesting that the albino mutant of *Schistocerca gregaria* in which the ommochrome pigments are much diminished also lacks the black markings on the thorax of the nymphs, although black spots on the fore wings of the adults develop normally and the spines, mouth parts, and condyles of the joints are sclerotized with a typical translucent brown sclerotin. Black cuticles which turn red in this way are not uncommon: for example, the black dorsal gills of larvae of *Ephemera danica*. Other black cuticles may not turn red themselves, but go through a stage in their development in which the underlying epidermal cells are colored a dark, dingy purple by a granular pigment which turns red on denaturation.

The chemical nature of the ommochromes has been investigated by Butenandt, who has shown that they are derived from the oxidation of

3-hydroxykynurenine (*80*), itself derived from tryptophan; the hydroxy-kynurenine is oxidized to the azoquinone, and two molecules then condense to give ommochrome. Butenandt's work has made clear the composition of the ommochromes, but the problem of their relation to sclerotin remains obscure. There are two main possibilities. The first of these is that 3-hydroxykynurenine might itself act as a tanning agent (*21*). It occurs in fairly high concentration in the blood of mature larvae of *Calliphora* and *Lucilia* at the time of pupation, when no dihydroxyphenol is easily demonstrated, and it seemed an attractive idea that the azoquinone derived from hydroxykynurenine might take the place of the usual orthoquinones. Hydroxykynurenine is indeed oxidized by maggot cuticle, but tests with gelatin gel showed that it does not tan the protein in such a way as to raise its melting point; if catechol or dihydroxyphenylpyruvic acid is oxidized under similar conditions it renders the gel resistant to boiling water. According to Butenandt the azoquinone derived from hydroxykynurenine reacts preferentially with another molecule of the same kind even in the presence of other aromatic amino acids. There is a mutant of *Bombyx mori* called "Akaaka" in which the skin contains a red pigment and in which the blood turns red instead of black on exposure to the air (*81*). It has been shown that there is an excess of 3-hydroxykynurenine in the blood (*82*), and the red pigment was thought to be a mixed reaction product of this and dopa. Butenandt (*80*), however, finds that only ommochrome is formed under these conditions; the simultaneous oxidation of dopa is essential because dopaquinone is the only natural catalyst for the oxidation of 3-hydroxykynurenine.

This brings us to the second alternative: that the tryptophan derivatives act as intermediaries in the production of tanning agents. On Butenandt's scheme, hydroxykynurenine would prevent the oxidation of dopa to melanin by reducing dopaquinone, and that may be its function; to prevent the oxidation of dopa before it can be deaminated, without interfering with the action of tyrosinase on the deamination products. Or again the ommochrome itself may be important, acting as a general respiratory carrier.

There does not seem to be any reason why a general respiratory pigment should become incorporated in the cuticle at all; or alternatively, if the pigment is essential for the production of some part of the tanning apparatus, why is it not equally present in brown sclerotin? The answer to these questions may be that the pigment is important for the production of any form of sclerotin, and that it is generally present in the epidermal cells under any cuticle that is to be intensely sclerotized, but that it is particularly well developed under black sclerotin and that there is some special adaptation which causes it to be secreted along with the products of its activity into the cuticle.

The most notable examples of the presence of ommochromes in the epidermis beneath brown sclerotin come from the pupae of Lepidoptera. The larvae of several large moths develop, just before the pupal molt an intense reddish purple color due to *ommochrome* granules in the epidermis. The most typical of these are the sphingids, which pupate underground, and species such as *Dicranura vinula*, which pupates within a dark silken cocoon; in both types the pupa is heavily sclerotized with a typical translucent brown sclerotin. The red color is evidently derived in part at least by the modification of existing ommochrome pigments in the larval epidermis, which may be almost any color and contribute during larval life to the cryptic or aposematic patterns of the larva; Bückmann (83, 84) has shown that this color change is one of the first effects of the injection of pupation hormone from corpora allata. After pupation the pigment disappears from the epidermis, and eventually reappears, probably by way of the Malpighian tubules, in the pupal gut.

With the idea that ommochromes may be acting as respiratory carriers in the production of sclerotins, we come back to something very like the idea that the tyrosinase system may be acting as a terminal oxidase, and as before there is circumstantial evidence in support of the idea, but no conclusive proof. Ommochromes are capable of a redox change, but it has not been seen to occur *in vivo*. Such pigments do occur in positions which suggest that they may have some respiratory function; for example, in the flight muscles of Odonata. In Odonata Anisoptera the flight muscles are bright cherry red with a pigment of this kind, which can be extracted with acid alcohol, and a similar pigment occurs in the walls of the thoracic air sacs, where it is buff, but can be reduced to the red form. Immediately after emergence, the tendons are the same cherry red color as the muscles, but they turn black as they harden.

The association of ommochrome pigments with sites of active sclerotization is so suggestive that one hesitates to put forward a third possible explanation of their presence: that they have no function at all, but are merely excretory products. The essential function of the ommochromes, if they have one, may lie elsewhere, and the epidermal cells may be acting as temporary storage organs which hold the pigments until they are excreted by the Malpighian tubules.

Whatever the function of ommochromes in black cuticle, there is no reason to suppose that tyrosine derivatives are not also concerned.

Fuzeau-Braesch (85) finds that radioactive tyrosine injected at about the time of molting into *Gryllus bimaculatus* is incorporated into darkly pigmented zones and that it is taken up more strongly than radioactive tryptophan under the same conditions. She adds the curious observation that in patches where darkening has been inhibited by the external application of hydroquinone, tryptophan is accumulated but not tyrosine. This is difficult to interpret because it is not known just what may be happening in the inhibited areas.

It is not difficult to imagine that black cuticles owe their color to oxidation products of dopa, whereas in amber-colored cuticles oxidation products of polyphenols with no amino groups in the side chain are more important; if different enzymes were concerned it would not be difficult to account for patterns of black cuticle by supposing localized activity of the appropriate enzymes.

VI. Conclusions

The requirements for shoe leather and for the exoskeleton of a terrestrial animal are similar; indeed what are boots and shoes but a kind of temporary exoskeleton? The starting material of both leather and arthropod cuticle is a flexible, strongly hydrated high polymer, which must be stabilized both chemically and mechanically to give it some degree of rigidity. To cross-link a high polymer and so stabilize it chemically, a reagent is required with more than one reactive site. If the high polymer is not crystalline and closely packed, there will be considerable gaps between its reactive sites; therefore the cross-linking agent must be capable of polymerizing to form aggregates big enough to bridge them. If it polymerizes enough to fill all possible voids between the high polymer molecules or crystalline aggregates it will also stabilize them mechanically and confer stiffness in compression.

These requirements call for a combination of properties most easily met by some aromatic reagent; no other will give such bulky, insoluble products of polymerization and at the same time react with polar groups in the high polymer. Particularly for sole leather, where some degree of rigidity and a high resistance to abrasion are needed, aromatic tanning agents are the only satisfactory solution that human ingenuity has discovered. The vegetable tannins used in the manufacture of leather react by forming relatively weak secondary bonds with the hide proteins, whereas the natural tannins concerned in sclerotization form covalent bonds, but it would be rash to assume that only covalent bonds were concerned in sclerotin, and the difference does not invalidate the comparison, which indeed, insofar as the vegetable tannins represent the raw materials of lignin, rests on a natural similarity of function.

The similarities between lignin and sclerotin may properly be called a case of biochemical convergence; the same functional end has been attained in two different ways, and although the final products are chemically and physically similar, they differ in their origins and biosynthesis. The phenol oxidase complex was probably part of the biochemical equipment of the common ancestors of plants and animals and seems to be concerned in the synthesis of both lignins and sclerotins, although operating at quite different levels. Within the animal kingdom there is some suggestion that the method of tanning by free polyphenols found in arthropods may perhaps have evolved from some kind of autotanning, but there is very little evidence available.

References

1. K. H. Gustavson, "The Chemistry of Tanning Processes." Academic Press, New York, 1956.
2. K. Freudenberg, H. Zocher, and W. Dürr, *Ber. deut. Chem. Ges.* **62**, 1814–1823 (1929).
3. W. Robinson, *Phil. Trans. Roy. Soc.* **B210**, 49–82 (1920).
4. A. B. Foster and R. H. Hackman, *Nature* **180**, 40–41 (1957).
5. M. G. M. Pryor, *Proc. Roy. Soc.* **B128**, 378–392 (1940).
6. P. C. J. Brunet, *Quart. J. Microscop. Sci.* **92**, 113–127 (1951).
7. P. C. J. Brunet and P. W. Kent, *Proc. Roy. Soc.* **B144**, 259–274 (1958).
8. M. G. M. Pryor, P. B. Russell, and A. R. Todd, *Biochem. J.* **40**, 627–628 (1946).
9. R. H. Hackman, M. G. M. Pryor, and A. R. Todd, *Biochem. J.* **43**, 474–477 (1948).
10. M. G. M. Pryor, P. B. Russell, and A. R. Todd, *Nature* **159**, 399 (1947).
11. H. S. Mason, *Advances in Enzymol.* **16**, 105–185 (1955).
12. E. M. Trautner and E. A. H. Roberts, *Australian J. Sci. Research* **B3**, 356–380 (1950).
13. M. G. M. Pryor, *J. Exptl. Biol.* **32**, 468–484 (1955).
14. R. H. Hackman, *Biochem. J.* **54**, 362–367 (1953).
15. R. H. Hackman, *Biochem. J.* **54**, 367–370 (1953).
16. R. H. Hackman, *Biochem. J.* **54**, 371–377 (1953).
17. G. Fraenkel and K. M. Rudall, *Proc. Roy. Soc.* **B129**, 1–35 (1940).
18. P. Karlson, *Proc. 4th Intern. Congr. Biochem., Vienna, 1958* **12**, 37–47 (1959).
19. R. H. Hackman and A. R. Todd, *Biochem. J.* **55**, 631–637 (1953).
20. R. H. Hackman, *Proc. 4th Intern. Congr. Biochem., Vienna, 1958* **12**, 48–62 (1959).
21. M. G. M. Pryor, *Nature* **175**, 600 (1955).
22. M. G. M. Pryor, Unpublished work (1959).
23. C. M. Myers and J. N. Smith, *Biochem. J.* **56**, 498–503 (1954).
24. R. Dennell, *Biol. Revs.* **33**, 178–197 (1958).
25. C. E. Dalgliesh, *Arch. Biochem. Biophys.* **58**, 214–226 (1955).
26. H. Wagreich and J. M. Nelson, *J. Am. Chem. Soc.* **60**, 1545–1548 (1938).
27. P. Karlson, *Proc. 4th Intern. Congr. Biochem., Vienna, 1958* **12**, 62 (1958).
28. R. H. Hackman, *Australian J. Biol. Sci.* **9**, 400–405 (1956).
29. C. H. Brown, *Quart. J. Microscop. Sci.* **93**, 487–502 (1952).

30. C. H. Brown, *Nature* **165**, 275 (1950).
31. J. D. Smyth, *Quart. J. Microscop. Sci.* **95**, 139–152 (1954).
32. G. Blower, *Quart. J. Microscop. Sci.* **92**, 141–161 (1951).
33. I. W. Sizer, *Advances in Enzymol.* **14**, 129–161 (1953).
34. V. J. Clancey, *Biochem. J.* **20**, 1186–1189 (1926).
35. C. T. Mörner, *Z. physiol. Chem.* **88**, 138–154 (1913).
36. M. E. Fauré-Fremiet and H. Garrault, *Bull. soc. chim. biol.* **20**, 24–30 (1938).
37. M. E. Fauré-Fremiet and C. Baudouy, *Bull. soc. chim. biol.* **20**, 14–23 (1938).
38. M. Lafon, *Bull. inst. océanogr.* **850**, 1–11 (1943).
39. G. Krishnan, *Quart. J. Microscop. Sci.* **94**, 11–21 (1953).
40. S. C. Shrivastava, *Proc. Natl. Acad. Sci. India* **B27**, 74–77 (1957).
41. M. T. Sewell, *Ann. Entomol. Soc. Am.* **48**, 107–118 (1955).
42. G. Krishnan, *Quart. J. Microscop. Sci.* **95**, 371–381 (1954).
43. J. Kennaugh, *Quart. J. Microscop. Sci.* **100**, 41–50 (1959).
44. C. H. Brown, *Quart. J. Microscop. Sci.* **91**, 331–339 (1950).
45. C. H. Ellenby, *Nature* **151**, 320 (1946).
46. W. Stephenson, *Parasitology* **38**, 128–144 (1947).
47. F. R. Nurse, *Nature* **165**, 570 (1950).
48. C. H. Brown, *Quart. J. Microscop. Sci.* **93**, 487–502 (1952).
49. E. R. Trueman, *Nature* **165**, 397 (1950).
50. C. F. A. Pantin and T. H. Rogers, *Nature* **115**, 639 (1925).
51. R. Dennell, *Nature* **164**, 370 (1949).
52. A. G. Richards, "The Integument of Arthropods." Univ. of Minnesota Press, Minneapolis, 1951.
53. A. G. Richards, *Ergeb. Biol.* **20**, 1–26 (1958).
54. C. R. Dawson and W. B. Tarpley, *in* "The Enzymes: Chemistry and Mechanism of Action" (J. B. Summer and K. Myrback, eds.), Vol. II, Part 1, pp. 454–491. Academic Press, New York, 1951.
55. B. Kisch, *Biochem. Z.* **242**, 1–20 (1931).
56. A. Szent-Györgyi, *Biochem. Z.* **162**, 399–412 (1925).
57. P. Karlson and E. Wecker, *Z. physiol. Chem.* **300**, 42–48 (1955).
58. W. O. James, "Plant Respiration." Oxford Univ. Press (Clarendon), London and New York, 1953.
59. A. S. Sussmann, *Biol. Bull.* **102**, 39–47 (1952).
60. R. Dennell, *Proc. Roy. Soc.* **B136**, 94–109 (1949).
61. S. Fuzeau-Braesch, *Compt. rend. soc. biol.* **153**, 57–60 (1959).
62. R. Dennell, *Proc. Roy. Soc.* **B133**, 348–373 (1947).
63. M. G. M. Pryor, *Proc. Roy. Soc.* **B128**, 393–407 (1940).
64. G. S. Salt, *Proc. Roy. Soc.* **B144**, 380–398 (1955).
65. G. S. Salt, *Proc. Roy. Soc.* **B147**, 167–184 (1957).
66. C. H. Williams, *Biol. Bull.* **103**, 120–138 (1952).
67. N. H. Horowitz and M. Fling, *in* "Aminoacid Metabolism" (W. D. McElroy and B. Glass, eds.) pp. 207–218. Johns Hopkins, Baltimore, 1955.
68. E. Ohnishi, *Japan. J. Zool.* **12**, 179–188 (1958).
69. E. Ohnishi, *J. Inst. Physiol.* **3**, 219–229 (1959).
70. D. Keilin and E. F. Hartree, *Proc. Roy. Soc.* **B119**, 114–140 (1935).
71. D. L. Whitehead, P. C. J. Brunet, and P. W. Kent, *Nature* **185**, 610 (1960).
72. L. Golberg and B. de Meillon, *Biochem. J.* **43**, 379–387 (1948).
73. S. Ishii and C. Hirano, *Proc. 10th Intern. Congr. Entomol., 1956* **2**, 295–298 (1958).

74. T. Fukuda, *Nature* **177**, 429 (1956).
75. C. E. Dalgliesh, *Advances in Protein Chem.* **10**, 31–150 (1955).
76. A. B. Lerner, *Advances in Enzymol.* **14**, 73–128 (1953).
77. M. Pavan, *Proc. 4th Intern. Congr. Biochem., Vienna, 1958* **12**, 15–35 (1959).
78. C. H. Waddington, *Proc. Zool. Soc. Lond.* **111**, 173–180 (1941).
79. T. W. Goodwin, *Biol. Revs. Cambridge Phil. Soc.* **27**, 439–460 (1952).
80. A. Butenandt, *Angew. Chem.* **69**, 16–23, 1957.
81. K. Makino, H. Takahashi, K. Satoh, and K. Inagami, *Nature* **173**, 586 (1954).
82. K. Inagami, *Nature* **174**, 1105 (1954).
83. D. Bückmann, *Naturwissenschaften* **43**, 43 (1956).
84. P. Karlson and D. Bückmann, *Naturwissenschaften* **43**, 43–44 (1956).
85. S. Fuzeau-Braesch, *Compt. rend. acad. sci.* **248**, 856–858 (1959).

CHAPTER 9

Silk and Other Cocoon Proteins

K. M. RUDALL

Department of Biomolecular Structure, The University of Leeds, England

I. Introduction

Knowledge of silk has been considered very recently in a most comprehensive manner by Lucas, Shaw, and Smith (*1*), and if we did not have that veritable treatise such an article as this should have endeavored to cover the same ground. As the main facts about silk are now so well recorded, we must consider principally the more recent investigations at the Shirley Institute which are particularly relevant from the comparative point of view. We also have the extensive work of Professor Florkin and his colleagues at Liège, where they are using the silkworm as a highly convenient biochemical factory for neat experimental studies with isotope-labeled amino acids. The amino acids of fibroin being so well known, it is comparatively simple to follow metabolic changes by injecting labeled acids into the hemolymph and tracing the processes involved in the production of the various amino acids of the silk. Although we will be considering matters of fiber structure rather than problems of metabolism, this Belgian work is so considerable and promising that we must clearly draw attention to it by a few references which should lead to acquaintance with the full series of papers. When the structural problems are better defined, the metabolic processes will become the center of interest (2).

This present article aims to be more comparative still than that of Lucas et al. (1), which should be consulted for many detailed expositions. Another most profitable treatise on related topics is "Synthetic Polypeptides" by Bamford, Elliott, and Hanby (3). Here, instead of waiting for an insect to do it, polypeptides are made in the laboratory; in these, very often, problems of configuration are more readily studied than in natural proteins.

Natural silk is the name given to the glossy fibers spun by silkworms, the larvae of certain moths. Sericulture is an ancient industry, and in the course of time the word silk has been applied to many other glossy fibers of animal origin. In modern times, silkworm silk and various kinds of spider silk have been shown to possess many similarities of chemical constitution and molecular structure. It has therefore been assumed that all "silks" are closely related substances and that by continuing to study them we should not find out much more than details within a generally accepted picture of a comparatively simple and inert protein, fibroin.

But as work has proceeded it has become clear that so-called silks are extremely varied in constitution and configuration, and so we would like to know more about them. Even within the confines of insect species, many silks turn out to be quite unlike the fully extended chain molecules of classic fibroins. Not only do we have various folded and helical forms of protein chains, but typical-looking silks may be collagenlike in structure or be composed of the polysaccharide chitin. The range of structure types is so great that we can form no generalization on the constitution of silk. Some unstudied silk may produce a new surprise and contribute greatly to the study of long-chain molecules.

In certain ways this diversity is embarrassing; not being able to study every case, we will often appear to consider things at random. Apart from lepidopteran silks, which have, to a pleasing extent, been studied systematically, the others may eliminate themselves because the species is too small to produce an easily studied quantity, or, in spite of this, may strongly recommend themselves because there is some pressing reason to make the effort worth while.

In insects, silk is most commonly produced by labial or serigenous glands opening in the head region; the usual purpose is to form a protective cocoon to cover the pupating larva. But adult insects also produce silk, and cocoons of other texture, to protect the eggs; in this case the material is produced by so-called colleterial glands which are accessory to the genital system. Silklike texture, i.e., an assemblage of microscopic, smooth fibers may occur in either of the above types. But other textures do occur, particularly in the adult secretions where the cocoon or ootheca consists of more or less coherent layers or films of material. These non silklike textures are also considered in this chapter.

II. Main Importance of Studies on Silk

As far as scientific knowledge is concerned the greatest contribution arising from the study of silk has come from the interpretation of its X-ray diffraction diagrams. Apart from the fibroins, few natural proteins exist in the comparatively fully extended form. But studies by Meyer and Mark (4) using silk established the concept of the extended polypeptide chain structure of proteins, that is, a linear series of amino acids joined end-to-end by peptide links; in this solid state the residues were arranged on a dyad-screw axis. This in turn assisted in the definition of the β-structure of keratin, myosin, etc., and in the study of synthetic polypeptides. More recently, silk has given important confirmation of the pleated sheet structures for the β-form of proteins. We owe these successes to the relatively simple amino acid constitution and to the good quality of the diffraction patterns, which allow relatively extensive interpretation.

In themselves, these X-ray studies readily demonstrate many important fundamental points of molecular structure and configuration. However, they cannot stand entirely by themselves, and much more is to be gained from a comparative study of molecular structure and chemical constitution (5, 6). This correlation of structure, physical properties, and composition is a second great achievement in the scientific study of silk.

We can expect a still wider range of important scientific information. Variation is so great that we can look forward to a host of comparative studies of the biochemistry of synthesis in this relatively simple group of proteins. This work might proceed through the isolation of the ribonucleoproteins and enzymes which are responsible. Leaving the primary synthetic processes behind, we are interested to know just how these large molecules are held in fairly concentrated solution and what molecular processes intervene between this state and the final insoluble fibrous state.

The complete study of silk and other cocoon proteins would bring us into contact with various cross-linking reactions, including those due to a tanning process. Again, the widespread occurrence of various pigments and chromoproteins raises the question of what part, if any, these play in the total biochemical picture of the formation and manipulation of the main structural protein. For the study of these things it is necessary to have the insects as laboratory animals. Some important molecular processes take place at the time of cocoon production, and these cannot be detected or defined unless the living insect is available. Also for X-ray and infrared studies it is desirable to make one's own fibers from the material stored in the serigenous or ootheca-forming glands. Then one can produce films of appropriate thickness or well-oriented fibers of suitable size.

In describing the X-ray results, we are concerned with the main significance of these. Comments rather than tabulations of measurements are given. Each of the new structures which have been discovered requires full-time work to achieve formal interpretation of details. The present results take us to the point where we can see that there is even more to be gained by further work.

III. The Protein "Fibroin" and Its Varieties

The term "fibroin" is used to describe the protein of the solid fibers of silkworm cocoons; the cement or "gum" coating the fibers, and frequently sticking them together, is another protein, called "sericin." Some workers use the term fibroin for any silken fibers of arthropods, but as some of these silks have turned out to be collagen, and others a chitin-protein complex, fibroin is clearly not the proper term in these cases. We propose to restrict fibroin to the range of structures described by Warwicker (6), namely, those silks whose X-ray diagram of the parallel-β form shows the polypeptide chains to be nearly fully extended with fiber axis period of 6.9–6.95 Å, with the dominating equatorial reflection being 120 and the double side-chain repeat being comparatively small and in the range 9.2–16 Å. These fibroins have in common a pleated sheet structure as described by Pauling and Corey (7), and also a definable method of chain packing (8, 9). The important difference between the various fibroins lies in the distance separating superposed pleated sheets, this distance depending on the average side-chain length of the constituent amino acids.

Fibroins defined in this way enable us to group together a considerable number of proteins and to contrast them sharply with other principal types, such as those which are like keratin, and those which are like collagen, in structure. In each of these major groups, according to X-ray studies, there is a characteristic configuration of the protein chains and a characteristic method of packing these chains. This is an X-ray diffraction classification of fibroin proteins, and within each group there are, of course, other distinctions to be made. But this fits with a chemical classification which indicates that the fibroin type of structure only occurs if there is some 50% of the amino acids as glycine, alanine, and serine, whereas the β-keratin type occurs where there is considerably less than 50% of the small amino acids. The collagen configuration is very different and results when there is a high content of glycine plus proline and hydroxyproline. The diffraction data and the chemical analysis thus go together, the chemistry giving the important clues as to the amino acids that would explain the particular configuration seen by X-rays. And to a certain extent the X-ray dimensions allow or forbid the presence of certain larger amino acids in the main crystalline region of the fiber.

A. CHEMICAL ANALYSIS

The amino acids of silk have been studied for about a hundred years, and a useful perspective of progress is given by Howitt (10). Only in recent times have methods of rapid analysis on small quantities become available, thus enabling comparative studies on a large number of different specimens of silk. There is the microbiological method used on fibroin hydrolyzates by Kirimura (11) and by workers in Belgium: Duchâteau, Florkin, and Leclercq (12). On the other hand, we have the rather more extensive work of Lucas et. al. (5), using both a modified DNP method and the ion exchange method of Moore and Stein; by these means they have analyzed over seventy different fibroins. The first important point is, how well do these methods agree? Kirimura's microbiological assays agree with the analytical results of Lucas et al. (5), but some considerably different results are obtained by microbiological assay as used by the Belgian workers (12). Much depends on the reliability of the quantitative results presented. We have two important tests of reliability, namely, that results by different methods should agree and secondly, with corrections made, all the nitrogen should be accounted for. On these counts, therefore, in the instance of disagreement noted above (5, 12), the preference in reliability should go to the DNP and ion exchange results (5).

For many years Lucas, Shaw and Smith have made a special study of silks, and preliminary details of their procedure using the DNP method have already been given (13); they promise further details in a recent paper (5), in which they also describe their use of the ion ex-change method of Spackman, Moore, and Stein (14). We are concerned here with the kind of results obtained. There is a remarkably fine table giving the amino acids found in some 26 widely different fibroins. The dominant feature is the relatively high quantity of the three smaller amino acids, glycine, alanine, and serine, which account for about 95% of the total residues in *Anaphe moloneyi* and show all variations between this high figure and the figure of about 43% for *Arctia caja* and *Lasio-campa quercus*. Again in frequency, acidic amino acids vary from some 13% to less than 1%, basic amino acids from about 6% to less than 1%, and aromatic amino acids from 7% to about 0.5%.

All these analyses form a starting point for the consideration of problems. The first direction in which they begin to make sense is in relation to the elastic properties where a general rule emerges that the fiber is more extensible in length, and less work is required for this extension, where there is a higher content of bulky or larger amino acids (15). The way in which the resistance to extension of *Anaphe moloneyi* fibroin is so little affected by the degree of hydration is just what we should expect from its dominating content of the nonpolar side chains of glycine and alanine. By contrast, the silk of *Bombyx mori* is considerably altered in the direction of easier extension when thoroughly wet with water, and this is readily related to the high serine content and the greater number of acidic and basic residues (15). The first profit, then, is to show ways in which the physical properties of the different types of fibroin can be explained. At a glance we can see the influences of the relative quantities of nonpolar and polar side groups. Also, we can see the high uniformity of side-chain sizes, or again that the lack of uniformity is about as great as could be expected. These various features will lead to good or to less good packing of the chain molecules and must have their effect upon the properties of extensibility.

Details of the sequence of amino acids will of course explain many things, such as the neatness of packing of the constituent chains, and should also lead to explanation of details within the X-ray diagram, such as fiber axis periodicities. Again we owe outstanding work along these lines to Lucas *et al.* (13), using the silk of *Bombyx mori*. First, the "crystalline" fraction was isolated by digestion with chymotrypsin, and it was found to be composed of the residues glycine, alanine, and serine in the ratio 3:2:1. The molecular weight was approximately 4000, and a small amount of tyrosine was present as the *C*-terminal residue. Here we have chain molecules some 60 residues long which "crystallize" to give extremely clear diffraction diagrams of the type less clearly evident in the untreated silk.

Lucas and co-workers (13) proceeded to determine the sequence of amino acids in this important fraction, which they refer to as CTP (chymotrypsin precipitate). Chymotrypsin of course, breaks the long chains at the tyrosine C-terminal position. The rest of the sequence in CTP was deduced from the study of numerous partial hydrolyses and by specific attack on the serine residues. This very patient work gave a plan for the CTP peptide as follows:

$$\text{Gly·Ala·Gly·Ala·Gly·[Ser·Gly·(Ala·Gly)}_2\text{]}_8\text{Ser·Gly·Ala·Ala·Gly·Tyr}$$

In this picture, at least for lengths of over 50 residues, glycine alternates along the chain with either alanine or serine. Surely these things tell us that the X-ray diffraction diagram of Bombyx mori fibroin comes from lengthy segments of polypeptide chains with glycine on one side of the chain and mostly alanine, but some serine, on the other side. This, of course, is essentially the model proposed by Marsh, Corey, and Pauling (8).

We certainly look forward to the extension of this work and its application to fibroins other than cultivated silk. However, the structure of this latter silk is about the most simple we are likely to meet with. It occurs, furthermore, in a very convenient experimental animal: it seems quite likely that the mechanism of coding, be it in RNA or RNP, may first be revealed in the formation of the fibroin of Bombyx mori.

B. X-RAY ANALYSIS

The history of studies on the crystalline structure of fibroin have been well reviewed recently by Marsh et al. (8), but mention should be made of one very early endeavor they do not include. We are indebted to Dr. S. G. Smith for pointing out the astonishing paper by Nishikawa and Ono dated September, 1913, barely a year following the demonstration of X-ray diffraction by Laue, Friedrich, and Knipping (1912). Nishikawa and Ono (16), using asbestos as their most successful fibrous material, found diffraction positions corresponding to the equatorial and layer line spots now so familiar to us. They rotated their fibers about the fiber axis, they tilted the fiber bundle in various ways, and made the correct deduction that the specimen consisted of "elementary crystals of a definite prismatic structure arranged parallel to the fiber." Furthermore, they stated: "It is, however, a remarkable fact that the organic fibers, silk, wood, bamboo or asa (hemp) gave rise to a similar phenomenon." It is a pleasure to acknowledge this remarkably enterprising work in Japan; the X-ray diffraction study of silk surely started there, and in recent times this same approach under better conditions has been very fruitful indeed.

Marsh, Corey, and Pauling have given considerably detailed inter-pretations of the X-ray diffraction diagrams of two principal forms of silk. In the first form, namely that of *Bombyx mori* (8), they concen-trate on a pseudounit composed of the simpler residues, glycine, alanine, and serine. They also consider a number of features of the diagrams, especially the 00*l* series of reflections, in a search for the true unit of structure. But the real satisfaction comes in their interpretation of the pseudounit as consisting of pleated sheets with antiparallel chains, with the alanine and serine side chains projecting on one side of the sheet and the negligible side group (hydrogen) of glycine residues projecting on the opposite side. It established an important concept in the consti-tution of polypeptide chains, in placing every other residue of a lengthy segment as glycine, and shows the possibility that the two sides of a pleated sheet can be quite different. If the alanine residues were all replaced by serine, then one side of the sheet would be polar and the other side nonpolar. The structure with all its glycine hydrogens pro-jecting on the same side of individual chains is effectively confirmed by the sequence studies of Lucas, Shaw, and Smith (13).

A principal additional axial period of 21 Å. has been confirmed by Marsh *et al.* (8) as previously found by Kratky and Schauenstein (17). A likely origin for this lies in the sequence of eight sets of hexapeptides (Ser $\cdot$ Gly $\cdot$ Ala $\cdot$ Gly $\cdot$ Ala $\cdot$ Gly $\cdot$)$_8$ in which the serine residue repeats every 21 Å. The ideas emerging from the interpretation of the pseudo-unit, and the existence of this axial repeat, thus agree very well with the data coming from the analysis of the CTP precipitate (13).

There is, however, a particular feature in Marsh, Corey and Pauling's study of this fibroin that led them to extensive discussion of the relation between the pseudounit and the real unit. Their accurate measurements gave a figure for the principal side chain reflection of 9.7 Å. compared with that of about 9.3 Å. given by other workers. What we should like to know is whether this difference could arise from experimental pro-cedures. Marsh, Corey and Pauling worked with commercial silk gut, and many samples were doubly oriented by stretching and rolling. Apart from the processing to produce the commercial gut, other exten-sive manipulation may have caused slipping of chains or pleated sheets past one another so that larger amino acids were brought into regions which in the more natural state contained only the simpler residues—glycine, alanine, and serine. On the other hand, Kratky and Kuriyama (18) worked on gut they prepared themselves whereas Warwicker (19) has worked with degummed silk from the cocoon. Some support for a change of spacing due to chain rearrangement is given below in considering the intramolecular transformation on stretching *Chrysopa* egg-stalk silk.

The second major contribution due to Marsh *et al.* was the accurate description of a structure for tussah or wild silk (*9*). In principle, it is the same type of structure as for cultivated silk, but now the pleated sheets of antiparallel chains are regularly separated by a distance of 5.3 Å. whereas in the *Bombyx mori* silk, similar pleated sheets were separated alternately by distances of 3.5 Å. and 5.7 Å. This means that in tussah silk side chains of similar average size project on both sides of the individual pleated sheets. It probably means that in the individual β-chain the sequence of residues is such that the average side-chain length is the same on both sides of the chain. The glycine is now likely to occur on both sides of the chain instead of on one side only, as in the simpler fibroin of *Bombyx mori*.

For our present purpose, these structures are extremely helpful in locating certain amino acids in those regions of the chain structure which give rise to the main features of the diffraction diagram.

IV. Fibroins of the Parallel-β Type

In the discovery of the $\alpha \rightleftarrows \beta$ transformation of proteins, Astbury recognized the existence of two main configurations of the same polypeptide chain (*20*). The α-form was folded up in such a way that when extended to about twice its length it reached a fully extended limit which he called the β-form. The silk fibroins then known were, according to the diffraction diagrams, in a similar extended or β-form. But as the extended chains are parallel to the fiber axis, or direction of stretching, it is necessary to describe them as in the parallel β-form to distinguish them from several cases we will describe presently.

The most extensive comparative study of these types of fibroin has been made by Warwicker (*6*), and it is fortunate that this fine work has been done in close collaboration with Lucas, Shaw, and Smith at the Shirley Institute, Manchester. Warwicker distinguishes seven types of fibroins according to their diffraction diagrams and gives extensive tables of data, some of which we bring together in Table I. It should be noted that while Marsh, Corey and Pauling refer to the axes *a*, *b*, and *c* as the letters were used in the pioneer studies of Meyer and Mark on a variety of fibrous structures both protein and polysaccharide, Kratky (*18*), Warwicker (*6*), and others (*21*) follow another convention which gives the fiber axis as *c* instead of *b*; it is sometimes difficult to draw attention to statements on the same reflection by the two groups of workers. Warwicker uses *a* as the side chain axis, *b* as twice the

TABLE I

THE SPACINGS OF TYPICAL FIBROINS[a,b]

Group	Typical fibroin	100	040	060	041	002	022	032	013	023	033
1	*Bombyx mori*	9.3	2.38	1.56	2.30	3.53	2.83	2.31	2.27	2.10	1.82
2a	*Anaphe moloneyi*	10.0	2.38	1.58	2.28	3.49	2.86	2.28	2.26	2.06	1.84
2b	*Clania* sp.	10.0	2.30	1.57	2.29	3.53	2.79	—	2.28	2.05	—
3a	*Antheraea mylitta*	10.6	2.38	1.58	2.28	3.44	2.92	2.29	2.25	2.07	1.85
3b	*Dictyoploca japonica*	10.6	—	1.58	2.23	3.45	2.92	2.29	2.28	2.09	1.88
4	*Thaumetopoea pityocampa*	15.0	2.36	1.55	—	3.40	—	—	2.26	2.10	1.88
5	*Nephila senegalensis*	15.7	2.35	1.57	2.19	3.43	2.77	—	2.23	2.06	1.87
	Calculated spacing (Å.)		2.36	1.57	2.23	3.48	2.80	2.31	2.25	2.08	1.87

[a] Values are in Angstrom units.
[b] Data from Warwicker (6).

distance between main chains in the plane of the pleated sheets, and c as the fiber axis in an orthorhombic system.

From Table I it is immediately apparent that the 100 spacing varies widely from 9.3 to 15.7 Å. whereas all other spacings are such as to indicate that the b and c axis periods are very nearly the same for all these fibroins, i.e., $b = 9.44$ Å. and $c = 6.95 \pm 0.05$ Å. From several workers one recognizes the fact that the fiber-axis period c varies slightly in different fibroins; some more accurate figures are given by Brown and Trotter (21) and by others (9). A striking thing is that even with the large side-chain dimensions of type 5 fibroin, the fiber axis period is still within the "fibroin" range and distinctly different from that of β-keratin. Also in type 5, the dominant reflection on the equator seems describable as the 120 spacing.

It would have been reasonable enough to suppose that in various fibroins, which have the high content of glycine, alanine, and serine ranging from 43% to over 95%, these residues formed a nearly constant type of polypeptide chain and that the differences between silks were due to the incorporation of another protein containing mainly the larger amino acids. From fibroins, then, we should have expected a fairly constant X-ray diagram with $d(100)$ ranging from 9.3 to 10.6 Å., but with a weak diagram from the other protein superposed when this latter was present in greater quantity. Warwicker's work clearly shows that this is not the case, but that each fibroin could be composed of but one molecular species.

As previously described (22), the calculation of the average residue volume from constituent groups in the protein bears a close relation to the average residue volume as measured by X-rays. Since these earlier calculations were made, we have acquired the considerably more accurate data for two synthetic polypeptides, poly-L-alanine (3, 21) and poly-β-n-propyl-L-aspartate (23). These form an excellent standard of reference. Whereas we know the composition in these polymers, in the natural fibroins there is reasonable argument that certain amino acids may not be within the crystalline region which gives the measurements we obtain in X-ray diagrams. Support for such argument is very strongly apparent in some of the measurements recorded in Table II.

In the calculation of the mean residue volume of fibroins from constituent groups we have used the analyses of Lucas et al. (5). Table II shows a number of interesting things. There is clearly room in the measured residue volumes of polyalanine and of poly-β-n-propyl-L-aspartate for the residue volume which is calculated. The polyalanine is packed very closely and, as might be expected from the bulky propyl groups, the poly-β-n-propyl-L-aspartate packs rather less closely. In the

TABLE II

CALCULATED AND OBSERVED MEAN RESIDUE VOLUMES[a]

Protein or peptide	Mean apparent molar volume of residue	Mean volume of residue from X-rays
Poly-L-alanine	87	88
Fibroins		
Bombyx mori		
CTP[b] peptide without tyrosine	74	75 $d(100) = 9.2$ Å.
CTP peptide plus tyrosine	76	80 $d(100) = 9.7$ Å.
All analyzed residues	86	
Anaphe moloneyi	78	82
Antheraea mylitta	98	87
Chrysopa flava	86	88
Thaumetopoea pityocampa	115	123
Nephila senegalensis	109	128
Complex proteins		
β-Keratin	133	150
β-Myosin	136	152
β-Tropomyosin	141	155?
Poly-β-n-propyl-L-aspartate	194	203

[a] Values are in cubic Angstroms.
[b] Chymotrypsin precipitate.

more complex proteins—keratin, myosin, and tropomyosin—there is abundant room in the crystalline region for the total variety of amino acids in the relative quantities measured. The same applies to the fibroins of *Anaphe moloneyi*, *Chrysopa flava*, and *Thaumetopoea* and *Nephila* species.

In sharp contrast are *Bombyx mori* and *Antheraea mylitta*, where the average volume of all the analyzed amino acids is considerably greater than the average residue volume as measured by X-rays. This surely means that there are long lengths of chain not containing the more bulky residues and that these simpler chain segments give rise to the main features of the diffraction diagram. By contrast, in *Thaumetopoea* and *Nephila* fibroins, we cannot say that there are long sequences of the simpler residues, but rather that the larger and the smaller amino acids are all well mixed up in some sequence along the chains. For the two latter proteins it would have been better to have the X-ray measurements under thoroughly dry conditions. It may be that there is less distinction between the diagrams for types 4 and 5 fibroins if both were taken under vacuum-dry conditions.

The fibroin of *Bombyx mori* attracts attention in Table II. If we take the CTP precipitate and the 100 spacing of 9.2 Å., then we find there is room only for the appropriate amounts of glycine, alanine, and serine. If even one tyrosine residue is brought into the crystalline structure, then the X-ray volume with $d(100) = 9.7$ Å. gives the better agreement. Taking all the amino acids of cultivated silk gives much too large a calculated volume, and the same is true of *Antheraea mylitta*. There seems to be no doubt that in the crystalline regions of these two fibroins there is not room for all the amino acids as analyzed.

DOUBLE ORIENTATION IN RIBBONS

In silk fibers there is much variation in the shape of cross section, and some typical photomicrographs have been published (*1*). Those of *Antheraea mylitta* show the fibers to be considerably flattened and almost ribbonlike. We have found a much more striking example of ribbons in the cocoon of the sawfly *Cimbex femorata* L. The usefulness of this material is that there is a very high natural double orientation of the crystal structure, the side-chain direction being perpendicular to the ribbon surface and, of course, the main chains closely parallel to the length of the ribbon. The structure is of type 3—probably 3a (*6*)—but it would need complete rotation diagrams to be conclusive on this point. Several other Symphyta cocoons, e.g. *Trichiosoma* species, show the same phenomenon.

Apart from the interest of the conditions which bring about this high double orientation, it will allow us to obtain X-ray diagrams with rotation of structure about an axis perpendicular to the main chains and lying in the plane of the pleated sheets. This is required for comparison with the naturally occurring cross-β structures as found in *Chrysopa* egg stalks.

Similar double orientation is found in many other cocoons having a compressed layer structure.

V. Fibroins of the Cross-β Type

All fibroins so far considered are of the parallel-β type, i.e. the chains are in the extended or β-configuration and they lie parallel to the fiber axis. The importance of these fibroins lies in their good definition of structure and the clear evidence of increasing complexity in a series. Much useful information about proteins has been gained in their study. Although we seem to have ranged widely, that is from spiders to insects, we have found only a rather narrow range of structure types, namely those having a fully extended β-configuration of the fibroin type. Maybe a greater range of phenomena will yet be found in Arachnida and Lepidoptera silks, but if we go to other insect groups we soon find many new phenomena. A number of these will be briefly described in this and the following sections.

The "silk" of the egg stalk of *Chrysopa* species was studied because it was a neat example of secretion from the colleterial glands (*24*) and we had previously been interested in such products (*25*). Realization of the significance of this *Chrysopa* silk came from an X-ray examination. This led to making a special effort to collect sufficient of this not abundant material so that chemical analyses could be made (*26*).

The term cross-β was first defined and used in a study of epidermal protein (*27*) to indicate that the polypeptide chains lie across or at right angles to the fiber axis, whereas in ordinary fibroins and β-keratin-like structures they lie parallel to the fiber axis. We call such structures parallel-β to distinguish them from cross-β; the former term does not imply that the individual neighboring chains are "parallel" as distinct from "antiparallel" in the sense of Pauling and Corey (*7*). They could be either.

The type of X-ray diagram obtained in the case of thermally contracted epidermal protein was interpreted as a folded form of an otherwise long β-polypeptide chain (*27*), as distinct from the previous interpretation of piles of short-length chains (*28*). The rather complex epidermal protein does not readily give crucial evidence that we are dealing with such a folded form in the cross-β structure. The importance of *Chrysopa* silk is that its behavior is overwhelmingly in favor of the cross-β condition being a regularly folded form of extended protein chains.

The main features of the cross-β diagram of *Chrysopa* silk, and the evidence for an intramolecular transformation during stretching, are illustrated in Figs. 1–4. Figure 1 is the type of diffraction diagram obtained from the natural fiber, though actually the fibers here have already been stretched to twice the natural length, which improves the orientation a little without as yet causing any other marked change in the diagram. [Unstretched natural fibers give the diagrams previously illustrated (*24, 29*).] The fiber axis is vertical and four distinct layer lines are clearly apparent, the major second layer having a moderately strong meridional reflection of 4.72 Å. Most of the reflections are easily interpreted in terms of the structure for tussah silk (*9*) if there is rotation about an axis perpendicular to the polypeptide chains and lying in the planes of the pleated sheets. This is the *a* axis of Marsh *et al.* (*9*); we use the same axes and keep them for both cross-β and parallel-β forms, i.e., *a* = chain separation in plane of pleated sheets, *b* = axis of polypeptide chains, *c* = side-chain direction.

As a β-fibroin structure, the two special features of the cross-β form are the several well-defined reflections on the first layer line and the series of reflections on the equator (Fig. 1).* Now, Fig. 2 is obtained from similar fibers, when stretched to five to six times their original length. In this case practically all the cross-β pattern has changed to a parallel-β pattern, i.e. one closely similar to that of tussah silk. The cross-β reflections on the first layer line and on the equator of Fig. 1 have now disappeared. Figure 3 is of material stretched to three times natural length, and Fig. 4 of fibers stretched to four times natural length, the varying intensities being due to the number of fibers that happen to survive in these difficult experiments. Figures 2, 3, and 4 demonstrate that the cross-β diagram disappears in relative strength without losing orientation. While a similar transformation from cross-β to parallel-β was indicated in the case of the more complex protein epidermin, the situation remained somewhat unsatisfactory because it could not be decided with certainty that the whole cross-β structure did not rotate round into the parallel-β form. In the case of *Chrysopa* there is no evidence for the rotation of micelles and all the evidence is in favor of a true intramolecular transformation from cross-β to parallel-β.

The reflections on the first layer line of Fig. 1 show that there is a larger unit of structure. They indicate periods of about 21 Å. in the side-chain direction and of over 25 Å. in the polypeptide chain direction. The folded form of the chain is viewed as in Fig. 5; more details about this are given elsewhere (30). In Fig. 5, the length of the folds is considered to be represented by the derived spacing of 25 Å. In stretching to the parallel-β form, this would give an extension of six to seven times, which is in reasonable agreement with the amount of fiber extension required to give the diagram of Fig. 2, i.e. five to six times the natural length.

The progress of the transformation is rather dramatically seen by concentrating one's view on the 211 arcs of Figs. 1–4. In Figs. 1 and 2, which are essentially pure cross-β and pure parallel-β, these arcs are in quite different positions; they are seen side by side in Figs. 3 and 4. In Fig. 3 they are of comparable strength while in Fig. 4, which is more highly extended, the parallel-β 211 is clearly stronger than the cross-β 211, and this latter has effectively disappeared in the wholly parallel-β structure of Fig. 2. These features merely reinforce the conclusion that one diagram does not rotate into the other, and that it is a case of the one diagram disappearing and the other taking its place, just as would be required by an intramolecular transformation.

A very prominent difference between Figs. 1 and 2 is the sharpness

---

* Figures 1–4 and 6–16 are grouped on Plates I–VIII, following page 424.

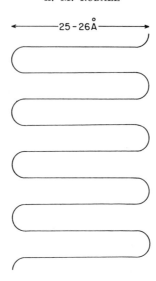

FIG. 5. Diagrammatic representation of folded form of chain; the length of the folds is considered to be represented by the derived spacing of 25–26 Å.

of the 5.4 Å. reflection, 002, in Fig. 1, and its greater breadth and spreading toward the central spot in the parallel-β diagram of Fig. 2. A similar and even more distinct difference is seen in comparing the 004 reflections. The cross-β form is the natural state in *Chrysopa* fibers, and the outstanding clarity of the diagram indicates that the chains find their best mode of packing in this configuration. But in the extensive unfolding to produce the parallel-β form it is likely that the larger amino acids (those other than glycine, alanine, and serine) become more involved in determining the average interchain separation. It is partly because of this phenomenon that we drew attention to the possibility of other fibroins, such as that of *Bombyx mori*, being altered by manipulation. It should be noted, in passing, that the parallel-β form of *Chrysopa* fibers shows a number of sharp meridional or near-meridional reflections at smaller angles than the first-layer line of the β-structure. Assuming that it is the repeating of serine every sixth residue that gives the 21 Å. axial period in *Bombyx mori* fibroin, then the plentiful serine residues in *Chrysopa* silk (*26*) may be responsible for the outstanding axial repeats there.

It is satisfactory to record that the study of fibroins has given two major contributions on the configuration of protein chains. First of all there is the view of the fully extended chain of Meyer and Mark, and secondly there is the present case of intramolecular transformation from cross-β to parallel-β.

Another item of importance coming from the study of *Chrysopa* silk is revealed by the "pedestal" or film of protein which is spread upon the surface of the leaf and from which the insect draws out the fiber to form the egg stalk (*24*). Although this pedestal film is formed on the rather uneven surface of a leaf, the protein is comparatively well oriented and in an interesting fashion. The configuration is the folded cross-β form, but now the chain direction, b axis, is perpendicular to the surface of the film, while the a and c axes lie in the plane of the film (Fig. 6). Thus with the X-ray beam directed parallel to the surface of the film we have effectively a rotation photograph about the main chain direction as axis. These are the conditions in which the usual photographs of parallel-β fibroins are taken. In Fig. 6 it is quite clear that the special equatorial reflections at smaller angles in Fig. 1 are now oriented on the meridian. Figure 7 is given for comparison with Fig. 6; it is the parallel-β structure of *Chrysopa* fibers purposely somewhat disoriented. In it there is no sign of the larger axial spacings of Fig. 6, which are regarded as coming from the folded nature of the cross-β form. Another important point is that only in Fig. 7 are reflections from planes ($h2l$) and ($h3l$) clearly defined; this is to be expected because of the very small number of amino acid residues in the short (25 Å.) segments of the folded polypeptide chains. Also we see, once again, the sharpness of 002 and 004 in Fig. 6 and the greater breadth of these reflections in Fig. 7.

The series of meridional reflections in Fig. 6 is not easy to interpret. Their spacings alter as between the wet and dry conditions, and this is reasonable in view of the layers that should exist parallel to the surface owing to the folded polypeptide chains. A fundamental spacing of about 50 Å. is indicated, i.e. twice that of the length of the fold. It seems certain that the orientation of the structure of Fig. 6 could be greatly improved by persuading the insect to form these pedestals on a glass surface. It is no use trying to improve the orientation by pressing—one merely unfolds the structure, thus proceeding toward a parallel-β system.

This study of *Chrysopa* fibers is important to our present position because it revealed the first of a number of entirely new types of structure in silks. The X-ray diffraction method is by far the best for drawing attention to specially interesting phenomena in small samples. It then becomes worth while to collect sufficient material for other studies.

VI. The α-Form of Silk

At the time the $\alpha \rightleftarrows \beta$ transformation was discovered in keratin (*20*), in addition to recognizing the close relation of β-keratin and the extended chain structure in silks, Astbury argued that there should be an α-form in silk. He carried out an examination of acid-contracted fibroin, but failed to find evidence for a regularly folded α-form. More recently a very beautiful α-form of polyalanine was discovered (31); this was found to be a simple α-helix of the type proposed by Pauling and Corey (7). But as the β-form of polyalanine is, in principle, identical with the protein chain form in tussah silks, one would expect any α-form of these silks to be similar to the α-form of polyalanine.

We are able to report finding many α-forms of silk; so far they are all confined to one group of the Hymenoptera, namely, the Aculeata. This was first discovered in our domestic bees, where the silk of the cocoon is spun by the larva before pupation, just as in Lepidoptera. While details may possibly vary, the same well-defined α-structure has been found in ants, bees, social wasps, and solitary wasps. The X-ray diagrams we show in Figs. 8 and 9 were obtained using the outer loose silken protection of the cocoons from a solitary wasp collected in southern Spain. This was identified by Dr. Yarrow, of The British Museum, as *Pseudopompilus humbolti*, Dahlbom. He describes it as an extremely rare wasp whose biology is quite unknown, but morphologically it is close to the pompilids. Its virtues for our present purpose lie in the relative ease with which regular lengths of undistorted fiber can be obtained. Material similar in nature is surely abundant in any aculeate cocoon.

The α-form of this aculeate silk is shown in Fig. 8. The principal strong meridional reflection shows signs of resolving into a central and two lateral spots. The spacing is very near to 5.0 Å., which is similar to the main fiber spacing of α-keratin-like structures, though here it is the smallest spacing recorded for this prominent arc, often referred to as the 5.1 Å. reflection. There are moderately strong reflections on a layer line having a spacing somewhat greater than 5 Å. (5.4–5.6 Å.), which is a feature more related to the simple α-helix, as in α-polyalanine. The strong equatorial reflection consists of at least three distinct spots and indicates a principal equatorial spacing of about 8.5 Å. There are a number of sharply defined reflections to smaller angles on the meridian and less sharp reflections close in on the equator. Finally, of course, there is a well-defined meridional reflection at about 1.5 Å. For the present purpose this must suffice to indicate the α-nature of this pattern and the possible great interest of it.

Next we are interested to know what kind of β-pattern this gives rise to on stretching. Extensions of 90–100% were achieved in warm water (70° C.) and the α → β transformation was substantially complete as is seen in Fig. 9. In general, this pattern resembles that of β-keratin (20), but there are two features that are quite different. First, the main side-chain spacing is only about 7.8 Å. whereas the stronger equatorial reflection outside this has a spacing of 4.52 Å. The fiber axis period is too indistinct to pronounce upon at present; on the whole this structure is more closely related to Warwicker's type 5 fibroin than to any other β-structure.

The α-form of aculeate silk, with its many longer spacings, indicates a highly regular structure; chemical analyses should eventually provide clues as to details of the diffraction pattern. In an attempt to provide more abundant well-oriented α-form fibers, the bulky "silks" of *Vespa cabro* (hornets) and of *Vespa sylvestris* were dissolved in dichloroacetic acid (3) and precipitated, first in acetic acid vapor and then by glacial acetic itself. This material, which could be readily extended as fibers, did not give any α-diagram, but, instead, a highly satisfactory cross-β diagram with a sharp, well-oriented meridional arc of spacing about 4.62 Å. Unlike the case of *Chrysopa* egg-stalk silk, where the packing of the chains in cross-β and parallel-β are closely the same, it seems that the chain packing could be considerably different in the two β-forms of aculeate silk. Nevertheless, apart from details, it appears once again that the cross-β form is as characteristic a configuration of protein chains as are the α- and parallel-β forms.

VII. Silk Which Is Collagen

These very interesting α-forms having been found in aculeate silk, other members of the Hymenoptera were examined as suitable material became available. During the brilliant summer of 1959 there were "plagues" of gooseberry sawfly (*Nematus ribesii*) in our gardens, and for several short periods abundant ripe larvae, about to pupate, could be obtained. The larva spins its silk after falling to the ground and burrowing into the top soil. In this position the cocoon rapidly goes a dark brown, probably as a result of a tanning process. But if cocoons are caused to pupate in dry glass vessels, the silk remains a pleasant yellow color and the "browning" does not occur, though it will rapidly do so if wetted with water. Wigglesworth describes a similar phenomenon in the case of several other cocoons (32). The X-ray examination of the gooseberry sawfly silk showed it to be mainly collagen with some β-protein structure as well.

By far the best preparations were obtained by dissecting the paired serigenous glands into "Insect Ringer" (33), then placing them in water and rapidly stretching the glands to the maximum extent. From a gland several centimeters long a meter or more of fiber is readily obtained, the broken gland walls remaining unextended at the ends. Though it is

tedious and not easy, this procedure yields a reasonable amount of we
oriented fiber which gives the X-ray diagram shown in Fig. 10. Th
is unmistakably the wide-angle diffraction diagram of the collagen typ
with strong meridional arcs at 2.86 Å. and equatorial reflections
12 Å. These 12 Å. reflections consist of two spots one above and on
below the equator, and there are other features in the wide-angle di
gram that are well resolved. The series of sharp meridional reflectio
nearer the center show that we have to deal with some series of lon
spacings, as is so characteristic of classic collagen of fibroblast origi
Equatorial reflections are also well defined at smaller angles, and bo
these and the meridional series are better defined and altered in positi
in wet material.

The above reflections are exactly those of collagen or what we migh
expect of collagen. The one rather special feature in Fig. 10 is the we
defined meridional arc at 4.65 Å., this being something we have come
expect of a cross-β structure, but no other reflections of the cross
system have been detected. There are several possible explanations f
this conspicuous reflection: there may be a separate protein lying
parallel with the collagen; there may be a thin protein shell intimate
surrounding an elementary collagen micelle; the same continuous cha
may have the collagen configuration along one segment and the cross
configuration in another segment; the 4.65 Å. reflection may be a specia
enhanced layer line in this particular collagen. In the course of time, v
shall know which, if any, is the correct explanation.

Collagen is not an easily detected product in insects, but was fin
established by X-ray in the tissues of mantids (34). Later its existence
insect tissues was confirmed by the demonstration of collagen in t
sheath surrounding the ventral nerve cord of the cockroach (35
Recently, electron microscope studies have defined a banded system
fibers in association with the nerve cord, and although this banding
similar in type to that found in known collagens, it is not identical wi
them (36). The production of collagen by the gooseberry sawfly lar
is very abundant for an insect, the paired serigenous glands being fu
of the protein just prior to pupation.

There is one outstanding feature in common between fibroins an
collagen—they both have a high content of the three small amino aci
glycine, alanine, and serine. In mammalian collagens these account f
over 40% of the structure (37), and in earthworm cuticle collagen, f
over 50% of the structure (38). If somehow we could introduce mo
proline into fibroin, we should end up with a collagen-like material.
an analysis of the sawfly "silk" Dr. F. Lucas of the Shirley Institute h
found a spectrum of amino acids not unlike that of known collagen

Compared with fibroins, the proline content is considerably increased. Strangely, hydroxyproline has not been found with certainty. We await with interest his further results with this material.

It seems that in this insect we have, superposed upon a fairly normal plan for producing fibroins, a special mechanism which incorporates considerable proline into the protein chains. We are a little surprised to realize how near the fibroins are to the collagens.

VIII. Silk Which Is Chitin

Praying mantids, in hatching from the ootheca, wriggle out and become suspended at the end of long, paired silken threads, up to 5 cm. in length. Some excellent photographs of the hatching are published by *Turtox News* (39), but one is scarcely able to see the threads, which are very fine—less than 5μ in diameter. Bundles of these fibers have been examined and as shown in Fig. 11, are typically chitin, of the kind usually found in insect cuticle structures. The diagram shows very clearly the sharply defined meridional series corresponding to the first four layer lines and also the two main equatorials, 002 and 100 (40). The relative absence of all other detail is that typical of chitin-protein complexes (41). Without examining this silk one might have dismissed it as yet another fibroin. As the dominant structure is the aminopolysaccharide, chitin, we would expect its protein content to be that normally associated with chitin—a protein we called "arthropodin" (41), which has been extensively studied by Hackman (42).

In the colleterial glands of cockroach and *Mantis* there are, associated with the columnar epithelial protein-secreting cells, small flattened chitogenous cells which secrete the chitinous intima. Thus, if the protein-secreting function in a gland were suppressed and the secreting function of the chitogenous cells increased and modified so as to give a free viscous fluid in the lumen of the gland, then the formation of a chitinous silk would be readily understood. We recall that the cocoon of *Donacia* larvae is secreted as a viscous chitinous layer (43). Likewise the peritrophic membrane in certain insects is best explained as originating from a fluid secretion (44).

In the case of the threads suspending the newly hatched *Mantis* larva, Williams and Buxton (45) have described them as arising from two papillae "beneath the sides of the posterior margin of the tenth tergite" and have stated that the threads frequently unite as a flat band a short distance behind the larva. However, these authors cite an older and not easily accessible paper by Pawlowa (1896) (46), who in studying the development of the thread "found that it was formed from a mass of cells arranged in a spiral series." According to this, the chitinous silk is

really a cellular filament, but because of morphological and chemi
change all indications of cellular structure have been lost. The situat.
needs looking at again to confirm or deny this cellular nature of silk
fibers some 5 μ in diameter. We are so used to thinking of silken fibers
being secreted protein, suitably molded by spinnerets, that it is diffic
to accept these chitinous fibers as being cellular filaments. If they a
in fact cellular, it would be a warning against always accepting a silk
fiber as a noncellular filament.

IX. Further Cases of "Silk" in the Cross-β Form

We have kept the large water beetle *Hydrophilus piceus* in a
laboratory because of the substantial fibrous cocoon which the ad
female makes for egg laying. Interesting descriptions of cocoon form
tion are given by Miall (47). The abundant protein is produced by a
colleterial glands and the fibrous raft subsequently darkens, app
ently by a tanning process. We mentioned our study of this mater
previously (24). Fine fibers can be selected from the freshly lay
cocoon and are noteworthy for giving the excellent cross-β diagram
Fig. 12. This differs markedly from that of *Chrysopa* egg stalks (Fig.
but is similar to that obtained from various keratin structures wh
supercontracted (27, 48). In Fig. 12 the main meridional arc gives
spacing of 4.72 Å. and there is clear evidence for an inner layer line
9.44 Å. The cross-β diagrams of Figs. 12 and 13 are the best of th
type so far obtained; the reflections corresponding to 210, according
the indexing of β-keratin (20), are now well-separated, nonaxial arcs
the second layer line. When looked for, there is no axial reflection abc
1.5 Å. on the meridian. The well-defined 210 reflections give a calculat
fiber period, oriented along the equator, of a little over 6.6 Å. In th
way, too, the structure is more like the β-keratin type than the fibre
structures where the fiber axis period is 6.9–6.95 Å.

The very clear cross-β diagram of Fig. 13 (better defined as the
was more material available) is produced by a dipteran larva, the Ne
Zealand glowworm *Arachnocampa luminosa* Skule. The material com
from labial, or so-called salivary glands, of the larva and either for.
the numerous moist hanging threads to trap insect prey, or at pupati
forms the stout stalk 1–1½ cm. long which suspends the pupa from t
roof of the cave. Pictures of these structures may be seen in Tour
Bulletins concerning the Waitomo Caves (e.g. 49), and an entomologis
account of the insect is given by Hudson (50). The suspension stalk
the pupa is much more convenient to handle, though less abunda
than the larval threads and web. It is extremely brittle in the dry sta
but when wet it is an easily handled elastic fiber. We are indebted

Dr. Aola Richards of Auckland for recent samples of this material, the main phenomena having been detected in samples we collected in 1955.

The cross-β diagram of Fig. 13 is noteworthy for showing a series of equatorial reflections which should be related to the length of folds in a cross-β structure. As the main equatorial reflection is in the region of 30 Å. we should expect an extension of approximately seven times to give rise to the parallel-β form. As yet there has not been an opportunity to follow the series of changes analogous to those illustrated in Figs. 1–4 for *Chrysopa* fibers. The special value of the glowworm material is that it represents the type of structure occurring in the cross-β form of keratins and proteins with high contents of the larger amino acids. It gives promise of providing more superior diffraction data than any other natural structure of this type so far known.

The *Hydrophilus* silk and the glowworm fibers are clearly related in structure. Compared with KMEF proteins (*51*) the side-chain reflection is considerably smaller, i.e., about 9 Å. or less in the glowworm fibers. Some years ago Dr. S. G. Smith made for us a survey by paper chromatography of the amino acids in the *Hydrophilus* silk; he found a wider range of frequently occurring amino acids than in typical fibroins. Nevertheless the four most abundant amino acids were alanine, aspartic acid, glycine, and serine, all being smaller amino acids. The apparent smaller side-chain separation in the fibers of the *Hydrophilus* cocoon is consistent with these indications from the qualitative survey of amino acids.

X. The Other Cocoon Protein—the Sericin Fraction

Sericin is the other main protein in the structure of the cocoon; it functions as a cement sticking the fibroin fibers together. Reviews on the structure and properties of sericin are given by Howitt (*10*), Lucas *et al.* (*1*), and Richards (*52*).

Our present interest in the molecular structure of sericin arises from the frequent appearance of the cross-β diagram in 'fibroins" which are more heavily cemented together. Of several examples in different cocoons, one of the best occurs in the characteristic stalks of *Antheraea paphia* L. The stalks give well-oriented diagrams of Warwicker's type 3a, but superposed is a substantial meridional arc of spacing 4.66 Å. Microscopic sections show the constituent fibers cemented together by an easily visible layer of material several microns thick. Examined in polarized light, these cross sections show the essentially isotropic fibroin fibers surrounded by birefringent layers, a finding consistent with the protein of the cement being "doubly oriented" or perhaps arranged in layers around the fibroin. In associating the cross-β pattern with the

cementing layers, we are influenced by the fact that in those region‍
the stalk where the cement layer is much more abundant, the cro‍
diagram is increased in relative strength to that of the fibroin. ‍
X-ray diagram of some cocoon stalks could well be that of a typ‍
fibroin, with a weaker diagram, such as that in Figs. 12 or 13, su‍
posed on it.

Qualitatively the amino acid spectrum of *Bombyx mori* sericin
is comparable with that quoted above for the *Hydrophilus* fibers. He‍
a cross-β structure in sericin proteins is not unexpected. The X-ray d‍
for isolated sericins have not been very informative (see ref. *10*). T‍
this is not surprising, as the excellent cross-β structure in Fig. 13 is v‍
easily transformed to an amorphous diagram, as seen in fibers was‍
and dried after swelling in strong urea solution.

The "sericin" layer of the stalk of *Antheraea paphia* is of furt‍
interest. It is distinctly brown in color and seems to be "tanned" in‍
same way as many insect proteins. This reminds us of the "arthropo‍
of insect cuticle, which reacts to tanning molecules, becoming colo‍
and insoluble (*41*). Trim sought to relate sericin to the structure of‍
insect cuticle protein and observed some possible relations (*53*).‍
Antheraea paphia the "sericin" of the "tanned" cocoon stalk is behav‍
in a similar way to the arthropodin of tanned insect cuticle. In X-‍
studies of isolated arthropodin, a well-defined β-structure has b‍
observed (*41*); when this material was doubly oriented by pressing ‍
stretching it gave X-ray diagrams of the cross-β type. These things s‍
gest there may be several features in common between "sericin" ‍
arthropodin.

For the time being we view the various fibroin fibers as contain‍
essentially one protein species; even the fibroin of *Thaumetopoea pit‍
campa*, which dissolves readily and gives at least two peaks in‍
ultracentrifuge, is viewed as containing one protein which is liable‍
break into various fractions during preparation of the solutions (5‍
The other main protein is the sericin, and there too it is possible that‍
have one "species" readily broken into several different fragment‍
sericin A, B, etc. Nevertheless we cannot rule out the possibility t‍
there are other "significant" proteins in small quantity or that b‍
the fibroin and the sericin do exist, at least sometimes, as more than ‍
protein species.

XI. The Proteins of Other Cocoons

The word "cocoon" derives from the diminutive of the French *coq‍*
a shell. While we usually think of a cocoon as composed of silken fib‍
there are other "small shells" for pupating larvae and for the eggs. Th‍

s the chitin-protein cocoon of *Donacia* larvae, and some interesting points about this have been discussed by Picken, Pryor, and Swann (43). The "small shell" or cocoon surrounding the eggs is usually called the ootheca, though the silken nature of the egg basket in *Hydrophilus* preserves the name of cocoon in that case.

In the previous section we have discussed sericins as the other cocoon proteins. Here we are concerned with the proteins of the other "cocoons," namely various oothecae.

A. Cockroach Ootheca

Modern interest in this structure was greatly stimulated by Pryor's work on the general nature of the tanning process which causes the hardening and darkening of the oothecal protein after laying (55). Knowledge of the processes involved has been much advanced by Brunet's studies (56) and by the more accurate resolution of the enzyme processes leading to hardening by Brunet and Kent (57). Nothing very characteristic is known about the main oothecal protein. Electron microscope studies have revealed the general nature of the secretion from type 4 cells of the left colleterial gland (58). The picture is that of protein globules about 700 Å. in diameter and not surrounded by any detectable membrane. Such a system of globules would form a mobile fluid easily manipulated by the ootheca-forming apparatus. X-rays tell us that the tanned protein is of the β-keratin type (55), and our own observations do not show any degree of orientation in the oothecal wall. We picture the general situation, then, as follows. Disoriented β-protein chain structures are present within the globules described by Mercer and Brunet (58), and there is no evidence, so far, that the globules change this structure markedly. Tanning molecules seem to penetrate the globules, "fix" them, and join them together without any definable transformation of the intrinsic globular structure.

We assume from the high reactivity of oothecal protein with quinones that basic amino acids are plentiful. Also from the X-ray diagram the protein appears to contain a wider range of amino acids, less dominated by the small amino acids than are the typical fibroins. It is a complex protein, but we should still seek relationships with those other nonfibroins, sericin, arthropodin, and the fibers of *Hydrophilus* cocoons and glowworm stalks.

B. *Mantis* Ootheca

A general account has been given elsewhere of the protein in this very elaborate egg case (25). The structure is membranous rather than fibrous, and the basic unit is a ribbon some 50 μ long, 1–2 μ wide, and

200–300 Å. in thickness. The ribbons develop externally to the animal by a molecular transformation of long thin fibrous units, 50 μ long and about 0.25 μ in diameter. These fibrous units are stored in large membrane-bounded, birefringent globules within tubules of the colleterial glands. The molecular transformation is not mediated by mechanical processes of the ootheca-forming apparatus. It occurs spontaneously in the test tube when the conditions are right. At present we are unable to define these conditions, but can refer to a number of partly successful experiments on the assumption that enzymes and calcium ions were important. Undoubtedly a major interest in the *Mantis* ootheca protein is this molecular change from a fibrous to a highly organized membranous or ribbonlike state.

The second outstanding feature of the ootheca is the highly crystalline nature of the ribbons. In this they show a doubly oriented α structure, as do some of the synthetic polymers and copolymers of amino acids (3). On stretching, the ribbons transform reversibly to a doubly oriented β-structure, but with the unusual orientation of pleated sheets standing perpendicularly to the ribbon surface. Again, this is a promising material in which to study the increasing complexity of α-protein structure, starting from the acceptable configuration for simple helixes. On the whole, we seem to be dealing with the relatively simple case of a two-strand coiled helix (25).

The ribbons tend to split longitudinally very readily [see Fig. 5 of ref. 25]. Yet in electron micrographs the major structural feature in the surface view of the ribbons is the regular series of striations making an angle of some 20 degrees with the principal cleavage edge as is shown in Fig. 14. More rarely cleavage occurs parallel to the striations, and indeed, the upper edges of Fig. 14 are clearly "faces" parallel to the striations. While we can be sure that the helical protein chains are parallel to the surface of the ribbons, it is not so certain how they lie in the plane of the ribbons. Because of the X-ray diagram and the marked tendency to cleave lengthwise, we think of the protein chains as lying parallel to the edge of the ribbons rather than parallel to the striations.

Thoughts on the structure of the oothecal protein based on some features of Fig. 14 have been given elsewhere (25). Since then electron micrographs have been better resolved and some additional features are shown in Fig. 15. The best way to observe this picture is at various glancing angles to the page, this serving to even out irregularities of contrast and to bring up a variety of axes in the plane of the ribbon. When viewed along the direction of the main striations (indicated by arrow), the striations, which appeared as rather narrow single lines in Fig. 14, now appear as broader double rows of spots, each spot being 20–30 Å. in diameter.

In order to obtain the separated ribbons we have used brief treatment with cold, commercial trypsin solution, and this proteolytic action may be contributing to the ease with which phosphotungstic acid is fixed at certain sites as in Figs. 14 and 15. However, the procedures do reveal a remarkably regular arrangement of reacting centers, as if the ribbons were formed of very uniform particles or "globular proteins" rather than fibers. In 1954, Dr. R. W. Burley made a partial analysis of the purified ribbons and found quantities of the basic amino acids as follows: arginine, 6.1%; histidine, 2.8%; lysine, 7.6%. This information is relevant to the staining behavior. In Fig. 14 the ribbons were only briefly washed after treatment with phosphotungstic acid (PTA) whereas they were extensively washed overnight in the case of Fig. 15. Thus, on recent views that lysine gives up its combined PTA much more readily than does arginine (59), the centers in Fig. 15 could be mainly arginine.

The *Mantis* ootheca protein is undoubtedly more complicated in amino acid structure than the fibroins. Also, there are clearly some specialized molecular processes which change a more fibrous condition, in itself analogous to the state in which fibroins seem to be stored within the tubules of the gland, to a highly crystalline ribbonlike condition. The contrast is that the highly oriented structure in the *Mantis* ribbon is brought about by molecular processes, but the orientation in silk fibers seems to be almost entirely due to mechanical spinning.

C. Ootheca of *Aspidomorpha*

The *Mantis* ootheca differs considerably in morphology and molecular structure from that of the cockroach although the two creatures are not so distantly related. In quite another group of insects, the Coleoptera, oothecae are found which in many ways closely resemble the *Mantis* ootheca. Prominent among these is the egg case of the beetle *Aspidomorpha puncticosta* (60). A fine batch of pupae of this creature was kindly provided for us by Dr. E. McC. Callan of Rhodes University, Grahamstown, Union of South Africa. After initial difficulties, we succeeded in maintaining the insects on the larger bindweed *Calystegia sylvestris;* new generations were reared from the many oothecae produced.

Some information on the colleterial glands producing this material

is given by Muir and Sharp (60); at present we are unable to describe
the gland contents or what molecular changes take place in the ootheca
after laying. Most of the ootheca is composed of thin membranes, bu
some advantage is taken of the fact that the edges of these membrane
are usually thickened as highly oriented birefringent fibers. X-ray
diagrams of such fibers appear as shown in Fig. 16. The structure does
not appear to be closely related to any of the cocoon materials so far
studied. The only resemblance it shows to the protein of the Mantis
ootheca is that in both cases there is considerable detail referring to
large units of structure. In principle it recalls the elaborations in the
"feather keratin" diagram, but in Fig. 16 there is much less evidence of
fibrous structure. It may be a case of the association of "globular protein"
units without extensive unfolding of intrinsic protein chains. None of
the features of α- or β-diagrams have been detected at either large or
intermediate angles. It is evident that this diagram will yield a very
large number of reflections when the material is suitably prepared from
the living insect.

The birefringence is so low in natural membranes from Aspidomorpha ootheca, which are of suitable thickness for infrared absorption
measurements, that it becomes uncertain what is the position of orienta
tion equivalent to that in the stoutish fibers giving the diagram of Fig
16. The typically protein infrared absorption shows little significant
dichroism, and in the 1600 cm.$^{-1}$ range there is C$=$O stretching absorp
tion corresponding to both α and β positions—again a situation recalling
that of feather keratin.

The oothecae of cockroach and mantids contain, in addition to the
protein, numerous crystals of calcium oxalate and calcium citrate, re
spectively. The calcium oxalate is present along with the structural
protein in the tubules of left colleterial gland, while the calcium citrate
of the praying mantis is added at the time of laying from a special
gland beneath the seventh ventral sternite or subgenital plate (61). The
ootheca of Aspidomorpha also contains numerous small crystals resistant
to solution in water but readily soluble in dilute acid. Their exact
chemical nature has not been determined as yet.

There is, of course, a vast number of other colleterial secretions still
to be examined; we have made some preliminary study of this material
in locusts. The colleterial gland products so far studied, i.e. Chrysopa
fibers, Hydrophilus cocoon, and these three types of ootheca, all show
features of great interest. They are all protein structures, but with folded
chains rather than the extended parallel chains of typical fibroins. Other
wise they are all different, showing once again the wide variation among
products of the one type of insect gland.

PLATE I

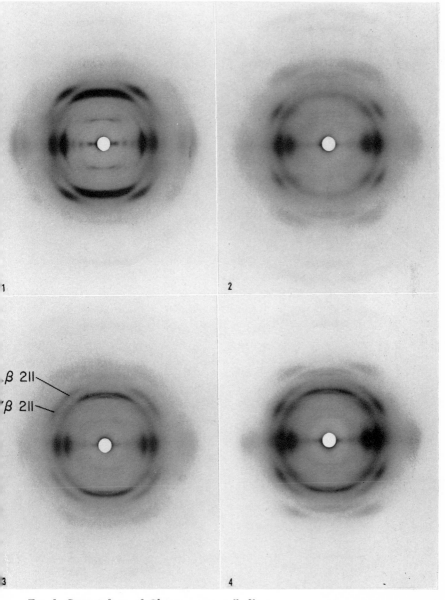

FIG. 1. Cross-β form of *Chrysopa* egg stalk fibers.

FIG. 2. Parallel-β form of *Chrysopa* fibers. Stretched to five to six times natural length.

FIG. 3. *Chrysopa* fibers stretched to three times natural length. KEY: $\times\beta$ 211 = 211 reflection of cross-β diagram; //β 211 = 211 reflection of parallel-β diagram.

FIG. 4. *Chrysopa* fibers stretched to four times natural length. Figures 1–4 are X-ray diffraction photographs taken on flat film in vacuum camera; fiber axis vertical.

Plates I–VIII face page 424.

PLATE II

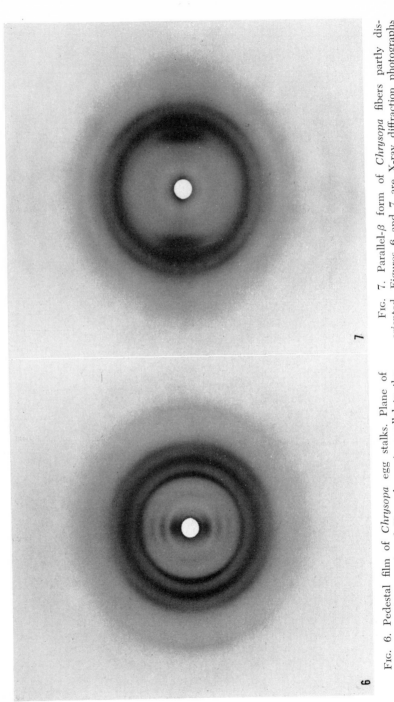

Fig. 6. Pedestal film of *Chrysopa* egg stalks. Plane of pedestal film is horizontal and X-ray beam is parallel to the surface of the pedestal film.

Fig. 7. Parallel-β form of *Chrysopa* fibers partly disoriented. Figures 6 and 7 are X-ray diffraction photographs taken on flat film in vacuum camera; fiber axis vertical.

PLATE III

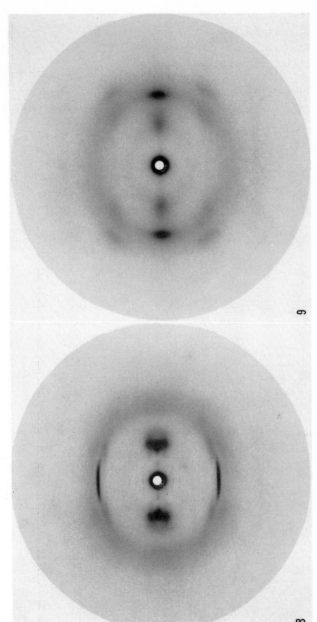

FIG. 8. The α-form of silk from a wasp cocoon.

FIG. 9. The silk shown in Fig. 8 when stretched to the parallel-β form. Figures 8 and 9 are X-ray diffraction photographs taken on flat film in vacuum camera; fiber axis vertical.

PLATE IV

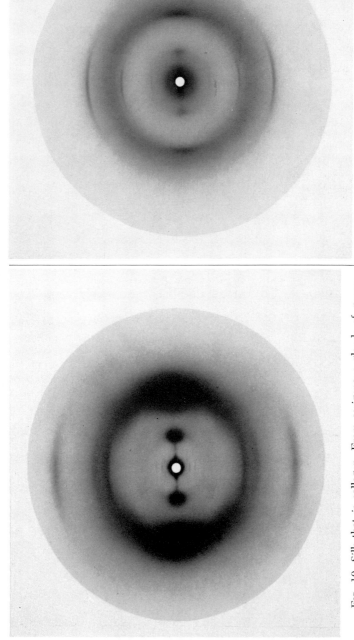

FIG. 10. Silk that is collagen. From serigenous glands of gooseberry sawfly larva (*Nematus ribesii*). X-ray diffraction photograph taken on flat film in vacuum camera; fiber axis vertical.

FIG. 11. Chitinous "silk" from *Mantis* larva. X-ray diffraction photograph taken on flat film in vacuum camera; fiber axis vertical.

PLATE V

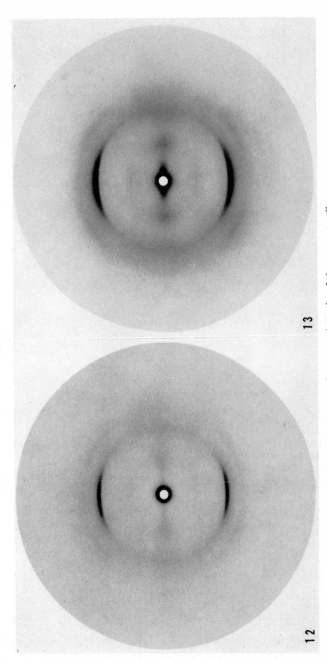

FIG. 12. Cross-β diagram of *Hydrophilus* cocoon silk.

FIG. 13. Cross-β diagram of pupal suspension stalk of New Zealand glowworm (*Arachnocampa luminosa*). Figures 12 and 13 are X-ray diffraction photographs taken on flat film in vacuum camera; fiber axis vertical.

PLATE VI

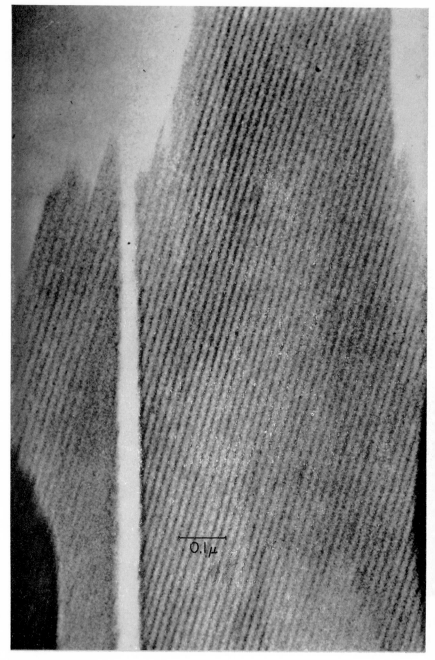

FIG. 14. Electron micrograph of "ribbons" in the ootheca of mantids. Stained with phosphotungstic acid.

PLATE VII

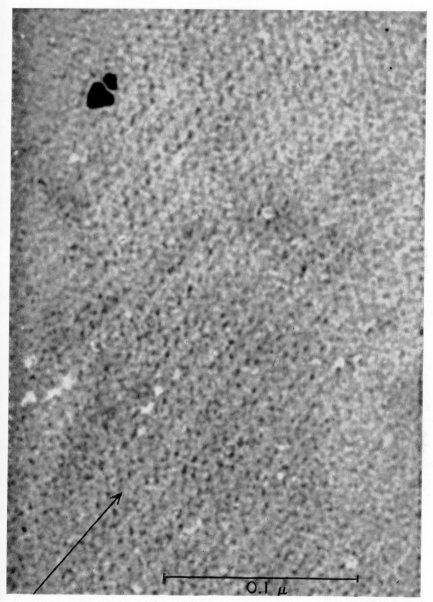

FIG. 15. Electron micrograph of similar ribbons extensively washed after staining with phosphotungstic acid. Arrow indicates direction of main striations. Regularity of detail is more easily appreciated by viewing at a glancing angle along the direction of the arrow.

PLATE VIII

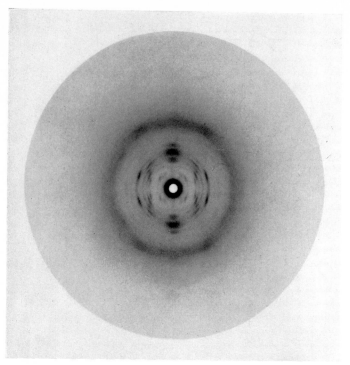

FIG. 16. Fibrous regions of *Aspidomorpha* ootheca. X-Ray diffraction photograph taken on flat film in vacuum camera; fiber axis vertical.

XII. Byssus Silk

Some consideration of the byssus silk found in various mollusks (Lamellibranchia) perhaps does not seem relevant to our present subject, which is apparently restricted to arthropod materials. However, such byssus has been used extensively as a textile fiber and is credited with the name of silk. It is secreted from skin glands and may become essentially a free fiber or remain rooted within the gland, in which case it grows in length by the addition of noncellular substance, much as mammalian hairs grow by the addition of cellular substance in the follicle. The present distinction between "free fiber" and "rooted fiber" is significant because the molecular structures of the two types are quite different.

The "rooted fiber" is represented by the classic byssus silk of *Pinna nobilis* and other *Pinna* species and by the byssus stalk or stem of *Mytilus edulis* (*34*). The characteristic molecular structure is essentially the same in both these "rooted" forms of byssus; it can be studied best in the stalk of *Mytilus edulis* or in the silk of *Pinna nobilis,* but before this latter type hardens and darkens. From its diffraction diagram it cannot be recognized as a collagen or as similar to β-keratin. Because of the considerable series of reflections at smaller angles, it may be largely a globular protein partly unraveled into fibrous regions. The maintenance of regular organized structural features depends on the presence of water; it is extensible, and contracts in hot water. Whatever the molecular unit may be, there seem to be chain regions that are folded and others unfolded.

Chemical analyses for the byssus silk of *Pinna nobilis* are given by Lucas, Shaw, and Smith (*15*) and are widely different from those of fibroins. In their analysis they gave the figures 14.7% nitrogen- and 7% sulfur-containing amino acids. It is interesting to note that the byssus stalk of *Mytilus edulis,* which has a closely similar molecular structure, gives almost identical analyses of 14.5% N and 1.5% S (*34*).

By contrast, the "free fibers" produced by *M. edulis* are quite different in molecular structure. By "free fibers" we mean that growth is not continued from a rooted end, but the fibrous material is secreted into the groove of the foot, fixed at one end on some external object and at the other end to the byssus stalk. It is a free fiber in the same sense that spider silk and insect silks are free fibers, being secreted by the animal and fixed between external points *A* and *B*. The byssus threads of *M. edulis* are mainly a collagen-type secretion, but with undoubted second proteins included, in or on the fibers. It might have been thought that collagen fibers have nothing to do with insect silks, but, of course, we have now discovered a silk, which is truly a collagen, in gooseberry sawfly cocoons.

"Silks and other cocoon proteins" constitute the most important section of the known cases of secretion of fibrous proteins. There are, of course, many others, and byssus is only one example. The study of all types helps to achieve a view of the whole picture.

XIII. Microscopy

There is much need for more extensive microscopical studies of various aspects. There are the fibers themselves and some interesting pictures have been published (1); we have mentioned the case of *Cimbex femorata*, where the fibers are very thin and ribbonlike, this being associated with the high double orientation of molecular structure. Furthermore, these particular ribbons seem to be spun in sets of three instead of the usual two filaments. Again, in a cocoon like that of *Dusona myrtillus* Desv. we have a scant external layer of coarse fibers overlying a number of layers of very fine uniform fibers, while the bulk of the cocoon wall within is composed of dense compacted layers containing a doubly oriented fibroin structure. We should like to have more knowledge of the significance of complications such as these.

We have referred to our study of cross sections of the suspension stalk of *Antheraea paphia*. This was primarily concerned with an estimation of the relative quantity of "fibroin" and "sericin" in a search for an explanation of two superposed molecular patterns in the X-ray diffraction diagram. We could see also that the "sericin" was yellow brown in color or "tanned," whereas the fibers were, for the most part, uncolored. However, in some regions, namely those first laid down, the core of the fibers was dark brown, a fact suggesting a different protein structure or different biochemical reactions. Such sections were also stained by the periodic acid-Schiff procedure and the "sericin" layers gave a distinctly stronger positive reaction than the fibers. This would be consistent with a higher content of serine in the "sericin" than in the fibroin, thus according with the results of chemical analysis. Indeed, there are many helpful microscopic studies to be made on both the morphology and histochemistry of cocoon structures.

Perhaps even more important are the details of the glands which produce the cocoon materials. In many the region of actual secretion can be located by radioisotopes (62), but in others it is more easily and directly observed (63). For some colleterial glands we have considerable knowledge, as from Ito's work on *Mantis* glands (63) and Brunet's excellent modern accounts of cockroach glands (56). We want to know all about the cells producing the main protein so that in the course of time we can locate the enzyme systems which produce the particular protein we have elaborately analyzed.

Electron microscopy also has very much to contribute on the structure of both the cocoon and the intracellular features of the various glands. Especially, we should hope for refined work on periodic structure such as cross banding in fibroin fibers. Such long and seemingly regular sequences of amino acids as in the chymotrypsin precipitate peptide (13) indicate that there are segments of fiber about 200 Å. long and terminated by tyrosine residues. This may be related to the older observations of Guba and Karolyhazi (64), who observed a beaded structure of periodicity 220–240 Å. after treatment with Millon's reagent. So great is the variation of silk structure, so very numerous are the materials available, and so many are produced in small quantities, that it is a question, really, of relying on the electron microscope to reveal problems that we would not be likely to know of by other means.

XIV. Taxonomy and the Structure of Silk

Demonstrating points of taxonomical interest is not the chief purpose of a comparative survey of silk structures. The overwhelming interest lies in revealing principles of protein structure and the relationship between different protein types. It is, however, to be expected that there are points of taxonomical interest coming from these studies, and this is pleasing because we rely so much on classification experts for determining the various species and for other guidance.

Duchâteau, Florkin and Leclercq attempt a molecular taxonomy and define the quantities of various amino acids that are characteristic of the silks in a number of lepidopteran families (12). We should, of course, expect the silks of related creatures to be similar, but there may be many exceptions. The most recent paper by Lucas et al. (5) gives a comprehensive view of their extensive findings. They conclude that no precise relationship exists between the biological classification of the various fibroins and their amino acid composition and structure. From a given constitution we may get different diffraction diagrams, which can be accounted for in terms of varying amino acid sequences. Thus, insofar as the diffraction analysis allows us to infer a few general points about sequences, the combined chemical and diffraction diagram information gives the best available picture of the structure of a given fibroin. It seems quite clear that a chemical and diffraction diagram classification often does not agree well with the biological classification.

We give these several excerpts from Lucas, Shaw, and Smith (5):

"There are two examples in which fibroins produced by moths, that are widely separated taxonomically, have similar amino acid compositions and are also placed in the same group by X-ray examination.

"Secondly, the fibroins of the species *Lasiocampa quercus, Thaumetopaea pityocampa* and *Arctia caja* belong to three different families, yet their amino acid analyses are similar, particularly with respect to their glycine and alanine contents, which are relatively low, and they are placed by X-rays in the same group.

"The fibroins of the two spiders *Nephila madagascariensis* and *N. senegalensis* . . . differ in amino acid composition and X-ray classification."

Warwicker speaks in terms of seven types of diffraction diagrams for fibroins and expects that there be differences within these types (6). From our studies we would expect many more types, even in the parallel-β fibroins, were we to give other 100-spacings than those recorded by Warwicker. All these measurements and subdivisions are important in recording closer or less close similarities between fibroins, which are so extremely varied in composition and structure.

Our own more limited X-ray work, mainly in Hymenoptera, has shown some useful points with reference to general classification. The silk of all aculeate cocoons studied is in a characteristic α-form as shown in Fig. 8. This should mean that there is a characteristic amino acid composition which favors this particular configuration of the chains. But in other members of the Apocrita, e.g. Parasitica, the structure is in the parallel-β form of fibroin, e.g. in various ichneumons and braconids. In Symphyta, the cocoon proteins must be particularly varied in structure and three types of diffraction pattern have been defined, namely, fibroin types of Warwicker in *Cimbex femorata* and *Trichiosoma* species, collagen in *Nematus ribesii,* and amorphous or undefinable patterns in some other species. But from the larger number of aculeate silks already studied, we would be surprised if any aculeate silk did not give the characteristic α-diagram of Fig. 8. We have collected unknown cocoons in the field and decided from an X-ray study that these should be an aculeate insect; it is pleasing to record that they hatched out as solitary wasps. But it would be rash to say that nowhere else among the arthropods is there another silk of similar structure.

XV. Summary and Conclusions

The comparative study of silks and other cocoon proteins is altogether larger than a comparison of fibroinlike proteins. It becomes a study of the complete functions of the epidermis in arthropods, and, as Wigglesworth has recently emphasized (65), these are of very considerable range. Cocoons and silken fibers secreted by insects may vary from a chitin-protein complex like the cuticle itself to protein fibers and membranes anologous to anything met with in the whole animal kingdom. One can see something of this wide capacity for varied chemical activity in the many types of cell within the colleterial glands of a single insect species (56). Of the protein fibers alone many, but by no means all, can be classified as fibroins according to Warwicker's types (6).

Similarity of amino acid composition does not mean identity, and we are faced with the necessity for refined studies of amino acid sequence (5). Again, there is the thought that the considerable replacement of one amino acid by another may lead to quite different chain configuration and properties, yet the two proteins must remain closely related and perhaps differ only in the action of a single gene. On the other hand, two proteins may be slightly different at a number of points and in general appear very similar. They may be slightly altered by a larger number of genes. Which pairs of proteins, then, are the more closely related?

The labial glands of insect larvae are the chief producers of silk, though on occasions the colleterial glands behave similarly. We knew already that the silk produced by adult spiders from their abdominal spinnerets was often similar to that produced by the labial or "salivary" glands of insect larvae. Within Insecta we can now make these statements. The labial glands of many insect larvae produce a similar kind of fibroin to that coming from the adult colleterial glands of *Chrysopa* although the amino acids differ in detail. Again, as Figs. 12 and 13 show so well, the colleterial glands of *Hydrophilus* and the labial glands of the New Zealand glowworm larva produce very similar kinds of protein fiber. We have insufficient knowledge of the complete range of functions of labial and colleterial glands, but the above examples give cases where their output has many points in common.

The universally occurring epidermal secretion of arthropods is the chitin-protein complex (41). In *Donacia* and the larval *Mantis* we have cocoon and "silk," respectively, which has the same general composition as the insect cuticle. One way of looking at the whole situation is to say that, whether the main fibrous constituent be chitin, collagen, or various β-fibroins and α-proteins, there is always a second protein: arthropodin, sericin, or that represented by the 4.66 Å. meridional reflection in Fig. 10. One cannot help wondering whether some structure in this second protein is not the constant common factor in the comparative study of silk and other cocoon proteins.

In this article little is said concerning the processes leading to insolubility of the silk; sufficient review on these points is given elsewhere

(*1, 3*). But we have several new cases to consider. There is the special molecular change which occurs external to the animal and which leads to the highly crystalline ribbons of the *Mantis* ootheca. There is the case of *Chrysopa* fibers which remain folded in the cross-β form and as a result of drying become highly insoluble. There are the α-forms of silk in Aculeata which remain folded, yet are considerably insoluble. Finally, there are the collagen fibers produced by the gooseberry sawfly larva, and their final insolubility seems to require a tanning action which takes place under moist conditions. There is certainly opportunity for many molecular changes after the cocoon protein has been secreted by the animal and these can range possibly from the fibrinogen-fibrin type of change as occurs in blood clotting (*66*) to the process of quinone tanning. The silks of large wasps, such as hornets, are α-protein structures and remain uncolored, yet they are highly insoluble. But there is no evidence for cross linking through cystine.

One of our most interesting observations is that silk can have the structure which is typical of the collagens. So far collagen has been found in the silk of only one species, i.e. *Nematus ribesii;* we can contemplate mapping its variation from this one species through its closest relatives until what was collagen is again a typical fibroin in structure. What are the steps in this change? The reasonable prospect of finding these steps shows one of the outstanding features of our materials. As the detail is not vitally important to the animal we might expect to see all possible variations on the theme of fiber production.

The relative simplicity of amino acid composition helps greatly in the analysis of X-ray diffraction patterns. In particular, we have the prospect of throwing light on the increasing complexity of structure, starting from a simple helix. In aculeate silk and in the *Mantis* oothecal protein we should be able to define the first simpler complications which occur in the association of α-helixes. Thus, the study of α-forms in silk should lead to sound views on the structure of the more complicated intracellular fibers like keratin and myosins.

Again, from the simplicity of composition, we might hope that a study of the intracellular synthesis of silks will show the way in which amino acid sequences are coded. Surely the common alternation of glycine with alanine and serine in the fibroin of *Bombyx mori* must depend on a simple code, and perhaps the principle underlying coding will first come to light in the further study of this protein.

We believe that the study of silk and other cocoon proteins is very much more interesting and important than is generally thought. We conclude by recalling some special achievements and pointing to some new prospects.

The intramolecular transformation from cross-β to parallel-β has been established in the case of the fibroin of *Chrysopa* egg stalks, and some other very fine cross-β forms have been discovered in *Hydrophilus* and *Arachnocampa*. These latter should allow us to give an equally satisfactory demonstration of a similar intramolecular transformation in proteins related to the β-keratin type. As yet, we have not found structures fully comparable with the parallel-β form of keratin; possibly the nearest occurs in the stretched form of the *Mantis* ootheca ribbons.

But, perhaps the most striking new viewpoint is the realization that fibroins and collagens are so nearly the same. In various Symphyta we can see this link, for some silks are fibroin and some collagen. Intermediates between these two contrasted configurations may be represented by the comparatively amorphous diagrams we have found with some Symphyta cocoons.

This does not break down the physical distinction between the collagen-like proteins and those of the KMEF group. However, it points to a transition between the two groups. On physical grounds, it has been customary to relate closely fibroins and other β-proteins of the keratin, myosin type, but it appears that, genetically as well as chemically the fibroins are more closely related to the collagens than to the KMEF proteins. It ought to be possible in the great variety of silks to find transitions between the fibroin type and the β-keratin type. Thus, fairly simply in one series, we should be able to relate, fibroins, collagens, and KMEF proteins. In the accompanying diagram we indicate that from simple proteins like the fibroins we can easily obtain collagens by incorporating adequate proline (a), whereas by incorporating a much greater proportion of the larger amino acids (b) we should obtain the KMEF proteins.

From these, we may find a relatively simple physical connection with apparently globular protein structures as in *Aspidomorpha* oothecas or again a wider relation, biochemical rather than physical, with the chitin-protein system. The close comparative study of silk and of the glands producing it, should provide many of the answers to problems concerning natural fibers.

References

1. F. Lucas, J. T. B. Shaw, and S. G. Smith, *Advances in Protein Chem.* **13,** 108 (1958).

432   K. M. RUDALL

2. S. Bricteux-Grégoire, W. G. Verly, and M. Florkin, *Arch. intern. physiol. et biochim.* **67**, 563 (1959); S. Bricteux-Grégoire, A. Dewandre, and M. Florkin, *ibid.* **68**, 281 (1960); *Biochem. Z.* **333**, 370 (1960).
3. C. H. Bamford, A. Elliott, and W. E. Hanby, "Synthetic Polypeptides." Academic Press, New York, 1956.
4. K. H. Meyer and H. Mark, *Ber.* **61**, 1932 (1928).
5. F. Lucas, J. T. B. Shaw, and S. G. Smith, *J. Mol. Biol.* **2**, 339 (1960).
6. J. O. Warwicker, *J. Mol. Biol.* **2**, 350 (1960).
7. L. Pauling and R. B. Corey, *Proc. Roy. Soc.* **B141**, 21 (1953).
8. R. E. Marsh, R. B. Corey, and L. Pauling, *Biochim. et Biophys. Acta* **16**, 1 (1955).
9. R. E. Marsh, R. B. Corey, and L. Pauling, *Acta Cryst.* **8**, 710 (1955).
10. F. O. Howitt, "Bibliography of the Technical Literature on Silk." Hutchinson, London, 1946.
11. J. Kirimura, "Protein Chemistry," Vol. 5. Kyovitsu Publ. Co., Tokyo, 1957.
12. G. Duchâteau, M. Florkin, and J. Leclercq, *Arch. intern physiol. et biochim.* **68**, 190 (1960).
13. F. Lucas, J. T. B. Shaw, and S. G. Smith, *Biochem. J.* **66**, 468 (1957).
14. D. H. Spackman, S. Moore, and W. H. Stein, *Anal. Chem.* **30**, 1185 (1958).
15. F. Lucas, J. T. B. Shaw, and S. G. Smith, *J. Textile Inst.* **46**, T440 (1955).
16. S. Nishikawa and S. Ono, *Proc. Tokyo Math. Phys. Soc.* [2] **7**, No. 8, 131 (1913).
17. O. Kratky and E. Schauenstein, *Discussions Faraday Soc.* **11**, 171 (1951).
18. O. Kratky and S. Kuriyama, *Z. physik. Chem.* **B11**, 363 (1931).
19. J. O. Warwicker, *Acta Cryst.* **7**, 565 (1954).
20. W. T. Astbury and A. Street, *Phil. Trans. Roy. Soc.* **A230**, 75 (1931); W. T. Astbury and H. J. Woods, *ibid.* **A232**, 333 (1933).
21. L. Brown and I. F. Trotter, *Trans. Faraday Soc.* **52**, 537 (1956).
22. K. M. Rudall, *in* "Progress in Biophysics and Biophysical Chemistry" (J. A. V. Butler and B. Katz, eds.), Vol. I, p. 39. Pergamon, New York, 1950.
23. E. M Bradbury, L. Brown, A. R. Downie, A. Elliott, R. D. B. Fraser, W. E. Hanby, and T. R. R. MacDonald, *J. Mol. Biol.* **2**, 276 (1960).
24. K. D. Parker and K. M. Rudall, *Nature* **179**, 905 (1957).
25. K. M. Rudall, "Scientific Basis of Medicine," Vol. 5 Athlone Press, London, 1956.
26. F. Lucas, J. T. B. Shaw, and S. G. Smith, *Nature* **179**, 905 (1957).
27. K. M. Rudall, *Soc. Dyers Colourists Symposium on Fibrous Proteins, Leeds, 1946* p. 15 (1946).
28. W. T. Astbury, S. Dickinson, and K. Bailey, *Biochem. J.* **29**, 2351 (1935).
29. W. T. Astbury, *Discussions Faraday Soc.* **25**, 80 (1958).
30. W. T. Astbury, E. Beighton, and K. D. Parker, *Biochim. et Biophys. Acta* **35**, 17 (1959).
31. C. H. Bamford, L. Brown, A. Elliott, W. E. Hanby, and I. F. Trotter, *Nature* **173**, 27 (1954).
32. V. B. Wigglesworth, "The Principles of Insect Physiology." Methuen, London, 1950.
33. G. Hoyle, *J. Exptl. Biol.* **30**, 121 (1953).
34. K. M. Rudall, *Symposia Soc. Exptl. Biol.* **9**, 49 (1955).
35. A. Glenn Richards and D. Schneider, *Z. Naturforsch.* **13b**, 680 (1958).
36. E. G. Gray, *Proc. Roy. Soc.* **B150**, 233 (1959).

37. J. E. Eastoe and A. A. Leach, "Recent Advances in Gelatin and Glue Research," p. 73. Pergamon, London, 1958.
38. L. Singleton, *Biochim. et Biophys. Acta* **24**, 67 (1957).
39. *Turtox News* **26**, No. 8 (1948).
40. D. Carlström, *J. Biophys. Biochem. Cytol.* **3**, 669 (1957).
41. G. Fraenkel and K. M. Rudall, *Proc. Roy. Soc.* **B134**, 111 (1947).
42. R. H. Hackman and M. Goldberg, *J. Insect Physiol.* **2**, 221 (1958); R. H. Hackman, *Proc. 4th Intern. Congr. Biochem.*, *Vienna, 1958* **12**, 48 (1959).
43. L. E. R. Picken, M. G. M. Pryor, and M. M. Swann, *Nature* **159**, 434 (1947).
44. D. F. Waterhouse, *Ann. Rev. Entomol.* **2**, 1 (1957).
45. C. B. Williams and P. A. Buxton, *Trans. Entomol. Soc. London* p. 87 (1916).
46. M. S. Pawlowa, *Arb. Zool. Lab. Warschauer Univ.* (1896). [Cited in reference 45.]
47. L. C. Miall, "The Natural History of Aquatic Insects." Macmillan, London, 1895.
48. N. Peacock, *Biochim. et Biophys. Acta* **32**, 220 (1959).
49. New Zealand Government Publicity Dept., The Strand, London.
50. G. V. Hudson, "Fragments of New Zealand Entomology." Ferguson & Osborn, Wellington, New Zealand, 1950.
51. W. T. Astbury, *Proc. Roy. Soc.* **B141**, 1 (1953).
52. A. G. Richards, "The Integument of Arthropods." Univ. of Minnesota Press, Minneapolis, 1951.
53. A. R. Trim, *Biochem. J.* **35**, 1088 (1941).
54. J. T. B. Shaw and S. G. Smith, *Biochim. et Biophys. Acta* **46**, 302 (1961).
55. M. G. M. Pryor, *Proc. Roy. Soc.* **B128**, 378 and 393 (1940).
56. P. C. J. Brunet, *Quart. J. Microscop. Sci.* **92**, 113 (1951); **93**, 47 (1952).
57. P. C. J. Brunet and P. W. Kent, *Proc. Roy. Soc.* **B144**, 259 (1955).
58. E. H. Mercer and P. C. J. Brunet, *J. Biophys. Biochem. Cytol.* **5**, 257 (1959).
59. See F. O. Schmitt and A. J. Hodge, *J. Soc. Leather Trades' Chemists* **44**, 217 (1960).
60. F. Muir and D. Sharp, *Trans. Entomol. Soc. London* p. 1 (1904).
61. K. D. Parker and K. M. Rudall, *Biochim. et Biophys. Acta* **17**, 287 (1955).
62. T. Fukuda and M. Florkin, *Arch. intern. physiol. et biochim.* **67**, 185, 190, and 214 (1959).
63. H. Ito, *Arch. anat. microscop.* **20**, 343 (1924).
64. F. Guba and M. Karolyhazi, *Acta Physiol. Acad. Sci. Hung.* **3**, 311 (1952).
65. V. B. Wigglesworth, "The Control of Growth and Form. A Study of the Epidermal Cell in an Insect." Cornell Univ. Press, Ithaca, New York, 1959; *Nature* **188**, 358 (1960).
66. see, e.g., K. Laki, J. A. Gladner, and J. E. Folk, *Nature* **187**, 758 (1960).

CHAPTER 10

Blood Coagulation

Charles Grégoire

Institut Léon Fredericq, Department of Biochemistry,
University of Liège, Belgium

and

Henry J. Tagnon

Department of Medicine and Clinical Investigation, Institut J. Bordet,
University of Brussels, Belgium

I. Introduction

Blood coagulation, as seen in vertebrates, has a conspicuous significance as part of the hemostatic mechanism of the body. It consists essentially of the transformation of a soluble protein, fibrinogen, into a gel, fibrin, followed sooner or later by dissolution of the fibrin in the form of protein breakdown products resulting from the action of proteolytic enzymes. In vertebrates and especially mammals, blood coagulation is recognized as a complicated process, proceeding by successive steps and calling into play a number of factors present in the plasma and some that are found in the blood platelets. Platelets play a role in hemostasis which is different, at least in part, from their role in the coagulation phenomenon. In addition, hemostasis depends on a number of factors which have no relation to blood coagulation as such, and these will not be discussed here. Thus, in its most elementary form, coagulation should be seen as the transformation of extracellular fluid, and especially in vertebrates of that part of the extracellular fluid present in the vascular system, from a fluid into a gel. It is under this aspect that it can be observed and followed through the animal kingdom from lower to higher species, although gelification of extracellular fluid in different species does not necessarily imply identity of mechanisms. As of now, attempts at establishing a line of evolution of the mechanisms implicated in this process of gelification are hampered by several factors, among which the most important is the lack of information in several main zoological groups.

In invertebrates, except perhaps for Crustacea, most investigations so far performed, chiefly consist of morphological descriptions, without precise chemical identification of the factors involved in the process, while in vertebrates, especially in mammals, considerable data are at hand and several factors are accurately defined. In addition, coagulation or gelification is known to be absent in many invertebrate species, a fact which indicates either that the hemostatic function is not indispensable for species survival at all levels of evolution, or that alternate hemostatic mechanisms exist without gelification. Therefore there appears to be a certain degree of freedom in the selection of various hemostatic mechanisms, especially in invertebrates. The resulting lack of unity makes attempts at correlation particularly difficult and hazardous.

This study represents an attempt to survey the known facts on coagulation of coelomic fluid and blood in the different species insofar as they lend themselves to comparison and correlation of mechanisms.

II. Systems of Coagulation in the Different Zoological Groups

A. Invertebrates

The literature on coagulation of coelomic fluid, hemolymph, and of the blood of various groups of invertebrates has been reviewed in several articles: Echinodermata (1, 2); "Vermes"* (1); Mollusca (3); Crustacea (4, 5, 6); Insecta (5, 7–11).

The evolution of the enzyme systems involved in coagulation has been recently surveyed in a well-documented pamphlet (12).

The main data available in the literature on the changes produced in the various groups of animals by shedding out of the coelomic fluid,

---

* Although the classification "Vermes" (or worms) as a subkingdom is no longer accepted by zoologists, it is retained in this chapter for the sake of convenience. For a breakdown of the specific groups included under this term, see Table I.

of the hemolymph, or of the blood, are summarized, without any claim to be exhaustive, in Table I.

In Coelenterata (27), the coelomic fluid is a mixture of sea water, metabolites, and small amounts of proteins. This mixture does not clot. In several other groups of invertebrates, echinoderms, worms, mollusks, and various arthropods, agglutination of the blood corpuscles or amebocytes without participation of plasma components is the simplest mechanism so far described of reaction of the coelomic fluid outside the body. This agglutination is followed by formation of cellular meshworks which shrink into clumps visible to the naked eye.

Whether the corpuscles forming these meshworks preserve their integrity (syncytia) (2, 21, 32) or fuse their cytoplasms into plasmodia and into gels (1, 2, 13, 19, 23, 28, 53) has long been a matter of controversy in investigations not directly connected with coagulation (90, 90a). These alterations taking place in the blood cannot be considered as a true coagulation, a term which implies biochemical and structural alterations confined to the plasma. The inappropriate and consistent use of the terms "cell coagulation" in the literature for defining these purely cellular mechanisms has confused the problem.

On the other hand, in the groups in which agglutination has been the only alteration generally reported, data suggest that the true process might not be as simple and that alterations of plasma proteins around the material derived from the agglutinated corpuscles could be involved in the formation of the cell clots (14, 23, 66, 67). For instance, in animals previously considered as possessing only an initial, cellular phase of coagulation, the weights of the coagulum were three to eight times more than the estimated maximum cellular contribution (73). After clotting of coelomic fluids in sea urchins, the reduction of plasma nitrogen is of the order of 15–25% (2), a finding which indicates that material from the plasma is involved in formation of the clots.

Among the few and conflicting data so far collected on the reactions of the coelomic fluid and of the blood in the worms, nothing is known about the chemical composition and the mechanism of coagulation of the coelomic fluids discharged from *Octochoetus multiporus* or from *Acanthodrilus annectens* (33): these fluids coagulate almost at once into thick gum mucilages resembling clotted cream, which are so tenacious that they clog scissors, stick to the fingers, and paste coverglasses on the slides unremovably. Similar observations were made in a Japanese giant earthworm (*Pheretima sieboldi*) (36).

Among the invertebrates, a true gelation or solidification, induced by enzymatic mechanism, of unstable proteins ("fibrinogen") present in substantial amounts in the plasma, was first described in arthropods,

TABLE I

OBSERVATIONS RECORDED IN THE LITERATURE CONCERNING THE ALTERATIONS OF HEMOCYTES OR AMEBOCYTES (SOURCES OF COAGULINS) AND OF PLASMA (SOURCE OF COAGULABLE MATERIAL) IN DIFFERENT CLASSES OF ANIMALS

The objective in compiling the table was to abstract in the most concise form the results and conclusions of the investigators, a task sometimes difficult, owing to the imprecision of several reports.

The data reported in the table have been arranged for the most part in chronological order for each zoological group; for Crustacea, however, unicists and dualists, with regard to the mechanism of the process of coagulation, have been placed in different groups.

With regard to invertebrates, the part played by the blood corpuscles (amebocytes, hemocytes) in the induction of the alterations in plasma has been the basis of subdivision into two groups. The first (left-hand) group reports the data in which no discrimination was made by the investigators among the various kinds of corpuscles with respect to their activity in altering the plasma. The second (right-hand) group reports the data in which a special category of blood corpuscles has been recognized to play an important part in the initiation of the process of coagulation. Such a subdivision appears to be justified in view of the important discovery made by Hardy of a category of highly labile explosive corpuscles selectively involved in the initiation of the process of coagulation in Crustacea.

The blanks in the table mean that no precise information could be found in the original publications with regard to the corresponding topics.

Investigator	Source of material	Hemocytes (amebocytes)		Plasma	Comments
		No discrimination made among the cell types involved in the plasma alterations	Recording of a special category of cells involved in plasma coagulation		
	Echinodermata ASTEROIDEA, ECHINOIDEA				
Geddes (1879–1880) (18)	Asteracanthion vulgare, Spatangus purpureus, Echinus sphaera, Toxopneustes lividus	Agglutination, shrinkage, and fusion into plasmodia		No coagulation	
Schäfer (1882) (14)	Echinus sp.	Exudation of coagulation-inducing material from the cells		Coagulation into a substance different from fibrin, resembling mucin	

Reference	Species	Observation		Coagulation
Haycraft and Carlier (1888) (15)	Echinus sp.	Agglutination and shrinkage; no alteration in the hemocytes without contact with solid matter		No coagulation
Cuénot (1891–1906) (16, 17)	Echinidae Asteridae	Agglutination Fusion into plasmodia (pseudocoagulation)		No coagulation
Griffiths (1892) (18)	Spatangus, Echinus, Uraster, Solaster			"Fibrin" present in the blood
Ducceschi (1903) (19)	Strongylocentrotus lividus	Agglutination		No coagulation
Henri (1906) (20)	Strongylocentrotus lividus	Agglutination		No coagulation
Goodrich (1920) (21)	Asterias glacialis	Spreading out of amebocytes, formation of membranes; no fusion into plasmodia		No coagulation
Théel (1918–1920) (23)	Parechinus miliaris, Asterias rubens	Syncytial networks		Development of a fibrin-like substance
Kindred (1921, 1924) (24)	Arbacia sp.	Agglutination		No coagulation
Donnellon (1938) (25)	Arbacia sp.	Agglutination accompanied by breakdown of granules from disintegrated cells. Possibility of intercellular clotting		No plasma clot
Bookhout and Greenburg (1940) (26)	Mellita quinquiesperforata	Agglutination		No coagulation
Grégoire (unpublished, 1953)	Paracentrotus lividus	Scattering or formation of small aggregates	Fragile hyaline hemocytes with threadlike expansions	Inconstant alterations around fragile corpuscles. Islands of coagulation questionable. Incidental veils
Davidson (1953) (30)	Echinarachnius parma	Aggregation		No coagulation

TABLE I (*Continued*)

Investigator	Source of material	Hemocytes (amebocytes)		Plasma	Comments
		No discrimination made among the cell types involved in the plasma alterations	Recording of a special category of cells involved in plasma coagulation		
	HOLOTHUROIDEA				
Krukenberg (1882) (*27*)	*Holothuria tubulosa, Cucumaria planci*	Agglutination		No coagulation	
Howell (1885) (*28*)	*Thyonella gemmata*	Fusion of the corpuscles into plasmodia		No coagulation	
Cuénot (1891, 1906) (*16, 17*)	7 Species of holothurians	Agglutination (pseudo-coagulation)		No coagulation	
Bottazzi (1902) (*1*)	*Holothuria* sp.	Agglutination (plasmodia)		No coagulation	
Théel (1921) (*23*)	8 Species of holothurians	Syncytial meshworks; subsequent fusion		Fast development of a fibrinlike substance, conspicuous in *Mesothuria intestinalis*	
Kindred (1924) (*24*)	14 Species from 4 classes of Echinodermata	Syncytial meshworks		Development of a fibrin-like substance	
Millott (1950, 1953) (*29*)	*Holothuria forskali, Thyone briareus*	Clot formed by free and compact amebocytes (agglutination)			
Boolootian and Giese (1959) (*2*)	15 Species from the 5 classes of Echinodermata	3 types of clot: 1. Reversible agglutination 2. Agglutination and fusion into plasmodia 3. Temporary agglutination and immeshing in extracellular fibrous clots	3. Rupture of hyaline hemocytes initiates the alterations	— — 3. Participation of plasma in formation of fibers in type 3	

	"Vermes" (coelomic fluid only)		
Schwalbe (1869) (31)	Phascolosoma sp.		No coagulation
Geddes (1879–1880) (13)	Lumbricus terrestris	Agglutination and fusion into plasmodia	No coagulation
Krukenberg (1882) (27)	Arenicola piscatorum, Sipunculus nudus, Lumbricus complanatus, Spirographis pallanzanii	Agglutination	No coagulation
Michel (1888) (32)	Lumbricus terrestris	Agglutination; no fusion into plasmodia	
Cuénot (1891) (16)	Various Polychaeta, Oligochaeta, and Hirudinea	Agglutination	No coagulation
	Among Gephyrea: Sipunculus nudus, Phascolosoma granulatum		
	Bonellia viridis		
Benham (1901) (33)	Octochoetus multiporus, Acanthodrilus annectens	Agglutination	Rapid formation of a hard, highly adhesive and sticky mass
Bottazzi (1902) (1)	Sipunculus nudus	Agglutination	No coagulation
Duceschi (1903) (19)	Phymosoma granulatum	Agglutination and fusion	Rapid formation of a compact transparent mass, with subsequent exsudation of fluid
	Sipunculus nudus	Precipitates; plasmodia not recorded	No coagulation
Nolf (1909) (34)	Oligochaeta, Polychaeta	Agglutination	No coagulation
Goodrich (1920) (21)	Arenicola piscatorum	Development of membranous expansions	No coagulation
	Lumbricus terrestris	No fusion into plasmodia	

TABLE I (Continued)

Investigator	Source of material	Hemocytes (amebocytes)		Plasma	Comments
		No discrimination made among the cell types involved in the plasma alterations	Recording of a special category of cells involved in plasma coagulation		
Romieu (1923) (22)	Arenicola marina	Agglutination		Rapid formation of a "fibrinous" clot embedding the hemocytes	
Cameron (1932) (35)	Lumbricus terrestris			Rapid coagulation	
Ohuye (1937) (36)	Pheretima sieboldi	Deformed (spindle-shaped) hemocytes scattered or agglutinated in the plasma clot		Rapid formation of an adhesive hard clot, unrelated to the coelomic corpuscles	
Mollusca					
Fredericq (1878) (37)	Octopus vulgaris	Agglutination		No coagulation	
Geddes (1880) (13)	Pholas sp., Patella vulgata, Buccinum undatum	Agglutination and fusion of the amebocytes into plasmodia		No alteration	
Krukenberg (1882) (27) Griffiths (1892) (18)	Planorbis corneus, Patella coerulea, Chiton sp.	Agglutination		No coagulation	
Cuénot (1891) (16)	Various cephalopods, gastropods, and pelecypods	Agglutination		No coagulation	
Camus (1900) (38)	Helix sp.			No coagulation	
Couvreur (1900) (39)	Helix sp.			No coagulation	
Bottazzi (1902) (1)	Octopus vulgaris, O. macropus, Eledone moschata, Aplysia limacina, A. depilans	Agglutination and development of plasmodia		No coagulation	

Author (year) (ref.)	Species	Reaction of the hemocytes	Coagulation	Remarks
Nolf (1909) (34)				Neither fibrinogen, nor thrombin
Drew (1909–1910) (40)	Cardium norregicum	Agglutination	No coagulation	
Goodrich (1920) (21)	Ostrea edulis, Mytilus edulis	Development of membranous expansions	No coagulation	
Sato (1931) (40a)	Arca inflata	Agglutination	No fibrin; no coagulation	
Takatsuki (1933–1934) (41)	Ostrea edulis	Agglutination	No coagulation	
George and Ferguson (1950) (42)	Busycon carica, B. canaliculatum, Fasciolaria tulipa	Agglutination into clumps	No coagulation	
Saunders Dundee (1953) (42a)	Freshwater mussels	Temporary clumping of the hemocytes; no agglutination	No coagulation	
Schwartzkopff (1954) (43)	Aplysia limacina, A. depilans	Agglutination (plasmodia)	No coagulation; increase in viscosity of the hemolymph	
Onychophora[a]				
Grégoire (1955) (44)	Peripatus sp.	Unaltered or undergo slow modifications. Scattering at random or formation of insignificant meshworks	No coagulation. Disintegration of a category of fragile hemocytes	"Differential sensitiveness" of the hemocytes to contact with foreign surfaces
Tuzet and Manier (1958) (45)	Peripatopsis moseleyi	Degeneration (including explosion of cells)		
Arthropoda				
MYRIAPODA				
Cuénot (1891) (16)	Scutiger coleoptrata, Scolopendra cingulata		Substantial gelatinous clot	
Yeager and Knight (1933) (46)	Spirobolus marginatus	"Cell coagulation"	No coagulation	Limulus type (Loeb)

[a] A primitive group having arthropod and annelid characteristics.

TABLE I (*Continued*)

Investigator	Source of material	Hemocytes (amebocytes)		Plasma	Comments
		No discrimination made among the cell types involved in the plasma alterations	Recording of a special category of cells involved in plasma coagulation		
Grégoire (1955, 1957, 1959); Grégoire and Jolivet (1957) (44, 47, 48, 49)	CHILOPODA-DIPLOPODA 17 Species (Neotropical and Old World)	Slow alterations. Scattering at random or insignificant agglutination. No disintegration	Swift alterations in a category of highly fragile hemocytes (intracytoplasmic dissolution or explosive discharges of granules)	No visible alteration in the plasma, but occasional inelastic pellicles	Picture of coagulation: pattern IV of insect hemolymph (see below)
Shipley (1909) (50)	TARDIGRADA Various species			No coagulation	
Howell (1885) (28)	XIPHOSURA Limulus polyphemus	Formation of cellular meshworks and of compact clumps		No fibrinlike substance in plasma	
Loeb (1903–1927) (51–56)	Limulus polyphemus	All hemocytes belong to a single category. Development of extensive meshworks. Dissolution of intracellular granules and fusion of the cytoplasms into gelatinous masses (cell fibrin) (= first or cell coagulation). Incidentally, insignificant jellyfication around the cell clumps: Limulus second coagulation (cell substances exclusively)		No coagulable fibrinlike substance recorded in plasma	"Cell fibrin" only. No true plasma coagulation

Reference	Species	Cell alterations	Immediate alterations	Plasma / coagulation result	Remarks
Alsberg and Clark (1908–1909) (57)	Limulus polyphemus	Confirm Loeb's findings about the second coagulation		No fibrinogen	
Copley (1947) (58)	Limulus polyphemus	Agglutination, gelation			
Grégoire (1952, 1955) (59, 44)	Limulus polyphemus	Several kinds of hemocytes. Development of substantial meshworks. No disintegration.	Immediate alterations (explosions and discharges of substance in a category of fragile hemocytes)	No alteration in plasma of some specimens. Jellyfication in the shape of conspicuous veils in others	
Morrison and Rothman (1957) (59a)	Limulus polyphemus	Cell agglutination in two phases: agglutination followed by gelation, different from a true coagulation		No fibrinogen	
Cuénot (1891) (16)	ARACHNIDA Scorpionidae Buthus occitanus, Scorpio europeus			Fibrinous coagulum, as in Crustacea	
Grégoire (1955); Grégoire and Jolivet (1957) (44, 49)	Uroplectes occidentalis, Opisthacanthus elatus, Pandinus sp., 8 undetermined species			No visible alteration	Picture of coagulation: pattern IV of insect hemolymph (see below)
Grégoire and Jolivet (1957) (49)	Amblypygae Phrynichus bacillifer	Slow alterations. Constitution of scattered meshworks	Swift alterations in a category of unstable hemocytes (explosive discharges of granules)	Veils	
Cuénot (1891) (16)	Araneae Tegenaria domestica, Epeira diadema			Scarce fibrinous coagulum	
Yeager and Knight (1933) (46)	Several species of spiders	Cell coagulation		No coagulation	Limulus type (Loeb)
Deevey (1941) (60)	Phormictopus cancerides	Aggregation into clumps		Unknown	

TABLE I (*Continued*)

Investigator	Source of material	Hemocytes (amebocytes)		Plasma	Comments
		No discrimination made among the cell types involved in the plasma alterations	Recording of a special category of cells involved in plasma coagulation		
Grégoire (1952, 1955, 1957, 1959); Grégoire and Jolivet (1957) (*61, 44, 47, 48, 49*)	53 Species from 17 families	Hemocytes scattered at random or agglutinated to the adhesive threadlike processes of the fragile hemocytes Development of meshworks No disintegration	Instantaneous intracellular dissolution or explosive discharges of granules by a category of hemocytes highly sensitive to foreign surfaces Extrusion of cytoplasmic expansions by other corpuscles of the same category In other specimens: no alteration	Inconstant reactions starting rapidly around altered fragile hemocytes and along their expansions: development of veils. No visible alterations in other specimens	High degree of "differential sensitiveness" of the hemocytes to contact with foreign surfaces Reactions resembling coagulation pattern II of insects (*Scarabaeidae*, lepidopteran larvae) Large variations in the reactions
(*44*)	Opiliones *Phalangiidae* sp., *Cosmetidae* sp.				
Grégoire (1955, 1959) (*44, 48*)	Pedipalpida *Tarantula palmata barbadensis*, *Tarantula fuscimana*, undetermined species			No visible alteration	Pattern IV (see Insecta)
Grégoire (1955, 1959) (*44, 48*)	Ixodidae *Ornithodorus rudis*, *Amblyomma humerale*, undetermined species			No visible alteration	Pattern IV (see Insecta)
Lochhead and Lochhead (1941) (*62*)	CRUSTACEA Primitive groups *Artemia salina* (Anostraca)	Agglutination		No coagulation	Pattern IV (see Insecta)

	Decapods and other groups Lobster, crab		Coagulation (in lobster)	
Wharton Jones (1846) (63)	Lobster, crab	Agglutination		Coagulation is a cellular process
Geddes (1879–1880) (18)	Carcinus maenas Pagurus bernhardus	Agglutination and fusion into plasmodia		Blood coagulation consists of two distinct processes
Fredericq (1879) (64)	Palinurus vulgaris Homarus vulgaris	Agglutination (plasmodia); 1st, or cellular, coagulation	True coagulation of a fibrinlike substance; 2d, plasma coagulation	
Howell (1885) (28)	Callinectes hastatus	Development of meshworks		
Heim (1892) (65)	Palinurus vulgaris, Homarus vulgaris Carcinus maenas, Maia squinado, Astacus fluviatilis	Aggregation Aggregation	True clot No coagulation	Blood coagulation consists of two distinct processes
Duceschi (1903) (19)	Homarus vulgaris, Palinurus vulgaris	Agglutination	Coagulation	
Loeb (1903–1927) (51–56)	Homarus americanus Callinectes hastatus	Agglutination. Constitution of meshworks. Fusion of the hyaline exoplasms into masses of fibrinlike substances. First or cell coagulation "cell fibrin"	Coagulation, induced by blood coagulin, into a fibrinlike substance (2d coagulation)	Blood coagulation consists of two successive and distinct processes
Krukenberg (1882) (27)	Cancer pagurus, Maia squinado	Coagulable material shed out from the cells	No coagulation (no fibrin)	Coagulation is a single process
Halliburton (1885) (66)	Homarus vulgaris, Carcinus maenas, Astacus fluviatilis, Nephrops norvegicus	The blood corpuscles supply a fibrin ferment, which induces coagulation of a fibrinogenous substance present in the plasma within the clumps of cells	Extension of coagulation due to action upon fibrinogen of the fibrin ferment yielded by the ameboid corpuscles	Coagulation is a continuous process and occurs first around the blood cells

TABLE I (Continued)

Investigator	Source of material	Hemocytes (amebocytes)		Plasma	Comments
		No discrimination made among the cell types involved in the plasma alterations	Recording of a special category of cells involved in plasma coagulation		
Cuénot (1891) (16)	20 Species of decapods, Lygia oceanica (isopod)			Fast and substantial coagulation, induced by a fibrin ferment	Coagulation is a continuous process
Bottazzi (1902) (1)	Palinurus sp., Maia sp., Homarus sp.	Agglutination and coalescence (plasmodia)		Coagulation starting around the corpuscles	Coagulation consists of two successive phases of the same process
Nolf (1909) (67)	Chiefly Palinurus vulgaris	Agglutination induced by deposition on the surface of the hemocytes of fibrin resulting from coagulation of B-fibrinogen by leucocyte coagulin (= Nolf's A-fibrinogen)		Chain process: extension with increasing rapidity to the whole plasma (coagulation of Nolf's B-fibrinogen or plasma fibrinogen) of the coagulation process initiated around the blood cells	Coagulation is a continuous process arising in plasma around the blood cells
Hardy (1892) (68)	Astacus fluviatilis, Daphnia sp.		Explosive corpuscles, source of fibrin ferment	Coagulation induced by the fibrin ferment shed out by the explosive corpuscles	Plasma coagulation initiated selectively around a category of fragile hemocytes
Tait (1910–1911); Tait and Gunn (1918) (69–71)	a.o. Maia squinado, Cancer pagurus, Gammarus marinus Carcinus maenas, Palaemon serratus, Portunus puber,	Agglutination		No jellying of the plasma (type A)	Classification of the coagulation process into three types: Type A
		Agglutination		Jellying of the plasma (type B)	Type B

Reference	Species	Insignificant agglutination and slow cytolysis (thigmocytes, amebocytes)	Hardy's explosive corpuscles, yielding a thrombinlike substance	Coagulation	Remarks
	Astacus fluviatilis, Palinurus vulgaris, Ligia oceanica and other isopods, Gammarus locusta			Jellying of the plasma. development of islands of coagulation around exploded Hardy's corpuscles. Later second jellying, involving the whole remaining plasma	Type of Coagulation, arising, continuous process, arising in plasma around a special category of fragile hemocytes
Goodrich (1920) (21)	Carcinus maenas, Astacus fluviatilis, Eupagurus prideauxi	Development of membranous processes		Coagulation	
Numanoi (1938) (72)	Ligia exotica		Hardy's explosive corpuscles	Islands of coagulation around Hardy's explosive corpuscles	Type C of Tait, inhibited by fluid of hepatopancreas
Glavind (1948) (6)	Homarus vulgaris and other decapods	Agglutination		Conversion of crustacea-fibrinogen into crustacea-fibrin, accelerated by crustacea-coagulin shed out from the hemocytes	Coagulation is a one-phase process
Morrison and Morrison (1952) (73)	12 Species from 7 families	Agglutination		Coagulation, absent in some species	
Grégoire (1955) (44)	Homarus americanus, Eriocheir sinensis, Oniscoidea sp. (isopods)		Hardy's explosive corpuscles	Islands of coagulation around Hardy's explosive corpuscles	Type C of Tait
Fredericq (1881) (74)	INSECTA Oryctes nasicornis, larva (Col.)			Coagulation	
Poulton (1885) (74a)	Phytophagous lepidopteran larvae			Solid black clots	

TABLE I (*Continued*)

Investigator	Source of material	Hemocytes (amebocytes)		Plasma	Comments
		No discrimination made among the cell types involved in the plasma alterations	Recording of a special category of cells involved in plasma coagulation		
Cuénot (1891) (16)	29 Species a.o. Stenobothrus parallelus (Orth.), Hydrophilus piceus, Blaps mortisaga (Col.)			No coagulation	
	a.o. Gryllotalpa vulgaris (Orth.), Nepa cinerea (Hemipt.), Meloe proscarabaeus (Col.)			Coagulation	
Mutkkowski (1924) (75)	6 Identified species and 10 specimens of caterpillars	Formation of cellular meshworks by thigmotactic amebocytes. Agglutination of chromophile leukocytes		Formation of a fibrin network and of gelatin, resulting in part from discharge of cell material	
Yeager et al. (1932) (76)	Periplaneta orientalis (Blattidae)	Agglutination, disintegration, and formation of a "cell coagulum"		No obvious alteration of the plasma	Limulus type of Loeb (cellular process only) or crustacean type A of Tait
Yeager and Knight (1933) (46)	47 different species of insects from various orders including a.o. 2 Cerambycidae (Col.)	No or negligible "cell coagulation"		No coagulation	Classification of the coagulation process in three groups: Group I
	Insects from various orders including 5 species of Orthoptera and species of Tenebrionidae (Col.)	Agglutination. "Cell coagulation"		No or negligible coagulation	Group II

Reference	Material		Some degree of cell coagulation	Conspicuous coagulation	Group III
	Insects from various orders, including *Gryllus* (Orth.) *Belostoma fluminea* (Hemiptera)		Cytolysis of certain cells	Alteration in plasma around the cytolyzed corpuscles	Alterations possibly corresponding to the crustacean type C of Tait
Recai (1939) (77)	*Periplaneta americana*	Formation of meshworks. Agglutination into syncytia		Coagulation starting independently from lymphocytes	
Beard (1948–1950) (78)	*Galleria mellonella*, larva (Lepidoptera)	Agglutination		Incidental formation of gelatin	
	Popilia japonica, larva (Coleoptera)	No agglutination		Plasma gel	
Grégoire and Florkin (1950) (79)	*Gryllus domesticus* (Gryllidae), *Carausius morosus* (Phasmidae)	Hemocytes not involved in the alterations of the plasma; scattered or agglutinated at random in small meshworks	Alterations in a category of fragile hemocytes (coagulocytes) homologous to Hardy's explosive corpuscles	Development of islands of coagulation around the coagulocytes	Crustacean type C of Tait
Åkesson (1953) (80)	*Calliphora erythrocephala* (Diptera)	Agglutination of sphaerule cells into lumps		Coagulation	
Grégoire (1951, 1955, 1957, 1959, and unpublished results); Grégoire and Jolivet (1957) (81, 82, 47, 48, 49)	About 1500 species from different orders. Orthopteroid complex (Blattodea, Mantodea, Isoptera, Phasmoptera, Orthoptera, Dermaptera) Plecoptera Hemiptera: Nepidae, Belostomatidae Homoptera: several families including Cicadidae, Fulgoridae, Cicadellidae, Dictyopharidae, Cercopidae Coleoptera: *Necrophorus* (Silphidae) *Cybister*	No disintegration of the hemocytes, scattered or agglutinated at random, passively entrapped in the plasma clot. Do not take part in the initiation of the process of coagulation.	Irreversible alterations affecting a category of highly unstable hemocytes (coagulocytes). Exudation or explosive discharge of cell material (cytoplasm and possibly nucleus) into the plasma	Development of islands of coagulation around the coagulocytes. Extension of the coagulation to the whole plasma	Classification of the coagulation process in 4 patterns: Pattern I (= crustacean type C of Tait); see Figs. 1 and 2

TABLE I (*Continued*)

Investigator	Source of material	Hemocytes (amebocytes)			Comments
		No discrimination made among the cell types involved in the plasma alterations	Recording of a special category of cells involved in plasma coagulation	Plasma	
	(Dytiscidae), Coprinae (Scarabaeidae), Meloidae, Cerambycidae, genera *Timarcha* and *Chrysolina* (Chrysomelidae) Panorpoid complex: Megaloptera-Sialodea (*Corydalus*, *Sialis*) Mecoptera (*Panorpa*) Trichoptera (*Leptomena*, Limnophilidae, *Anabolia*) Hymenoptera: various species of Formicidae (*Paraponera*), Vespidae, Pompilidae, Sphecidae				
	Coleoptera: Scarabaeidae: species from 8 subfamilies including Rutelinae, Melolonthinae, Dynastinae, Geotrupinae, Trichinae, Cetoninae, Valginae Panorpoid complex: lepidopteran larvae from Lymantriidae, Arctiidae, Notodontidae, Phalenidae, Agrotidae, Noctuidae, Lasiocampidae, Sphingidae, Nymphalidae	No disintegration of the hemocytes, agglutinated at random along the highly adhesive cytoplasmic expansions of the fragile hyaline hemocytes	Extrusion of cytoplasmic expansions by unstable hemocytes resembling the coagulocytes. Constitution of pseudopodial meshworks	No islands of coagulation. Outgrowth of jellylike veils in plasma, within the systems of expansions of the unstable hemocytes	Pattern II

Reference	Insects			Pattern III (= association of the reactions observed in patterns I and II) / Pattern IV
	Diptera: larvae of Tipulidae			
	Homoptera: species of Cercopidae and of Cicadellidae Coleoptera: Elateridae Coprinae Former superfamily Heteromera: Tenebrionidae, Lagriidae, Oedemeridae, some species of Meloidae Lepidoptera: possibly Saturniidae Hymenoptera: species from Tenthredinidae, Formicidae, Vespidae, Pompilidae, Sphecidae, Mutillidae	As in patterns I and II	Alterations in unstable hemocytes, as in pattern I (explosive discharges). Production, by the same corpuscles, of cytoplasmic expansions, as in pattern II	Islands of coagulation as in pattern I. Veils as in pattern II (**Pattern III**)
	Hemiptera-Heteroptera: species from 14 families including, a.o., Reduviidae, Coreidae, Pentatomidae, Scutellaridae Coleoptera: Hydrophilidae, Staphylinidae Curculionidae (except for a few species—see reference 83), Brenthidae Panorpoid complex: Mantispidae Diptera: adult specimens Hymenoptera: several Apidae	Scattered or agglutinated at random in small groups	No modification, or alterations (discharges of material in the corpuscles resembling coagulocytes	No visible alteration by phase contrast microscopy (see the text) (**Pattern IV**)
Grégoire (1955, 1959) (82, 83)	Curculionidae (33 species) Diptera (10 species)	Constitution of loose networks by extensive pseudopodial arborizations developed in a category of hemocytes	See above (pattern IV)	Except in a few species of Curculionidae and in Dipteran larvae, no visible alteration

TABLE I (*Continued*)

Investigator	Source of material	Hemocytes (amebocytes)		Plasma	Comments
		No discrimination made among the cell types involved in the plasma alterations	Recording of a special category of cells involved in plasma coagulation		
Jones (1956) (84)	Sarcophaga bullata (Diptera)	Formation of plasmodial networks			
Cuénot (1891) (16)	Amphioxus	Amebocytes not seen		Unknown	
	Protochordata TUNICATA				
Krukenberg (1882) (27)	Ciona intestinalis, Ascidia mentula, A. mammillata, A. fumigata			No coagulation	
Nolf (1909) (34)	Botryllus violaceus, Ciona intestinalis			No coagulation	
Cuénot (1891) (16)	Phallusia mammillata, Ciona intestinalis, Ascidia mentula and sanguinolenta, and other species	In perivascular fluid: amebocytes not recorded. In blood: agglutination		No information	
Henze (1911) (85)	Phallusia mammillata, Ascidia mentula, A. fumigata	Blood: agglutination		No coagulation	
Fry (1909) (86)	Ciona intestinalis	Blood: agglutination		No coagulation	
Huus (1937) (87)	Ciona intestinalis, Appendiculariae	In perivisceral fluid: amebocytes not seen. In blood: no information		No coagulation	
Robertson (1954) (88)	Phallusia mammillata, Salpa maxima			No coagulation	
Webb (1956) (89)				No coagulation	

especially in Crustacea. In arthropods, one finds a series of types showing every gradation of evolution, from complete absence of clotting to the occurrence of firm jelly coagulums (69).

In 1846, Wharton Jones (63) observed in crustacean blood collected *in vitro* the formation of plugs consisting of agglutinated corpuscles. The remaining fluid exhibited in various species all gradations in its clotting properties. The reactions of blood corpuscles and those of the plasma of Crustacea, were subsequently described in a great number of papers (Table I).

In Crustacea, the process of coagulation has been reported as taking place either in two successive phases; the phases are considered to be two distinct and independent processes (by dualists) or a single continuous process (by unicists). For the dualists (51–56, 64, 65), agglutination of the blood corpuscles (first or cell coagulation) is followed in some species by gelification of the plasma (second or plasma coagulation). On the other hand, for the unicists (1, 16, 27, 66, 67), coagulation of soluble components of the plasma occurs first around the blood corpuscles, which furnish thromboplastic substances, and spreads out more or less rapidly to the whole plasma.

In all these studies, no special part in the process of coagulation was recognized as being played by a special category of cells. All the corpuscles were described as undergoing common alterations, resulting in formation of "cell fibrin" or supplying substances (blood coagulins) that induce clotting of the plasma.

A considerable advance in the knowledge of the coagulation process in Crustacea was realized when Hardy (68), confirmed by Tait (69, 70) and Tait and Gunn (71), showed that in several Crustacea a category of highly fragile blood cells (explosive corpuscles) were selectively altered and that coagulation of the plasma occurred first around these corpuscles in the shape of islands. These investigators suggested, in agreement with a previous interpretation of Halliburton (66), that disruption of these corpuscles and dispersion of their granules would set free a substance (fibrin ferment) affecting a coagulable component in the plasma. Tait (69, 70; Tait and Gunn, 71), however, did not exclude the possibility that the other, more stable categories of blood cells (thigmocytes), might also discharge active substances in later stages. Among the three distinct modes of coagulation in Crustacea recognized by Tait (69) (see Table I), type C is the only one characterized by jellying of the plasma in the shape of islands of coagulation around Hardy's explosive corpuscles. The occurrence of such a category of unstable hemocytes, especially sensitive, in contrast with the other kinds of blood corpuscles, to contact with foreign surfaces, has been questioned by some (91), but confirmed by others (44, 72) in Crustacea.

In other arthropods, similar fragile hemocytes were first observed in insects (79, 81, 82), then in myriapods (44), Xiphosura (44, 59), scorpionids (44, 49), in spiders (44, 47, 48, 49), and in Onychophora (*Peripatus*) (44), a highly primitive group associating annelidan and arthropodan characteristics.

In insects, coagulation type C of Tait, observed incidentally in a specimen of *Belostoma fluminea* (46), was first described in *Gryllus domesticus* and in *Carausius morosus* (79). In these insects, alteration of the hemolymph *in vitro*, recorded by phase contrast microscopy and by microcinematography, started in a category of labile hyaline hemocytes characterized by a generally small, eccentric nucleus and a pale hyaline cytoplasm containing a few scattered granules. These cells, called coagulocytes (79), are highly sensitive to solid surfaces and to physical interfaces. Alterations in these fragile elements consist of exudation or discharge of cell substance (79, 81, 82, 82a), followed by the development in the surrounding plasma of typical islands of coagulation and by subsequent jellyfication of the whole plasma. Further studies (47, 48, 49, 81, 82, 83, 92) showed that large disparities occur in insects with regard to the microscopical picture of the films of clotting hemolymph, and especially in the nature of the alterations in the fragile hemocytes.

Hemocytes which resemble the coagulocytes in their cytological appearance and are similarly unstable to contact with foreign surfaces, upon shedding of the hemolymph undergo changes consisting of extrusion of highly adhesive threadlike cytoplasmic expansions; these changes result in the constitution of systems of cytoplasmic meshworks of various complexity. Confined to these systems of cytoplasmic meshworks, the reactions in the plasma developed in the shape of elastic, contractile, and transparent veils. In other insects, islands of coagulation were found together with these alterations; in yet others, a visible reaction could not be recorded in the plasma, at least under the phase contrast microscope (see below).

These different reactions in unstable hemocytes and in the plasma have been classified into four tentative patterns, whose characteristic features are summarized in Table I. Owing to resemblances in the microscopic reactions, this classification has also been used for other groups of arthropods (see below). The patterns of hemolymph coagulation representative for each species have been determined in fifteen hundred species of insects and other arthropods (Myriapoda, Arachnida)

($44, 47, 48, 49, 59, 61, 81, 82, 83, 92$). Predominance of one of the patterns has been recorded in several groups (see Table I), at different levels of the taxonomic hierarchy.

The results of this survey suggest that the coagulation patterns are not individual particularities but represent, in Insecta and possibly in Myriapoda and in various groups of Arachnida (e.g., Araneae, Scorpionidae), stable characters of species and more frequently of supraspecific taxonomic categories (genera, families, suborders, orders). The investigations on the distribution of the patterns of hemolymph coagulation in the different orders of insects are recorded below in a condensed form ($47, 48$).

(a) In the orthopteroid complex, a great uniformity of reaction (pattern I). (See Fig. 2.)

(b) In 14 families of Hemiptera-Heteroptera, no visible reaction in plasma (pattern IV), in striking contrast to two families of the same suborder, Nepidae-Ranatridae and Belostomatidae (substantial coagulation of pattern I). (See Fig. 1.)

(c) Among Hemiptera-Homoptera, extremely rapid coagulation (especially in Fulgoridae) and predominance of pattern I in 6 families.

(d) Among Coleoptera, as a taxonomic group, great heterogeneity in the reactions. However, in this order, uniformity of the reactions or predominance of a pattern was recorded at the infra-order level, especially in the families Hydrophilidae and Staphylinidae, in most Curculionidae (pattern IV), in the former superfamily Heteromera (pattern I and/or III), in the families Cerambycidae and Meloidae (pattern I), in several subfamilies of Scarabaeidae (pattern II).

(e) In the panorpoid complex, predominance of pattern II in larval Lepidoptera, of pattern IV in Mantispidae and in adult Diptera, of pattern I in Sialodea and Trichoptera.

(f) In Hymenoptera, occurrence of patterns I and/or III in several families.

Other groups from various orders, e.g., Carabidae (Coleoptera), exhibit large individual and species variations in their coagulation pattern. However, in these groups, a distinct predominance of one of the patterns was recorded in scattered genera or species. Among all the insects investigated, the most dense coagulation was observed in several species of Blattidae and of Gryllidae, in Gryllotalpa (orthopteroid complex), in all Nepidae and Belostomatidae (Hemiptera-Heteroptera), in Fulgoridae (Hemiptera-Homoptera), in Cerambycidae (Prioninae, Lamiinae), and in Heteromera (Meloidae) (Coleoptera) ($47, 49, 81, 82$).

Random coincidence does not seem entirely to explain some correlations between phylogenetic position of certain groups of insects and the microscopic aspect of the coagulation of their hemolymph. For instance, pattern I has been recorded in various unrelated groups, especially in those characterized by the retention of various primitive characters (82). As shown in comparisons between the microscopic pictures of films of hemolymph spread out under glass by the standard procedure used and in clot plugs spontaneously formed at the wound sites in different insects, the patterns are faithful reproductions of the corresponding alterations that occur during the undisturbed natural processes (47, 82). The uniformity in the pattern recorded in taxonomic groups as broad as the orthopteroid complex offers provisionally, as far as qualitative aspects are concerned, little prospect for the detection of differences in more limited subgroups belonging to this complex. However, differences in the relative number of coagulocytes capable of initiating coagulation (coagulocyte index) and differences in the amount of clotted material developed around these cells bring evidence that a quantitative appreciation of differences between species and groups might be possible by means of adequate methods.

In none of the patterns did the other categories of hemocytes take part in the process of coagulation, in contrast with the unstable corpuscles. These hemocytes remained unaltered or underwent slow modifications without cytolysis. They were passively entrapped at random in the plasma clots (pattern I), in the veils (pattern II), in both formations (pattern III), or they gathered along the highly adhesive expansions already developed by the fragile corpuscles.

The differences recorded in the patterns probably reflect differences among species and higher taxonomic groups of insects and other arthropods in the relative number and in the degree of sensitiveness of the fragile hemocytes to contact with foreign surfaces, in the nature of the alterations undergone by these unstable cells, in their content in coagu-

---

Fig. 1. *Lethocerus cordofanus* Mayr (Hemiptera, *Belostomatidae,* Congo). Pattern I of coagulation: circular island of coagulation around a coagulocyte. In this preparation, extension of the coagulation process took place in the shape of successive waves. Two of these waves are illustrated in the picture. At the periphery of the second wave, channels between the islands of coagulation contain still fluid hemolymph (×600). Courtesy Institut des Parcs Nationaux du Congo et du Ruanda-Urundi (*49*).

Fig. 2. *Orxines* sp. (*maclotti* De Haan, Java). Phasmoptera. Selective development of an island of coagulation around a fragile hyaline hemocyte (coagulocyte). Two granular hemocytes do not take part in the process of coagulation (×600). Courtesy *Archives de biologie* (*82*).

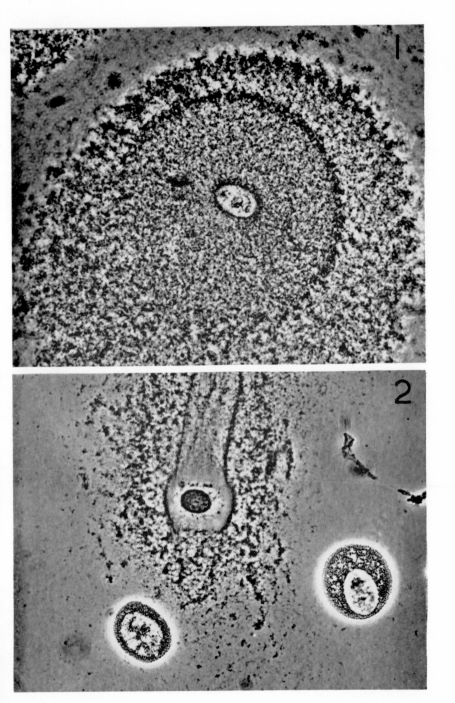

lins, in the amounts in coagulable substances in the surrounding plasma. A similar degree of sensitiveness of the fragile hemocytes is frequently shared by insects belonging to a same taxonomic group (47, 82).

Numerous other factors, still insufficiently known, such as seasonal, developmental, nutritional, cryptic pathological conditions, affect the behavior of the hemolymph in insects (49, 81, 82) and probably also in other arthropods and invertebrates, either by altering the contact sensitiveness of the coagulocytes and similar unstable hemocytes, or by changing the amounts of coagulable substances in the plasma. For instance, a decrease in the clotting ability of the blood has been reported at pupation (89a). Similarly, the hemolymph of insects, characterized in normal conditions by a substantial coagulation, does not clot any more when infection is observed (49, 82) or in starved animals (as in other groups of invertebrates 2, 6, 16, 89b). When only a limited number of specimens are available, these factors are a serious handicap to recording the actual reactions.

From these observations, hemolymph coagulation in insects appears to be a continuous process, initiated by alterations taking place on contact with foreign surfaces in a single category of highly fragile hemocytes, and followed by various degrees of gelification of the plasma. These results are at variance with the conclusions of previous studies (75, 76, 78), in which the hemolymph coagulation in insects was described as consisting of two physiologically distinct processes, which can occur independently or together: (a) cell agglutination or cell coagulation, with no participation of a special category of blood elements, and/or (b) plasma coagulation. These differences in the conception of the mechanism of coagulation of the hemolymph in insects and in the criteria used for appreciating the reactions of the hemolymph in vitro are responsible for the profound divergencies recorded in the literature about a same group of insects. As shown in Table I, species belonging to groups characterized by a consistent and substantial coagulation of the hemolymph, such as Orthoptera (47, 48, 49, 79, 81, 82), have been reported to have no coagulation at all (46, 76).

In Onychophora and in the groups of arthropods, other than Crustacea and Insecta, which were the subject of investigation (Myriapoda, Xiphosura, Scorpionidae, Araneae) (44, 47, 48, 49), the alterations in fragile hyaline hemocytes containing granules in variable amounts were frequently instantaneous (Araneae) and consisted of intracytoplasmic explosion and dissolution of the granules and of ejection of these organelles into the surrounding fluid. After these changes, the altered hemocytes closely resembled the insect coagulocytes. In these groups of arthropods, the rapid cytologic alterations in the fragile corpuscles were not (Onychophora, Myriapoda)* or were inconstantly (Xiphosura, Araneae) followed by alterations in the plasma.

In the films of Limulus and of spider blood (44), the changes in the plasma consisted predominantly of veils, frequently confined within pseudopodial systems built up by the unstable hemocytes, a picture resembling that described as pattern II of coagulation and found in groups of insects such as Scarabaeidae and lepidopteran larvae. These veils developed with great suddenness, when all hemocytes, except the unstable corpuscles were still unaltered. Modification in the plasma around unstable hemocytes, assuming a resemblance with islands of coagulation, found in a few samples of Limulus blood and in one sample of spider blood (Lycosa), suggest that a mechanism of coagulation involved in Crustacea (type C of Tait) and in Insecta (pattern I) (81, 82) might also occur in other groups of Arthropoda.

Identification of the fragile hyaline hemocytes of insects (coagulocytes) with the functionally corresponding unstable hemocytes in other arthropods has been attempted in several papers (44, 47, 81, 82, 92). Differential counts of these hyaline hemocytes performed in 12 species of insects characterized by different coagulation patterns of their hemolymph (82) have shown that these corpuscles represent from 8% to 95% of the hemocytes.

In certain groups of insects [larval Odonata, Hemiptera-Heteroptera (93), larval and adult Coleoptera and Diptera, larval Lepidoptera, Trichoptera, some Hymenoptera] and in various spiders, some of the unstable corpuscles exhibit cytological features which are also observed in oenocytoids. In the films of hemolymph, these hemocytes appear as highly refractile or as dark hyaline corpuscles of large size, which undergo a sudden clarification after discharge of cytoplasmic and perhaps of nuclear substance. However, the same corpuscles differ in other cytological characters from the classic description of the oenocytoids (82).

Hemostasis in Invertebrates

The role in hemostasis of the different mechanisms of hemolymph or of blood coagulation has been always more or less tinted with teleological considerations. Frequently also, apparently consistent theories are invalidated by spectacular exceptions (69, 70). The interrelations of the different factors affecting the potential loss of blood in Crustacea (autotomy, hemocyte agglutination, clotting ability, strength of the integument) have been discussed (73).

---

* Inelastic pellicles or scanty veil-like reactions were observed incidentally in thick blood films exposed to air in this group (44).

Among invertebrates, coagulable substances in conspicuous amounts appear first in arthropods, while in several other groups, such as mollusks and worms, such substances are absent or still ill defined. It has been pointed out (16) that in arthropods, when the process of autotomy is not functioning, puncturing of the rigid integument leaves a hole which remains yawning. In that condition, formation of a fibrinlike material is a highly efficient process to stop bleeding. On the other hand, in mollusks and in worms, contraction of musculature is sufficient to stop bleeding and is helped by a plug of agglutinated corpuscles.

The process of cell agglutination, which characterizes the reactions of the extravasated coelomic fluid in many other groups of invertebrates, has been considered by most investigators (Table I) as adequate to stop bleeding in these invertebrates. A similar process might even exist in sponges (4, 94) in which agglutination of archeocytes might play the same part as the amebocytes in the other groups. This hemocyte reaction, responsible for development of initial plugs of wounds, has been considered (51–56) to be the prototype of the analogous spindle cell agglutination in amphibians and of platelet agglutination in mammals.

Among the arthropods, the prominent part played by the explosive corpuscles of Hardy in the arrest of hemorrhage has been vividly described by Tait (69) in Crustacea, especially in *Gammarus*, at the stump of sectioned antennae examined under coverglass. Hardy's explosive corpuscles aggregate rapidly at the end of the stump. Soon, a small globular mass, homogeneous and transparent, appears from among these cells and is accompanied by vibrations and upheavals due to successive explosions of the fragile hemocytes. The globules still attached to the stump grow in size, very much as a blown soap bubble expands. Numerous other globules of firm consistency appear rapidly in succession, clinging to the end of the stump. These globules are actually explosion coagula or islands of coagulation, around which a true passive agglutination of other categories of cells takes place. The primary function of these explosive coagula seems therefore to be the formation of a mechanical obstruction.

The successive steps of coagulation at a wound site described by Tait in Crustacea have been also observed by phase contrast microscopy in insects characterized by pattern I of coagulation (Table I) corresponding to type C of Tait (47, 82). In arthropods in which the hemolymph or blood does not exhibit visible alterations in plasma [crustacean type A (62, 69) or pattern IV in insects (49, 81, 82, 83)], and in which explosive corpuscles are inactive with regard to induction of modifications in plasma, hemostasis might be realized by different mechanisms. In these animals, formation of plugs by agglutinated hemo-

cytes (62) or development of extensive networks of cytoplasmic arbor-
izations resembling the dendritic expansions of nerve cells in vertebrates,
e.g., Diptera (82, 84), Curculionidae (83), might functionally compen-
sate for the failure of the fragile hemocytes, homologous to the coagulocytes of other groups, to induce coagulation of the plasma. However,
as pressure of the hemolymph inside the insect hemocoele is below the
atmospheric pressure under normal circumstances, it has been objected
that little hemolymph is lost from a wound and that the clotting property is not necessary to all members of the insect group (7).

In Crustacea, Fredericq's autotomy is another procedure for stopping
bleeding. It has been pointed out that coagulation and autotomy might,
in certain species, substitute for one another (69) and that some inverse
correlation between autotomy and clotting ability may be seen in the
fact that heavy clots come from genera in which it is difficult to induce
autotomy while light clots come from genera prone to autotomy (73).
Other factors such as thickness of the integument have been also considered (6, 51–56, 65, 73, 95).

B. CHORDATES

1. Tunicates

The plasma of tunicates is very similar in composition to sea water
(27, 89) and contains only small amounts of proteins. No coagulation
of this fluid has been so far reported (Table I).

2. Vertebrates

Most of the studies on blood coagulation in vertebrates deal with
the blood of the higher mammals, especially man. These investigations
carried out by a large number of laboratories and investigators have
led to a consideration of blood coagulation as a complex set of reactions
involving numerous factors and quite unlike the apparent simplicity
described in lower animals. For purposes of discussion, the scheme of
blood coagulation depicted in Tables II and III can be used at present,
with the realization that it does not necessarily represent all the views
presently held on the subject. This is not the place to discuss the significance of every step in this reaction and the experimental support
for each of them except as they may relate to similar or analogous
phenomena in the lower animals.

(a) The coagulation factors listed as participants in the reaction do
not all necessarily correspond to chemical entities. Several have never
been isolated in a state approaching purity and chemical identification.
This applies particularly to the more recently recognized factors: factor

TABLE II
SCHEME OF BLOOD COAGULATION

A. FIBRINOGENESIS

1. Proteolysis:

$$\text{Fibrinogen} \xrightarrow{\text{thrombin (FCA, Ca}^{2+}\text{)}} \text{Fibrin monomer and Peptides}$$

2. Polymerization:

$$\text{Fibrin monomer} \xrightarrow{\text{colloids, Ca}^{2+}} \text{Fibrin polymer (soluble)}$$

3. True coagulation:

$$\text{Fibrin polymer (soluble)} \xrightarrow{\text{FSF. Ca}^{2+}} \text{Fibrin (insoluble)}$$

B. EXTRINSIC THROMBINOGENESIS

1. Thromboplastin + Ca^{2+} + Proconvertin $\underset{\text{tissue}}{\overset{\text{Stuart-Prower}}{\rightleftharpoons}}$ Activated thromboplastin (convertin)

2. Prothrombin $\xrightarrow{\text{activated thromboplastin (convertin)}}$ Thrombin

3. Proaccelerin $\xrightarrow{\text{thrombin}}$ Accelerin

4. Convertin + accelerin $\rightleftharpoons$ Complete thromboplastin (prothrombinase)

5. Prothrombin $\xrightarrow{\text{complete thromboplastin}}$ Thrombin

C. FORMATION OF PLASMA THROMBOPLASTIN AND INTRINSIC THROMBINOGENESIS

1. Hageman $\xrightarrow{\text{contact}}$ Activated Hageman

2. Precursor $\xrightarrow{\text{activated Hageman, PTA}}$ Antihemophilic B activated + PPA

3. Activated antihemophilic A + B $\xrightarrow{\text{Stuart-Prower}}$ Intermediary product

4. Intermediary product I + Platelets → Activated thromboplastin (intermediary product II)

5. Activated thromboplastin + Accelerin → Complete thromboplastin (plasma thromboplastin)

6. Prothrombin $\xrightarrow{\text{complete thromboplastin}}$ Thrombin

III and factors V to X. Prothrombin and fibrinogen have a more precise definition as chemical entities (96).

(b) The coagulation reaction consists of a series of steps, but in addition, there are interactions of reaction products with initial reagents in such a way that the velocity of the general reaction can be influenced positively or negatively by intermediary products. Thus thrombin activates Ac-globulin (factor V) and in this way speeds up the conversion of prothrombin to thrombin (96). Another example is provided by fibrinolysin (plasmin) which splits fibrin into fragments having antithrombin activity capable of delaying coagulation. These actions and

TABLE III

PLASMA COAGULATION FACTORS

Factor number	Synonyms
I	Fibrinogen
II	Prothrombin
III	Thromboplastin
IV	Calcium
V	Proaccelerin, labile factor, plasma Ac-globulin
(VI)	(Accelerin, serum Ac-globulin)
VII	Proconvertin, stable factor, SPCA (serum prothrombin conversion accelerator)
VIII	Antihemophilic factor A, antihemophilic globulin, thromboplastinogen, platelet cofactor I
IX	Antihemophilic factor B, Christmas factor, PTC (plasma thromboplastin component), platelet cofactor II
X	Stuart-Prower factor, Stuart factor, Prower factor
—	PTA (plasma thromboplastin antecedent)
—	PPA (prephase accelerator)
—	Hageman factor

interactions probably account for the contrast between the stability of circulating blood and the rapidity of clot formation when hemostasis is needed. A simpler system might not be able so precisely to satisfy these two opposite requirements.

Proteolysis is an important biochemical aspect of the blood coagulation reaction: thus the transformation of prothrombin into thrombin is the result of a proteolytic action (97). Thrombin is a proteolytic enzyme (98). The last step of the coagulation process consisting of the gradual disappearance of the clot of fibrin is brought about by the action of the proteolytic enzyme plasmin, resulting from the activation of the precursor plasminogen present in the plasma.

(c) A recently proposed concept of the nature of prothrombin and its evolution during the coagulation reaction would tend to consider several plasma factors listed in Table II as simple derivatives of the initial prothrombin molecule. This view would attribute to the prothrombin molecule the unique ability to undergo, spontaneously or otherwise, important chemical modifications, some of them reversible, demonstrable in certain experimental conditions and occurring perhaps physiologically as well. Through these modifications, certain plasma factors listed as independent entities would evolve from the original molecule (99). This new interpretation should suggest a re-examination of the "coagulation ferment" (Table I) described in invertebrates, in order to explore similar capabilities in this molecule.

(d) There are several possible pathways for the conversion of prothrombin into thrombin, the clotting enzyme. One of these can be demonstrated under experimental conditions which do not seem to have a physiological counterpart: the spontaneous transformation of prothrombin into thrombin in 25% sodium citrate solution more or less free of other coagulation factors does not occur *in vivo*. On the other hand, thrombin formation in plasma without intervention of platelet or tissue factors is possible and may have physiologic significance. The participation of factors derived from platelets or tissues represent two other possibilities, each of which alone may create a speedy enough reaction for hemostatic purposes, although maximum velocity is probably ensured when both platelet and tissue factors add their effects, e.g., when bleeding results from a traumatic disruption of tissue (97, 99).

In contrast, in the case of invertebrates, one can say that participation of cellular elements in blood coagulation appears to be necessary; possible exceptions are suggested by observations on *Calliphora erythrocephala* (80) and on other insects [around air bubbles (74a, 82)] in which apparently coagulation of cell-free fluid was observed (see below).

III. Comparison of Coagulation Systems among the Zoological Groups

The number of species of invertebrates which have been studied with respect to coagulation of hemolymph or blood is very small in comparison with the number of existing species, which is estimated as approximately one million. Even crude morphological information on entire important groups is completely lacking. Under such conditions, generalizations are liable to be untimely and questionable.

On the other hand, coagulation in vertebrates has been studied more extensively, and this applies especially to mammals. Unfortunately studies, with few exceptions, on nonmammalian species were conducted before the recognition of factors subsequent to factor V. Yet it is the discovery of these newer factors which has elucidated much that could not properly be interpreted earlier.

A. THE COAGULABLE PROTEINS OF PLASMA

Little is known of the chemical nature of the substances involved in the process of hemolymph or blood coagulation in invertebrates. The terms fibrin and gelatin used in the literature for the characterization of the coagulum do not imply a chemical identification, but rather a morphological analogy with the coagulum of vertebrate blood. Among the data collected on the protein components of invertebrate blood by means of modern methods of biochemistry, a single study (100) so far has been directly focused on the coagulation process in an attempt to clarify the concept of "coagulable protein" of plasma and to prepare electrophoretically homogeneous lobster fibrinogen. Except for this paper, most investigations do not concern themselves with the coagulation process. Several protein fractions have been separated by starch or paper electrophoresis in the hemolymph of various insects, especially from the serum (101–108). These studies have shown that the cell-free pupal blood of the silkworm (Platysamia) (101, 102) exhibits electrophoretic patterns comparable in complexity with those of mammalian serum.

A recent review (10) states that there is no reason to suppose that the clotting system of Arthropod blood will prove to be much less complex than that of human plasma. However, Duchâteau and Florkin (100) showed in Homarus that purified, electrophoretically homogeneous fibrinogen is clotted by simple addition of muscle coagulin obtained by ultracentrifugation. Though purified by elimination of a part of its components, the muscle coagulin used by the authors was not electrophoretically homogeneous and still consisted of three components. Attempts at isolation and at identification of the active coagulin factor or factors among these three components have failed so far owing to the instability of the preparation.

As far as true fibrin formation is concerned, it seems well established that it occurs in all vertebrates as well as in certain invertebrates (Crustacea) (Table I). However, fibrinogen in mammals differs from crustacean fibrinogen in solubility and electrophoretic mobility (100). Differences exist also between the clots of vertebrates and invertebrates as far as structure and appearance are concerned. During the clotting of mammalian blood, fibrin is deposited as crystallike needles with the formation of a network.

Extending some old observations with the ultramicroscope on fibrin formation in arthropods and in vertebrates (28, 109, 110), recent studies with the phase contrast microscope (79, 81) have detected granular material in the islands of coagulation of insect hemolymph. In thin films of hemolymph spread out between slide and coverglass, the granular precipitates become gradually organized into beaded threads or into strings loaded with granular particles and form delicate meshworks. Absence of crystallike needles, developed during the clotting of mammalian blood (28, 109, 110), has been generally reported in invertebrate blood clots (Crustacea, *28, 73, 110;* Insecta, *110*). However, transformation of the granular material of the coagulum in the peripheral parts of the islands of coagulation into needlelike structures, especially in the vicinity of air bubbles, has been observed in films of hemolymph, spread out between glass and coverglass, of two species of insects [*Laccotrephes vicinus* (*49*); *Ranatra linearis* (*111*)] characterized by the pattern I of coagulation.

Under the electron microscope, the granular substance of the islands of coagulation, unmixed with cellular products of disintegration of the coagulocytes, studied in species belonging to various orders of insects and characterized by pattern I of coagulation of their hemolymph (*111, 112*), appears in the shape of spongelike masses or rugged pebbles (microflocs) scattered or agglutinated at random against a background of small, rounded particles. The substance of the granulum, stretched mechanically into pseudofilaments or strings or organized secondarily into meshworks, exhibits the same spongelike appearance.

Microflocs were observed also in other forms of coagulation of insect plasma, such as the veils in pattern II (*83, 111*). At the electron microscope level, these structures differed from those observed in the granular substance of the coagulation islands (pattern I) in their texture, in their size, and in the mode of their dispersion in the films.

In pattern IV (*83*), characterized by absence of visible changes in plasma in the optical conditions of phase contrast microscopy, microflocs, with the same spongelike structure detected in the clots of other insects, were dispersed in the films; however, they were fewer than in film preparations from insects having blood that clots and were not visible with conventional microscopes.

These discrete reactions suggest that clotted material might not be absent from the reactions of the hemolymph outside the body cavity, in which no perceptible modification of the fluidity or of the microscopic appearance of the plasma has been detected by phase contrast microscopy (*83, 111*). The clear gel developed in *Limulus* blood (second coagulation, see Table I) and associated with the clumping of the cells, appears under the electron microscope in the shape of extremely thin filaments (*113*).

Except for incidental findings (*49, 111*) (*Laccotrephes vicinus, Ranatra linearis*), no periodicity similar to that observed in vertebrate fibrin fibrils (*114, 115, 116*) has been so far recorded in the fibrillar structures forming the clots in invertebrates.

A general handicap in such investigations on invertebrate blood is that, in contrast with the studies on vertebrate blood performed on purified preparations of fibrinogen and of thrombin of known content and activity, all these electron microscope observations were made on the whole hemolymph (without hemocytes in some cases), a much too complex system, in which numerous unpurified components probably interfere with each other.

B. The Cells Involved in Production of Coagulation-Inducing Substances (Coagulins)

Analogies between amebocytes of invertebrates and spindle cells, thrombocytes, and platelets of vertebrates had been long established (51–$57, 117$) at a time when agglutination, described as an alteration common to all these elements upon shedding of blood, was considered as the only process of coagulation in many invertebrates, including several arthropods (Table I).

The findings of Hardy and others ($47, 48, 49, 68$–$71, 79, 81, 82, 83$) have shown that in physiological coagulation in several arthropods, the source of the blood coagulins must probably not be sought, at least in the early phases of the process, in the whole-cell fraction of the blood, as a result of common alterations undergone by all the hemocytes, but rather in a special category of fragile cells. These fragile cells are much more sensitive to contact with foreign surfaces than the other categories of hemocytes, and are selectively involved, like ruptured vertebrate platelets, in the initiation of the process of coagulation by discharge of a blood coagulin.

In arthropods, the explosive cells of Hardy and the coagulocytes represent a high degree of selective adaptation and of functional specialization of a category of blood corpuscles, which coincide, in some groups (crustacean type C, insect pattern I) with the simultaneous presence in plasma of coagulable substances in conspicuous amounts, a peculiarity typical of arthropods—at least in the present conditions of ignorance about other groups of invertebrates.

Detection in other orders of arthropods and possibly in echinoderms (Table I) of similar blood corpuscles ($44, 47, 48, 49, 59$), characterized by a higher sensitiveness than other categories of hemocytes to contact with foreign surfaces, suggests that this specialization represents a general character, at a morphological level, of the Arthropoda and at the same time may be considered to be an example of functional convergence in zoological groups as distant as are arthropods and vertebrates. In vertebrates, and especially in mammals, the platelets, in contrast with the other categories of blood cells, exhibit a similar specialization: as the explosive cells in Crustacea and as the coagulocytes in Insecta, platelets are unstable on contact with foreign surfaces, on which they undergo spectacular alterations, and they play similarly a selective role in the initiation of the alterations in plasma. However, the morphological reactions of these corpuscles and those of the plasma in their vicinity differ in invertebrates and in vertebrates. Some of these differences are reported in Sections III, B, 1–5, below.

1. Early Alterations in and around Vertebrate Platelets and Invertebrate Fragile Hemocytes

In mammals, the initial event in hemostasis appears to be the agglutination of platelets in the wound, with formation of long pseudopodia. This process, called viscous transformation of platelets, precedes the formation of fibrin (118, 118a). It is induced by contact with a modified endothelial surface in the case of a wound or, experimentally, with glass. If and when fibrin formation occurs, the altered platelets seem to provide the network on which the coagulable proteins precipitate. In invertebrates, neither Hardy's explosive corpuscles nor insect coagulocytes exhibit, at least in vitro, the property of autoagglutinability that characterizes the platelets.

In mammals, it is not entirely clear whether the viscous transformation of platelets occurs without participation of plasma factors. Thrombin appears to play an important role, and it has also been demonstrated that many of the soluble coagulation factors can be extracted from washed platelets to which they are attached by adsorption or some other process (119). These observations illustrate once more the difficulties experienced in attempting to separate experimentally formed elements and plasma factors in the production of hemostasis.

In mammals, when fibrin formation takes place, there is apparent orientation of fibrin fibers in relation to the pseudopods of the platelets generated by their viscous transformation (120). On the other hand, in Crustacea and in Insecta, after explosive discharge of substance by the fragile corpuscles followed by formation of islands of coagulation, such precise orientation of the clotting material has so far not been described, except incidentally (49). If the participation of certain plasma clotting factors, among which are calcium ions, the antihemophilic and the Christmas factor, is required for the viscous transformation of platelets, such participation of noncellular factors of the hemolymph or blood of lower animals to the alterations of the explosive cells, coagulocytes, and spindle cells is not demonstrated, but cannot be excluded. Removers of calcium ions prevent disintegration of coagulocytes in insects (121).

The fragility of the explosive corpuscles and of the coagulocytes seems to be much greater than that of the platelets. In contrast with the blood of vertebrates, no modification or delay in clotting was noticed (121) when hemolymph of insects was collected on nonadhesive water-repellent surfaces such as those of various plastic materials, resins, and glass coated with silicone. In oily environments negative results were obtained even when hemolymph, during transfer from the coelomic cavity to the coated slide, was preserved from contact with air and from contamination with the tissues at the wound before falling onto the silicone-coated surfaces. The consistent failure of the silicone-coated surfaces to prevent coagulation of insect hemolymph may be explained by assuming that alterations in the coagulocytes and liberation of coagulins may have already started before the hemolymph reaches the silicone surfaces, possibly in contact with injured tissue fragments incompletely coated with oil at the wound site.

2. Anticoagulants

Substances which decrease, delay, or prevent the alterations in the platelets (122–125) in the crustacean explosive corpuscles (19, 71, 126) and in the fragile hemocytes of insects (coagulocytes) (121) decrease, delay, or prevent blood coagulation.

In studies of this kind, development or absence of alterations in the unstable hemocytes and of subsequent formation of islands of coagulation around these corpuscles (coagulation pattern I) constitutes an expedient morphological test for appreciating anticoagulant effects. By means of this test, 33 substances, most of them anticoagulants of vertebrate blood, have been investigated in vitro on hemolymph of different species of insects, chiefly characterized in normal conditions by a conspicuous coagulation pattern I (121).

Several compounds, which act on vertebrate blood as removers of calcium ions, deionizing agents, or preventers of platelet disintegration, were also efficient anticoagulants of insect hemolymph. It has not been established whether these compounds interfere with the insect coagulation process either, like other strong salts, in preventing the release of coagulins by the fragile hemocytes or in inactivating these substances, or by removing calcium salts possibly involved in the mechanism of the clotting process of the plasma. It is worth mentioning that among the organic esters of sulfuric acid, which were found to be efficient anticoagulants of insect blood, the trypanocidal drug suramin is an inhibitor of enzymatic activity (127). Proteolytic enzyme inhibitors, such as the soybean trypsin inhibitor (128) and the pancreatic trypsin inhibitor (129) which exhibit definite anticoagulant activity on the blood of mammals, have not been investigated on lower animals.

3. Effects of Ionizing Radiations on Coagulation

Among the factors of the hemorrhagic syndrome which develops in vertebrates exposed to total body irradiation by X-rays, a decrease in coagulability of the blood, inhibition of the adhesive properties of the platelets (130), and thrombocytopenia have been reported (131, 132).

Similarly, after total irradiation by X-rays of insects (Periplaneta americana, Carausius morosus, and Locusta migratoria) characterized by coagulation pattern I of their hemolymph, the alterations observed in the coagulation process (133) consist (Locusta: 10,000 r) of a progressive decrease in the number of coagulocytes efficient in inducing formation of coagulation islands and a decrease in the size of these islands, finally reduced to thin fringes of clotted material around the coagulocytes. These changes result after a few days in total incoagulability of the hemolymph in which hemocytes of all categories have disappeared or are found in small numbers. The same doses of X-rays applied to other species did not induce clear-cut modifications of the process.

4. The Clotting Process without Participation of Blood Corpuscles

In mammals, fibrin formation occurs after the agglutination of platelets and probably serves the purpose of ensuring a more permanent hemostasis. Plasma factors contribute to the initial hemostatic process represented by the viscous transformation of platelets as well as to the second phase represented by fibrin formation. Blood coagulation in mammals can take place in the absence of platelets in vitro (134). However, in vivo, for purposes of hemostasis, it is probable that the different mechanisms available to the organism for the conversion of prothrombin to thrombin are called into play and the initiating factors, such as tissue juice, platelet action, and the plasma foreign surface, are all functioning synergistically.

In invertebrates, information about the possibility of clotting plasma deprived of cellular elements is scarce and contradictory. The blood of Calliphora erythrocephala (80) has been reported to clot if the blood corpuscles have been removed by centrifugation, like the blood of vertebrates deprived of platelets. Suggestion (10) that, by centrifugation, a factor from the coagulocytes might have been liberated into the blood seems to be confirmed by examination with the phase contrast microscope (82) of sediments of centrifugation of insect hemolymph: many hemocytes were found to be altered by this procedure. Debris of cells, appearing as a granular jelly, were gathered at the upper layer of the sediment. In certain insects (Silphidae, especially Necrophorus,

49, 82) thick muffs of clotted plasma developed rapidly around air
bubbles in films between glass and coverslip, in areas in which coagulocytes were apparently absent. On the other hand, no clot appeared in
Periplaneta when small portions of plasma were isolated from the
hemocytes before coagulation (82a).

From these inconsistent data, the possibility of a cell-free type of
coagulation in insects is not demonstrated but it distinctly exists in
mammals. However, it is the biochemical analysis of the process in the
higher mammals which has revealed these other mechanisms whereas the
role attributed to spindle cells and the fragile hemocytes (coagulocytes)
in lower animals is mainly based on morphologic observations and the
simple type of chemical analysis used several decades ago. If these were
the only methods available in the case of the higher animals, it is conceivable that platelets would still be considered the only initiating factor
in the onset of coagulation. This consideration should introduce the
element of doubt in any interpretation of the evolutionary process by
virtue of which, on the basis of presently available information, blood
coagulation in the higher vertebrates, as compared in lower animals, is
characterized by: (a) increased complication; (b) the gradual emergence of alternate pathways of fibrin formation; (c) the appearance of
plasma factors capable of substituting to a variable extent for the
initiating action of platelets and tissue products.

The recurring theme of cellular elements that contain coagulation
factors in unavailable form but easily released from these elements on
contact with foreign surfaces could be interpreted as a convergence
phenomenon by virtue of which blood is maintained fluid unless and
until it is shed and the cellular elements are injured.

5. *Hemostasis without Participation of the Plasma*

In Echinodermata, Vermes, and Mollusca, agglutination of blood
corpuscles without participation of plasma components seems to be the
simplest mechanism, so far described, of reaction of the coelomic fluid
outside the body. A superficial analogy to this hemostasis by "cell coagulation" is provided, in man, by the hemostasis through platelet agglutination which apparently is effective in the total absence of fibrinogen in
plasma (118). No real similarity between the two processes can be
stated with the existing information, but it is interesting to observe the
possible fulfillment of a hemostatic function by a purely cellular process
at two widely separated points of the zoological scale.

The viscous modification of the platelets resembles at first sight the
"cell coagulation" extensively described in the literature on invertebrates,
especially by Loeb (51–56). In mammals, however, this process is selec-

tively limited to the platelets. The other categories of blood cells are not involved in the process.

C. PLASMA FACTORS IN COAGULATION

If we turn now to an analysis of the clotting agents in plasma, it is immediately apparent that in arthropods technical difficulties have so far delayed isolation of blood coagulins from the explosive corpuscles or coagulocytes. These difficulties are responsible for many controversial and inconsistent results recorded in experiments destined to separate plasma constituents from cell components. Such separation is difficult because in several arthropods, and especially in insects, explosive discharges and dissemination of material from the Hardy's corpuscles or from coagulocytes represent extremely fast processes, which proceed to instantaneous completion as soon as these cells come into contact with foreign environment: instances of this phenomenon can be observed in larval Tenthredinidae (Hymenoptera) (82, 83) and in larval Tipulidae (Diptera) (82, 83). In such conditions, separation of the cellular and plasma components of the blood may furnish a cell fraction already agglutinated by small amounts of clotted plasma (66, 67) on the one hand, and a plasma fraction contaminated by coagulins or deprived of part of its coagulable substances left in the cell fraction on the other hand.

In vertebrates, separation of cellular and plasma factors of coagulation has been easier. As far as plasma factors are concerned, prothrombin has been studied in different species (135). It is present in much smaller amounts than fibrinogen and differentiation among the species is more difficult to achieve. However, measurements of prothrombin by the two-stage method have been carried out in different vertebrate species including birds, fishes and reptiles (136–138). The variable amounts found in these species may be due to true quantitative differences or to different molecular compositions associated with differences in the activity or availability of the newly recognized coagulation factors.

In vertebrates, especially in mammals, many other coagulation factors have been recognized, the existence of which has not been detected so far in invertebrates. These factors are listed in Table III. As a result, the coagulation mechanism in these higher animals is now interpreted as a complex process and, as a result of this complexity, it provides opportunities among the different zoological groups for variations in the proportion of the different reagents with maintenance of an adequate hemostatic mechanism through compensatory changes in other reagents. An example of this adaptability is observed in studies of blood coagulation in birds: recent studies have shown the presence in chicken blood of factors V, VII, VIII, and IX. However, the factor responsible for foreign surface activation (Hageman factor) appears to be lacking, and this should perhaps be correlated with the fact that bird spindle cells are not labile when placed in contact with glass, in which respect they behave differently from those of lower vertebrates (138). Another difference between birds and mammals, on the one hand, and other vertebrates, on the other, is found by experimenting on citrated plasma: citrated turtle plasma does not clot on recalcification unless tissue extracts are added (139) but bird and mammalian plasma do not need tissue extract. All these observations indicate the greater adaptability of the coagulation mechanism in birds and mammals with acquired relative independence from any single initiating reaction, in this case the tissue factor effect, for the onset of coagulation.

A recent interesting study of blood coagulation in amphibians (*Bufo marinus* Linn) (139a) reveals that cellular dependence is still great at this zoological level: in this animal, the blood leucocytes are a source of complete thromboplastic activity, while the plasma lacks the factors (factors V and VII) which are present in mammals and are indispensable for the elaboration of plasma thromboplastic activity. This example illustrates the gradual emergence in the evolutionary process of mechanisms in the plasma capable of substituting for intracellular mechanisms, and the greater role progressively assumed by soluble plasma coagulation factors. The presence of key coagulation factors in an intracellular location, as illustrated previously by the example of *Homarus* (100), offers the obvious advantage of preventing to a large extent the possibility of intravascular coagulation. The availability of these same factors in plasma in soluble forms would increase the tendency to intravascular coagulation, were it not for the multiple anticoagulant mechanisms which have appeared in the blood of higher animals.

It is more difficult to evaluate the significance of differences found within a class, as for instance between the teleost and elasmobranch. Teleost blood clots more rapidly than elasmobranch blood, and this has been attributed to enhanced activity of the granules of spindle cells in teleost as compared to elasmobranch (140–143). In all these studies, recently discovered coagulation factors were not taken into account so that interpretation of the observed differences is doubtful. One interest of these studies on fishes is that they brought about the important concept of species specificity in the clotting reaction (143, 144): tissue extract from elasmobranch is less active on teleost plasma than on elasmobranch plasma. Failure to take into account the factor of species specificity by investigators who used heterologous reagents in their experiments may render invalid many conclusions found in the old literature.

Species specificity is found in many species and applies especially to the action of tissue extracts (139), but also to a variable extent, to the other coagulation factors; it is less marked or may be completely absent in many groups of species (Table IV). At the branch level, tissue coagulin and coagulable substances are active inside a 'same branch. However, among vertebrates, the blood coagulins of selachian blood (145) are an exception. These factors are strongly specific: they are active on selachian fibrinogen only and inactive on bovine fibrinogen, Conversely, invertebrate tissues coagulins are inactive on vertebrate fibrinogen, and reciprocally. However, in all these studies, except for isolated data (100), the invertebrate substances investigated had not been purified by modern procedures. Some of these substances were crude products. Some even were extracts from whole organisms.

Species specificity applies also, although in an entirely different way, to the observations on certain anticoagulants secreted by invertebrates: for instance, the anticoagulant hirudin, secreted by the leech, strongly inhibits vertebrate coagulation but has no effect on invertebrate blood (54). The usefulness of such a specificity is based on the fact that leeches feed on vertebrate blood and the anticoagulant secreted by the leech plays no role in the coagulation reaction of the leech itself.

As far as mammals are concerned, it appears that the whole sequence of reactions in this group is identical, although the concentrations of factors may vary widely from one species to another. The essential homogeneity of the mammalian group is exemplified by the experimental breeding of a strain of hemophilic dogs characterized by a deficiency of antihemophilic factor (AHF) in the plasma: this canine hemophilia is indistinguishable from human hemophilia (146). Adaptation of the clotting system to living conditions is shown by the summer bat: in a cold environment, the number of mast cells in this species increases: mast cells contain heparin, and this increase may be responsible for the prolongation of the clotting time observed in a cold environment (147).

IV. Conclusions

With the limited data available on blood coagulation in invertebrates as compared with the abundant information existing on higher vertebrates, correlations are difficult to establish on a firm experimental basis. However, three main conclusions seem to emerge from this review.

TABLE IV

DEGREE OF ZOOLOGICAL SPECIFICITY OF THE FACTORS INVOLVED IN THE PROCESS OF COAGULATION[a]

Investigator	Coagulation-inducing substances ("coagulins") from	and Coagulable substances from	Results
Nolf (1909) (145, 67, 34)	Vertebrates: fish, selachians excluded: thrombozym and thrombogen	Vertebrates (Mammalia): bovine fibrinogen	Coagulation
	Crustacea: various species Blood and muscle coagulins	Crustacea: plasma and blood from different species	Coagulation
Loeb (1905) (54)	Crustacea (lobster and other closely related species): fibrinous coagulin; crab muscle coagulin	Crustacea: lobster plasma	Coagulation
Loeb and Fleisher (1910) (145a)	Vertebrates: muscle coagulin	Vertebrates: fibrinogen	Coagulation
Zunz (1933) (144)	Crustacea: muscle extract of lobster	Crustacea (lobster): plasma	Coagulation
Donnellon (1938) (25)	Crustacea, Mollusca, Echinodermata: extracts	Echinodermata: coelomic fluid	Coagulation
Glavind (1948) (6)	Crustacea: muscle extracts of various species of decapods	Crustacea: plasma of various species of decapods	Coagulation
Duchâteau and Florkin (1954) (100)	Crustacea: electrophoretically homogeneous muscle coagulins (lobster)	Crustacea: electrophoretically homogeneous fibrinogen of lobster	Coagulation
Halliburton (1885) (66)	Mammalia: thrombin	Crustacea: lobster blood	Coagulation
Heim (1892) (65)	Crustacea: thrombin	Mammalia: plasma and blood	Coagulation

Loeb (1905) (54)	Amphibia: frog thrombin	Crustacea: lobster plasma	No coagulation
	Vertebrates (rat, rabbit) and invertebrates (other than arthropods): tissue coagulins	Crustacea: lobster plasma	No coagulation
	Invertebrates: tissue coagulins	Vertebrates: plasma	No coagulation
Nolf (1909) (34)	Echinodermata: cell plasmodia and coelomic fluid	Mammalia: bovine fibrinogen	No coagulation
	Crustacea: muscle and blood coagulins	Mammalia: bovine fibrinogen	No coagulation
	Mammalia: muscle and blood coagulins	Crustacea: plasma of *Palinurus*	No coagulation
	Vermes: blood corpuscles; perivascular fluid	Mammalia: bovine fibrinogen	No coagulation
	Vertebrates (fish): muscle coagulin	Crustacea: plasma of *Palinurus*	No coagulation
	Vertebrates (fish): selachian thrombozym	Mammalia: bovine fibrinogen	No coagulation
Howell (1914–1916) (28)	Mammalia: thrombin of pig	Crustacea: crab blood	No coagulation
Zunz (1933) (144)	Vertebrates (fish): thrombin	Crustacea: lobster plasma	No coagulation
Glavind (1948) (6)	Crustacea: muscle coagulin	Mammalia: fibrinogen	No coagulation
George and Nichols (1948) (91)	Crustacea: blood coagulin (crab)	Mammalia: bovine fibrinogen	No coagulation
George and Ferguson (1950) (42)	Mammalia: bovine thrombin	Mollusca: blood of *Busycon*	No coagulation
	Mollusca: blood of *Busycon*	Mammalia: bovine fibrinogen	No coagulation
Duchâteau and Florkin (1954) (100)	Mammalia: electrophoretically homogeneous bovine thrombin (with or without calcium)	Crustacea: electrophoretically homogeneous lobster fibrinogen	No coagulation

 ª The data have been arranged in two groups, each in approximately chronological order; the first records use of substances from the same branch (vertebrate or invertebrate); the second group, mixtures of vertebrate and invertebrate substances.

(*a*) Coagulation of coelomic fluid and blood in invertebrates appears to be a relatively simple process; however, this apparent simplicity may be entirely due to the methods employed, none of which, with few exceptions, includes the use of the modern methods of biochemistry. Yet, it is by the use of these modern methods that blood coagulation in higher vertebrates has finally revealed itself as a very complex and delicate mechanism. Until invertebrates have been studied by these methods, the concept that coagulation in invertebrates is fundamentally a simpler process than in vertebrates may be very misleading.

(*b*) The main evolutionary process of blood coagulation in higher animals can be interpreted as the extension into the extracellular plasma of mechanisms primitively confined to the intracellular medium. There is an increasing independence of blood coagulation in higher animals from cellular participation, although this participation may persist as an alternate pathway of coagulation (*148*). Hemostasis, considered as a general phenomenon of which blood coagulation is just one step, remains more dependent on cellular participation even in higher animals. The main physiological significance of coagulation in this latter group appears to be the production of a more permanent type of hemostasis, while the initial and immediate hemostasis is still ensured by platelet action.

(*c*) Striking manifestations of highly selective adaptation and of functional convergence emerge from a comparative study of coagulation processes. The most remarkable example probably is represented by the analogous role of Hardy's explosive cells and coagulocytes in invertebrates and platelets in mammals in the initiation of blood coagulation, as well as by their similar sensitiveness to contact with foreign surfaces.

References

1. F. Bottazzi, *in* "Handbuch der vergleichenden Physiologie" (H. Winterstein, ed.), Vol. I, Physiologie der Körpersäfte, Part 1: Echinodermen, pp. 519–528; Würmer, pp. 589–592. Fischer, Jena, 1925; see also *Arch. ital. biol.* **37**, 49–63 (1902).
2. R. A. Boolootian and A. C. Giese, *J. Exptl. Zool.* **140**, 207–229 (1959).
3. G. Quagliariello, *in* "Handbuch der vergleichenden Physiologie" (H. Winterstein, ed.), Vol. I, Physiologie der Körpersäfte, Part 1: Mollusken, pp. 597–668. Fischer, Jena, 1925.
4. M. Silberberg, *Physiol. Revs.* **18**, 197–228 (1938).
5. F. N. Schulz, *in* "Handbuch der vergleichenden Physiologie" (H. Winterstein, ed.), Vol. I, Physiologie der Körpersäfte, Part 1: Crustaceen, pp. 669–746; Tracheaten (Insekten), pp. 747–812; Tunicaten, pp. 813–826. Fischer, Jena, 1925.
6. J. Glavind, "Studies on the Coagulation of Crustacean Blood," pp. 1–137. Nyt Nordisk Forlag, Arnold Busck, Copenhagen, 1948.

7. K. Mellanby, *Biol. Revs. Cambridge Phil. Soc.* **14**, 243–260 (1939).
8. N. S. R. Maluf, *Quart. Rev. Biol.* **14**, 149–191 (1939).
9. J. L. C. Rapp, *J. N. Y. Entomol. Soc.* **55**, 295–308 (1947).
10. H. E. Hinton, *Sci. Progr.* **44**, 684–696 (1956).
11. V. B. Wigglesworth, *Ann. Rev. Entomol.* **4**, 1–16 (1959).
12. R. F. Doolittle, "The Evolution of a Unique Enzyme System. The Comparative Physiology of Blood Coagulation," 42 pp. Bowdoin Prize in Natural Sciences, Dept. of Biological Chemistry, Harvard University, Cambridge, Massachusetts, 1960.
13. P. Geddes, *Proc. Roy. Soc.* **B30**, 252–255 (1879–1880); *Arch. zool. exptl. et gén.* [1] **8**, 483–496 (1879–1880).
14. E. A. Schäfer, *Proc. Roy. Soc.* **B34**, 370–371 (1882).
15. J. B. Haycraft and E. W. Carlier, *Proc. Roy. Soc. Edinburgh* **15**, 423–426 (1887–1888).
16. L. Cuénot, *Arch. zool. exptl. et gén.* [2] **9**, 13–670 (1891).
17. L. Cuénot, *Compt. rend. soc. biol.* **61**, 255–256 (1906).
18. A. B. Griffiths, *Proc. Roy. Soc. Edinburgh* **19**, 116–130 (1892).
19. V. Ducceschi, *Beitr. chem. Physiol. u. Pathol.* **3**, 378–384 (1903).
20. V. Henri, *Compt. rend. soc. biol.* **58**, 880–881 (1906).
21. E. S. Goodrich, *Quart. J. Microscop. Sci.* **64**, 19–26 (1920).
22. M. Romieu, *Thèse fac. sci. Paris* **A919** (1923).
23. H. Théel, *Arkiv Zool.* **12**, No. 4, 1–38; No. 14, 1–48 (1918–1920); **13**, No. 25, 1–40 (1921).
24. J. E. Kindred, *Biol. Bull.* **41**, 144–152 (1921); **46**, 228–251 (1924).
25. J. A. Donnellon, *Physiol. Zoöl.* **11**, 389–398 (1938).
26. C. G. Bookhout and N. D. Greenburg, *Biol. Bull.* **79**, 309–320 (1940).
27. C. F. W. Krukenberg, "Vergleichend-physiologische Studien" (2), Part 1, pp. 87–138. C. Winter, Heidelberg, 1882.
28. W. H. Howell, *Am. J. Physiol.* **35**, 143–149 (1914); **40**, 526–546 (1916); *Studies Biol. Lab. Johns Hopkins Univ.* **3**, 267–287 (1885).
29. N. Millott, *Biol. Bull.* **99**, 342–344 (1950); *J. Marine Biol. Assoc. United Kingdom* **31**, 529–539 (1953).
30. E. Davidson, *Biol. Bull.* **105**, 372 (1953).
31. G. Schwalbe, *Arch. mikroskop. Anat. u. Entwicklungsmech.* **5**, 250 (1869), quoted by Krukenberg (27).
32. A. Michel, *Compt. rend. acad. sci.* **106**, 1555–1556 (1888).
33. W. B. Benham, *Quart. J. Microscop. Sci.* **44**, 565–590 (1901).
34. P. Nolf, *Arch. intern. physiol.* **7**, 280–301 (1909).
35. G. R. Cameron, *J. Pathol. Bacteriol.* **35**, 933–972 (1932).
36. T. Ohuye, *Sci. Repts. Tôhoku Imp. Univ., Fourth Ser.* **12**, 255–263 (1937).
37. L. Fredericq, *Bull. acad. roy. méd. Belg.* [2] **46**, 722 (1878).
38. L. Camus, *Compt. rend. soc. biol.* **52**, 495–496 (1900).
39. E. Couvreur, *Compt. rend. soc. biol.* **52**, 395–396 (1900).
40. G. H. Drew, *Quart. J. Microscop. Sci.* **54**, 605–622 (1909–1910).
40a. T. Sato, *Z. vergleich. Physiol.* **14**, 763–783 (1931).
41. S. I. Takatsuki, *Quart. J. Microscop. Sci.* **76**, 379–431 (1933–1934).
42. W. C. George and J. H. Ferguson, *J. Morphol.* **86**, 315–328 (1950).
42a. D. Saunders Dundee, *Trans. Am. Microscop. Soc.* **72**, 254–264 (1953).
43. J. Schwartzkopff, *Z. Naturforsch.* **9b**, 155–158 (1954).
44. C. Grégoire, *Arch. biol.* (*Liége*) **66**, 489–508 (1955).
45. O. Tuzet and J. F. Manier, *Bull. biol. France et Belg.* **92**, 7–23 (1958).

46. J. F. Yeager and H. H. Knight, *Ann. Entomol. Soc. Am.* **26,** 591–602 (1933).
47. C. Grégoire, *Smithsonian Inst. Publs., Misc. Collections* **134,** No. 6 (1957).
48. C. Grégoire, *Smithsonian Inst. Publs., Misc. Collections* **139,** No. 3 (1959).
49. C. Grégoire and P. Jolivet, *Explor. Parc Natl. Albert* (2), Fasc. 4 (1957).
50. A. E. Shipley, *in* "The Cambridge Natural History" (S. G. Harmer and A. E. Shipley, eds.), Vol. 4, pp. 477–487. Hafner, New York, 1909.
51. L. Loeb, *Biol. Bull.* **4,** 301–318 (1903).
52. L. Loeb, *Protoplasma* **2,** 512–553 (1927).
53. L. Loeb, *Virchows Arch. pathol. Anat. u. Physiol.* **173,** 35–112 (1903); **176,** 10–46 (1904); **185,** 160–193 (1906).
54. L. Loeb, *Beitr. chem. Physiol. Pathol.* **5,** 191–207, 534–557 (1904); **6,** 260–286 (1905); **8,** 67–94 (1906); **9,** 185–204 (1907).
55. L. Loeb, *Biochem. Z.* **16,** 157–163 (1909); **24,** 478–495 (1910).
56. L. Loeb, *Pflügers Arch. ges. Physiol.* **131,** 465–508 (1910); *Washington Univ. Studies* **8,** 1, 3–79 (1920).
57. C. L. Alsberg and E. D. Clark, *J. Biol. Chem.* **5,** 323–329 (1908–1909).
58. A. L. Copley, *Federation Proc.* **6,** 90–91 (1947).
59. C. Grégoire, *Arch. intern. physiol.* **60,** 97–99 (1952).
59a. P. Morrison and W. H. Rothman, *Proc. Soc. Exptl. Biol. Med.* **94,** 21–23 (1957).
60. G. B. Deevey, *J. Morphol.* **68,** 457–487 (1941).
61. C. Grégoire, *Arch. intern. physiol.* **60,** 100–102 (1952).
62. J. H. Lochhead and M. S. Lochhead, *J. Morphol.* **68,** 593–632 (1941).
63. T. Wharton Jones, *Phil. Trans. Roy. Soc.* pp. 89–101 (1846).
64. L. Fredericq, *Bull. acad. roy. méd. Belg.* [2] **47,** 409–413 (1879).
65. F. Heim, Etudes sur le sang des crustacés décapodes, Thesis. Paris, 1892.
66. W. D. Halliburton, *J. Physiol.* (*London*) **6,** 300–335 (1885).
67. P. Nolf, *Arch. intern. physiol.* **7,** 411–461 (1909).
68. W. B. Hardy, *J. Physiol.* (*London*) **13,** 165–190 (1892).
69. J. Tait, Proc. Physiol. Soc., *J. Physiol.* (*London*) **40** (1910); *J. Marine Biol. Assoc. United Kingdom* **9,** 191–198 (1911).
70. J. Tait, *Quart. J. Exptl. Physiol.* **3,** 1–20 (1910).
71. J. Tait and J. D. Gunn, *Quart. J. Exptl. Physiol.* **12,** 35–80 (1918).
72. H. Numanoi, *Japan. J. Zoöl.* **7,** 613–641 (1938).
73. P. R. Morrison and K. C. Morrison, *Biol. Bull.* **103,** 395–406 (1952).
74. L. Fredericq, *Bull. acad. roy. méd. Belg.* [3] **1,** 489–492 (1881).
74a. E. B. Poulton, *Proc. Roy. Soc.* **38,** 269–314 (1885).
75. R. A. Muttkowski, *Bull. Brooklyn Entomol. Soc.* **19,** 128–144 (1924).
76. J. F. Yeager, W. E. Shull, and M. D. Farrar, *Iowa State Coll. J. Sci.* **6,** 325–344 (1932).
77. E. Recai, *Z. Zellforsch. u. mikroskop. Anat.* **29,** 613–669 (1939).
78. R. L. Beard, *Anat. Record* **101,** 736 (1948); *Physiol. Zoöl.* **23,** 47–57 (1950).
79. C. Grégoire and M. Florkin, *Physiol. Comparata et Oecol.* **2,** 126–139 (1950); *Experientia* **6,** 297–298 (1950).
80. B. Åkesson, *Arkiv Zool.* **6,** 203–211 (1953).
81. C. Grégoire, Proc. Physiol. Soc., *J. Physiol.* (*London*) **114,** (1951); *Blood* **6,** 1173–1198 (1951).
82. C. Grégoire, *Arch. biol.* (*Liége*) **66,** 103–148 (1955).
82a. H. Franke, *Zool. Jahrb.* (*Abt. allgem. Zool.*) **68,** 499–518 (1960).
83. C. Grégoire, *Explor. Parc natl. Albert* (2), Fasc. 10 (1959).

84. J. C. Jones, *J. Morphol.* **99**, 233–258 (1956).
85. M. Henze, *Hoppe-Seylers Z. physiol. Chem.* **72**, 494–501 (1911).
86. H. J. B. Fry, *Folia Haematol.* **8**, 467 (1909).
87. J. Huus, *in "Handbuch der Zoologie"* (W. Kükenthal, ed.), Vol. **5**, Part 2, Tunicata pp. 614–616. de Gruyter, Berlin and Leipzig, 1937.
88. J. D. Robertson, *J. Exptl. Biol.* **31**, 424–442 (1954).
89. D. A. Webb, *Pubbl. staz. zool. Napoli,* **28**, 273 (1956).
89a. I. R. Taylor and N. Millman, *Anat. Record* **72**, 107–108 (1938).
89b. Z. Gruzewska, *Compt. rend. soc. biol.* **110**, 920–922 (1932).
90. A. Dehorne, *Compt. rend. acad. sci.* **180**, 333 (1925); E. Fauré-Frémiet, *Arch. anat. microscop.* **23**, 99 (1927); *Protoplasma* **6**, 521 (1929).
90a. G. Cattaneo, *Atti soc. ital. sci. nat.* **31**, 231–266 (1888); *Arch. ital. biol.* **10**, 267–272 (1888); **15**, 409–417 (1891).
91. W. C. George and J. Nichols, *J. Morphol.* **83**, 425–442 (1948).
92. C. Grégoire, *Arch. intern. physiol.* **60**, 94–96 (1952); **61**, 234–236, 394–397, 391–393 (1953); **62**, 117–119 (1954).
93. C. Grégoire, *Arch. intern. physiol.* **61**, 237–239 (1953).
94. P. S. Galtsoff, *J. Exptl. Zool.* **42**, 183–217, 223–256 (1925).
95. F. D. Wood and H. E. Wood, *J. Exptl. Zool.* **62**, 1–55 (1932).
96. W. H. Seegers, *in* "Proceedings of the International Conference on Thrombosis and Embolism, pp. 31–46. Schwabe, Basel, Switzerland, 1954.
97. R. H. Landaburu and W. H. Seegers, *Am. J. Physiol.* **197**, 1178–1180 (1959).
98. R. H. Landaburu and W. H. Seegers, *Am. J. Physiol.* **198**, 173–179 (1960).
99. E. F. Mammea, W. H. Seegers, W. R. Thomas, and R. H. Landaburu, *Record Chem. Progr.* (*Kresge-Hooker Sci. Lib.*) **21**, 1–18 (1960).
100. G. Duchâteau and M. Florkin, *Bull. soc. chim. biol.* **36**, 295–305 (1954).
101. W. H. Telfer, *Federation Proc.* **12**, 734 (1953); *J. Gen. Physiol.* **37**, 539–558 (1954).
102. W. H. Telfer and C. M. Williams, *J. Gen. Physiol.* **36**, 389–413 (1953).
103. A. Drilhon, *Compt. rend. acad. sci.* **238**, 2452 (1954).
104. T. J. Bowen and B. A. Kilby, *Arch. intern. physiol.* **61**, 413–416 (1953).
105. J. Oda, K. Hayashi, and S. Sasaki, *J. Agr. Chem. Soc. Japan* **30**, 342 (1956).
106. J. M. Denucé, *Z. Naturforsch.* **13b**, 215–218 (1958).
107. M. van Sande and D. Karcher, *Science* **131**, 1103 (1960).
108. A. Krieg, *Naturwissenschaften* **43**, 60 (1956).
109. C. Schimmelbusch, *Virchows Arch. pathol. Anat. u. Physiol.* **101**, 201 (1885).
110. H. Stübel, *Pflügers Arch. ges. Physiol.* **156**, 361–400 (1914); **181**, 285–309 (1921).
111. C. Grégoire, *Arch. intern. physiol.* **67**, 329 (1959).
112. C. Grégoire, G. Duchâteau, and M. Florkin, *Arch. intern. physiol.* **57**, 117–119 (1949).
113. F. H. Bang and J. L. Frost, *Biol. Bull.* **105**, 361 (1953).
114. C. Wolpers, *Klin. Wochschr.* **24/25**, 424–427 (1947); C. Wolpers and H. Ruska, *Klin. Wochschr.* **18**, 1077 (1939).
115. C. van Zandt Hawn and K. R. Porter, *J. Exptl. Med.* **86**, 285–292 (1947).
116. C. E. Hall, *J. Biol. Chem.* **179**, 857–864 (1949).
117. M. C. Dekhuyzen, *Anat. Anz.* **19**, 529–540 (1901).
118. Hémostase spontanée, plaquettes sanguines et parois vasculaires." Premier Symposium de la Fondation Valentino Baldacci, 1955, pp. 159–160. Omnia Medica, Pisa, Italy.

118a. G. Bloom, *Z. Zellforsch.* **42**, 365–385 (1955); G. Köppel, *ibid.* **47**, 401–439 (1958).

119. "Hémostase spontanée, thrombose et coagulation sanguine." Deuxième Symposium de la Fondation Valentino Baldacci, 1957, pp. 34–57. Omnia Medica, Pisa, Italy.

120. M. Bessis and M. Burstein, *Rev. hématol.* **3**, 48–91 (1948).

121. C. Grégoire, *Biol. Bull.* **104**, 372–393 (1953).

122. J. Bizzozero, *Virchows Arch. pathol. Anat. u. Physiol.* **90**, 261–332 (1882).

123. K. Bürker, *Pflügers Arch. ges. Physiol.* **102**, 36–94 (1904).

124. H. P. Wright, *J. Pathol. Bacteriol.* **53**, 255–262 (1941).

125. R. Feissly and H. Ludin, *Helv. Physiol. et Pharmacol. Acta* **7**, C9 (1949).

126. J. S. Hensill, *Anat. Record* **101**, 736 (1948).

127. E. D. Willis and A. Wormall, *Nature* **165**, 813–814 (1950).

128. H. J. Tagnon and J. P. Soulier, *Proc. Soc. Exptl. Biol. Med.* **61**, 440–441 (1946).

129. D. Grob, *J. Gen. Physiol.* **26**, 423–442 (1943).

130. J. P. Savitzky and S. Sherry, *Proc. Soc. Exptl. Biol. Med.* **85**, 587–590 (1954).

131. H. J. Curtis, *Ann. Rev. Physiol.* **13**, 41–56 (1951).

132. L. F. Lamerton, *in* "Künstliche radioaktive Isotope in Physiologie und Therapie" (H. Schwiegk, ed.), pp. 163–199. Springer, Berlin, 1953.

133. C. Grégoire, *Arch. intern. physiol.* **63**, 246–248 (1955).

134. R. C. Hartmann, C. L. Conley, and J. S. Lalley, *Bull. Johns Hopkins Hosp.* **85**, 231 (1949).

135. E. D. Warner, K. M. Brinkhous, and H. P. Smith, *Am. J. Physiol.* **125**, 296–300 (1939).

136. J. Tait and F. Green, *Quart. J. Exptl. Physiol.* **16**, 141–148 (1926).

137. J. P. Soulier, O. Wartelle, and D. Menache, *Brit. J. Hematol.* **5**, 121 (1959).

138. O. Wartelle, *Rev. hérmatol.* **12**, 351 (1957).

139. S. E. Dorst and C. A. Mills, *Am. J. Physiol.* **64**, 160–166 (1923)

139a. E. Hackett and R. LePage, *Australian J. Exptl. Biol. Med. Sci.* **39**, 57–65; 67–77 (1961).

140. H. J. B. Fry, *Folia Haematol.* **8**, 467 (1909).

141. S. Kaname, *Bull. Japan. Soc. Fisheries* **19**, 1139 (1954).

142. P. Nolf, *Arch. intern. physiol.* **4**, 216–259 (1906).

143. E. Zunz, *Arch. intern. physiol.* **37**, 282–287 (1933).

144. E. Zunz, *Bull. acad. roy. méd. Belg. Cl. Sci.* [5] **19**, 929–937; 938–944; 1107–1125 (1933).

145. P. Nolf, *Arch. intern. physiol.* **4**, 98–216 (1906–1907); **7**, 379–410 (1909).

145a. L. Loeb and M. S. Fleischer, *Biochem. Z.* **28**, 169–175 (1910).

146. K. M. Brinkhous and J. B. Graham, *Science* **111**, 723–724 (1950).

147. D. E. Smith, Y. S. Lewis, and G. Svihla, *Proc. Soc. Exptl. Biol. Med.* **86**, 473–475 (1954).

148. L. V. Heilbrunn, "An Outline of General Physiology." Saunders, Philadelphia, Pennsylvania, 1937.

CHAPTER 11

Metamorphosis and Biochemical Adaptation in Amphibia*

THOMAS PETER BENNETT† and EARL FRIEDEN‡

Department of Chemistry, Florida State University, Tallahassee, Florida

* The preparation of this chapter was aided by a research grant, C-3006, from the United States Public Health Service. The various researches from the Department of Chemistry, Florida State University reported here covers a ten-year period of research supported by several grants to Earl Frieden from the United States Public Health Service. Acknowledgment is made to the many individuals who contributed to this work, especially A. E. Herner, F. Finamore, the late J. L. Dolphin, E. J. C. Lewis, H. Mathews, B. Naile, W. Westmark, and others (see references). We are greatly indebted to Carla Ferguson for her valuable aid in the preparation of this chapter. Some of this discussion was presented by E. Frieden at a symposium on metamorphosis at the 1960 meeting of the American Institute of Biological Science, Stillwater, Oklahoma [*Am. Zool.* **1,** 115 (1961)].

† *Present address:* Graduate School, Rockefeller Institute, New York City.

‡ To whom inquiries concerning this review should be sent.

I. Introduction *

Metamorphosis may be defined as postembryonic developmental changes in nonreproductive structures of an organism; these changes occur in a discrete period or periods during which there are alterations in the biochemical, physiological and anatomical structures of the

---

* Abbreviations which are used frequently in this chapter: T_4, L-thyroxine; T_3, 3,5,3'-triiodo-L-thyronine; ATP, adenosine-5'-triphosphate; G-6-Pase, glucose-6-phosphatase; RNA, ribonucleic acid; DNA, deoxyribonucleic acid; TSH, thyroid-stimulating hormone; A : G, albumin-to-globulin ratio.

organism. Many alterations which occur during metamorphosis have adaptive value in that they involve the preparation of an organism for a transition from one environment to another which is usually strikingly different. In other words, metamorphosis is a developmental transition from a larval form specialized for a particular existence to an adult form adapted for another environment, a controlled remodeling of the animal to fit his environment. It has been pointed out (1, 2) that metamorphosis anticipates changes in environment and is essentially preparation for existence in a new environment, not a response to it. Those changes which occur as a response to environmental changes are to be distinguished from true metamorphosis. For the more adaptive aspects of metamorphosis, such anticipation of the environment to come is essential, for the animal cannot move to the new environment until metamorphosis has made it ready. Moreover, "every first metamorphosis invites a second metamorphosis" (2). The completion of the essential circularity of the life cycle of some metamorphosing species is therefore briefly discussed in Section XII. The mechanisms by which these metamorphic changes are effected constitute the subject matter of the biochemistry of metamorphosis.

As Etkin (3) has written: "The evolutionary process producing divergent specialization between larva and adult has occurred repeatedly and independently in different animal groups." Those groups for which there exists an extensive literature on the morphological and biochemical nature of the metamorphic process are insects, crustaceans, fish, and amphibians. In this review, we shall compare briefly the salient aspects of various metamorphoses and then concentrate on the significant features of the biochemical adaptations involved in anuran metamorphosis.

II. Comparative Morphological Alterations at Metamorphosis[*]

A. INSECTS

According to Snodgrass (4) insects can be divided into three groups with respect to the type of metamorphosis they undergo. Parametabolous insects undergo a small degree of metamorphic change between the larval and adult form. In hemimetabolous forms the young differs conspicuously from the adult or has distinctive adaptive characteristics of its own, but makes the transition to the adult form in one molt. Holo-

[*] The following paragraphs are intended only as a brief introduction to the comparative aspects of metamorphosis. A recent detailed discussion of these phenomena entitled "Metamorphosis in the Animal Kingdom" appeared in February, 1961 [Am. Zool. 1, (1), 1–171 (1961)].

metabolous insects have at least two molts involved in the change and therefore an intervening pupal stage between the larval and adult. Numerous examples of insects that undergo one or another of the three types of metamorphosis are known, and the nature of the morphological changes are summarized in numerous reviews (3–6). These morphological alterations can be collated with the change in habitat which occurs at the time of metamorphosis. A transition occurs in the locomotor, respiratory, feeding, and other structures during the change from an aquatic to a terrestrial or aerial habitat. Alterations in the type of parasitism of a species are also reflected in morphological changes at metamorphosis. For specific morphological variations correlated with environment the original literature should be consulted (7, 8).

B. Crustaceans

Snodgrass (9) and Waterman and Chace (10) have reviewed the general aspects of crustacean development. As they have pointed out, a large proportion of these animals undergo a series of ten or more molts before sexual maturity is reached. These are gradual developmental changes unmarked by specialized ontogenetic alterations which we have defined as metamorphosis. Many crustaceans, however, undergo a real metamorphosis in which special adaptations occur in certain phases of the life history. Thus, in forms such as Brachyura, Anomura, Scyllaridea, and Stomatopoda a transition occurs during metamorphosis from a pelagic larval form to a benthic adult animal with changes occurring in feeding, locomotion, and other habits.

More dramatic than the adaptation of the appendages and feeding parts of these animals is the total metamorphic reconstruction of some crustacea for a parasitic way of life. In some copepods, isopods, and cirripeds striking alterations occur between the larval and adult form, one of which may be a parasitic stage and demonstrate marked host specificity. These alterations are structural adaptations to a parasitic life and constitute the most extreme examples of metamorphic changes in crustacea. The major differences between crustacean and insect metamorphosis are that in the former, alterations occur earlier, usually before segmentation is complete and in the absence of true pupal phases comparable to those of some orders of insects.

C. Fish

The fishes that undergo a true metamorphosis may be placed in one of two groups: (a) animals that remain aquatic, although they may transfer from a freshwater to a marine habitat, but acquire modified physiological and behavioral patterns at the time of metamorphosis; and

(b) animals that assume a semiterrestrial existence after metamorphosis. Wald (11) has discussed the transformations that occur in the first group; Harms (12), in the latter. Hoar (13) has briefly reviewed aspects of metamorphosis in both groups.

A real metamorphosis of the first type occurs during development of several fishes, e.g., lamprey (Petromyzon), eel (Anguilla), flounder (Pleuronectes), and a modified metamorphosis, the parr-smolt transformation, occurs in salmon. The sea lamprey begins its life in streams as a blind larva, buried in mud or sand. While still in that location, it undergoes a series of changes preparatory to migrating downstream to the ocean for its growth phase. The young freshwater eel migrates from its marine spawning ground to the shores of Europe or America. There it metamorphoses to the adult form and usually, though not always, migrates into freshwater for its growth phase (11). In these animals metamorphic changes involve alterations in feeding structures, locomotor and sensory organs, in preparation for the new habitat the animal will enter.

The gobies, Boleophthalmus and Periophthalmus, and the blenny Salarias studied by Harms (12) undergo a migration from an aquatic to a semiterrestrial habitat, as do members of other animal groups discussed in the present paper. The larval form is strictly aquatic. During metamorphosis the animal keeps its head out of the water much of the time. The metamorphosed form spends much of its time on the dry surface near water. Harms (12) has described the transformation in the skin of these animals during metamorphosis—a transformation analogous to that discussed in this paper for anurans. He also discussed the changes in the respiratory, locomotor, and sensory organs during this metamorphosis and has compared the changes to those that occur during metamorphosis in crustaceans and amphibians.

D. Amphibians

Within the class Amphibia, animals can be divided into several groups based on the nature of their transition from the larval to adult form. The members of one group, e.g., Necturus and Proteus, display total neoteny, a condition in which no metamorphosis occurs. These animals retain their gills and remain as permanently aquatic forms throughout their lives. Another group displays partial neoteny. For example, the Mexican axolotl lives its larval and adult life as an aquatic animal. However, if dry conditions prevail, such animals undergo metamorphic changes and thus become adapted to a terrestrial life. Hormonal treatment will also cause them to metamorphose from an aquatic to a terrestrial form, as discussed in the next section. Another group, exemplified by *Xenopus laevis,* undergo a complete metamorphosis but remain aquatic in both the larval and adult stage. A fourth important group includes the anurans, animals which are aquatic in the tadpole or larval stage and after metamorphosis exist as terrestrial animals.

For those animals which make an environmental transition during metamorphosis the contrast between the larval and adult habitat is chiefly that between an aquatic and a terrestrial or semiterrestrial environment. The successful colonization of either environment requires certain adaptive features which may be generally summarized for aquatic environments as follows: aquatic respiratory mechanism (gills), muscular system for swimming, and mucus-covered skin; and for terrestrial environments as follows: air respiratory mechanism (lungs and skin), skeletal system for crawling or walking, and water conservation mechanism (kidneys and cornified skin).

E. Anurans

The literature is replete with detailed descriptions of the structural changes that occur during anuran metamorphosis. Much of the morphological information has been collected in the texts of Needham (*14*), Witschi (*15*), and Rugh (*16*), in the reviews of Lynn and Wachowski (*17*) and of Roth (*18*), and in the paper of Taylor and Kollros (*19*). A lengthy repetition of this material would be redundant. Lynn and Wachowski (*17*) give an excellent brief summary of the morphological changes during anuran metamorphosis which is excerpted here. Prior to the onset of metamorphosis, the frog tadpole is an aquatic animal with well-developed gills, a long flattened tail, lidless eyes, horny rasping teeth, and a long coiled intestine. The frog, in contrast, is an air-breathing animal with no tail, well-developed limbs, eyelids, and other structures adapted for its terrestrial habits. Even structures that persist in the adult undergo extensive alterations. The skin thickens, becomes more glandular, and attains an outer cornified layer. The intestine decreases in length and becomes more highly differentiated. Alterations also occur in the liver, pancreas, skin pigments, tongue, tympanae, cloaca, and the opercular perforation. The disappearance of the tadpole tail is one of the most striking structural features of anuran metamorphosis. The tail appears to responds rapidly to relatively high concentrations of thyroid hormone. In fact, reduction in tail length or tail width of tadpoles has served as the basis for many convenient bioassays for the thyroid hormone (*20*).

The obvious morphological changes of amphibian metamorphosis must be reflected in more subtle cellular changes. Explorations of various organ systems have revealed possible intracellular differentiation of the cells of several internal tissues. For example, in 1936 Kaywin (21) reported evidence for the fragmentation of the Golgi apparatus and the mitochondria and possibly for nuclear changes in cells of the tadpole liver, stomach, intestine, and pancreas in response to thyroid hormone treatment. In his emphasis on the modifications of certain intracellular structures in response to thyroid, Kaywin may have anticipated some of the very interesting recent observations by Lehninger (22) and others on the effects of thyroid hormones on the gross properties of the mitochondria. However, it should be realized here that no claim can as yet be made for a direct or primary effect of thyroid on the cytology of tadpole cells although we do not doubt that this will be found. The sensitivity of intracellular structures to environmental factors such as diet, temperature, etc., is not yet adequately appreciated. Finally, it is of interest to note, as did Kaywin, the essential similarity of histological changes in several of these tissues during normal and accelerated metamorphosis. It is likely that many new points of interest could be found by a searching cytological comparison of tadpole cells before and after metamorphosis.

In order to collate the facts about anuran metamorphosis, it is necessary to relate the chemical or enzymatic effects to some standard structural yardstick. A variety of criteria have been used by various workers to indicate the progress of metamorphosis. These descriptions range from very general qualitative criteria to the detailed characterizations of Taylor and Kollros (19), Roth (18), and Witschi (15). It is best to use the excellent division of metamorphosis into the discrete stages defined by Taylor and Kollros for *Rana pipiens*. In the earlier literature a broader subdivision was used which involved prometamorphosis, a period involving maximum growth. Prometamorphosis leads to the metamorphic climax which begins externally with the emergence of the forelimbs and includes the resorption of the gills and tail, perhaps the most striking external changes of anuran differentiation. Postmetamorphosis refers to the period immediately following the metamorphic climax.

In specific situations in this laboratory, we have found it convenient to use the ratio of the hind limb length to tail length, introduced by Roth (18) to attempt to compare normal and thyroxine-induced metamorphosis, particularly at the later stages. Ratios of limb length to tail length can be accurately determined, thus permitting an arbitrary quantitative index of metamorphic development (Fig. 1). In agreement with Brown and Cohen (23), we have found a close relationship between this ratio and the intermediate metamorphic stages; this ratio is also

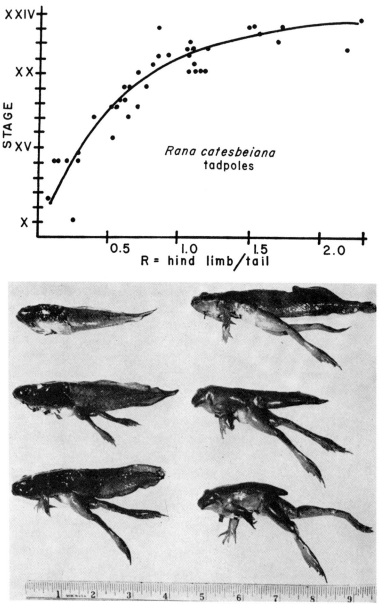

FIG. 1. Spontaneous metamorphosis of *Rana catesbeiana:* Top, correlation of stage of tadpole development with ratio of hind limb length to tail length. Bottom, Taylor-Kollros stages of normal development. Top to bottom, left to right: Stages X, XVIII, XX, XX½, XXIII, XXIV. From Brown and Cohen (23).

frequently used in this review to express the changes occurring during induced metamorphosis, since normal staging is frequently disrupted and inadequate to express the appropriate changes (Fig. 2).

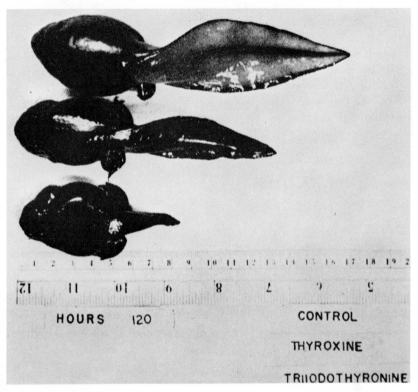

FIG. 2. Induced metamorphosis of *Rana heckscheri:* Tadpoles injected 5 days earlier with saline and 0.50 ml. $1.0 \times 10^{-4} M$ thyroxine and triiodothyronine and maintained at 29°. From Dolphin and Frieden (75).

In considering the anatomical, physiological, and biochemical aspects of the metamorphosis of the various animal groups, it is important to recognize, as Etkin has pointed out (3), that the evolutionary process producing divergent specialization between larva and adult has occurred repeatedly and independently in different animal groups. On this basis one might expect analogous metabolic characteristics during metamorphosis of the different animal groups although homologous characteristics would be expected only in the more closely related members of the group. It is these analogous control factors and metabolic alterations which will be considered in the next sections.

III. Comparative Endocrine Regulation of Metamorphosis

The biochemical questions related to metamorphosis of any species center around two major areas:

(a) The neuroendocrine control of the metamorphosis-initiating hormone (e.g., T_4);

(b) The interaction of the intiating hormone with the mosaic of larval tissues to produce the multidifferentiation of metamorphosis and its resulting end products (e.g., frog).

We will briefly consider the first point, but concentrate on the second, particularly in relation to the interaction of thyroid hormones and tadpole tissues (Fig. 3).

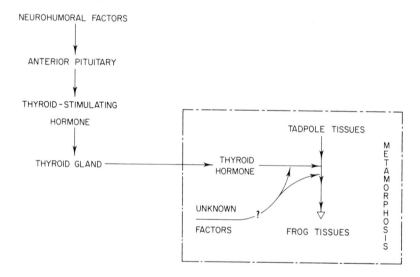

Fig. 3. Major steps involved in anuran metamorphosis. The enclosure indicates the portion of the subject emphasized in this paper.

Extensive studies have been made on the chemical nature and interrelations of initiators and control factors of metamorphosis in various animal groups (3, 6, 24). Etkin (3) has reviewed the comparative aspects of the control of metamorphosis in two animal groups, anurans and insects, and the control of molting in Crustacea has been described by Scharrer (25) and expanded to a general hypothesis of metamorphic control via a neuroendocrine axis. The general features of the Scharrer scheme for anurans and insects are presented in Fig. 4. The effects of environmental stimuli and inherent intrinsic stimuli are integrated by the central nervous system. Neurosecretory cells release a chemical

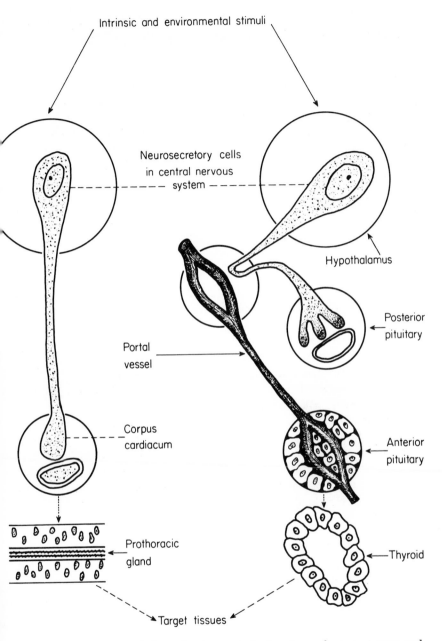

FIG. 4. Comparison of the endocrine control of metamorphosis in insects and anurans. Modified from Scharrer (25).

mediator which incites the first in a series of hormonal factors which ultimately interact with target tissues.

A. INSECTS

There are several reviews about the control axis of insect metamorphosis (3, 5, 7). As summarized in Fig. 4, the control pathway involves the production of a brain or prothoracotropic hormone by the neurosecretory cells of the insect protocerebrum. This substance stimulates the prothoracic gland of the insect thorax to produce a growth and differentiating hormone. This hormone seems to interact directly with the tissues, stimulating them to assume the adult condition. It is of interest that all the insect hormones are lipid in contrast to the corresponding known anuran hormones, the protein TSH and the iodothyronines.

B. CRUSTACEANS

The control of crustacean metamorphosis appears to be via a pathway analogous to that in insects (9, 25, 26). As various investigators have pointed out, no studies on the control of crustacean metamorphosis comparable to those on insects have been made, but the studies which have been made suggest a control mechanism which is fundamentally the same in both groups. A chemical mediator produced by the neurosecretory cells (X-organ) of the crustacean stimulates the sinus gland via axon transport. The sinus gland produces a molt-inhibiting hormone which interacts with the Y-organ, which in turn produces the metamorphosing hormone (26). This metamorphosing hormone then interacts with target tissues to result in the characteristic pattern of change. The major difference between the control mechanism for crustaceans and insects is that the insect prothoracotropin stimulates the metamorphosing gland whereas the X-organ neurosecretory hormone apparently inhibits the comparable crustacean gland.

C. FISH

The control of metamorphosis in fish has been briefly discussed by Harms (12), Hoar (13), and Gorbman (27). The endocrinology of the transition from aquatic to terrestrial life made by several gobies and the blenny Salarias has been studied by Harms (12). These animals showed an enlargement of the thyroid at the time of migration to land suggesting a role of this gland in the metamorphic phenomena. Further evidence for the involvement of the thyroid comes from the demonstration that these changes could be induced prematurely by the use of thyroid materials (12).

The control of metamorphosis in ammocoetes and other members of the fish group has not been elucidated. The importance of a control axis involving the thyroid gland, as occurs in most vertebrates undergoing metamorphosis, is doubtful. Attempts to induce metamorphosis of lamprey larvae with thyroid material have been unsuccessful (28, 29). In the metamorphosis of the eel, Vilter (30) has claimed a role for T_4 but this has not been confirmed (17).

D. AMPHIBIANS

Experimental data supporting the control of amphibian metamorphosis by the pituitary-thyroid axis are voluminous [see reviews by Lynn and Wachowski (17) and Etkin (3)]. The dependence of amphibian metamorphosis upon thyroid hormone has been demonstrated by thyroid feeding or injection (31), thyroidectomy (32), and reimplantation studies (33). Histological studies (34, 35) have shown clearly that the secretory activity of the gland can be correlated with the rate of metamorphic change. The secretory activity of the thyroid is controlled by a thyrotropic hormone (TSH) secreted by the beta cells of the anterior lobe of the pituitary.

The failure of neotenous amphibians such as axolotl to metamorphose has been variously ascribed to a deficiency in the animal's thyroid secretion, exceptional tissue insensitivity to thyroid influence, or impairment of thyrotropic function of the pituitary. The experiments of Blount (36, 37) indicate that the latter explanation is probably the correct one. The ability of an environmental stimulus such as dryness to precipitate metamorphosis of these amphibians makes possible an interpretation similar to that of Scharrer (25) for these amphibians.

A number of reviews are available concerning the various aspects of the endocrine control of metamorphosis in anurans (3, 17, 38). The classic Gudernatsch experiments (31, 39) in which anuran tadpoles fed with mammalian thyroid gland underwent precocious metamorphosis whereas those fed with any other mammalian tissue displayed no change, initiated studies which firmly established the thyroid as a controlling factor in metamorphosis. Subsequently Kendall (40) extracted thyroxine from the thyroid and demonstrated the ability of this compound to cause precocious metamorphosis of tadpoles. Many criteria have been used to establish the importance of the thyroid gland and its products as a stimulus that precipitates metamorphosis. Studies of the effect on metamorphosis of feeding and injection of T_4, thyroidectomy and reimplantation of thyroid (33, 41), and correlations of increase in thyroid activity with metamorphic changes (42, 43) are a few of the types of investigations that have established the thyroid in this regard. The apparent greater activity of several thyroxine and triiodothyronine analogs in inducing metamorphosis is considered in Section III, E (20).

Very early studies on hypophysectomy in anurans established the dependence of metamorphosis on the presence of secretions of the pituitary (32, 44). Subsequent studies established that the anterior region of the pituitary was necessary for the activation of the thyroid and that its influence on metamorphosis can be attributed to its control of the thyroid rather than to a direct effect on the peripheral tissues (45, 46). This has been well established by experiments with implants, extracts, and transplants of the anterior pituitary (47). The control of the thyroid by the anterior pituitary is effected by a thyrotropic hormone (TSH) which is produced in this lobe of the gland. The possibility of a direct metamorphic effect by the pituitary has been eliminated by the demonstration that transplanted anterior lobes from adult frogs are effective in inducing metamorphosis in normal and hypophysectomized tadpoles, but not in thyroidectomized larvae (48). Chang (49) has investigated the neurohumoral control of hypophyseal function in tadpoles by using hypothalectomy. Tadpoles, hypothalectomized at the open neural fold stage, develop normally up to the time of the extrusion of the forelegs. The metamorphic climax is delayed or inhibited. Since TSH production seems normal during the larval stage, Chang has suggested that ordinarily a sudden increase in the output of TSH may be required during this critical stage and that this extra production probably depends on hypothalmic stimulation.

E. The Anomalous Activity of Thyroxine Analogs in Anura

It has been frequently reported that certain side-chain variants of T_4 and T_3 showed many times the activity of T_4 when compared for their ability to induce metamorphosis in anura (50–54). For example, the compound, 3,5,3'-triiodothyropropionic acid has been variously reported to be 20 to 300 times as active as T_4. Many of these data have been summarized in Pitt-Rivers and Tata's recent book (54). However, the abnormally high activity of these T_4 analogs does not appear in T_4 activity comparisons in other *in vivo* or in the many *in vitro* systems. While there is ample evidence for the presence of T_3 and T_4 in the tadpole, the quantitative aspects of the tadpole response to certain T_4 analogs seemed to be unique. Therefore the question of the anomalous activity of the substituted thyronines and analogs in anura was re-examined (20). It was found that the unusual activity of T_4 analogs in tadpoles is a result of a unique testing method—immersion of the tadpoles in a solution of the test compound instead of injection. When the test compounds are administered to the tadpole by intraperitoneal injection, the relative activity of the various T_4 analogs are comparable to the *in vivo* activities observed in man.

Relative activities of five compounds administered by both immersion and injection routes in *Rana grylio* tadpoles are presented in Fig. 5. The most active compound is seen to be T_3, when injected, which exceeds the activity of 3,5,3'-triiodothyropropionic acid and any of the

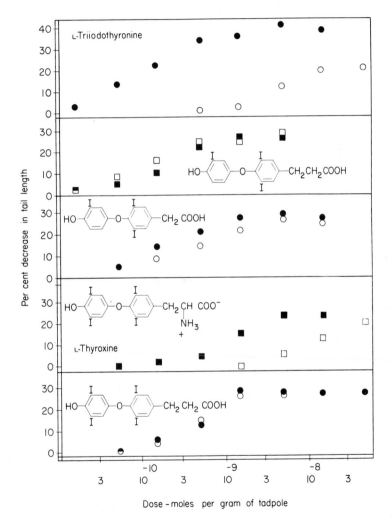

FIG. 5. Comparison of injection and immersion activity for thyroxine analogs in *Rana grylio* at 24°. The percentage decrease in tail length was measured after 5 days. For each test compound, a single injection (filled symbols) was compared with a 48 hour immersion (open symbols). From Frieden and Westmark (20).

other compounds tested. The activity of these compounds on immersion of R. grylio is in general agreement with previously reported data (54). The most interesting feature of the data in Fig. 5 is the great disparity between the injected and immersed activity of both T_3 and T_4. On the other hand, triiodo- and tetraiodothyropropionic acids show virtually the same activity regardless of the mode of administration. Activity is slightly favored for injected triiodothyroacetic acid.

Similar data, not presented in detail here, were obtained with two different subspecies of Rana pipiens using the percentage decrease in tail breadth as the morphological criterion. The divergence between activity of T_3 administered by both methods was not quite as large but was still highly significant. It is important to note that the difference between injection and immersion responses to T_3 and T_4 remain despite some variation in tadpole response due to seasonal and possibly other environmental factors that are difficult to control.

TABLE I

COMPARATIVE ACTIVITY OF THYROXINE AND ANALOGS

Animal.........	Man	Rat	Rat	Tadpole		
				Rana grylio	Rana spp.[a]	
Test...........	BMR	Oxygen uptake	Goiter prevention	Tail	Tail	
Route..........	Inj.	Inj.	Inj.	Inj.	Immersion	
Compound	Activity compared to thyroxine					Activity ratio, injection: immersion[b]
Thyroxine (T_4)	1.0	1.0	1.0	1.0	1.0	17
T_4-propionate	Active	0.1–0.6	0.2–0.4	3.2	21–100	1.0
Triiodothyronine (T_3)	0.9–1.4	1.0–2.0	2.5–10	17	5.0–20	~100
T_3-propionate	Active	0.1	0.5	6.7	15–300	0.37
T_3 acetate	0.1	0.3	0.5–1.5	6.8	10–24	3.3

[a] Data in this column summarize experiments with several species including R. grylio, R. clamitans, R. catesbeiana, and R. pipiens.

[b] Calculated from data as in Fig. 5. Considerable experimental variation was observed in this ratio.

Table I summarizes the response of different animals to these five compounds. It is clearly indicated that the tadpole immersion test yields unique data. When these compounds are injected, their activities are comparable regardless of the test animal used. In the last column, the activity ratio of injected : immersed compounds necessary for a 20% decrease in tail length was estimated from the data in Fig. 5. The figures vary from over 100 for T_3 to less than 1 for triiodothyroacetic acid.

The implications of the wide differences in the immersion and injection responses to T_3 and T_4 are of considerable import. We are inclined to believe that the activity after injection gives a more accurate picture of the comparable T_4 activity of T_4 analogs in the tadpole tested by the tail response. Activity comparisons also should be made using other criteria, e.g., forelimb emergence and growth. The immersion response is probably strongly influenced by relative rates of penetration of the various compounds tested. It is consistent with the classic rules of permeability that a compound with only an acetate or propionate side chain should be more permeable than a compound with a divalent zwitter ion side chain. Immersion tests might also be more subject to difficulties arising from the instability of T_4 compounds (53, 55) and to adsorption on glass in dilute solutions (56, 57). These results may help to explain certain enhancements and inhibition of tadpole responses in immersion experiments (58). The many varied and confusing results obtained in this area may be due to effects on the rates of permeability of T_4 and T_3 rather than to an effect on the peripheral tissue response to the thyroid hormone.

IV. Importance of Intrinsic Tissue Sensitivity in the Tadpole

Stimulation of metamorphosis by the complex of endogenous hormones or by exogenous thyroid hormone constitute the extrinsic factor in anuran differentiation. Probably of even greater importance are the intrinsic factors contributed by the mosaic of sensitive tissues. As Witschi has commented in his book, "Development of Vertebrates" (59):

> The experiments with hormones and hormone glands raise again the question of the relative importance of extrinsic and intrinsic factors as determiners of embryonic differentiation. As in previous discussions on the primary organizers and on the determinations in limb development, it must be answered in favor of the latter. Thyroxin, like the inductors of the early embryonic epoch, acts as an activator, but only if it comes in contact with responsive tissues. Responsiveness and determination of the specificity of reaction are intrinsic tissue factors.

It is thus more accurate to speak of metamorphosis as resulting from the interaction of thyroid hormone with tadpole tissue because it emphasizes that the many phenomena of metamorphosis depend not only on the action of thyroxine, but also on the presence of an inherent tissue sensitivity.

The intrinsic susceptibility of tadpole tail tissue is dramatically illustrated in Fig. 6 taken from the work of Schwind (60). Schwind transplanted an eye cup to a tadpole tail. During metamorphosis the eye moved gradually forward during tail resorption and finally came to rest in the sacral region at the termination of metamorphosis. Similarly transplanted limbs are unaffected by the degenerative processes in the surrounding tail tissues. The impressive degenerative changes of the tail have afforded an extremely convenient tool for bioassay for thyroid hormones in tadpoles.

As might be expected, the differences in the morphological response of tissues have their counterpart in metabolic differences. Using radioactive phosphate, Finamore and Frieden (61) found that the effect of triiodothyronine on nucleic acid biosynthesis in the tail was directly opposite to that in the liver. In induced metamorphosis, tail tissue showed a reduction in phosphate incorporation into RNA and DNA while liver showed an increase in phosphate incorporation. The results were consistent with the frequently observed association of protein biosynthesis and nucleic acid metabolism. During metamorphosis, tadpole liver increases in size and number of functions while tadpole tail is undergoing resorption.

A. Thyroxine Implantation

The acute and differential sensitivity of amphibian tissues were also shown in a different way by Hartwig (62). Hartwig obtained local metamorphic changes by thyroxine implants in salamander larvae. This technique has been improved and extended by Kollros (63), Kaltenbach (64), and others. Using thyroxine-cholesterol pellet implants, these workers have reproduced locally many of the individual tissue changes relatively independent of general systemic effects. For example, Kaltenbach (64) implanted thyroxine-cholesterol pellets into early larval tadpoles and induced prematurely and unilaterally in the vicinity of the pellets such effects as change in head outline, resorption of labial fringe and shedding of labial teeth, maturation and molting of the skin, lengthening and ossification of bones of a hind limb, complex changes in eye structure, and tail resorption depending upon the site of implantation. Thus thyroxine is shown to be the direct initiator of a wide variety of cellular differentiations in various tissues.

An additional approach emphasizing inherent tissue response has come from the recent work of Kollros and his associates (65). Kollros

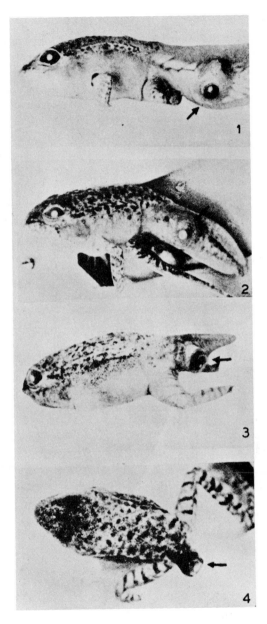

FIG. 6. Photographs showing the specific sensitivity of tail tissue. From Schwind (*60*).

exposed hypophysectomized *R. pipiens* tadpoles to extremely low doses of thyroxine or triiodothyronine and observed unique responses. At extremely low immersion levels of exogenous hormone, disappearance of skin tissue in the opercular region, characteristic changes in the mouth region, and skin pigment alterations were noted. Under the same conditions little change in tail tissue, limb development, or certain other morphological features was detected. These interesting experiments await further elucidation because of the possible effects of the removal of hormones, other than thyroid-stimulating hormone, which accompany hypophysectomy. Since the tadpole was immersed in solutions of the thyroid hormone, it is also possible that the skin and related structures received a relatively larger proportion of the very dilute hormone used than did internal organs.

B. GENETIC CONTROL

Finally it should be stressed that we are only beginning to understand the possible role of hormones on the genetic apparatus of differentiating tissue. Herein rests a complete explanation for the different responses of different animal or plant tissues. That chromosomal activity can be affected by a hormone is suggested from the very recent work of Clever and Karlson (66). They injected ecdysone—the hormone of the prothoracic glands—into the last instar larvae of *Chironomus tentans*. Within 2 hours a new puff in the first chromosome appeared while another puff disappeared. This chromosomal change also occurred in normal development. It was postulated that the primary effect of ecdysone is to alter the activity of specific genes.

V. Biochemical Changes of Direct Adaptive Value during Anuran Metamorphosis

Only brief references to the biochemical alterations that occur during anuran metamorphosis have been discussed in the earlier reviews of Etkin (3), Lynn and Wachowski (17), and Wald (1, 2). A more complete review has been given by Urbani (67). We are not aware of a comprehensive review in which the diverse biochemical modifications that occur during anuran metamorphosis have been integrated about a unified concept. In the text which follows, biochemical changes during anuran metamorphosis will be discussed as pertinent to the adaptive value they contribute to an organism transforming from an aquatic larval form to a terrestrial adult form.

During metamorphosis, biochemical alterations are occurring that may be considered to: (*a*) have an apparent direct adaptive value, or (*b*) serve as a basis for morphological, chemical, or other changes that have adaptive value.

It is not always easy to decide whether a significant chemical change is directly adaptive or only indirectly so. Possibly all the transitions observed will prove to be directly adaptive to land living when properly appreciated. Therefore we emphasize the arbitrary and temporal nature of this distinction and anticipate a steady migration of the less well understood chemical alterations into the primary adaptive category.

In relating biochemical changes to the anuran's adjustments to land, it is not meant to deny the many useful descriptions of metamorphosis as an extended embryological process. Indeed, many embryologists consider metamorphosis as merely a terminal phase of embryonic development. Witschi includes three chapters on metamorphosis in his recent book "Development of Vertebrates" (*68*). Many of the biochemical changes during metamorphosis parallel fetal to adult changes including the increase in serum albumin, the reduction in oxygen binding by the prevailing hemoglobins, and the development of the urea cycle enzymes. Some of the most useful arguments in support of the classic recapitulation theory are drawn from the events of anuran metamorphosis. The transition from tadpole to frog illustrates many of the essential features of the biochemical evolution. Since these two outlooks are well known, an equally general but less used viewpoint based on chemical adaptation has been preferred in an attempt to integrate the biochemical changes observed during anuran metamorphosis.

The biochemical changes accompanying anuran metamorphosis which contribute to land adaptation may be listed as follows: (*a*) the shift from ammonotelism to ureotelism during metamorphosis; (*b*) the increase in serum albumin; (*c*) the change in the structure and biosynthesis of hemoglobins; (*d*) the change in digestive enzymes; (*e*) the augmentation of respiration.

VI. The Shift from Ammonotelism to Ureotelism during Anuran Metamorphosis

It is axiomatic in the classic approach to comparative biochemistry as developed, particularly by Needham (*14*) and Baldwin (*69*) and more recently by Cohen and Brown (*70*), that the nature of an animal's nitrogenous excretory product is a function of its environment and phylogenetic position. As early as 1931 Needham emphasized that ammonia is the principal end product of protein metabolism of aquatic animals, but is supplanted by urea or uric acid in amphibians, birds, reptiles, and mammals. An abundance of water is required for the efficient elimination of ammonia because of its great toxicity. Terrestrial animals have urea or uric acid as the predominant excretion product. Mammals are ureotelic, urea being the main end product, whereas birds and reptiles are primarily excretors of uric acid, i.e., uricotelic. Needham (14) correlated these differences among higher vertebrates with the mode of reproduction. Ureotelic metabolism is associated with viviparity, uricotelic with development within a cleidoic egg. Between these permanently aquatic vertebrates and strictly terrestrial animals are the amphibians—vertebrates making a transition from an aquatic to a terrestrial environment in their life cycle.

From these results it is apparent that the nitrogen excretion pattern of amphibians might fluctuate between that of their aquatic ammonotelic, and their terrestrial ureotelic, relatives. At the outset of metamorphosis or under the influence of the metamorphic stimulus T_4, alterations in the nitrogen excretion pattern begin to occur—alterations which have adaptive value for terrestrial existence. The anurans make the transition from ammonotelism to ureotelism very dramatically. Baldwin (69) has summarized the change as follows:

> The common frog hatches from the egg as an aquatic ammonia-excreting tadpole, but at about the time that it develops the ability to go on to the land, ammonia excretion ceases and is superceded by that of urea. This is evidently an adaptation without which it would be impossible for the animals to spend even a part of their time on the land on account of the difficulty of getting rid of ammonia. Urea, like the ammonia which it replaces, is a very soluble and very diffusible substance, but differs from it in that it is non-toxic even in relatively high concentrations. It could therefore be formed and remain in the body for some time before being excreted, a fact of which these amphibious animals have taken full advantage.

A. Ammonia and Urea Excretion

Forty years ago it was demonstrated that anuran tadpoles excrete a large fraction of their nitrogen in the form of ammonia whereas the adults excrete almost all their nitrogen as urea (71). Munro (72) found that prometamorphic R. temporaria excrete approximately 92% of their nitrogen as urea. As Fig. 7 shows, at the metamorphic climax the excretion pattern changes, urea becoming the principal nitrogen-containing product. Froglets excrete only some 12% of their nitrogen as ammonia. A similar change has been observed in other species including Bufo vulgaris (73), R. catesbeiana (23), Bufo bufo (73). This change has also been observed during T_4-induced metamorphosis of R. temporaria and other species (73).

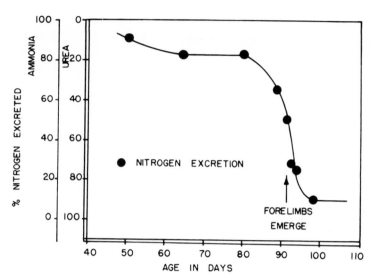

FIG. 7. The transition from ammonia to urea excretion in *Rana temporaria* tadpoles. Data adapted from Munro (72).

Unlike *Rana* and the other toads studied, the adult clawed toad, *Xenopus laevis*, a permanently aquatic form, continues to excrete most of its nitrogen as ammonia (73). Underhay and Baldwin (74) reported that the relative percentage of ammonia excreted decreases and reaches a minimum at the time when the animal enters the metamorphic climax, then begins to increase and continues to increase into the adult stage. Munro (73) found only a slight decrease in ammonia excretion for this animal just prior to the metamorphic climax. The apparent discrepancy between these studies may be resolved by a consideration of the experimental conditions; the conditions of Munro being much less satisfactory for observing pronounced changes in excretory products.

Even the permanently aquatic *Xenopus laevis* fits into this general picture. Under the influence of intrinsic stimuli, the *Xenopus laevis*, for which there is no adaptive value associated with ureotelism, continues as an ammonotelic organism into adulthood. If, however, adult *Xenopus* is subjected to the environmental stimulus of dryness it does undergo a change toward greater ureotelism.

B. INCREASE IN THE ACTIVITY OF THE KREBS ORNITHINE-UREA CYCLE ENZYMES

Does the shift from ammonotelism to ureotelism find an expression in the enzymatic personality of tadpole tissues? There is a remarkably complete correlation of the alteration in principal nitrogenous excretory products with enzyme developments in the liver. The important metabolic sequences involving the conversion of ammonia to urea are depicted in the Krebs ornithine-urea cycle shown in Fig. 8. A key enzyme in this

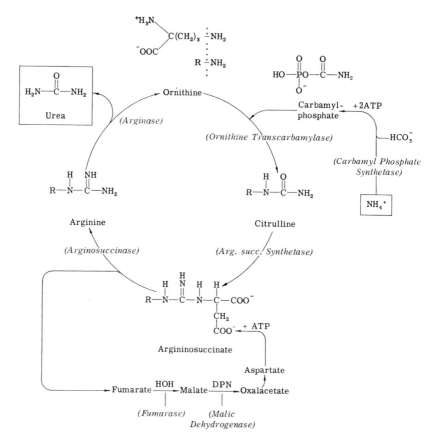

FIG. 8. The Krebs-urea-ornithine cycle emphasizing the position of ammonia and urea. Adapted from Brown and Cohen (23).

cycle is arginase which is directly responsible for urea production. Following the work of Munro (72), a thorough study of liver arginase activity during induced and spontaneous metamorphosis was made (75). The most significant results are summarized in Fig. 9. In both *Bufo* and *R. heckscheri*, a direct relationship was obtained between the morphological stage and an increased arginase activity. The arginase activity responded more rapidly to T_3 and T_4 than did the morphological

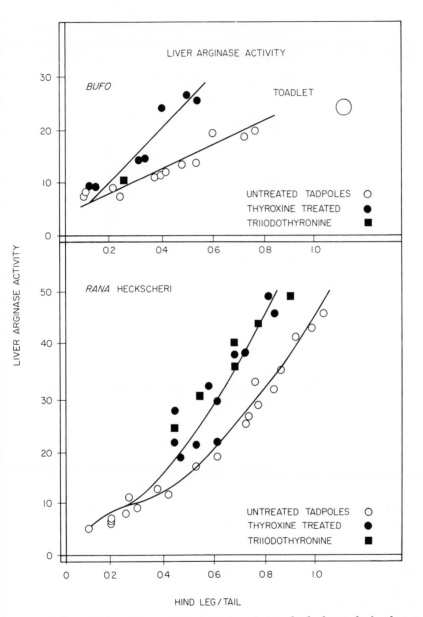

FIG. 9. Increase in arginase activity in *Bufo* and *Rana heckscheri* tadpoles during induced and spontaneous metamorphosis. Data from Dolphin and Frieden (75).

conversion. The increase in arginase was confirmed subsequently by Brown and Cohen (23) in another species, *R. catesbeiana*.

A thorough study of the liver enzymes involved in the synthesis of arginine from ornithine was also recently made by Brown, Brown, and Cohen (76). As illustrated in Fig. 10, all three enzymes, carbamyl-

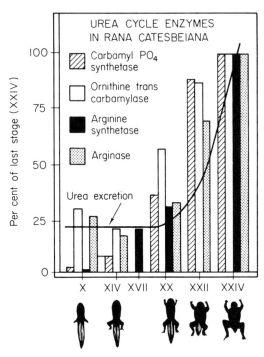

FIG. 10. Increase in arginine-synthesizing enzymes during spontaneous metamorphosis. Figure modified from that of Brown, Brown, and Cohen (76).

phosphate synthetase, ornithine transcarbamylase, and argininosuccinate synthetase, increase in activity at the onset of metamorphosis and remain at an elevated level in the frog. The fiftyfold increase in carbamylphosphate synthetase is especially striking. Mixed activity studies of tadpole and frog extracts failed to demonstrate the presence of inhibitors or activators which might account for changes in the specific activity of this enzyme. The absence of inhibitors or activators suggests that an increased rate of de novo synthesis of this enzyme takes place at the time the animal becomes anatomically and physiologically attuned to moving from its aquatic habitat to a terrestrial one. Further evidence for the synthesis of this urea cycle enzyme during metamorphosis comes from the studies of Paik and Cohen (77). The livers of T_4-induced metamorphosing tadpoles showed a marked increase in the synthesis of carbamylphosphate synthetase as indicated by immunochemical studies. A linear relation between the specific activity of the enzyme and metamorphic changes (hind leg length : tail length) was found for T_4-induced metamorphosis. Since these and other investigators have found no increase in succinoxidase and a delayed increase in catalase activities in liver, selective stimulation of protein biosynthesis by the thyroid hormone has been proposed (77, 78).

On the basis of a comparison of the activities of the urea cycle enzymes, assuming each in turn to be rate limiting, and calculation of the amount of urea synthesized in the tadpole liver, Brown *et al.* (76) concluded that the rate-limiting step of the urea cycle could be that catalyzed by the argininosuccinate synthetase condensing enzyme. Thus the cause per se for the increase in rate of urea synthesis and excretion in metamorphosing tadpoles would appear to be the increase in activity of the citrulline-aspartate condensing enzyme.

The picture emerging from these studies is that of a stimulation of *de novo* urea cycle enzyme synthesis by T_4. The appearance and increase in activity of these enzymes results in the preparation of the organism for a terrestrial existence by a shift from ammonotelism to ureotelism.

VII. The Increase in Serum Albumin and Serum Protein*

The physiological versatility of the serum proteins is well known. Probably their most important role, particularly that of albumin, is the maintenance of blood volume through osmoregulation (79). Therefore it is not unexpected that in the transition from fresh water to land, there would be a significant adjustment of the osmotic pressure regulatory mechanism. The extent of this change is so large that it must be of major significance in the biochemical adaptation involved in metamorphosis (80).

A. Increase in A : G Ratio and Albumin Concentration with Metamorphosis

The method of paper electrophoresis proved to be ideal for the study of numerous small samples of tadpole serum. A striking change in the four species studied was the increase in, and the eventual predominance of, the fastest-moving fraction, corresponding to the increased metamorphic development of the tadpoles (80). For Ranidae this fraction

---

* The published and unpublished work on the serum proteins and hemoglobins during metamorphosis is from the Ph.D. dissertation of Dr. A. E. Herner while at Florida State University, Tallahassee, Florida.

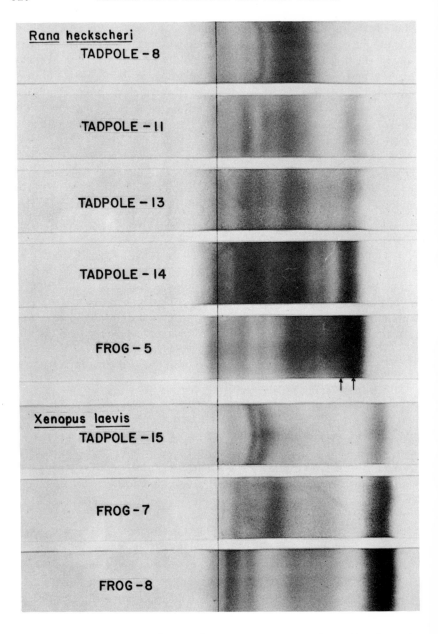

FIG. 11. Serum protein changes during anuran metamorphosis. Top five strips: *Rana heckscheri*. The albumin peak in Tadpole-8 is very small, increasing during metamorphosis to a maximum in Frog-5. Bottom three strips: *Xenopus laevis*. The changes in the serum proteins of the fully metamorphosed animal upon maturation can be seen by a comparison of the strip for the small frog (Frog-7) with that for the larger frog (Frog-8). From Herner and Frieden (80).

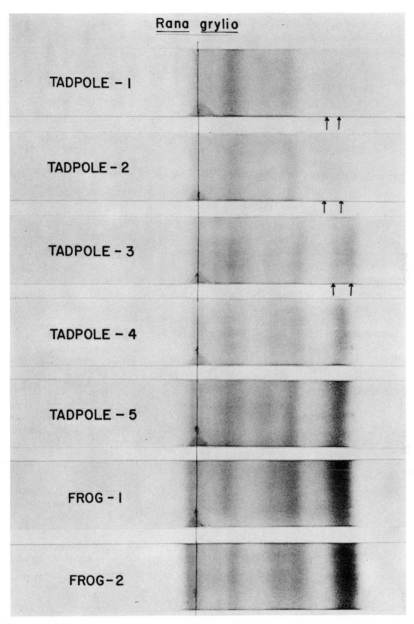

FIG. 12. Typical paper strips showing the electrophoretically separated serum proteins stained with bromophenol blue for *Rana grylio*. Group designations are as in Fig. 14 and Table II, and are explained in the text. The gradual increase in the intensity of the albumin fraction during metamorphosis is striking and the redistribution of the globulins can be seen.

has the same electrophoretic mobility as human serum albumin and also shares the intensive staining properties of human serum albumin. Under the experimental conditions this fraction has an anodal migration of 7 cm. for the Ranidae and 8 cm. for the *Xenopus* samples. The slower-moving fractions are considered to be globulins.

The migration of the 7-cm. fractions remains relatively constant for all stages of a given species so that its presence may be conveniently surveyed as the tadpole develops into the adult frog. Further, this frac-

TABLE II

Changes in Hind Leg to Tail (L:T) and Albumin to
Globulin (A:G) Ratios during Anuran Metamorphosis

Designation	Number of animals	Description	L:T[a]	A:G[a]
Rana grylio				
Tadpole-1	9	Early metamorphosis	0.09 ± 0.04	0.12 ± 0.03
Tadpole-2	3	3 Days after T$_3$ inj.	0.18 ± 0.03	0.16 ± 0.04
Tadpole-3	6	5 Days after T$_3$ inj.	0.28 ± 0.08	0.22 ± 0.05
Tadpole-4	4	6 Days after T$_3$ inj.	0.36 ± 0.07	0.35 ± 0.08
Tadpole-5	3	Intermediate	1.22 ± 0.12	0.54 ± 0.14
Frog-1	7	Postmetamorphosis	—	0.81 ± 0.11
Frog-2	3	Adult	—	0.90 ± 0.01
Rana catesbeiana				
Tadpole-6	5	Early metamorphosis	0.04 ± 0.03	0.12 ± 0.02
Tadpole-7	7	6–7 Days after T$_3$ inj.	0.39 ± 0.09	0.23 ± 0.08
Frog-3	4	Postmetamorphosis	—	0.64 ± 0.09
Frog-4	4	Adult	—	0.70 ± 0.07
Rana heckscheri				
Tadpole-8	10	Early metamorphosis	0.11 ± 0.02	0.02 ± 0.02
Tadpole-9	3	1 Day after T$_3$ inj.	0.07 ± 0.02	0
Tadpole-10	5	2 Days after T$_3$ inj.	0.10 ± 0.05	0.08 ± 0.05
Tadpole-11	7	3 Days after T$_3$ inj.	0.14 ± 0.05	0.07 ± 0.02
Tadpole-12	3	5 Days after T$_3$ inj.	0.18 ± 0.03	0.09 ± 0.02
Tadpole-13	6	6 Days after T$_3$ inj.	0.41 ± 0.16	0.11 ± 0.03
Tadpole-14	2	Intermediate	0.60	0.14
Frog-5	5	Adult	—	0.48 ± 0.05
Rana clamitans				
Frog-6	2	Adult	—	0.31
Xenopus laevis				
Tadpole-15	12+[b]	Early metamorphosis	—	0.20
Frog-7	2	Weight ca. 3 gm.	—	0.52
Frog-8	2	Weight ca. 20 gm.	—	1.49

[a] Including standard deviations.

[b] Two groups of 6 each.

tion has the same migration for all stages of the Ranidae species studied. The actual chemical relationship of the fast-moving fractions to each other or to human serum albumin is open to conjecture; however, on the basis of identical electrophoretic mobilities, we may postulate that they are similar. *Xenopus laevis* serum affords the only instance of an albumin of a different mobility (see Fig. 11). Dialysis of these sera against water did not alter the electrophoretic picture or the pattern of the proteins in an analytical ultracentrifuge. The sedimentation patterns of tadpole and frog serum also reveal the differences in albumin content noted here. The sedimentation properties of these albumins are identical with human serum albumins.

In Fig. 11 the appearance of the fast-moving albumin band is easily observable. This species, *R. heckscheri,* is noteworthy in that the tadpole

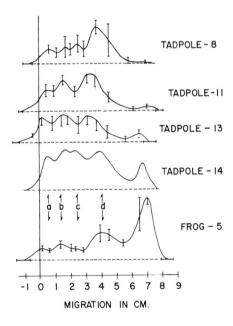

FIG. 13. Composite electrophoretic patterns for the serum proteins of *Rana heckscheri* at various stages of metamorphosis. Spontaneous metamorphosis: Tadpole-8 (early metamorphosis), Tadpole-14 (intermediate), Frog-5 (adult). T₃-induced metamorphosis: Tadpole-11 and Tadpole-13 (3 and 6 days after T₃ injection). Details for the group designations are in the text. Globulin fractions a, b, c, and d are indicated. The fraction with the greatest migration is the albumin. Serum volume: tadpoles, 40 µl.; Frog-5, 20 µl. From Herner and Frieden (*80*).

seems to have almost no detectable serum albumin. In other species, the albumin is always very low but usually discernible. If albumin is added to tadpole serum it appears in the expected place, a fact indicating that the albumin is not being held in the globulin region by some chemical interaction. Albumin production can also be induced in young tadpoles by injecting T_3.

Figure 12 shows representative electrophoregrams for various stages of *R. grylio*. The quantitative picture is essentially similar to that of *R. heckscheri* although some albumin is detectable in the young tadpole. The postmetamorphic froglet has a picture similar to that of the mature frog.

The photographs show single representative animals from appropriate groups identified in Table II. To obtain group statistics, dye intensity measurements were averaged for the results in Figs. 13–16. These averages and the indicated deviations again represent the animals described in Table II and provide the basis for the more detailed discussion given below.

B. Changes in the Serum Proteins of *Rana heckscheri*

Changes in the *Rana heckscheri* patterns (Fig. 13) are most dramatic in that the young tadpole (Tadpole-8) starts with an extremely low level of albumin (0.007 gm. per 100 ml.) which increases to a level of 0.7 gm. per 100 ml. in the mature adult (Fig. 13). This is reflected in an increase in the A : G ratio from 0.02 to 0.48 (Table II). From Fig. 13 it is seen that the increase in albumin coincides with the progress of spontaneous metamorphosis. Smaller but significant increases in serum albumin are observed for T_3-induced metamorphosis (tadpole groups 11–14 of Table II and Fig. 13).

C. Changes in the Serum Proteins of *Rana grylio* and *R. catesbeiana*

R. grylio (Tadpole-1) and *R. catesbeiana* (Tadpole-6) tadpoles have a higher A : G ratio (0.12 for both) and higher albumin concentrations than the comparable *R. heckscheri* tadpole (Tadpole-8). The A : G ratios in the mature animals of both these species (Frog-2 and Frog-4) reach 0.90 and 0.70, respectively. The albumin concentrations for the frogs *R. grylio* and *R. catesbeiana* are similar (about 1 gm. per 100 ml.) and higher than that for the *R. heckscheri* frog. Included in Fig. 14 and Table II are results obtained for the species *R. grylio* and *R. catesbeiana* both for postmetamorphic frogs (Frog-1 and Frog-3) and for the mature animals (Frog-2 and Frog-4). The data for these species show that after the animals have completed metamorphosis their serum protein picture remains essentially unchanged. Growth of the animals does

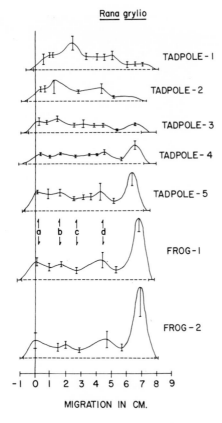

FIG. 14. Composite electrophoretic patterns for the serum proteins of *Rana grylio* at various stages of development. Spontaneous metamorphosis: Tadpole-1 (early metamorphosis), Tadpole-5 (intermediate), Frog-1 (postmetamorphosis), Frog-2 (adult). T_3-induced metamorphosis; Tadpoles-2, -3, and -4, (respectively 3, 5, and 6 days after T_3 injection). The volume of serum used was 20 μl. in all cases. From Herner and Frieden (*80*).

not lead to any further change either in the distribution of these proteins or the total concentrations. In both these species, T_3 treatment stimulated albumin production and caused redistribution of the globulins.

D. COMPARISON OF THE ELECTROPHORETIC PATTERNS OF THE RANIDAE

The patterns of the *R. catesbeiana* tadpole in early metamorphosis (Tadpole-5) and both the postmetamorphic and adult frogs (Frog-3 and Frog-4) of this species have the same general shape as the patterns of comparable animals of the species *R. grylio* (Tadpole-1, Frog-1, and

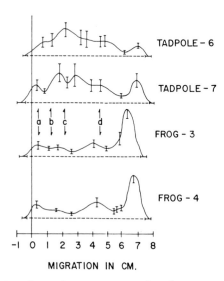

FIG. 15. Composite electrophoretic patterns for the serum proteins of *Rana catesbeiana* at various stages of development. Tadpole-6 (early metamorphosis), Tadpole-7 (6–7 days after T₃ injection), Frog-3 (postmetamorphosis), and Frog-4 (adult). 20 μl. of serum were applied for the tadpoles and 10 μl. for the frogs. From Herner and Frieden (*80*).

Frog-2). The difference for these two species in their terminal T₃-treated animals (Tadpole-4 and Tadpole-7) is noted above.

Though the albumin level is low in the terminal T₃-treated animal (Tadpole-13) and the intermediate animal (Tadpole-14) of *R. heckscheri*, the globulin distribution of these animals is comparable to that in corresponding animals of *R. grylio*. The frog patterns of all three species are almost identical but with the slight variation mentioned previously for *R. heckscheri* frogs. It is surprising that the adult frog of another Ranidae species, *Rana clamitans* (Fig. 16), has so low an albumin fraction in comparison to the other three Ranidae studied.

The composite electrophoretic patterns clearly show an extensive redistribution of the globulins during metamorphosis. However, we feel that the multiplicity and interactions of the globulins necessitate cautious interpretation of these data. Therefore, we cite only the shift of the globulins from arbitrarily labeled fraction *c* to fraction *a*, and to a lesser extent fraction *d*, during metamorphosis. Only in *R. heckscheri* is there an increase in fraction *b*. The T₃-treated tadpoles in the three species reflected these migrations to fractions *a* and *b*, but not to *d*.

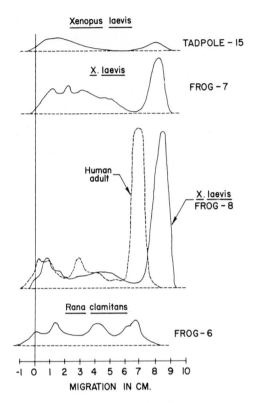

Fig. 16. Composite electrophoretic patterns for the serum proteins of *Xenopus laevis* at three stages of normal development and for the adult *Rana clamitans*. The albumin peak for the *X. laevis* animals is displaced to the right of the position for this peak in the Ranidae and adult human sera (shown). Two peaks are present in the albumin area in the serum of the adult *R. clamitans*. Serum volumes: Tadpole-15, 100 μl.; Frog-6, -7, and -8, 20 μl.; adult human, 10 μl. From Herner and Frieden (*80*).

The young tadpole serum patterns of *R. heckscheri* are dissimilar to those of *R. grylio* and *R. catesbeiana*. Yet these three species change to a similar pattern at the completion of metamorphosis. This effect has its counterpart in the morphology of embryological development. De Beer (*81*) notes that there are cases of structurally divergent embryos which will, in the course of their development, become similar in structure. This phenomenon was named *caenogenesis* by Haeckel (*82*).

E. Alterations of Serum Proteins of *Xenopus laevis*

Electrophoretic patterns for *Xenopus laevis* animals are presented in Figs. 11 and 16 and the A:G data in Table II. The A:G ratio for the earliest tested stage of tadpoles of this species (Tadpole-15) is considerable (0.20). It increases to 0.52 with the completion of metamorphosis. At variance with the Ranidae species discussed above, the A:G ratio and the total protein concentration continue to increase as the frog matures. The A:G ratio reaches 1.49 and the total protein concentration becomes 3.5 gm. per 100 ml. for the 20-gm. frog (Frog-8).

There is an increase in all the globulins during metamorphosis and the appearance of faster-moving globulins in the more advanced animals (Fig. 16). During growth of the *Xenopus* frogs, the globulins appear to redistribute, the most noticeable effect being the diminution of the fractions with a mobility in the middle range. The globulin distribution of the larger *Xenopus* frog (Frog-8) is more comparable to that of adult human serum than to the globulin patterns of the Ranidae frogs.

TABLE III

VARIATIONS IN TOTAL SERUM PROTEIN CONCENTRATION
DURING ANURAN METAMORPHOSIS

Species	Group	Number of animals	Protein concentration (gm./100 ml.)
Rana grylio	Tadpole-1	7	1.42 ± 0.30
	Tadpole-2	3	1.28 ± 0.27
	Tadpole-3	4	1.47 ± 0.10
	Tadpole-4	4	1.41 ± 0.40
	Frog-1	4	2.19 ± 0.17
	Frog-2	4	1.97 ± 0.12
Rana catesbeiana	Tadpole-6	7	1.16 ± 0.19
	Tadpole-7	8	1.74 ± 0.39[a]
	Frog-3	3	2.56 ± 0.50[a]
	Frog-4	4	2.56 ± 0.53[a]
Rana heckscheri	Tadpole-8	7	0.35 ± 0.04
	Tadpole-13	8	0.92 ± 0.22[a]
	Frog-5	4	2.03 ± 0.19
Xenopus laevis	Tadpole-15	12[b]	0.2[c]
	Frog-7	2	2.3[c]
	Frog-8	2	3.5[c]

[a] Trichloroacetic acid-insoluble nitrogen $\times$ 6.25.
[b] Two pooled samples of serum, each from six animals.
[c] Estimated from the electrophoretic patterns, including standard deviations.

F. TOTAL SERUM PROTEIN CONCENTRATION

Table III shows that as an animal undergoes metamorphosis, either T_3-induced or spontaneous, there is usually an increase in the total serum protein concentration associated, to a large extent, with an increase in the albumin concentration. Of the Ranidae, on the basis of percentage increase, the effect is most marked for R. *heckscheri* and least so for R. *grylio*. The T_3-treated R. *grylio* does not show a significant change in serum protein. For the *Xenopus* frogs there is a significant increase in the total protein concentration with growth.

G. Adaptive Role of the Serum Proteins

The increase in albumin in the Ranidae can be ascribed to new needs which the animals acquire in developing from the water-dwelling form to a complex terrestrial animal. The frog, with its more intricate circulatory system, requires a greater serum protein concentration for peripheral osmotic exchange and for the maintenance of blood volume (79). Albumin, by virtue of its small molecular weight and its highly charged state at physiological pH's, is a superior protein for achieving the necessary osmotic balance. Whipple (83) even suggests that the osmotic parameter may itself be stimulatory for the biosynthesis of albumin.

Collateral to the osmotic requirements of the blood is the necessity for greater carrying capacity per unit volume of blood for the small molecules required by the tissues. The transport function of serum proteins particularly of albumin, is well known. An increase in albumin concentration fulfills both the osmotic and the transport needs, resulting in a blood more efficient for metabolic exchange in the frog than in the tadpole.

H. Comparative Embryology of the Serum Proteins

There is a precedence for an increased serum protein concentration in embryological differentiation. Moore, Shen, and Alexander (84) have followed the changes in the serum proteins during the embryological development of the higher vertebrates and found that the sera of developing chick and pig embryos increase in total protein concentration. The serum albumin of chicks and pigs becomes the predominant fraction during the later developmental stages. In the early embryos, the α- and β-globulins predominate. The component with a mobility similar to mammalian γ-globulins does not appear until rather late.

I. Role of the Liver in Serum Protein Synthesis

Because of the importance of the liver in the synthesis of serum proteins, the changes in the nature and quantity of the serum proteins that are observed during metamorphosis would be expected to be reflected in the metabolic and structural nature of the liver. Henriques and co-workers (85) have shown that, in the rabbit, the serum proteins synthesized by the liver represent 40% of the total protein output of this tissue. Kaywin (21) demonstrated the effect of thyroid hormone in altering the cytological structure of the liver during accelerated anuran metamorphosis. An increase in the size and a change in the gross structure of the liver have also been noted (78). Modifications of the metabolic nature of the liver are indicated by the studies of enzymatic activities (67, 77, 78) and changes in nucleic acid metabolism (61). Extrahepatic changes may account for electrophoretic alterations in the γ-globulins and the hemoglobins that accompany anuran metamorphosis (86).

VIII. The Change in the Molecular Properties and Biosynthesis of Hemoglobin

Another significant adaptive change that occurs during metamorphosis is the alteration in the properties and biosynthesis of hemoglobin. It was shown earlier by McCutcheon (87) and later by Riggs (88) that hemoglobin isolated from tadpole red cells has a greater oxygen affinity and is virtually independent of pH, whereas the binding of oxygen by frog hemoglobin is very sensitive to pH (Bohr effect). This is clearly revealed in Rigg's data summarized in Fig. 17 (88). At pH's 6.28, 7.32, and 9.0, oxygen binding by tadpole hemoglobin scarcely varies while frog hemoglobin varies considerably in oxygen binding from pH 6.9 to 8.4. At physiological pH's the difference in binding between the two hemoglobins is pronounced. Tadpole blood has a large oxygen "loading capacity" whereas the blood of the adult has a lesser "loading capacity" but a greater "unloading capacity." The Bohr effect is widespread in nature and its appearance after anuran metamorphosis is a striking example of molecular evolution.

The adaptive feature of this change in hemoglobin oxygen affinity during anuran metamorphosis may arise from the necessity for a superior oxygen-capturing mechanism for the tadpole because of its essential limitation to the dissolved oxygen in its aqueous environment. It is also conceivable that the lowered oxygen binding of frog hemoglobin provides for its rapid and prodigious needs for oxygen to permit its greater powers of locomotion on land. Thus it is believed that this biochemical alteration as well as gross morphological changes (resorption of gills; development of lungs) prepare anurans for the passage from their aquatic environment with a low oxygen tension to their terrestrial habitat with an increased availability of oxygen. Alternatively, it may be reasoned that the presence of the Bohr effect in the frog promotes the discharge of CO_2 in the lungs. Presumably the tadpole, whose gills are constantly bathed in water, needs no aid in getting rid of CO_2.

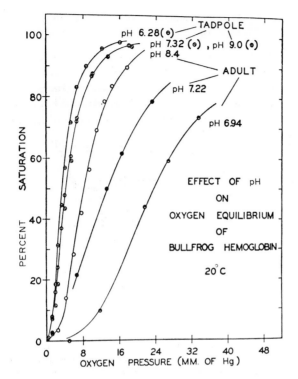

FIG. 17. Comparison of the oxygen dissociation curves of the tadpole and frog hemoglobins of *R. catesbeiana*, showing the pH (Bohr) effect in the frog and the relative absence of this effect in the tadpole. From Riggs (88).

Riggs (88) also found that tadpole hemoglobin had the normal vertebrate molecular weight of 68,000. Recently Riggs (89) has shown a correlation of the available sulfhydryl groups in various hemoglobins with Bohr effect. He notes that frog hemoglobin has more available sulfhydryl groups than tadpole hemoglobin. Obviously the difference in the properties of tadpole and frog hemoglobin must be reflected in this and possibly other molecular differences. This question has been examined in detail by Herner and Frieden (86).

First of all, the fact that the heme portion is the same for both the tadpole and frog hemoglobins of several species was confirmed. The absorption spectra for oxyhemoglobin solutions all show the same shape with identical visible maxima at 541 and 578 mμ. Thus the difference observed must be attributed to the changing character of the protein moiety, the globin.

A. Reduction in Electrophoretic Mobility of Hemoglobin during Metamorphosis

Variation in the amino acid composition of hemoglobin usually shows up in different electrophoretic mobilities. When a hemoglobin solution from the red blood cells of tadpoles or frogs of *R. grylio* is subjected to paper electrophoresis at pH 8.6 for 18 hours, data such as those depicted in Fig. 18 and Table IV were obtained. In tadpoles, there

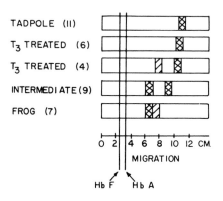

Fig. 18. Metamorphic changes in the electrophoretic character of the hemoglobins of *R. grylio*. T_3 refers to animals treated with triiodothyronine for 5 or 6 days. The numbers in parentheses are the numbers of animals in each group. The crosshatched areas represent intense fractions; the striped areas are lighter fractions. The migrations of the human hemoglobins F and A are included for comparison. Reduced mobilities are observed when thicker paper is used. From Herner and Frieden (86).

is only one band with the characteristic reddish brown color of hemoglobin at 11 cm. in the anodal direction from the origin. This is a relatively high mobility compared to human hemoglobins F and A which migrate to respective positions of 2.5 and 3.5 cm. under identical experimental conditions. T_3 treatment results in an apparent decreased mobility of the major hemoglobin band to 10.5 cm. and eventually in the appearance of a new fraction at 7 cm. In the spontaneous partially metamorphosed tadpole, two principal hemoglobin bands are evident at 7.0 and 9.5 cm. Just prior to final metamorphosis the hemoglobin of lesser mobility becomes predominant until the hemoglobin of 6.5 cm. mobility is present in a greater proportion than the hemoglobin of 7.5 cm. mobility. Thus there appears to be a marked transition in the electrophoretic mobility of tadpole hemoglobin as metamorphosis proceeds. It is expected that the higher electrophoretic mobility of tadpole hemo-

TABLE IV

ELECTROPHORETIC DISTRIBUTION OF SOLUBLE RED CELL PROTEINS OF
Rana grylio AT VARIOUS STAGES OF METAMORPHOSIS

	Group	Number of samples	Nonhemoglobin fractions[a]			Hemoglobin fractions[a]		
Number	Description		I	II	III	III	IV
1	Tadpole (L:T = 0.12)	11	−5.3	−3.8	7.6	—	11.2
2	T₃-Treated (L:T = 0.3)	7	−4.9	−3.9	7.5	—	10.4
3	T₃-Treated (L:T = 0.3)	4	−5.2	−3.8	—	7.2	10.6
4	Part. metamorphosed (L:T = 0.6)	3	−5.0	−3.7	7.0	—	9.7
5	Part. metamorphosed (L:T = 0.6)	2	−5.2	−3.9	—	6.8	9.7
6	Part. metamorphosed (L:T = 7.2)	5	—	—	—	5.6	8.3
7	Frog	7	—	—	—	6.4	7.6

[a] Figures represent migration of components in centimeters.

globin reflects a lower isoelectric point and a higher incidence of acidic amino acids such as glutamic or aspartic acids (or a lower proportion of basic amino acids such as lysine or arginine). The lower mobility of frog hemoglobin and the report of Riggs (89) might signify a partial substitution of cysteine residues for acidic amino acids in the metamorphic process. The progressive change in the mobilities of the hemoglobins suggests that the substitution process may be gradual.

B. ALTERED BIOSYNTHESIS OF HEMOGLOBIN

McCutcheon (87) noted that red cells of R. catesbeiana become more elliptical after differentiation, and this has now been confirmed for several other species (86). The red cell count increases proportionately with the increase in blood hemoglobin concentration. Not only have the properties and structure of hemoglobin been altered during metamorphosis, but we have evidence for a significantly different biosynthetic mechanism.

To gain insight into the mechanism of hemoglobin biosynthesis, the nonchromogenic, water-soluble proteins of tadpole and frog erythrocytes have been examined. These were detected by typical bromophenol blue staining techniques of paper electropherograms and densitometric tracings made as with the serum proteins. In the young tadpole a prominent nonhemoglobin protein fraction appeared at 7.6 cm. (see Fig. 19; fraction III). One or two other proteins with cathodal migrations, probably globins, also were detected (fraction II; I is not shown). A similar protein picture was obtained for T_3-treated tadpoles except for the cathodal proteins. During normal development little change in these proteins is seen until close to the completion of metamorphosis (leg:tail $\cong 2$) when the nonhemoglobin protein fractions are present, such as designated fractions III and IV in Fig. 19. The changes in the red cell proteins reach a final state in the young frog. No difference was observed between red cell extracts from young and mature frogs. Thus, as in the case of the serum proteins (80), the differentiation of the red cell proteins is complete just after metamorphosis.

Using radioactive iron, it was observed that in the tadpole, there was no localization of Fe^{59} in the area corresponding to fraction III (7.6 cm.). There is considerably greater Fe^{59} uptake during spontaneous metamorphosis, again exclusively in the hemoglobin areas on paper electrophoresis. The Fe^{59} which appears in the 0–4 cm. range is probably ghost or stroma-bound iron (Fig. 20).

Thus it has been found that the tadpole produces one principal hemoglobin and a nonheme precursor of a new hemoglobin. As meta-

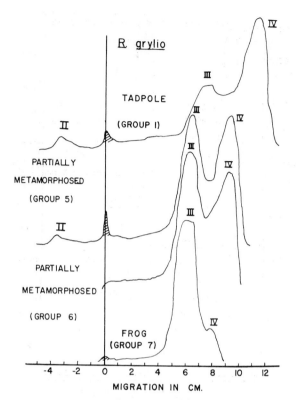

Fig. 19. Representative electrophoretic patterns showing the changes in the red cell proteins during spontaneous metamorphosis in *Rana grylio*. Patterns are densitometric tracings of the bromophenol blue-dyed paper strips. Fractions II and III are referred to in the text. Not appearing in the patterns shown is fraction I which, when present, is at a position of −5.1 cm. and to the left of fraction II. The shaded peaks at the origin are due to ghost cells. Data of Herner and Frieden (86).

morphosis proceeds this nonheme protein is converted to a red hemoglobin in a process which is also accompanied by demonstrable Fe[59] uptake. The process for the synthesis of this new low mobility hemoglobin may be pictured using a scheme modified from Eriksen (90) (Fig. 21). In tadpoles there is evidence for the presence of globin and the porphyrinogen-globin with a break indicated by the dashed line. As metamorphosis proceeds, the capacity to conduct the additional steps to complete the synthesis of a new hemoglobin may be acquired. Presumably, it is this new hemoglobin which shows a different oxygen binding and the Bohr effect.

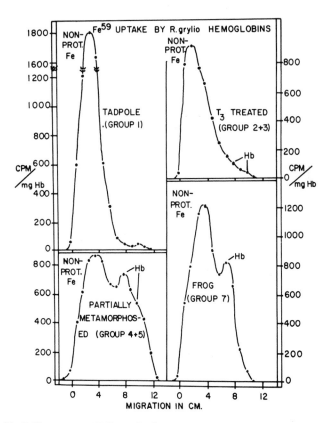

Fig. 20. Differences in Fe^{59} uptake by red cells and in the incorporation of Fe^{59} into hemoglobin in *Rana grylio* at various stages of metamorphosis. The hemoglobin solutions prepared from the Fe^{59}-incubated red cells (details in text) were subjected to paper electrophoresis. Paper strips were cut into 1-cm. segments for counting. The dosage was 4 μc. of Fe^{59} per milliliter of whole blood. All bloods were pooled samples from 3 or 4 animals. Data of Herner and Frieden (*86*).

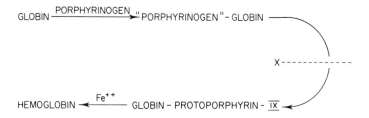

Fig. 21. Possible mechanism of the biosynthesis of hemoglobin. An omission or block in the tadpole may occur at the point indicated by X. An alteration might also exist in the formation of globin from "globin precursors."

C. COMPARATIVE RED CELL PROTEIN DISTRIBUTION IN AMPHIBIA

The main hemoglobin fraction in *R. catesbeiana* and *R. heckscheri* tadpoles migrates farther than the hemoglobin of the frog extracts, as in comparable *R. grylio* animals. Also, as in the case of *R. grylio*, the nonhemoglobin proteins, present in the extracts of the tadpole red cells, are not found in the solutions prepared from frog red cells.

The positions of the hemoglobins of the frog and the tadpole of *R. grylio* and *R. catesbeiana* as well as the position of fraction III in *R. grylio* and the comparable fraction in the tadpole of *R. catesbeiana* are quite similar. This corresponds well to the similarity of the respective serum proteins of the frogs and the tadpoles of these two species.

The hemoglobins of the *R. heckscheri* tadpole and frog are slower moving than the hemoglobins of the other two Ranidae species. In addition, a fraction corresponding to fraction III in the *R. grylio* tadpole extract is not discernible in the tadpole pattern of *R. heckscheri*. The lack of similarity of the *R. heckscheri* patterns to those of the other two species also agrees with the findings in the serum protein studies (80). There is evidence for multiple hemoglobins in both the frogs and tadpoles of the above species.

The *Xenopus laevis* patterns are quite different from those of the above species in that the hemoglobin fractions are slower moving in both the tadpole and the frog, though they are in the same sequence. An additional hemoglobin fraction, near the origin, is present in the tadpole sample. There is no evidence for any nonhemoglobin proteins either in the tadpole or in the frog of *Xenopus*.

The change to slower-moving hemoglobins in anuran metamorphosis has its parallel in phylogeny. In a thorough study of the electrophoretic properties of amphibian and reptilian adult hemoglobins, Dessauer, Fox and Ramirez (91) have shown that there is a tendency toward slower-moving hemoglobins in the transition from the lower amphibia to the higher reptiles.

IX. Alterations in Digestive Mechanisms

The transformation of the tadpole to the frog produces a profound change in dietary habits. The aquatic tadpole is primarily an herbivorous animal whereas the land-dwelling frog thrives on insects or other invertebrates, a protein-rich diet. This shift in diet is accompanied by many morphological changes in the digestive tract [see description by Ratner (92), supplemented by Janes (93), Liu and Li (94), and Lim (95)]. Alterations in the enzymatic machinery of digestion also contribute to the frog's ability to cope with its new, essentially carnivorous diet. The cytological structures of the pancreas are also geared to cope with new secretory demands on the pancreas. Aron (96) and Gennaro (97) have demonstrated an augmentation of increased pancreatic activity occurring just before metamorphosis and continuing into the adult stage. Intestinal secretory and functional activity is also greatest prior to metamorphosis, as indicated by $P^{32}O_4$ incorporation studies (97). The phosphate uptake drops markedly when the reorganization processes of the gut begin.

In this instance the cytological and anatomical evidence exceeds the biochemical data on the adaptation of the digestive system. There is confusion because of experimental difficulties and of the occurrence of a nonfeeding period at the metamorphic climax. Moreover, levels of many digestive enzymes are high in the tadpole, fall during early larval development, and then increase at metamorphosis. Therefore the times selected for comparison may be crucial.

Enzyme trends. Kuntz (98) found a decrease in amylase activity coincident with the period of fasting during metamorphosis. As the animal resumes feeding after metamorphosis, there is an acceleration of carbohydrate digestion and a higher amylase activity in both the pancreas and small intestine. Lipase activity also is shown to increase in the whole-animal studies by Urbani (99). Very recently Kaltenbach *et al.* (100) have observed no appreciable change in liver esterase, but a marked increase (up to 20 times) in serum esterase during the metamorphosis of *R. grylio*. The injection of T_3 caused a two- to threefold increase in serum esterase. Blacher and Liosner (101) reported an increase in intestinal trypsin activity; pepsin activity, however, seemed to disappear in the later stages of metamorphosis. An increase in acid proteinase (pH 4.2) but no change in basic proteinase in *Bufo vulgaris* was noted (102). Coromaldi (103) reported an increase in the acid ribonuclease (RNase) (pH 5.6) of *B. vulgaris* tail and body. Alkaline RNase decreases during all stages of metamorphosis. Clearly stronger evidence is needed to clinch this evidence of biochemical adaptation of the digestive machinery during anuran metamorphosis.

X. The Effect on Respiration

It is paradoxical that we still cannot firmly associate two of the oldest facts regarding the thyroid hormone and anuran metamorphosis. It has been known for almost 50 years that the thyroid hormone initiates metamorphosis (31). That mammalian respiration is under the profound control of the thyroid hormone has been realized for an even longer period (104). Yet decisive experimental evidence associating a heightened oxygen uptake with spontaneous metamorphosis is still lacking [for a more detailed discussion see Lewis and Frieden (*105*)].

A. EFFECT OF THYROID HORMONES ON RESPIRATION

Significant increases in oxygen consumption after injections of T_3 or T_4 were reported by Lewis and Frieden (*105*). As shown in the representative data of Fig. 22, T_3 produces a greater oxygen uptake whether

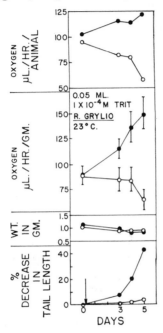

FIG. 22. Effect of 50 μl. of $1.0 \times 10^{-4} M$ T_3 on the respiration of *Rana grylio* tadpoles at 23°C. The T_3-treated group is indicated by the filled circles; a single injection was made, as indicated by the arrow, after 3 hours from the zero time measurement. Here, open circles designate control groups. From Lewis and Frieden (*105*).

calculated on the basis of the individual animal or wet weight. That the tadpole is highly capable of a calorigenic response was shown decisively in data presented in Fig. 23. Injected 2,4-dinitrophenol caused a 100% increase in oxygen uptake within 2 hours. As expected, a smaller more durable elevation in respiration was observed on immersion of tadpoles in the same total amount of dinitrophenol. Data similar to that illustrated above were also reported in brief by Martensson (*106*).

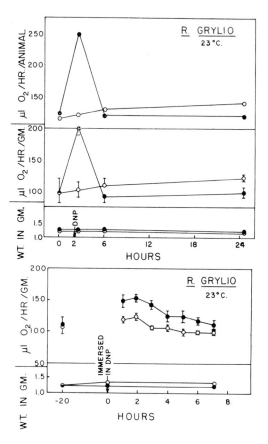

Fig. 23. Upper figure: Effect of injected 2,4-dinitrophenol (DNP) on the respiration of *Rana grylio* tadpoles. The tadpoles were injected with 50 μl. of 3.0 × 10^{-3} M DNP (filled circles) 2 hours after the initial respiration was determined. The respiration was then determined as soon as possible after injection.

Lower figure: Effect of immersion in DNP on the respiration of *R. grylio* tadpoles. The DNP group (filled circles) was immersed in 3.0 × 10^{-5} M DNP at zero time. From Lewis and Frieden (*105*).

B. RESPIRATION DURING SPONTANEOUS METAMORPHOSIS

Experiments designed to follow respiration during normal metamorphosis are handicapped by the changing structure of the animal. Methods suitable for following the oxygen uptake of an aquatic tadpole are frequently unsuitable for frogs. The problem is further complicated by the difficulty in selecting suitable criteria for comparison of the tissue unit of these animals. Etkin (*107*) has correctly emphasized the danger of not properly correcting for the loss in body weight. This is why the results reported in Fig. 22 were obtained by several different measurements.

Detailed oxygen consumption data during the various stages of normal metamorphosis have been published by Wills (108), Witschi (59), and Lewis and Frieden (105). Witschi notes a rapid fall in respiration at the conclusion of egg development and the outset of feeding for *R. pipiens*. The data of Lewis and Frieden (105) agree essentially with those of Wills and Witschi, but a sharp rise at the end of metamorphosis is ascribed to the greater activity of *Bufo* froglets since at this stage they possessed functional limbs. In an extensive study Barch (109) has already established that there is an almost twofold increase in the metabolic rate of *R. pipiens* skin during both normal and induced metamorphosis.

If an increase in respiration during metamorphosis is assumed, then we contend that an essential biochemical adaptation is involved. This adaptation may be transitory and may not persist throughout the entire life of the frog. A greater metabolic rate may be involved, as Barker (110) has emphasized, in making the necessary energy available for the many specialized processes of metamorphosis. The greater mobilization of enzymatic machinery for metamorphosis is briefly discussed in Section XI, I. The possibility of atypical metabolic cycles being involved in the respiration increase is considered in Section XI, D on carbohydrate metabolism.

XI. Additional Biochemical Alterations during Anuran Metamorphosis

The foregoing discussion has dealt with biochemical changes which may be described as having immediate survival value to the metamorphosing tadpole. We now consider a number of interesting biochemical properties of the metamorphic process which relate only indirectly to some structural differentiation or are unrecognized in their contribution to adaptation. Yet some of the ideas to be presented, e.g., the transition of the visual-pigment system, form an extremely fascinating chapter in evolution and in comparative biochemistry. As emphasized earlier, it is anticipated that there will be a steady migration of these "secondary" changes into the directly adaptive group. The major categories of other biochemical changes that have been traced during anuran metamorphosis are discussed in Sections A–I.

A. TRANSFORMATION OF THE VISUAL PIGMENTS

One of the more complete stories of comparative biochemistry has been the evolutionary correlations involving the visual pigments as developed by Wald (*111*). In metamorphoses of certain tadpole species, the anuran visual system is accompanied by a change from the porphyropsin (vitamin A_2) to the rhodopsin (vitamin A_1) visual system as shown in Fig. 24. The survival value of the conversion from the A_2 to A_1

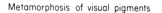

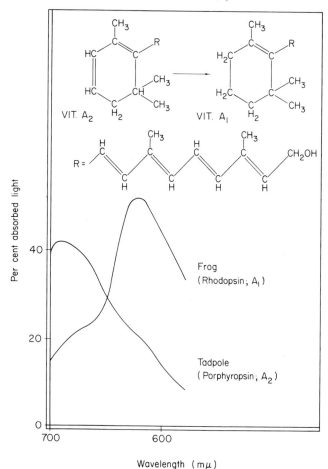

FIG. 24. Difference in the absorption spectra of *Rana catesbeiana* tadpole and frog visual pigments. The difference in chemical structure of the vitamin A moiety is also given. Data from Wald (*113*).

visual pigment system for terrestrial existence is not known. As Wald (*1*) has pointed out, the small differences in the absorption spectra of porphyropsin and rhodopsin would not be expected to be of significance to the survival and propagation of the different systems. In his book on biochemical evolution, Florkin (112) suggests that it would be important to determine whether a particular visual pigment pattern has survival value in a particular environment or was a fortuitous innovation in the adventures of the evolutionary process.

The visual system of the adult form of a number of frogs is that characteristic of other land vertebrates—the rhodopsin pigment system (113, 114, 115). A number of species of anurans have aquatic larvae that have the porphyropsin visual system which is characteristic of fresh-water inhabitants in general. Those larvae found to have the A_2 pigment are *R. catesbeiana* (116), *R. pipiens* (114), and *Hyla rigilla* (115). The finding that *R. temporaria* (115), *R. esculenta* (115), and *Bufo boreas* (117) tadpoles have only the A_1 system raises a question as to the generality of the occurrence of the A_2 system in the aquatic life stage of the frogs and toads. The permanently aquatic clawed toad, *Xenopus laevis*, has been shown to have vitamin A_2 almost exclusively in both the larval and adult retina (118).

The early generalization of Wald (1, 113) that the visual pigment patterns of marine, freshwater, and terrestrial animals reflect the evolutionary course of development of the vertebrate visual system is consistent with most of the available data. In this scheme the anurans are phylogenetically interpolated between aquatic and the terrestrial vertebrates, the metamorphosis of their visual system paralleling the visual changes in the evolutionary transition of vertebrates from water to land.

The major objection to Wald's view for anurans has come from the work of Collins, Love, and Morton (115) and their interpretation of Wald's studies in relation to their own. On the basis of their studies involving *R. esculenta* and *R. temporaria*, which have vitamin A_1 in the larva as well as the adult retinas, these investigators argue for a dietary basis for the changes in visual pigment occurring during metamorphosis. Their explanation assumes the dietary presence of preformed vitamin A_2 or a specific provitamin A_2 or both. All differences in the proportions of vitamin A_1 and vitamin A_2 in the retinal or liver tissues are ascribed to differences in food. However, Wilt (119, 120) could find vitamin A_2 only in the eye—not in the liver, intestine, or blood of *R. catesbeiana* larvae. This and other data suggest that diet is not responsible for the Wald (113) and Wilt (119, 120) data. By local implantation of T_4-cholesterol pellets, Wilt demonstrated that an eye which has received a pellet consistently shows a greater increase in the vitamin A_1 content, rhodopsin system, than does the contralateral sham-operated eye or eyes from animals with pellets placed in the abdominal cavity. Thus T_4 may act directly on the tissues of the eye rather than on some other organ which is responsible for the metabolic change.

1. Enzyme Systems

Wilt (119) examined the specificity of the visual system enzymes concerned with visual pigment formation of R. catesbeiana to determine whether the larval retinal enzymes have a vitamin A_2 specificity and whether during metamorphosis a conversion to A_1 specificity occurs. If one of the enzymes concerned with the formation of visual pigment has a specificity for vitamin A_2 or retinine 2 but during metamorphosis changes its specificity to include vitamin A_1, then the changes from the porphyropsin to the rhodopsin system would have a rational enzymatic basis. Extracts of larval retina were incubated with adult retinine 1 and reduced diphosphopyridine nucleotide (DPNH). A quantitative conversion of retinine 1 to vitamin A_1 occurred. From this Wilt concluded, in agreement with Wald (116), that larval retinal alcohol dehydrogenase does not have a vitamin A_2 specificity alone. The isomerizing enzyme, retinine isomerase was tested and likewise found to be nonspecific. Mixed substrate studies should indicate whether enzymes specific for both vitamin A_1 and vitamin A_2 compounds were present in larval extracts or whether a vitamin A_1-A_2 nonspecific enzyme is present. Opsin, another component concerned with the formation of the visual pigment, was tested to determine its specificity. As had been shown by Wald and Brown (121) the larval and adult opsin were interchangeable in their reaction with retinine 2 or retinine 1. This apparent lack of specificity indicates that the metabolic availability of the vitamin A prosthetic group determines the nature of the visual pigment produced.

B. Nucleic Acid Metabolism

Alterations in nucleic acid content and biosynthesis may be concomitant with the multiple reorientation of proteins and enzymes which occur during anuran metamorphosis. It is, of course, now well accepted that RNA is involved in protein biosynthesis and that DNA is a major component of the hereditary units of the cell.

1. Nucleic Acid Content

An increase in RNA per individual B. vulgaris was shown by Urbani and Coromaldi (102) until the beginning of the metamorphic climax. Zacchei (122) found an increase in tail RNA of B. vulgaris, beginning at the time of tail resorption. More recently, Minelli and Rossi (123) reported a twofold increase in RNA and DNA per unit weight during the spontaneous metamorphosis of B. vulgaris. During the last stages of the change, the RNA to DNA ratio dropped sharply from 1.9 to 1.1. In R. grylio liver, Finamore and Frieden (61) observed a rapid fall in

TABLE V

NUCLEIC ACID CONTENT OF *R. grylio* TADPOLE LIVER[a,b]

Days after injection	Control groups						Triiodothyronine groups					
	Number of animals	L:T	Total nucleic acid (mg./gm.)	RNA (mg./gm.)	DNA (mg./gm.)	RNA:DNA	Number of animals	L:T	Total nucleic acid (mg./gm.)	RNA (mg./gm.)	DNA (mg./gm.)	RNA:DNA
1	23	0.08	4.6	2.0	2.1	0.98	22	0.06	5.0	2.2	2.5	0.86
2	22	0.09	5.2	1.8	2.5	0.70	22	0.09	4.4	1.7	2.3	0.76
3	—	—	—	—	—	—	22	0.10	4.6	2.0	1.8	1.1
4	21	0.07	4.8	2.1	2.3	0.91	22	0.16	4.4	2.7	1.6	1.7
5	—	—	—	—	—	—	19	0.19	4.0	2.8	1.2	2.2
6	20	0.06	4.2	2.6	1.9	1.4	13	0.29	4.0	2.7	1.4	1.9
5	14	0.11	5.8	2.2	2.7	0.82	14	0.26	2.3	2.1	0.67	3.1
Froglet	50	—	6.9	3.2	3.7	0.89	50	—	6.8	3.1	3.9	0.80
	27	—	4.0	2.2	2.1	1.0	—	—	—	—	—	—

[a] From Finamore and Frieden (61).

[b] Summary of nucleic acid analysis for several experiments reported earlier in this paper. The average hind leg length to tail length ratio (L:T) has been included to indicate the morphological effect of triiodothyronine treatment.

DNA (0.25% to about 0.10%) and a slight increase in RNA at the end of induced metamorphosis (Table V). The control animals showed no appreciable change. More will be said about these data in the following section on biosynthesis.

2. Biosynthesis of RNA and DNA

A comparison of nucleic acid biosynthesis during induced metamorphosis has been made (61). The specific activity of $P^{32}O_4$ in key phosphorus-containing fractions was measured in two divergent tissues, liver and tail. Only the nucleic acid fraction showed marked differences in $P^{32}O_4$ uptake when T_3-treated tadpoles were compared with normal tadpoles (Fig. 24). The nucleic acid fraction was resolved; the results are summarized in Figs. 25 and 26.

During induced metamorphosis the rate of incorporation of P^{32} as orthophosphate into the RNA, DNA and protein of the liver is increased and is observable before a tail response is discernible (Fig. 25). There is a marked alteration of the liver RNA:DNA ratio during this time due to a net synthesis of RNA coinciding with an apparent liver hypertrophy (Table V). Incorporation of $P^{32}O_4$ into the RNA, DNA, and protein of the tail increases for 2 days after initiation of metamorphosis and then is maintained at a relatively constant level throughout the experimental period even though the tail is resorbing. This suggests the establishment of an apparent "steady state" in these tail constituents (Fig. 26). No differences were observed in the nucleotide composition of either liver or tail RNA.

3. Liver Hypertrophy

The decrease in liver DNA even though $P^{32}O_4$ incorporation increases suggests an important feature of liver response to T_3. If triiodothyronine produces hypertrophy of the tadpole liver, the liver weight should increase even though the cell number remains essentially constant and the amount of DNA per unit of wet weight should decrease. A 25–30% increase in liver weight on hormone treatment during the experimental period accompanied by an approximate 40% decrease in the DNA content has been observed. Thus the weight increase could account for the most part for the observed decrease in DNA content of the tadpole liver; this observation strongly suggests that hypertrophy of the liver occurs during induced metamorphosis. Assuming this effect exists, then the slight tendency for the liver RNA content on a wet weight basis to increase, coupled with the stimulation of $P^{32}O_4$ uptake, indicates a substantial net synthesis of RNA in the tadpole liver during induced metamorphosis.

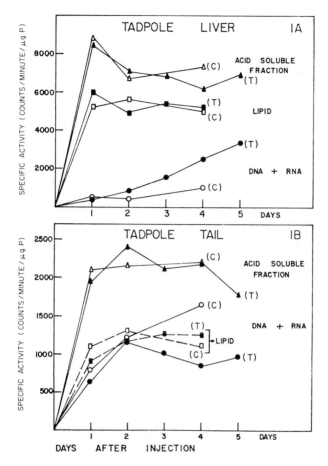

FIG. 25. Specific activity of acid-soluble, lipid, and total nucleic acid fractions at various times after P[32] injection. Groups of about 20 animals received single injections of 1×10^{-9} moles of T_3 per gram of body weight at 0 days to induce metamorphosis; approximately 1 hour later they were administered 100 μc. of carrier-free P[32] as orthophosphate. Comparable control groups received only P[32]. Open symbols (C), control group; filled symbols (T), T_3 group. From Finamore and Frieden (61).

In view of the fact that hormone treatment does not alter the nucleic acid content, RNA:DNA ratio, or incorporation of $P^{32}O_4$ in the froglet liver, the nucleic acid effect is restricted to the liver of tadpoles undergoing metamorphosis. Since the RNA-to-DNA ratio of froglet liver corresponds to that of the control tadpole liver, triiodothyronine treatment of the tadpole produces only a temporary alteration of this ratio.

During induced and spontaneous metamorphosis an increase in activity of many liver enzymes has been noted, but no enzymatic effects

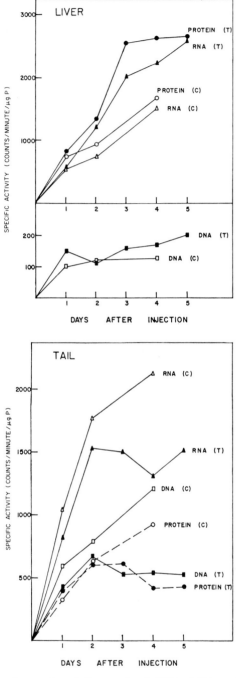

Fig. 26. Specific activity of liver and tail RNA, DNA, and protein at various times after P^{32} injection. Experimental conditions and symbols as in Fig. 25. From Finamore and Frieden (61).

have been recorded prior to the appearance of morphological changes. In contrast, the stimulation by triiodothyronine of $P^{32}O_4$ incorporation into the liver RNA is apparent as early as 2 days after injection of the hormone, before any morphological changes are obvious. Therefore, the increased incorporation of $P^{32}O_4$ into liver RNA represents an early response in induced amphibian metamorphosis, presumably a prelude to increased protein biosynthesis.

C. Nitrogen Metabolism

In an animal, such as the metamorphosing tadpole, in which enormous tissue breakdown and pronounced tissue build-up are occurring simultaneously in preparation of the organism for a transfer from one environment to another, it is evident that the picture of nitrogenous metabolism will be exceedingly complex. Studies on nitrogen metabolism in specific tissues and organs where primarily either degenerative or synthetic processes are taking place could be expected to result in a relatively clear picture of some of the molecular changes associated with morphological destruction or construction. The tail and the gills are particularly suitable for catabolic studies. In the limbs, liver, and kidney anabolic processes predominate during metamorphosis. Studies on whole animals represent the summation of degradative and fabricative processes. Of the biologically important nitrogen-containing compounds, amino acids, polypeptides, and proteins will be considered briefly in this section. The conversion of ammonia to urea was considered in Section VI.

1. Total Nitrogen

The total nitrogen content of the tail and gills has been shown to increase during metamorphosis in the same manner as does amino nitrogen (101). The total nitrogen content of the blood showed an increase at the beginning of metamorphosis and during resorption (101). This increase in blood nitrogen can be attributed to an increase in total serum protein, as shown by Herner and Frieden (80). Urbani (67) showed a decrease in total nitrogen for individual Bufo vulgaris from the prometamorphic to the adult stage. Lewis and Frieden (105) reported a relative constancy of total nitrogen per unit weight for Bufo tadpoles and froglets. If the results of Urbani were expressed per unit weight, this general trend might also result since a decrease in weight occurs at the terminal stages of metamorphosis. In the studies of Lewis and Frieden (105) T_3-treated tadpoles showed an increase in their total nitrogen content per unit wet weight.

2. Amino Acids and Peptides

Blacher and Liosner (101) have shown an increase in the amino nitrogen of the blood of R. ridibunda just prior to the beginning of the metamorphic climax with a decrease to a constant value during the later stages of metamorphosis. These investigators demonstrated a similar effect in tail and gill tissues—tissues which are undergoing rapid resorption. These changes probably reflect the protein degradation that is going on in these tissues. Dolphin and Frieden (75) studied changes of the amino acid pattern in metamorphosing R. heckscheri. A decrease in the concentration of liver arginine and tyrosine was observed. This effect was even more dramatic for animals undergoing precocious metamorphosis initiated by T_4 and T_3. The decrease in free arginine of the liver correlates with a rapid increase in arginase activity and despite the initiation of the Krebs ornithine-urea cycle (75). The decrease in tyrosine may mirror primarily an enhanced utilization in protein biosynthesis or in pigment formation. No decisive alterations in the concentrations of the other amino acids identified could be detected.

Roberts et al. (124) found a progressive increase in γ-aminobutyric acid in the brain of R. catesbeiana from larval to adult stages. These investigators also noted small amounts of taurine in brain of adult frogs but none in the larval stages. The investigators found no change in the pattern of other amino acids of the brain. A change in the concentration of γ-aminobutyric acid, which is possibly a transmitter substance in the central nervous system, reflects the developments in the central nervous system during metamorphosis. The transition to a more highly differentiated nervous system associated with the adult form may involve the effects cited here.

Polypeptide nitrogen undergoes marked changes in several tissues during metamorphosis (101). A fourfold increase in the early period of metamorphosis with a subsequent decrease in later stages has been found to occur in the blood. An increase occurs at the beginning of the metamorphic climax in gill tissue. A similar change in the tail polypeptide nitrogen occurred during the period of tail resorption. These changes parallel those of amino nitrogen and probably mirror the protein breakdown occurring in these tissues.

3. Protein Metabolism

In regard to protein metabolism it will only be mentioned here that Herner and Frieden (80) have demonstrated a significant increase in the concentration of serum albumins in several tadpole species undergoing metamorphosis. The serum proteins are significant to protein biosynthesis because they represent the most important means of supplying peripheral tissues with amino acids for synthetic processes. Some of the substrates for the synthesis of serum proteins may arise from the degradative changes in tissues such as the tail. Products of protein degradation are transported from this region to sites of utilization or elimination. A more complete discussion of the significance of both the serum protein and hemoglobin changes appeared earlier in this paper.

The early work of Braus (125) claimed immunological differences between larval and adult forms of the toad *Bombinator pachypus*. But later Kritchevsky (126), using saline extracts of entire larvae as antigens in complement fixation tests, obtained reactions with antisera against extracts of entire larval and adult *R. esculenta*. Wilkoewitz and Ziegenspeck (127) confirmed this work with *R. esculenta*, observing no quantitative differences in the serological reactions of extracts of embryos, larvae, and adults. Cooper (128) has criticized the work of Kritchevsky (126) and Wilkoewitz and Ziegenspeck (127) because their techniques possibly caused denaturation of some proteins. Using *R. pipiens* embryos and larvae, Cooper demonstrated the presence of antigens of combining groups closely related to or identical with those of adult frog serum.

4. Enzyme Changes

The changes in amino and polypeptide nitrogen have their basis in alterations in enzymatic activities. Since it is not known whether certain enzymes function only in protein biosynthesis or exclusively in protein breakdown or possibly in both, it is possible to interpret results of enzymes studies in several ways. Studies have been made on many enzymes involved in nitrogen metabolism. Liver cathepsin and trypsin have been shown to decrease during metamorphosis (67). Since these enzymes have primarily proteolytic functions this decrease is not unexpected in view of the primarily protein anabolic processes underway in the liver at this time.

The activities of various proteolytic enzymes have been studied frequently on whole-animal preparations. Recognition of the important role that various ions and compounds play in determining enzyme activities makes one wary of whole-animal studies especially when the animals are in a relatively uncontrolled environment with qualitative and quantitative variations in food, light, and temperature. The studies of Urbani (67) on this subject express enzyme activity per individual *Bufo vulgaris*, making his studies difficult to relate to studies in which the basis of calculation is per unit weight or per unit nitrogen since the weight of *B. vulgaris* is presumed to change during metamorphosis as does that of other species. Whole-animal studies by Blacher and Liosner (101) indicate a decrease in cathepsin and trypsin for the whole animal during the metamorphic period. This might reflect the predominance of anabolic over catabolic processes during this time. Urbani (67) reported an increase in the dipeptidase for leucylglycine per individual with a decrease in alanylglycine and glycylglycine. No particular trend could be seen for the tripeptidase of glycylglycylglycine. Acid proteinase increases whereas alkaline proteinase shows an almost unchanged activity. An impressive thirtyfold increase in tail cathepsin was found by Weber (129).

D. Carbohydrates

Since the catabolism of carbohydrates is a prime source of energy, augmented energy demands during metamorphosis could be met by alterations in carbohydrate metabolism. These alterations could take the form of an increased rate of catabolic processes in certain tissues or perhaps the shift from one predominant pathway of metabolism to another.

Bilewicz (130) has demonstrated an increase in the percentage of glycogen of the liver and the whole body of R. temporaria during prometamorphosis. At the metamorphic climax a reversal occurs and a pronounced utilization of glycogen occurs as reflected in a drastic decrease in the percentage of glycogen in the liver and the body. In a study of the carbohydrates of several species, Faraggiana (131) and Urbani (67) both noted a decline in these constituents during prometamorphosis in contrast to the findings of Bilewicz. A heightened rate of decrease was observed at the beginning of the metamorphic climax. These studies suggest that glycogen reserves in the liver acquire importance as a source of nourishment during the period of metamorphosis when dramatic changes occur in the digestive system and the animal stops feeding.

The results of Aron (96) suggest a control mechanism for these trends in carbohydrate metabolism. Aron has demonstrated that the endocrine activity of the pancreas is influenced by the thyroid. Tadpoles undergoing spontaneous or T_4-induced metamorphosis reveal extensive changes in the islet cells of the pancreas. Increase in size and decrease in pigmentation of the islet cells are several of the changes which occur during the early phases of metamorphosis just before the marked changes in glycogen reserves occur. Gennaro (97) corroborated this work in noting an increased P^{32} uptake by the pancreas of R. sylvatica at approximately the period when glycogenic activity in the liver began. This is of particular importance if the functional basis of this increase in P^{32} uptake lies in the initiation of the endocrine secretion. Thus the thyroid hormone stimulates pancreatic alterations which are important in the regulation of glycogenolysis as well as the digestive enzymes.

1. Enzyme Changes

The enzymatic basis for alterations in carbohydrate metabolism has been explored by a number of investigators. Frieden and Mathews (78) have studied hepatic glucose-6-phosphatase (G-6-Pase) during spontaneous and T_3-induced metamorphosis of R. grylio. An impressive increase in the activity of this enzyme was noted during normal metamorphosis of R. grylio. One influence on the activity of this enzyme has been shown to be the nutritional state of the organism. Fasting results in an increase in activity of this enzyme in rats (132). Since many anurans stop feeding at the outset of metamorphosis one could rationalize the changes in G-6-Pase activity as being controlled by this factor. Studies on liver G-6-Pase during induced metamorphosis have revealed that the thyroid is also an important controlling factor of the enzymatic activity. Fasting T_3-induced metamorphosing tadpoles had a significantly higher G-6-Pase level than fasting control animals. Thus the thyroid hormone effect was superimposed on a nutritional effect. Paralleling enhanced utilization of glycogen, there is an increased activity of a key glycolytic enzyme, an enzyme that plays an important role in the mobilization of liver glycogen.

The importance of ATP-hydrolyzing enzymes (ATPase) in the cellular economy is well established. The central role of ATP in the energy metabolism of the cell is well recognized. It is not unlikely that the balance between ATP and its hydrolytic products may be of major significance in glycolysis and respiration. Liver ATPase activity shows a marked increase, particularly in the latter stages of normal metamorphosis (78). The ATPase activity rises to over four times the level of the enzyme in the young tadpole. No significant effect of diet or nutritional state was noted on liver ATPase activity. A statistically significant increase (2.5 times the increase in controls) in tadpole liver ATPase was also observed when metamorphosis was induced by T_3.

The question whether an increase in respiration occurs during normal metamorphosis has yet to be decisively answered. T_3 or T_4 injections produce an increase in oxygen consumption (105). In the rat, thyroid hormone invariably causes an increase in succinoxidase activity concomitant with an increase in respiration. Yet Lewis and Frieden (105) found no increase in liver or tail succinoxidase activity in R. grylio in spontaneous or induced metamorphosis. Yamamoto and Suzuki (133) and Paik and Cohen (77) reported a decrease in liver succinic dehydrogenase and succinoxidase activity, respectively, during various phases of metamorphosis. If the lack of increased activity among the Krebs cycle enzymes during metamorphosis is general, then alternative pathways of carbohydrate utilization may be implicated.

E. Lipids

Lipids have the potential of serving as a source of metabolic energy as well as a source of biochemical intermediates for the tricarboxylic acid cycle. Their rapid utilization during periods of starvation usually follows when the glycogen reserves of the liver are almost depleted. Therefore alterations in lipid metabolism will serve as an indirect factor in the formation of structures with adaptive value for the adult.

In the course of his studies Urbani (99) found an approximate four-fold decrease in the total body lipid of B. vulgaris during the metamorphic period. Since the organism stops eating and undergoes metamorphosis in a period of several weeks, the changes which occur in lipids probably reflect a utilization of these substances as a supplement to the glycogen reserves.

Aquatic animals have depot fat characteristically composed of a majority of unsaturated fatty acids—approximately 80% unsaturated versus 20% saturated fatty acids. Since terrestrial animals have predominantly saturated fatty acids (134), a shift to saturated fats during metamorphosis is predicted.

Urbani (67) studied the alterations in lipase activity of whole animals during metamorphosis. During the prometamorphic period a threefold decrease in activity occurred. At the outset of the metamorphic climax a rise in lipase activity occurred with a subsequent slight increase into the later stages of metamorphosis. As in other studies on the enzymatic activity of whole-animal preparations, the significance of such measurements is difficult to evaluate.

F. Water Balance

The demonstration by Etkin (107) and Irichimovitch (135) that a significant decrease in the water content of the whole body of animals takes place during metamorphosis can be interpreted as a gross adaptation of tissue to decreased water availability which occurs in terrestrial habitats. In anurans there is a very rapid decrease in water content at the beginning of the growth of the hind limbs. This change continues and becomes more marked during the metamorphic climax.

This alteration is of special significance because of its pertinence to other studies in which chemical changes in a metamorphosing system have been expressed on a wet weight basis. Subtle increases of biochemical components will be magnified when expressed on a wet weight basis. Small decreases in components will be masked or undetectable when expressed on the basis of wet weight. For example, the confusion as to the increase of respiration during spontaneous and induced metamorphosis depends in part on the method of expressing the data in terms of wet weight or some other unit of tissue such as nitrogen content. The change is also of interest because of the similar dehydration effect which has been observed for other organisms during their developmental transition from an aquatic natal environment to a less aqueous neonatal environment (14).

Urbani (67) cites the decrease in cell size or cell shrinkage during metamorphosis observed by Contronei as a reflection of water loss. He also suggests that the increase of vitamin C during metamorphosis demonstrated by Bucci (136) may be of importance in regulating dehydration phenomena in view of the effect of ascorbic acid on cellular permeability.

Studies on water changes during induced metamorphosis have revealed parallel changes. Etkin (107) has demonstrated a tissue dehydration of approximately 35% for thyroid-treated tadpoles. Lewis and Frieden (105) have found a comparable change in R. grylio on treatment with T_3. The problem of water balance during metamorphosis has also been developed in the studies of Herner and Frieden (80). The conservation of body water and the maintenance of plasma volume, operations which are of the utmost importance for terrestrial forms, are enhanced by a high plasma protein content, a condition found in more advanced periods of metamorphosis.

G. MECHANISM OF TAIL RESORPTION

The disappearance of the tadpole tail is a most impressive feature of metamorphosis. Recently Kaltenbach (33) has demonstrated a striking local metamorphic response in the dorsal and ventral tail fins of R. pipiens tadpoles brought about directly by localized concentrations of T_4 resulting from T_4-cholesterol pellet implants. This study along with the early studies on tissue competence gives a vivid demonstration of a tissue which has the potential to undergo demolitive changes when triggered by T_4. It has been suggested that T_4 stimulated tail tissue metabolic processes resulting in the production of acidic metabolites, e.g., lactic acid. These metabolites bring about increased acidity of tail tissues. The increased acidity activates acid proteases and other degradative enzymes. This increased enzymatic activity results in a heightened production of acid products which are transferred via the blood from the tail to other sites in the organism [see discussion by Needham (14)].

1. *pH Changes and Enzymatic Hydrolysis*

Existing data can be marshaled to support this general view of the biochemical changes that occur in tail tissue during resorption. Helff (137) has demonstrated that the injection of small amounts of lactic acid or butyric acid results in tail atrophy. Autolysis began at the site of injection and spread over the whole tail. A slight increase in acidity of tail tissue before the first sign of morphological change has been demonstrated by Aleschin (138). The pH is 7.1 for normal tissues and 6.6 for tail tissue during resorption. During the course of the resorptive phenomenon a conspicuous increase occurs in amino and polypeptide nitrogen, reflecting an increase in protein hydrolysis in tail tissue (101). The transport of the acid products of protein hydrolysis and other acid metabolites from the tail could contribute to the decrease in blood pH (7.5 to 7.2) shown by Helff (139) for animals between prometamorphosis and the end of metamorphosis.

An enzymatic basis for these increases in nitrogen-containing compounds of low molecular weight is an increased activity of proteolytic enzymes in the tail during resorption. The most significant change in tail enzyme, noted thus far, is the thirtyfold increase in tail cathepsin activity during the resorption in *X. laevis* reported by Weber (129). The dipeptidase for alanylglycine, lysylglycine, and glycylglycine have been shown by Urbani (67) to increase markedly in the tail of *B. vulgaris* between prometamorphosis and the end of the tail resorption period. Zacchei (122) has also demonstrated a heightened alanylglycine dipeptidase activity during tail involution. The tripeptidase for glycylglycylglycine increases some sevenfold during the same period of time (129). The acid protease in the tail of *B. vulgaris* increases ninefold whereas the alkaline protease activity shows only a very slight increase. These studies support a heightened proteolysis and acid production for resorbing tail tissue.

Elevation of the activity of several other enzymes can be considered to be the basis of degradative changes in other structural components of tail tissues. Tail lipase has been shown to increase slightly and amylase very markedly in activity from the premetamorphic stage to the time when absence of tail made further studies impossible (67). Yanagisawa's (140) demonstration of an enhanced acid phosphatase activity may contribute to the transportation of decomposed substances from the tail. The decreased ATPase activity in resorbing tail shown by Frieden and Mathews (78) is consistent with a decreased protein biosynthesis and enhanced hydrolysis of protein.

2. Metabolic Differences

The deviation from normal RNA and DNA synthesis that occurs in the tail after T_3 injection was discussed in detail in Section XI,B. Rather than a continued increase in $P^{32}O_4$ uptake, a premature steady state was reached. This may mean a failure in adequate RNA and DNA synthesis, dooming the tail to eventual dissolution.

Contronei (141) in an early publication, suggested the general idea that the tail constituted a reserve of materials and energy necessary for metamorphosis. Aleschin (138) postulated a rather direct dependence of limb growth on materials from autolysis of tail tissues. Irichimovitch (135) and Woitkewitsch (142) have pointed out that, since the most active growth of the limbs begins before the onset of tail resorption, the two processes may not be dependent. Paik and Cohen (77) have reported that the removal of up to 60% of the tadpole's tail had no significant effect on the rate of liver carbamylphosphate synthetase synthesis.

H. Transition of Skin Pigments

It is obvious that pigment patterns can change greatly during metamorphosis. The adaptive feature of this alteration may be the protective anonymity conferred on the frog rather than a reflection of any internal adjustment. Hormones also frequently have an effect, directly or indirectly, on the development of pigment patterns in vertebrates. The

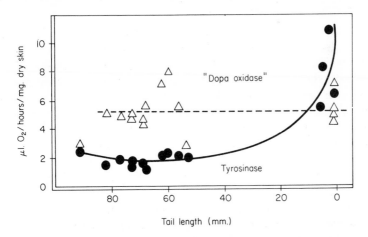

Fig. 27. Tyrosinase and "dopa oxidase activity" during spontaneous metamorphosis. The enzyme activity is plotted as a function of the size of the tail. Data from Hunter and Frieden (144).

complex cytological events in the skin have been summarized by Stearner (143).

The basis for the alteration of pigment patterns during the metamorphosis of the Florida swamp frog, R. *heckscheri*, was studied some years ago (144). It was found that on the completion of metamorphosis the melanin content of frog skin had almost doubled. Since melanin is a product of tyrosinase and "dopa oxidase" this enzyme (or enzymes) was also studied. The results, shown in Fig. 27, indicated that skin tyrosinase activity increases severalfold at the completion of spontaneous metamorphosis. An even greater increase in tyrosinase activity was obtained after thyroxine treatment. Changes in "dopa oxidase" activity were much smaller and of dubious statistical significance.

I. Alteration of Enzymatic Activities

Repeatedly, in discussing the biochemical features of anuran metamorphosis, we have mentioned enzymatic changes in connection with some more direct chemical or structural adaptation. So far we have avoided cataloguing enzymes although this in itself may be worth while. As Paul Weiss (144a) has pointed out:

> To be sure, much of this work is no more than sequential descriptive chemistry, just as old-time embryology was descriptive morphology; but we may expect that once a complete record of the biochemical history of a particular ontogenetic series of stages has been obtained, the succession of events in this chain of transformations may furnish a clue to the underlying dynamics of differentiation.

Great difficulty was encountered in attempting to correlate enzyme changes during metamorphosis in order to draw quantitative conclusions. While we have emphasized the significant chemical aspects of metamorphosis, there are suggestions of possible physical environmental influences on metamorphosis. Huxley (145) reported that, at temperatures below 5° C., R. *temporaria* failed to metamorphose even after moderate doses of thyroid substance. What is known of the role of ionic environment and other chemical agents on the metamorphic process has been summarized in the review of Lynn and Wachowski (17) and more recently explored by Frieden and Naile (58). Obviously more information is needed in this area.

Other complications appear in evaluating enzymatic effects during metamorphosis. Many enzymes increase during the egg stage of anurans and decline during the early free-swimming larval stages (146). Metamorphic effects occur subsequent to this. Thus the selection of appropriate stages for comparison becomes important. The occurrence of a second metamorphosis could also influence any comparison. Finally the

TABLE VI

ENZYME ACTIVITIES THAT INCREASE SIGNIFICANTLY DURING ANURAN METAMORPHOSIS

Enzyme	Tissue	Relative effect[a]	Species[b]	Reference
Urea cycle enzymes				
1. Arginase	Liver	3–5	B.t., R.h., R.c.	(75, 76)
2. Carbamyl-PO₄ synthetase	Liver	29	R.c.	(76)
3. Ornithine-transcarbamylase	Liver	5	R.c.	(76)
4. Argininosuccinate synthetase	Liver	3	R.c.	(76)
Peptidases and proteases				
5. Cathepsin	Tail	30	X.l.	(129)
6. Alanylglycine dipeptidase	Tail	7	B.v.	(67)
7. Glycylglycine dipeptidase	Tail	5	B.v.	(67)
8. Glycylglycylglycine tripeptidase	Tail	7	B.v.	(67)
9. Leucylglycine dipeptidase	Tail	3	B.v.	(67)
10. Protease (pH 4.2)	Tail	9	B.v.	(67)
11. Protease (pH 4.2)	Total animal	4	B.v.	(67)
Phosphatases				
12. ATPase	Liver	4	R.g.	(78)
13. Glucose-6-phosphatase	Liver	4	R.g.	(78)
14. Acid phosphatase (pH 4.4)	Liver	3	R.s.a.	(140)
15. Alkaline phosphatase (pH 10.1)	Liver	2	R.s.a.	(140)
16. Acid phosphatase (pH 4.4)	Tail	4	B.v.f.	(140)
17. Alkaline phosphatase (pH 10.1)	Tail	3	B.v.f.	(140)
18. Tyrosinase	Dorsal skin	3	R.h.	(144)
19. Uricase	Liver	3	R.t.	(147)

[a] Relative effect is defined as the ratio of the enzyme activity after metamorphosis (either spontaneous or induced) to the enzyme activity before metamorphosis.

[b] Species are abbreviated as follows: B.t., *Bufo terrestris*; B.v., *Bufo vulgaris*; B.v.f., *Bufo vulgaris formosus*; R.c., *Rana catesbeiana*; R.g., *Rana grylio*; R.h., *Rana heckscheri*; R.s.a., *Rhacophorus schlegerii arborea*; X.l., *Xenopus laevis*; R.T., *Rana temporaria*.

basis for comparison of enzyme activities should be made on some basis other than on a whole animal basis even for the smaller species of tadpoles.

Is a general picture emerging from the observed enzymatic changes? The information is too incomplete for an accurate reply. As shown in Table VI a number of important enzymes show a striking increase during metamorphosis—as much as a thirtyfold increase. Prominent among this group are the urea-ornithine cycle enzymes, peptidases, proteases, phosphatases, and two oxidative enzymes. Many enzymes, principally hydrolases, show little or no increase (Table VII). Only a

TABLE VII

ENZYMES THAT DECREASE OR DO NOT INCREASE
DURING ANURAN METAMORPHOSIS

No appreciable increase in activity:
  1. ATPase (tail)
  2. Cathepsin (liver)
  3. Dipeptidases: alanylglycine; leucylglycine; glycylglycine (total animal)
  4. Protease (pH 8.7) (total animal, tail)
  5. RNase (pH 5.6, 8.0) (total animal, tail)
  6. Lipase (tail)
  7. Dopa oxidase (skin)
  8. Succinoxidase (total animal)

Decrease in activity:
  1. Glycylglycylglycine tripeptidase (total animal)
  2. Trypsin (total animal, liver)
  3. Amylase (total animal, pancreas, intestine)
  4. Lipase (total animal)
  5. Alkaline phosphatase (pH 10.1) (tail)
  6. Succinoxidase (liver)

limited few enzymes show a fall in activity (Table VII), and these are probably associated with tissues undergoing extensive resorption, as tail and intestine. Thus metamorphosis is most frequently accompanied by an increase in enzyme activity. We regard this as at least a partial mobilization of the biochemical resources of the tadpole to meet the metabolic demands of the process itself and of the subsequent change in environment.

XII. The Second Metamorphosis

Some animals undergo adaptive changes at the time of reproduction which prepare them for re-entry into a previous environment. This return of sexually mature vertebrates to their natal environment has been described by Wald (2) as a second metamorphosis. Evidence for this additional transition is accumulating from studies in amphibians, fish, and possibly arthropods. Recently Nash and Fankhauser (148) and Grant (149) have also supported the existence of the second metamorphosis.

The newt *Triturus viridescens* exhibits morphological and biochemical changes which can conveniently be considered as a second metamorphosis. In the first transformation, the aquatic larva changes into the terrestrial red eft which shows many morphological adjustments to land living. At the end of 2–3 years of terrestrial life, the sexually mature eft returns permanently to water—a return accompanied by both morphological and biochemical changes. The epidermis returns to its smooth state with a thin cuticle. The lateral line organs return to the surface and become functional again; the tongue becomes smaller and loses its protrusibility and secretory glands. Concomitant biochemical changes observed so far include the reappearance of porphyropsin as the principal retinal pigment (2) and a partial return to ammonotelism in the nitrogen excretory pattern (148).

XIII. Conclusion

Metamorphosis encompasses the postembryonic developmental changes in nonreproductive structures of an organism—a remodeling of the animal preparatory for a change in environment. The process expresses itself in a variety of morphological changes for insects, crustaceans, fish, and amphibians. Although controlling hormones vary in chemical nature, there is a fundamental similarity in the endocrine regulatory mechanisms. The regulatory mechanisms in anurans parallel the thyroid function in mammals involving the hypothalamus, pituitary, and thyroid secretions, in that order. In addition to these extrinsic stimuli, the intrinsic tissue sensitivity of anurans are dramatically demonstrated in the divergent responses of tadpole tissues such as tail, limbs, and liver.

The biochemical changes that occur during anuran metamorphosis appear to have either direct or indirect adaptive value in facilitating the transition from fresh water to land. Among the most important adaptive changes are the shift from ammonotelism to ureotelism, the increase in serum albumin and other serum proteins, the alteration in the properties and biosynthesis of the hemoglobins. The development of certain digestive enzymes and possible effects on respiration also contribute to the success of the differentiation process. During metamorphosis, there are many additional important chemical developments which may be secondary to other more primary morphological or cytological transformations which aid in the adjustment to land. These include alterations in carbohydrate, lipid, nucleic acid, and nitrogen metabolism.

Major modifications in water balance, visual pigments (vitamin A), pigmentation, and tail metabolism are also observed. Finally there is a partial mobilization of the enzymatic machinery to effect the metamorphic process and the colonization of land.

Addenda

Since this review was written early in 1960, several important papers bearing directly on topics mentioned in this paper have appeared. A complete symposium on the comparative aspects of metamorphosis in the animal kingdom appeared as the first issue of the *American Zoologist* (February, 1961). The subjects included a survey of: (i) endocrine control and biochemical aspects of insect metamorphosis; (ii) regulation and mechanisms of metamorphosis in bryozoa, ascidia, crustacea, fish, and lamprey; (iii) hormonal mechanisms and types of amphibian metamorphosis; (iv) second metamorphosis; and (v) biochemical adaptation and anuran metamorphosis. A comprehensive review of the metabolism of amphibia by G. W. Brown, Jr. is also in press in "Physiology of the Amphibia," edited by J. A. Moore (Academic Press, New York).

Changes in the electrophoretic character of hemoglobin during the metamorphosis of *Rana esculenta* similar to those described here (Section VII, A) were reported by G. Chieffi, M. Siniscalco, and M. Adinoifi [*Acad. Nazl. Lincei* **28**, 233 (1960)]. Using starch gel electrophoresis, they detected two hemoglobins in tadpole red blood cell preparations and two prominent slower moving hemoglobins in frog erythrocytes. All these hemoglobins also moved faster than typical human hemoglobin.

K. Fletcher and N. B. Myant [*J. Physiol. (London)* **145**, 353 (1959)] observed a fall in Q_{O_2} during the spontaneous metamorphosis of *Xenopus laevis*. In other anuran species, they reported a decrease in Q_{O_2} after the administration of thyroxine or triiodothyronine. These results are relevant to some of the data discussed in Section X, A of this chapter.

Paik, Metzenberg, and Cohen [*J. Biol. Chem.* **236**, 536 (1961)] reported that the amount of liver DNA and RNA phosphorous did not change in thyroxine-treated tadpoles. They also observed a decreased rate of incorporation of adenine-8-C^{14} into RNA. They concluded that thyroxine induced a rearrangement within RNA molecules. These data are pertinent to the discussion in Section XI, B.

References

1. G. Wald, *in* "Modern Trends in Physiology and Biochemistry" (E. S. G. Barron, ed.), p. 337. Academic Press, New York, 1952.
2. G. Wald, *Science* **128**, 1481 (1958).
3. W. Etkin, *in* "Analysis of Development" (B. H. Willier, P. Weiss, and V. Hamburger, eds.), p. 631. Saunders, Philadelphia, 1955.
4. R. E. Snodgrass, *Smithsonian Inst. Publs., Misc. Collections* **122**, No. 9 (1954).
5. V. B. Wigglesworth, "The Physiology of Insect Metamorphosis." Cambridge Univ. Press, London and New York, 1954.
6. J. B. Buck, *in* "Insect Physiology" (K. D. Roeder, ed.), p. 191. Wiley, New York, 1953.
7. M. Rockstein, *Science* **123**, 3196 (1956).

8. J. Briggs, *Science* **129,** 532 (1959).
9. R. E. Snodgrass, *Smithsonian Inst. Publs., Misc. Collections* **131,** No. 10, (1956).
10. T. H. Waterman and F. A. Chace, Jr., *in* "The Physiology of Crustacea (T. H. Waterman, ed.), Vol. 1, p. 1. Academic Press, 1960.
11. G. Wald, *Science* **129,** 534 (1959).
12. J. W. Harms, *Z. wiss. Zool.* **133,** 211–397 (1929).
13. W. S. Hoar, *in* "The Physiology of Fishes" (M. Brown, ed.), Vol. I, p. 287. Academic Press, New York, 1957.
14. J. Needham, "Biochemistry and Morphogenesis," p. 447. Cambridge Univ. Press, London and New York, 1942.
15. E. Witschi, "Development of Vertebrates," p. 124. Saunders, Philadelphia, 1956.
16. R. Rugh, "Experimental Embryology," p. 56, Burgess, Minneapolis, 1948.
17. W. G. Lynn and H. E. Wachowski, *Quart. Rev. Biol.* **26,** 123 (1951).
18. P. C. J. Roth, *Mém. mus. natl. hist. nat.* (*Paris*) **21,** 175 (1946).
19. C. A. Taylor and J. J. Kollros, *Anat. Record* **94,** 7 (1946).
20. E. Frieden and W. Westmark, *Science* **133,** 1487 (1961).
21. L. Kaywin, *Anat. Record* **64,** 413 (1936).
22. A. L. Lehninger, *Proc. Intern. Symposium on Enzyme Chem., Tokyo and Kyoto, 1957* pp. 297–301.
23. G. W. Brown, Jr., and P. P. Cohen, *in* "The Chemical Basis of Development" (W. D. McElroy and B. Glass, eds.), p. 495. Johns Hopkins, Baltimore, 1958.
24. E. Witschi, "Development of Vertebrates," p. 183. Saunders, Philadelphia, 1956.
25. E. Scharrer, *in* "Comparative Endocrinology" (A. Gorbman, ed.), p. 233. Wiley, New York, 1959.
26. L. M. Passaus, *in* "The Physiology of Crustacea" (T. H. Waterman, ed.), Vol. I, p. 473. Academic Press, New York, 1960.
27. A. Gorbman, *in* "Comparative Endocrinology" (A. Gorbman, ed.), p. 266. Wiley, New York, 1959.
28. W. J. Leach, *Physiol. Zool.* **19,** 365 (1946).
29. M. Stokes, *Proc. Soc. Exptl. Biol. Med.* **42,** 810 (1939).
30. V. Vilter, *Compt. rend. soc. biol.* **140,** 783 (1946).
31. J. F. Gudernatsch, *Arch. Entwicklungsmech. Organ.* **35,** 457 (1912).
32. B. M. Allen, *Science* **44,** 755 (1916).
33. J. C. Kaltenbach, *J. Exptl. Zool.* **140,** No. 1, 1 (1959).
34. Z. Mayerowna, *Compt. rend. soc. biol.* **87,** 1175 (1922).
35. S. A. D'Angelo and H. A. Charipper, *Anat. Record* **72,** 40 (1938).
36. R. F. Blount, *J. Exptl. Zool.* **113,** 717 (1950).
37. R. F. Blount and I. H. Blount, *Anat. Record* **97,** 380 (1947).
38. B. M. Allen, *Quart. Rev. Biol.* **4,** 325 (1929).
39. J. F. Gudernatsch, *Am. J. Anat.* **15,** 431 (1914).
40. E. C. Kendall, *Am. J. Physiol.* **49,** 136 (1919).
41. W. Etkin, *J. Exptl. Zool.* **82,** 463 (1939).
42. W. Etkin, *J. Morphol.* **59,** 69 (1936).
43. A. Mazzeschi, *Arch. zool. ital.* **28,** 297 (1940).
44. P. E. Smith, *Science* **44,** 280 (1916).
45. P. E. Smith, *Am. Anat. Mem.* **No. 11** (1920).
46. B. M. Allen, *Anat. Record* **54,** 65 (1932).

47. M. Grant, *Anat. Record* **49,** 373 (1931).
48. B. M. Allen, *Univ. Calif. Publs. Zool.* **31,** 53 (1927).
49. C. Y. Chang, *Anat. Record* **128,** 531 (1957).
50. E. Frieden and R. J. Winzler, *J. Biol. Chem.* **176,** 155 (1948).
51. T. C. Bruice, N. Kharasch, and R. J. Winzler, *J. Biol. Chem.* **210,** 1 (1954).
52. K. Tomita and H. A. Lardy, *J. Biol. Chem.* **219,** 595 (1955).
53. W. L. Money, R. I. Meltzer, J. Young, and R. W. Rawson, *Endocrinology* **63,** 20 (1958).
54. R. Pitt-Rivers and J. Tata, "The Thyroid Hormones," Pergamon, New York, 1959.
55. N. E. Stasili, R. L. Kroc, and R. I. Meltzer, *Endocrinology* **64,** 62 (1959).
56. N. Freinkel, S. H. Ingbar, and J. T. Dowling, *J. Clin. Invest.* **36,** 25 (1957).
57. S. Lissitzky, M. Roques, and M. J. Benevent, *Biochim. et Biophys. Acta* **41,** 252 (1960).
58. E. Frieden and B. Naile, *Science* **121,** 37 (1955).
59. E. Witschi, "Development of Vertebrates," p. 186. Saunders, Philadelphia, 1956.
60. J. L. Schwind, *J. Exptl. Zool.* **66,** 1 (1933).
61. F. Finamore and E. Frieden, *J. Biol. Chem.* **235,** 1751 (1960).
62. H. Hartwig, *Biol. Zentr.* **60,** 473 (1940).
63. J. Kollros, *Physiol. Zoöl.* **16,** 269 (1943).
64. J. Kaltenbach, *Anat. Record* **108,** 38 (1950).
65. J. Kollros, *in* "Comparative Endocrinology" (A. Gorbman, ed.), p. 340. Wiley, New York, 1959.
66. U. Clever and P. Karlson, *Exptl. Cell Research* **20,** 623 (1960).
67. E. Urbani, *Rend. ist. lombardo Sci.* **B92,** 69 (1957).
68. E. Witschi, "Development of Vertebrates," Chapters 9, 10, and 11. Saunders, Philadelphia, 1956.
69. E. Baldwin, "An Introduction to Comparative Biochemistry," 2nd ed. Cambridge Univ. Press, London and New York, 1940.
70. P. P. Cohen and G. W. Brown, Jr., *in* "Comparative Biochemistry" (M. Florkin and H. S. Mason, eds.), Vol. II, Chapter 4, p. 161. Academic Press, New York, 1960.
71. K. Bialaszewicz and M. Mincowna, *Prace. Zakladu fizjol., Inst. Biol. Nenck.* **1,** 1 (1923).
72. A. F. Munro, *Biochem. J.* **33,** 1957 (1939).
73. A. F. Munro, *Biohem. J.* **54,** 29 (1953).
74. E. Underhay and E. Baldwin, *Biochem. J.* **61,** 544 (1955).
75. J. Dolphin and E. Frieden, *J. Biol. Chem.* **217,** 735 (1955).
76. G. W. Brown, Jr., W. Brown, and P. P. Cohen, *J. Biol. Chem.* **234,** 1775 (1959).
77. W. Paik and P. P. Cohen, *J. Gen. Physiol.* **43,** 683 (1960).
78. E. Frieden and H. Mathews, *Arch. Biochem. Biophys.* **73,** 107 (1958).
79. J. Shaw, *in* "Comparative Biochemistry" (M. Florkin and H. S. Mason, eds.), Vol. II, Chapter 9, p. 471. Academic Press, New York, 1960.
80. A. E. Herner and E. Frieden, *J. Biol. Chem.* **235,** 2845 (1960).
81. G. De Beer, "Embryos and Ancestors," 3rd ed., p. 40. Oxford Univ. Press (Clarendon), London and New York, 1958.
82. E. Haeckel, *Jena. Z. Naturw.* **9,** 402 (1875).
83. C. H. Whipple, "The Dynamic Equilibrium of Body Proteins," p. 61. Charles C. Thomas, Springfield, Illinois, 1956.

84. D. H. Moore, S. C. Shen, and C. S. Alexander, *Proc. Soc. Exptl. Biol. Med.* **58,** 307 (1945).
85. O. B. Henriques, S. B. Henriques, and A. Neuberger, *Biochem. J.* **60,** 409 (1955).
86. A. E. Herner and E. Frieden, *Arch. Biochem. Biophys.* in press (October, (1961).
87. F. H. McCutcheon, *J. Cellular Comp. Physiol.* **8,** 63 (1936).
88. A. Riggs, *J. Gen. Physiol.* **35,** 23 (1951).
89. A. Riggs, *J. Gen. Physiol.* **43,** 737 (1960).
90. L. Eriksen, *Exptl. Cell Research* **13,** 624 (1957).
91. H. C. Dessauer, W. Fox, and J. R. Ramirez, *Arch. Biochem. Biophys.* **71,** 11 (1957).
92. G. Ratner, "Zur Metamorphose des Darmes bei den Froschlarvae." Schnakenburg, Dorpat, 1891.
93. R. G. Janes, *J. Exptl. Zool.* **67,** 73 (1935).
94. C. Lui and J. C. Li, *Peking Nat. Hist. Bull.* **4,** 67 (1930).
95. R. K. S. Lim, *Quant. J. Exptl. Physiol.* **12,** 303 (1920).
96. M. Aron, *Compt. rend. soc. biol.* **99,** 215 (1928).
97. J. F. Gennaro, *Univ. Pittsburgh Bull.* **49,** 1 (1953).
98. A. Kuntz, *J. Morphol.* **38,** 581 (1924).
99. E. Urbani, *Atti acad. nazl. Lincei* **21,** 498 (1956).
100. J. Kaltenbach, E. Frieden, and W. Westmark, unpublished data (1960).
101. L. J. Blacher and L. D. Liosner, *Biol. Zentr.* **50,** 285 (1930).
102. E. Urbani and L. DeCesaris Coromaldi, *Ricerca sci.* **24,** 2364 (1954).
103. L. DeCesaris Coromaldi, *Rend. ist. lombardo sci.* **B92,** 357 (1958).
104. A. Magnus-Levy, *Berlin. Klin. Wochschr.* **32,** 650 (1895).
105. E. J. C. Lewis and E. Frieden, *Endocrinology* **65,** 273 (1959).
106. J. Martenson, *Skand. Arch. Physiol.* **77,** 59 (1937). *Chem. Abstr.* **32,** 652 (1938).
107. W. Etkin, *Physiol. Zoöl.* **1,** 129 (1934).
108. T. A. Wills, *J. Exptl. Zool.* **73,** 481 (1936).
109. S. H. Barch, *Physiol. Zoöl.* **26,** 223 (1953).
110. S. B. Barker, *Physiol. Revs.* **31,** 205 (1951).
111. G. Wald, *in* "Comparative Biochemistry" (M. Florkin and H. Mason, eds.), Vol. I, Chapter 7, p. 311. Academic Press, New York, 1960.
112. M. Florkin, "Biochemical Evolution" (S. Morgulis, ed.), p. 71. Academic Press, New York, 1949.
113. G. Wald, *Harvey Lectures 1945–1946* **41,** 148 (1947).
114. J. C. Peskin, *Anat. Record* **128,** 600 (1957).
115. F. D. Collins, R. M. Love, and R. A. Morton, *Biochem. J.* **53,** 632 (1953).
116. G. Wald, *Science* **109,** 482 (1949).
117. F. Crescitelli, *Ann. N. Y. Acad. Sci.* **74,** 230 (1958).
118. H. J. A. Dartnall, *J. Physiol. (London)* **125,** 25–42 (1954).
119. F. Wilt, *Develop. Biol.* **1,** 199 (1959).
120. F. Wilt, *J. Embryol. Exptl. Morphol.* **7,** 556 (1959).
121. G. Wald and P. K. Brown, *J. Gen. Physiol.* **40,** 627 (1956).
122. A. M. Zacchei, *Ricerca sci.* **24,** 1489 (1954).
123. G. Minelli and M. R. Rossi, *Ricerca sci.* **30,** 539 (1960).
124. E. Roberts, J. Lowe, L. Guth, and B. Jelinek, *J. Exptl. Zool.* **138,** 313 (1952).
125. H. Braus, *Arch. Entwicklungsmech. Organ.* **22,** 564 (1906).
126. J. L. Kritchevsky, *Centr. Bakteriol.* **72,** 81 (1914).

127. K. Wilkoewitz and H. Ziegenspeck, *Botan. Arch.* **22,** 227 (1928).

128. R. S. Cooper, *J. Exptl. Zool.* **101,** 143 (1946).

129. R. Weber, *Experientia* **13,** 153 (1957).

130. S. Bilewicz, *Biochem. Z.* **297,** 379 (1938).

131. R. Faraggiana, *Atti. accad. nazl. Lincei* **18,** 580 (1933).

132. J. Ashmore, A. B. Hastings, F. B. Nesbett, and A. E. Renold, *J. Biol. Chem.* **218,** 77 (1956).

133. K. Yamamoto and M. Suzuki, *Endocrinol. Japon.* **4,** 262 (1957).

134. T. P. Hilditch, "The Chemical Constitution of Natural Fats." Wiley, New York, 1956.

135. A. I. Irichimovitch, *Biol. Zentr.* **56,** 639 (1936).

136. G. Bucci, *Riv. Biol.* (*Perugia*) **43,** 529 (1951).

137. O. M. Helff, *Anat. Record* **34,** 129 (1926).

138. B. Aleschin, *Biochem. Zeit.* **171,** 79 (1926).

139. O. M. Helff, *Biol. Bull.* **63,** 405 (1932).

140. T. Yanagisawa, *Repts. Liberal Arts. Fac. Shizuoka Univ., Nat. Sci.* **5,** ·53 (1954).

141. G. Contronei, *Mem. soc. ital. sci. detta dei XL* Ser. 3ª, p. 24 (1919).

142. A. A. Woitkewitsch, *Biol. Zentr.* **57,** 196 (1937).

143. S. P. Stearner, *Physiol. Zoöl.* **19,** 370 (1946).

144. A. S. Hunter and E. Frieden, unpublished data (1951).

144a. P. Weiss, *Arch. Neerland. Zool.* **10,** Suppl. 2, 165 (1953).

145. J. S. Huxley, *Nature* **123,** 712 (1929).

146. S. Løvtrup, *Compt. rend. trav. lab. Carlsberg* **29,** 262 (1955).

147. R. Truzkowski and H. Czuperski, *Biochem. J.* **27,** 66 (1933).

148. G. Nash and G. Fankhauser, *Science* **130,** 714 (1959).

149. W. Grant, *Am. Zool.* **1,** 163 (1961).

CHAPTER 12

Porphyrins: Structure, Distribution, and Metabolism

C. RIMINGTON

Department of Chemical Pathology, University College Hospital
Medical School, London, England

and

G. Y. KENNEDY

Cancer Research Unit, The University of Sheffield, Sheffield, England

557

I. Introduction

In 1898, Marion Newbigin (1) maintained that "there are three reasons why it is desirable that the biologist should concern himself with colour in organisms. The first is the conspicuousness of colour phenomena in a merely objective survey of animals and plants; the second is the relation of these colours to current theories in evolution; and the third is their importance in comparative physiology." Jean Verne (2) in his book "Les Pigments dans l'Organisme animal," published in 1926, wrote in the preface: "Je crois inutile d'insister ici sur l'importance de l'étude des pigments. Quelle que soit la branche de la biologie que l'on cultive, on est tenu de s'intéresser à eux. Le systématicien, le physiologiste, l'anatomiste, le cytologiste, le chimiste, le généticien, le pathologiste ont, à un moment donné, à considérer, sous des angles divers, la question pigmentaire. Cet intérêt général se conçoit, un pigment ne représente autre chose d'après notre définition, qu'un stade, naturellement coloré, du métabolisme de composés résultant des réactions, normales ou pathologiques, de la substance vivante."

Porphyrins are widely distributed throughout the animal and vegetable kingdoms. In the free form they occur in small amount, but the iron complexes of porphyrins, or hemes, are quantitatively more important and play a vital role in the living cell. Ferroprotoporphyrin IX is the prosthetic group of several important enzymes such as, for example, catalase, peroxidase, and cytochrome b, whereas hemes derived from porphyrins of slightly different structure occur in chlorocruorin, cytochrome c, and cytochrome oxidase. The macrocyclic rings of chlorophylls a and b are derivable from the same parent structure, porphin, and recent evidence shows that they are built up in a way comparable to that of the animal porphyrins (3). Chlorophyll-like pigments also occur in brown and red algae and in some bacteria, and although experimental evidence is still lacking, it seems likely that their biosynthesis follows the same general pattern. Finally, hemoglobin and myoglobin are both chromoproteins whose prosthetic group is ferroprotoporphyrin IX. Thus, functions of oxygen storage or transport, photosynthesis, intracellular oxidation in the most lowly to the most developed forms of life, electron transport, and so on are dependent upon this class of compounds. Porphyrin synthesis would appear to be one of the most fundamental attributes of cells. Relatively simple materials are employed and the steps involved seem to follow a general plan, as will be made clear in the following pages. Thus, although our knowledge has been gained chiefly from study of the biosynthesis of the heme of hemoglobin, the results are applicable in a much wider context and probably reveal processes contemporaneous with the emergence of life itself.

II. Porphyrins and Their Metal Complexes

A. THE CHEMISTRY OF THE PORPHYRINS

1. General Aspects

As a result of the work largely of the school of Hans Fischer (4), of Lemberg (5), and MacDonald (6) and their collaborators, the chemistry of the porphyrins now rests upon a very firm foundation and most of the naturally occurring porphyrins have been prepared by unambiguous syntheses. They may be considered as derivable from porphin, which has itself been synthesized and studied although it does not occur naturally. Porphin (Fig. 1) is a macrocyclic structure in which four

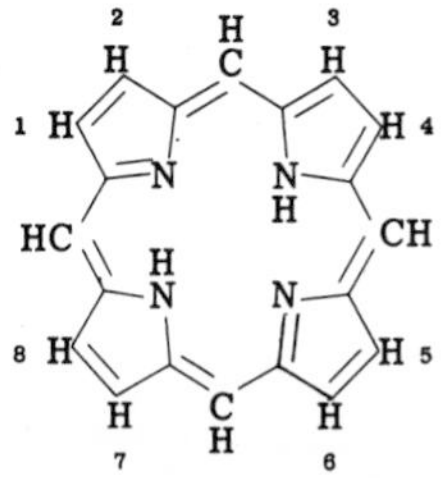

FIG. 1. The structure of porphin.

heterocyclic rings, namely one pyrrole, two pyrrolenine, and one maleinimide ring, are joined by methene groups —CH=. The two hydrogen atoms attached to nitrogen are replaceable by metals (iron, copper, magnesium, etc.) which are coordinatively bound. The whole structure is capable of a high degree of resonance and exhibits well-marked spectral absorption in the visible and infrared regions (7).

Porphyrins may be regarded as derived from porphin by substitution of the H atoms occupying the $\beta\beta'$-positions of the rings. Replacement by two dissimilar groups, e.g., CH_3 and C_2H_5 as in the etioporphyrins, can be made in four possible ways leading to four position isomers. Fischer synthesized all four etioporphyrins (Fig. 2) and proposed that all porphyrins should be referred to them for designation of isomeric type. There are thus four coproporphyrins (substituent groups CH_3 and CH_2CH_2COOH) and four uroporphyrins (substituent groups CH_2COOH and CH_2CH_2COOH). When one comes to the protoporphyrins with four methyl, two vinyl, and two propionic acid residues and the meso-

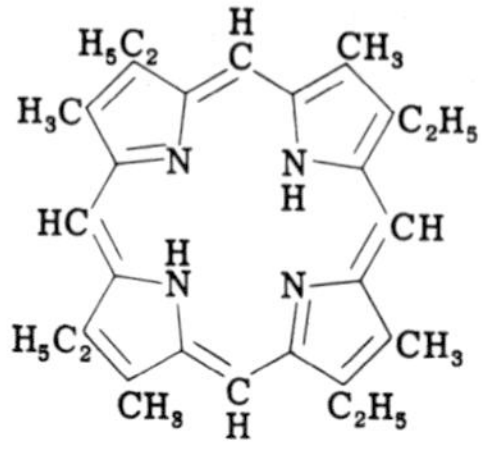

Fig. 2. Structures of the four isomeric etioporphyrins.

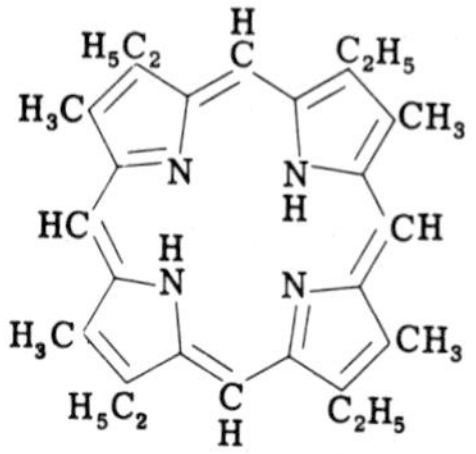

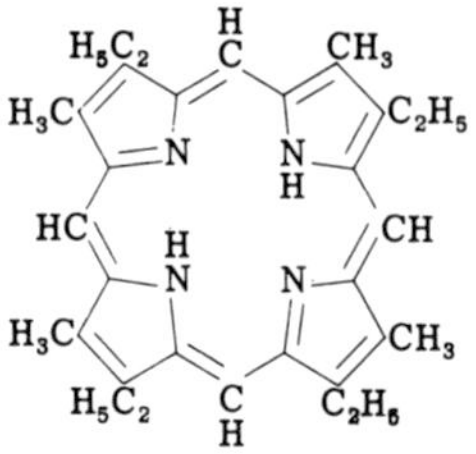

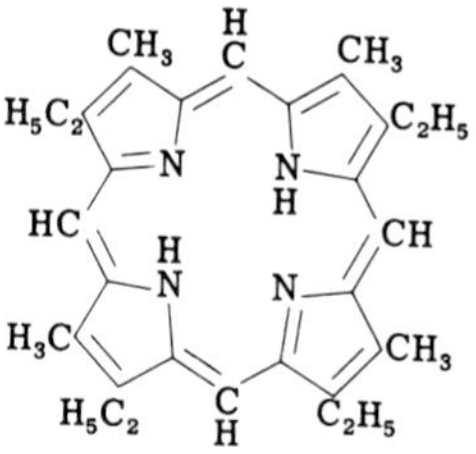

porphyrins, derivable from them by the reduction of the vinyl to ethyl groups, the number of isomers becomes fifteen. Fischer synthesized twelve of the fifteen possible mesoporphyrins to provide reference materials for constitutional analysis. As it happens, only the single protoporphyrin IX (Fig. 3) has so far been encountered in nature,

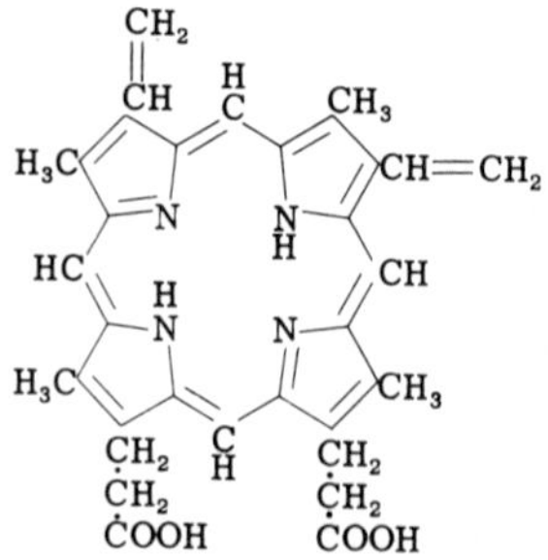

Fig. 3. The structure of protoporphyrin IX.

either in the free state or as the iron complex or heme (Fig. 4), and only coproporphyrins I and III and uroporphyrins I and III. These structural relationships and additional data are summarized in Table I.

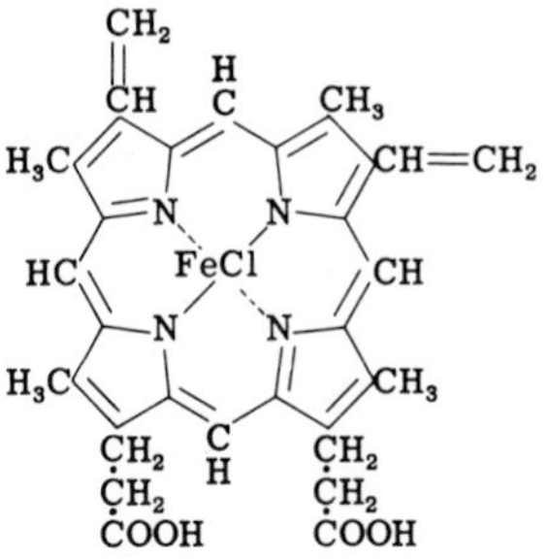

FIG. 4. The structure of hemin.

Vigorous reduction of a porphyrin, e.g., coproporphyrin I with an agent such as sodium amalgam, leads to addition of six H atoms and production of the colorless, nonfluorescent porphyrinogen (Fig. 5).

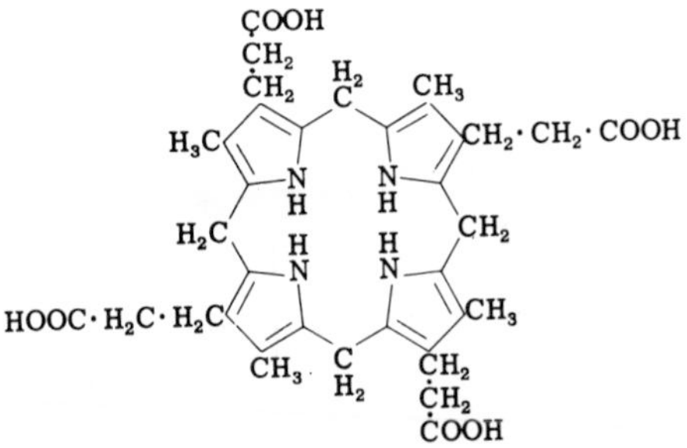

FIG. 5. The structure of coproporphyrinogen I.

Reoxidation takes place readily in contact with air or by treatment with dilute aqueous iodine. The porphyrinogens have recently assumed considerable importance in connection with the biosynthetic pathway. Minute quantities of porphyrins may be detected by taking advantage of their intense fluorescence and spectral absorption. They can be separated by extraction or chromatographic procedures and determined quantitatively. Elucidation of isomeric configuration is also possible by application of paper chromatography (8).

2. Hemes

Porphyrins have the property of combining very readily with a

TABLE I

NATURE AND POSITION OF SIDE CHAINS IN DIFFERENT PORPHYRINS

Substance	1	2	3	4	5	6	7	8
Porphin	H	H	H	H	H	H	H	H
Uroporphyrin I	A	P	A	P	A	P	A	P
Uroporphyrin III	A	P	A	P	A	P	P	A
Coproporphyrin I	Me	P	Me	P	Me	P	Me	P
Coproporphyrin III	Me	P	Me	P	Me	P	P	Me
Protoporphyrin IX	Me	V	Me	V	Me	P	P	Me
Mesoporphyrin IX	Me	Et	Me	Et	Me	P	P	Me
Deuteroporphyrin IX	Me	H	Me	H	Me	P	P	Me
Chlorocruoroporphyrin	Me	CHO	Me	V	Me	P	P	Me
Chlorophyll a	Me	V	Me	Et	Me	Iso	Pp + H	Me + H
Chlorophyll b	Me	V	CHO	Et	Me	Iso	Pp + H	Me + H
Chlorophyll d	Me	CHO	Me	Et	Me	Iso	Pp + H	Me + H
Bacteriochlorophyll	Me	$COCH_3$	Me + H	Et + H	Me	Iso	Pp + H	Me + H
Phylloerythrin	Me	Et	Me	Et	Me	CH_2—CO	P	Me

The β,β'-Positions[a]

[a] The $\beta\beta'$-positions on the pyrrole rings are numbered 1 to 8 (see Fig. 1). Me = CH_3; A = CH_2COOH; P = $CH_2 \cdot CH_2 \cdot COOH$;

Et = CH_2CH_3; V = $CH = CH_2$; Pp = $CH_2 \cdot CH_2 \cdot COOC_{20}H_{39}$; Iso = isocyclic ring C_6 to C_7, CH—CO (see Fig. 7).

$COOCH_3$

variety of metals to form metalloporphyrins in which the metal is coordinatively bound to the nitrogen atoms. Thus vanadium-porphyrin complexes have been identified in shale oils (9), a copper-uroporphyrin III constitutes the red coloring matter, named turacin, of the wings of certain Central African birds (10), and by purely chemical means complexes have been prepared of porphyrins with magnesium, zinc, manganese, cobalt, nickel, silver, tin, cadmium, etc. (4). By far the most important metalloporphyrins, however, are the iron complexes or hemes. In these nature has exploited the valency change from the ferric to ferrous state and vice versa to establish an electron transport system connecting the intracellular dehydrogenases with atmospheric oxygen. In the myoglobins and hemoglobins the combination with protein is such that coordination of the iron atom with oxygen can take place without valency change in the iron atom. These substances thus act as oxygen carriers or storers.

That no other isomer of protoporphyrin except protoporphyrin IX occurs in the natural hemes was a puzzling fact, since both uroporphyrin I and coproporphyrin I occur in nature, but it is now evident that this is occasioned by the isomer specificity of the enzyme system converting coproporphyrinogen to protoporphyrin. It acts only upon coproporphyrinogen III whereas uroporphyrinogen decarboxylase will transform either uroporphyrinogen I, II, III, or IV into the corresponding coproporphyrinogen (11). That the presence of the vinyl groups in protoporphyrin is a necessary condition for the biological insertion of iron to produce heme was demonstrated by Granick and Gilder (12) in the case of *Hemophilus influenzae* which requires for growth either heme or protoporphyrin plus iron; it cannot grow when supplied with deuteroheme or mesoheme or these porphyrins together with iron.

3. Cytochromes

It was stated above that the ability to synthesize porphyrins and heme is a fundamental property of the cell, possibly contemporaneous with the emergence of life itself. The heme-containing cytochromes provide the mechanism for linking oxygen of the air with metabolic substrates within the cell and thus providing energy for vital processes. Many bacteria will produce quantities of porphyrins under suitable cultural conditions, and they possess more or less complete cytochrome systems depending upon their degree of aerobiosis (13). Thus true aerobes contain most of the cytochrome components, facultative anaerobes have an incomplete cytochrome spectrum, and anaerobes have none. The position of the latter is interesting since some obligate anaerobes such as *Clostridium sporogenes* and *C. histolyticum* have been shown by Topley and Wilson (14) to contain small quantities of catalase. They must be able, therefore, to synthesize heme, and one may wonder whether their lack of cytochromes is due to loss of this function in the course of evolution. In this connection it is of interest that Gilder (15) found that the facultative anaerobe Leuconostoc mesenteroides produces catalase when grown in the presence of heme, but not in its absence; this finding suggests that the property of heme synthesis has been lost, but not the ability to produce the specific apoprotein of catalase. In these experiments, heme acted inductively. No attempt will be made to discuss the chemical structures of the different cytochromes or to particularize their occurrence in different organisms since an excellent modern review is available (13) and this chapter is primarily concerned with a survey of the porphyrins in nature.

4. Hemoglobins (Erythrocruorins, True Hemoglobins, Chlorocruorins) and Myoglobins

We have adopted a convention in which we use the term "hemoglobin" to embrace all respiratory pigments containing a heme united to a protein. By "true hemoglobins" we understood such pigments in which ferroprotoporphyrin IX is associated with globin, a basic protein of molecular weight up to 68,000. Erythrocruorins cover associations of the same heme with specific proteins of much higher molecular weight, usually of the order of 1–3 million. In chlorocruorins, a large protein moiety is combined with a different heme, namely, ferrochlorocruoroporphyrin (5).

The production of hemoglobins appears to be confined to the animal kingdom, with one notable exception—the presence of a pigment of this type in root nodules of the Leguminosae, which are the site of symbiosis between the plant and bacteria of the genus Rhizobium. Only nodules which are effective in nitrogen fixation contain the pigment and are able to synthesize porphyrins in vitro. The function of the hemoglobin is not definitely known, but it is thought to be one of oxygen transport or storage.

Vertebrate and many invertebrate bloods contain an oxygen-carrying hemoglobin in which protoporphyrin IX is united to an apoprotein of comparatively small molecular weight (31,000–68,000). In such cases the pigment is confined within specialized cells, the erythrocytes, no doubt to avoid the consequences which would otherwise follow upon the presence of a protein in simple solution in such concentrations. In other invertebrates the same heme is combined with much larger apoproteins and is then found freely dispersed in the hemolymph. Thus Arenicola and *Lumbricus,* for example, have erythrocruorins or hemoglobins with a molecular weight of about 3 million (5).

In yet other invertebrates, the pigment moiety differs structurally from protoheme. The most familiar example is to be found in the sabellid worms (Polychaeta) such as *Spirographis,* the greenish hemoglobin of which, chlorocruorin or spirographis hemoglobin, consists of a large apoprotein united to a heme of the constitution shown in Fig. 6 (*16*).

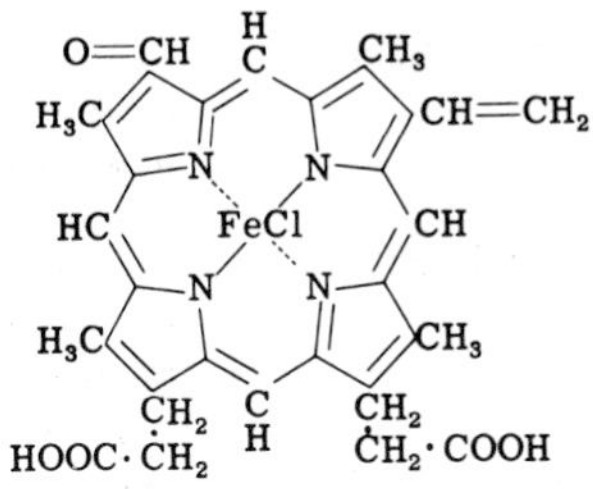

Fig. 6. The structure of chlorocruoro (*Spirographis*) hemin.

Oxygen-storing or -transporting pigments of the hemoglobin type are often found associated with muscular tissue, in which they occupy an intracellular position and impart a red color to the fibers and to the muscle as a whole. Such pigments have been termed myoglobins or myohemoglobins. It is of interest that in many Gastropoda (e.g., *Buccinum undatum*) the heart and radula muscles contain a myoglobin in which protoheme is the prosthetic group, but the oxygen-carrying pigment of its blood is a hemocyanin, a copper-containing pigment devoid of any tetrapyrrolic nucleus (*17*). The distribution of some of the hemoglobins and myoglobins is set out in Table II.

5. Chlorophylls

No survey of porphyrin production and distribution in nature can neglect reference to the occurrence of chlorophyll in higher and lower plants and many protozoa or of bacteriochlorophyll in some bacteria. The metal with which the tetrapyrrolic nucleus is chelated is magnesium, and the ring itself is a modification of the porphin structure. Nevertheless, it is probable that chlorophyll arose before heme; and the work of Granick (*18*) and others on the alga *Chlorella vulgaris* has demonstrated that the same fundamental steps are followed up to the stage of protoporphyrin in the biosynthesis of the two pigments. Thereafter, the subsequent changes would appear to take place (Fig. 7) in which the isocyclic ring is formed by oxidative ring closure between one propionic

TABLE II

DISTRIBUTION OF HEMOGLOBINS AND MYOGLOBINS

Phylum	Pigment	Examples
Protozoa	Hemoglobin in cytoplasm	Ciliata, e.g., *Paramecium*
Nemathelminthes	Erythrocruorin in body cavity	Several species of *Ascaris*, intestinal parasitic worm in mammals. Two
	Erythrocruorin in body wall	distinct pigments
Annelida	Erythrocruorin in blood fluid	*Amphitrite johnstoni, Terebella lapidaria, Audouinia tentaculata, Nephthys caeca, Lumbriconereis fragilis, Platynereis dumerilli*
	Erythrocruorin in gut	*Aphrodite aculeata, Hermione hystrix, Harmothoe imbricata, Lepidonotus squamatus, Panthalis oerstedi, Phyllodoce maculata*
	Erythrocruorin in coelomic corpuscles	Several species of order Polychaeta, e.g., *Glycera convulata*, the blood worm.
	Erythrocruorin in blood fluid	Several species of order Polychaeta, e.g., *Spirographis, Sabella pavonina, Branchiomma vesiculosus, Myxicola infundibulum, Anabothrus gracilis, Ampharete grubei, Sabellides octocirrata, Amphictenus gunneri, Pomatoceros triqueter, Euchone rubrocincta, Dasychone bombyx, Stylariodes plumosa, Serpula vermicularis*
Arthropoda		
Crustacea	Erythrocruorin in blood fluid	Found in several species, e.g., *Daphnia*, the water flea, and *Ernoecera*, a parasitic copepod of fish
Insecta	Erythrocruorin in blood fluid	*Chironomus*, midges (order Diptera)
Mollusca	Erythrocruorin in blood fluid	*Planorbis*, freshwater snail (order Gastropoda)
	Erythrocruorin in corpuscles	*Arca*, a mussel (order Lamellibranchiata)
	Myohemoglobin	*Buccinum undatum* (order Gastropoda), the whelk. Pigment in heart and radula muscles (hemocyanin in circulation)
Echinodermata	Erythrocruorin	*Thyone*, a holothurian
Chordata		
Protochordata	?	So far, neither hemoglobin nor myohemoglobin reported present in members of this subphylum. Redfield reports absence of hemoglobin in *Amphioxus*. (? *Balanoglossus*)

TABLE II (*Continued*)

Phylum	Pigment	Examples
Vertebrata	True hemoglobin in corpuscies	Present throughout, including *Lampetra* (suborder Cyclostomata)
	Myohemoglobin	Probably present throughout the lower orders, e.g., Pisces, Amphibia, and Reptilia; most in the heart muscle.

acid side chain and one methene bridge. This oxidation is partly counterbalanced by reductions of the porphin ring itself to the dihydroporphin structure and reduction of a vinyl to an ethyl group (in chlorophyll a). Bacteriochlorophyll has a tetrahydroporphin structure (*19*). The chlorophyll c present in Phaeophyceae (*20*) is a pheoporphyrin-like compound, while the chlorophyll d of the Rhodophyceae has recently been characterized by Holt and Morley (*21*) as 2-devinyl-2-formyl chlorophyll a (Fig. 8).

The quantity of chlorophyll synthesized annually on the earth's surface is stupendous. As Lemberg (*22*) has remarked: "Our earth seen from outside is a green star"; and he goes on to calculate that the human race alone biosynthesizes some 160,000 tons of protoporphyrin annually for its hemoglobin! The production of chlorophyll by plant life must be incomparably greater.

One result of the ingestion of chlorophyll-containing food by the ruminant herbivores, is its transformation into the porphyrin phylloerythrin (Fig. 9). The bacteria and protozoa of the rumen are considered to be responsible for this change (*23*); the pigment is normally absorbed and excreted in the bile so that it ultimately passes out of the body in the feces (*24*). Should jaundice, however, occur for any reason in these species, phylloerythrin enters the peripheral circulation together with other bile pigments and may cause severe photosensitization (*25*) since it is highly photoactive. Diseases of stock are now well recognized in which this syndrome occurs (*26*).

Accompanying phylloerythrin in the feces of herbivores, rhodoporphyrin-γ-carboxylic acid and various phorbides have been identified (*27*). The latter are degradation products of the chlorophylls formed by the removal of magnesium and the phytol residue.

B. THE BIOSYNTHESIS OF PORPHYRINS

Present knowledge concerning the pathway of porphyrin and heme synthesis is set out in Fig. 10. This knowledge has been accumulated during the past thirteen years and represents a major accomplishment

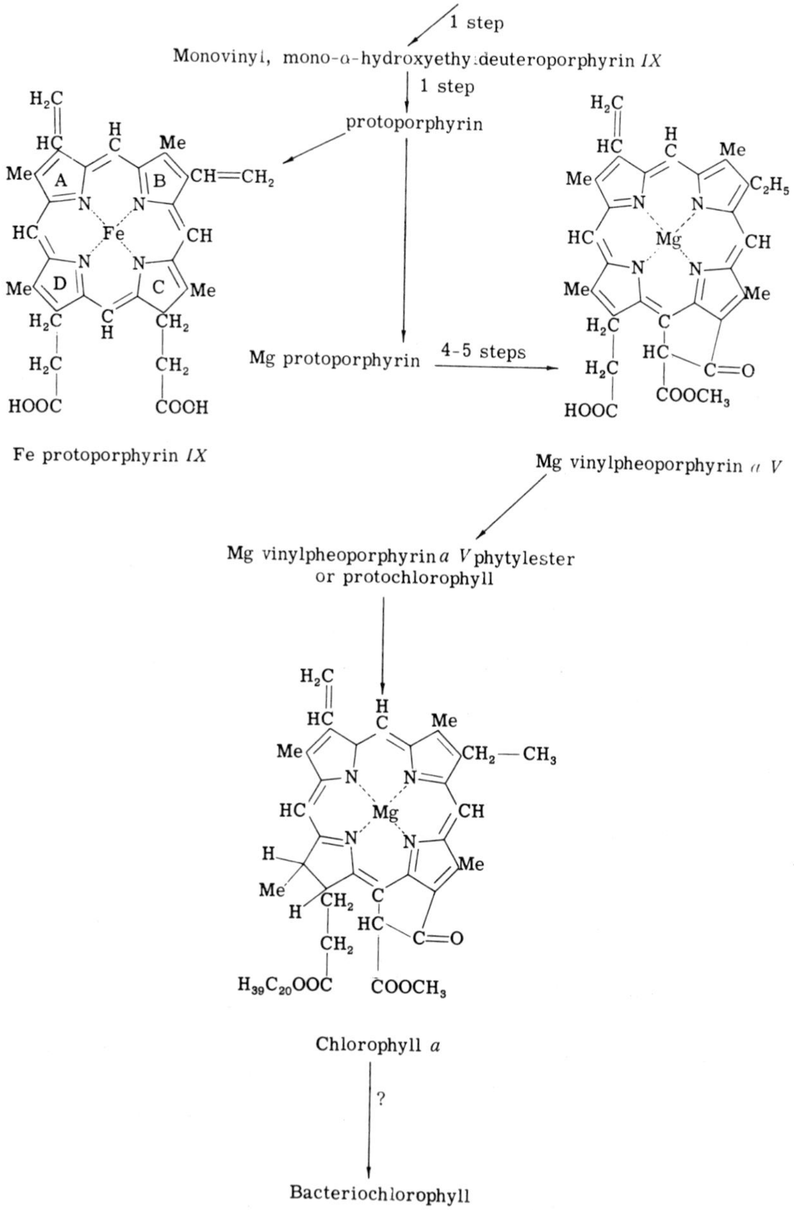

FIG. 7. Steps in the biosynthesis of chlorophyll a from the protoporphyrin stage. After Granick (18a).

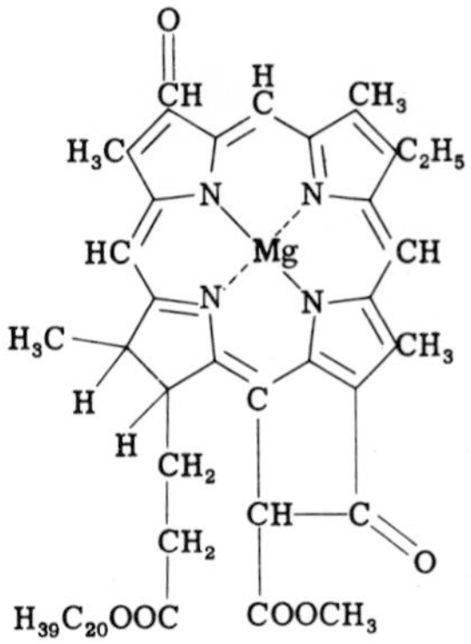

FIG. 8. Structure of chlorophyll d. From Holt and Morley (*21*).

of modern biochemistry. The final scheme has been pieced together from discoveries made at different times, but there still remain significant details to be filled in. Nevertheless, the way in which this complicated yet vital synthesis is achieved may be regarded as firmly established (for review with references see Rimington, *28*).

The first recognizable building units are glycine and succinyl coen‑zyme A (CoA), the latter being derived from operations of the Krebs cycle involving substrates like acetate and cofactors such as magnesium ions and lipothiamide. The combination of glycine and succinyl CoA is brought about by a system requiring pyridoxal (probably as phosphate) and ferrous iron (*29*). The participation of the metal at this stage is of particular interest; it probably favors Schiff's base formation, the tendency for which at physiological pH is only slight (*30*). The unstable β-ketonic acid, α-amino-β-ketoadipic acid is thought to be formed as the first product of the union but to lose carbon dioxide very rapidly, yielding δ-aminolevulinic acid, which is the identifiable product of the reaction. An enzyme, δ-aminolevulinic acid dehydrase, promotes con-

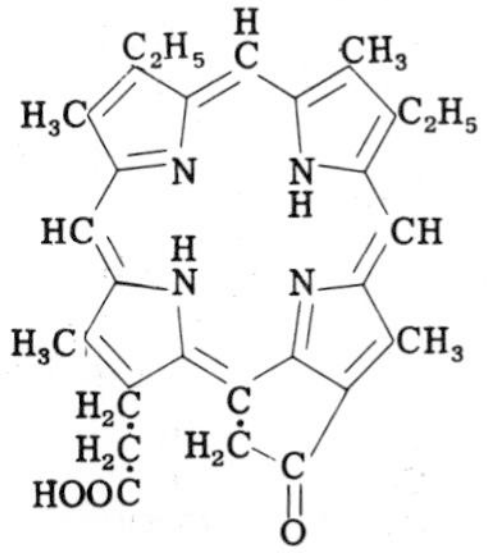

FIG. 9. The structure of phylloerythrin.

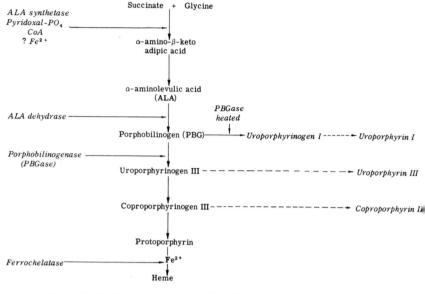

FIG. 10. A scheme showing established steps in heme biosynthesis.

densation of two molecules of the acid in such a manner that a pyrrolic substance, porphobilinogen, is formed (Fig. 11). This is a highly re-

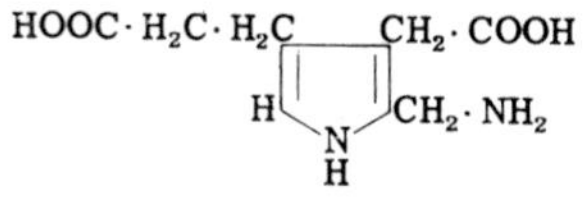

FIG. 11. The structure of porphobilinogen.

active material which in dilute acid solution readily gives rise to a mixture of uroporphyrinogens among which uroporphyrinogen of the isomeric series III predominates (Fig. 12). Enzymatic preparations

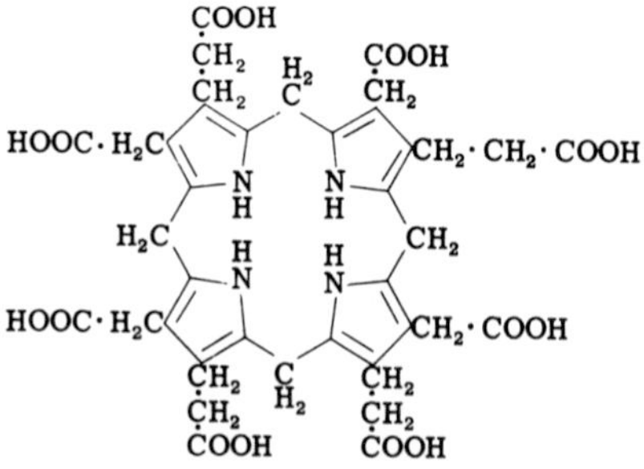

FIG. 12. The structure of uroporphyrinogen III.

made from red blood cells, liver, or many other tissues of animal or plant origin convert porphobilinogen into uroporphyrinogen III and "pseudouroporphyrinogen," the constitution of which is not yet clear although it is known also to belong to the isomeric series III. If any of the above-named enzyme systems is heated for a short time at 60–65° and then allowed to react with porphobilinogen, uroporphyrinogen I (Fig. 13) is produced. The mechanism by which four molecules of the

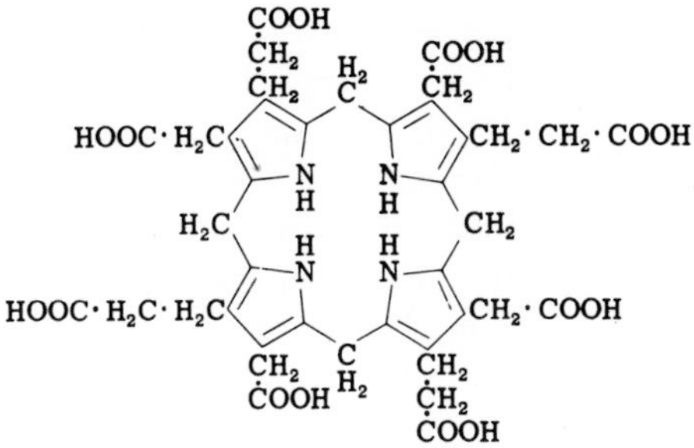

FIG. 13. The structure of uroporphyrinogen I.

pyrrole porphobilinogen are normally combined to give an unsymmetrical III-series pigment has given rise to much speculation, and various hypothetical reaction schemes have been proposed. Bogorad (31) was able to separate two factors concerned in the enzymatic synthesis of uroporphyrinogen III. The first is a relatively stable enzyme, named by him "porphobilinogen deaminase," which if present alone converts porphobilinogen into uroporphyrinogen I and ammonia. The second factor, "uroporphyrinogen isomerase," has itself no action upon porphobilinogen, but if present together with the deaminase, it modifies the action of the latter so that uroporphyrinogen III results. One could assume that action of the deaminase upon porphobilinogen leads to some intermediate, such as that postulated by Wittenberg (32), which can be further transformed into porphyrinogen in two different ways, isomerase favoring that leading to the III-series pigment. Alternatively, and it would appear to us with greater plausibility, one may picture combination of porphobilinogen through the unsubstituted α-position with the enzyme "porphobilinogen deaminase" followed by activation of the side-chain and consequent attack upon other porphobilinogen molecules as envisaged by Bullock et al. (33), until a linear pyrrolic chain is built up. The "uroporphyrinogen isomerase" may be regarded as an enzyme inducing cyclization of four such units to form a molecule of uroporphyrinogen III. Detachment of this would leave the enzymatic surface free to reinitiate the process, and thus only uroporphy-rinogen III molecules would be formed. In the absence of the isomerase or its destruction by heat, it may be assumed, however, that the union of linear pyrrol units will continue, cyclization of a terminal four only taking place spontaneously. According to any scheme based on the hypothesis of Bullock *et al.* (*33*), this would necessarily lead to production of uroporphyrinogen I while a single pyrrolic moiety remained attached to the surface of the porphobilinogen deaminase. This fragment might eventually appear, when all substrate was used up, as opsopyrrole-dicarboxylic acid or some closely related structure. Quite clearly further evidence must be accumulated in order to make possible a choice between the available hypotheses.

Returning to the main biosynthetic pathway of the porphyrins, the next step is the decarboxylation of uroporphyrinogen III to coproporphy-rinogen III. The enzyme accomplishing this step in *Rhodopseudomonas spheroides* appears to decarboxylate all four isomers equally well but to require a heat-stable cofactor, the nature of which has not yet been elucidated. The enzyme is without action upon the uroporphyrins, a finding which has interesting biological implications.

Between coproporphyrinogen and protoporphyrin there occurs not only a decarboxylation, but also a desaturation step, two vinyl groups ultimately taking the place of two propionic acid residues. The mechanism of this transformation is little understood apart from the fact that mitochondria supply some essential element. Whether protoporphy-rinogen or protoporphyrin appears initially is also a matter for conjecture, but we do know that the step is isomer specific since systems active with coproporphyrinogen III have no effect upon coproporphy-rinogens I, II, or IV. Herein lies the explanation for the occurrence in natural products of only protoporphyrin IX, that configuration belonging to the isomer III series.

The introduction of iron to form heme would appear to take place enzymatically with protoporphyrin as substrate, but not protoporphy-rinogen. The system derivable from red blood cells has been extensively studied by Goldberg and others, and the participation of ascorbic acid, glutathione, or cysteine as cofactor has been demonstrated (*34*).

From recent work, it would appear that in the process of hemoglobin formation it is a protein-bound form of iron and a protein-bound form of protoporphyrin which react to produce heme. This heme may then be transferred to separately synthesized globin (*35*).

III. Occurrence of Porphyrins in Invertebrates

There can be few more fruitful spheres for the chromatologist than the study of invertebrate pigments, particularly the marine forms, and it is therefore strange that so many of these pigments should have remained incompletely identified for so long. Much of the careful, indeed classic, work of C. A. MacMunn has been almost disregarded for upwards of sixty years, and only in the last six years has any of his interesting work on porphyrins in invertebrates been exhaustively re-examined (36–39a).

The first reported experimental work on invertebrate porphyrins seems to be that of Moseley (40) in 1877, who extracted a red pigment which he called "polyperythrin" from some madreporarian corals, from the anemones *Discosoma* and *Actinia*, and from the scyphozoans *Cassiopeia* and *Rhizostoma*. MacMunn (41) later showed that this pigment was a porphyrin and identified it with the hematoporphyrin of Hoppe-Seyler, then the only porphyrin known. MacMunn also found a porphyrin in the integument of the starfish, then known as *Uraster rubens*, in the slug *Arion*, and in the earthworm, and he considered that these pigments too were all hematoporphyrin. In the light of recent work mentioned above, it is curious that this careful man, working with a reliable spectroscope, should not have noticed that the absorption spectra of these porphyrins were appreciably different from that of hematoporphyrin.

An examination of Table III will reveal that in the invertebrates so far investigated, the occurrence of porphyrins in the free state seems confined to eight phyla, and is widespread in only two, the Annelida and the Mollusca. It will be interesting to discuss the table phylum by phylum and to speculate on the biological significance of the pigments and their interest to the taxonomist.

A. PORIFERA

MacMunn (42) examined the sponge *Suberites wilsoni*, sent to him by Sir Ray Lankester, which contains a purplish pigment that Lankester had called "spongioporphyrin." This gave a two-banded absorption spectrum with centers at 571 and 527 mμ and is very suggestive of a copper porphyrin: MacMunn, however, added that although Lankester's name "spongioporphyrin" was descriptively accurate, it "must not lead to the supposition that the pigment is in any way related to haematoporphyrin . . ." as he had suggested from the fact that concentrated sulfuric acid did not liberate a free porphyrin from the pigment. Mac-Munn concluded ". . . hence spongioporphyrin is not allied to haemoglobin or to haematin." There is no mention of fluorescence in his paper, although the red fluorescence of the porphyrins (43) was by then well known and he himself had observed it in his study of "haematoporphy-

TABLE III

OCCURRENCE OF PORPHYRIN PIGMENTS IN INVERTEBRATA

Occurrence	Pigment	Location	Reference
Porifera			
Tethya aurantium	Unidentified	General	37
Tethya lyncurium			
Suberites flavus			
Halichondria panicea			
H. caruncula			
H. rosea			
H. bucklandi			
H. incrustans			
H. seriata			
Hymeniacidon sanguineum	Chlorophyll-like pigments	General	44
Leuconia gossei			
Pachymatisma johnstonia			
Grantia seriata			
Hircinia variabilis			
Aplysina aerophoba			
Tedania muggiana			
Reneira aquaeductus			
Clathria coralloides			
Coelenterata			
Actinia equina	"Actiniohaematin" (cytochromes a_1, b_1, and c, with b_1 predominating)	Column	45, 46
Metridium senile			
Tealia felina			
Hormathia coronata			
Cereus pedunculatus			
Anemonia sulcata			
Adamsia palliata			
Cerianthus membranaceus			

Organism	Compound	Location	Ref.
Flabellum variabile	"Haematoporphyrin"	General	*41*
Fungia symmetrica			
Cassiopeia	"Polyperythrin" (later said to be	General	*40, 41*
Rhizostoma octopus	"haematoporphyrin")		
Discosoma			
Madreporarian corals			
Platyhelminthes			
Dugesia dorotocephala	Coproporphyrin + uroporphyrin	General	*47*
Tetrathyridium sp.	?Copro- or protoporphyrin	General	*49*
Taenia solium	?Protoporphyrin	Cysticercus	*49*
Nemathelminthes			
Eustrongylus gigas	Proto- and coproporphyrins	General	*50*
Nemertinea			
Lineus longissimus	Protoporphyrin	Integument	Unpublished
Annelida			
Nereis diversicolor	Coproporphyrin III, biliverdin and pheophorbides a	Viscera	*57*
Chaetopterus variopedatus	Coproporphyrin III, a pentacarboxylic porphyrin, pheophorbides a and b + other tetrapyrrols		*37, 39*
Sabella pavonina	Chlorocruorin	Blood	*118*
Branchiomma vesiculosus			
Myxicola infundibulum			
Anabothrus gracilis	Chlorocruorin	Blood	*131*
Ampharete grubei			
Sabellides octocirrata			
Amphicteus gunneri			
Pomatoceros triqueter			
Euchone rubrocincta			
Dasychone bombyx			
Stylariodes plumosa			

TABLE III (Continued)

Occurrence	Pigment	Location	Reference
Serpula vermicularis	Chlorocruorin + hemoglobin	Blood	118
Nephthys caeca	Hemoglobin	Blood	131
Lumbriconereis fragilis	Hemoglobin	Blood	131
Platynereis dumerilii	Hemoglobin	Blood	131
Aphrodite aculeata	Methemoglobin	Gut	131
Hermione hystrix	Hemochromogen	Gut	131
Harmothoe imbricata	Hemochromogen	Gut	131
Lepidonotus squamatus	?Hematin	Gut	131
Panthalis oerstedi	?Hematin	Gut	131
Phyllodoce maculata	?Hematin	Gut	131
Phyllodoce lamillosa	?Hematin	Gut	131
Glycera convoluta	Hemoglobin	Coelomic corpuscles	131
Glycera alba	Hemoglobin	Coelomic corpuscles	131
Amphitrite johnstoni	Hemoglobin, coproporphyrins I and III, tricarboxylic porphyrins, hematin	Blood, heart body	
	Coproporphyrin III, hematin	Coelomic cells (pink and brown), body wall	
Terebella lapidaria	Hemoglobin	Blood	
	Coproporphyrin III	Heart body	48
	Hematin	Coelomic cells	
Lanice conchilega	Coproporphyrin III	Heart body, gut	
Cirratulus cirratus	Coproporphyrin III and hematin	Heart body	
Audouinia tentaculata	Hematin	Body wall and gut	
	Hemoglobin	Blood	
Melinna palmata	Coproporphyrins I and III	Heart body, blood, gut	
Flabelligera affinis	Coproporphyrin III	Heart body	
	Coproporphyrin III	Heart body, gut	

Organism	Porphyrin	Location	Ref.
Polycirrus caliendrum	Coproporphyrin III	Whole body, body wall, gut	*48*
Myxicola infundibulum	Coproporphyrin III, hematin	Body wall, gut	*48*
Arenicola marina	Coproporphyrins I and III, tricarboxylic porphyrins, hematin	Extravasal tissue and body wall (dark and pink)	*48*
Eisenia foetida	Protoporphyrin, hemoglobin	Integument, blood	*81, 83*
Lumbricus terrestris	Protoporphyrin	Integument	*41, 81, 82*
Echiuroidea			
Bonellia viridis	Dioxymesopyrrochlorin	Integument	*89*
Thalassema lankesteri	Dioxymesopyrrochlorin	Integument + mucus	*90*
Mollusca			
Arion ater (black)	Uroporphyrin I	Integument	*127*
Duvaucelia plebia	Uroporphyrin I	Integument	*37*
Aplysia punctata	Uroporphyrin I	Integument	*37*
	Aplysioviolin + aplysiorhodin	"Ink gland"	*132*
Akera bullata	Uroporphyrin I	Integument	*129*
	Cu-pheophorbide a	Viscera	*129*
	?"Aplysiopurpurin"	"Ink gland"	*40*
Ianthina janthina			
The genera:	Uroporphyrin	Shell	*105*
Monodonta			
Angaria			
Leptothyra			
Lithopoma			
Tricolia			
Theodoxus			
Neritodryas			
Neritina			
Torinia			
Trivia			
Erato			

TABLE III (*Continued*)

Occurrence	Pigment	Location	Reference
Velutina	Uroporphyrin	Shell	105
Cyproea			
Marginella			
Clypidina			
Fissurella			
Lucapina			
Acmoea			
Trochus			
Clanculus			
Ethalia			
Isanda			
Monilia			
Thalotia			
Elenchus			
Umbonium			
Gibbula			
Livona			
Hydatina			
Bulla			
Acteon			
Haminea			
Aplustrum			
Umbraculum			
Enigmonia			
Anomia			
Pteria			
Pinctada			
Malleus			

	Uroporphyrin →	Shell →	
Isognomon		Shell	*105* →
Pinna			
Venus			
Turbo regenfussi	Turboglaucobilin	Shell	*109*
Turbo marmoratus	Turboglaucobilin	Shell	
Turbo elegans	Turboglaucobilin	Shell	
Haliotis cracherodii	Haliotiviolin	Shell	
Echinodermata			
Astropecten irregularis	Proto- and chlorocruoroporphyrins	Integument	*37*
Luidia ciliaris	Proto- and chlorocruoroporphyrins	Integument	*37*
Asterias rubens	Protoporphyrin	Integument	*37, 44*
Arthropoda			
Crustacea			
Cambarus	Biliverdin	Digestive gland	*92*
Pellogaster paguri	Biliverdin	Attachment "roots"	*50*
Insecta			
Tineola bisselliella	Proto- and coproporphyrins	Excreta of lanae	*93*
Acherontia atropos	"Phyllobombicin"	Larvae	*50*
Bombyx mori	"Phyllobombicin"	Larvae	*50*

rin" in 1886; it would therefore appear that "spongioporphyrin" was not fluorescent and did not give rise to fluorescent derivatives. The true nature of this pigment is still in doubt.

The sponge *Tethya aurantium*, which was examined by Kennedy and Vevers (37), contains a very small amount of a pigment which is red fluorescent and has an acid number of 5 or less, which suggests that it may be a porphyrin. Owing to the scarcity of the material, nothing further could be said about this pigment.

MacMunn (44) reported that he had extracted chlorophyll-like pigments from a series of sponges (see Table III). He described these pigments as "green to green-yellow pigments, which on the grounds of their spectral properties resemble chlorophyll." Extracts were made in absolute alcohol which were red fluorescent and presented a pheophytin-like spectrum; they appear now to have been a mixture of the a and b components. It is possible that these pigments are derived from algae present on the sponges either as epiphytes or as symbionts (37).

B. Coelenterata

MacMunn (45) obtained a brownish purple pigment which he called "actiniohaematin" from *Actinia equina* (then known as *A. mesembryanthemum*) and some other anemones. This was later examined by Roche (46) and stated to be a mixture of cytochromes a_1, b_1, and c, with b_1 predominating.

Moseley (40) described a pigment, which he called "polyperythrin," from some corals and scyphozoans mentioned in Table III. Later, MacMunn (41), after examining Moseley's specimens, considered this pigment to be hematoporphyrin. He also extracted a red-brown porphyrin from *Fungia symmetrica* and *Flabellum variabile* and identified this too with hematoporphyrin. This work has never been repeated. *Fungia* is the "mushroom coral," common on reefs, and *Flabellum* is a deep-water variety, not a reef builder.

C. Platyhelminthes

The first report of a porphyrin in planarians seems to be that of Krugelis-Macrae (47). According to this account, coproporphyrins and uroporphyrin (isomers unspecified) were found in extracts of *Dugesia dorotocephala* in all individuals examined. The pigment is distributed generally, not stored in inert tissue, and is to be found in starved and regenerating animals. Krugelis-Macrae suggests that a physiological porphyria exists in these animals and that the porphyrin may be responsible for the well-known sensitivity to light of planarians. The question of porphyria in the invertebrates has been considered by Kennedy and Dales (48).

Some parasitic worms have been shown to contain porphyrins, and Derrien (49) reported a porphyrin in *Tetrathrydium,* a cestode parasite of the hedgehog. The same author also described a porphyrin in the cysticercus of *Taenia solium,* the tapeworm of the pig and man. The nature of these porphyrins is uncertain since Derrien was very vague about them but "believed" them to be "coproporphyrin or proto-porphyrin."

D. NEMATHELMINTHES

Lederer (50) in his review "Les Pigments des Invertébrés" mentions the presence of proto- and coproporphyrins in the nematode *Eustrongylus gigas,* parasitic in the dog. The pigments are thought to be derived from the hemoglobin of the host.

E. NEMERTINEA

At the suggestion of Professor Munro-Fox, Kennedy (unpublished) examined the nemertine worm *Lineus longissimus* and found proto-porphyrin in the integument. Thomas Rymer Jones (51), in his book "The Aquarian Naturalist," described the color of this worm. "It varies very considerably in colour as it contracts or extends itself, changing from a dusky to a reddish-brown; but it has, when placed in a strong light, especially in the sunshine, a gloss of fine rich purple all over; when most contracted it appears nearly black." Bürger (52) described the epithelium as consisting of three kinds of cells—slender, threadlike cells, interstitial cells, and gland cells. In *Lineus* and its related forms, the pigment occurs in the gland cells, whose secretion is often green. It would be interesting to examine other nemertines, e.g., *Nemertopsis* and *Amphiporus.*

F. ANNELIDA

The variable color of the polychete *Nereis diversicolor* has been known since Müller (53) described the species as "die bunte Nereide" in 1771. Most of the worms belonging to this species appear to be orange or brown in color, though close examination reveals that some green pigment is invariably present. However, others may be found that are predominantly green in appearance, and a few that are completely green and appear to lack brown or orange pigments in the epidermis.

Several previous authors have given attention to this. Mendthal (54) considered the green color of some worms to be due to a diet of green algae. McIntosh (55) rejected this idea and suggested that the green color was due to "pale greenish ova." However, it may be pointed out that males are also green and that in our experience the oocytes of this species are colorless or have only a pale straw color. Various other writers have commented on the variability of the color of this animal without contributing to the elucidation of the problem; Thomas (56) alone has attempted an analysis of the different pigments. He concluded that the green pigment was probably a porphyrin, possibly a modified chlorophyll.

Dales and Kennedy (57), working at the Plymouth Laboratory, showed that the variable color is due to variations in the proportion of green, orange, and brown pigments. The orange and brown pigments are mainly carotenoids; the green color is due to biliverdin. Pheophorbide a and coproporphyrin III also occur, but both these pigments may be restricted to the gut wall; biliverdin occurs both in the wall of the gut and in the epidermis and coelomic cells.

Bloch-Raphaël (58) concluded, in her review of the seat of hemoglobin synthesis and breakdown in polychetes, that in nereids these processes probably take place in the body wall and around the proboscis and that the bile pigments are excreted into the gut. This view agrees with present observations on N. diversicolor. The granules of biliverdin may gradually be removed from the epidermis by the coelomic cells and conveyed to the gut, the cells traveling down the septa and oblique muscles. Coelomic cells loaded with biliverdin, often in granules 4–5 μ across, can be seen in these positions in spawned females. When the rate of hemoglobin breakdown is increased as in ripe males and spawned females, the rate of elimination is not increased in proportion, so that the pigment accumulates in the body.

Kennedy and Dales (48) examined the heart bodies and other tissues of a number of polychete worms; the results are summarized in Table III. The chief interest in this work is centered in the presence of relatively large amounts of coproporphyrin III, together with traces of coproporphyrin I, a tricarboxylic porphyrin, and hematin in the heart body. The fact that all these pigments can be isolated from the heart-body tissue is very strong evidence in support of the view expressed by Meyer (59) that the heart body is an hematopoietic organ. It is possible that in the polychetes with hemoglobin which we have examined there exists a kind of idiopathic porphyria in which the heme biosynthesis system is inefficient. In such a system the intermediates in the chain of reactions in Fig. 10, namely coproporphyrinogen III, coproporphyrinogen I, and also tricarboxylic porphyrinogen, have been deposited in the tissues in their oxidized form and their metabolism to heme cannot, consequently, be carried further.

It is of interest to note here that the suggestion of Picton (60) that the heart body is formed from an infolding of extravasal epithelia is amply borne out by the equivalence, as shown by the porphyrins present, of the heart bodies with the extravasal tissue in *Arenicola*—tissue frequently referred to by previous authors as "chloragogen" (*61*). It thus seems possible that such extravasal "chloragogen" in polychetes fulfills a hematopoietic role, without excluding the possibility that it participates in excretion or food storage as well (*62*). Romieu (*61*) regarded the results of his histochemical and histological investigations as providing evidence for regarding the heart body as a "storage-kidney," or intravascular "chloragogue." Eisig (*63*) considered that the brown or brown-green pigment of the heart body in *Terebella lapidaria* was a derivative of hemoglobin. Romieu (*61*) did not agree with this and did not elicit the reactions for hematin or biliverdin; he was of the opinion that this brown pigment was a "urochrome" and compared it with chaetopterin, which he said was a modified chlorophyll—the comparison resting solely on its solubility in acetic acid and on its color. Kennedy and Dales (*48*) describe experiments which confirm Eisig's view that the brown granules in the heart body of *Arenicola* and also in the extravasal tissue are a derivative of hemoglobin; in fact, hematin.

The green coloration of *Chaetopterus* gut has been repeatedly investigated. The pigment, called "chaetopterin" by Lankester (*64*), occurs in the gut wall, and early workers found abundant green granules in the intestinal epithelium, especially of the middle region (*64–66*). These granules were generally regarded as a pigmented cell secretion concerned in some way with digestion, an idea originating in the resemblances between the green pigment and chlorophyll.

The intestinal epithelium of *Chaetopterus*, especially of the middle region, contains many small spherules, and it is in these spherules that the green pigment chaetopterin appears to be localized. Earlier suggestions that the green spherules are plant cells were supported by Berkeley (*67*), who examined *Mesochaetopterus taylori*, *Phyllochaetopterus prolifica*, and *Leptochaetopterus pattsi*. In these animals, as in *Chaetopterus variopedatus*, the intestine is green in color and replete with green granules. Berkeley believed that the granules were palmelloid stages of one of the Chrysophyceae, which he designated *Chrysocapsa chaetopteri*. The green bodies are similar in the three genera of worms which Berkeley examined. They range in size from 1 to 8 μ and are abundant in the intestinal epithelial cells throughout most of the gut. In *C. variopedatus*, the green bodies are most abundant in the gut of the middle region but are absent from the anterior region of the body (*66*).

Chaetopterin has been extracted from the gut with ethanol, benzene, chloroform, and other solvents used for chlorophyll, to which its solubility characteristics are similar. Chaetopterin is insoluble in water but can be extracted with aqueous or alcoholic hydrochloric acid. The pigment displays a strong red fluorescence in ultraviolet light; it is olive green in neutral or alkaline solutions and deep blue in acid, the color change being reversible (1, 42, 64).

There has been general agreement in the literature that chaetopterin is a pigment closely allied to chlorophyll (1, 2, 42, 64, 68–71). Alavarez, Sheard, and Higgins (72) considered chaetopterin to be chlorophyll occurring in protophytes or symbionts in the animal's tissue.

As reported in the literature, the absorption characteristics of chaetopterin are certainly very similar to those of chlorophyll. In organic solvents (ethanol, benzene, etc.) the main absorption bands have been reported with maxima at 657, 604, (560), 538, 504, and 400 mμ (approximately). The absorption band at 560 mμ is feeble (42).

Abderhalden's *Biochemisches Handlexikon* describes the properties of chaetopterin as reported by Lankester, MacMunn, and Newbigin. MacMunn emphasized the very close similarity between the absorption spectra and spectrographic curves of chaetopterin and those of "modified" (acid-treated) chlorophyll. Most workers since have concluded that chaetopterin is a slightly modified chlorophyll derivative. Dhéré (73), following the paper of Romieu and Obaton (71), wrote: ."La chétoptérine ne serait d'ailleurs que de la chlorophylle d'Ulva, par example, transformée en phéophytine." Lederer (50) concluded that the absorption bands of chaetopterin in neutral alcohol at 655, 600, 535, and 500 mμ indicate a pheophytin or pheophorbide ("il pourrait s'agir d'une phéophytine ou phéophorbide") (cf. Fox, 74).

The conspicuous greenish color of the midgut and hindgut of *Chaetopterus* was shown by Kennedy and Nicol (39) to be due predominantly to a mixture of pheophorbides a and b. These substances are derivatives of chlorophylls a and b. Kennedy and Nicol believe that pheophorbide a occurs in much greater quantity than pheophorbide b. This mixture of pheophorbides a and b is the "chaetopterin" of older workers (Lankester and others), now resolved for the first time after sixty-one years. The pheophorbides occur almost entirely in small green spherules packing the epithelial cells of the gut, although a small amount is present in the feces. The pigments are free, not esterified. In the animal they appear to be loosely bound to a carbohydrate—a polysaccharide or mucopolysaccharide—which probably accounts for the fact that they are not fluorescent *in vivo*. There is some similarity here to the state of chlorophyll in the chloroplasts of green leaves, in which the chlorophyll is probably present in the form of a complex with lipids or protein. This complex is very weakly fluorescent *in vivo*, but after treatment with boiling water, the chlorophyll becomes fluorescent. The same is probably true of green algae. Seybold and Egle (75) held the opinion that all chlorophyll-protein complexes are nonfluorescent. However, according to Rabinowitch (76), while this appears to be true of such complexes, it does not apply to complexes which contain both proteins and lipids—coacervates, as described by Hubert (77).

Kennedy and Nicol (39) also found the following pigments in their extracts of *Chaetopterus:*

A. Chlorophyll derivatives
    Isopheophorbide d
    Dioxymesophyllochlorin
    Rhodoporphyrin g₇ carboxylic acid (possibly)
    Copper pheophorbide chelation compounds
B. Coproporphyrin III
C. A pentacarboxylic porphyrin in traces
D. Bile pigment derivatives
    Turboglaucobilin
    Helioporobilin or a pigment closely resembling it
    An unidentified pigment
    Mesobiliviolin
E. Carotenoids
    β-Carotene
    A xanthophyll
F. Melanins

All the chlorophyll derivatives listed in A above, together with pheophorbides a and b, were found in extracts of the midgut region, and certain of them (see below) were found in extracts of the feces. *Chaetopterus* is a filter feeder, and it might be expected that these chlorophyll derivatives, including the pheophorbides, originate in the food of the animal. Chlorophyll a, from which pheophorbide a is derived, occurs in all marine algae, but chlorophyll b (the source of pheophorbide b) is found only in the Chlorophyceae, Siphonales, and Euglenineae. Chlorophyll d, from which the pheophorbides d are derived, occurs only in the Rhodophyceae (78). Dead remnants of algae become broken down into free particles by mechanical and bacterial action and contribute to the detritus suspended in the sea water, on which *Chaetopterus* feeds. According to Fox (74), who has reviewed recent literature, chlorophyll, various porphyrins, and carotenoids are found in the surface deposits of shores and the ocean floor. Quantitative estimations of the amounts of chlorophyll derivatives in marine sediments have been made by Orr and Grady (79). They found quantities, calculated as pheophytin a, ranging from 4 to 100 parts per million (dry sediment) in surface samples from marine basins.

Kennedy and Nicol (39) showed that the pheophorbides are retained tenaciously by the animal, even during prolonged starvation. Moreover, the pheophorbide content of *Chaetopterus* remains at a high level throughout the year. They believe that the green pigment occurs freely in green spherules in the tissues of the animal, and not in algal symbionts. Since the animal retains its content of green pigment at such a high level under such rigorous conditions, one may reasonably conclude that the pigment plays some important role in its economy.

Metcalf (*80*) examined the pigments of the squash bug *Anasa tristis* and discovered a system of breakdown of chlorophyll which he suggested was analogous in part to the breakdown of hemoglobin in the bug *Rhodnius prolixus*. In the fat body and pericardial cells he found a pheophorbide (unspecified) and a Gmelin-positive green pigment that was a tetrapyrrolic chlorophyll derivative analogous to biliverdin. A urobilin type of pigment was also present.

This work of Metcalf is very similar in result to that reported by Kennedy and Nicol (*39*). *Chaetopterus* appears to need pheophorbides for its economy and probably obtains them in that form from its detrital diet. In this material, there is a good deal of pheophorbide—sometimes in the form of a copper complex (Kennedy, unpublished)—and the pigments could then be put straight into the gut wall. There appears to be no intake of chlorophyll as such and no deposition of magnesium in the tissues (incineration tests, etc.).

An analogous case of pheophorbide accumulation is presented by another polychete, *Owenia fusiformis*. The midgut of this animal is also deep green in color owing to the presence of numerous granules of green pigment in the epithelial cells. These granules are rather irregular in shape, about the same size as the green spherules in *Chaetopterus* ($3-7\,\mu$) and are structureless. When freed from the epithelial cells they did not appear to be motile. The green pigment, when extracted, proved to be pheophorbide b plus some coproporphyrin and possibly carotenoid (*62*).

The pheophorbide spherules inside the cells have a large intracellular surface area, and it is tempting to speculate that this surface may be utilized in enzymatic processes concerned with digestion and assimilation. Nutrient substances, congregated on the surfaces of these spheres, may be decomposed into smaller units, a process in which the pheophorbide molecules may play a part.

MacMunn (*41*) examined the deep-purple streak which runs along the dorsal surface of the earthworm *Lumbricus terrestris* and thought it to be hematoporphyrin. This pigment was later investigated by Hausmann (*81*) and by Dhéré (*82*) and considered by them to be protoporphyrin. Hausmann thought that this pigmented streak had a photosensitizing effect upon the animal, but if the pigment is protoporphyrin—and there is still some doubt about that—then such an effect would be unlikely since this porphyrin is the least active in this respect.

Fischer and Schaumann (83) detected a similar pigment in *Eisenia foetida,* an allied species of oligochete. This had previously been noted by Hausmann (81).

The echiuroid *Bonellia viridis,* as the specific name would suggest, is bright green and for a long time was thought to contain chlorophyll. The pigment occurs in the skin and subepidermal cells of the female in particular, and in the wandering cells which partly fill the coelom in the degenerate male. A solution of the pigment in alcohol is brilliantly red fluorescent and gives a complex absorption spectrum. Gottlieb, who investigated the pigment at the instigation of Schmarda (84), found that it was soluble in hydrochloric acid, sulfuric acid, potassium hydroxide, alcohol, and ether with a beautiful green color. The alcoholic extract was dichroic, resembling an alcoholic extract of green leaves— green in transmitted, red in reflected, light. Sorby (85) gave the name "bonellin" to the pigment, and both he and Krukenberg (86) showed that it was not chlorophyll. Dubois (87) discussed the pigment under the confusing name "fluoro-chlorobonellin." Dhéré and Fontaine (88) concluded that bonellin (or bonelline) had some similarities with the porphyrins and phylloerythrin and appeared to be derived from the chlorophyll of the food. Lederer (89) made a careful analysis of the pigment and came to the conclusion that it is a dioxymesopyrrochlorin containing the isocyclic nucleus of chlorophyll a.

Thalassema lankesteri, another echiuroid, is also a very vivid green, and has hemoglobin in the perivisceral fluid and muscles (90). According to Lederer (50), the pigment is not fluorescent, and has only one absorption band, at about 617 mμ. However, Lönnberg and Gustafson (91) reported that the pigment was readily extracted with acetone, giving in ultraviolet light a strongly fluorescent solution whose absorption spectrum matched that of bonellin. They found that the acetic acid solution gave a band at 616 mμ, and they identified the pigment as "bonellin." Some confusion seems to have arisen over the fact that some solutions were in acid and some in neutral alcohol or acetone.

A similar pigment was reported in another echiuroid, *Hamingia arctica,* but the literature is rather scanty and vague here.

G. ARTHROPODA

1. *Crustacea*

Bradley (92) found biliverdin in the digestive gland of the crayfish *Cambarus.* It is possible that the pigment of the so-called "green gland" in these animals is also biliverdin. Lederer (*50*) reported that he had made studies of the "roots" of the parasite *Peltogaster paguri*, which parasitizes crabs; he deduced from the solubility and the positive Gmelin reaction that the pigmentation was due to biliverdin.

2. Insecta

Fischer and Fink (*93*) extracted the feces of moth caterpillars (probably *Tineola bisselliella*) obtained from feathers, and found coproporphyrin and protoporphyrin, the former predominating. In another piece of work, they used moth caterpillar feces from brown wool, and this time found coproporphyrin only. Fischer and Hendschel (*94, 95, 96*) isolated a pigment which they called "phyllobombicine" from the larvae of the silk moth *Bombyx mori*. This pigment is a degradation product of chlorophyll, formed probably by the opening of the isocyclic ring of phylloerythrin. It is transformed into chlorin by alcoholic potash, into phylloporphyrin by hydrobromic acid, and into pheoporphyrin by reduction by hydriodic acid. Fischer and Hendschel also found the same pigment in the feces of the larvae of *Acherontia atropos*. Seybold and Egle (*97*) believe that phyllobombicin is only an artifact formed during isolation of the pigment, and stated that in fresh feces of *Acherontia* larvae, only chlorophylls a and b could be found. Phyllobombicin and phylloerythrin are degradation products of chlorophyll a. It appears that very little work has been done on the pyrrol pigments of insects.

H. MOLLUSCA

This is a very large and diverse phylum, embracing more examples of land, freshwater, and marine forms than any other. It is of great interest, therefore, that, as will be seen, the only actual porphyrin found in the Mollusca so far is uroporphyrin I.

Arion ater is the common black garden slug previously called *Arion empiricorum*, which was a synonym introduced by de Férussac, de Férussac, and Deshayes (*98*) to cover the numerous color and pattern varieties of *Arion ater*. MacMunn (*41*) extracted from this slug a pigment that he identified with hematoporphyrin. Dhéré and Baumeler (*99*) confirmed the presence of a porphyrin in the integument but did not specify which porphyrin. Kennedy (*100*) isolated uroporphyrin I from *Arion ater* integument and found that such is the amount present that isolation and crystallization could be done on one large specimen of the animal. The associated black melanin may be present as a protection against the effects of light upon the animal, since uroporphyrin is known to cause photosensitivity (*101, 102, 103*) and in those individuals which have little or no associated pigment, there is no uroporphyrin in the integument. It seems also that the red, brown, and orange pigments occurring in the integuments of the various colored forms of *Arion ater* are protective in this way since, as the color becomes paler, the amount of porphyrin decreases. Perhaps these red, brown, and orange pigments are stages in the formation of melanin, each of which is sufficient to protect the animal according to the amount of uroporphyrin present.

Specimens of the land snail *Cepaea nemoralis,* which had brown and yellow or brown and pink striped shells with gray integuments, had no uroporphyrin at all in either the shell or the soft parts.

The finding of uroporphyrin in the upper soft integument of *Duvaucelia plebia* (better known as *Tritonia*) and *Aplysia punctata* (*36*) is of considerable interest in view of the presence of this pigment in some mollusk shells (*104*).

In an excellent review on the pigmentation of molluskan shells, Comfort (*105*) describes his own work on their chemistry and distribution. Krukenberg (*106, 107*) and Schulz (*108*) reported the presence of linear pyrrolic pigments in the shells of some marine mollusks. Dhéré and Baumeler (*99*) published some rather vague results in this field; in a careful study later, Tixier (*109*) described the presence of glaucobilin and haliotiviolin in the shells of green *Turbo* and in *Haliotis cracherodii,* respectively.

Free uroporphyrin was isolated from the shells of species of *Pteria, Pinctada,* and *Trochus* by German workers, among them Hans Fischer and his pupils (*110, 111, 112*); they were followed by Waldenström (*113*) and Tixier (*114*). Traces of coproporphyrin (subsequently unconfirmed) were also reported, and of "conchoporphyrin," which has had five and sometimes seven carboxyl groups attributed to it. This status of conchoporphyrin has never been satisfactorily settled; it may in fact have been present in minute traces in some individuals but not in others. One may recall that the pentacarboxylic porphyrin reported in *Chaetopterus* by Kennedy and Vevers (*36*) was quite clearly and definitely demonstrated by chromatography, but the same workers have not encountered it since. Nicholas and Comfort (*104*) could not detect conchoporphyrin in *Pteria radiata* L. by partition chromatography or in a number of gastropod and pelecypod species possessing abundant uroporphyrin. They found Fischer's original material to contain both uroporphrin and coproporphyrin.

Comfort (*115, 116*) has shown that within this group the distribution of free porphyrins follows the accepted anatomical classification of the Mollusca. They occur widely in the Archaeogastropoda, not in *Pleurotomaria, Patella,* or *Haliotis,* and are replaced in the Turbinidae by the open-ring pyrroles. Free porphyrins occur in some of the Lamellariacea, in several Cypraea, in *Marginella ornata,* in several tectibranchs (which Comfort does not name), in *Umbraculum,* in several loricates, scaphopods, and bivalve Aomiidae, and in some isolated Veneridae. The main genera in which Comfort (*116*) found porphyrins are listed in Table III.

Comfort mentions that the pattern of distribution in an individual species may or may not coincide with the visible pigment, being in some forms generalized and in others confined to a single locus. Shell porphyrins are very stable, as shown by the fact that porphyrins can be detected in post-Pleistocene and Upper Eocene fossil shells.

I. Echinodermata

Kennedy and Vevers (*117*) confirmed the presence of a porphyrin, reported by MacMunn (*41*), in the integument of the starfish *Asterias rubens,* and showed that it was protoporphyrin. A yield of 33.6 mg. of protoporphyrin dimethyl ester was obtained from 548.5 gm. of *Asterias* integument. Following this work, and the investigation of porphyrins in mollusk shells by Nicholas and Comfort (*104*), it was naturally of interest to examine the distribution of porphyrin pigments in other echinoderms.

The presence of free chlorocruoroporphyrin in *Luidia ciliaris* and also in *Astropecten irregularis* is of great interest, since this porphyrin has hitherto only been found to occur naturally in the form of its heme as chlorocruorin, the blood pigment of sabellid worms (*118*). Lemberg and Legge (*5*) have suggested that "since this pigment is found only in a small group of worms which live in the same type of environment as do others containing erythrocruorin with protohaem IX as prosthetic group, the peculiarity does not appear to be of adaptive importance, and may be an evolutionary relic."

Among the three species of echinoderms shown to contain porphyrins, *Asteria rubens* has only protoporphyrin (*117*) bearing two vinyl groups, while *Luidia ciliaris* and *Astropecten irregularis* have both chlorocruoroporphyrin, which has one vinyl and one formyl group, and also protoporphyrin. Warburg (*119*) considered that the presence of a carbonyl (=CO) group in a side chain, where other species elaborate a vinyl group, is a primitive characteristic. The occurrence of chlorocruoroporphyrin in *Luidia* and *Astropecten,* both phanerozonian asteroids, may therefore be regarded as an additional argument for classifying the Phanerozonia as less specialized than the Forcipulata exemplified by *Asterias rubens* (*120*). This consideration apart, it would appear that the distribution of integumentary porphyrins in starfishes is random not only in relation to their taxonomic position but also in relation to their ecology and mode of life. Thus the presence of protoporphyrin in

A. rubens and its absence in *Marthasterias glacialis* is surprising, for not only are these two starfishes classified in the same family (Asteriidae), but their larvae are almost identical in form and scarcely distinguishable (*121*) and the adults feed in the same way on the same type of food. In areas where their geographical ranges overlap, as they do off Plymouth, England, these two species may, in fact, be said to occupy the same ecological niche.

J. TUNICATA

According to Webb (*122*) the vanadium-containing chromogen of tunicates is not a porphyrin complex but may be related to the linear pyrrole pigments.

IV. Origin and Function of the Porphyrins in Invertebrates

The origin and function of the porphyrins in the invertebrates presents one of the most difficult, and therefore stimulating, problems of biochemistry. This question has engaged the attention of many workers for a very long time. Verne (*123*) in his "Couleurs et Pigments des Êtres Vivants" said: "Contrairement à ce que l' on pourrait croire, le fait d'être colorés ne confère pas aux pigments une propriété physiologique commune, un rôle biologique général. Il n'existe pas une fonction universelle attribuable au différents corps auxquels les êtres vivants sont redevables de leurs couleurs. La signification physiologique varie essentiellement suivant la constitution chimique de ces corps, et selon leur situation dans l'organisme."

Verne divided the pigments into three classes according to their roles:

1. Roles of pigments in metabolism
   a. Fixation of energy
   b. Respiration
   c. Nutrition
   d. Excretion
2. Roles of pigments in protection against external factors, and especially against the effects of light.
3. Roles of pigments in adaptation of the animals to their environment.

It is only possible to place the porphyrins in the first class, and in groups a, b, and d in particular; even then, porphyrins can play a part in respiration only when they are associated with a metal and a specific protein as in the hemoglobins and other respiratory pigments. The same is largely true in the case of energy fixation since the chlorophylls contain chelated magnesium and the alcohol phytol and cannot be said to be free porphyrins.

Porphyrins do not contribute very much to the color patterns of invertebrates; here they rather hide their lights under the bushel of the carotenoids and melanins. In some of the mollusks, however, like *Trochus* and *Calliostoma* and *Venus*, the shell bands are definitely due to a porphyrin, uroporphyrin I.

The significance of the relatively large amounts of porphyrins in the heart body of some polychetes has already been discussed. Kennedy and Dales (48) suggested that the heart body is a hematopoietic organ and produced evidence for this by the isolation of the two coproporphyrins, a tricarboxylic porphyrin and hematin (Fe-protoporphyrin) from these tissues.

Dales and Kennedy (57) showed that the biliverdin of *Nereis diversicolor* is derived from the hemoglobin of the blood. The other colors of this "diversely coloured" worm are due to carotenoids and pheophorbide a. Just why these colors should be present is not known; one can only suggest that here is some possible adaptation mechanism to different environments, e.g., different-colored muds and sands.

The origin of the porphyrins in the mollusks is a much more difficult problem. Some mollusks contain hemoglobin. In *Solen, Pectunculus,* and the clam *Arca* it is in corpuscles; in *Planorbis*, a small gastropod, it is in the plasma. The large clam *Tivela stultorum* (the Pismo clam occurring along the coast of Southern California) has hemoglobin in the mantle, gills, foot, and adductor muscle, and the same pigment has been identified in the brain of this mollusk, which is dark brown (124). The large mussel *Pinna fragilis* contains a brown pigment, pinnaglobin, which contains manganese (125). Comfort (105) in his review said that uroporphyrins in the higher forms have been regarded as by-products of the synthesis of the protoporphyrin of heme, but that in mollusks some other explanation is required for their presence. This is not necessarily the case, since there are other ways of looking at this point. It is striking that none of the mollusks so far examined, which produce hemoglobin or a similar pigment, have porphyrin in the shell or soft parts. It could be that the uroporphyrin seen in many of the mollusks—shells and integument (in the tectibranch and nudibranch forms)—is indeed the end product in what was intended far back in geological time to be heme synthesis. Now that hemocyanin has taken the place of heme for the respiratory pigment, probably for reasons of adaptive efficiency, the rudimentary mechanism stops at uroporphyrin. The porphyrin, being redundant is stored in the shell or the integument; where the pigment would cause photosensitization, melanins or other protective pigments have been developed to screen the animal. As Comfort says in connection with *Enigmonia,* an animal which contains a great deal of porphyrin, it is possible that there is a retention in phylogeny of the power of porphyrin synthesis by forms which can no longer dispose of it metabolically—a condition analogous to uric acid formation in the human subject.

According to Comfort (*105*), the general picture emerging from his and other workers' experiments on shell pigments is one "in which the porphyrins and atypical pyrroles of the primitive marine forms give place first to bile pigments, and later in phylogeny to chromoproteins of increasing complexity, bound to the conchiolin of the shell by a process of tanning. In no case does the primitive pattern of pigment metabolism succeed in crossing the sea-land barrier." It is interesting that Kennedy and Vevers (*36*) found that the only mollusks which have been definitely shown to contain a porphyrin in their soft parts are either species without shells (*Duvaucelia* and *Arion*) or species with uncalcified shells (*Aplysia*), whereas uroporphyrin, with traces of coproporphyrin, occurs in several of the shells of shell-bearing species. This suggests that in mollusks the porphyrin is normally laid down in the shell (an integumentary product) or, failing that, in the uncalcified integument. The former would be in keeping with the deposition of uroporphyrin I in the bones and teeth in congenital porphyria, and in the bones of the Pennsylvania fox squirrel *Sciurus niger,* to be discussed later. Turner (*126*) connected the formation of the uroporphyrin I with the megaloblasts of the bone marrow, and postulated that in *Sciurus* there exists a unique persistence into the adult span of a fetal method of hemoglobin synthesis. Certainly an association of porphyrin with calcified structures has frequently been recognized and commented upon.

In mollusks, if free porphyrin is present it is uroporphyrin I (*36, 127*). In those mollusks which have a shell, the porphyrin is laid down in the shell, very often in a definite pattern, and in those mollusks which are without shells or have very reduced shells, such as the tectibranchs and land slugs, if uroporphyrin I is present, it occurs in the integument. It is significant that it is the black variety of the slug *Arion ater* in which the greatest amount of uroporphyrin I occurs (*127*), the amount of porphyrin being closely parallel to the amount of melanin in the integument, so that in the very pale gray specimens, no uroporphyrin I is detectable. *Sciurus niger* has black hair, so that in these two widely differing animals an additional pigment is present, namely melanin, which protects these animals from the photosensitizing effects of the porphyrin. *Aplysia* and *Akera,* which are more darkly colored, have more uroporphyrin I than *Duvaucelia,* which has a bright orange pigment. A greater concentration of coproporphyrin III occurs in the body wall of the dark-colored *Arenicola* and *Amphitrite* than in the lighter, pink specimens. Also the more darkly pigmented *Asterias* contained more protoporphyrin IX than the paler animals (*36*) although protoporphyrin is not noteworthy for its photosensitizing action. Fischer and Zerweck (*101*) have shown in mammals that photosensitivity to ultraviolet light increases with the number of carboxylic groups in the porphyrin molecule, the action of proto-, deutero- and mesoporphyrin is very slight, but copro- and uroporphyrin have an intense photosensitizing action. The exception to this generalization is hematoporphyrin, which has not been detected in nature so far, but which has the greatest photosensitizing effect of all and which carries two carboxyl groups and two hydroxyethyl groups.

A further interesting point is provided by the sea cucumber *Holothuria forskali* Delle Chiaje, which has two pigments in the integument, a melanin and a yellow pigment with a very intense green fluorescence visible even in daylight. The animal is black all over, except for the ventral surface which is yellow, and if it is turned with the yellow ventrum to the light the animal immediately begins to turn back so that the yellow part is concealed. This suggests that the yellow pigment photosensitizes the animal and that the black melanin protects that portion of the integument which is normally exposed to light. The yellow pigment may act as an orientating mechanism, as suggested by Crozier (*128*). Grassé (*120*) wrote: "La surface dorsale tout entière est photoréceptive; quand on fait tomber en un point quelconque une lumière ponctiforme, la peau se déprime à l'endroit touché; presque toutes les espèces ont un phototropisme négatif et fuient la lumière d'une fenêtre; le passage d'une ombre devant un animal épanoui le fait se contracter; il y a sans doute un rapport entre cette sensibilité à la lumière et la présence dans les téguments d'un pigment jaunâtre à belle fluorescence verte." Preliminary experiments (unpublished) suggest that the pigment behaves in many ways like a flavin. The integument of *Cucumaria normani* Pace when exposed to the light darkens and becomes black.

In their work on the tectibranch *Akera bullata,* Kennedy and Vevers (*129*) found pheophorbide a and its copper derivative. It is curious that only pheophorbide a was detected, in view of the fact that *Akera*—like *Aplysia*—grazes on *Ulva* (*130*), which contains chlorophylls a and b. Dales and Kennedy (*57*) reported a similar result from *Nereis diversicolor.* Both chlorophylls a and b must be ingested by the animals, and it is very difficult to account for the absence of the b degradation component. The reason may lie, as far as *Akera* is concerned, in the fact that pheophorbide b is only sparingly soluble in ether, and if present originally in very small amounts, as is most likely, (the ratio of chlorophyll a to chlorophyll b is often as high as 3:1), the pigment may have been washed out in the process of removal of the acetic acid. Such an explanation is not entirely satisfactory, and the problem deserves further investigation.

The presence of a copper complex of pheophorbide a is of great interest. Some mullusks are known to concentrate copper from the sea, and of course the respiratory pigment hemocyanin, which is a copper polypeptide, occurs in the cephalopod and gastropod mollusks and in the arthropods. However, there is no doubt that the green nonfluorescent pigment isolated from *Akera* is a copper pheophorbide. That it is not an artifact, caused by the coordination of copper ions with pheophorbide during the course of extraction, is supported by the fact that free pheophorbide also occurs; the affinity of copper for porphyrin pigments is so great that if free copper were present in the animal, *all* the pheophorbide would have become changed to the metal complex.

Many of the chlorophyll derivatives found in invertebrates have their origin in the diet. This is true of other pigments, e.g., carotenoids and the dibromindigo pigments. Kennedy and Nicol (39) reported that the chaetopterin content of *Chaetopterus* varied considerably and reached its maximum in May. However, starvation did not deplete the animal of the pigment. Many animals become colored by the pigment of their food, e.g., *Spinther miniaceus,* a small polychete worm that feeds on the sponge *Hymeniacidon sanguineum,* and thus escape the notice of potential predators. This is not the case with the porphyrins but may well be true of the chlorophyll pigments.

The distribution of the porphyrins in the Echinodermata, as has already been mentioned, seems to be at random, closely related forms like *Asterias* having a lot of porphyrin and *Marthasterias* having none. This may not be so surprising in the light of other biochemical differences, e.g., the presence of a diguanidine arcaine in *Arca noae* but not in *Mytilus edulis* and the occurrence of urea in the tissues of elasmobranch, but not of teleost, fishes.

The porphyrins and bile pigments form part of the excreted material in some invertebrates, just as they do in the vertebrates. In some cases, the excretory material is voided in true feces, and in others in liquid form. In the sea slug *Aplysia* and in *Ianthina,* the biliviolins and bilirhodins are derived from the food, which contains phycocyanins and phycoerythrins, and these pigments are degraded and used by the animals in their protective "ink."

V. Occurrence of Porphyrins in Vertebrates

Since the ability to synthesize the tetrapyrrole nucleus appears to be almost a fundamental property of living matter, it is not surprising that free porphyrins are found in minute quantities in nearly all tissues of the higher organisms. The literature recording these occurrences is immense and no attempt will be made to survey it in detail. Attention will be drawn, rather, to certain peculiarities of distribution and to the possible biological and biochemical significance of porphyrins in these situations.

We are today much better able to speculate upon the biological role of different porphyrins since we know that they represent stages in the synthetic pathway toward heme and are not, as had been previously supposed, products of heme or hemoglobin destruction (except in certain exceptional circumstances). Lemberg (133) has even suggested that the reason for the sporadic and quantitatively scanty occurrence of free porphyrins in living matter may be the fact that protoheme formation is biochemically so efficient. Before the steps of heme synthesis had been revealed, it was generally assumed, following Hans Fischer, that coproporphyrin was derived from protoporphyrin by a process of carboxylation, and uroporphyrin from coproporphyrin in the same way. This led to hypotheses, such as that of the detoxication of porphyrins for urinary elimination, for which no experimental support could be found and which retarded true biochemical progress. The concept of the dualism of the porphyrins, introduced by Fischer as a result of his chemical work, has on the contrary proved fruitful. Fischer realized that position isomerism provided for the possible existence of four different uroporphyrins, four different coproporphyrins, and no less than fifteen different protoporphyrins and mesoporphyrins. His degradative and synthetic studies revealed, however, that only two of the four possible coproporphyrins occurred in nature, isomers I and III, respectively, and natural protoporphyrin was always protoporphyrin IX, stemming from coproporphyrin III. The uroporphyrin which he first isolated from pathological urine was uroporphyrin I, and at a later date uroporphyrin III was also discovered in nature. His concept of dualism asserted that all porphyrins in nature were members of either the I or III isomeric series (4).

As already pointed out, the protoporphyrin or heme of hemoglobin, myoglobin, cytochrome b, catalase, peroxidase, and in fact all the naturally occurring hemoproteins, is always the same, i.e., isomer number IX derived from the III series. Coproporphyrin I occurred in normal urine and feces, together with smaller quantities of coproporphyrin III, but no physiological importance or function could be found for the I-series porphyrins, which were therefore regarded as unnatural and useless isomers. This conception that the I-series porphyrins were by-products arising during the biosynthesis of the III-series porphyrins was formulated simultaneously by Rimington (*134*) and by Dobriner, Localio, and Strain (*135*); it may be depicted as shown in Scheme I.

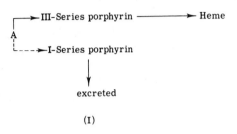

(I)

In congenital porphyria, there is an enzymatic defect manifesting itself as a failure to direct the change of porphobilinogen into uroporphyrinogen III (*136*). Instead, uroporphyrinogen I is produced, and the excretion of uroporphyrin I and coproporphyrin I is greatly increased as a consequence. Protoporphyrin I is not formed since the enzyme directing the step coproporphyrinogen → protoporphyrin is specific for the III-series isomer.

A. PORPHYRINS IN BONY STRUCTURES

The frequent occurrence of uroporphyrin I and coproporphyrin I in calcified structures such as shells is almost certainly due to the ready adsorption of these by-products of heme synthesis by calcium phosphate under certain conditions (*137*). They are deposited, therefore, in any structure undergoing calcification where these conditions obtain, namely an excess of calcium rather than of phosphate ions. The situation is exactly analogous with the adsorption of fluorescein by silver chloride; so long as chloride ions remain they are adsorbed in preference to the fluorescein, but the moment the silver ion is in excess, the dye disappears from the solution onto the precipitate. Injected uroporphyrin is strongly adsorbed by calcifying bone or callous tissue, and the inference seems permissible that the ultimate step in such calcification takes place in an excess of calcium, and not of phosphate, ions.

The bones of young animals exhibit a sharp zone of red fluorescence due to uroporphyrin at the region of active calcification (*138*), and it is a well-known fact that the bones of humans or animals suffering from congenital porphyria are colored a deep brown by the uroporphyrin deposited in them. The teeth also show brown to red discoloration, but cartilage remains unpigmented. Paul, Engström, and Engfeldt (139) have also demonstrated deposition of porphyrin in the bones of cases of porphyria cutanea tarda in which free porphyrin is present in the circulating plasma. Rodents are remarkable for the large amount of porphyrins they produce naturally. In some species, as for example *Sciurus niger* the American fox squirrel, this is so marked that the animals have been described as suffering from a "physiological porphyria" (140). The bones and teeth fluoresce brightly owing to the uroporphyrin they contain, and urinary and fecal porphyrin content is high. Ordinary squirrels', rabbits', and rats' bones and teeth may show faint to marked red fluorescence. Occasionally porphyrin fluorescence may be seen when the teeth of human patients are examined by ultraviolet light in a dark room, but this may be due merely to deposits of bacterial slime or to decay (141). Carrié (142) has described the production of porphyrins by various organisms normally inhabiting the human skin and mouth.

B. PORPHYRINS IN BLOOD AND BONE MARROW

Blood contains small quantities of porphyrin, by far the greater proportion of which is within the cells. Coproporphyrin was, however, detected in normal serum by Fischer and Zerweck (143), and its presence was confirmed by Hijmans van den Bergh and Grotepass (144). Since coproporphyrin is eliminated in the urine, it is not surprising that it should be found in transit in the blood plasma. Hijmans van den Bergh and Hyman (145) demonstrated the presence of protoporphyrin in normal red cells where, according to Watson and Clarke (146), it is present mainly, but not exclusively, in the reticulocytes and may be responsible for their typical staining by combining with the dye brilliant cresyl blue to form an insoluble precipitate (146).

The protoporphyrin content of blood which is normally around 20 μg. per 100 ml. (147) is subject to considerable alteration in pathological conditions. It is raised, for example, in fever, hepatic disease, lead poisoning, nutritional iron deficiency, and pernicious anemia, especially during the reticulocyte crises following therapy. In addition to protoporphyrin, small quantities of coproporphyrin are also present in normal red cells (148) and the erythrocyte coproporphyrin appears to afford a more satisfactory index of erythropoietic activity than does the erythrocyte protoporphyrin level (148).

In conditions such as congenital porphyria, large increases are observed in coproporphyrin content of both erythrocytes and plasma and in cellular protoporphyrin. The plasma also contains uroporphyrin in considerable quantity.

The porphyrins are now well recognized as intermediates in the biosynthesis of hemoglobin, and it is therefore not surprising to detect their presence in erythropoietic bone marrow. Borst and Königsdörffer (149) identified uroporphyrin and coproporphyrin in fetal bone marrow by ultraviolet fluorescence microspectroscopy and suggested that the bone marrow in congenital porphyria showed an atavism, a return to this primitive state. The work of Salomon, Richmond, and Altman (150) using radioisotopes provided evidence for the presence of uroporphyrin III in normal adult rabbit marrow, and since then numerous investigations have confirmed the participation of the series III porphyrins, or their products of hydrogenation, the corresponding porphyrinogens, in normal hemopoiesis.

C. PORPHYRINS IN LIVER AND BILE

The presence of porphyrins in bile has been known for a long time; Hijmans van den Bergh et al. (151) give the normal concentration as 40–60 μg. per 100 ml. Since in man the volume of bile secreted during 24 hours is of the order of 700–1000 ml., this means a daily influx into the intestine of some 280–600 μg., a figure agreeing with the findings of Brugsch (152). A considerable quantity of this porphyrin undergoes an enterohepatic circulation so the quantity of endogenous porphyrin eliminated daily in the feces is considerably less. Owing to the enterohepatic circulation, bile will also contain porphyrin derived from the intestine. Thus breakdown products of chlorophyll such as pheophytins and pheophorbides are usually present in small quantities, and in the case of ruminant herbivores such as the sheep, phylloerythrin (Fig. 9) may be present in very large quantities in bile and feces. It is formed from chlorophyll by microbial action mainly in the rumen. Since phylloerythrin is highly photosensitizing, any interruption of bile flow leading to jaundice can cause severe photosensitization in these animals.

Liver tissue possesses the enzymes capable of synthesizing porphyrins from simple materials such as glycine and succinate, and it is possible that even in adult life these contribute to the total of porphyrins excreted. Certainly, on the other hand, there is a quite rapid turnover of hemoproteins, such as catalase in the liver, and one may expect to find porphyrin by-products of these syntheses. Direct extraction of fresh liver tissue yields protoporphyrin IX together with smaller quantities of other porphyrins.

A remarkable case has been put on record (153) of a hepatic tumor, a liver cell adenoma, which apparently produced very large quantities of porphyrins, mainly protoporphyrin and coproporphyrin. The patient was a woman of 80 with raised porphyrin excretion and symptoms of cutaneous porphyria. After removal of the tumor, her symptoms disappeared and her porphyrin excretion returned to normal; the inference seemed justifiable that the tumor cells had been displaying an exaggeration of the intrinsic capacity of liver cells to synthesize porphyrin.

D. PORPHYRINS IN THE EXCRETA

1. Feces

The feces contain porphyrins of both endogenous and exogenous origin. The former enter the gut in the bile and are represented mainly by protoporphyrin and coproporphyrin. These same two porphyrins may be formed as exogenous products by gut microorganisms either acting upon heme-containing constituents of the food or synthesizing them from simple materials. In any case, protoporphyrin, of whatever origin, is exposed to bacterial transformation and is almost certainly the source of the mesoporphyrin and deuteroporphyrin, which have been detected in feces (154).

A large amount of research has been done upon the production of porphyrins during the putrefaction of heme-containing materials (155) from which it is abundantly evident that, even during sterile autolysis of meat, porphyrins may arise but that the synergistic action of various bacteria is probably largely responsible for the porphyrin formation in the gut. This would appear to occur in the small intestine and upper segments of the colon. No porphyrin formation occurs normally in the stomach or during in vitro action of digestive juices (156) and the introduction of food rich in hematin into the stomach of a patient with pyloric stenosis did not result in porphyrins being produced (157). Similarly Carrié (142) emphasized that the lower segment of the colon and rectum could not be sites of porphyrin formation since hemorrhages in these situations were not accompanied by increase in deuteroporphyrin excretion. Boas (158) claims that the fecal deuteroporphyrin test for occult internal hemorrhage in a subject on a heme-free diet is superior to and more accurate than the benzidine reaction and, from what has been said above, some measure of localization of the lesion is clearly possible.

That porphyrin is eliminated via the bile and feces even under sterile conditions is proved by the finding of quite large quantities of porphyrin in meconium in various species (159). This is mainly coproporphyrin I, but porphyrins with seven, six, or five carboxyl groups per molecule are also present in smaller quantities (160). From calf meconium, Nicholas and Rimington (160) isolated a pentacarboxylic porphyrin with crystalline methyl ester, m.p. 231–232°. Uroporphyrin rarely occurs in feces but is occasionally to be found in severe cases of porphyria cutanea tarda. The occurrence of porphyrins in coprolites from remote geological ages has already been mentioned.

The range of porphyrin concentration in normal human feces is: coproporphyrin 0–20 and protoporphyrin 0–30 μg. per gram dry weight. This corresponds to about 150–400 μg. total porphyrin per 24 hours. It is greatly raised in congenital porphyria, in porphyria cutanea tarda, in sprue, and in some other conditions. Any increase in acute intermittent porphyria is relatively slight.

2. Urine

Saillet (*161*) is generally credited with the first observation of porphyrin in normal urine. He called the pigment "urospectrine" and noted that a considerable proportion of the total was excreted in the form of a colorless precursor, an observation which lay neglected for many years. It is now realized that over 95%, or possibly all, of the urinary coproporphyrin is actually excreted by the kidney in the form of coproporphyrinogen which oxidizes spontaneously into porphyrin. Estimates of the quantity of total porphyrin in normal urine have varied very widely on account of neglect of the presence of porphyrinogen and also on account of the relatively crude and inaccurate methods which have been available in the past for quantitative determination. The most reliable figures found by modern techniques are for human males 166 ± 45 μg. and for females 134 ± 42 μg. of total coproporphyrin per day (*162*). It must be pointed out, however, that the total porphyrin elimination is proportional to body weight (*163*) and also that alteration in diet, particularly the ingestion of only quite moderate amounts of alcohol, can cause relatively large fluctuations (*164*). In normal urine, small quantities of uroporphyrin are definitely present (*165*) and also porphyrins containing seven, six, or five carboxyl groups per molecule. The presence of protoporphyrin in normal urine was reported by Boas (*166*), but this has not been confirmed by other workers (*167*).

As mentioned above, it is probable that all the urinary coproporphyrin is excreted in the reduced form of coproporphyrinogen. In agreement with this conclusion is the observation that intravenous injection of coproporphyrin into a *normal* animal causes no rise in urinary porphyrin, although injection into an animal with its liver injured by carbon tetrachloride is followed by elimination of a proportion of the pigment via the kidney. Liver function is thus an important factor in determining the route of coproporphyrin excretion, and it may be recalled that Nesbitt and Snell (*168*) actually claimed that there was a good correlation between the urinary:fecal coproporphyrin ratio and the extent of injury of the parenchymatous hepatic cells in various conditions. Now, since it would appear that only porphyrinogen passes through the kidney and that renal tissue is incapable of reducing porphyrin brought to it in the blood stream to the porphyrinogen level (failure of intravenously injected coproporphyrin to raise urinary porphyrin in the normal animal), one must conclude that the route of coproporphyrin elimination is governed by the ratio between porphyrin and porphyrinogen established in the liver and that under normal circumstances this is predominantly in favor of porphyrin. It may be mentioned at this point that one of us (C. R.) together with collaborators has recently shown (169) that if freshly prepared coproporphyrinogen III is injected intravenously into the normal rabbit, a considerable proportion of the dose is excreted in the urine, injected coproporphyrin III being entirely eliminated in the feces.

One may ask by what mechanism does disturbance of hepatic function result in increased porphyrinogen, and a clue may be available in the known action of alcohol, a very effective porphyrinurogenic agent, in raising the level of hepatic DPNH at the expense of DPN (diphosphopyridine nucleotide) (170). The hypothesis tentatively sketched below (II) is at present under experimental investigation. In porphyria

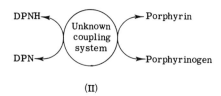

(II)

cutanea tarda one observes a continuously raised level of porphyrinogenesis, but during periods of remission of the clinical symptoms such as photosensitization, the bulk or all of this excess is excreted via the bile and feces. It is only during periods of clinical exacerbation that the content of porphyrin in the urine rises at the expense of that of the feces, and during such times jaundice and urobilinogenuria are common (171). It would appear from what has been said above that these periods of hepatic dysfunction are accompanied by a change in the DPN:DPNH and porphyrin:porphyrinogen balance in the liver. In lead poisoning also, one might infer that the metal has profoundly affected these ratios, although the possibility of lead interfering at other stages in the biosynthetic pathway to heme is not by any means excluded thereby.

There has been much discussion concerning the ratio of the coproporphyrin isomers I and III in normal urine. Analytical methods are not very satisfactory. Grotepass (172) considered they were present in approximately equal amounts; most observers, however, have considered isomer I to be much in excess. Watson and collaborators (173) have paid particular attention to this problem and found a mean percentage for the series III isomers for a sample of the normal population in Minneapolis of 25%. He noted, however, one most puzzling fact, namely that a group of Divinity students selected for their temperate habits and studied in Chicago in 1946 consistently excreted a much higher proportion of coproporphyrin III (58–82%). Another group of similar students studied in 1948 were now found to excrete 12–44% of the series III isomer. Some possible change in the water supply was the only reasonable suggestion that could be put forward in explanation of this very extraordinary finding.

That the urinary coproporphyrin was a by-product of heme or porphyrin synthesis and not derived from degradation of hemoglobin was proved in isotopic labeling experiments by Grinstein, Kamen, Wikoff, and Moore (174). Dobriner and Rhoads (175) had already demonstrated a rise in urinary coproporphyrin excretion during times of enhanced erythropoiesis. It may be mentioned that the urinary clearance rate of coproporphyrin has been shown to be equal to that of creatinine (176). The recent finding that myocardial infarction is followed by coproporphyrinuria (177) has attracted much interest.

E. PORPHYRINS IN THE FETAL FLUIDS

Coproporphyrin occurs in amniotic fluid and is said to be present also in the serum of embryos and of newborn babies. Fikentscher (178), who made these observations, could not detect it in maternal serum and so concluded that coproporphyrin cannot pass the placental barrier. Kench et al. (179) have recorded a case, however, of a woman with congenital porphyria bearing a normal child. The infant excreted an excess of porphyrin during only the first few days of life, a fact that suggests that maternal porphyrin had entered its circulation and was being progressively eliminated. The porphyrin:porphyrinogen ratio may be of importance in this connection as it is in renal excretion. Embryonated hen's eggs develop quite considerable quantities of coproporphyrin during incubation (180); the pigment is almost certainly a by-product of the active heme synthesis which is there proceeding.

F. PORPHYRINS IN THE NERVOUS SYSTEM

Very considerable interest has been aroused by Klüver's (181) demonstration of coproporphyrin as a regular, though minor, constituent of certain regions of the nervous system. The distribution has also been investigated by Solomon and Figge (182) and is summarized in Table IV.

TABLE IV

DISTRIBUTION OF PORPHYRIN IN THE CENTRAL NERVOUS SYSTEM OF THE PIG[a,b]

Cerebrum	Midbrain	Medulla oblongata	Cerebellum	Spinal Cord
3.05 ± 0.1	4.23 ± 0.27	.4.85 ± 0.31	3.10 ± 0	3.16 ± 0.22

[a] From Solomon and Figge (182).

[b] Values are micrograms of coproporphyrin III per 100 gm. tissue.

The function of this porphyrin in nervous structures is not understood; it is present only in warm-blooded animals. One attractive speculation is that the occurrence of porphyrin in the optic tracts and pituitary gland may play some part in the connection between photoperiodicity and reproductive functions in birds. As is well known, gonadotropins are secreted by the pituitary gland, and this organ appears to be stimulated in birds by the duration and intensity of light to which the eyes are exposed.

Poliomyelitis is a disease that affects the nervous system, and Watson and collaborators (183) have reported increased urinary porphyrin excretion in this and in some other nervous diseases.

G. PORPHYRINS IN SPECIALIZED TISSUES AND MISCELLANEOUS STRUCTURES

1. Harderian Gland

While studying the fluorescence of regions of ossification in young rats, Derrien and Turchini (184) established the presence of an intense red fluorescence in Harder's gland in rodents. This retrobulbar gland is associated with the lachrymatory apparatus and has been carefully described by Grafflin (185). It appears to possess all the enzymatic requirements for synthesis of protoporphyrin from simple materials (186), and it is its secretion, rich in protoporphyrin, which is normally swallowed by the rat and imparts such a high protoporphyrin content to the feces in this species. The real function of the porphyrin-rich secretion is unknown, but it is suggested that it acts as a lubricant to the third eyelid (187). A certain parallelism has been observed between the porphyrin content of the gland and the appearance of mammary carcinoma in mice (188).

In pantothenic acid deficiency in rats, the Harderian secretion, rich in protoporphyrin, becomes very viscous and encrusts the nasolabial region, causing the appearance popularly called "bloody whiskers." Raised environmental temperature will also induce this condition, according to Collins (189), without, however, in the rat increasing the actual porphyrin content of the gland. In the mouse gland, Collins (189) found the porphyrin content to be normally much lower but to be raised by a higher environmental temperature. Administration to these animals of eserine followed by acetylcholine produced definite chromo-dacryorrhea ("bloody whiskers"). One of us (G. Y. K.) has isolated a tricarboxylic porphyrin ester, m.p. 144° uncorrected, from Harderian glands of rats. The glands appear to be able to form porphyrin from porphobilinogen or δ-aminolevulic acid. This is under investigation at present.

2. Oviduct and Eggshells

As early as 1883, Krukenberg (190) observed that the shells of hen's eggs showed a red fluorescence in ultraviolet light. This was found to be due to porphyrin, by Derrien (191) in 1924, and the observation was extended to other species (192) such as the sea gull, plover, swan, Guinea fowl, and also the ostrich. Porphyrin fluorescence was observed even in the fossilized shells of eggs dating from the Tertiary epoch. The pigment was identified as protoporphyrin by Königsdörffer (193) and Gouzon (194), the latter finding it also in the egg yolk. Finally Derrien and Turchini (195) were able to prove the presence of protoporphyrin in the region of the oviduct where the eggshell is formed. They put forward the hypothesis that the pigment is functionally related to the calcification process, but it has been pointed out in Section V, A that this association may be merely a result of physicochemical properties and circumstances. Little is known about the way in which the porphyrin is deposited in the eggshell. Giersberg (196) considered it to be conveyed in wandering cells which penetrate the uterine epithelium in the final stages of calcification of the shell. Hijmans van den Bergh and Grotepass (197) believe that the uterine glands excrete the porphyrin together with calcium albuminate. The occurrence of an excessive deposition of protoporphyrin and iron-containing material on the surface of a duck's egg has been described by Rimington (198), the circumstances suggesting that the porphyrin could have been derived from extravasated blood. Hutt and Sumner (199) record a somewhat similar occurrence in a hen's egg, but in this instance iron was present only in traces.

An interesting observation made recently by Polin (200) would seem to call for further examination. He found that Nicarbazin (4,4'-dinitrocarbanilide) reduced the deposition of porphyrin in brown egg-shells although it had no demonstrable effect upon the *in vitro* bio-synthesis of porphyrin from δ-aminolevulic acid (ALA) by preparations from red blood cells, vagina, uterus, follicular membrane, or small intestine of hens. The possibility would seem to be that it interferes with porphyrin synthesis at a stage prior to ALA production, no doubt some reaction of the tricarboxylic acid cycle.

3. *Feathers and Feather Follicles*

The most remarkable and well-known occurrence of a porphyrin derivative in birds' feathers is that of turacin in the red portions of the flight feathers of many touracos, or plantain-eater (Musophagidae, N. O. Scansores), birds inhabiting Central Africa and adjacent regions. The pigment was first described in 1869 by Church (*201*), who correctly deduced that it contained copper. It was shown to be the copper com-plex of a uroporphyrin by Fischer and Hilger (*202*), who concluded that it was a series I isomer, only uroporphyrin I being known at that time. Final identification as copper uroporphyrin III was reported by Rimington (*203*) in 1939, and this has been confirmed several times since (*204*). The anatomical distribution of turacin in the feather structure has been investigated in detail by Auber (*205*) and Moreau (*206*). The pigment is confined to cortical strata of the barb and to barbules, the medulla being devoid of turacin.

Why these birds, belonging to the genera *Turacus, Musophaga, Gallirex, Ruwenzorornis*, should lay down this pigment in such a precise location is not known; there seems to be nothing otherwise unusual about their porphyrin metabolism. Turacin is easily soluble in slightly alkaline water and it has been observed that if the birds are kept in captivity in such a way that their feces contaminate water in which they can bathe, the red color is readily washed out of their feathers. On placing them in aviaries where such contamination can no longer occur, the red color gradually returns (*207*). It must be resynthesized and transported to the proper site. Turacin is quite nontoxic (*208*), its copper being extremely firmly coordinated with the porphyrin.

Porphyrin fluorescence has been described as present in the spines of the feathers of a young pigeon and the quills of a hedgehog (*209*). Völker (*210*) has drawn attention to the relatively intense porphyrin fluorescence in the downy feathers of the bustards (Otides), an ob-servation confirmed by With (*211*), and he also detected porphyrin fluorescence in the feathers of about one-quarter of all natural orders of Aves.

4. Porphyrins in Ambergris

The porphyrins of ambergris were studied by Lederer and Tixier (212), who found the relatively large quantities of 30 μg./gm. of protoporphyrin and 10 μg./gm. of mesoporphyrin. The total porphyrin is of the same order as is found in human feces.

VI. Conclusion

In the above discussion of the occurrence of porphyrin in various situations in the animal body we have made no attempt at completeness. Porphyrin biosynthesis is a well-nigh universal property of cells and only some of the more striking and more interesting localizations have been discussed.

As we have pointed out, porphyrins can be regarded as accidentally colored stages in the metabolism of organic material. But nature has in some instances made use of them for decorative purposes, and investigators have over and over again been attracted by them as pigments. What a drab world it would be without color! But porphyrins have an importance far greater than their ornamental qualities. They have been utilized by the living cell to provide the most indispensable catalysts of all but the very lowliest forms of living matter. Life without the porphyrins could be but a poor shadow of the great and wonderful thing it has become. Their study is therefore a task of prime importance to the biologist. Chemical knowledge is a prerequisite requirement to biochemical study, but the labors of Hans Fischer furnished in his lifetime an imposing edifice of porphyrin chemistry, which has been enlarged but little in the last twenty years. The biochemistry of the porphyrins, on the other hand, has for some strange reason lagged sadly behindhand. Only during the last decade has some understanding of their biosynthesis and metabolism been achieved, and as our pages have tried to show, there still awaits a vast and fascinating field for exploration in comparative porphyrin biochemistry.

References

1. M. Newbigin, "Colour in Nature." John Murray, London, 1898.
2. J. Verne, "Les Pigments dans l'Organisme animal." Gaston Doin, Paris, 1926.
3. S. Granick, Ann. Rev. Plant Physiol. 2, 115 (1951).
4. H. Fischer and H. Orth, "Chemie des Pyrrols." Akad. Verlagsges., Leipzig, 1937.
5. R. Lemberg and J. W. Legge, "Haematin Compounds and Bile Pigments." Interscience, New York, 1949.
6. S. F. MacDonald and R. J. Stedman, J. Am. Chem. Soc. 75, 3040 (1953); Can. J. Chem. 32, 896 (1954); S. F. MacDonald and K. H. Michl, ibid. 34, 1768 (1956); S. F. MacDonald and A. H. Jackson, ibid. 35, 715 (1957).

7. C. Rimington, S. F. Mason, and O. Kennard, *Spectrochim. Acta* **12**, 65 (1958).
8. J. E. Falk, *Brit. Med. Bull.* **10**, 211 (1954).
9. A. Treibs, *Angew. Chem.* **49**, 551, 682 (1936).
10. A. Church, *Phil. Trans. Roy. Soc.* **154**, 627 (1869); C. Rimington, *Proc. Roy. Soc.* **B127**, 106 (1939); R. E. H. Nicholas and C. Rimington, *Biochem. J.* **50**, 194 (1951); T. K. With, *Scand. J. Clin. Lab. Invest.* **9**, 398 (1957).
11. D. Mauzerall and S. Granick, *J. Biol. Chem.* **232**, 1141 (1958); D. S. Hoare and H. Heath, *Biochem. J.* **73**, 679 (1959).
12. S. Granick and H. Gilder, *J. Gen. Physiol.* **30**, 1 (1946).
13. R. K. Morton, *Revs. Pure and Appl. Chem.* (*Australia*) **8**, 161 (1958).
14. G. S. Wilson and A. A. Miles, "Topley and Wilson's Principles of Bacteriology and Immunity," 4th ed., pp. 719, 998, 1000. Arnold, London, 1955.
15. H. Gilder, cited from S. Granick and H. Gilder, *Advances in Enzymol.* **7**, 305 (1947).
16. H. Fischer and C. von Seemann, *Z. physiol. Chem.* **242**, 133 (1936); H. Fischer and G. Wecker, *ibid.* **272**, 1 (1941); R. Lemberg and J. Parker, *Australian J. Exptl. Biol. Med. Sci.* **30**, 163 (1952).
17. H. M. Fox and H. G. Vevers, "The Nature of Animal Pigments." Sidgwick & Jackson, London, 1960.
18. S. Granick, *Ann. Rev. Plant Physiol.* **2**, 115 (1951); J. R. Della Rosa, K. I. Altman, and K. Salomon, *J. Biol. Chem.* **202**, 771 (1953).
18a. S. Granick, *in* "Chemical Pathways of Metabolism" (D. M. Greenberg, ed.), Vol. 2, p. 287. Academic Press, New York, 1954.
19. H. Fischer, R. Lambrecht, and H. Mittenzwei, *Z. physiol. Chem.* **253**, 1 (1938); J. R. Barnard and L. M. Jackman, *J. Chem. Soc.* p. 1172 (1956).
20. W. M. Manning and H. H. Strain, *J. Biol. Chem.* **151**, 1 (1943).
21. A. S. Holt and H. V. Morley, *Can. J. Chem.* **37**, 507 (1959).
22. R. Lemberg, "The Tetrapyrrole Pattern in Nature," Presidential address to Section N, *Rept. Australian New Zealand Assoc. Advance. Sci., 1954* p. 243 (1955).
23. J. I. Quin, C. Rimington, and G. S. Roets, *Onderstepoort J. Vet. Sci. Animal Ind.* **4**, 463 (1935).
24. L. Marchlewski, *Bull. soc. chim. biol.* **6**, 464 (1924).
25. C. Rimington, and J. I. Quin, *Onderstepoort J. Vet. Sci. Animal Ind.* **3**, 137 (1934); *Nature* **132**, 178 (1933).
26. N. T. Clare, "Photosensitization in Diseases of Domestic Animals." Commonwealth Agricultural Bureaux, Farnham Royal, Bucks, England, 1952.
27. H. Fischer and A. Hendschel, *Z. physiol. Chem.* **216**, 57 (1933); H. Fischer and G. Stadler, *ibid.* **239**, 167 (1936).
28. C. Rimington, *Revs. Pure Appl. Chem.* (*Australia*) **8**, 129 (1958).
29. E. G. Brown, *Nature* **182**, 313 (1958).
30. D. E. Metzler, M. Ikawa and E. E. Snell, *J. Am. Chem. Soc.* **76**, 648 (1954).
31. L. Bogorad, *J. Biol. Chem.* **233**, 501, 510 (1958).
32. J. Wittenberg, *Nature* **184**, 876 (1959).
33. E. Bullock, A. W. Johnson, E. Markham, and K. B. Shaw, *J. Chem. Soc.* p. 1430 (1958).
34. A. Goldberg, H. Ashenbrucker, G. E. Cartwright, and M. M. Wintrobe, *Blood*, **11**, 821 (1956); A. Goldberg, *Brit. J. Haematol.* **5**, 150 (1959); S. Schwartz, G. E. Cartwright, E. L. Smith, and M. M. Wintrobe, *Blood* **14**, 486 (1959); M. Grinstein, R. M. Bannerman, and C. V. Moore, *ibid.* p. 476 (1959).

35. L. Eriksen, "Biosyntesen av Porfyriner og Hemoglobin." Akad. Trykningssentral, Oslo, 1955; *Exptl. Cell. Research* **13**, 624 (1957); M. Rabinovitz and M. E. Olson, *Nature* **181**, 1665 (1958); S. Minakami, *J. Biochem.* (*Tokyo*) **45**, 833 (1958); Y. Kagawa, S. Minakami, and Y. Yoneyama, *ibid.* **46**, 771 (1959); S. Minakami, Y. Yoneyama, and H. Yoshikawa, *Biochim. et Biophys. Acta* **28**, 447 (1958); G. Nishida and R. F. Labbe, *ibid.* **31**, 519 (1959); R. F. Labbe, *ibid.* p. 589; M. Rabinovitz and H. McGrath, *J. Biol. Chem.* **234**, 2091 (1959); M. Faber and I. Falbe-Hansen, *Nature* **184**, 1043 (1959); P. Clark and R. J. Walsh, *ibid.* p. 1730.

36. G. Y. Kennedy and H. G. Vevers, *Nature* **171**, 81 (1953).

37. G. Y. Kennedy and H. G. Vevers, *J. Marine Biol. Assoc. United Kingdom* **33**, 663 (1954).

38. G. Y. Kennedy, *J. Marine Biol. Assoc. United Kingdom* **38**, 27 (1959).

39. G. Y. Kennedy and J. A. C. Nicol, *Proc. Roy. Soc.* **B150**, 509 (1959).

39a. G. Y. Kennedy and H. G. Vevers, *J. Marine Biol. Assoc. United Kingdom* **32**, 235 (1953).

40. H. N. Moseley, *Quart. J. Microscop. Sci.* **17**, 1 (1877).

41. C. A. MacMunn, *J. Physiol.* **7**, 240 (1886).

42. C. A. MacMunn, *Quart. J. Microscop. Sci.* **43**, 337 (1900).

43. J. L. Thudichum, "Tenth Report of the Medical Officer to the Privy Council," Appendix, p. 228. London, 1868.

44. C. A. MacMunn, *Quart. J. Microscop. Sci.* **30**, 51 (1898).

45. C. A. MacMunn, *Phil. Trans. Roy. Soc.* **176**, 661 (1885).

46. J. Roche, *Bull. soc. chim. biol.* **18**, 825 (1936).

47. E. Krugelis-Macrae, *Biol. Bull.* **110**, 69 (1956).

48. G. Y. Kennedy and R. P. Dales, *J. Marine Biol. Assoc. United Kingdom* **37**, 15 (1958).

49. E. Derrien, *Compt. rend. acad. sci.* **184**, 480 (1927).

50. E. Lederer, *Biol. Revs. Cambridge Phil. Soc.* **19**, 121 (1944).

51. T. Rymer Jones, "The Aquarian Naturalist." van Voorst, London, 1858.

52. O. Bürger, "Die Nemertinen des Golfes von Neapel," Monogr. 22: Friedländer, Berlin.

53. O. F. Müller, "Von Würmen des süssen und salzigen Wassers." Heinlok and Faber, Copenhagen, 1771.

54. M. Mendthal, *Schr. Phys.-Ökon. Ges. Königsberg* **30**, 27 (1889).

55. W. L. McIntosh, "A Monograph of the British Marine Annelids," Vol. 2, Part 2, p. 233. The Ray Society, London, 1910.

56. J. A. Thomas, *Bull. soc. zool. France* **55**, 97 (1930).

57. R. P. Dales and G. Y. Kennedy, *J. Marine Biol. Assoc. United Kingdom* **33**, 699 (1954).

58. C. Bloch-Raphaël, *Ann. inst. océanogr. Monaco* **19**, 1 (1939).

59. E. Meyer, *Mitt. zool. Sta. Neapel.* **7**, 592 (1887).

60. L. J. Picton, *Quart. J. Microscop. Sci.* **41**, 263 (1898).

61. M. Romieu, Thèse, Fac. Sci. Univ. Paris. Gaston Doin, Paris, 1923.

62. R. P. Dales, *J. Marine Biol. Assoc. United Kingdom* **36**, 91 (1957).

63. H. Eisig, "Die Capitelliden des Golfes von Neapel," Monogr. 16. Friedländer, Berlin, 1887.

64. E. R. Lankester, *Quart. J. Microscop. Sci.* **40**, 447 (1897).

65. C. Lespès, *Ann. sci. nat., Zool.* **15**, Art. 14 (1872).

66. J. Joyeux-Laffuie, *Arch. zool. exptl. et gén.* [2] **8**, 245 (1890).

67. C. Berkeley, *Quart. J. Microscop. Sci.* **73**, 465 (1930).
68. E. R. Lankester, *Quart. J. Microscop. Sci.* **19**, 434 (1879).
69. M. Newbigin, *Quart. J. Microscop. Sci.* **41**, 391 (1898).
70. M. Romieu, *Bull. Biol.* **56**, 579 (1922).
71. M. Romieu and F. Obaton, *Compt. rend. acad. sci.* **175**, 51 (1922).
72. W. C. Alvarez, C. Sheard, and G. M. Higgins, *Proc. Soc. Exptl. Biol. Med.* **25**, 302 (1928).
73. C. Dhéré, "La Fluorescence en Biochimie," Presses Univ. Paris, 1937.
74. D. L. Fox, "Animal Biochromes and Structural Colours." Cambridge Univ. Press, London and New York, 1953.
75. A. Seybold and K. Egle, *Botan. Arch.* **41**, 578 (1940).
76. E. I. Rabinowitch, "Photosynthesis and Related Processes," Vol. II, Part 1. Interscience, New York, 1951.
77. B. Hubert, *Rec. trav. bot. néerl.* **32**, 323 (1935).
78. G. E. Fogg, "The Metabolism of Algae," Wiley, New York, 1953.
79. W. L. Orr and J. R. Grady, *Deep-Sea Research* **4**, 263 (1957).
80. R. L. Metcalf, *Ann. Entomol. Soc. Am.* **38**, 397 (1945).
81. W. Hausmann, *Biochem. Z.* **77**, 268 (1916).
82. C. Dhéré, *Compt. rend. acad. sci.* **195**, 1436 (1932).
83. H. Fischer and O. Schaumann, *Z. physiol. Chem.* **128**, 162 (1923).
84. L. C. Schmarda, *Sitzber. Wiener Akad. Wiss.* **4**, 121 (1852).
85. H. C. Sorby, *Quart. J. Microscop. Sci.* **15**, 166 (1875).
86. C. F. W. Krukenberg, *Vergl. Studien.* Reihe 1, Abt. 2, 76 (1880).
87. R. Dubois, *Compt. rend. soc. biol.* **62**, 654 (1907).
88. C. Dhéré and M. Fontaine, *Ann. inst. océanogr. Monaco* **12**, 349 (1932).
89. E. Lederer, *Compt. rend. acad. sci.* **209**, 528 (1939).
90. E. R. Lankester, *Quart. J. Microscop. Sci.* **40**, 447 (1898).
91. E. Lönnberg and G. Gustafson, *Arkiv. Zool.* **B32**, 1 (1939).
92. H. C. Bradley, *J. Biol. Chem.* **4**, 36 (1908).
93. H. Fischer and H. Fink, *Z. physiol. Chem.* **150**, 243 (1925).
94. H. Fischer and A. Hendschel, *Z. physiol. Chem.* **198**, 33 (1931).
95. H. Fischer and A. Hendschel, *Z. physiol. Chem.* **206**, 255 (1932).
96. H. Fischer and A. Hendschel, *Z. physiol. Chem.* **222**, 250 (1933).
97. A. Seybold and K. Egle, *Sitzber. Heidelberger Akad. Wiss.* **7** (1939).
98. J. B. L. d'A. de Férussac, A. E. J. P. J. F. d'A. de Férussac, and G. P. Deshayes, "Histoire naturelle générale et particulière des Mollusques terrestres et fluviatiles," 4 vols. and Atlas J.-B. Baillière, Paris, 1820–1851.
99. C. Dhéré and C. Baumeler, *Compt. rend. soc. biol.* **99**, 726 (1928).
100. G. Y. Kennedy, *J. Marine Biol. Assoc. United Kingdom* **38**, 27 (1959).
101. H. Fischer and W. Zerweck, *Z. physiol. Chem.* **137**, 176 (1924).
102. H. Fischer and K. Schneller, *Z. physiol. Chem.* **130**, 302 (1923).
103. E. Mertens, *Z. physiol. Chem.* **250**, 57 (1937).
104. R. E. H. Nicholas and A. Comfort, *Biochem. J.* **45**, 208 (1949).
105. A. Comfort, *Biol. Revs.* **26**, 285 (1951).
106. C. F. W. Krukenberg, *Zbl. Med. Wiss.* **21**, 785 (1883).
107. C. F. W. Krukenberg, *Vergleichphysiol. Vorträge* **1**, 142 (1886). Publ. by C. Winter, Heidelberg, Germany.
108. F. N. Schulz, *Z. allgem. Physiol.* **3**, 91 (1904).
109. R. Tixier, *Mém. mus. hist. nat. Paris. Sér. A, Zool.* **5**, 41 (1952).
110. H. Fischer and E. Haarer, *Z. physiol. Chem.* **204**, 101 (1931).

111. H. Fischer and K. Jordan, *Z. physiol. Chem.* **190**, 75 (1930).

112. H. Fischer and H. J. Hoffmann, *Z. physiol. Chem.* **246**, 15 (1937).

113. J. Waldenström, *Acta Med. Scand.* Suppl. 82 (1937).

114. R. Tixier, *Bull. soc. chim. biol.* **28**, 394 (1945).

115. A. Comfort, *Nature* **162**, 851 (1948).

116. A. Comfort, *Biochem. J.* **44**, 111 (1949).

117. G. Y. Kennedy and H. G. Vevers, *J. Marine Biol. Assoc. United Kingdom* **32**, 235 (1953).

118. H. M. Fox, *Proc. Roy. Soc.* **B99**, 199 (1926); **136**, 378 (1949).

119. O. Warburg, *Z. angew. Chem.* **45**, 1 (1932).

120. P. P. Grassé, "Traité de Zoologie," Vol. 11. Masson et Cie, Paris, 1948.

121. T. Mortensen, "Echinoderms of the British Isles." Oxford Univ. Press, London and New York, 1927.

122. D. A. Webb, *J. Exptl. Biol.* **16**, 499 (1939).

123. J. Verne, "Couleurs et Pigments des Êtres Vivants." Masson, Paris, 1930.

124. A. C. Redfield, *Quart. Rev. Biol.* **8**, 31 (1933).

125. A. B. Griffiths, *Compt. rend. acad. sci.* **114**, 840 (1892).

126. W. J. Turner, *J. Biol. Chem.* **118**, 519 (1937).

127. G. Y. Kennedy, *J. Marine Biol. Assoc. United Kingdom* **38**, 27 (1959).

128. W. J. Crozier, *Am. J. Physiol.* **36**, 8 (1914).

129. G. Y. Kennedy and H. G. Vevers, *J. Marine Biol. Assoc. United Kingdom* **35**, 35 (1956).

130. J. E. Morton and N. A. Holme, *J. Marine Biol. Assoc. United Kingdom* **34**, 101 (1955).

131. E. Phear, *Proc. Zool. Soc. London* **125**, 383 (1955).

132. E. Lederer and C. Huttrer, *Trav. membres soc. chim. biol.* **24**, 1055 (1942).

133. R. Lemberg, *Fortschr. Chem. org. Naturstoffe* **11**, 300 (1954).

134. C. Rimington, *Onderstepoort J. Vet. Sci. Animal Ind.* **7**, 567 (1936); *Compt. rend. trav. lab. Carlsberg, Sér. chim.* **22**, 454, (1938).

135. K. Dobriner, S. Localio, and W. H. Strain, *J. Biol. Chem.* **114**, xxvi (1936).

136. H. L. Booij and C. Rimington, *Biochem. J.* **65**, 4P (1957); C. Rimington, *Proc. Roy. Soc. Med.* **52**, 963 (1959).

137. S. L. Sveinsson, C. Rimington and H. D. Barnes, *Scand. J. Clin. & Lab. Invest.* **1**, 2 (1949).

138. E. Fränkel, *Virchow's Arch. pathol. Anat. u. Physiol.* **248**, 125 (1924); M. Borst and H. Königsdörffer, "Untersuchungen über Porphyrie mit besonderer Berückrichtigung der Porphyria congenita." Hirzel, Leipzig, 1929; R. Finkentscher, H. Fink, and E. Emminger, *Klin. Wochschr.* **10**, 206 (1931).

139. K. G. Paul, A. Engström, and B. Engfeldt, *J. Clin. Pathol.* **6**, 135 (1953).

140. W. J. Turner, *J. Biol. Chem.* **118**, 519 (1937).

141. E. Derrien and J. Turchini, *Compt. rend. soc. biol.* **92**, 1028 (1925); S. Loos, *Z. Stomatol.* **29**, 1294 (1931).

142. C. Carrié "Die Porphyrine." Thieme, Leipzig, 1936.

143. H. Fischer and W. Zerweck, *Z. physiol. Chem.* **132**, 12 (1924).

144. A. A. Hijmans van den Bergh and W. Grotepass, *Klin. Wochschr.* **12**, 586 (1933).

145. A. A. Hijmans van den Bergh and A. J. Hyman, *Deut. med. Wochschr.* **54**, 1492 (1928).

146. C. J. Watson and W. O. Clarke, *Proc. Soc. Expt. Biol. Med.* **36**, 65 (1937).

147. G. E. Cartwright, M. A. Lauritsen, S. Humphreys, P. J. Jones, I. M. Merrill, and M. M. Wintrobe, *Science* **103**, 72 (1946); S. Schwartz and H. M. Wikoff, *J. Biol. Chem.* **194**, 563 (1952).

148. S. Schwartz and H. M. Wikoff, *J. Biol. Chem.* **194**, 563 (1952); C. J. Watson, *Arch. Internal Med.* **86**, 797 (1950).

149. M. Borst and H. Königsdörffer, "Untersuchungen über Porphyrie mit besonderer Berücksichtigung der Porphyria Congenita." Hirzel, Leipzig, 1929.

150. K. Salomon, J. E. Richmond, and K. I. Altman, *J. Biol. Chem.* **196**, 463 (1952).

151. A. A. Hijmans van den Bergh, W. Grotepass, and F. E. Revers, *Klin. Wochschr.* **11**, 1534 (1932).

152. J. T. Brugsch, *Z. ges. exptl. Med.* **95**, 471 and 482 (1935); J. T. Brugsch, *ibid.* **98**, 49 and 57 (1936).

153. T. H. Tio, Beschouwingen over de Porphyria Cutanea Tarda, Thesis, University of Amsterdam (1956); T. H. Tio, B. Leijnse, A. Jarrett, and C. Rimington, *Clin. Sci.* **16**, 517 (1957).

154. K. Zeile and B. Rau, *Z. physiol. Chem.* **250**, 197 (1937).

155. O. Schumm, *Z. physiol. Chem.* **133**, 308 (1924); **141**, 153 (1924); H. Kämmerer, *Deut. Arch. klin. Med.* **145**, 257 (1924); H. Kämmerer and Y. Gürsching, *Verhandl. deut. Ges. inn. Med.* (*Wiesbaden*) **41**, 486 (1929); A. Jakob, *Klin. Wochschr.* **18**, 1024 (1939); R. Hoagland, *J. Agr. Research Wash.* **7**, 41 (1916); H. Fischer, H. Kämmerer, and A. Kühner, *Z. physiol. Chem.* **139**, 107 (1924).

156. F. Haurowitz, *Arch. Verdauungs-Krankh. Stoffwechselpathol. u. Diäfetik* **50**, 33 (1931); G. Barkan, *Z. physiol. Chem.* **148**, 124 (1925); F. Haurowitz, *ibid.* **188**, 161 (1930).

157. I. Boas, *Klin. Wochschr.* **11**, 1051 (1932); L. A. Hulst, Bloedsporen in de Ontlasting, Dissertation, Utrecht (1933).

158. I. Boas, *Klin. Wochschr.* **11**, 1051 (1932).

159. H. Günther, *Ergeb. allgem. Pathol. u. pathol. Anat. Menschen u. Tiere* **20**, 608 (1922); A. Papendieck, *Z. physiol. Chem.* **128**, 109 (1923); **133**, 97 (1924).

160. R. E. H. Nicholas and C. Rimington, *Biochem. J.* **48**, 306 (1951); R. E. H. Nicholas, The Chromatography of the porphyrins and its application to natural products, Thesis, London (1951).

161. Saillet, *Rev. méd.* (*Paris*) **16**, 542 (1896).

162. L. Zieve, E. Hill, S. Schwartz, and C. J. Watson, *J. Lab. Clin. Med.* **41**, 663 (1953).

163. L. A. Strait, H. R. Burman, B. Eddy, H. Hrenoff, and J. J. Eiler, *J. Appl. Physiol.* **4**, 699 (1952); D. Y. Hsia and M. Page, *Proc. Soc. Exptl. Biol. Med.* **85**, 86 (1954); R. A. Neve and R. A. Aldrich, *Pediatrics* **15**, 553 (1955).

164. K. Franke and R. Fikentscher, *Münch. med. Wochschr.* **82**, 171 (1935); K. Franke, *Z. klin. Med.* **130**, 222 (1936).

165. R. E. H. Nicholas and C. Rimington, *Scand. J. Clin. Lab. Invest.* **1**, 12 (1949); W. H. Lockwood, *Australian J. Exptl. Biol. Med. Sci.* **31**, 453 (1953); S. Schwartz, *Veterans Admin. Tech. Bull.* TB—10–94 (1953); T. K. With and H. C. A. Petersen, *Lancet* **ii**, 1148 (1954).

166. I. Boas, *Klin. Wochschr.* **12**, 589 (1933).

167. H. T. Schreus and C. Carrié, *Klin. Wochschr.* **12**, 745 (1933); A. Vannotti, "Porphyrin und Porphyrinkrankheiten." Springer, Berlin, 1937.

168. S. Nesbitt and A. M. Snell, *Arch. Internal Med.* **69**, 573 and 582 (1942).

169. T. Heikel, B. C. Knight, C. Rimington, H. D. Ritchie, and E. J. Williams, *Proc. Roy. Soc.* **B153**, 47 (1960).

170. C. S. Lieber, L. M. De Carli, and R. Schmid, *Biochem. Biophys. Research Communs.* **1**, 302 (1959).

171. C. H. Gray, C. Rimington, and S. Thomson, *Quart. J. Med.* [N.S.] **17**, 123 (1948); G. C. Wells and C. Rimington, *Brit. J. Dermatol.* **65**, 337 (1953); A. G. MacGregor, R. E. H. Nicholas, and C. Rimington, *Arch. Internal Med.* **90**, 483 (1952); G. Holti, C. Rimington, B. Tate, and G. Thomas, *Quart. J. Med.* [N.S.] **27**, 1 (1958).

172. W. Grotepass, *Z. physiol. Chem.* **253**, 276 (1938).

173. C. J. Watson, *J. Clin. Invest.* **15**, 327 (1936); C. J. Watson, V. Hawkinson, S. Schwartz, and D. Sutherland, *J. Clin. Invest.* **28**, 447 (1949).

174. M. Grinstein, M. D. Kamen, H. M. Wikoff, and C. V. Moore, *J. Biol. Chem.* **182**, 715 and 723 (1950).

175. K. Dobriner and C. P. Rhoads, *J. Clin. Invest.* **27**, 105 (1938).

176. O. Schück and J. Berman, *Časopis lékáru českých* **5**, 125 (1956).

177. P. Koskelo, *Ann. Med. Internae Fenniae* **45**, Suppl. 24 (1956).

178. E. Derrien, *Bull. soc. chim. biol.* **8**, 218 (1927); R. Fikentscher, *Zool. Anz.* **103**, 20 (1933).

179. J. E. Kench, F. A. Langley, and J. F. Wilkinson, *Quart. J. Med.* **22**, 285 (1953).

180. A. A. Hijmans van den Bergh and W. Grotepass, *Compt. rend. soc. biol.* **121**, 1253 (1936); F. Schønheyder, *J. Biol. Chem.* **123**, 491 (1938).

181. H. Klüver, *Science* **99**, 482 (1944).

182. H. M. Solomon and F. H. J. Figge, *Proc. Soc. Exptl. Biol. Med.* **94**, 356 (1957).

183. C. J. Watson, W. N. Schulze, V. Hawkinson, and A. B. Baker, *Proc. Soc. Exptl. Biol. Med.* **64**, 73 (1947).

184. E. Derrien and J. Turchini, *Compt. rend. soc. biol.* **91**, 637 (1924).

185. A. L. Grafflin, *Am. J. Anat.* **71**, 43 (1942).

186. R. H. Davidheiser and F. H. J. Figge, *Proc. Soc. Expt. Biol. Med.* **90**, 461 (1955).

187. F. A. Davis, *Trans. Am. Ophthalmol. Soc.* **27**, 401 (1929).

188. L. C. Strong, *Proc. Soc. Exptl. Biol. Med.* **57**, 78 (1944).

189. K. J. Collins, *Quart. J. Exptl. Physiol.* **42**, 24 (1957).

190. C. Krukenberg, *Verhandl. Würzburger physik.-med. Ges.* **17**, 109 (1883).

191. E. Derrien, *Compt. rend. soc. biol.* **91**, 634 (1924).

192. H. Bierry and B. Gouzon, *Compt. rend. soc. biol.* **194**, 653 (1932).

193. H. Königsdörffer, *Strahlentherapie* **28**, 132 (1928).

194. B. Gouzon, *Compt. rend. soc. biol.* **116**, 925 (1934).

195. E. Derrien and J. Turchini, *Bull. soc. chim. France* **35**, 687 (1924); *Compt. rend. soc. biol.* **91**, 637 (1924).

196. H. Giersberg, *Z. wiss. Zool.* **120**, 1 (1923); *Biol. Zentr.* **43**, 167 (1923).

197. A. A. Hijmans van den Bergh and W. Grotepass, *Compt. rend. soc. biol.* **121**, 1253 (1936).

198. C. Rimington, *Bull. Brit. Ornithologists' Club* **73**, 24 (1953).

199. F. B. Hutt and J. B. Sumner, *Science* **116**, 35 (1952).

200. D. Polin, *Proc. Soc. Expt. Biol. Med.* **100**, 695 (1959).

201. A. Church, *Phil. Trans. Roy. Soc.* **154**, 627 (1869).

202. H. Fischer and J. Hilger, *Z. physiol. Chem.* **138**, 49 (1924).

203. C. Rimington, *Proc. Roy. Soc.* **B127**, 106 (1939).

204. O. Völker, *Z. Naturforsch.* **2b**, 316 (1947); R. E. H. Nicholas and C. Rimington, *Biochem. J.* **50**, 194 (1951); T. K. With, *Scand. J. Clin. & Lab. Invest.* **9**, 398 (1957).

205. L. Auber, Personal communication (1960).
206. R. E. Moreau, *Ibis* **100**, 67 (1958).
207. A. Church, *Phil. Trans. Roy. Soc.* **183**, 511 (1892).
208. J. Keilin, *Biochem. J.* **49**, 544 (1951).
209. E. Derrien and J. Turchini, *Compt. rend. soc. biol.* **92**, 1030 (1925).
210. O. Völker, *J. Ornithol.* **86**, 438 (1938); *Z. physiol. Chem.* **258**, 1 (1939).
211. T. K. With, Personal communication (1960).
212. E. Lederer and R. Tixier, *Compt. rend. acad. sci.* **224**, 531 (1947).

CHAPTER 13

Pteridines: Structure and Metabolism

Hugh S. Forrest

Genetics Foundation, The University of Texas, Austin, Texas

I. Introduction

The pteridine ring system probably occurs in all living organisms. Chemically it can be related to the hydrocarbon naphthalene (it is a tetraazanaphthalene), or it can be considered to be a fused pyrimido-pyrazine (pyrimido-4,5-b-pyrazine). It resembles the purine ring system and was originally numbered (I) to conform with it (II). This system is still used in some European countries but the *Chemical Abstracts* numbering system (III) is now most generally accepted.

The majority of naturally occurring pteridines have a 2-amino and a 4-hydroxy group. The large number of compounds so far isolated vary only in the substituents in, and the state of oxidation of, the pyrazine ring. It has been shown in the last few years that 2,4-dihydroxypteridines also exist in nature and that they are intimately concerned with ribo-

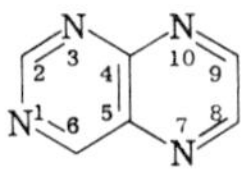

(I)

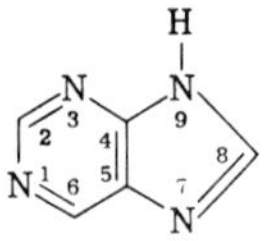

(II)

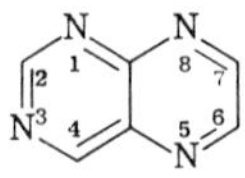

(III)

flavin biosynthesis (riboflavin itself is a fused benzpteridine related to this group). It is quite possible that other derivatives with different substituents in the pyrimidine portion of the ring remain to be discovered.

The first naturally occurring pteridines were isolated from butterfly wings by Hopkins in 1889 (1). The correct structures of these pigments were not elucidated until fifty years later although the ring system was synthesized chemically at about the same time as the natural compounds were described (2). Because of their chemical resemblances to uric acid and their close physical proximity in the wings of butterflies, the pteridines were thought to be purine derivatives. Difficulties inherent in their physical and chemical properties made the establishment of their correct structures a long and tedious process. The white pigment leucopterin (IV) was synthesized in 1940 (3), and the pale yellow pigment xanthopterin (V) in 1941 (4). A third compound, isoxanthopterin (VI), was also synthesized in 1941 (5), and the structures and relationships of all three were finally established.

At about this time reports were beginning to appear in the literature of the occurrence of pteridines in places other than butterfly wings. Uropterin (6), later shown to be xanthopterin (7), was isolated from human urine in 1936 and a second compound, urothion (8), in 1943, but more significant discoveries came from nutritional studies with microorganisms. Two factors required for the growth of *Lactobacillus casei* (norite eluate factor) and *Streptococcus faecalis* R (folic acid) were purified in 1940 (9, 10); their identity and pteridine nature were demonstrated in 1946 with the complete characterization of a pure material obtained from liver (11). A number of other growth factors for microorganisms and/or antianemic agents were described about this time. These have either been shown to be identical to the substance described above or to be closely related to it (see Section II, A). This

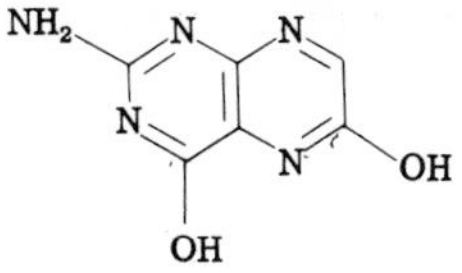

(IV)

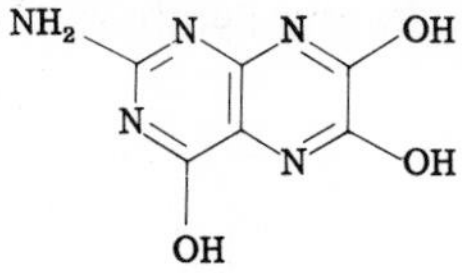

(V)

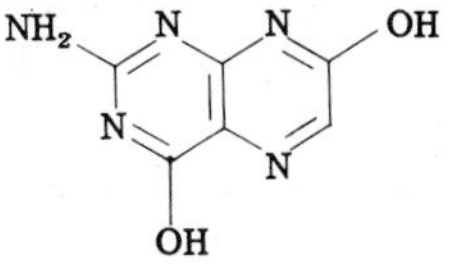

(VI)

substance (VII) has been given the name N-pteroylglutamic acid, the prefix deriving from the trivial name pteroic acid given to

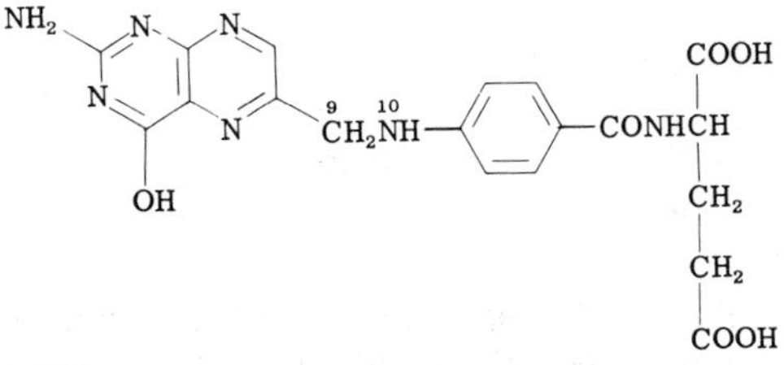

(VII)

2-amino-4-hydroxy-6-(p-carboxyanilinomethyl)pteridine. The term folic acid is frequently used in a general sense for any compound containing the pteroyl radical showing biological activity (12). The biological activity is generally considered to be associated with derivatives of these compounds in which the pyrazine ring is reduced. Furthermore these tetrahydro compounds are often bound through a glutamic acid residue to small peptides and/or proteins. Numerous reviews on the chemical and nutritional aspects of this group of compounds are available (13–17).

A new growth factor for a trypanosome, Crithidia fasciculata, (18) was isolated in 1955 from human urine (19). Simultaneously, it was isolated from the fruit fly Drosophila melanogaster (20). It was given the name biopterin and its structure was shown to be (VIII) by degradation and synthesis. It has since been found to occur in a number

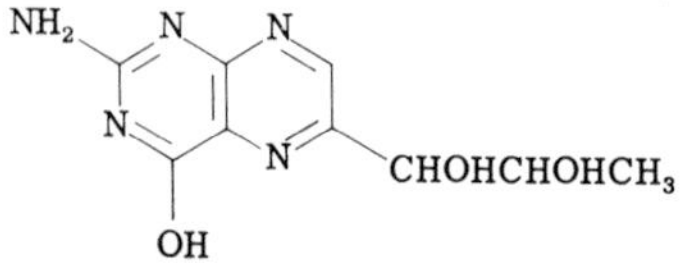

$$NH_2 \quad N \quad N$$
$$\text{CHOHCHOHCH}_3$$
$$OH$$

(VIII)

of organisms. A number of other recently isolated pteridines, e.g., ichthyopterin from fish scales (*21*), sepiapterins (*22*) and drosopterins (*23*) from *D. melanogaster* have now been related to biopterin. These will be discussed in more detail in Section III along with additional butterfly pigments and simple pteridines from other sources.

For convenience in further discussion the naturally occurring pteridines are divided into two groups, the folic acid compounds and the simple pteridines. Functionally and metabolically, however, these are interrelated in some cases, and more inter-relationships may be recognized with increasing knowledge of their biochemistry.

II. Folic Acid Compounds

A. CHEMISTRY

1. *Rhizopterin*

A growth factor for *Streptococcus faecalis* R, but not for *Lactobacillus casei*, was isolated from the mold *Rhizophus nigrans* in 1947 (*24*). It was shown to be formylpteroic acid (IX), by degradation and synthesis (*25*).

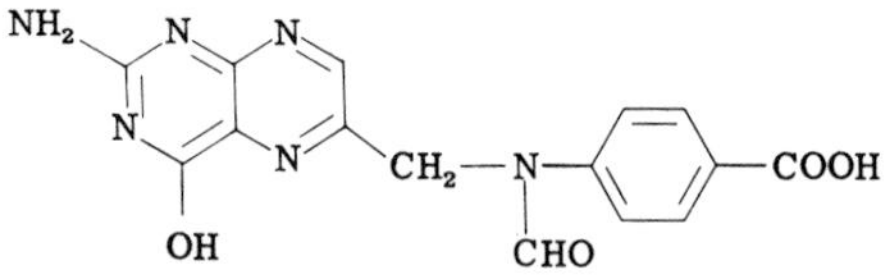

$$NH_2 \quad N \quad N$$
$$\text{CH}_2\text{—N—}\bigcirc\text{—COOH}$$
$$OH \qquad CHO$$

(IX)

An analog, N^{10}-formylpteroylglutamic acid, has been isolated from horse liver (*26*).

2. *Pteroylglutamic Acid (VII)*

This compound was isolated from liver in 1946 (*11*) and details of the structure proof, by degradation and synthesis, were given in 1948 (27). It has been shown to be the compound responsible for the biological activities of the older impure materials, norite eluate factor from liver and yeast (9), the original folic acid from spinach (10), and vitamin B_c from liver (28). It is therefore an essential growth factor for S. faecalis R and L. casei, and for chicks.

3. Fermentation L. casei factor (Teropterin)

A compound isolated from Corynebacterium (29) had little growth activity for S. faecalis R, but was fully active for L. casei. It could be hydrolyzed to pteroylglutamic acid and glutamic acid and was subsequently shown to be pteroyl-γ-glutamyl-γ-glutamylglutamic acid by synthesis (30). Isomers containing one or more α links are not biologically active.

4. Vitamin B_c Conjugate

A substance was isolated from yeast in 1945 having no growth activity for L. casei or S. faecalis, yet being almost identical, spectrally, with pteroylglutamic acid. Its structure was deduced by hydrolysis to be pteroylglutamic acid with six additional glutamic acid residues (31). It is assumed that only γ-linkages are present.

5. Citrovorum Factor—Folinic Acid S. F., Leucovorin

An optically active substance necessary for the growth of Leuconostoc citrovorum (now called Pediococcus cerevisiae) was isolated from liver in 1951 (32). A synthetic compound made by reducing N^{10}-formyl-pteroylglutamic acid and autoclaving the product (33) [later shown (34) to cause a migration of the formyl group from the 10- to the 5-position] was half as active on a molar basis (the synthesis produces a racemic mixture arising from the asymmetric carbon atom resulting from hydrogenation). The compound is therefore 5,6,7,8-tetrahydro-5-formylpteroylglutamic acid (X). It replaces folic acid as a growth

(X)

factor for both *S. faecalis* and *L. casei.* Knowledge of its structure is fundamental to an understanding of the biological function of folic acid compounds.

6. *Coenzyme Forms*

It has been surmised for some time that natural coenzyme forms containing the essential pteroic acid moiety may be more complex than any of the compounds described above. Thus, to explain some of the results of inhibition studies of sulfonamides on various microorganisms, a compounds, coenzyme F, has been postulated (*35*). There is no real evidence as to its chemical identity. It has been suggested that it may be 5, 6, 7, 8-tetrahydro-5-formylpteroylglutamic acid with a ribosyl, ribosyl phosphate, or a more complicated substituent on the N^8-position.

Coenzyme C is the name given to a group of folic acid-containing compounds isolated and partially purified from extracts of *Clostridium cylindrosporum* (*36*). The important feature of these compounds is that, in addition to the pteroic acid moiety and glutamic acid, some of them were claimed to contain other amino acids (serine, glycine, alanine) and three analyzed for a mole of pentose and up to four moles of phosphate (*37*).

B. FUNCTION

Folic acid or its reduction product probably has several functions in living systems. The one that has been most studied is concerned with the transfer of a one carbon unit in the synthesis or degradation of a number of important biological compounds. Many enzymes involved in these processes have now been shown to have the reduced form of folic acid or a derivative containing one more carbon atom as their cofactor. This subject has been reviewed in great detail recently (*38, 39, 40*). A brief account of the well-authenticated enzyme reactions in which folic acid participates follows.

1. *Reduction*

Folic acid is probably always reduced to tetrahydrofolic acid through a dihydro compound. Reduced triphosphopyridine nucleotide or reduced diphosphopyridine nucleotide supply the reducing power (*41*). A system from chicken liver which reduces both folic acid and a synthetic dihydrofolic acid to tetrahydrofolic acid has been partially purified (*42*), and a highly purified enzyme for the reduction of dihydrofolic acid has been described (*43*).

The hydrogens in the dihydro compound are considered to be located at the 7- and 8-positions.

A second method of reducing folic acid has been shown to occur in extracts of *Clostridium sticklandii* (*44*), in the following way:

$$\text{Folic acid} + \text{Pyruvate} + \text{CoA} \rightarrow \text{Acetyl CoA} + \text{Dihydrofolic acid}$$

2. Addition of One Carbon Unit

Two oxidation states of the 1-carbon fragment can be found combined with reduced folic acid, and both appear to be involved in different metabolic reactions. The 1-carbon unit can be at the formic acid level of oxidation, or it can be at the formaldehyde level. The active transfer of the carbon fragment at the formic acid level of oxidation takes place in the form of N^5- or N^{10}-formyl compounds or as an N^5,N^{10}-bridge compound loosely called N^5,N^{10}-methenyltetrahydrofolic acid (XI). At the formaldehyde level the analogous N^5,N^{10}-methylenetetrahydrofolic acid (XII) appears to be the key intermediate.

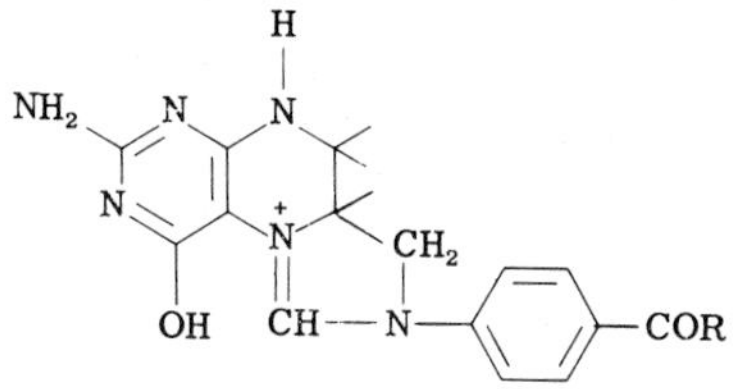

(XI)

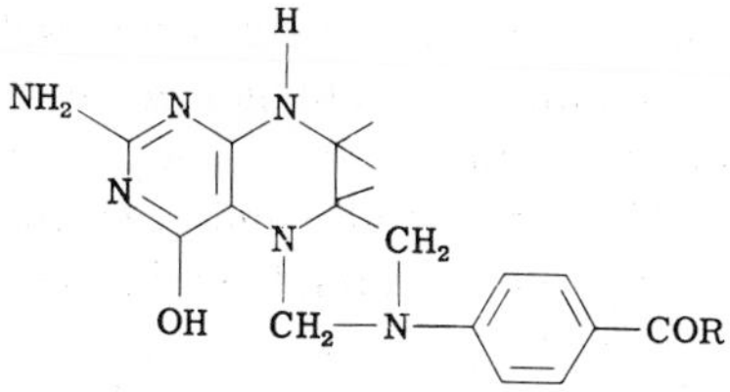

(XII)

Compound (XI) can be synthesized from tetrahydrofolic acid and formic acid through the N^{10}-formyl derivative (*45*) or from tetrahydrofolic acid and N-formyl glutamic acid through the N^5-formyl derivative (*46*), or in a more complex reaction from the catabolism of purines through an N^5-formimino derivative (*47*).

Compound (XII) can be synthesized directly from formaldehyde

(48) or from the breakdown of serine to glycine (39, 40) or from a reversal of a number of reactions that normally accept this carbon fragment (see later). (XI) and (XII) are interconverted by a triphosphopyridine nucleotide-linked dehydrogenase (49).

3. Metabolic Reactions Catalyzed by These Compounds

a. *Purine Synthesis.* Folic acid enzymes are involved in purine synthesis at two points, the formylation of glycinamide ribotide and the insertion of carbon 2 of the pyrimidine ring (Eqs. 1 and 2).

$$(1)$$

Inosinic acid $\quad(2)$

Different forms of folic acid are involved in the two reactions. For the first, the coenzyme is N^5,N^{10}-methenyltetrahydrofolic acid, for the second it is N^{10}-formyltetrahydrofolic acid (50).

Frequently folic acid deficiency in microorganisms manifests itself first as a breakdown of purine biosynthesis. In such a state of deficiency added purines will restore normal growth; conversely purine synthesis is quite sensitive to compounds that antagonize the action of folic acid. The historical importance of this in the study of purine biosynthesis lies in the discovery (51) that in sulfonamide inhibition in *Escherichia coli* a compound, 4-amino-5-carboxamidoimidazole, derived from the immediate precursor of the purine ring accumulated. This observation was the key one for the later understanding of purine biosynthesis. A detailed review of subsequent developments is given by Buchanan and Hartman (50).

b. *Thymidylic Acid Synthesis.* Tetrahydrofolic acid is an essential cofactor in the conversion of uridylic acid to thymidylic acid (Eq. 3) (52). The active cofactor in this reaction is probably N^5,N^{10}-methylenetetrahydropteroylglutamic acid, and probably vitamin B_{12} is also involved. Enzymes catalyzing the reaction have been shown to be present in microorganisms and in the animal kingdom.

$$(3)$$

Thymidine
Thymidylic acid

c. *Methionine Synthesis.* The synthesis of methionine from homocysteine (Eq. 4) requires N^5,N^{10}-methylenetetrahydropteroylglutamic acid and probably vitamin B_{12} (53), although the nature of the natural cofactor is not yet clear. In *E. coli*, for example, the substance most closely approaching it appears to be a derivative of tetrahydropteroyltriglutamic acid (54), in the presence of which vitamin B_{12} is not essential.

$$\begin{array}{ccc}
SH & & SCH_3 \\
| & & | \\
CH_2 & & CH_2 \\
| & \longrightarrow & | \\
CH_2 & & CH_2 \\
| & & | \\
CHNH_2 & & CHNH_2 \\
| & & | \\
COOH & & COOH
\end{array} \qquad (4)$$

Homocysteine   Methionine

d. *Serine-Glycine Interconversions.* The β carbon atom of serine is transferred to receptor molecules such as uridylic acid or homocysteine through N^5,N^{10}-methylenetetrahydrofolic acid (39, 40, 55). The reaction is reversible, and this may represent a major route of glycine catabolism.

e. *Histidine Catabolism.* Histidine is considered to break down through urocanic acid to formiminoglutamic acid (Eq. 5).

$$(5)$$

Histidine   Urocanic acid   Formiminoglutamic acid

The formimino group is then transferred to tetrahydrofolic acid to give an N^5-formiminotetrahydrofolic acid. This compound is then broken down enzymatically to ammonia and N^5,N^{10}-methenyltetrahydrofolic acid (47). This, of course, can then enter into reactions previously described for it. As already mentioned, the formimino group can also arise from formiminoglycine resulting from the catabolism of purines.

f. Other Metabolic Reactions. The folic acid coenzymes by virtue of their 1-carbon transferring capacities have been implicated in a number of other biochemical reactions. These include panthothenic acid biosynthesis, valine-leucine transformations, vitamin B_{12} synthesis, choline synthesis, sarcosine catabolism, etc.

In addition to these reactions, an extremely important part in cell division appears to be played by the reduced form of folic acid. According to Jacobson (56), leucovorin causes nucleoprotein to be shed into the cytoplasm and this initiates metaphase-anaphase transformations. This work is based on the effect of folic acid antagonists on mammalian cells in tissue culture and the reversal of these effects by leucovorin. Presumably, also, the aberrant cell formations caused by folic acid antagonists in bacteria (57) are another manifestation of this phenomenon. Unfortunately, nothing is known of the biochemistry of this process, although obviously it may be of fundamental importance in the regulation not only of bacterial growth, but also of the more highly coordinated growth of higher organisms.

Although no well-authenticated case is known, it is obvious that folic acid or one of its reduced compounds could function in a redox system. Examples of enzymes that bring about the reduction of folic acid have already been given, but these seem to be involved only in the synthesis of the active cofactors for 1-carbon transfer. However, tetrahydrofolic acid can act in at least one redox system, the oxidation of phenylalanine to tyrosine, although it is not the natural cofactor (see Section III, B).

Finally, there is evidence from the classic *E. coli* sulfonamide inhibition system and from work on animal nutrition that addition of all the known metabolites in whose synthesis folic acid has been implicated still does not completely overcome the action of inhibitors. There must therefore still be folic acid-requiring reactions to be discovered.

C. Occurrence

It is evident from the previous section that folic acid is involved in reactions essential to life. Therefore it must be present in all cells. However, cells have varying capacities for synthesizing it. Many bacteria, for instance, are capable of synthesizing their requirement using only common nutrients whereas others must be supplied with some part of the molecule (most commonly the *p*-aminobenzoic acid moiety). This latter fact, of course, was utilized to great effect in the discovery of the mode of action of the sulfonamide drugs, which prevent the growth of many bacteria by inhibiting the incorporation of p-aminobenzoic acid into the coenzyme form of folic acid. The differential response of bacteria to growth factors of the folic acid group seems to be concerned with the absorption or utilization of the form in which the p-aminobenzoic acid is added.

Folic acid has been detected in algae, lichens, and fungi, and it is probable that these organisms are able to synthesize their total requirement. Higher plants contain significant quantities [the name folic acid is derived from the Latin *folium*, a leaf (10)], and it is presumed that they are able to synthesize it.

In the animal kingdom, however, it appears that folic acid, or possibly the pteridine ring, must always be obtained exogenously. Some protozoa [e.g., *Tetrahymena pyriformis* (58)] have been shown to have an absolute requirement, and in higher animals folic acid is generally classed as a vitamin. However, it has been shown that "germ-free" rats are able to synthesize folic acid and its reduced forms (59).

It is interesting to note, however, that although "conjugases," i.e., enzymes able to liberate free folic acid from the bound forms, have been found in bacteria, they appear to be much more common, and to be widely distributed, in animal tissue (40). Since folic acid probably occurs frequently in the form of conjugates (severe conditions are frequently used in the isolation of the growth factors discussed in Section II, A, conditions that tend to break down such conjugates), the presence of such an enzyme may be an important requirement for these organisms. Indeed it has been suggested that in the clinical condition known as sprue, which responds to massive doses of folic acid, the primary deficiency is in an intestinal enzyme that liberates conjugated folic acid (60).

III. Simple Pteridines

A. CHEMISTRY

The simplest naturally occurring pteridine known is 2-amino-4-hydroxypteridine, which has been isolated from *Drosophila melanogaster* (61, 62) and from the blue-green alga *Anacystis nidulans* (63). It can be reduced to a 5, 6, 7, 8-tetrahydro compound which reoxidizes through all three possible dihydro compounds (5, 6-, 5, 8-, and 7, 8-) to the original compound. A variety of anionic reagents can be added to one of these derivatives to give 6-substituted pteridines (64, 65). The possible biological significance of this is discussed in Section IV.

Xanthopterin, leucopterin, and isoxanthopterin, the classic butterfly wing pigments, have been discussed briefly. They are, respectively, 2-amino-4, 6-dihydroxypteridine, 2-amino-4, 6, 7-trihydroxypteridine, and 2-amino-4, 7-dihydroxypteridine. Xanthopterin and leucopterin are interchangeable chemically. They have all been synthesized. An excellent account of their discovery and the work on their constitution is given by Gates (13). Two other reviews incorporating a large amount of information on the chemical properties of the pteridine ring system and of simple pteridines are available (16, 17).

Two further butterfly wing pigments are chrysopterin (yellow) and erythropterin (orange red). These were identified as 7-methylxanthopterin (66) (XIII) and 7-propenylxanthopterin (67). Erythropterin is now considered to be a fused furano (2, 3-g) pteridine (XIV) (68). They are unique in that they have a carbon-containing side chain in the 7-position. The carbon-containing side chain in all other naturally occurring pteridines is in the 6-position. Both compounds have been synthesized.

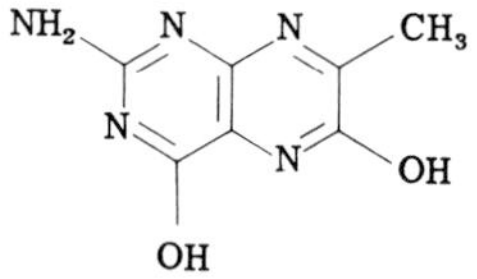

(XIII)

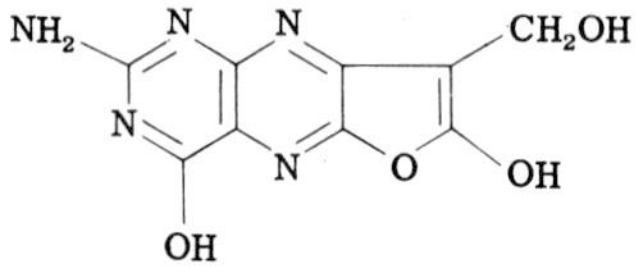

(XIV)

2,6-Diamino-4-hydroxypteridine has been isolated from *Drosophila melanogaster* and blue-green algae (65). It is very probable, however, that it is an artifact arising from the action of ammonia on a reduced pteridine derivative during the isolation procedure.

Urothione is a yellow, optically active pigment isolated from human urine (8). It is not strictly a pteridine since it appears to have a sulfur-containing ring fused to the pyrazine portion of the pteridine ring (69). Its biochemical origin is a complete enigma.

2-Amino-4-hydroxy-6-[(L-*erythro*)-1'2'-dihydroxypropyl-]pteridine (biopterin) was isolated from human urine (*19*) and from the fruitfly *Drosophila melanogaster* (*20*). Its structure (VIII) was proved by degradation and synthesis. A series of glycosylbiopterins yielding biopterin and a variety of sugars on acid hydrolysis have been isolated from blue-green algae (*70, 71*). The sugar is attached to one or other of the hydroxyl groups of the side chain.

One of the older pteridines, ichthyopterin (also known earlier as fluorescyanine), has now been related to the biopterin series (*72*). It is 7-hydroxybiopterin (XV).

(XV)

Two yellow pteridines have been isolated from *Drosophila melanogaster* (*22, 73, 74*). Their isolation is facilitated by the fact that they accumulate in a *sepia* mutant. They have been named sepiapterin and isosepiapterin by the Swiss workers (*74*). Isosepiapterin has also been isolated from the blue-green alga *Anacystis nidulans*. The relationship between the two has been established, isosepiapterin (XVI) having an H in place of the OH of sepiapterin (XVII) on C-2 of the side chain. There is still some doubt about their formulas, but they are closely related to biopterin to which sepiapterin can be converted by reduction and reoxidation (75) and from which an oxidation product of iso-sepiapterin can be obtained (71).

The name drosopterine was applied to an impure red pigment isolated from *Drosophila melanogaster* in 1946 (76). Three crystalline compounds (drosopterin, isodrosopterin and neodrosopterin) have since been isolated from the same source (77) and there is evidence of the occurrence of many more red pigments in these insects (78). Drosopterin and isodrosopterin are evidently geometrical isomers, and neodrosopterin is in the keto form. Provisional formulas (XVIII–XX) have been given for all these compounds (75).

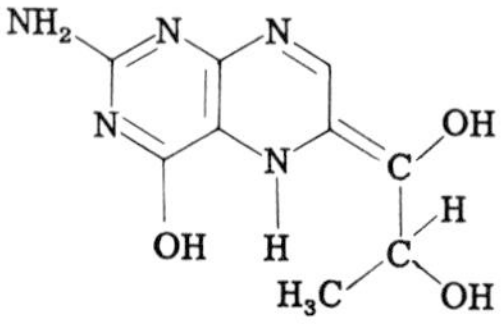

Drosopterin
(XVIII)

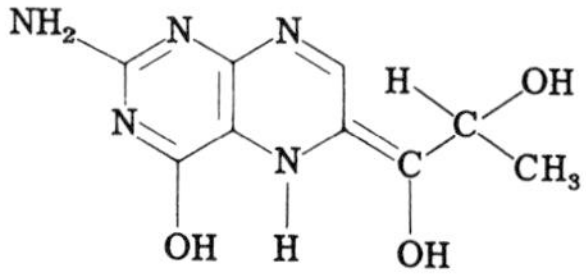

Isodrosopterin
(XIX)

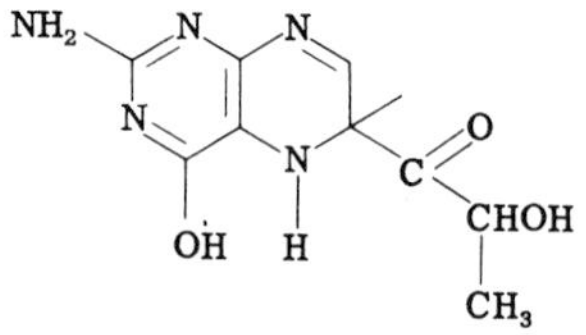

Neodrosopterin
(XX)

Their relationship to biopterin has been demonstrated by their conversion to it by reduction and reoxidation. A close relation to the yellow pigments sepiapterin and isosepiapterin is also evident and is supported by the known genetic information. The two types of pigment have not been interconverted chemically or biochemically.

B. FUNCTION

In contrast to the rapid advance is knowledge of the nature and functions of the folic acid group in the last ten to fifteen years, little is known about the biochemistry of the simple pteridines.

An enzyme has been purified from *Drosophila melanogaster* which converts 2-amino-4-hydroxypteridine to isoxanthopterin (79). Diphos-phopyridine nucleotide is required as a cofactor, and the enzyme which can also convert hypoxanthine through xanthine to uric acid is therefore a xanthine dehydrogenase. Two genetic loci in *Drosophila* are known to affect its production (80, 81). Xanthine oxidase will also catalyze the conversion of 2-amino-4-hydroxypteridine to isoxanthopterin (82). A scheme utilizing this enzyme has been proposed for the degradation of folic acid in humans (83), and a theory based on the inhibiting action of isoxanthopterin on melanogenesis places it, and hence the enzyme, at a crucial point in the control of pigment production in the elytra of the lady beetle, *Harmonia axyridis* (84).

A similar scheme (85) has been suggested for the control of ommatin (brown eye pigment) production in *Drosophila* to explain the well-known genetic relationship between brown and red eye pigments, also found in the meal moth *Ephestia* (86).

Xanthopterin does not arise through the action of xanthine oxidase, although it is oxidized by this enzyme and by xanthine dehydrogenase to leucopterin. Tetrahydropteridines, including those of the folic acid series, reoxidize spontaneously to a number of simple pteridines in-cluding xanthopterin. In slightly alkaline solution the yield of this can be quite high. Presumably some such degradation is the source of the naturally occurring material. Over the years xanthopterin has been implicated in a number of biological effects, the most striking of which is the observation that when injected into rats it produced an increase in growth of the kidneys caused by increased cell division in the tubules. Xanthopterin, although a substrate at low concentrations, acts as an inhibitor of xanthine oxidase at higher concentrations (87). Perhaps, then, all four compounds, 2-amino-4-hydroxypteridine, xanthopterin, isoxanthopterin, and leucopterin, are delicately interrelated through the action of this enzyme.

Biopterin is necessary for the growth of the protozoan *Crithidia fasciculata* (18). Curiously a number of other polyhydroxyalkyl com-pounds are more or less as effective. It has been stated that the require-ment for activity is the presence of a hydroxyl group at the 1′-position of a side chain in the 6-position, and a second hydroxyl in the L-configura-tion at carbon 2′ (88). There appears to be no simple relationship between biopterin and folic acid, as evidenced by their noninterconverti-bility (89). However, no biochemical function has yet been found for this compound. This is also the situation with the glucoside of biopterin. The glucosyl moiety becomes radioactive in photosynthetic experiments with $C^{14}O_2$, but this radioactivity is much too small to arise from primary photosynthetic processes (90).

Although the chemical relationships between biopterin, sepiapterin, isosepiapterin, and the drosopterins have been more or less established, there is again no information on their biochemical transformations. Isosepiapterin obtained from *Anacystis nidulans* is now believed to be an artifact arising by oxidation and degradation during the process of isolation (*91*). This may explain the failure to obtain evidence of biochemical activity of these compounds, since they may all be in a reduced state when acted upon metabolically. For example, in *Drosophila melanogaster* sepiapterin and isosepiapterin accumulate in the sepia mutant, which contains no drosopterins. It is reasonable to assume then that these yellow compounds are precursors of the drosopterins. However, the conversion of one to the other has not been observed either chemically or enzymatically, but, by analogy with the folic acid series, the compounds may have to be in the reduced, colorless state for metabolic transformations to take place.

The conversion of phenylalanine to tyrosine in rat liver preparations is catalyzed by a tetrahydropteridine in the following way:

$$\text{Tetrahydropteridine} + O_2 + \text{Phenylalanine} \rightarrow \text{Oxidized pteridine} + \text{Tyrosine} + H_2O$$

Reduced triphosphopyridine nucleotide and a second enzyme are necessary for the resynthesis of the tetrahydropteridine (*92*). The natural cofactor has not yet been identified, but the most active material so far discovered is 2-amino-4-hydroxy-5,6,7,8-tetrahydro-6-methylpteridine. Tetrahydrofolic acid is also active, but apparently its side chain is not necessary. This represents an oxidation-reduction catalysis such as was mentioned as a possible function of the folic acid group (Section II, B). The elucidation of the structure of the natural material is awaited with great interest.

An extract from *Alcaligenes metalcaligenes* oxidatively deaminates pteroylglutamic acid, and it acts also on some simple pteridines, e.g., 2-amino-4-hydroxy-6-carboxypteridine (*93*). A reaction of this type, or its reverse, may be the link which has been postulated (*94*) between the 2-amino-4-hydroxypteridines and the 2,4-dihydroxypteridines involved in riboflavin biosynthesis.

C. Occurrence

No systematic investigation of the occurrence of simple pteridines in nature has been made. Therefore, it is difficult to make valid generalizations concerning their comparative biochemistry. Aspects of the subject have been dealt with in reviews (*95, 96*).

Very few well-authenticated isolations of simple pteridines from bacteria have been reported. The human tubercle bacillus produces a substance which has been tentatively identified as erythropterin (*97*), and the isolation of the same material from *Mycobacterium lacticola* is recorded (98). A yellow pigment from a chromoprotein in *Mycobacterium smegmata* may be a pteridine (99). 2-Amino-4-hydroxypteridine has been isolated from *Pseudomonas fluorescens* and from *Azotomonas insolita* (71).

Blue-green algae are probably the most abundant source of simple pteridine yet found. The pteridine content may run as high as 0.05–0.1% of the dry weight (63). Other algae, on the other hand, have not been shown to contain any free pteridines. Certain fungi probably produce considerable quantities of pteridines (100, 101), but these have not been rigorously identified. Higher plants probably contain simple pteridines, but no study has been made of their occurrence.

In the animal kingdom the most extensively studied class has been the insects. Pteridines belonging to the group described in Section III have been isolated from *Drosophila melanogaster* (20, 22, 23), from the silkworm *Bombyx mori* (102), and from a number of species of butterflies (95), wasps (103), ladybugs (84), grasshoppers (104) and bees (105).

In the crustaceans, the only recorded isolation of a pteridine is xanthopterin from the crab *Cancer pagurus* (106), although numerous species contain blue fluorescent materials which are almost certainly pteridines.

In the phylum Chordata, xanthopterin has been identified from the tunicate *Microcosmus polymorphus* (107), and among the vertebrates pteridines have been isolated from fishes (21), frogs (108), toads (109), snakes (110), and humans (6, 7).

In the work cited above, the pteridines have not always been identified with known compounds. It is quite probable that some, as yet unknown, compounds will be found in the organisms listed or in others. An interesting attempt has been made to study the evolution of pteridine metabolism within the genus *Drosophila* (111). Finally, there is a remarkably high correlation between the pteridines found in some fishes and the pteridines of *Drosophila*, even to the production by the former of drosopterins (112). It is to be expected that future work will reveal more correlations of this type.

IV. Biosynthesis of the Pteridine Ring

Information on the biosynthesis of the pteridine ring is fragmentary. It has long been supposed that the ring arises from the purine ring, and this has been supported, to some extent, recently by chemical and microbiological work. It is possible to convert 2-hydroxypurine into a pteridine in the test tube, and in good yield in the presence of a 2-

carbon fragment such as glyoxal (*113*), but purines such as 6-hydroxy- or 2-amino-6-hydroxypurine are converted in very low yield. It has been shown in butterflies that C^{14}-labeled precursors are incorporated into the pyrimidine portion of the pteridine nucleus of leucopterin in the same manner as into the purine ring (*114*) and that 1-C^{14}-labeled glucose appears predominantly in the 6- and 7-positions (*115*). C^{14}-Labeled glucose has also been claimed to be incorporated into the pteridines of *Drosophila*, but not into the purines (*116*). The synthesis of a radioactive pteridine from guanine-2-C^{14} in the larva of the amphibian *Xenopus* has been claimed (*117*), but the experimental technique is open to objection in this case. The one clear-cut case of the incorporation of a purine into a pteridine is in connection with the biosynthesis of riboflavin in the mold *Eremothecium ashbyii*. The pyrimidine ring of adenine-U-C^{14} is incorporated into riboflavin *in toto* (*118*). An authentic pteridine (XXI), which appears to be a by-product of riboflavin biosynthesis in this mold, is also synthesized from a purine (*119*).

(**XXI**)

It is possible then that an intermediate of this type could represent a common precursor for riboflavin and the 2-amino-4-hydroxypteridines. Such a scheme has been postulated (*94, 120*).

The biosynthesis of the folic acid group is beginning to be understood (Eq. 6). There are two reports of enzyme reactions in bacteria which combine 2-amino-4-hydroxy-6-hydroxymethyl-5,6,7,8-tetrahydropteridine and *p*-aminobenzoic acid (*p*-ABA) or *p*-aminobenzoylglutamic acid (*p*-ABGA) to give folic acid-like compounds (*121, 122*).

This pteridine is almost certainly not the natural substrate, which could be a phosphate (*123*) or a pyrophosphate. Possibly an even simpler compound could be involved in view of the known reactivity (see above) of reduced 2-amino-4-hydroxypteridine. 2-Amino-4-hydroxy-6-carboxypteridine or xanthopterin (in the presence of cocarboxylase and biotin) may also be used for the synthesis of folic acid-like compounds in *Mycobacterium avium* (*124*).

V. Riboflavin

A. CHEMISTRY

Riboflavin is 6,7-dimethyl-9-(D-1′-ribityl)isoalloxazine (XXII).

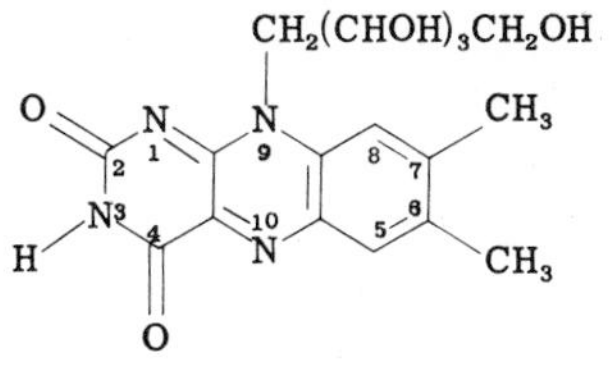
$CH_2(CHOH)_3CH_2OH$
O
N
N
CH_3
H
N
N
CH_3
O
1
2
3
4
5
6
7
8
9
10

(XXII)

The basic ring structure can be considered as a benz(1,2-*g*)pteridine, and this serves to connect riboflavin with the pteridines chemically. Biologically a pteridine is implicated in the biosynthesis of riboflavin (see below), and numerous observations have been recorded of a close association of riboflavin and pteridines in animal tissues (*125*).

Although riboflavin is frequently found in biological materials, it is active as a catalyst or cofactor only in the form of one of two derivatives, flavin mononucleotide (FMN) and flavin adenine dinucleotide (FAD). Flavin mononucleotide was first isolated from old yellow enzyme (*126*) and it has been synthesized (*127*). It is riboflavin-5′-phosphoric acid. The second and probably most common coenzyme, FAD (XXIII), was isolated in 1938 (*128*) in a sufficient state of purity to determine its structure. It was synthesized in 1954 (*129*).

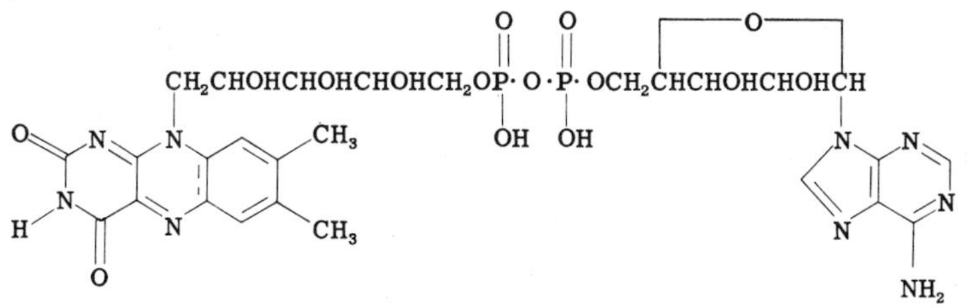
O O
O
$CH_2CHOHCHOHCHOHCH_2OP\cdot O\cdot P\cdot OCH_2CHCHOHCHOHCH$
OH OH
O
N
N
CH_3
H
N
N
CH_3
O
N
N
N
N
NH_2

(XXIII)

A riboflavin-5'-glucoside has been prepared from riboflavin by the action of an enzyme preparation from rat liver (*130*), and some microorganisms appear to be able to make similar glycosides (*131*). The significance of these compounds is not understood. Flavin compounds of a more complex nature have been reported (*132*), but none of these is well characterized.

Many excellent articles and reviews are available on the chemistry and biochemistry of riboflavin and its derivatives (*14, 15, 132,* etc.).

B. Function

The biological activity of the flavin compounds FMN and FAD resides in the redox properties of the isoalloxazine ring. Addition of hydrogens to the 1- and 10-positions produces a colorless, leuco form which spontaneously reoxidizes in the presence of oxygen. In biological systems, this addition probably takes place in two steps through a stabilized semiquinone radical, and it is possible that metals bound to a protein and chelated to the riboflavin coenzyme through position 10 and the oxygen at position 4 are involved (*133*).

It is beyond the scope of this article to deal with the many enzymes having FMN or FAD as prosthetic groups. These have been dealt with in great detail in many recent reviews and text books.

C. Occurrence

Riboflavin or one of its phosphorylated derivatives has been isolated from a wide variety of natural sources, and it probably occurs in all living cells. For example, an extensive survey (*14*) utilizing materials from eight different phyla (Chordata, Arthropoda, Mollusca, Annelida, Protozoa, Bacteria, Fungi, and Spermatophytes) revealed the universal presence of riboflavin (and folic acid). Quantitative figures for the riboflavin (or folic acid) content of these different organisms are not very reliable, however, in view of the multiple and tightly bound forms now known to occur. The ability to synthesize riboflavin, however, is probably restricted to microorganisms and to the plant kingdom. Higher animals require it as a vitamin. Some microorganisms produce very large amounts of flavin compounds and are used extensively in the commercial production of the compound. They have also been utilized to good effect in studying the biosynthesis of riboflavin.

D. Biosynthesis

The general outline of the biosynthesis of riboflavin, at least in the molds *Eremothecium ashbyii* and *Ashbya gossypii* and in the yeast *Candida flaveri,* all of which produce large amounts of it, has been elucidated in the last few years. As with the pteridines it has long been felt that riboflavin arises from a purine ring, and some nutritional data have been adduced in support of this (*134*). In 1956, however, more precise evidence was obtained when it was shown that the pyrimidine portion of adenine-U-C^{14} was incorporated intact into the riboflavin molecule in *E. ashbyii* (*118*). About the same time a greenish fluorescent compound was isolated from cultures of *E. ashbyii* and its structure (XXIV) was determined by degradation and synthesis (*135, 136*). This

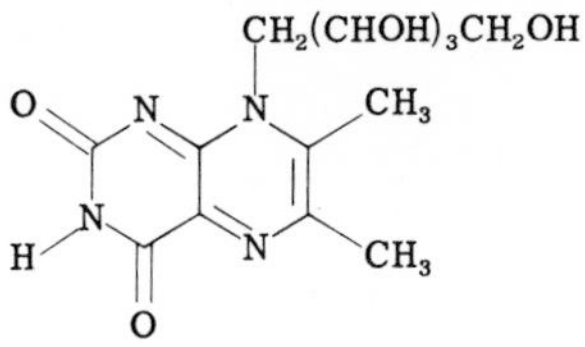

(XXIV)

compound could be converted chemically, by reaction with diacetyl or acetoin, to riboflavin (*137*). More recently this conversion has been brought about by the use of enzyme extracts from a number of organisms (*120, 138*), although in this case the extra four carbons appear to come from two molecules of pyruvic acid rather than from acetoin (see, however, *139*). It appears, then, that the purine precursor is first converted to a pyrimidine, which then in the form of a ribityl derivative condenses with acetoin (*140*) to give (XXIV), and thence to riboflavin (Eq. 7).

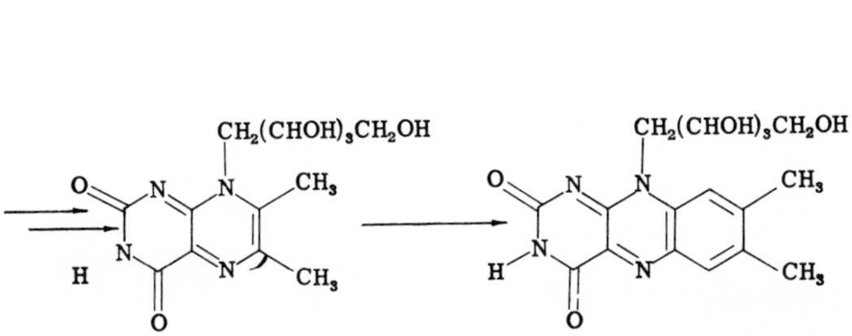

(7)

In support of the concept of a pyrimidine intermediate, a small amount of 2,4-dihydroxy-5,6-diaminopyrimidine has been isolated in the form of a derivative from cultures of *A. gossypii* (*141*).

The nature of the immediate purine precursor remains to be demonstrated, since it is obviously not adenine. In growth experiments correlated with flavin production in *C. flaveri* it has been shown that guanine and xanthine stimulate the production of flavins (*142*). In one form or another, then, one of these is probably the immediate precursor. The origin of the ribityl group and the place in the reaction sequence at which it becomes attached are also not known. Guanosine, for example, loses its ribosyl group before it is incorporated into riboflavin.

A second colorless, purple fluorescing pteridine has been isolated from *E. ashbyii* (*143*). Its structure has been shown by degradation and synthesis to be (XXI) (*144*). As mentioned previously this also derives its pyrimidine ring from a purine (*119*). However, it is not incorporated into riboflavin and indeed appears to be on a side pathway, being derived enzymatically (*138*) from (XXIV) (Eq. 8).

$$(8)$$

The synthesis of FMN and FAD follow conventional pathways. Thus the formation of FMN is catalyzed by a flavokinase from yeast (*145*) according to the scheme:

$$\text{Riboflavin} + \text{ATP} \xrightarrow{\text{Mg}^{++}} \text{FMN} + \text{ADP}$$

A similar enzyme has been shown to be present in rat intestinal mucosa (*146*), plants (*147*), and other microorganisms.

The synthesis of FAD involves FMN in the following way (*148*):

$$\text{FMN} + \text{ATP} \rightarrow \text{FAD} + \text{Pyrophosphate}$$

Again, enzyme activity has been found in a variety of different sources (*132*). There may be a second pathway to FAD directly from riboflavin (*149*):

$$\text{Riboflavin} + \text{ATP} \rightarrow \text{FAD} + \text{Pyrophosphate}$$

but this is not well established.

VI. Conclusion

A brief outline has been presented of the chemistry, biochemistry, and biological activity of compounds that contain the pteridine ring.

This has been extended to include riboflavin, which, although not strictly a pteridine, appears to be closely related biosynthetically. The chemistry and some of the functions of the folic acid groups are now well understood, as is the case with riboflavin. Also, the majority of the simple pteridines have probably been described. However, many important questions remain to be answered. For example, what is the biochemistry underlying the effect of leucovorin on cell division? What is the relationship between the folic acid group and the simple pteridines? It is to be noted that, in general, simple organisms produce only folic acid-like compounds, whereas more complex organisms may not be able to make these, yet have an abundance of simple pteridines. Are the simple compounds, then, to be considered as degradation or excretion products of folic acid, or do they have important biological functions in their own right? How is the pteridine ring made in nature, and what complex interactions are involved in the control of its synthesis? These and many other questions remain to be answered by future work in this fascinating field of natural materials.

References

1. F. G. Hopkins, *Nature* **40**, 335 (1889).
2. O. Kühling, *Chem. Ber.* **28**, 1968 (1895).
3. R. Purrmann, *Ann. Chem. Liebigs* **544**, 182 (1940).
4. R. Purrmann, *Ann. Chem. Liebigs* **546**, 98 (1941).
5. R. Purrmann, *Ann. Chem. Liebigs* **548**, 284 (1941).
6. W. Koschara, *Z. physiol. Chem.* **240**, 127 (1936).
7. W. Koschara, *Z. physiol. Chem.* **277**, 159 (1943).
8. W. Koschara, *Z. physiol. Chem.* **277**, 284 (1943).
9. E. E. Snell and W. H. Peterson, *J. Bacteriol.* **39**, 273 (1940).
10. H. K. Mitchell, E. E. Snell, and R. J. Williams, *J. Am. Chem. Soc.* **63**, 2284 (1941).
11. R. B. Angier, J. H. Boothe, B. L. Hutchings, J. H. Mowat, J. Semb, E. L. R. Stokstad, Y. SubbaRow, C. W. Waller, D. B. Cosulich, M. J. Fahrenbach, M. E. Hultquist, E. Kuh, E. H. Northey, D. R. Seeger, J. P. Sickels, and J. M. Smith, Jr., *Science* **103**, 667 (1946).
12. J. R. Totter, *Ann. Rev. Biochem.* **26**, 192 (1957).
13. M. Gates, *Chem. Revs.* **41**, 63 (1947).
14. R. J. Williams, R. E. Eakin, E. Beerstecher, Jr., and W. Shive, "The Biochemistry of the B Vitamins." Reinhold, New York, 1950.
15. E. L. R. Stokstad, R. S. Harris, and F. H. Bethell, *in* "The Vitamins" (W. H. Sebrell, Jr., and R. S. Harris, eds.), Vol. III, Chapter 13. Academic Press, New York, 1954.
16. A. Albert, *Quart. Revs.* **6**, 197 (1952).
17. A. Albert, *Fortschr. Chem. org. Naturstoffe* **11**, 351 (1954).
18. H. A. Nathan and J. Cowperthwaite, *J. Protozool.* **2**, 37 (1955).
19. E. L. Patterson, H. P. Broquist, A. M. Albrecht, M. H. von Saltza, and E. L. R. Stokstad, *J. Am. Chem. Soc.* **77**, 3167 (1955).
20. H. S. Forrest and H. K. Mitchell, *J. Am. Chem. Soc.* **77**, 4865 (1955).
21. R. Huttel and G. Sprengling, *Ann. Chem. Liebigs* **554**, 69 (1943).

22. H. S. Forrest and H. K. Mitchell, *J. Am. Chem. Soc.* **76**, 5656 (1954).
23. M. Viscontini, E. Hadorn, and P. Karrer, *Helv. Chim. Acta* **40**, 579 (1957).
24. E. L. Rickes, L. Chaiet, and J. C. Keresztesy, *J. Am. Chem. Soc.* **69**, 2749 (1947).
25. D. E. Wolf, R. C. Anderson, E. A. Kaczka, S. A. Harris, G. E. Arth, P. L. Southwick, R. Mozingo, and K. Folkers, *J. Am. Chem. Soc.* **69**, 2753 (1947).
26. M. Silverman, J. C. Keresztesy, and G. J. Koval, *J. Biol. Chem.* **211**, 53 (1954).
27. J. H. Mowat, J. H. Boothe, B. L. Hutchings, E. L. R. Stokstad, C. W. Waller, R. B. Angier, J. Semb, D. B. Cosulich, and Y. SubbaRow, *J. Am. Chem. Soc.* **70**, 14 (1948).
28. J. J. Pfiffner, S. B. Binkley, E. S. Bloom, R. A. Brown, O. D. Bird, A. D. Emmet, A. G. Hogan, and B. L. O'Dell, *Science* **97**, 404 (1943).
29. B. L. Hutchings, E. L. R. Stokstad, N. Bohonos, N. H. Sloane, and Y. SubbaRow, *J. Am. Chem. Soc.* **70**, 1 (1948).
30. J. H. Boothe, J. Semb, C. W. Waller, R. B. Angier, J. H. Mowat, B. L. Hutchings, E. L. R. Stokstad, and Y. SubbaRow, *J. Am. Chem. Soc.* **71**, 2304 (1949).
31. J. J. Pfiffner, D. G. Calkins, E. S. Bloom, and B. L. O'Dell, *J. Am. Chem. Soc.* **68**, 1392 (1946).
32. J. C. Keresztesy and M. Silverman, *J. Am. Chem. Soc.* **73**, 5510 (1951).
33. W. Shive, T. J. Bardos, T. J. Bond, and L. L. Rogers, *J. Am. Chem. Soc.* **72**, 2817 (1950).
34. A. Pohland, E. H. Flynn, R. G. Jones, and W. Shive, *J. Am. Chem. Soc.* **73**, 3247 (1951).
35. *cf.* D. D. Woods, *in* "Chemistry and Biology of the Pteridines" (G. E. W. Wolstenholme, and M. P. Cameron, eds.), p. 220. Churchill, London, 1954.
36. B. E. Wright, *J. Am. Chem. Soc.* **77**, 3930 (1955).
37. B. E. Wright, *Proc. 4th Intern. Congr. Biochem. Vienna, 1958* **11**, 266 (1960).
38. F. M. Huennekens, M. J. Osborn, and H. R. Whitely, *Science* **128**, 120 (1958).
39. F. M. Huennekens and M. J. Osborn, *Advances in Enzymol.* **21**, 369 (1959).
40. J. C. Rabinowitz, *in* "The Enzymes" (P. D. Boyer, H. Lardy, and K. Myrbäck, eds.), Vol. 2, p. 185. Academic Press, New York, 1960.
41. J. M. Peters and D. M. Greenberg, *Nature* **181**, 1669 (1958).
42. S. Futterman, *J. Biol. Chem.* **228**, 1031 (1957).
43. M. J. Osborn and F. M. Huennekens, *J. Biol. Chem.* **233**, 969 (1958).
44. B. E. Wright, M. L. Anderson, and E. C. Herman, *J. Biol. Chem.* **230**, 271 (1958).
45. G. R. Greenberg, L. Jaenicke, and M. Silverman, *Biochim. et Biophys. Acta* **17**, 589 (1955).
46. M. Silverman, J. C. Keresztesy, G. J. Koval, and R. C. Gardiner, *J. Biol. Chem.* **226**, 83 (1957).
47. J. C. Rabinowitz and W. E. Pricer, Jr., *J. Am. Chem. Soc.* **78**, 5702 (1956).
48. M. J. Osborn, E. N. Vercamer, P. T. Talbert, and F. M. Huennekens, *J. Am. Chem. Soc.* **79**, 6565 (1957).
49. M. J. Osborn and F. M. Huennekens, *Biochim. et Biophys. Acta* **26**, 646 (1957).
50. J. M. Buchanan and S. C. Hartman, *Advances in Enzymol.* **21**, 199 (1959).
51. W. Shive, W. W. Ackermann, M. Gordon, M. E. Getzendaner, and R. E. Eakin, *J. Am. Chem. Soc.* **69**, 725 (1947).
52. M. Friedkin and A. Kornberg, *in* "The Chemical Basis of Heredity" (W. D. McElroy and B. Glass, eds.), p. 609. Johns Hopkins, Baltimore, 1957.
53. R. L. Kisliuk and D. D. Woods, *Biochem. J.* **75**, 467 (1960).

54. J. R. Guest and K. M. Jones, *Biochem. J.* **75,** 12p (1960).
55. R. L. Kisliuk and W. Sakami, *J. Biol. Chem.* **214,** 47 (1954).
56. W. Jacobson, *in* "The Chemistry and Biology of the Pteridines" (G. E. W. Wolstenholme and M. P. Cameron, eds.), p. 329. Churchill, London, 1954.
57. M. Webb, *in* "The Chemistry and Biology of the Pteridines" (G. E. W. Wolstenholme and M. P. Cameron, eds.), p. 253. Churchill, London, 1954.
58. G. W. Kidder, *Arch. Biochem. Biophys.* **9,** 51 (1946).
59. T. D. Luckey, J. R. Pleasants, M. Wagner, H. A. Gordon, and J. A. Reyniers, *J. Nutrition* **57,** 169 (1955).
60. S. H. Hutner, H. A. Nathan, and H. Baker, *Vitamins and Hormones* **17,** 1 (1959).
61. H. S. Forrest and H. K. Mitchell, *J. Am. Chem. Soc.* **77,** 4865 (1955).
62. M. Viscontini, M. Schoeller, E. Loeser, P. Karrer, and E. Hadorn, *Helv. Chim. Acta* **38,** 397 (1955).
63. H. S. Forrest, C. Van Baalen, and J. Myers, *Science* **125,** 699 (1957).
64. M. Viscontini and H. R. Weilenmann, *Helv. Chim. Acta* **42,** 1854 (1959).
65. C. Van Baalen and H. S. Forrest, *J. Am. Chem. Soc.* **81,** 1770 (1959).
66. R. Tschesche and F. Korte, *Chem. Ber.* **84,** 641 (1951).
67. R. Purrmann and F. Eulitz, *Ann. Chem. Liebigs* **559,** 169 (1948).
68. R. Tschesche and H. Ende, *Chem. Ber.* **91,** 2074 (1958).
69. R. Tschesche, F. Korte, and G. Heuschkel, *Chem. Ber.* **88,** 1251 (1955).
70. H. S. Forrest, C. Van Baalen, and J. Myers, *Arch. Biochem. Biophys.* **78,** 95 (1958).
71. H. S. Forrest, Private communication (1959).
72. T. Kauffmann, *Ann. Chem. Liebigs* **625,** 133 (1959).
73. H. S. Forrest, D. Hatfield, and C. Van Baalen, *Nature* **183,** 1269 (1959).
74. M. Viscontini and E. Mohlmann, *Helv. Chim. Acta* **42,** 836 (1959).
75. M. Viscontini and E. Mohlmann, *Helv. Chim. Acta* **42,** 1679 (1959).
76. E. Lederer, *Biol. Revs. Cambridge Phil. Soc.* **15,** 273 (1946).
77. M. Viscontini, E. Hadorn, and P. Karrer, *Helv. Chim. Acta* **40,** 579 (1957).
78. C. V. Tondo, F. Lewgoy, and A. R. Cordeiro, *Rev. brasil. biol.* **19,** 367 (1959).
79. H. S. Forrest, E. Glassman, and H. K. Mitchell, *Science* **124,** 725 (1956).
80. E. Hadorn and I. Schwinck, *Nature* **177,** 940 (1956).
81. E. Glassman and H. K. Mitchell, *Genetics* **44,** 153 (1959).
82. O. H. Lowry, O. A. Bessey, and E. J. Crawford, *J. Biol. Chem.* **180,** 389 (1949).
83. J. A. Blair, *Biochem. J.* **68,** 385 (1958).
84. C. Oshima, T. Seki, and H. Ishizaki, *Genetics* **41,** 4 (1956).
85. H. S. Forrest, *in* "Pigment Cell Biology" (M. Gordon, ed.), p. 619. Academic Press, New York, 1959.
86. A. Butenandt, *in* "Perspectives in Organic Chemistry" (A. R. Todd, ed.), p. 495. Interscience, New York, 1956.
87. E. G. Krebs and E. R. Norris, *Arch. Biochem. Biophys.* **24,** 49 (1949).
88. A. Wacker and E.-R. Lochmann, *Z. Naturforsch.* **14b,** 222 (1959).
89. A. Wacker, E.-R. Lochmann, and S. Kirschfeld, *Z. Naturforsch.* **14b,** 150 (1959).
90. C. Van Baalen, H. S. Forrest, and J. Myers, *Proc. Natl. Acad. Sci. U. S.* **43,** 701 (1957).
91. H. S. Forrest, *Abstr. 17th Intern. Congr. Pure and Appl. Chem., Munich, 1959* **2,** 40 (1960).
92. S. Kaufman, *J. Biol. Chem.* **234,** 2677 (1959).

93. B. Levenberg and O. Hayaishi, *J. Biol. Chem.* **234,** 955 (1959).

94. H. A. Nathan, S. H. Hutner, and H. L. Levin, *Nature* **178,** 741 (1956).

95. D. L. Fox, "Animal Biochromes and Structural Colors." Cambridge Univ. Press, London and New York, 1953.

96. I. Ziegler-Gunder, *Biol. Revs. Cambridge Phil. Soc.* **31,** 313 (1956).

97. M. O'L. Crowe and A. Walker, *Science* **110,** 166 (1949).

98. R. Tschesche and F. Vester, *Chem. Ber.* **86,** 454 (1953).

99. F. B. Cousins, *Biochim. et Biophys. Acta* **40,** 532 (1960).

100. F. T. Wolf, *Nature* **180,** 860 (1957).

101. Y. Kaneko, *J. Agr. Chem. Soc. Japan* **31,** 118 (1957).

102. M. Polonovski, H. Jerome, and P. Gonnard, *in* "Chemistry and Biology of the Pteridines" (G. E. W. Wolstenholme and M. P. Cameron, eds.), p. 124. Churchill, London, 1954.

103. J. Leclercq, *Nature* **165,** 367 (1950).

104. L. E. Burgess, *Arch. Biochem. Biophys.* **20,** 347 (1949).

105. A. Butenandt and H. Remboldt, *Z. physiol. Chem.* **311,** 79 (1958).

106. M. Polonovski and E. Fournier, *Compt. rend. soc. biol.* **138,** 357 (1944).

107. P. Karrer, C. Manunta, and R. Schwyzer, *Helv. Chim. Acta* **31,** 1214 (1948).

108. T. Hama, *Experientia* **9,** 299 (1953).

109. T. Hama and M. Obika, *Experientia* **14,** 182 (1958).

110. J. A. Blair, *Nature* **180,** 1371 (1957).

111. J. L. Hubby and L. H. Throckmorton, *Proc. Natl. Acad. Sci. U. S.* **46,** 65 (1960).

112. T. Kauffmann, *Z. Naturforsch.* **14b,** 358 (1959).

113. A. Albert, *Biochem. J.* **65,** 124 (1957).

114. F. Weygand and M. Waldschmidt, *Angew. Chem.* **67,** 328 (1955).

115. F. Weygand, H. J. Schliep, H. Simon, and G. Dahms, *Angew. Chem.* **71,** 522 (1959).

116. O. Brenner-Holzach and F. Leuthardt, *Helv. Chim. Acta* **42,** 2254 (1959).

117. I. Ziegler-Gunder, H. Simon, and A. Wacker, *Z. Naturforsch.* **11b,** 82 (1956).

118. W. S. McNutt, *J. Biol. Chem.* **219,** 365 (1956).

119. W. S. McNutt and H. S. Forrest, *J. Am. Chem. Soc.* **80,** 951 (1958).

120. G. F. Maley and G. W. E. Plaut, *J. Am. Chem. Soc.* **81,** 2025 (1959).

121. T. Shiota, *Arch. Biochem. Biophys.* **80,** 155 (1959).

122. G. M. Brown, *Abstr. 17th Intern. Congr. Pure and Appl. Chem., Munich, 1959* **2,** 28 (1959).

123. T. Shiota and M. N. Disraely, *Bacteriol. Proc.* (*Soc. Am. Bacteriologists*) **60,** 174 (1960).

124. N. Katunuma, T. Shoda, and H. Noda, *J. Vitaminol.* (*Osaka*) **3,** 77 (1957).

125. R. G. Busnel, *Compt. rend. acad. sci.* **214,** 189 (1942).

126. H. Theorell, *Biochem. Z.* **278,** 263 (1935).

127. R. Kuhn, H. Rudy, and F. Weygand, *Chem. Ber.* **69,** 1543 (1936).

128. O. Warburg and W. Christian, *Biochem. Z.* **298,** 150 (1938).

129. S. M. H. Christie, G. W. Kenner, and A. R. Todd, *J. Chem. Soc.* p. 46 (1954).

130. L. J. Whitby, *Biochem. J.* **50,** 433 (1952).

131. S. Tachibana and H. Katagiri, *Vitamins* (*Kyoto*) **8,** 304 (1955).

132. H. Beinert, *in* "The Enzymes" (P. D. Boyer, H. Lardy, and K. Myrbäck, eds.), Vol. 2, p. 339. Academic Press, New York, 1960.

133. H. R. Mahler, *Advances in Enzymol.* **17,** 233 (1956).

134. J. A. McLaren, *J. Bacteriol.* **63,** 233 (1952).

135. T. Masuda, *Pharm. Bull.* (*Tokyo*) **4,** 375 (1956).

136. T. Masuda, T. Kishi, M. Asai, and S. Kuwada, *Chem. & Pharm. Bull.* (*Tokyo*) **7,** 361 (1959).

137. T. Masuda, *Pharm. Bull.* (*Tokyo*) **5,** 136 (1957).

138. S. Kuwada, T. Masuda, T. Kishi, and M. Asai, *Pharm. Bull.* (*Tokyo*) **6,** 619 (1958).

139. T. W. Goodwin and D. H. Treble, *Biochem. J.* **70,** 14p (1958).

140. T. Kishi, M. Asai, T. Masuda, and S. Kuwada, *Chem. & Pharm. Bull.* (*Tokyo*) **7,** 515 (1959).

141. T. W. Goodwin and D. H. Treble, *Biochem. J.* **67,** 10p (1957).

142. E. G. Brown, T. W. Goodwin, and O. T. G. Jones, *Biochem. J.* **68,** 40 (1958).

143. H. S. Forrest and W. S. McNutt, *J. Am. Chem. Soc.* **80,** 739 (1958).

144. W. S. McNutt, *J. Am. Chem. Soc.* **82,** 217 (1960).

145. E. B. Kearny and S. Englard, *J. Biol. Chem.* **193,** 821 (1951).

146. K. Yagi, *J. Biochem.* (*Tokyo*) **41,** 757 (1954).

147. K. V. Giri, P. R. Krishnaswamy, and N. A. Rao, *Biochem. J.* **70,** 66 (1958).

148. A. W. Schrecker and A. Kornberg, *J. Biol. Chem.* **182,** 795 (1950).

149. F. Ito and K. Ota, *Vitamins* (*Kyoto*) **3,** 27 (1950).

CHAPTER 14

Carotenoids: Structure, Distribution, and Function

T. W. GOODWIN

Department of Agricultural Biochemistry, University College of Wales,
Penglais, Aberystwyth, United Kingdom

I. Introduction

The carotenoids probably represent the most widespread group of naturally occurring pigments, for they are universally present in photosynthetic organisms, spasmodically encountered in the nonphotosynthetic tissues of higher plants and in fungi and bacteria, and present in at least one species of almost all forms of animal life. They are synthesized *de novo* only by the higher plants and the protista; all animal carotenoids are derived from these two sources, although they may have been slightly altered, by oxidative metabolism, before being accumulated in the various animal tissues.

The carotenoids belong to the terpenoid group of compounds which are built up from isoprenoid residues:

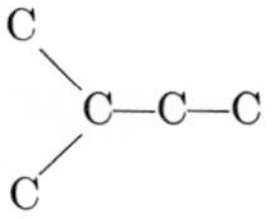

$$\begin{array}{c} C \\ \diagdown \\ C{-}C{-}C \\ \diagup \\ C \end{array}$$

643

Almost all naturally occurring carotenoids are tetraterpenoids (the exceptions are crocetin and bixin) containing 8 isoprenoid residues (40 carbon atoms) arranged in the molecule as if two 20 C units, formed by the head-tail condensation of 4 isoprenoid residues, had combined tail to tail; one implication of this structure is that the two lateral methyl groups near the center of the molecule are in position 1,6 whereas all other lateral methyl groups are in position 1,5 (Fig. 1).

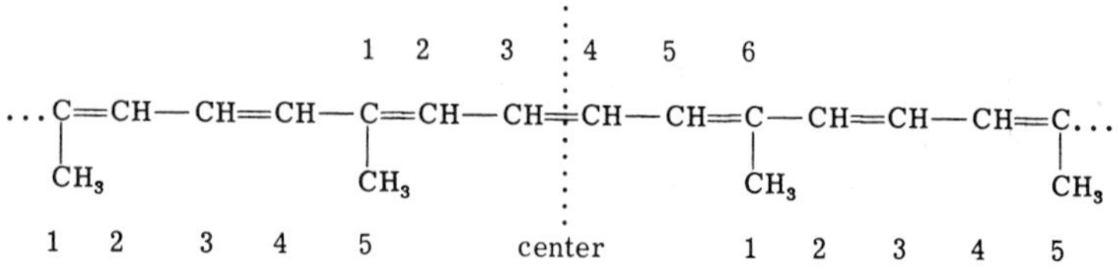

Fig. 1. Arrangement of methyl groups at the center of a carotenoid molecule.

Both cyclic and acyclic carotenoids are known; their color is due to the long series of double bonds in the molecule. Hydrocarbon carotenoids are termed carotenes, and oxygenated carotenoids xanthophylls; carotenoids containing other elements are not known. The fundamental work on the structure of carotenoids was carried out in the early 1930's mainly by Karrer and by Kuhn and their associates (1), and many have now been elegantly synthesized by Isler and his colleagues (2). The basic structure and numbering of the carotenoid molecule is illustrated in detail by reference to α-carotene (I).

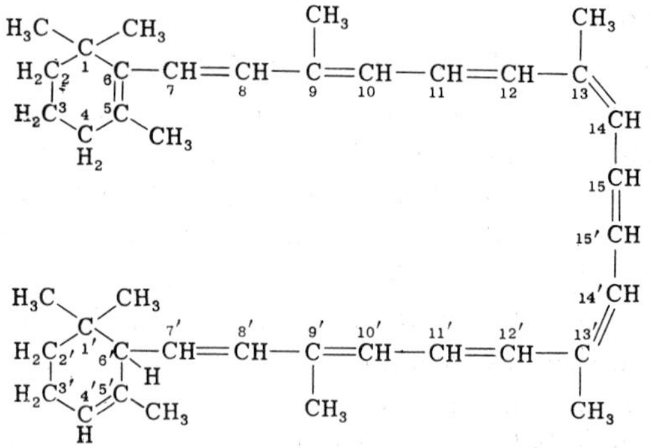

(I)

This pigment contains a β-ionone and an α-ionone residue. When a carotenoid molecule is not symmetrical, the plain numerals are assigned to the half of the molecule containing a β-ionone residue, and the prime numerals to the remaining half. Two shorthand formulas are used in this chapter. These are illustrated here as β-carotene (two β-ionone residues) (II) and lycopene (two pseudoionone residues) (III); formulas based on (II) are used when the structure between

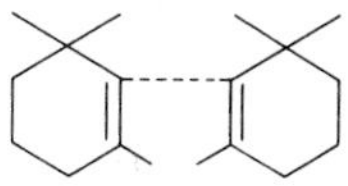

(II)

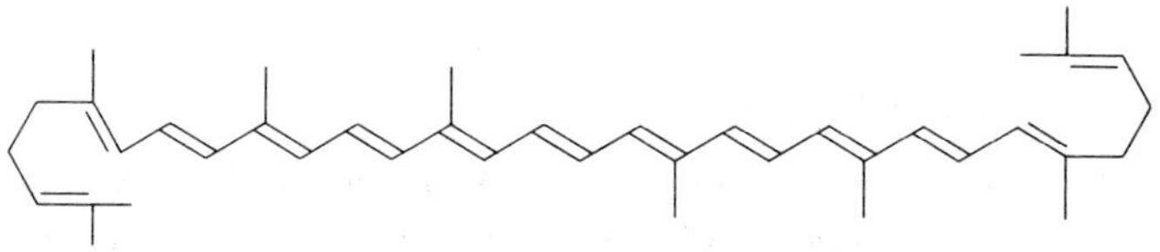

(III)

C-7 and C-7′ is the same as in α-carotene, and formulas based on (III) are used when there has been some modification in this region of the molecule.

The oxygen function in carotenoids can take many forms and these are dealt with in the appropriate sections.

The *cis*-isomers occur in nature and can also be produced chemically in a number of ways; this aspect of carotenoid chemistry has been the special province of Zechmeister (3, 4). The isomers most frequently encountered usually have *cis*-configurations around the ethylenic bonds attached to C-9,-9′,-13,-13′,-15 and -15′. Rotation about the bonds attached to C-7,-7′,-11, and -11′ is hindered because of the overlap of the methyl group on the carbon atoms attached to the double bonds; however, some hindered *cis* isomers are known to exist naturally. Stereoisomers of carotenoids are named according to their chromatographic behavior. An isomer is named by prefixing neo- to the name of the pigment and suffixing T,U,V, etc., or A,B,C, etc., according to the position on a chromatogram relative to the parent pigment; T,U,V, etc., are used if the pigments are more strongly adsorbed, and A,B,C, etc., if they are less strongly adsorbed. Some naturally occurring isomers that possess hindered configurations have been termed procarotenoids. As the configurations of the various isomers are elucidated, then this nomenclature can gradually be replaced by a more direct system; for example neo-β-carotene B (IV) is 3,6,-di-*cis*-β-carotene; the italicized numerals apply to the double bonds in the molecule.

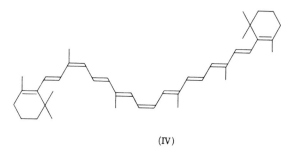

(IV)

II. Structures of Naturally Occurring Carotenoids

A. CAROTENES

1. *Fully Unsaturated Polyenes*

Apart from α- and β-carotenes and lycopene, which have just been discussed, the only other fully unsaturated carotenes known are γ-carotene (V), δ-carotene (VI), and leprotene. This structure of δ-carotene is still in doubt. The structure of leprotene ($C_{40}H_{54}$) is not known. Torulene has recently been reported to be 3′,4′-dehydro-γ-carotene (*4a*).

(V)   (VI)

2. *Partly Saturated Carotenes*

A series of partly saturated carotenes has recently been observed in various plant tissues (Table I) (*5*). All the compounds appear to be lycopene derivatives; phytofluene and phytoene are colorless and exhibit characteristic absorption maxima in the ultra violet region of the spectrum.

3. *Cis Isomers*

Many *cis* isomers of the various carotenes already discussed have been unequivocally detected in nature (Table II) (*1, 4, 6, 7, 8*). It should be emphasized that extreme care is necessary in order to exclude the appearance of some *cis* isomers as artifacts. Phytofluene is interesting in that its naturally occurring configuration is *cis* (*9*); there is no evidence that all-*trans*-phytofluene is a natural product.

TABLE I
NATURALLY OCCURRING, PARTLY SATURATED CAROTENES

Name	Structure	Original source
ε-Carotene	Unknown	Diatoms
ζ-Carotene	7,8,7′,8′-tetrahydrolycopene	Carrot, root
θ-Carotene	Unknown	*Neurospora crassa*
Flavacene	Unknown	*Aphanizomenon flos-aquae*
Neurosporene	5,6-Dihydrolycopene	*Neurospora crassa*
Phytoene[a]	7,8,11,12,7′,8′,11′,12′-Octahydrolycopene	Tomato, fruit
Phytofluene[a,b]	7,8,11,12,7′,8′-Hexahydrolycopene[c]	Tomato, fruit
α-Zeacarotene	7′,8′-dihydro-δ-carotene	Maize
β-Zeacarotene	7′,8′-dihydro-γ-carotene	Maize

[a] These compounds are colorless.
[b] The naturally occurring isomer has a *cis* configuration.

TABLE II
NATURALLY OCCURRING *cis* ISOMERS OF CAROTENES

Name	Configuration	Original source
Neo-β-carotene B	3,6-di-*cis*	Green leaves
Neo-β-carotene U	3-*cis*	Green leaves
Neoneurosporene P	Unknown	*Pyracantha angustifolia*, berries
Phytofluene[a]	Unknown	Tomato, fruit
Pro-γ-carotene[b]	poly-*cis*	*Butia capitata*, fruit
Prolycopene[b,c]	poly-*cis*	*Pyracantha angustifolia*, berries

[a] The all-*trans* form does not occur naturally.
[b] These contain hindered *cis* configurations.
[c] Other poly-*cis* lycopenes are also present.

B. XANTHOPHYLLS

1. *Hydroxylated Carotenoids*

The hydroxylated carotenoids of known structure are listed in Table III (*1, 10*). An important common property is that the hydroxyl groups are, with only two known exceptions (chloroxanthin and rhodopin), always attached to carbons 3 and/or 3′. The hydroxyl group can exist either free or esterified. Xanthophylls that are well characterized but whose structures are still unknown include taraxanthin (*1*), sarcinaxanthin (*1*), myxoxanthophyll (*1*), and corynexanthin (*11*). A new structure appears in eschscholtzxanthin (VII); in all structures so far considered the link between the ring systems and the aliphatic chain joining the rings is a

TABLE III

NATURALLY OCCURRING HYDROXYLATED CAROTENOIDS

Name	Structure	Original source
Celaxanthin	3′,4′-Dehydrorubixanthin	*Celastus scandens*, berries
Chloroxanthin	1-Hydroxy-2-hydro-neurosporene	*Rhodopseudomonas spheroides*, mutant
Cryptoxanthin	3-Hydroxy-β-carotene	*Physalis* spp., berries
α-Cryptoxanthin	3′-Hydroxy-α-carotene	*Physalis* spp., berries
Diadinoxanthin	Closely related to lutein	Diatoms
Diatoxanthin	Closely related to zeaxanthin	Diatoms
Eschscholtzxanthin	3,3′-Dihydroxyretro-β-carotene[a]	*Eschscholtzia californica*, petals
Gazaniaxanthin	1′,2′-Dihydrorubixanthin	*Gazania rigens*, petals
3-Hydroxy-α-carotene	—	Orange, fruit
Lutein	3,3′-Dihydroxy-α-carotene	Green leaves
Lycophyll	3,3′-Dihydroxylycopene	*Solanum dulcamara*, berries
Lycoxanthin	3-Hydroxylycopene	*Solanum dulcamara*, berries
Phytofluenol[b]	Hydroxyphytofluene	Tomato, fruit
Rhodopin	1-hydroxy-2-hydrolycopene	Purple bacteria
Rubixanthin	3-Hydroxy-γ-carotene	*Rosa rubiginosa*, berries
Zeaxanthin	3,3′-Dihydroxy-β-carotene	Maize
Zeinoxanthin	3′-Hydroxy-α-carotene	Maize

[a] Also termed 3,3′-dihydroxydehydro-β-carotene.
[b] Colorless.

single bond and the compounds are said to have a *normal* (cyclo-hexenyl) structure. When a double bond forms the link, as in esch-scholtzxanthin, a *retro* (cyclohexylidene) structure is obtained (*6*).

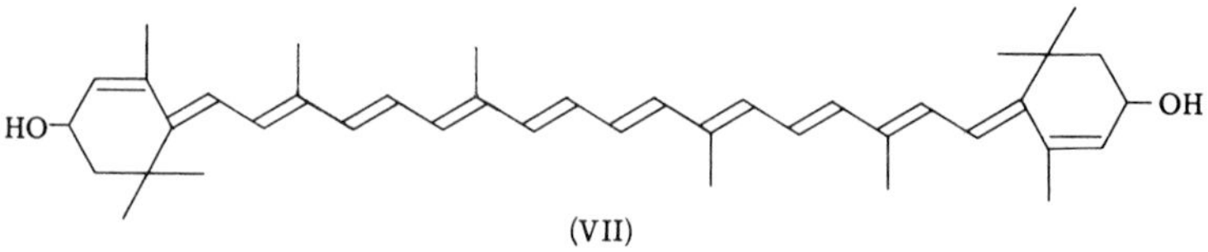

(VII)

2. Methoxylated Carotenoids

The methoxylated carotenoids of known structure are listed in Table IV (*5, 13*). They are all lycopene derivatives, and in contrast to all hydroxylated xanthophylls with the exception of rhodopin and chloroxan-thin (*12*) they are substituted at position 1, but not at position 3. Fur-thermore, rhodopin and chloroxanthin exist only in association with the methoxylated carotenoids and are, in fact, their biosynthetic precursors.

TABLE IV
NATURALLY OCCURRING METHOXYLATED CAROTENOIDS

Name	Structure	Original source
P-481[a]	(VIII)	*Rhodospirillum rubrum*
P-512[a]	Unknown	*Rhodopseudomonas gelatinosa*
Pigment Y	(IX)	*Rhodopseudomonas spheroides*
Rhodovibrin (Hydroxy P-481)	(X)	*Rhodospirillum rubrum*
Spheroidenone[b]	(XI)	*Rhodopseudomonas spheroides*
Spirilloxanthin[c]	(XII)	*Rhodospirillum rubrum*

[a] The number indicates the position of the main absorption maximum in light petroleum.

[b] Also called pigment R.

[c] Also called rhodoviolascin.

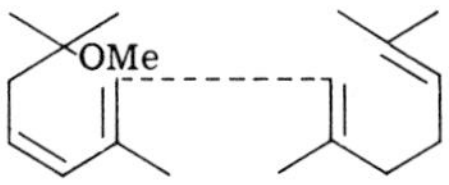

(VIII)

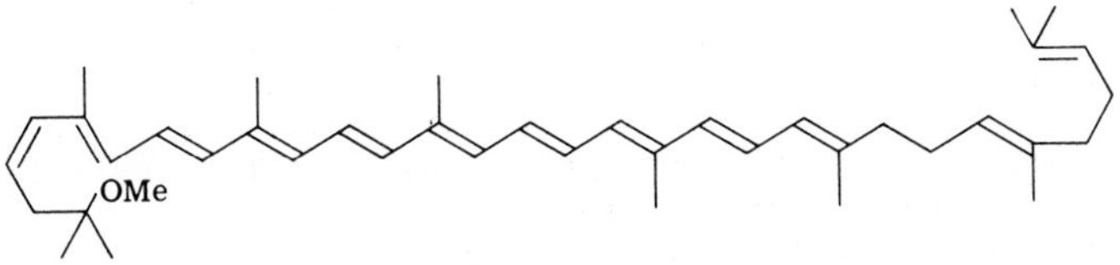

(IX)

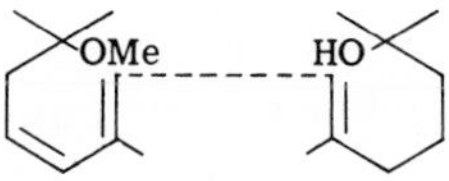

(X)

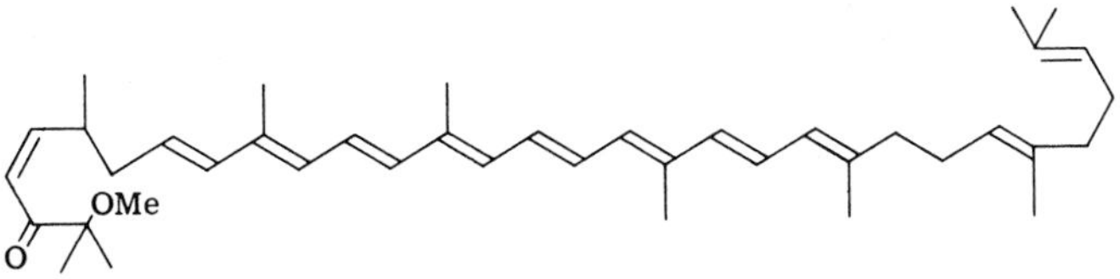

(XI)

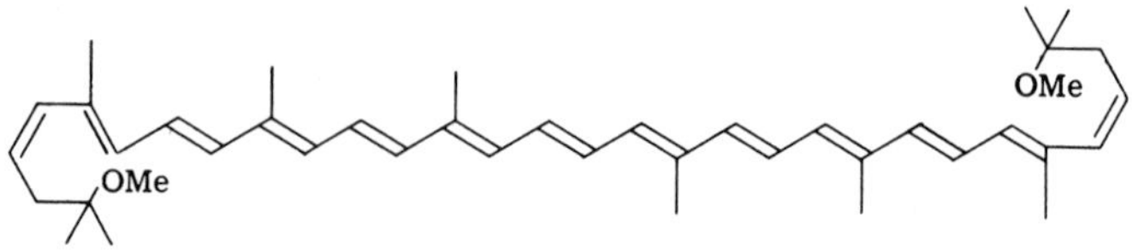

(XII)

3. Oxocarotenoids

The various carotenoids known to contain oxo groupings are given in Table V. With one exception, rhodoxanthin (XIII) which has a

TABLE V
NATURALLY OCCURRING OXOCAROTENOIDS

Name	Structure	Original source
Astaxanthin[a]	3,3'-Dihydroxy-4,4'-dioxo-β-carotene	*Homarus vulgaris*, eggs and carapace
Canthaxanthin	4,4'-Dioxo-β-carotene	*Cantharellus cinnabarinus*
Capsanthin	See formula (XIV)	*Capsicum annuum*
Capsorubin	See formula (XV)	*Capsicum annuum*
Echinenone[b]	4-Oxo-β-carotene	*Strongylocentrotus lividus*, gonads
Rhodoxanthin	3,3'-Dioxoretro-β-carotene	*Potamogeton natans*
Spheroidenone	See Table IV	*Rhodopseudomonas spheroides*

[a] Under alkaline conditions rapidly oxidized to astacin (3,3',4,4'-tetraoxo-β-carotene), which is generally considered to be an artifact.

[b] Probably identical with myxoxanthin and aphanin.

retro structure, the oxo function does not appear at C-3 and C-3'. Of special interest is the recent work on the structures of capsanthin (XIV) and capsorubin (XV). The pigments are unique among the carotenoid series in that they contain pentane rings (*14*).

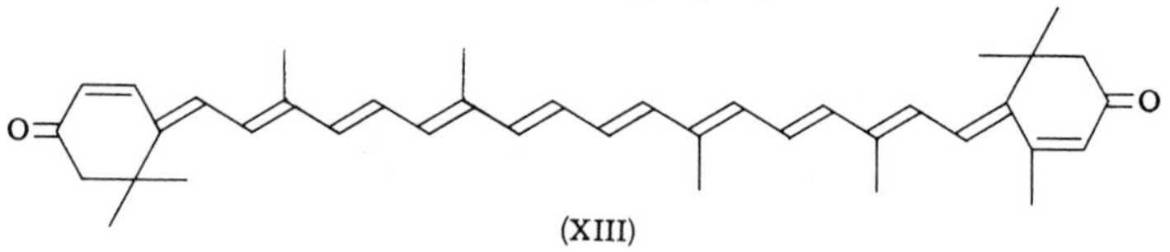

(XIII)

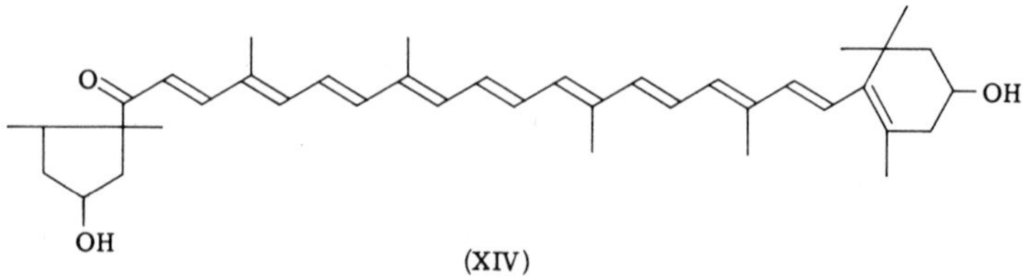

(XIV)

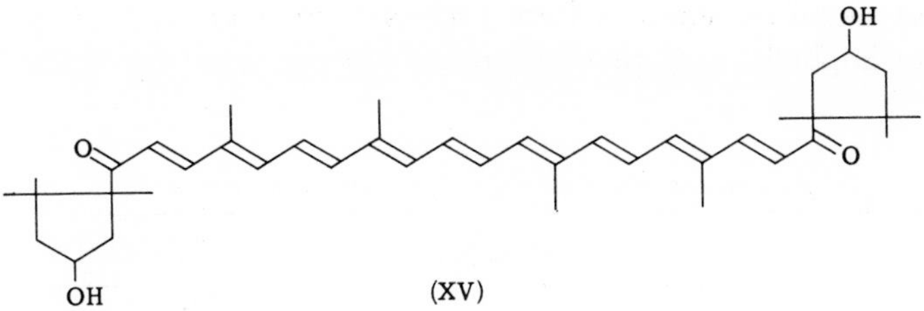

(XV)

4. Epoxycarotenoids

Two types of carotenoid epoxide exist in nature: they are 5,6-epoxides (XVI) and 5,8-epoxides (XVII). Mono and di-5,6- or 5,8-epoxides of both carotenes and xanthophylls are regularly encountered, but molecules containing both the 5,6- and 5,8-structures (luteochrome) (XVIII) have been reported only occasionally (*15, 16*). Tables VI and VII summarize the known naturally occurring epoxides. Many strongly

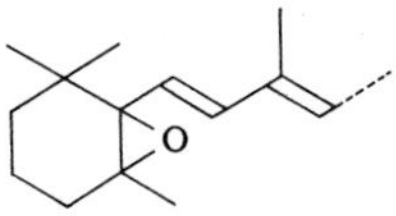

(XVI)

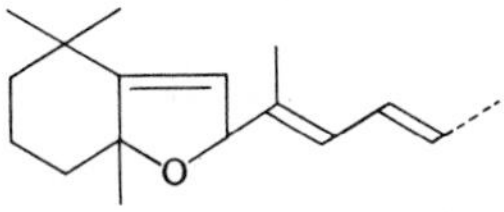

(XVII)

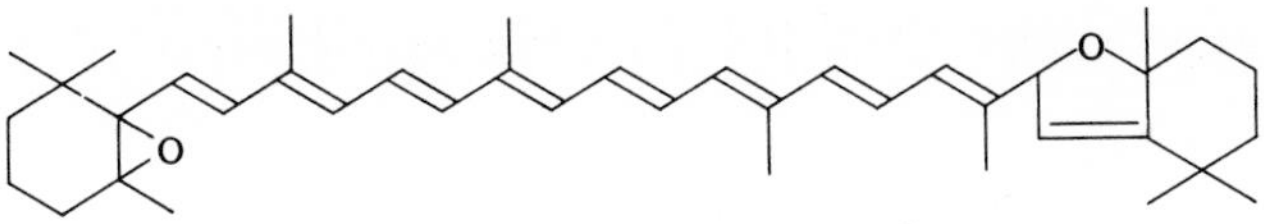

(XVIII)

TABLE VI
NATURALLY OCCURRING CAROTENOID 5,6-EPOXIDES

Name	Structure	Original source
Antheraxanthin[a,b]	5,6-Epoxyzeaxanthin	*Lilium tigrinum*, pollen
α-Carotene 5,6-epoxide	—	*Tragopogon pratensis*, flowers
Isolutein[c]	5,6-Epoxylutein	Green leaves
Neoxanthin	3,3',5'(or 6')-trihydroxy-6'-(or 5')-hydro-5,6-epoxy-β-carotene	Green leaves
Trollixanthin[b]	(?) 6'-Hydroxylutein 5,6-epoxide	*Trollius europaeu.*, petals
Violaxanthin	5,6,5',6'-diepoxyzeaxanthin	*Viola tricolor*, petals

[a] Probably identical with petaloxanthin.

[b] *Cis* isomers also occur.

[c] Identical with eloxanthin.

adsorbed pigments reported from various sources (1, 10) are probably epoxyxanthophylls, e.g., pectenoxanthin (1).

TABLE VII

NATURALLY OCCURRING CAROTENOID 5,8-EPOXIDES

Name	Structure	Original source
Aurochrome	5,8,5′,8′-Diepoxy-β-carotene	*Cotoneaster bullata*, berries
Auroxanthin	5,8,5′,8′-Diepoxyzeaxanthin	*Viola tricolor*, petals
Chrysanthemaxanthin	5,8-Epoxylutein	Aster, petals
Cryptochrome	5,8,5′,8′-Diepoxycryptoxanthin	Orange, fruit
Cryptoflavin	5,8-Epoxycryptoxanthin	Orange, fruit
Flavochrome	5,8-Epoxy-α-carotene	Orange, fruit
Flavoxanthin	5,8-Epoxylutein	*Ranunculus acer*, petals
Mutatochrome	5,8-Epoxy-β-carotene	Orange, fruit
Mutatoxanthin	5,8-Epoxyzeaxanthin	Orange, fruit
Rubichrome	5,8-Epoxyrubixanthin	*Tagetes patula*, petals
Trollichrome	Furanoid form of trollixanthin	*Trollius europaeus*, petals

5. Carboxycarotenoids

If the structural criteria laid down in the definition of a carotenoid (page 644) are strictly applied, then only two carotenoid acids are known, bixin (XIX) and crocetin (XX). The configuration of naturally occurring bixin has recently been settled with the aid of nuclear magnetic resonance studies (17). It is an 8-mono-*cis* derivative. It will also

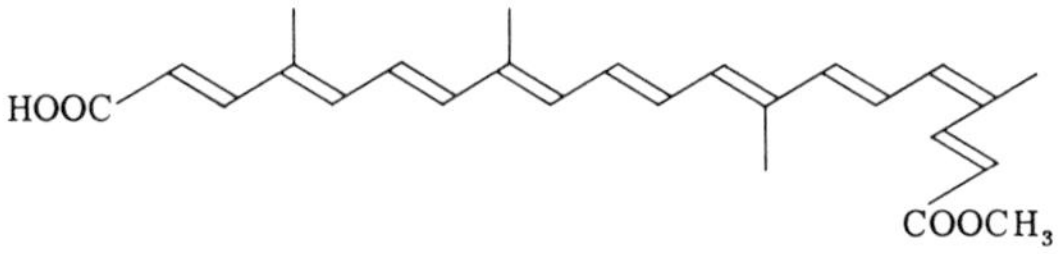

(XIX)

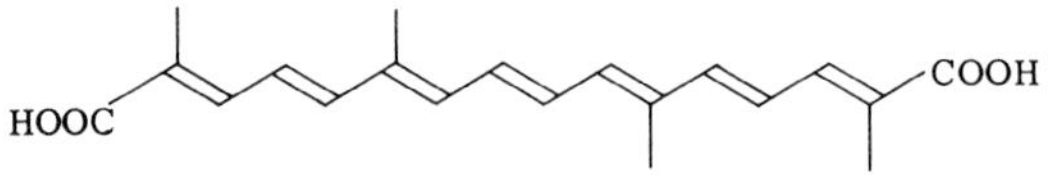

(XX)

be noted that it is a monomethylester of a dicarboxylic acid. Crocetin is very similar to bixin but contains four carbon atoms less. It occurs in either the free state or, in greater amounts, as the digentiobioside crocin (1). A labile naturally occurring methyl ester is a *cis* isomer of undetermined configuration. Two other polyene acids have been described. Torularhodin (XXI) occurs in red yeasts (18) and azafrin (XXII) is found in the roots of *Escobedia* spp. (1).

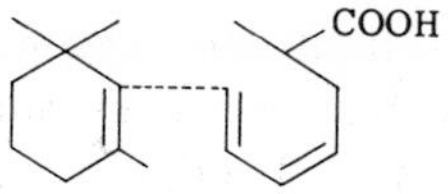

(XXI)

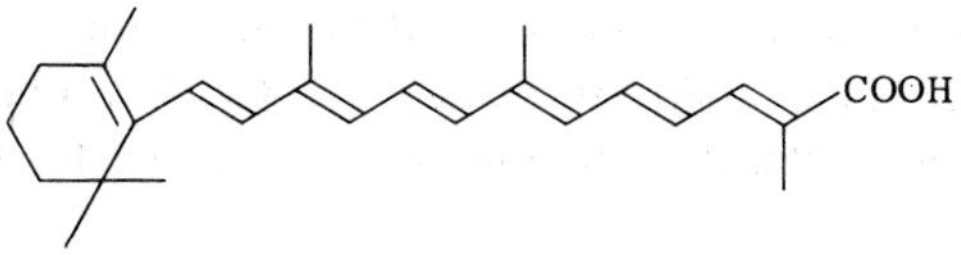

(XXII)

C. CAROTENOIDS WITH UNIQUE STRUCTURES

Mention has already been made of capsanthin and capsorubin (Section II, B, 3), which contain pentanoid rings. Further unique pigments are renieratene (XXIII) and isorenieratene (XXIV), isolated from the sponge *Reniera japonica* (*19*); these pigments contain two aromatic rings. Fucoxanthin ($C_{40}H_{56}O_6$), probably the most abundant naturally occurring carotenoid, still defies the efforts of the organic chemist. It is

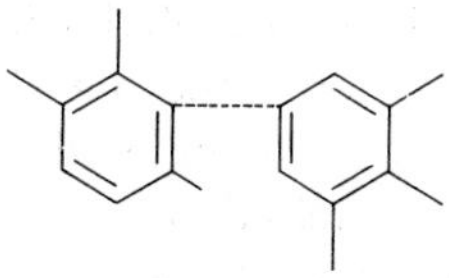

(XXIII)

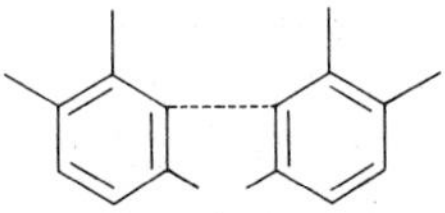

(XXIV)

destroyed by alkali and uniquely contains a $C=C=C$ grouping (*8*). Two carotenoids isolated from sea urchin eggs, paracentrotin A and paracentrotin B, must have unique structures, judging from their behavior toward alkali. As isolated they exhibit slightly unsymmetrical spectra (λ_{max}, light petroleum, 488–490 $m\mu$ and 480 $m\mu$, respectively). On addition of KOH their spectra shift to shorter wavelengths and exhibit a typical triple-banded carotenoid spectrum (λ_{max}, light petroleum, 435, 460, and 486 $m\mu$ and 430, 455, and 480 $m\mu$, respectively) (*20*).

III. Distribution in Nature

A. OCCURRENCE IN PHOTOSYNTHETIC ORGANISMS

All photosynthetic organisms contain, in addition to chlorophylls, carotenoid pigments. The investigations of Stanier and his colleagues (*21*) on carotenoidless mutants of photosynthetic bacteria indicate that carotenoids function primarily by protecting the cells against photosensitization caused by light absorbed by the chlorophyll molecule. The combined effect of light and oxygen is lethal to the mutant; neither light nor oxygen alone has any deleterious effect. On this view aerobic photosynthesis as we know it today exists only because the synthesis of carotenoids and chlorophylls have run parallel during the evolution of the chloroplast. Furthermore, this hypothesis relegates to an ancillary role the function of carotenoids in absorbing light in the blue region of the spectrum and passing the energy on to chlorophyll; this increases the efficiency of photosynthesis but is not essential to the process (22).

1. Higher Plants

All green plants so far examined contain the same major carotenoids, β-carotene, lutein, violaxanthin, and neoxanthin; α-carotene may or may not accompany β-carotene, and cryptoxanthin and zeaxanthin may or may not accompany lutein (5, 8). They are located in the grana of the chloroplasts, where they exist as water-soluble chromoproteins, probably within the lamellae of the grana (23). The xanthophylls are always unesterified; this is unlike the situation in many fruits. The quantitative variations in the carotenoid components of chloroplasts of different plants can, however, be considerable. The reported existence of cis isomers of β-carotene and of epoxides must be accepted with reserve. The first could be artifacts whereas the latter could be due to the oxidation of the normal constituent carotenoids in material which was not examined immediately after collection. Excised leaves when kept in the dark soon accumulate carotenoid epoxides at the expense of the original pigments present (24). All the carotenoids in green leaves contain two ring systems. No acyclic carotenoids have ever been reported in green leaves, but the colorless polyenes phytofluene and phytoene are present in minute traces in many plants (25, 26); it would be interesting to determine whether they are located in the chloroplasts or not. Phytoene does, however, accumulate in the leaves of a peculiar tomato phenotype (ghost, gh) which appears spontaneously in tomato lines carrying normal red fruit (27).

Rhodoxanthin has been reported in certain Potamogeton spp. and in the bronze winter needles of conifers [e.g., Cryptomeria japonica (5)]. There is yet no information as to the location of this pigment in these plants.

2. Bryophytes and Pteridophytes

All the rather meager information concerning the bryophytes and pteridophytes points to a carotenoid distribution qualitatively very similar to that in green leaves (8), although two pteridophytes Equise-

tum and *Selaginella* contain rhodoxanthin. As with *Potamogeton* and *Cryptomeria,* the location of this pigment in the cells of these pterido-phytes is not known.

3. Thallophytes

a. Lichens. Only one lichen, *Ramelia reticulata,* has been examined in detail; its carotenoid distribution is similar to that in green leaves (28).

b. Algae. The general distribution of carotenoids in the various algal classes is given in Table VIII (5, 8, 10, 29). In all cases the pigments are concentrated in the chloroplasts. The unicellular green algae have the same carotenoid composition as green plants.

The photosynthetic regions of all the colonial Chlorophyceae, with the exception of the Siphonales, also contain the "leaf plastid" carote-noids. The Siphonales are unique in that they synthesize a character-istic pigment, siphonaxanthin, structure unknown, as their main xantho-phyll (28). It would again be very interesting to know if this pigment was present in the plastids or not, especially as it exists mainly in the esterified form as siphonein. α-Carotene rather than β-carotene appears to be the chief carotene in Siphonales.

The Euglenophyta (Euglenineae) have a unique carotenoid distribu-tion for the main pigments are β-carotene, antheraxanthin and neoxan-thin; traces of echinenone and other keto-carotenoids are also present (29a).

The Phaeophyceae and Bacillariophyceae are characterized by the presence of large amounts of fucoxanthin, which replaces lutein as the major xanthophyll. The conjugation of fucoxanthin with its apoprotein causes a marked bathochromic shift (about 40 mμ) in its absorption spectrum; this is the main cause of the characteristic color of these classes. Apart from the report of minute amounts of a β-carotene chromo-protein in green leaves (30) with a bathochromic shift of about 60 mμ, the fucoxanthin complex is the only example of such a complex in photosynthetic tissues. Many, however, occur in lower animals, espe-cially marine invertebrates. The diatoms (Bacillariophyceae) contain small amounts of two pigments, diatoxanthin and diadinoxanthin, which closely resemble but are not identical with zeaxanthin and lutein, respectively (28).

The Heterokontae (Xanthophyceae) are characterized by the syn-thesis of β-carotene and 3 or 4 xanthophylls (31), which are unique and which appear to be related to zeaxanthin.

The component carotenoids of pure cultures of members of the class Chrysophyceae have only recently been investigated (32). *Ochromonas*

TABLE VIII

MAJOR CAROTENOID DISTRIBUTION IN VARIOUS ALGAL CLASSES[a,b]

(+ = present; − = absent; ? possibly present in traces)

	Chlorophyta		Xanthophyceae (Heterokontae)	Phaeophyta			Rhodophyta	Pyrrophyta	Euglenophyta	Archephyta	Cryptophyta
	Charophyceae[c]	Chlorophyceae		Bacillariophyceae (Diatomophyceae)	Chrysophyceae	Phaeophyceae	(Rhodophyceae)	(Dinophyceae)	(Euglenineae)	(Cyanophyceae)	(Cryptophyceae)
Carotenes											
α-Carotene	−	+[c]	−	−	−	−	+	−	−	−	+
β-Carotene	+	+[c]	+	+	+	+	+	+	+	+	+
γ-Carotene	+	+[f]	−	+	−	−	−	−	−	−	−
ε-Carotene	−	?	−	+	−	−	−	−	−	+	−
Flavacene	−	−	−	−	−	−	−	−	−	+	−
Xanthophylls											
Echinenone	−	−	−	?	−	−	−	−	+	+	−
Lutein	+	+	−	+	+	−	+	−	+	?	−
Zeaxanthin	+	+	−	−	−	−	−	−	+	+	+[g]
Violaxanthin	+	+	−	−	−	−	−	−	+	−	−
Flavoxanthin	−	−	−	−	−	?	−	−	−	−	−
Neoxanthin	+	+	−	−	−	−	−	−	+	−	−
Antheraxanthin	−	−	−	−	−	−	−	−	−	−	+
Fucoxanthin	−	−	−	+	+	+	−	−	−	−	−
Diatoxanthin	−	−	−	+	−	?	−	−	+	−	−
Diadinoxanthin	−	−	−	+	−	−	−	−	−	−	−
Dinoxanthin	−	−	−	−	−	−	−	+	−	−	−
Peridinin	−	−	−	−	−	−	−	+	−	−	−

Myxoxanthophyll	—	—	—	—	—	—	—	+	—	—
Siphonaxanthin	+[d]	—	—	—	—	—	—	—	—	—
Astaxanthin	+[e]	—	—	—	—	—	—	+[h]	—	—
Oscillaxanthin	—	—	—	—	—	—	—	—	+[h]	—

[a] Occasional variations from this general picture are discussed in the text.
[b] No information exists on the carotenoids of the Chloromonadophyta (Chloromonadineae).
[c] Only one species (*Chara fragilis*) studied; lycopene also reported present.
[d] The main pigments of the Siphonales.
[e] The main pigments (haematochrome).
[g] The pigment present may be diatoxanthin.
[h] Not present in every species.

danica and *Prymnesium parvum* have a carotenoid distribution similar to that found in the brown algae and diatoms. β-Carotene is present, but fucoxanthin is the main pigment, representing some 75% of the total. Zeaxanthin and diatoxanthin are also present in traces.

The carotenoids in the members of the Dinophyceae, Cryptophyceae, and Cyanophyceae so far examined are all characteristically different from those of the members of the other classes examined. The main pigment of the Dinophyceae is a xanthophyll of unknown structure, peridinin, which is said to be identical with sulcatoxanthin ($C_{40}H_{52}O_8$), first isolated from the sea anemone *Anemonia sulcata* (*1, 8*). The single member of the Cryptophyceae so far examined in pure culture, *Cryptomonas ovata*, synthesizes zeaxanthin or the closely related diatoxanthin (*33*) as the main xanthophyll; no other photosynthetic organism yet examined has this distribution.

The carotenoids synthesized in the blue-green algae are also unique, the main pigments being β-carotene, echinenone, and myxoxanthophyll (*34*). The last has not been found in any other photosynthetic plant or in fruit, flowers, or roots. Echinenone occurs in certain marine invertebrates but because of its very restricted distribution in the plant world, its quantitative determination in lake deposits may be a means of determining the growth of blue-green algae in the past (*35*). Myxoxanthophyll, of unknown structure (*1*), was until recently considered specific to the Cyanophyceae, but it is now reported to be synthesized by a strain of *Mycobacterium phlei* (*36*).

Perhaps the most interesting of the algae recently examined with respect to pigments is *Cyanidium caldarium*. Taxonomically it can be considered a green alga, although its claims to be classed as a blue-green alga would appear to be strong when considered on purely biochemical grounds, because it synthesizes phycocyanins and chlorophyll a but not chlorophyll b. Both these properties are characteristic of the Cyanophyceae. The carotenoids present are, however, characteristic of neither the Chlorophyceae nor the Cyanophyceae; they consist of a relatively large proportion of β-carotene (over 50% of the total pigments), with zeaxanthin the main xanthophyll (*32*). The high percentage of β-carotene is reminiscent of the Cyanophyceae (*34*), but the only other alga which is known to produce zeaxanthin or a closely related pigment as the main xanthophyll is, as just discussed, *Cryptomonas ovata* (Cryptophyceae). The carotenoid distribution in *C. caldarium* is, therefore, not incompatible with the view that it is a transitional form between the cryptomonads and the green algae, because it is possible that the cryptomonads represent a primitive flagellate group from which the Chlorophyceae have developed.

The carotenoids in the algae exist along with the chlorophylls in the chloroplasts. They are confined to the lamellae, which are unrestricted in distribution and not concentrated into grana as in higher plants (22).

4. Photosynthetic Bacteria

The photosynthetic bacteria are usually classified by being placed in suborder III (Rhodobacterineae) of the order Eubacteriales. The Rhodobacterineae are further subdivided into purple bacteria and green sulfur bacteria. The purple bacteria are separated into two families: the Thiorhodaceae, which accumulate intracellular sulfur globules when grown in the presence of H_2S, and the Athiorhodaceae, which do not accumulate such globules (37).

a. *The Purple Bacteria.* The carotenoid distribution in the purple bacteria is summarized in Table IX (38). The two marked differences between this group of organisms and all other photosynthetic organisms are: (a) the bacterial pigments are all open-chain carotenoids derived from lycopene; and (b) the oxygen function in the xanthophylls frequently exists as the methoxyl grouping. The purple bacteria can be divided into those that produce spirilloxanthin and those that do not. Those that do not can be further subdivided into two subgroups. One group comprises organisms that under anaerobic conditions are yellowish and brown and synthesize mainly pigment Y, but under aerobic conditions or after exposure of anaerobic cultures to air are brownish red, owing to the conversion of pigment Y into spheroidenone (pigment R) (*R. capsulatus, R. gelatinosa, R. spheroides*) (5, 21). The second group *Rhodospirillum molischianum, R. photometricum,* and probably *R. fulvum* do not produce carotenoids more unsaturated than lycopene or P-481 and are thus brownish rather purple (39). *Rhodomicrobium vannielii* is an interesting organism in that according to its carotenoid make up it could be considered a typical member of the purple bacteria (40); on morphological grounds, however, this classification is doubtful (41).

b. *The Green Sulfur Bacteria. Chlorobium* is the only genus of the green sulfur bacteria that has been investigated. All species of *Chlorobium* contain the same carotenoids, γ-carotene together with small amounts of pro-γ-carotene and rubixanthin (42). *Chlorobium* spp. are unique among photosynthetic organisms in a number of ways; for example, (a) they contain more carotenes than xanthophylls; (b) they contain γ-carotene as their main pigment; (c) they contain a poly-*cis* isomer (pro-γ-carotene).

The purple bacteria do not contain chloroplasts but submicroscopic photoactive particles (diameter about 50 mμ) called chromatophores in

TABLE IX

Carotenoid Distribution in Purple Photosynthetic Bacteria[a]

Organism	Lycopene	P-481	Y	Spheroidenone (R)	Spirilloxanthin	Rhodopin	Rhodovibrin	Hydroxy-Y	P 512	Hydroxyspheroidenone	(?) Demethylated spirilloxanthin
Athiorhodaceae											
Rhodopseudomonas capsulatus	+	−	+	+	−	−	−	+	−	+	−
Rhodopseudomonas gelatinosa	?	−	+	+	+	−	−	+	+	+	−
Rhodopseudomonas palustris	+	+	−	−	+	+	+	−	−	−	+
Rhodopseudomonas spheroides	+	−	+	+	?	−	−	+	−	+	−
Rhodospirillum molischianum	+	+	−	−	−	+	+	−	−	−	−
Rhodospirillum photometricum	+	+	−	−	−	+	+	−	−	−	?
Rhodospirillum rubrum	+	+	−	−	+	+	+	−	−	−	+
Thiorhodaceae											
Chromatium spp.	+	+	−	−	+	+	?	−	−	−	−

[a] Symbols: +, present; −, absent; ?, possibly present in traces.

which the carotenoids and chlorophylls are concentrated (*43*). Similar particles exist also in the green sulfur bacteria (*44*). These particles correspond to the grana of the higher plants. Nothing is known of the fine structure of the chromatophores.

B. General Comparison of Photosynthetic Organisms

1. Carotenoid Formation during Growth

a. Qualitative Changes. During the growing period the carotenoids of higher plants and most algae examined do not alter qualitatively (*5*). On the other hand, young cells of some photosynthetic bacteria synthesize pigments which, as the cells mature, are converted into the characteristic pigment of fully developed cultures. For example, 24–36-hour cultures of *Rhodospirillum rubrum* contain lycopene, rhodopin, P-481, and hydroxy P-481 (rhodovibrin) (*45*); on resuspension of these cells in phosphate buffer the pigments are converted sequentially into spirilloxanthin (*5*). The relative amounts of β-carotene and echinenone in the blue-green alga *Anabaena variabilis* vary with the cultural conditions, but the details have not yet been fully examined (*46*).

As the leaves of deciduous trees reach senescence and fall, the carotenoids change qualitatively and gradually disappear; no such changes have been observed in old cultures of algae or photosynthetic bacteria. The changes that occur during leaf senescence can vary according to species; for example in both the oak (*Quercus robur*) and sycamore (*Acer pseudoplatanus*) β-carotene and neoxanthin disappear first and xanthophyll epoxides appear in small amounts; in sycamore leaves, however, lutein and violaxanthin are esterified during the later stages of necrosis. These esters are found almost entirely in the cell sap—not in the chloroplasts (*47*).

b. Quantitative Changes. In all three cases growth tends to proceed faster than carotenogenesis during the early stages, later they run parallel, and finally, in the case of the higher plants only, the carotenoids disappear (*5*). The disappearance is much less marked in leguminous than in nonleguminous plants (*10*).

2. Effect of Light

Etiolated seedlings of monocotyledons generally synthesize small amounts of xanthophylls qualitatively similar to the plastid carotenoids, but with β-carotene present only in minute traces; these pigments are extraplastidic. On illumination, the seedlings develop chloroplasts in which the typical "plastid carotenoids" and chlorophylls are synthesized

(48). In the one dicotyledon so far examined in detail (dwarf bean, *Phaseolus vulgaris*), the situation is different; the true leaves synthesize the expected carotenoids, whereas the main carotenoids in the cotyledons are chrysanthemaxanthin and auroxanthin. On illumination, both types of leaf produce functional chloroplasts containing the plastid carotenoids (49).

The effect of light on algae varies with genus. Complete exclusion of light has no effect on carotenoid levels of *Chlorella vulgaris* growing heterotrophically (50) whereas under the same conditions the levels in *Euglena gracilis* var. *bacillaris* are only one-fifth of those found in light cultures (51). The photosynthetic bacteria cultured semi-anaerobically in the dark will synthesize carotenoids, but this synthesis is stimulated by light (52).

High light intensities reduce carotenoid levels in leaves (53), algae (54), and photosynthetic bacteria (21). There is an optimal intensity for leaves (bean) (55) and algae (*Anacystis nidulans* and *Anabaena* spp.) (56), but not for the photosynthetic bacteria. Maximal carotenoid levels in a green mutant of *Rhodopseudomonas spheroides* were obtained at the lowest light intensity examined (50 foot-candles); at 5000 foot-candles the pigment levels were some five times less (21).

3. *Carotenoids and Evolution of Photosynthetic Organisms*

The information now available on carotenoid distribution in photosynthetic organisms (discussed in Section III, A) allows one to visualize the evolution of these organisms in terms of carotenoid pigments. If one accepts as a working hypothesis the views of Dougherty and Allen (57a) on the evolution of protista, then Fig. 2 indicates the pattern of protistan evolution revealed by carotenoid studies. The evidence for these conclusions has been recently discussed in detail (57b). It is necessary here only to emphasize some of the most important points: (i) The green photosynthetic bacteria which synthesize monocyclic carotenoids (γ-carotene derivatives) can reasonably be considered as an intermediate stage between the purple bacteria (acyclic, lycopene, derivatives) and the blue green algae (bicyclic, β-carotene, derivatives). (ii) The red algae represent an increase in complexity over the blue-green algae in that they synthesize both α- and β-carotene derivatives; they can thus be considered as occupying a central position in the evolutionary development of algae. (iii) Morphologically the Cryptophyta appear to be an intermediate group between the Rhodophyta and the Phaeophyta and this is supported by carotenoid studies. (iv) All the Phaeophyta except the Heterokontae (Xanthophyceae) are characterized by the formation of fucoxanthin, a highly oxidized pigment of unknown structure; the heterokonts also synthesize highly oxidized pigments, which appear to

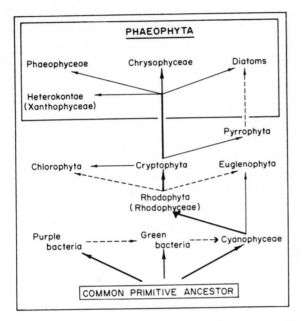

FIG. 2. Possible pattern of protistan evolution based on carotenoid studies.

be related to zeaxanthin. (v) The common formation of diadinoxanthin suggests a close relationship between the Dinophyceae (Pyrrophyta) and the diatoms (Bacillariophyceae), but in contrast, the Dinophyceae never synthesize fucoxanthin and diatoms never synthesize dinoxanthin or peridinin. (vi) The pigments of the green algae, with the exception of the Siphonales, are identical to the "mixed" (α- and β-carotene) line of the red algae, and they would appear to be closely related; in this connection it should be recalled that the green alga *Cyanidium caldarum* synthesizes mainly zeaxanthin and also phycocyanins; this supports the view that the cryptomonads may be transitional between the red and green algae. (vii) The main carotenoids of the Euglenophyta would ally this class with the blue-green algae—this is confirmed by the presence of echinenone, once considered characteristic of blue-green algae, in trace amounts in *Euglena gracilis;* however, the chlorophylls of the Euglenophytes place them with the Chlorophyta for they both synthesize chlorophylls *a* and *b*. (viii) It would appear that the Bryophyta (mosses and liverworts), Pterophyta (ferns) and Spermatophyta (seed plants) have evolved from the same stem as the Chlorophyta because, with only minor variations, they all synthesize the same carotenoid pigments.

The proposals outlined in Fig. 2 may have little contact with reality but it will be useful if they stimulate further work on carotenoid distribution in algae. This type of research is now more feasible than was possible previously; many algal species are being grown in the laboratory in pure culture for the first time, and simple screening tests for carotenoids are now available.

C. Pigment Accumulation in Nonphotosynthetic Regions of Plants

1. Algae

A group of flagellate algae are unique in that under certain conditions they form cysts in the resting state and in doing so they accumulate massive amounts of cytoplasmic carotenoids and change in color from green to red. The pigment was first known as hematochrome, but, because different algae produce various pigments, this name should now be abandoned. *Trentepohlia aurea* and *Dunaliella salina*, for example, accumulate β-carotene, whereas *Haematococcus pluvialis* accumulates astaxanthin (8, 10, 57).

2. Higher Plants

a. Fruit. Carotenoid distribution in fruit is spasmodic and unpredictable and no taxonomic correlations can be satisfactorily established. However, carotenogenic fruit can be divided into five main groups according to the pigments they synthesize on ripening (58): (a) those containing chlorophylls and the normal "plastid carotenoids" (e.g., *Sambucus nigra*); (b) those in which there is a marked synthesis of acyclic carotenoids but little stimulation of β-carotene synthesis (e.g., tomato); (c) those that synthesize large amounts of β-carotene (e.g., red palm); (d) those that synthesize large amounts of species-specific carotenoids (e.g., capsanthin in *Capsicum annuum*); and (e) those that synthesize mainly poly-*cis* carotenes (e.g., *Pyracantha angustifolia*). Many carotenoids observed in berries were previously thought to be specific to fruit (10), but as further investigations are reported, the number of such pigments is dwindling and only capsanthin and capsorubin can now be considered specifically fruit carotenoids. Rubixanthin, for example, is now known to occur in the green sulfur bacteria.

Fruit carotenoids are present in chromoplasts and, from the general properties of fruit juices, they are obviously attached to proteins. This has not, however, been demonstrated directly.

b. Flower Petals. Carotenoid distribution in flowers resembles that in fruit in being apparently fortuitous and not amenable to systemization. Almost all yellow flowers contain considerable amounts of xanthophylls and only traces of carotenes (10). The main characteristic of the xanthophyll fraction is that the pigments consist in large measure of

5,6- and 5,8-epoxides; pigments specific to petals are also encountered occasionally (e.g., eschscholtzxanthin and gazaniaxanthin), but as with fruit the list becomes smaller as information on other sources of carotenoids accumulates. The orange and orange-red colors of flower petals are also often due to the presence of carotenoids; in these cases the usual yellow epoxides are accompanied by relatively massive quantities of carotenes. The orange strains of *Calendula* spp. contain large amounts of lycopene (59) and β-carotene represents 2% of the dry weight of the red coronas of cultivated narcissi; in the red fringes of the corona of *Narcissus poeticus recurvis* it reaches the truly astonishing value of 16.5% (60).

The pigments are present in the chromoplasts, but it is not known whether they are attached to protein or not.

c. Roots. Very few roots contain significant amounts of carotenoids; in those varieties that do, carotenes generally preponderate (e.g., carrot, sweet potato) (10). In some cases poly-*cis* carotenes are synthesized (61). It is interesting that in wild carrots and in certain yellow varieties, xanthophylls preponderate among the small amounts of carotenoids present (10). β-Carotene is present in carrot roots in the form of crystalline chromoplasts which contain, in addition to protein, RNA, DNA, and phospholipids (62).

d. Pollen. The apparently haphazard distribution of carotenoids in nonphotosynthetic plant tissues is also discernible in pollen (10). The major pollen pigments are usually well-known xanthophylls, e.g., lutein and lutein 5,6-epoxide.

D. OCCURRENCE IN NONPHOTOSYNTHETIC ORGANISMS (FUNGI AND BACTERIA)

1. *Fungi*

The carotenoid distribution in fungi is, as in the case of the nonphotosynthetic regions of higher plants, apparently fortuitous (10), and no taxonomic generalizations can be made.

It is not even safe to generalize on one genus. For example, it was always considered that *Fusarium* spp. and *Penicillium* spp. did not synthesize carotenoids; recent investigations, however, have demonstrated their presence in *Fusarium aquaeductuum* (63) and *Penicillium sclerotiorum* (64).

Fungal carotenoids differ from carotenoids of higher plants and algae in three main respects: (a) β-carotene is by no means ubiquitous; (b) lutein, violaxanthin, and neoxanthin have never been detected, and zeaxanthin and cryptoxanthin only very occasionally (10, 65, 66);

(*c*) pigments characteristic of fungi are often acidic in nature, for example, torularhodin (*18*) and neurosporaxanthin (*67*). They occur in oil droplets (e.g., *Phycomyces*) or in pericapsular fat (e.g., the red yeasts) (*10*). There has as yet been no direct demonstration that they occur as chromoproteins.

Differential carotenoid distribution occurs in the two sexual forms of certain Phycomycetes. For example, the asexual and female plants of *Allomyces* spp. synthesize no carotenoids, but the male forms produce γ-carotene which is stored in the oil droplets in the cytoplasm of the gametangia (*68*). Similar differential distributions are found in the reproductive regions of certain colonial algae. For example in *Ulva* spp. (*69*).

It will be recalled that light can stimulate carotenoid synthesis in many photosynthetic systems (e.g., *Euglena*) whereas it is essential for synthesis in others (e.g., *Chlorella*). This picture is paralleled in the fungi. Light stimulates carotenoid synthesis in, among others, *Phycomyces blakesleeanus*, *Penicillium sclerotiorum*, and *Rhodotorula gracilis* (*69*). It is essential for carotenoid formation in, for example, *Fusarium oxysporum* (*70*) and certain *Cephalosporia* spp. (*71*). The photoreceptor for this effect is not known.

A triggering action of light on carotenogenesis is observed with some fungi; this has not been reported in any other class of living organisms. Exposure of dark-grown colorless conidia of *Neurospora crassa* to light and oxygen for as short a period as 1 minute allows such cultures, when returned to darkness and incubated aerobically, to synthesize carotenoids almost as effectively as when the cultures are continuously illuminated. Oxygen is mandatory both for activation and for synthesis in the dark after activation. The primary effect is not temperature dependent, but the over-all pigment production is (*72*). A similar triggering effect is observed with *Phycomyces blakesleeanus* (*73*) and *Fusarium oxysporum* (*70*).

2. Nonphotosynthetic Bacteria

In the bacteria we again encounter what appears on our present knowledge to be a completely fortuitous carotenoid distribution. The only generalization which appears from the data so far amassed is that carotenoids are absent from anaerobic organisms.

The carotenogenic bacteria are characterized by the very rare appearance of carotenes—β-carotene and leprotene in *Mycobacterium* spp., (*74*), lycopene in *Corynebacterium michiganese* (*75*), and sarcinene in *Sarcina lutea* and *Staphylococcus aureus* (*76*)—and the preponderance of highly oxygenated specific pigments whose structures have not yet been resolved (*10*, *77*).

There are no reports of the pigments existing in fat globules, but in *Corynebacterium* spp. a carotene-protein complex has been isolated and purified (*78*) and in *Micrococcus lysodeikticus* the carotenoids are located in the protoplast membrane (*79*).

There is no effect of light on carotenoid synthesis in nonphotosynthetic bacteria as there is in fungi.

Attempts to provide evidence that carotenoids have a function in nonphotosynthetic bacteria similar to that in photosynthetic bacteria have not been successful. Colorless mutants of *Corynebacterium poinsettiae* and colorless cells of the native strain (produced by growing the cells in the presence of the specific carotenoid inhibitor diphenylamine) do not show photosensitization under high light intensity (4000 foot-candles for 4 hours). However, in the presence of toluidine blue, the sensitivity to light of carotenoid-deficient cells was very marked compared with that of the normal strain. It would appear that the colorless cells do not contain sufficient amounts of a natural photosensitizing pigment to allow photosensitization to occur (*80*).

E. OCCURRENCE IN ANIMALS

The general distribution of carotenoids in the animal kingdom was discussed in detail some ten years ago (*10*, *81*). In the meantime much less new information on animal carotenoids has become available compared with information on plant carotenoids. In this section the work prior to the publication of the monographs just mentioned will be briefly summarized and the newer work discussed in more detail.

1. *Invertebrates*

a. Marine Invertebrates. The general carotenoid distribution in marine invertebrates is summarized in Table X. With the notable exception of the Cephalopoda (*10*, *82*), most marine invertebrates accumulate considerable amounts of carotenoids. The Porifera, Echinoidea, and Gastropoda accumulate mainly carotenes [including the unique renieratene (Section II, C)] and echinenone (*10*); the other phyla are characterized by polyoxygenated pigments including astaxanthin and other, less well characterized, acidic pigments. Astaxanthin is almost universally present in the Crustacea (*83–86*) and the Asteroidea (*10*, *81*) whereas the other acidic pigments are found in the Coelenterata (*10*) and Lamellibranchiata (*82*).

The Asteroidea and Crustacea resemble each other in accumulating

TABLE X

GENERAL CAROTENOID DISTRIBUTION IN MARINE INVERTEBRATES

Classification	Predominant pigments
Porifera	Carotenes, echinenone
Coelenterata	Xanthophylls and acidic carotenoids (not astaxanthin)
Echinodermata	
Asteroidea	Mainly astaxanthin
Echinoidea	Mainly β-carotene and echinenone
Mollusca	
Lamellibranchiata	Xanthophylls and acidic carotenoids (not astaxanthin)
Cephalopoda	Carotenoids present only in traces
Gastropoda	β-Carotene and echinenone, mainly
Arthropoda	
Crustacea	Astaxanthin, with traces of β-carotene, almost universally distributed

large amounts of astaxanthin both in an uncombined form and as chromoproteins of varying color; examples of chromoproteins are ovoverdin from lobster eggs and crustacyanin from lobster carapace (83). However, the Asteroidea and Crustacea differ in the fact that whereas astaxanthin is the major pigment in Crustacea, existing either alone or in conjunction with trace amounts of β-carotene (83–86), a complex mixture of carotenoids accompany astaxanthin in the asteroids (87, 88, 89). These are intermediate in oxidation state between β-carotene and astaxanthin and as such may represent intermediates in the conversion of β-carotene into astaxanthin.

Carotenoids are generally distributed throughout the body of marine invertebrates, but also they tend to accumulate in large amounts in the gonads and integument (10).

b. *Freshwater Invertebrates.* Much less is known about carotenoids in freshwater invertebrates than in marine invertebrates. Rare examples of carotenoid-free crustaceans are the cavernicolous amphipods *Niphargus* and *Gammarus pulex* sp. *subterraneus* (10) and the isopod *Asellus aquaticus cavernicolus* (90). Brought from the natural habitat to the laboratory *Gammarus* began to synthesize carotenoid, but individuals varied and eventually three genetically pure strains were separated: brown (R), olive gray ($\gamma+$), and red (90).

The carotenoprotein in the eggs of the gastropod *Pomacea canaliculata australis* has been isolated and termed ovorubin; its prosthetic group is astaxanthin (91). No marine gastropod that contains astaxanthin has been reported up to the time of writing. It is interesting that the main pigment in some herbivorous species of *Pomacea* is β-carotene (92).

c. Insects. β-Carotene is almost a universal component of the carotenoids in insects that accumulate these pigments (*10*). Occasionally lycopene is encountered, and as the insects concerned (*Coccinella septempunctata* and *Pyrrhocoris apterus*) do not consume lycopene-containing foodstuffs, its mode of formation would be well worth investigating.

The xanthophylls found in insects include lutein, taraxanthin, violaxanthin, and astaxanthin. Astaxanthin is formed in locusts and is almost certainly synthesized from dietary β-carotene (*98*).

Carotenoids play important parts not only in the general color patterns of insects (e.g., the characteristic green color of many insects is due to a mixture of blue and yellow chromoproteins, the prosthetic groups being bile pigments and carotenoids, respectively), but also in sexual dichroism. For example, immature locusts (*Locusta migratoria*) are brownish purple, but on reaching sexual maturity the females change color only slightly whereas the males turn bright yellow. This is due to the mobilization of β-carotene from the body fat into the integument (*98*).

2. Vertebrates

a. Fish. Fish are no exception to the general conclusion that most aquatic animals accumulate xanthophylls rather than carotenes. They differ from other aquatic animals, however, in the limited number of different xanthophylls detected, although the pigments are widely distributed in the various genera (*10*). The main pigments present are lutein, taraxanthin, and astaxanthin together with traces of β-carotene (*10*); astacene may also be present in some neon fishes (*93*) and a new xanthophyll, tunaxanthin, has been reported in some marine fishes (*94*). The pigments are found mainly in the skin and in ovaries. In skin they often occur in specialized cells, the chromatophores, and thus they can play an important part in producing color patterns in fish (*95*). The ovaries can accumulate large amounts of carotenoids but the pigments rarely occur in the male gonads. They are present in muscle in considerable amounts only in the Salmonoideae. As in some marine invertebrates, astaxanthin can exist in the skin as blue and purple chromoproteins (*96, 97*).

No differences in carotenoid distribution have ever been satisfactorily established between marine and freshwater fish.

Carotenoids often play an important part in sexual dichroism in fish (e.g., *Labrus mixtus* and *Crenilabius parvo* (*96, 97*)); we shall see that this happens also in insects and birds.

b. Amphibia. The carotenoids that are found in amphibia are mainly β-carotene and lutein; no new carotenoids have been reported (*10*).

c. Birds. Birds resemble all the animals so far discussed in that they accumulate mainly xanthophylls in their tissues. These are found in yolk, skin, body fat, liver, eyes, and feathers (*10*). The feather pigments are generally highly oxygenated and are formed by oxidation of dietary pigments. Lutein is a constant component of bird carotenoids and with "canary-xanthophyll" (unknown structure) and taraxanthin, is present in many yellow feathers. The coloration of red and pink feathers is often due to rhodoxanthin, e.g., in *Phoenicirens nigricollis* (*99*), or astaxanthin, e.g., in *Laniarius atrococcineus* (*100*) and *Phoenicopterus ruber* (*101*). Carotenoids play the same role in birds as in fish and insects: they contribute to the color pattern of the animals and play an essential part in sexual dichroism. For example, the nuptial display plumage of bishop birds is rich in carotenoids which are mobilized from the body fat under the influence of sex hormones (*10*).

d. Mammals. Mammals can be sharply divided into three main groups according to whether they accumulate (*a*) carotenes and xanthophylls, (*b*) primarily carotenes, or (*c*) no carotenoids. Apart from a genetic variant of the rabbit, no mammal is known that accumulates mainly xanthophylls (*10*). No mammal stores carotenoids other than those found in its diet; that is, mammals do not have the ability, noted in the lower animals, to transform dietary carotenoids into "animal carotenoids."

Man is the main animal falling into category (*a*), and the pigment distribution in human tissues tends to reflect closely the carotenoid distribution in the diet (*102*). Oxen are the main members of category (*b*), but horses, deer and Indian buffalo, among others, behave in the same way.

By far the largest number of animals fall into category (*c*); this means that, apart from converting vitamin A-active carotenoids into vitamin A, they very efficiently oxidize other carotenoids to colorless products and eventually to CO_2 and H_2O.

IV. Conclusions

A biochemist tends to look for a rationale of carotenoid distribution in nature at a molecular level; this may not always exist. We have an almost completely satisfying biochemical explanation of the universal presence of carotenoids in photosynthetic tissues, although the details are not yet known. We have no satisfactory biochemical explanation for the apparently fortuitous and haphazard distribution of carotenoids in flowers and fruit. The true explanation may be the obvious biological one which cannot be given more precise definition: the pigments may have developed during the countless years of evolution in order to attract the insects and birds which are the most effective agents for pollination and seed dispersal. However, one is completely at a loss to give even the most superficial explanation of the accumulation of carotenoids in certain plant roots.

In photosynthetic organisms, it is clear that the development of a pigment with the spectral characteristics of the fucoxanthin-protein complex was a *sine qua non* for the evolution of algae (Phaeophyceae) that would most effectively use the complete visible spectrum for photosynthesis and thus produce the largest algae (giant kelps) in the oceans. It is much more difficult at the moment to explain why the photosynthetic bacteria should evolve such very different carotenoids from those developed by other photosynthetic systems.

The β-carotene in the sporangia of many Phycomycetes probably acts as mediator in phototropic bending, but the significance of the spasmodic appearance of carotenoids in other fungi and in various bacteria is, at present, impossible to assess.

The accumulation of carotenoids in the ova of many fishes and invertebrates (asteroids, echinoderms, insects) is obviously a result of the need of the newly hatched larvae to have the correct color pattern; the pigments may also be necessary for a functional eye in animals which possess eyes. A number of lower invertebrates, e.g., hydroids, which are attached to the sea bed by stalks, move toward the light by differential growth in the same way as do plants. Carotenoids may be the photoreceptors for such responses. The comparatively huge amounts of carotenoids in other invertebrates is less easy to justify at the present time, especially in the Mollusca, for example in *Patella* and in *Pecten*. Further investigations into the early stages of the free-living larvae of these forms may reveal microscopic color patterns requiring carotenoids for their completion, or phototactic responses mediated by carotenoids.

The mobilization of carotenoids into the eggs of many avian species occurs in order to provide these animals with the right color pattern in their feathers. This, as we have seen, occurs also in many fishes and invertebrates. The same mobilization in many other avian species, such as the domestic hen, can only be considered as an evolutionary loose end, although the yellow color of the down of newly hatched chicks may have some significance.

The importance of carotenoids in mammalian metabolism is confined to the vitamin A-active carotenoids (the most important is β-carotene), which in herbivores under natural conditions are the only source of the essential vitamin A. Carotenoids per se have no function in mammals. The various ways in which mammals deal with carotenoids that are not vitamin-A-active can be satisfactorily explained on our present knowledge, but the reasons for the development of the different metabolic reactions are not immediately apparent. β-Carotene is converted into vitamin A as it passes across the intestinal wall; so that animals with β-carotene in their body tissues and circulating blood (e.g., man) are inefficient in converting β-carotene into vitamin A and/or inefficient in completely oxidizing β-carotene to CO_2 and H_2O whereas those with no tissue β-carotene (e.g., the rat) are efficient converters and/or oxidizers. The non-vitamin-A-active carotenoids (mainly xanthophylls) are presumably effectively oxidized in the rat as they cross the intestinal wall, less effectively in the cow, and least effectively in the human (102).

References

1. P. Karrer and E. Jucker, "Carotenoids" (E. A. Braude, transl.). Elsevier, Amsterdam, 1950.
2. O. Isler, M. Montavon, R. Rüegg, and P. Zeller, Ann. Chem., Liebigs 603, 129–144 (1957).
3. L. Zechmeister, Chem. Revs. 34, 267–344 (1944).
4. L. Zechmeister, Experientia 10, 1–11 (1954).
4a. R. Rüegg, U. Schwieter, G. Ryser, P. Schudel, and O. Isler, Helv. Chim. Acta 44, 985–993 (1961).
5. T. W. Goodwin, Advances in Enzymol. 21, 295–368 (1959).
6. L. Zechmeister, Fortschr. Chem. org. Naturstoffe 15, 32–82 (1958).
7. T. W. Goodwin, in "Handbook of Plant Analysis" (K. Paech and M. V. Tracey, eds.), Vol. 3, pp. 272–311. Springer, Berlin, 1955.
8. T. W. Goodwin, Ann. Rev. Biochem. 24, 497–522 (1955).
9. B. K. Koe and L. Zechmeister, Arch. Biochem. Biophys. 46, 100 (1953).
10. T. W. Goodwin, "Comparative Biochemistry of the Carotenoids." Chapman & Hall, London, 1952.
11. W. Hodgkiss, J. Liston, T. W. Goodwin, and M. Jamikorn, J. Gen. Microbiol. 11, 438–450 (1954).
12. J. B. Davis, L. M. Jackman, P. T. Siddons, and B. C. L. Weedon, Proc. Chem. Soc. pp. 261–263 (1961).
13. S. L. Jensen, Acta Chem. Scand. 13, 842–845 (1959).
14. M. S. Barber, L. M. Jackman, C. K. Warren, and B. C. L. Weedon, Proc. Chem. Soc. (London) pp. 19, 20 (1960).
15. T. W. Goodwin, Biochem. J. 62, 346–352 (1956).
16. J. Baraud, Rev. gén. botan. 65, 221 (1958).
17. M. S. Barber, L. M. Jackman, and B. C. L. Weedon, Proc. Chem. Soc. (London) pp. 23, 24 (1960).
18. R. Rüegg, W. Guex, M. Montavon, U. Schwieter, G. Saucy, and O. Isler, Chimia (Switz.) 12, 327 (1958).
19. M. Yamaguchi, Bull. Chem. Soc. Japan 31, 51, 739 (1958).
20. M. di Nicola and T. W. Goodwin, Exptl. Cell Research 7, 23–41 (1954).
21. G. Cohen-Bazire, W. R. Sistrom, and R. Y. Stanier, J. Cellular Comp. Physiol. 49, 25–67 (1957).
22. T. W. Goodwin, Atti 2° congr. intern. fotobiol., Turin, pp. 361–369 (1957).

23. T. W. Goodwin, *in* "Handbuch der Pflanzenphysiologie" (W. Ruhland, ed.), Vol. 5, pp. 394–443. Springer, Berlin, 1960.

24. J. Glover and E. R. Redfearn, *Biochem. J.* **54,** viii (1953).

25. L. Zechmeister and G. Karmakar, *Arch. Biochem. Biophys.* **47,** 160–164 (1953).

26. W. J. Rabourn and F. W. Quackenbush, *Arch. Biochem. Biophys.* **44,** 159–164 (1953).

27. G. Mackinney, C. M. Rick, and J. A. Jenkins, *Proc. Natl. Acad. Sci. U. S.* **42,** 404–408 (1956).

28. H. H. Strain, *in* "Manual of Phycology" (G. M. Smith, ed.), pp. 243–262. Chronica Botanica, Waltham, Mass., 1951.

29. T. W. Goodwin, *in* "Comparative Biochemistry of Photoreactive Systems" (M. B. Allen, ed.), pp. 1–10. Academic Press, New York, 1961.

29a. N. I. Krinsky and T. H. Goldsmith, *Arch. Biochem. Biophys.* **91,** 271–279 (1960).

30. H. H. Strain, "Chloroplast Pigments and Chromatographic Analysis." Penn. State, University Park, Pennsylvania, 1958.

31. M. Nishimura and K. Takamatsa, *Nature* **180,** 699–700 (1957).

32. M. B. Allen, T. W. Goodwin, and S. Phagpolngarm, *J. Gen. Microbiol.* **23,** 93–103 (1960).

33. F. T. Haxo and D. C. Fork, *Nature* **184,** 1061–1062 (1959).

34. T. W. Goodwin, *J. Gen. Microbiol.* **17,** 467 (1958).

35. J. R. Vallentyne, *Science* **119,** 605–606 (1954).

36. H. G. Schlegel, *Arch. Mikrobiol.* **31,** 231–239 (1958).

37. C. B. van Niel, *Ann. Rev. Microbiol.* **8,** 105–132 (1954).

38. T. W. Goodwin, *Souvenir Soc. Biol. Chem. India* pp. 271–276 (1955).

39. T. W. Goodwin, *Arch. Mikrobiol.* **24,** 313–322 (1956).

40. W. A. Volk and D. Pennington, *J. Bacteriol.* **59,** 169–170 (1950).

41. E. Duchow and H. C. Douglas, *J. Bacteriol.* **58,** 409–416 (1949).

42. T. W. Goodwin and D. G. Land, *Arch. Mikrobiol.* **24,** 305–322 (1956).

43. A. B. Pardee, H. K. Schachman, and R. Y. Stanier, *Nature* **169,** 282–283 (1952).

44. A. K. Bicknell, *Lloydia* **12,** 183–184 (1949).

45. C. B. van Niel, T. W. Goodwin, and M. E. Sissins, *Biochem. J.* **63,** 408–412 (1956).

46. P. P. Shah, Ph.D. Thesis, University of Liverpool (1957).

47. T. W. Goodwin, *Biochem. J.* **68,** 503–511 (1958).

48. T. W. Goodwin, *Biochem. J.* **70,** 612–617 (1958).

49. T. W. Goodwin and S. Phagpolngarm, *Biochem. J.* **76,** 197–199 (1960).

50. T. W. Goodwin, *Experientia* **10,** 213 (1954).

51. T. W. Goodwin and M. Jamikorn, *J. Protozool.* **1,** 216–219 (1954).

52. T. W. Goodwin and H. G. Osman, *Biochem. J.* **53,** 541–546 (1953).

53. A. Seybold and K. Egle, *Jahrb. wiss. Botan.* **86,** 50–80 (1938).

54. R. S. Bandurski, *Botan. Gaz.* **111,** 95–109 (1949).

55. J. B. Thomas, *Progr. in Biophys. and Biophys. Chem.* **5,** 109 (1955).

56. M. H. Handke, *Wiss. nat. Z. Martin Luther Univ. Halle-Wittenberg* **4,** 89–94 (1954).

57. T. W. Goodwin and M. Jamikorn, *Biochem. J.* **57,** 376–381 (1954).

57a. E. C. Dougherty and M. B. Allen, *in* "Comparative Biochemistry of Photoreactive Pigments" (M. B. Allen, ed.), pp. 129–144. Academic Press, New York, 1961.

57b. T. W. Goodwin, *Proc. 5th Intern. Congr. Biochem., Moscow, 1961* Symposium III (Pergamon Press, London, in press).

58. T. W. Goodwin, *Biochem. J.* **62**, 346–352 (1956).

59. T. W. Goodwin, *Biochem. J.* **58**, 90–94 (1954).

60. V. H. Booth, *Biochem. J.* **65**, 660–663 (1957).

61. A. E. Joyce, *Nature* **173**, 311 (1954).

62. W. Straus, *Exptl. Cell Research* **11**, 289–296 (1956).

63. W. Rau and C. Zehender, *Arch. Mikrobiol.* **32**, 423–428 (1959).

64. Y. Mase, W. J. Rabourn, and F. W. Quackenbush, *Arch. Biochem. Biophys.* **68**, 150–156 (1957).

65. F. T. Haxo, *Fortschr. Chem. org. Naturstoffe* **12**, 169–197 (1955).

66. T. W. Goodwin, *Biochem. J.* **53**, 538–540 (1953).

67. M. Zalokar, *Arch. Biochem. Biophys.* **70**, 568–571 (1957).

68. R. Emerson and D. L. Fox, *Proc. Roy. Soc.* **B128**, 275–293 (1940).

69. T. W. Goodwin, in "Handbuch der Pflanzenphysiologie" (W. Ruhland, ed.), Vol. 10, pp. 186–222. Springer, Berlin, 1958.

70. M. J. Carlile, *J. Gen. Microbiol.* **14**, 643–654 (1956).

71. R. C. Codner and B. C. Platt, *Nature* **184**, 741 (1959).

72. M. Zalokar, *Arch. Biochem. Biophys.* **56**, 318–325 (1955).

73. C. O. Chichester, P. S. Wong, and G. Mackinney, *Plant Physiol.* **29**, 238–241 (1954).

74. T. W. Goodwin and M. Jamikorn, *Biochem. J.* **62**, 269–275 (1956).

75. S. Saperstein, M. P. Starr, and J. A. Filfus, *J. Gen. Microbiol.* **10**, 85–92 (1954).

76. T. Ohta, T. Miyazaki, and T. Ninomiya, *Chem. & Pharm. Bull. (Tokyo)* **7**, 254–255 (1959).

77. D. P. Courington and T. W. Goodwin, *J. Bacteriol.* **70**, 568–571 (1955).

78. S. Saperstein and M. P. Starr, *Biochim. et Biophys. Acta* **16**, 482 (1955).

79. A. R. Gilbey and A. V. Few, *Nature* **182**, 55 (1958).

80. R. Kunisawa and R. Y. Stanier, *Arch. Mikrobiol.* **31**, 146–156 (1958).

81. D. L. Fox, "Animal Biochromes and Structural Colours." Cambridge Univ. Press, London and New York, 1953.

82. L. R. Fisher, S. K. Kon, and S. Y. Thompson, *J. Marine Biol. Assoc. United Kingdom* **35**, 41, 61, 63–80 (1956).

83. T. W. Goodwin, in "The Physiology of Crustacea " (T. H. Watermann, ed.), Vol. 1, pp. 101–140. Academic Press, New York, 1960.

84. L. R. Fisher, S. K. Kon, and S. Y. Thompson, *J. Marine Biol. Assoc. United Kingdom* **31**, 229–258 (1952).

85. L. R. Fisher, S. K. Kon, and S. Y. Thompson, *J. Marine Biol. Assoc. United Kingdom* **33**, 589–612 (1954).

86. L. R. Fisher, S. K. Kon, and S. Y. Thompson, *J. Marine Biol. Assoc. United Kingdom* **34**, 81–100 (1955).

87. M. de Nicola, *Biochem. J.* **56**, 555–558 (1954).

88. M. de Nicola, *Expt. Cell. Research* **10**, 441–446 (1956).

89. H. G. Vevers and N. Millott, *Proc. Zool. Soc. London* **129**, 78–80 (1957).

90. F. Anders, *Z. indukt. Abstamm.-u. Vererbungsl.* **87**, 567–579 (1956).

91. D. F. Cheeseman, *J. Physiol. (London)* **131**, 3–4P (1955).

92. G. G. Villela, *Nature* **178**, 93 (1956).

93. R. Mayer, *Z. physiol. Chem.* **307**, 154–160 (1957).

94. S. Hirao, J. Yamada, and R. Kikuchi, *Tokai Regional Fisheries Research Lab. Rept.* **16,** 53–58 (1957).

95. T. W. Goodwin, *Biochem. Soc. Symposia (Cambridge, Engl.)* **6,** 63–82 (1951).

96. L. Aboliñš and A. Aboliñš-Krogis, *Pubbl. staz. zool. Napoli* **29,** 389–406 (1957).

97. L. Aboliñš, *Acta Zool. (Stockholm)* **38,** 223–238 (1957).

98. T. W. Goodwin, *Biol. Revs. Cambridge Phil. Soc.* **27,** 439–461 (1952).

99. O. Völker, *Z. physiol. Chem.* **292,** 75–77 (1953).

100. O. Völker, *J. Ornithol.* **96,** 50–53 (1955).

101. D. L. Fox, *Nature* **175,** 492 (1955).

102. T. W. Goodwin, *Biochem. Soc. Symposia (Cambridge, Engl.)* **12,** 71–84 (1954).

CHAPTER 15

Comparative Biochemistry of the Alkali Metals*

H. B. STEINBACH

Department of Zoology, University of Chicago, Chicago, Illinois

* Chapters 7, 8, 9, and 10 of Volume II of this treatise may be consulted for authoritative accounts of various aspects of the physiology of sodium and potassium.
Since this chapter was completed, a comprehensive treatment of many aspects of the subject has appeared (H. H. Ussing, P. Kruhoffer, J. H. Thysen, and N. A. Thorn, The Alkali Metal Ions in Biology. "Handbuch der experimentellen Pharmakologie" Vol. 13. Springer, Berlin, 1960) which is highly recommended.

I. Chemistry of the Alkali Metals

There are six alkali metals: lithium, sodium, potassium, rubidium, cesium, and francium. Of these, francium, of short half-life, has no known biological significance. Lithium, rubidium, and cesium, while having important biological effects, are known not as critical components of living matter but rather as toxic agents or, at best, partial substitutes for Na or K.

Organisms share with the earth's crust the characteristic of having major components of K and Na, the other alkali metals normally being present in trace amounts.

General chemistry of the alkali metals has recently been well summarized (1). Useful tables and diagrams are to be found in a Symposium on Potassium (2). These references may be consulted for a more extensive discussion of chemical properties of the alkalies than is justified here.

Due to the soluble nature of most alkali salts and to the low complexing power of the ions, it is probable that their major contributions to biological systems will be those of ions in water solution rather than as precipitable salts or firmly bound complexes.

Table I lists a series of properties relating to parameters that might be most influential in determining the activities of the alkali metal compounds in solution. Suttle's (1) treatise may be consulted for further information and, especially, a useful table of isotopes.

For many years, in attempts to account for the biochemical and physiological actions of the alkalies, major emphasis was focused on ionic mobilities. These in turn have been related to inferred hydrated sizes of ions, in some instances invoking the difference between Na and K hydrated sizes as indicating a sharp and exclusive cut-off between penetrating and nonpenetrating ions (3).

Since it is now clear that in all probability neither partitioning nor physiological actions of the alkalies are to be completely explained on the basis of ionic mobilities, it is necessary to scrutinize other parameters.

In general, it might be assumed that the alkali metals participate in physiological processes in any one of several fashions:

(a) By influencing the state of the bulk water of protoplasm. Current discussions (4) place much emphasis on the role of metal ions in the structure of water. As suggested by viscosity effects (B of Table I), the small high-charge-density ions such as lithium can be regarded as structure promoting for water; K has little effect, Cs a disrupting effect, and the other ions have a relative action as indicated by the atomic number series.

TABLE I
SOME PROPERTIES OF THE ALKALIES[a]

Property	Li	Na	K	Rb	Cs	Fr
Atomic number	3	11	19	37	55	87
Atomic weight	6.940	22.997	39.096	85.48	132.91	—
Atomic radii (Å.)	1.379	1.80	2.21	2.45	2.69	—
Crystal dimensions (Å.)	3.46	4.24	5.25	5.62	6.05	—
Crystal radii (Å.)	0.60	0.95	1.33	1.48	1.69	—
Volume of ions (10^{-23} cc.)	0.14	0.37	0.99	1.36	1.95	—
Magnetic susceptibility[b]	−0.3	5.6	14.0	23.0	37.3	—
Entropies, aqueous ions (cal./mole/°C.)[c]	4.7	14.0	24.2	28.7	31.8	—
B-Ion (25°C.)[d]	0.1495	0.0863	−0.007	−0.03	−0.045	—
ΔE H_2O[e]	0.73	0.25	−0.25	—	−0.33	—
Ionic mobilities 25°C. (H_2O)	39.6	50.9	74.4	77.6	78.1	—
Ionic radii H_2O[f]	2.30	1.79	1.22	1.17	1.17	—
Gm./100 gm. Solubility, chlorides 0° H_2O	67	35.7	27.6	77	161.4	—
Solubilities of chlorides in NH_3	0.342	2.20	0.0177	0.024	0.0227	—

[a] Data from Suttle (1) except where noted.

[b] Magnetic susceptibility in dilute solution. Interpreted to indicate that there is no hydration of the larger ions.

[c] From I. M. Klotz, "Chemical Thermodynamics." Prentice-Hall, Englewood Cliffs, N. J., 1950.

[d] From $n/n_0 = 1 + AM^{1/2} + BM$. See M. Kaminsky, Discussions Faraday Soc. **24** (1957).

[e] Calculated activation energy for exchange of H_2O between hydration shell of ion and liquid phase. From O. Y. Samelov, Discussions Faraday Soc. **24** (1957).

[f] A variety of values are given by different sources. Samelov (loc. cit.) discusses some of the difficulties in considering hydration of ions.

In another sense, the bulk water phase can be said to hold the smaller ions (Li and Na) and reject the larger (Rb and Cs).

(b) The alkalies could act by chelating with various components, notably such cellular constituents as the polyphosphates. The rule to be expected is that Cs would have the lowest stability constant, Li the highest (5).

(c) The alkali ions could, either by electrostatic or covalent binding, alter "active centers" or other configurational aspects of the proteins and other polymers of cells. It is well known that some enzyme systems are specifically activated by K.

(d) The alkali metals could alter the activity of macromolecules of protoplasm. Szent-Györgyi (6), for example, has pointed out that K is just the right size to fit in the water lattice adsorbed to proteins; Na would disrupt the structure.

There exists, then, the distinct possibility that the alkali metals could influence biochemical processes by competitive interaction at any of the levels noted above.

Unfortunately, there is little information in the literature that allows one to judge the nature of the modes of action of the ions in any given case.

The solubilities of alkali salts show some interesting variations. In watery solutions, the chlorides exhibit no very distinctive behavior, but phosphates, sulfates, and carbonates do. Also, there is the strikingly high solubility of NaCl in liquid ammonia (Table I) which may indicate an important role of nonpolar interfaces in protoplasmic systems. In guaiacol solutions, on the other hand, K as the hydroxide shows a much greater solubility than Na (7).

Recent studies have focused attention on ion exchange systems, especially as devices for separating the alkalies [cf. Suttle (1) for references]. As yet there is no clear-cut relationship between the ion exchangers and protoplasmic systems. However, it is suggestive that phosphonic resins preferentially take up Na; sulfonic resins have a higher affinity for K.

II. General Distribution of the Alkalies

A. Biogeochemistry of the Alkalies

Since the alkalies typically form quite soluble compounds it is to be expected that extensive cycling should occur on a planet-wide basis. Figure 1, adapted from geochemical literature (8), illustrates the general course of the cycles concerned with the alkali metals.

The components of the biosphere are so intimately related to those of the general cycle that ideally a discussion of the biochemistry of the alkalies should include soil and water chemistry and meteorology as well as the usual treatment of plants and animals and their products. This approach will need to be recognized in the future, especially as the pattern that is unfolding out of the present day biochemistry of these elements lays major stress on cell-fluid gradients (nonhomogeneous distribution) rather than on specific chemical action.

It is, unfortunately, impossible in a short space to do justice to the widely scattered literature relating to what could be called the general ecology of the alkalies. In broad outline the cycle is summed up well by Fenn (9), who remarks that potassium is of the soil and the cell, sodium of the oceans and body fluids.

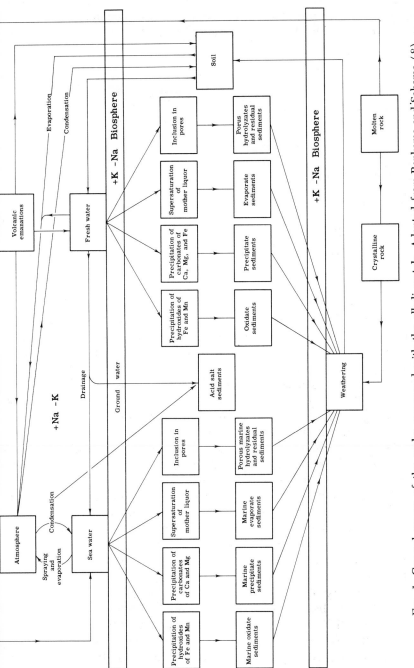

Fig. 1. General course of the cycles concerned with the alkali metals. Adapted from Rankama and Sahama (8).

If for the moment we focus attention on sodium and potassium, igneous rocks of the lithosphere have a sodium : potassium ratio not far from unity (Table II). As the surface layers of rocks weather, the first

TABLE II

RELATIVE MOLAR PROPORTIONS OF THE ALKALI ELEMENTS IN SEVERAL REGIONS OF THE EARTH[a]

Source	K	Rb	Cs	Na	Li
Igneous rock	1	5.10^{-3}	7.10^{-5}	1.9	14.10^{-3}
Shales, etc.	1	5.10^{-3}	13.10^{-5}	6.10^{-1}	9.10^{-3}
Limestones	1	?	?	2.10^{-1}	55.10^{-3}
Sea water	1	2.10^{-4}	2.10^{-6}	39	$1.5.10^{-3}$
Spring water	1	?	?	3.1	?
Plants	1	3.10^{-4}	5.10^{-4}	6.10^{-3}	?
Animals (vertebrates)	1	?	?	7.10^{-1}	?

[a] Figures are estimated from Rankama and Sahama (8) and other sources and should be taken as order-of-magnitude estimates.

leachate also would have nearly this ratio. However, the run off water, the water of the rivers and the streams, does not have the sodium : potassium ratio of the primitive lithosphere. In these waters sodium is typically in excess by three to four times over potassium. In large part this involves a fundamentally simple series of reactions. The solution of the rock releases, in addition to sodium and potassium salts, silicates that contribute to the mineral types found in clays and soils. Potassium is selectively taken up between the lattice planes of many of these minerals, thus effectively enriching the runoff waters with sodium. Potassium depletion is continued along the same lines aided by a relative selective inclusion of the metal in sedimentary rocks (e.g., limestones), especially those associated with the activities of the biosphere.

The net result of these several processes is the creation of the high-sodium oceans as they are known today. Without worrying about the details at the moment, it appears to be a fairly close approximation to assume that there has not been any very drastic change in either the proportions of the alkali metals or the amounts of them in sea water [cf. Rankama and Sahama (8) for discussion] over the major portion of the evolutionary history of organisms.

Against this background it is quite remarkable that the protoplasmic portions of all living forms are composed of high-potassium electrolyte systems. This statement appears to be true in general when protoplasmic electrolytes are compared to normal environments. It is almost universally true as meaning that potassium is the predominant protoplasmic cation, although as noted later there are exceptions to this.

On an over-all basis the sodium-potassium content of the biosphere (e.g., whole organisms including body fluids) displays a ratio not too far from unity, as was originally found in the primitive lithosphere. Thus in this sense living stuff although existing in water is truly of the soil with regard to its metallic components.

In general, then, the over-all cycle of the alkali metals involves the following steps: (a) the leaching of rocks (potassium:sodium ratio about unity); (b) formation of the hydrosphere (potassium:sodium ratio much less than unity; (c) formation of the soil (potassium:sodium ratio greater than 1); (d) biogenesis (potassium:sodium ratio considerably greater than 1); (e) formation of whole organisms, cells, and cell products (potassium:sodium ratio approaching unity).

Also, to speak in general terms, lithium tends to follow sodium; cesium and rubidium follow potassium. There are notable exceptions, especially the tendency of lithium to be associated in minerals with magnesium. Similarly, cesium is in some instances accumulated in excess of potassium in the lithosphere (8).

B. THE GENERAL DISTRIBUTION OF THE ALKALIES IN ORGANISMS

The alkali metals are widely distributed in nature. Several useful tabulations are available in addition to such sources as *Tabulae Biologica* (10) and the Handbook (11) series of the National Research Council. Prosser (12) has extensive figures on the ionic composition of body fluids of a variety of animals and of physiological saline solutions. Buck (13) presents a most comprehensive survey of the composition of insect bloods; and the monumental collection of data by Vinogradov (14), while concerned with all elements found in marine organisms, gives much valuable data on the alkalies. There is a scattered literature on cesium, rubidium, and lithium which will be discussed later. The findings may be summarized roughly as follows: (a) K is ubiquitous and is usually the predominant cation of protoplasm, plant or animal. (b) Na is variable in protoplasm but is generally found in body fluids of animals. (c) While the minor alkali elements (Li, Rb, Cs) are reported as frequent constituents, there is no evidence of special concentrating or excluding devices in protoplasm except as Cs and Rb may follow K, Li following Na.

1. Potassium in Organisms

Potassium is a normal constituent of all organisms or parts of organisms that have been analyzed. Tables III, IV, V, VI, and VII and

TABLE III
SELECTED VALUES OF SODIUM AND POTASSIUM CONTENTS
OF VARIOUS PLANT TISSUES[a]

Plant	Na	K
Asparagus	1	50
Beet, leaves	60	130
Beet, roots	30	75
Lettuce	6	60
String beans	1	60
Broccoli	7	75
Celery	50	90
Spinach	30	120
Yucca, leaves	19	70
Yucca, stems	98	50
Vetch	40	156
Salt grass (sea shore)	70	45
Salt bush	23	63
Rye, tops	4	120
Clover, tops	20	150

[a] From Handbook (11) data.
[b] Concentrations are expressed as millimoles per kilogram wet weight.

the references cited indicate this. In all cases, also, potassium is present in protoplasm in concentrations higher than environmental fluid concentrations. This is also evident from the tables cited. In almost all instances, K is also the predominant intracellular cation. Notable exceptions are to be found in the mammalian erythrocytes, where high or low K (Na related inversely to K) is a species characteristic so far as is known.

In certain sheep and opossums (15) the high K condition appears to be inherited as a dominant trait. Interestingly enough, the high Na condition appears only after a definite interval of postnatal development (16).

In most plants also, K is the predominant ion. In certain marine and shore forms (Table III) total body Na content may exceed that of K. In most plants, it is difficult to tell what fractions of Na or K are to be regarded as extracellular or vacuolar rather than protoplasmic. "Apparent free space" in plants (17) is at least as difficult to define as "extracellular space" in animals. Of the coenocytic marine forms (Table VII), one species (*Valonia ventricosa*) has high vacuolar K, another (*Halicystis osterhoutii*) has high vacuolar Na (18).

Eppley (19) reports an interesting case in the brown algae, where most of the K has been replaced by H, yielding a highly acidic cell

TABLE IV

Sodium and Potassium Content of Muscle Tissue[a,b]

Organism	Na	K
Bluefish (M)	30	79
Dogfish (M)	30	73
Catfish (F)	26	83
Mackerel[c] (M)	55	118
Barracuda[c] (M)	43	102
Beef	30	87
Lamb	40	82
Pork	25	65
Chick[d]		
Young	96	45
Old	16	98
Rat[d]	23	102
Rabbit[d]	17	115
Dog[d]	32	82
Oyster[e] (M)	16	95
Clam[f] (M)	160	84
Squid[g] (M)	53	113
Clam (F)	5	10
Crayfish[h] (F)	28	95
Cockroach[i]	35	83
Grasshopper	35	100
Dolphin[j] (M)	17	107
Spider crab[k] (M)	93	115

[a] From Handbook (11) data unless otherwise stated. For extensive tables of Na and K contents of various vertebrate tissues, see Hoppe-Seyler and Thierfelder, "Handbuch der physiologischund pathologisch-chemischen Analyse," Vol. 1. Springer, Berlin, 1953.

[b] Concentrations given as millimoles per kilogram wet weight. M = marine; F = freshwater.

[c] E. L. Becker, R. Bird, J. W. Kelley, J. Schilling, S. Solomon, and N. Young, *Physiol. Zoöl.* **31**- 224–228 (1958).

[d] J. S. Barlow and Manery, J. F. *J. Cellular Comp. Physiol.* **43**, 165–191 (1954).

[e] G. F. Humphrey, *Australian J. Exptl. Biol. Med. Sci.* **24**, 261–267 (1947).

[f] E. B. Meigs, *J. Biol. Chem.* **22**, 493–498 (1915).

[g] J. F. Manery, *J. Cellular Comp. Physiol.* **14**, 365–369 (1939).

[h] H. Clark, Thesis, University of Minnesota (1958).

[i] J. M. Tobias, *J. Cellular Comp. Physiol.* **31**, 125–142 (1948).

[j] L. Eichelberger, E. M. K. Geiling, and B. Vos, *J. Biol. Chem.* **133**, 661–666 (1940).

[k] W. K. Stephenson, *Biol. Bull.* **105**, 368–369 (1953).

interior. Perhaps a similar situation exists in some of the highly acid cells of ascidians.

For a few cases in which reliable estimates of intracellular K are available, an interesting fact is noted. At least for similar tissues (e.g., muscle, Table VIII) the intracellular K content is relatively constant

TABLE V

Sodium and Potassium in Erythrocytes and Serum or Plasma[a]

Organism	Erythrocytes[b]		Plasma or serum[c]	
	Na	K	Na	K
Man	11	91	138	4.2
Beef	70	25	142	4.8
Sheep (average)	82	11	160	4.8
Dog	106	5	150	4.4
Rabbit	16	99	158	4.1
Elephant seal[d]	95	7	142	4.5
Rat	12	100	151	5.9
Duck[e]	7	112	141	6.0
Chicken[c]	18	119	154	6.0
Dolphin (mammal)[f]	13	99	153	4.3
Fish (mackerel)[g]	—	—	188	10.0
Frog	—	—	105	4.8
Reptile (turtle)	—	—	140	4.6

[a] See also (12) for extensive tabulations, especially for body fluids of invertebrates.

[b] From C. W. Sheppard, W. R. Martin, and G. Beyl, *J. Gen. Physiol.* **34**, 411–429 (1951), unless otherwise noted.

[c] From "Standard Values of Blood" (Abritton, ed.) Saunders, Philadelphia, 1952.

[d] J. Eadie and R. L. Reik, *Australian J. Sci.* **14**, 26–27 (1952).

[e] D. C. Tosteson and J. S. Robertson, *J. Cellular Comp. Physiol.* **46**, 147–166 (1956).

[f] L. Eichelberger, E. M. K. Geiling, and B. J. Vos, *J. Biol. Chem.* **133**, 145–152 (1940).

[g] E. L. Becker, R. Bird, J. W. Kelley, J. Schilling, S. Solomon, and N. Young, *Physiol. Zoöl.* **31**, 224–227 (1958).

TABLE VI

Sodium and Potassium Contents[a] of Ova

Organism	Na	K
Salmon[b]	8	60
Cyprinus[b]	3	70
Asterias[b]	300	190
Arbacia lixula[c]	280	162
Paracentrotus lividus[c]	52	210
Psammechinus militaris[c]	343	266
Strongylocentrotus droebachensis[c]	316	200

[a] Concentrations as millimoles per kilogram wet weight.

[b] From (14).

[c] From Lord Rothschild and H. Barnes, *J. Exptl. Biol.* **30**, 534–544 (1953).

TABLE VII
SODIUM AND POTASSIUM CONTENTS OF COENOCYTIC MARINE ALGAE[a,b]

Alga	Na	K
Valonia ventricosa (per liter cell sap)	35	576
Valonia macrophysa (per liter cell sap)	90	500
Halicystis osterhoutii (per liter cell sap)	557	6
Ulva lactuca (per kilogram tissue H_2O)	192	310
Porphyra perforata (per liter cell volume)	51	482
Chara[c] (per liter cell sap)	66	65

[a] From Eppley (*18*).
[b] Concentrations as millimoles per liter or per kilogram, as indicated in column 1.
[c] C. T. Gaffney and L. J. Mullins, *J. Physiol.* **144,** 505–524 (1958).

TABLE VIII
INTRACELLULAR CONCENTRATIONS OF SODIUM AND POTASSIUM IN MUSCLE TISSUE[a]

Organism	Na	$\dfrac{Na_i}{Na_o}$	K	$\dfrac{K_i}{K_o}$
Mytilus	121	0.24	137	6
Eriocheir	3	0.07	136	18
Carcinus	54	0.11	112	9
Nephrops	27	0.05	177	20
Phascolosoma[b]	82	0.17	153	14
Frog[b]	16	0.15	127	49
Squid[c]	11	0.03	157	11
Rat[c]	2	0.02	154	38
Chicken[c]	8	0.05	147	20

[a] Intracellular ion concentrations calculated as millimoles per liter intracellular water. From Robertson (*20*) except where indicated.
[b] From Steinbach (*21*).
[c] J. S. Barlow and J. F. Manery, *J. Cellular Comp. Physiol.* **43,** 165–191 (1954).

regardless of the osmotic pressure of the environmental (internal or external) fluids (*20, 21*). This suggests a regulation of protoplasmic K relative to a constant protoplasmic composition rather than to an osmoregulatory function (*21*).

"Osmotic deficits," especially in cells of marine invertebrates, appear to be corrected in part by intracellular Na but to a greater extent by amino acids and related compounds (*22*). It is noteworthy that the organic components, apparently needed to balance osmotic strengths of protoplasm and extracellular media, are themselves regulated with respect to concentrations. In squid blood, for example, all of the low molecular weight organic compounds of squid nerve are present, but the concentration-in-protoplasm/concentration-in-blood ratios are highly variable (22a).

If there is indeed an "optimum" protoplasmic K concentration, then it may well be this feature that, in turn, sets the level for total molar concentration of body fluids of the vertebrates as they develop, with respect to both phylogeny and ontogeny. The remarkably constant salt concentration level of vertebrate blood may thus be truly a reflection of a vital structure of cells, rather than a reflection of the salt levels of ancient oceans.

In keeping with the low osmotic concentrations in the body fluids, freshwater invertebrates, such as clams, have low K concentrations in their tissues (22a). Estimates have been made of protoplasmic osmolar concentrations of Hydra (23) and some freshwater protozoa (24, 24a). These fall into the general range of concentrations found in clam blood, and it may be suggested that 0.03 M internal K represents about the lowest level for maintenance of animal cells. Florkin (24a) has reviewed many aspects of the problem of survival of organisms in fresh water and regulation of the ion concentrations of the cells of fresh water animals.

2. Sodium in Organisms

As contrasted with K, the Na content of both whole organisms and cells is highly variable. For example, the analysis of some 15 different plants and parts of plants reported in Table III indicates a standard deviation from the mean of ±90% for the Na contents, of only 48% for K. The standard deviation of the mean for the K: Na ratio exceeds ±150%. Thus, comparing different organisms, neither is the Na content regulated in any general fashion nor is the Na content of cells regulated with specific reference to K content. A similar great variability of Na as contrasted with K is noted in Tables IV to VI.

There is some question as to whether Na is essential as a general constituent of protoplasm. There is no doubt that it is essential for the body fluids of higher animals, and in some instances it can be shown to be necessary for the normal functioning of whole plants. On the other hand, during pupal development of some insects Na may virtually disappear from the organism (13).

There is evidence that Na can replace much of the K in some of the blue-green algae (25), and it is possible to prepare a Na-rich yeast that can still show considerable metabolic activity (26).

The role of extracellular Na in the nerve impulse is discussed elsewhere in this treatise (cf. Vol. II, Chapters 8 and 10).

3. Cesium and Rubidium

Cesium and rubidium appear to be present in organisms in a fashion
that would indicate that these two metals tend to follow potassium.
There is no indication of any pronounced selective concentration or
exclusion of either element by cellular systems. Table IX gives a few

TABLE IX

SODIUM, POTASSIUM, AND RUBIDIUM CONTENTS[a] OF SELECTED PLANTS
FROM THE GARDENS OF THE PASTEUR INSTITUTE[b]

Plant	K	Na	Rb
Cynodon dactylon	50.4	0.42	11.8
Euphorbia peplus	27.4	2.68	21.2
Amaranthus retroflexus	50.7	0.18	36.7
Lymaria cymbalaria	25.6	0.74	32.1
Solanum nigrum	21.6	0.12	23.7
Convolvulus sepium	50.2	0.48	17.5
Galinsoga parviflora	31.0	0.30	11.3
Erigeron canadensis	29.8	0.20	25.4
Lychnis dioica	49	0.31	25.1
Average	37	0.66	22.8

[a] In milligrams per gram (Na and K) or per kilogram (Rb) dry weight.
[b] Adapted from Bertrand and Bertrand (27).

selected figures for Rb from the more extensive compilations by
Bertrand (27). In general Rb occurs in plants on the order of $<1.10^{-3}$
that of the K content, which is not far from the general relation of the
two metals in the earth's crust. Bertrand, however, notes some instances
of relatively high Rb (K:Rb = 50). In the absence of figures for
exchangeable Rb and K of the soil in which the plants were grown it
suffices to note no evidence of special treatment of Rb as compared to K.

In a selected variety of plants grown in water culture, Collander
(28) found K, Rb, and Cs about evenly distributed between roots and
shoots, with the relative amounts of the metals roughly in proportion to
concentrations in the medium, thus indicating no preferential treatment
of any one of the three ions.

In animal tissues Rb[86] has occasionally been advocated as a possible
tracer for K. However, careful studies have shown (29) that while K
and Rb are distributed similarly in muscle and erythrocytes, there is a
selective distribution in most other tissues of man and rabbit. Hence
these authors (29) conclude that there is some discrimination between
the two ions. Similar careful studies are not available comparing Cs and

K, but most of the evidence indicates that Cs is even less able to take the place of K than is Rb. Earlier work (30) indicated that frog muscle does allow substitution of K by either Rb or Cs in part at least. In the sugar cane plant it has been found that the distribution of Rb follows that of K (31).

Of incidental interest is the report that Cs is present in fossils in excess of the Rb content (32).

Bertrand, in an extensive series of papers, gives figures for Cs and Rb contents of a variety of organisms (see 33 and 34 for references). Cs is reported as having a general distribution, both in plants and animals, with concentrations ranging up to over 100 mg. per kilogram dry weight. Rb levels are somewhat similar, and Bertrand also notes the similarity of distribution of Rb to K between cells and plasma of mammalian blood.

4. Lithium in Organisms

The distribution and physiological activity of lithium is covered in an excellent review by Schou (35). This review also contains valuable information about the other alkali metals. Unless otherwise noted, material for this section will be taken from Schou's review, which may be consulted for detailed references.

Normal distribution of Li indicates that the metal is not concentrated to any great extent. As with Cs and Rb in relation to K, there are no special ion-accumulating systems for Li relative to Na.

In many types of cellular systems, Li does appear to follow Na, especially as tested on tissues isolated from whole organisms. On the other hand, in plants growing in water culture, Li, together with Ca and Sr is more concentrated in shoots than roots. Na, by comparison, is more concentrated in roots than shoots (28).

Li, as is Na, is actively transported by frog skin and related systems. However, when injected into whole animals Li appears to be evenly distributed throughout the body water, showing neither the extracellular localization of Na nor the intracellular accumulation of K.

It should be recalled that Li, with its small high-charge-density ion, tends to follow group II elements of the periodic system, such as Mg, as well as to behave like an alkali in geochemical distributions.

With yeast it has been reported that as much as 98% of the internal cation content (normally K) can be substituted by Li (36). In this instance, Li thus behaves as does Na in taking the place of K.

That Li is very widespread in occurrence is shown by the extensive studies of Bertrand (37). Concentrations recorded, however, are low.

III. Alkali Metals as Required Nutrients

As fair generalizations, the following statements hold true with but few exceptions:

(a) K is an essential nutrient for all forms of life. In many forms Rb and, to a lesser extent, Cs can partially substitute for the K requirement.

(b) Na is shown to be required by only two groups of organisms: multicellular organisms that regulate their body fluids and some marine microorganisms. There is need for further work to demonstrate whether or not there is a more widespread requirement for Na. The majority of nonmarine plants do not require Na.

(c) Although Li can sometimes substitute for Na and Rb or Cs for K, there is no evidence of a strict requirement for these three trace alkalies under normal conditions.

Nutrition is a subject that is by no means easy to discuss on a comparative basis. There appear to be almost as many facets to nutritional requirements as there are types of organisms. In this section an attempt will be made to isolate certain general findings that may serve as a background to a comparative discussion of the alkalies as nutrients. Further information can be obtained from various reviews, many of them appearing on an annual basis (38).

A. Basic Nutritive Requirements for Alkalies

The general requirement for K is rather completely indicated for a variety of forms. Standard texts may be consulted for the detailed dietary needs of higher animals and plants. Snell (39) states that K is essential for all microorganisms tested, and his paper should be consulted for further review.

Similarly, reviews (40, 41) on nutrient requirements of algae and of higher plants note that there is a general requirement for K.

Specific levels of K requirements of course vary widely for different organisms and cells. Especially for whole multicellular organsims, there is a complex interplay between availability in the diet, excretion and retention, and uptake by individual cells of the body. In crabs, for example, Gross (42) has shown the outlines of a complicated interplay among various body fractions of K during water stresses. With protozoa (43) the absolute requirement of K for growth varies depending upon the amounts of other ions present.

A striking example of the ability of the mammalian body to regulate cellular K in the absence of any dietary supply is found in the rat during acute starvation. With a weight loss averaging 32%, muscle K concentration changed slightly if at all (44). The complexity of K requirements is illustrated in certain grafting experiments with peach trees. Variety A shoots grafted to B roots show no K deficiency while the same type of shoots show a K deficiency when grafted to variety C roots (41).

On the cellular level, fibroblast cells in tissue culture require 1–10 mM K in the medium (45).

As noted previously, Na is not universally required as a nutrient. Trees and most lower plants (e.g., bacteria, algae) do not require sodium (40, 41). Various crop plants do contain Na, and marked effects of excess of Na can be observed, but it seems possible that most of the forms could flourish in the absence of this element. Snell (39) lists Na as required by only a very few microorganisms. Na can apparently almost replace K in certain algae (40). Sodium, in trace amounts, is reported essential for the proper growth of *Hydra littoralis* (40a).

In some marine forms a clear-cut requirement for Na has been shown. *Labyrinthula* (sometimes classed with Myxomycetes) shows no growth with less than approximately 0.1 M NaCl and optimum growth at about 0.3 M NaCl (46). Similarly it is shown that marine bacteria (probably *Pseudomonas* or *Spirillum*) have maximal growth at 0.15 M NaCl (47).

It is notable that the concentration of Na needed for these marine forms is 50 to 100 times that required for K. As will be noted later, the requirement for Na of multicellular animals with body fluids appears to satisfy two needs: (a) the need to maintain osmotic strength of the extracellular fluids and (b) the need to participate in phenomena relating to irritability by permitting an ion gradient, outside to inside, of Na^+. In a few forms (see below), such as marine crabs and some insects, the existence of the Na gradient is not essential for maintained excitability of the neuromuscular system. There is no evidence in any of the forms shown to require Na that the metal is needed intracellularly. Indeed, MacLeod *et al.* (47) point out that in the marine bacteria, Na is without effect upon extracted enzyme systems. Thus it appears that the requirement for Na, where found, is different both quantitatively and qualitatively from the K requirement by all organisms.

There is no requirement known for Cs and Rb, although Rb especially can partially substitute for K. In bacterial nutrition, Rb decreases the K requirement of *Leuconostoc mesenteroides*, whereas Cs decreases the requirement of *Lactobacillus arabinosus* for K (48).

Somewhat similar sparing actions to a limited extent have been noted for most forms studied. As a general rule, Cs is considerably more toxic than Rb. That is, the extent to which the normal K requirement can be lowered is less for Cs than for Rb. For example, in rats developing heart or kidney lesions on low-K diets, Rb could prevent the necrosis, Cs only partly (49).

The role of lithium in nutrition is not known precisely except that there is no evidence that it is an essential element in the diet. The extent to which Li can replace Na appears to depend on the circumstances. For short terms, Li can apparently replace Na. For chronic situations, any considerable amount of Li causes toxic symptoms (35).

There is relatively little information on nutrition requirements of subcellular units such as viruses. Various rickettsiae (50) survive better in an artificial medium made up with K⁺ salts rather than Na. In a provocative study of comparative susceptibility to malarial infections (51), it was noted that high K, low Na erythrocytes (e.g., man, mouse) were more susceptible to infection than low K, high Na cells (dog, cow, etc.). The differentiation of susceptibility on this basis was, however, not precise.

Studies have been made on acclimatization of organisms to unnatural ionic environments. See, for example, an extensive series of reports on NaCl-yeast (52). Yeast adapted to high NaCl no longer shows normal plasmolysis behavior to NaCl solutions. The ability of fish to select a preferred salt level in the environment and the levels selected are influenced by endocrine functions (53).

In some instances, one ion may be substituted for another with respect to one physiological function but not another. For example, with *Bacillus subtilis*, Rb may replace K for growth, but not for the production of subtilin (54).

Li has been of particular interest to students of growth because of its marked effects on morphogenesis (35). Morphogenesis is altered in such diverse forms as *Hydra* (55), sea urchins (56), and flowering plants (57). There appears to be no good biochemical explanation for these specific effects, although metabolic upsets are noted.

B. Salt, Mythology, and Anthropology

Sodium chloride, common salt, has occupied a special niche in human history which may seem odd in view of the fact that one of the main items of cellular business is either to push sodium out or to keep it out. Preoccupation with salt appears to reflect the need for sodium chloride to maintain a proper gradient between blood cells, but the human attitude must rest on many complicated factors.

Perhaps one of the best discussions of the need for salt in the diet of human and domestic animals is that of von Bunge (58), translated into the English in 1902. Von Bunge cites figures for sodium and potassium contents of average diets of herbivores, carnivores, and omnivores.

He points out that carnivores have a balanced diet with respect to the alkali metals; all others must suffer a relative Na deficiency because of the high K content of the average plant diet. Table X illustrates with

TABLE X
YEARLY BALANCE SHEET FOR A COW[a]

Alkali metal	Income (gm.)	Outgo (gm.)			Balance (gm.)
		Milk	Excreta	Total	
Na	15,559	3,457	12,155	15,612	−54
K	40,618	10,155	30,283	40,439	+179

[a] Data from H. H. Dukes, "The Physiology of Domestic Animals." Comstock (Cornell Univ. Press), Ithaca, N. Y., 1947.

more modern data the yearly balance sheet for minerals of a cow fed on a diet plantlike in that it is high in K as compared to Na. Many similar tables are available (59).

The necessity for sodium chloride is occasionally cited as having had profound effects on the origin of civilization, as for example, the early settlement around the Dead Sea.

In anthropology (60) and mythology (61) ample evidence is found of a widespread and ancient preoccupation with salt. Salt cults are well known among American Indians, and such phrases as "worth his salt" and the practice of throwing a pinch of salt over the shoulder to ward off evil spirits appears to be widespread. The story of Lot's wife is of course a case in point.

Whether there is any sound physiological basis for this ancient attitude is debatable (62). While it is true that adrenalectomized rats will self-select a diet providing NaCl, there appears to be no evidence that normal animals will do so. The regulatory mechanisms of excretion appear to be adaptable to a high degree of salt conservation and adjustment, as attested, e.g., by starvation experiments.

With respect to human populations, there are Indian tribes in Brazil (63) where the individuals, without ever having developed salt licks or salt cults, voluntarily take little salt, sweat a great deal, and as a result suffer from a chronic chloropenia.

It seems probable that social attitudes toward salt reflect esoteric factors more than physiological needs. Taste mechanisms appear to be quite specific for sodium salts (64), and it seems reasonable to suppose that taste rather than physiological needs is important in developing human attitudes toward salt. In certain primitive tribes salt is eaten as a special treat, seemingly quite in excess of any known physiological needs.

C. CELLULAR NUTRITION. THE UPTAKE OF ALKALI METALS BY LIVING CELLS

If a substance is needed by a cell or an organism it presumably plays some role in vital phenomena. When K, for example, is required by all cells, it may be inferred that the metal has some specific relationship to other cellular constituents. The whole series of phenomena known collectively as the ion balance of cells may be properly thought of as a special case of assimilation (65). As more instances of ionic transport (active or otherwise) across cell boundaries are studied, more evidence is added that uptake or expulsion of ions in some way involves direct combination of the ions with other protoplasmic constituents.*

In the case of plant systems, with cell membranes of high impedance (low degree of leakiness for ions), uptake of the alkali ions appears to be entirely by combination with the cell boundary. The important studies of Epstein (see 66) showed that Rb, Cs, and K competed for identical sites on plant roots whereas Na appeared to have a more complex behavior. Rothstein (66a) in his studies on yeast has made pertinent measurements of the affinities of the alkalies for combining sites on the cell surface. In somewhat analogous fashion *Escherichia coli* cells bind K, Cs, and Rb internally with little evidence of external membrane participation (cf. Cowie *et al.*, 66b), while Na appears not to combine.

Animal cells appear to be considerably leakier with respect to ions in the sense that simple diffusion of ions appears to be one pathway involved in the ionic balance between cells and environment. Indeed much older work was based on the assumption that ionic size and diffusion velocity were critical parameters in ion penetration (67). However, careful studies are indicating that competition between ions is a factor in penetration into the cell. Solomon (68), working with human erythrocytes, notes that Rb competes with K for entry into the cell; Na and Li do not. Li, on the other hand, competes with Na, but Rb and K do not. Tosteson (69) discusses similar competition phenomena in relationship to the relative roles of diffusion and carrier processes.

Phenomena of active transport and secretion and excretion are reviewed elsewhere in this series. It is well to remember, however, that

* A recent review [M. Fried and R. E. Shapiro, *Ann. Rev. Plant Physiol.* **12**, 91–112 (1961)] lists many K_m values for the alkali metals with respect to the uptake of the elements by plant roots.

these phenomena are facets of the general problem of mineral nutrition of cells.

IV. Selective Combination of Alkali Metals with Cell Constituents and Particulates

Almost since the first analyses of the alkali metals in living material were performed there has been the vexing question of the state of the metal ions in the protoplasm system. Whereas earlier views tended to regard the high K content of cells as evidence of some type of chemical binding (immobilization) of ions, later biophysical studies have placed more emphasis on the free mobility of K in the interior of cells.

A. Intracellular Binding of Potassium and Sodium

A series of papers by Ernst and his collaborators (70) may be consulted for the evidence for internal binding of K based upon attempts to wash out the alkali in K-free solutions. Perfusion of frog limbs in situ for up to 18 hours fails to reduce the K level by more than 15% (71).

More recently, somewhat analogous types of evidence for some selective site attraction for intracellular K has come from uptake and washout studies using radioactive isotopes. The evidence appears to be consistent on at least one point, namely, that exchange or loss of intracellular K does not indicate a homogeneous intracellular distribution of K (see 72–76, for references).

Also in the older literature, considerable evidence was presented to indicate specific localizations of K intracellularly. For example, Macallum (77) on the basis of histochemical studies concluded that K was in the cytoplasm, not in the nuclei, of many cell types and was characteristic of the A bands of striated muscle rather than the I bands (see Dubuisson, 78, and Steinbach, 79, for further references).

A striking indication that ionic distribution within cells is not uniform comes from recent microelectrode studies on ascites tumor cells (80). First penetration of the cell by the electrode shows an area electropositive to the medium by 5–10 mv. Further penetration shows the inside electrode negative to the medium by 20–40 mv.

An illustration of selective distribution of Na (81) deserves further study. Amphibian ova incubated in Na^{24} exchanged only 12% of the total Na. Radioautographs showed the distribution of the radioactive Na to be nearly uniform throughout the cytoplasmic portion.

Studies of the migration of K^{42} along squid axons (82) and muscle fibers (83) indicate a mobility of K nearly that found in free solution. On the other hand, impedance studies of erythrocytes (84) indicate an internal conductance about half of that calculated for the known internal chemical composition. Furthermore, internal conductance is nearly the same for high K or high Na cells.

All this work, coupled with the recent interest in active transport, has led to an extensive search for selective combination of various substances with the alkali metals. A certain amount of confusion has been generated during the investigations by loose usage of the term "binding." Given a system providing relatively immobile negative (anionic) charges, cations will be held within the system and in that sense are bound although their activities may or may not be reduced. On the other hand, to help explain the specific retention of a given alkali (e.g., K) a selective binding must be sought, almost certainly involving a reduction in the activity of the ion selected.

B. The Selective Combination of Alkalies by Purified Chemical Systems

As a group, polyphosphates are able to distinguish between the alkali metals, affinity constants decreasing from Li to Cs (85, 86) in the order to be expected on the basis of charge density of the metal ions (Table XI). In general, for a given metal, the stability of the com-

TABLE XI
Stability Constants for Some Naturally Occurring Polyphosphates[a]

Compound[b]	K	Na	Li
AMP	1.6	2.9	4.1
ADP	5.5	6.7	14.0
ATP	11.5	14.3	37.5

[a] From R. M. Smith and R. H. Alberty, J. Phys. Chem. 60, 180–184 (1956).
[b] AMP, ADP, ATP = adenosine mono-, di-, and triphosphate, respectively.

plex increases with the number of phosphate groups involved. Whether the adenosine triphosphate-adenosine diphosphate (ATP-ADP) balance is involved in K changes during cellular activity is not known although in some cells ATP is strongly implicated in K transport (87).

Perhaps related to the selection of alkalies by phosphate compounds is the finding that phosphoproteins bind ions in the order Li > Na > K (88). Some muscle proteins select Na over K (89).

Although the behavior of the phosphate compounds is provocative, it should be noted that the degree of selective binding is quite small, especially when compared to the affinity of the same compounds for such elements as the alkaline earths. The constants with Mg, for example, are several orders of magnitude greater than for Li. Therefore any mechanism for selection of K over Na by polyphosphates should be greatly influenced by traces of Mg or Ca. This sensitivity may, of course, be reflected in the drastic changes in protoplasmic viscosity (90) with small changes in internal Ca.

Lipids extracted from white matter of mammalian brain with $CHCl_3$–CH_3OH mixtures show selective retention of K when partitioned against salt solutions (91). Phospholipids from swine erythrocytes (91a), on the other hand, show a slight retention of Na over K. Further work with lipid or lipoprotein complexes is definitely needed.* Certainly the earlier work of Osterhout (7) indicated a vital role of nonaqueous layers in the partitioning of ions between cells and environments. It is interesting to note that the K:Na ratio of milk fat (cow) is about 0.7 whereas that of the skim milk is nearer 3.0, thus indicating a preference of the lipid fraction for Na (11).

Since much work has been done with the ion-selection properties of muscle cells and erythrocytes, it is natural that selective ion binding by the major colloidal constituents of these two systems should be invoked to explain potassium retention. After some initial claims that hemoglobin selected K in preference to Na, careful studies have shown no discrimination between the two ions so far as hemoglobin in solution is concerned (92). In discussing the relatively low K of sickle-cell erythrocytes, Tosteson (93) lays major emphasis on structural changes rather than binding properties of normal and abnormal hemoglobins.

While some muscle proteins may bind a slight excess of Na (89), there is little evidence that the actomyosin system shows any marked preference for any single alkali. By careful manipulation of the ionic environment, washed glycerinated psoas threads can accumulate about 10% excess K over Na (6). Contraction of actomyosin threads occurs equally well in Na- or K-containing solutions (94).

Suggested by its peripheral localization, hyaluronic acid has been invoked as a selective ion-binding agent (95). However, studies of purified materials show that, despite marked ion-binding power, hyaluronic acid does not discriminate between ions such as Na and K (96). Aldrich (96) should also be consulted for an excellent discussion of the use and misuse of the term "binding" as applied to ions.

A study of ion binding by DNA (97) indicates that alkali ions are held in a nonselective fashion in an electrostatic field. Certain common metabolites (lactate, pyruvate, etc.) are shown to complex with Na

* The proposed role of phosphatidic acid in ion transport has been reviewed [L. E. Hokin and M. R. Hokin, *Intern. Rev. Neurobiol.* 2, 99–136 (1960)]. There is as yet no evidence to show the nature of the proposed carrier-cation complex.

(98). Unfortunately, the method used has not been applied to K or other alkalies. The close association between creatine and K in muscle tissues (99) should be reinvestigated. Washed algal material binds ions, but with no marked selection evident (100).

From this brief summary it is evident that a large gap exists between the marked discriminating powers of cells to select specific ions and the ability of purified cell constituents to provide chemical models. In a trenchant fashion, Glynn (101) reviews this problem, and his article should be consulted for further references and for an outstanding discussion of the phenomena of active transport of ions.

It seems clearly indicated that the ultimate model system to explain ion accumulation must involve the structural relations of protoplasmic units as well as the basic chemical properties of the pure substances in isolation.

C. THE SELECTIVE UPTAKE OF IONS BY CELLULAR PARTICULATES

As noted earlier, the actomyosin fiber system of muscle shows little ability to select K over Na or vice versa. Washed particulate matter from homogenized muscle shows a slight preference for Na (86; see, however, Stone and Shapiro, 102).

Mitochondria and microsomes, however, show definite ability not only to take up and extrude alkali ions, but also selectively to hold them, especially K, in nonexchangeable fashion (see Amoore and Bartley, 103, for discussion and references). However, only a part of K retention of whole cells can be accounted for on this basis (104). Prior adrenalectomy of the donor animal (rat) had little influence on the general behavior of liver mitochondria but did enhance the Na uptake somewhat (105).

Microsomes from different rat tissues bind varying amounts of Na and K, with the K:Na ratio fluctuating from 3 to 4 (106). Brain and muscle microsomes bind almost twice as much Na and K as do liver and kidney microsomes. Threads can be drawn from microsomal material, and, with the aid of microelectrodes, potential differences can be measured between thread interiors and external solution. With material of neural or muscular origin the potential differences exceed 30 mv.; with liver microsomal material, they were under 15 mv.

If microsomes are indeed related to the endoplasmic reticulum (107), then results with these particulates may well ultimately be shown to have a direct bearing on ion transport and accumulation phenomena. Microsomes from rat brain have been shown to have a sodium-activated ATPase. Potassium does not stimulate this system (101a).

D. Ion Selection and Exchange Resins

No attempt will be made to give a complete discussion of the rapidly growing field of ion exchange systems. Standard works (cf. Suttle 1) and the yearly volumes of *Annual Reviews of Physical Chemistry* should be consulted. The literature is old and very voluminous. Earlier work is to be found mainly in the literature on water purification.

The interest of physiologists and biochemists in ion exchange systems is of long standing. Macallum (108) describes his observations on percolating salt solutions through zeolites and other sards. K is preferentially retained in such columns. Artificial resins can now be obtained with preferential uptake of either K or Na (109). At the moment, any comparison between exchange resins and living systems can be only suggestive. It is only with a relatively high degree of cross-linking that much ion selectivity is noted. In living systems, the high cross-linking might conceivably be found in erythrocytes packed with hemoglobin or in muscle cells (striated) packed with actomyosin but would not be expected in plant cell vacuoles, amebas, etc.

V. The Action of Alkali Metals on Enzyme Systems and Cellular Metabolism

As a result of many observations by many scientists a series of generalizations about the effects of Na and K have arisen which hold more or less for many forms of life.

(a) The best medium for normal activity of cells not adjusted to low-salt environments involves a balance between Na and K.

(b) Na, in many cases, as an extracellular component, appears essential for maintenance of normal irritability.

(c) K in excess causes marked depolarization of cell boundaries.

(d) Within limits, Li tends to have effects similar to Na; Rb and Cs act more like K. NH_4^+ ion also acts similarly to K, and organic cations such as choline may in some instances be substituted for Na.

Because of these well-known general effects, interest has been strong in finding biochemical reaction systems preferentially activated or inhibited by specific alkali cations.

A. Effects of Alkalies on Isolated Enzyme Systems

Table XII lists a number of enzyme systems that have been studied with reasonable care. In the relatively simple systems shown, K is the only ion with marked activation effects. Where studied, Rb also activates, Cs inhibits or has only a slight activating effect.

Na is listed as inhibiting the reactions and has been thought to act

TABLE XII

ALKALI ION EFFECTS[a] ON ENZYME SYSTEMS

Enzyme system	Li	Na	K	Rb	Cs
Muscle pyruvic phosphoferase[b]	−	0	+++	+	
β-Galactosidase activity[c]	±	−	+++	++	+
Tryptophanase[d]	− −	−	+++	++	−
Yeast aldehyde dehydrogenase[e]	−	−	+++	++	−
Phosphotransacetylase[f]	−	−	+++		
Acetate activation[g]	−	−	+++	++	
Fructokinase substrate affinity[h]	+		+++		
Bacterial apyrase[i]	+	+	+	+	+

[a] +, Activation; −, inhibition; 0, no marked effect.
[b] P. D. Boyer, H. A. Lardy, and P. H. Phillips, *J. Biol. Chem.* **149**, 529–541 (1943).
[c] M. Cohn and J. Monod, *Biochim. et Biophys. Acta* **7**, 152–174 (1951).
[d] F. C. Happold and A. Struyvenberg, *Biochim. J.* **58**, 379–382 (1954).
[e] S. Black, *Arch. Biochem. Biophys.* **34**, 86–97 (1951).
[f] E. R. Stadtman, *J. Biol. Chem.* **196**, 527–534 (1952).
[g] R. W. von Korff, *J. Biol. Chem.* **203**, 265–271 (1953).
[h] H. G. Hers, *Biochim. et Biophys. Acta* **8**, 424 (1952).
[i] J. A. Clark and R. A. MacLeod, *J. Biol. Chem.* **211**, 531–540 (1954).

antagonistically to K. However, the Na effect is certainly not that of simple antagonism (*110*). Although not listed in Table XII, NH_4 has a K-like effect.

Little comparative work has been done, but one study by Boyer (*111*) reports the K activation of pyruvate kinase in sample organisms from six different phyla of animals. Since the other enzymes listed in Table XII are from a variety of organisms, it is safe to assume that the K activation, especially of the phosphate transfer systems, is very widespread.

Skow (*112*) reports some very interesting work on ATPase particulate system isolated from crab nerves. In the presence of Mg, Na markedly stimulates hydrolysis of ATP by the system. With both Na and Mg present in the system, K in low concentrations activates still further; in higher concentrations K inhibits the Na-activated system, but not the Mg-activated fraction. Evidence for the participation of an ATPase in active movements of the alkali metal ions is now highly suggestive (*112a*). As yet, however, there is no direct evidence concerning the nature of the carrier complex involved.

Skow interprets his results as consistent with an Na effect resting on the formation of an Na-Mg-substrate complex, K ions stimulating the enzyme directly.

It is worthy of note that the optimal concentrations of K necessary to stimulate enzymatic activities are high, as are inhibitory concentrations of Na. Thus for the pyruvic-kinase systems the optimum is above 0.1 M KCl added, for tryptophanase it is in the same general range. Only in the case of the Mg-ATPase system does an alkali metal have an optimum effect at a low concentration, 0.02 M for Na.

Thus in the K-activated systems at least, there would seem to be little reason for invoking the alkali metals as regulating devices or trigger mechanisms. Large changes in free intracellular monavalent cations would not be expected on a short-time basis. In the case of the natural experiment, that of the highly variable internal Na:K ratio of erythrocytes of different species, there appears to be no basic difference in metabolic activity, quantitative or qualitative.

B. EFFECTS OF THE ALKALIES ON TISSUE METABOLISM

The effects of the alkali metals on tissue slices and cell fragments have been studied extensively. The usual finding is that of some stimulation with moderate addition of K ions, excess K causing inhibition. A useful summary of effects is to be found in the "Handbook of Respiration" (113).

Variations in the Na content of the medium have little or no effect on the respiration or rate of glycolysis of brain slices (114), provided osmotic pressure is maintained with sucrose or by substitution of choline or Li for Na. The same evidence indicates little effect of Li on the respiration of this system.

There is little information available on the effects of Cs and Rb on metabolic activity except as they simulate the effects of K in low concentrations, becoming toxic in high.

Interesting interactions between amino acids such as glycine (ascites cells) (115) or glutamic acid (brain tissue) (116) have been studied extensively. Brain slices incubated in physiological salt solutions containing glutamate maintain a higher K content (but not concentration) than slices in the salt solution alone.

The range of effects of the alkali metals on purified enzyme systems is thus not very great when compared to the variety of effects of the same ions on physiological activities such as heartbeat, nerve action, and response of effectors. Differences probably relate to differences in modes of action on isolated chemical systems and on intact cells. In many instances, with intact cells effects are to be ascribed to action at external surfaces (117), the longer-term effects of intracellular ion changes being much less studied.

VI. The Physiological and Pharmacological Effects of the Alkali Metals

It is beyond the scope of this chapter to outline in detail the physiology and the pharmacology of the alkali metals. Standard works of physiology, especially Heilbrunn's "General Physiology" (90) and the "Comparative Animal Physiology" (12) edited by Prosser, should be consulted. A great wealth of information is also to be found in various Handbook series (118). Much information on the effects of Na and K on various biological systems is to be found in Fleckenstein's (119) monograph.

Excessive alteration of internal alkali composition leads to a variety of necrotic manifestations both in plants and animals. The general picture can best be summed up simply by saying that either depletion of intracellular K or excess of any other alkali leads to sick cells which, however, may be viable (cf. section on nutrition).

A. Effects of Extracellular Alkali Ions

With the vast majority of cell types, extensive alteration of the concentrations of alkali ions in the external medium leads to pronounced physiological changes. The monumental review by Shanes (120) gives much detailed information of the effects of various agents, including the alkalies, on phenomena of irritability, especially of animal cells.

By and large, K (and to a lesser extent, Cs and Rb) appears to be a most potent extracellular agent. The major effect of K and the K-like ions would seem to relate to a depolarizing effect upon the cell surface, the mechanism of action being entirely unknown. Moderate excesses of extracellular K increase excitability, higher concentrations lead to complete inexcitability. The sensitivity of various systems to K can be altered by means of "sensitizers" (121) such as guanidine and SCN, insect muscles showing slight response to sensitizers; those of holothurians, little or none, and worm and vertebrate muscles displaying pronounced effects.

Studies of the depolarizing action of K and Rb on frog muscle (117) lead to the conclusion that the effects of these ions are essentially on the cell surfaces. Even in insects with low-Na, high-K blood, a typical depolarization is found with excess K (122).

Throughout the years there has been a remarkably consistent tendency to ascribe the depolarizing action of K and related ions to an "increase in permeability." Unfortunately, from the biochemical point of view this idea is not very useful inasmuch as the term "permeability" gives no help in describing a biochemical mechanism. Since, as previously noted, there is reason to believe that alkali ion assimilation by living cells involves direct combination with other cellular components, it may be more fruitful in the future to search for chemical combinations of alkalies rather than devices to alter the rate at which a given ion travels a certain distance in free solution or in pores. No violence would be done to most of the electrophysiological observations on ion movements since all the formulations contain a "mobility" (e.g., P or U) function which could involve either an average rate of movement of a single ion or the population density of ions per unit of surface being crossed. An apparent increase of permeability could be due either to increased rate of movement of ions through pores or an increased number of ions per unit area. There is some evidence to show the normal external surface is a "low-concentration" region for ions as compared to the inner protoplasm (123).

The extensive studies by Heilbrunn and his students (90) deserve careful attention since they demonstrate the extreme sensitivity of protoplasm to ionic alterations and, conversely, the ability of changes in protoplasm to produce ionic changes. No chemical models are available as yet to explain these phenomena.

The effects of Na ions in the external medium are less drastic and a considerable variation can be tolerated by most cells, provided osmotic relationships are maintained by indifferent electrolytes, such as choline chloride, or by nonelectrolytes.

As noted previously, there is little evidence that Na is an essential nutrient except for some marine forms and the cells of vertebrates in tissue culture. This does not mean, of course, that further study will not demonstrate a requirement, but the evidence to date would indicate that in those forms where Na is required, the need is as an essentially extracellular component rather than as a part of the protoplasm itself.

Since Overton's time it has been recognized that lack of Na in the external medium will produce a nonirritable condition in many types of muscle and nerve. The pioneering work of A. L. Hodgkin and his co-workers (see Shanes, 120, for references) made good sense of this by demonstrating that an inwardly directed Na current was largely responsible for the rising phase of the action potential. In some forms, however, this Na current is not necessary (see Tobias, 124). Other ions such as Ca may be involved in, for example, the production of the action potential of crustacean muscle (125). In the case of Nitella cells, chloride serves to carry part of the current needed to generate the action potential (126).

B. Effects of Intracellular Alkali Ions

The physiological action of the alkalies on the interior protoplasm of cells is even more obscure than the external actions. As noted previously, some cell types can be drastically depleted of K by substituting NH_4, Na, or Li, yielding viable but physiologically impaired systems (see Danowski and Elkinton, 127). In view of the known activating effects of K on many transphosphorylating systems (see Table XII) these effects may be due to a fairly general slowing of synthetic processes.

Experiments on the effects of injecting excess electrolyte into squid giant axons (128, 129) lead to somewhat conflicting interpretations, but it seems clear that an increase in internal K by no means has effects comparable to similar alterations in external K concentrations. Depletion and repletion of intracellular K of frog muscle has little effect on the electrical parameters measured (130), and a similar independence of the action potential from internal Na content is claimed for toad muscle fibers (131).

Treatment of a variety of cell types with salt solution leads to characteristic changes in viscosity and sol:gel ratios (see Heilbrunn, 90, for references). The conditions of the experiments would certainly indicate that intracellular changes in ionic composition have taken place, but quantitative measurements are not available.

Since the early papers of H. Zwaardemaker (see Fenn, 9, for references) there have been suggestions that the natural radioactivity of K^{40} is an important factor in the physiological action of the metal. In spite of all contrary evidence, research continues to be reported indicating such effects of radioactivity (132). However, there are contrary reports also appearing (see, e.g., Vinogradov, 133), and the subject can be dismissed by saying that there is no compelling evidence for either the specific action or specific accumulation of any single K isotope naturally occurring.

VII. The Regulation of the Alkali Metals in Body Fluids and Cells

It may now be assumed that the protoplasmic content of the alkalies of cells in general is a result of the active participation of the cells themselves, probably with processes of uptake and extrusion both operative, either, as seems to hold for plant cells, with very little leakage by simple diffusion of ions, or against the background of an appreciably leaky system, as appears to be found in the case of erythrocytes.

The subject of active transport and accumulation is dealt with elsewhere in this treatise,* and the fundamental biochemistry concerned

* See Vol. II, Chapter 7.

must await further studies of the mechanisms involved, the ion-binding systems and the relationships of ions in the various protoplasmic phases —aqueous, nonaqueous, and surface. It is remarkable that the same cells that have the power of regulating their internal composition toward a high K condition can act in certain organ or tissue systems to provide body fluids closely regulated with respect to high Na and low K. This is especially true for body fluids of multicellular animals.

In an excellent series of papers, Robertson (*134, 135, 136*) has examined the composition of body fluids of marine invertebrates and chordates. He reports evidence of active regulation of ion content of body fluids in examples from five different phyla. Regulation ranges from relatively minor deviations from sea water ion ratios to quite pronounced variations in the decapod Crustacea. In all forms, at least slight accumulation of K was found in body fluids as contrasted with sea water. In the decapods, active regulation of Na was found as well.

The nonvertebrate chordates and hagfishes (Myxinoidei) maintain body fluids approximately isosmotic with respect to sea water, but with evidence of some regulation of each ionic constituent. Other vertebrates show the well-known regulation toward a low salt concentration down to one-third to one-fifth that of sea water. The regulation of body fluids of fish to a level lower than sea water and similar for both freshwater and marine forms has been widely interpreted as lending support to the theory of the freshwater origin of the vertebrates. Robertson's discussion (*137*) presents interesting evidence against this interpretation.

That the regulation of the body fluids of bony fishes to the low level normally found is not essential for the existence of all types is indicated by the provocative findings (*138*) that shallow water, marine arctic fishes, exposed to low temperatures, develop high-osmotic-strength bloods. Detailed analyses of blood compositions under these conditions are not available. Deep-sea forms under similar low temperature conditions maintain a low osmotic pressure of the blood, becoming supercooled at the near freezing temperatures for sea water.

Representative values for the Na and K contents of blood plasma and sera are given elsewhere (Table V; see also Prosser, *12*). Values for lymph, cerebrospinal fluids, etc., show specific variations from blood serum values of the same body, but the variations are quantitatively relatively small. Selected values for some other vertebrate secretions are shown in Table XIII. A considerable variation in both Na and K is to be noted, and the composition of a given secretion can vary widely depending upon the general physiological state of the animal. As is well known, body fluid electrolytes are regulated in part via hormone mechanisms (see Selkurt, *139*).

TABLE XIII

SODIUM AND POTASSIUM CONTENTS[a] OF CERTAIN SECRETIONS AND EXCRETIONS

Secretion	Na	K
Sweat, human (average)	70	17
Tears, man	145	24
Saliva, man	24	17
Gastric juice, man	49	12
Gastric juice, dog	22	7
Pancreatic juice, man	138	5
Pancreatic juice, dog	151	5
Rat submaxillary secretion[b]	40.7	92.1
Rat sublingual secretion[b]	43.2	83.1
Rat parotid secretion[b]	60.7	65.4
Rat pancreatic secretion[b]	32.5	72.4
Milk, dolphin[c]	44.6	32.2
Milk, human, colostrum[d]	21	18
Milk, human, mature[d]	6	13
Milk, goat[d]	17	42
Milk, cow[d]	33	35

[a] Values are in millimoles per liter. Unless otherwise stated, they are taken from National Research Council (U. S.) handbooks.

[b] L. H. Schneyer and C. A. Schneyer, *Am. J. Physiol.* **196**, 365–367 (1959).

[c] L. Eichelberger, E. S. Fetcher, E. M. K. Geiling, and B. J. Vos, *J. Biol. Chem.* **134**, 171–176 (1940).

[d] Composition of milks. *Natl. Acad. Sci.—Natl. Research Council Publ.* **254** (1953).

Prolonged deprivation of water and food illustrates the remarkable ability of animals to regulate internal Na and K contents (*140, 141*). Some animals, such as the kangaroo rat, are able to maintain a proper body fluid composition while drinking sea water (*142*), and gulls and other birds living near the sea make use of nasal glands (*143*) as Na (and presumably K) regulating devices in order to survive high salt intakes. Recent work shows that cats can ingest large quantities of sea water without undue upset of the ion balance of their body fluids (*144*).

With a normal diet, the parotid secretion of sheep normally contains 180 meq. Na and 10 meq. K per liter. Depletion of Na by withholding the element from the diet leads to a secretion containing 60 meq. Na and 120 meq. K per liter. Restoration of Na to the diet leads to a recovery of the normal pattern (*145*).

Semen from a wide variety of animals is characterized by a high K content relative to that of blood, Na usually being lower. In the case of man and dog, the secretion of the prostate has only a slightly increased K level, seminal vesicle secretion has considerably more K (*146*).

Satisfactory data are not at hand to evaluate properly either onto-genetic or phylogenetic changes in body fluid composition with respect to individual ions. In a very interesting paper Howard has given evidence that there is, in the body and embryonic fluids of the chick "an ontogenetic shift between an initial osmolarity characteristic of the blood of amphibia and the more primitive freshwater vertebrates, to the osmolarity characteristic of mature birds and mammals" (147). After hatching, blood salts remain virtually constant during further development (148), as does intracellular muscle K.

Shifts in total osmotic concentrations of embryonic fluids from a lower level to a high may indeed be indicative of various phases in the evolutionary history of animals, and such shifts have been used to bolster the arguments for the freshwater origin of vertebrates (see Wald, 149, for references).

Howard (147) points out that, so far as the evidence goes, several different types of organisms start early development with a relatively low osmolar concentration of the fluids bathing the cells. In the case of the chick egg, the low osmolar values of the white (albumen portion) may be compared to the generally low value of many of the external secretions of mammals or birds, as may the follicular fluids of mammals. If this is true, the rise in osmolar concentration of the blood during development would be more nearly a reflection of the process of cellular regulation setting in, rather than an indication that cellular regulation of body fluids necessarily had to start with dilute external media.

With man, the total cation content of serum rises during development from fetus to adult, the major quantitative change involving Na (+ about 14 mmoles per liter); Cl remains nearly constant and K drops from 10 to about 5 mmoles per liter. Thus much of the change in osmolarity must involve regulation by addition of plasma proteins (150). Certainly in the case of the amphibia and the freshwater fishes, the sudden dilution of the osmotically active constituents after deposition of ova in fresh water need indicate no more than that a short time interval is needed before the developing cellular systems can make the proper adjustment from the isotonic conditions of the maternal reproductive tract to the highly hypotonic external medium.

It is regrettable that there is relatively little basis on which to base speculations about the evolution of intracellular electrolytes or their ontogeny. In an interesting discussion, MacLeod and Onfrey (151) consider the adaptations that might account for the shift of primitive marine bacteria to terrestrial or holophytic forms. Marine bacteria, although they require Na, nevertheless maintain a relatively low intracellular content of Na while concentrating K. In this respect they closely resemble tissue culture cells of vertebrate origin.

As previously noted, while whole-tissue Na and K contents change during posthatching development, calculated intracellular K concentrations remain nearly constant (148). Similarly the intracellular K concentration of reticulocytes is the same as that of mature erythrocytes in rabbits (152). In other forms, marked changes during maturation of erythrocytes have been reported. With the Welsh sheep showing genetically controlled erythrocyte K and Na contents, all fetal cells are found to have high K contents, the high Na condition developing postnatally (153). In general fetal cells of sheep and cattle have more K and less Na than mature erythrocytes; in man, pig, and guinea pig the reverse is found (154). There is good evidence that young and old erythrocytes can be separated by centrifugation (155), the different classes having different ionic compositions.

VIII. The Sodium and Potassium Balance of the Whole Organism

The general acid:base balance of the mammalian body is well documented in standard text books of physiology and biochemistry. The subject is reviewed at frequent intervals, most notably perhaps in the *Annual Review of Physiology* (see Selkurt, 139). Major responsibility for regulation of Na in the body fluids is a function of the excretory system, which has remarkable properties of Na resorption. Excess Na, especially in forms facing a water shortage or NaCl excess, is removed by the kidney up to a certain point beyond which several odd types of extrarenal mechanisms may come into play in such forms as sea gulls, cormorants (see Schmidt-Nielsen, 143), and salt-water teleosts. Some mammals (e..g, kangaroo rat) are able to excrete a highly hypertonic urine. A provocative countercurrent diffusion theory has been developed to account for such renal phenomena (156).

The over-all regulation of Na and K in whole organisms is, to be sure, complicated and rests upon a number of special mechanisms in the different groups. In many of the simpler invertebrates, including the protozoa, and in plants the major alkali regulation appears to be concerned with intracellular K. With most plants and with single-cell forms there is no evidence for a widespread regulation of protoplasmic Na nor, indeed, extracellular Na, except insofar as the Na concentration of protoplasm is kept low. With some bacteria, the K regulation appears to involve a selective chemical binding ion on a matrix, Na moving freely in the interstices (see Epstein, 66, Cowie 66b, etc., for references); in most other systems some form of active Na extrusion perhaps backed up by active intake appears to be the rule.

With multicellular animals, a pattern emerges of variable degrees of regulation of body fluid composition superimposed on the basic regulation of K content of cells.

While this regulation seems to involve all inorganic ions to a greater or lesser degree (see Robertson, 157 and 137 for discussion and references), the major effect is that of maintaining a high Na and low K content of the internal environment—just the reverse of the protoplasmic picture. Interestingly enough, this ionic regulation of body fluids does not necessarily involve osmotic regulations.

With the development of vertebrates and in some other forms such as decapod Crustacea, osmotic regulation becomes prominent. Vertebrates, especially from the lampreys on, not only regulate ionic composition of the body fluids but osmotic concentrations as well, so that bloods are markedly hypertonic to fresh water and hypotonic to sea water. The level of osmotic regulation in all cases is reasonably close to the range of cellular K concentrations noted previously (cf. Table VIII).

Animals regulating body fluid Na while living under Na-deficient conditions (freshwater, terrestrial, etc.) make use of active uptake mechanisms (e.g., Na uptake by the skin of Amphibia) and the Na-conserving system of renal filtration-resorption. In both instances the process appears to be mainly one of active Na transport into the body fluids. To a lesser extent this process is also found in intestinal absorption. Other secretions may be "regulatory" in part. Sweat, for example, is normally hypotonic to blood with respect to Na, hypertonic with respect to K. However, with an increased secretion rate, Na concentration goes up, K concentration goes down (158), and severe salt loss may occur.

Regulation against high Na environments or intake involves both renal and extrarenal mechanisms, as previously noted.

Cellular regulation toward high K, low Na appears general for all cells with but few exceptions. These same cells, arranged in epithelial sheets, are able to regulate transcellular transport of Na to the high Na body fluids while still retaining their propoplasmic identity with respect to Na and K.

An excellent review of the complex interrelations in mammals is given by Darrow and Hellerstein (159), and Gross has discussed the situation in some Crustacea (160). In mammals, certain tissues act as definite reservoirs for Na and K. Bone, for example, appears to have little importance as a K reservoir although it functions well as a sort of buffer system for Na (See McLean, 161, for references). During K depletion, muscles lose intracellular K, replaced by Na. K-Depleted rats can tolerate considerably higher injections of KCl than can normal rats, and this appears to be a function of the ability of the depleted muscle fibers to take up the extra K, thus maintaining more nearly normal blood levels (162).

Many studies have pointed out the delicate balance between blood and cell ionic concentrations (see e.g., Darrow and Hellerstein, 159), and ions other than the alkali ions are generally involved. As noted previously, osmotic balance is not necessarily associated with ionic balance. Intracellularly, amino acids and related compounds are used as solutes to assist osmotic regulation; in body fluids, amino acids (e.g., insects) and urea (elasmobranch fish) are brought into service apparently for similar reasons.

IX. The Evolution of the Ionic Balance of Cells and Body Fluids

The general knowledge relating to this subject may be summarized in part as follows:

(a) K is the ubiquitous cation-forming element of protoplasm.

(b) Cellular concentrations of K tend to vary only slightly (mostly within the limits 100–200 mM) as contrasted to wide variations in osmotic concentrations of the environment.

(c) Ionic composition of body fluids is generally regulated to provide a high Na environment, not necessarily related to osmotic adjustments.

(d) In those forms that regulate total osmotic concentrations in the body fluids, as well as ionic ratios, the final concentration approached is comparable to that matching the protoplasmic K concentration.

In general, two types of K-concentrating devices appear in nature: (a) the apparent binding found in some bacteria and in some cell particulates and (b) the concentration mechanisms arising because of the establishment of an electromotive force across the membrane (Donnan effect) (see Theorell, 163). When the first mechanism is operative, Na seems to wander freely in the interstices of a matrix; as the second mechanism comes into play Na is actively extruded as it leaks in, K being further concentrated by electrostatic forces. It is indeed remarkable that even in an environment nearly equivalent to sea water, cells can hold the total protoplasmic inorganic cation content to a relatively low level, the system behaving as though there was an upper limit to the number of base-binding sites compatible with life. In a few cases (e.g., muscles of some marine forms, some plant cells) (164) new binding sites appear, but this is probably exceptional behavior. In most instances, as previously noted, osmotic adjustments are made by raising the organic solute concentration of cells as needed. This critical ion regulation, apparently for chemical rather than osmotic reasons, is one of the most tantalizing problems in the biochemistry of the alkalies.

There is no direct evidence relating to the evolution of the high-K condition of cell interiors. However, if the general scheme of origin of life followed the pattern: organic molecules → polymers → aggregates → formed structures → cells, a suggested pattern for accumulation of K would be (*a*) selection by polymers followed by (*b*) development of extrusion mechanisms for other ions (e.g., Na). The first mechanism would provide for relatively low levels of concentration and, since K is less likely to be bound by ordinary chelating processes, might be expected to relate to steric factors. In this sense, K can be said to be selected as the ion which has least chemical effect, either on water structure or on molecular configuration of the organic constituents.

This preliminary phase of K selection may well be reflected in K activation of enzyme systems as found in many cell types (Table XII).

To speculate further, the development of more pronounced ionic gradients (Na gradient and K gradient) may have been conditioned by the processes leading to the establishment of "active surfaces" or plasma membranes functional in ion transport processes. Indeed, because of the possible orienting influence of the electrical gradients, the development of "active surfaces" and ion gradients may well have been mutually dependent. As noted in the next section, there is some reason to assume that the development of ion gradients marks the step at which cells first become responsive and reactive to environmental changes.

The evolution of body fluids has been the subject of considerable speculation (see Roberton, *137*, Wald, *149*, and Romer, *165* for references), and the similarity of both concentrations and ionic ratios in the vertebrates has been held as consistent with the freshwater origin of vertebrates. While the evidence discussed in this chapter does not give any definitive evidence on this point, it is worth reiterating that the ionic concentrations of vertebrate blood are regulated in such a direction as to match, osmotically, the highly regulated internal K concentration of cells. As pointed out, internal regulation of osmotic concentrations of cells does not take place by elevated K concentrations. Therefore, with the advance of evolutionary processes, the active cells have, in a sense, adapted the body fluids to their own standard concentrations. This tendency is apparent even in some invertebrates, but has been perfected only in the vertebrates. As seen from this point of view, the development of a relatively uniform vertebrate blood pattern may have occurred during colonization of fresh water, but it represents a tendency that might have been expected in any milieu.

X. The Significance of Ion Gradients

As noted above, there are some reasons for thinking that the K gradient between living substance and the environment may have developed in the precellular stage, being enhanced and supplemented by ion extrusion mechanisms with the development of true cells. So far as formal cells are concerned then, K gradients (outwardly directed) and Na gradients (inwardly directed) arose at about the same period of history. The major excuse for the development of these gradients appears to be that of providing a storage battery system of readily available free energy. A more minor reason would be the establishment of a more favorable internal medium for catalyzed reactions.

The K gradient has been implicated as a source of energy for muscle contraction (119); Fleckenstein's book should be consulted for a comprehensive discussion. However, the nature of any coupling between ion gradients and production of mechanical energy remains obscure.

There is highly suggestive evidence that ion gradients can be directly responsible for the electrical variations associated with phenomena of irritability of cells. Squid axons with active transport processes poisoned will still conduct impulses (166). Nerves poisoned with excess KCl can still show some electrical variations if the electrical gradient is re-established from external sources (167).

Even though an internally directed Na gradient may have arisen as a primary event during the development of irritable cells, the necessity for the specific gradient is not ubiquitous. In *Chara* the double ionic gradient necessary for a reversal of sign during the action potential is obtained from two outwardly directed ion gradients: the usual K gradient and a chloride gradient (126). With crustacean muscles other ions (e.g., Ba and Sr) can serve in the external environment instead of Na (125), and with neuron cell bodies a variety of onium ions may take the place of much of the Na (168). As noted before Li can partially substitute for Na.

XI. Conclusion

"The discipline called 'biochemistry' deals with the study of (1) the nature of the chemical constituents of living matter and of the chemical substances produced by living things, (2) the functions and transformations of these chemical entities in biological systems, and (3) the chemical and energetic changes associated with these transformations in the course of the activity of living matter" (169).

While the alkali metals are neither produced nor transformed by living matter, they have, as a part of the living system, a biochemistry in the proper sense. "Potassium is an essential part of the physico-chemical structure of the cell. It is not fixed in position but can move about freely according to the demands of shifting membrane equilibria" (9). Sodium provides the ubiquitous metallic component of the environment against which protoplasm apparently likes to work. Extruded from cells but tolerated in variable amounts, sodium is the element actively conserved as a part of the cellular milieu in many different living systems. Potassium proves to be a comfortable protoplasmic constituent but is highly irritating to most cells when in excess in the environment. In contrast to sodium, there appear to be no extrusion mechanisms for potassium and, while active uptake devices may exist, they seem to play no dominant role; potassium usually follows an electrochemical gradient.

Special complexes of sodium and potassium with organic constituents have been sought; a few have actually been found. So far, however, they fall, in the main, into three categories: (i) binding of potassium as indicated by "Michaelis constants" of enzymes; (ii) "nondiffusible" sodium retained by cell particulates and by certain phospholipid fractions; and (iii) binding constants of both ions, as determined by competitive interaction during the transport processes involved in cell penetration. It is notable that there are no instances of massive binding or combinations of either potassium or sodium on a scale which would account for the marked concentration or depletion of the elements within cells. Although it may be possible for internal structures to be so arranged that a massive selection might take place due to forces depending on some "closest distance of approach" factor, such structures remain to be demonstrated.

While there can be no doubt that there is a tendency for all cells to have a characteristic level of potassium in their protoplasms, it is equally evident that the regulation of the exact level depends on the over-all metabolism of the living systems and also on genetic constitution. The inheritance of sodium-potassium patterns in erythrocytes has been known for some time. Recent work by Lubin (170) has demonstrated the genetic control of potassium uptake by *Escherichia coli* and indicates the future usefulness of such studies in unravelling the delicate mechanisms involved in ion transport generally.

Thus the biochemistry of the alkalies rests primarily on the dynamics of living systems. Sodium and potassium are concerned with specific parts of the vital machinery that can select the necessary small amounts of cation with the rapid turnover needed to keep an active process going. This active machinery is lost on the death of the cell and is turned off and on during responses to stimulating agents. Insofar as the behavior of sodium and potassium is concerned, response to a stimulus is a reversible form of death.

In the general cycles of the alkali metals on earth, sodium is associated with unformed aqueous phases, and potassium with soils and with protoplasm (9). As indicated by viscosity changes of solutions, sodium provides an ion promoting a tighter structure of water whereas potassium fits nicely into water lattice systems associated with natural ice structures (6). Further study of the interactions of the alkali ions with water, both in the fluid phases and as ordered ice-like patterns investing macromolecular units, should go far toward providing a true biochemistry of the elements. Klotz (171) has suggested that the marked changes in ionic mobilities attending the water-ice transformation may be associated with the drastic permeability changes that have been invoked to account for the ion migrations during the generation of the action potential. According to Eigen and De Maeyer (172) the mobility of the hydrogen ion is over a hundred times greater in ice than in water. Lithium, on the other hand, has a mobility over a thousand times *less* in ice than in water. Changes in the ordered lattice structure of water around the macromolecular elements of the cell membrane should be rapid and reversible and could be accompanied by large-scale alterations in either concentrations or mobilities of associated alkali ions. At present there is no evidence on which a scheme for discrimination between the metallic ions could be formulated, based on water structures; however, sodium and potassium have sufficiently divergent properties to encourage studies from this point of view.

References

1. J. F. Suttle, *in* "Comprehensive Inorganic Chemistry" (M. C. Sneed, J. L. Maynard, and R. C. Brasted, eds.), Vol. VI. Van Nostrand, New York, 1957.
2. Potassium Symposium. Intern. Potash Inst., Berne, Switzerland, 1954.
3. P. J. Boyle, E. J. Conway, *J. Physiol. (London)* **100**, 1–63 (1940).
4. See *Discussions Faraday Soc.* **24**, 1957.
5. A. E. Martell and M. Calvin, "Chemistry of the Metal Chelate Compounds." Prentice-Hall, Englewood Cliffs, N. J., 1952.
6. S. L. Baird, G. Kaneman, H. Mueller, and A. Szent-Györgyi, *Proc. Natl. Acad. Sci. U. S.* **43**, 705–708 (1957).
7. W. J. V. Osterhout, *Ann. Rev. Physiol.* **20**, 1–12 (1958).
8. K. Rankama and T. G. Sahama, "Geochemistry." Univ. of Chicago Press, Chicago, 1950.
9. W. O. Fenn, *Physiol. Revs.* **20**, 377 (1940).
10. "*Tabulae Biol.*" (*Hague*) **3** (1928), et seq.
11. "Handbook of Respiration," N.A.S. Series. Saunders, Philadelphia, 1958, and earlier volumes; Composition of cereal grains and forages, *Natl. Acad. Sci. —Natl. Res. Council Publ.* **No. 585** (1958); Sodium restricted diets, *ibid.* **No. 325** (1954).

716   H. B. STEINBACH

12. C. L. Prosser, D. W. Bishop, F. A. Brown, Jr., T. L. Jahn, and V. J. Wulff, eds., "Comparative Animal Physiology." Saunders, Philadelphia, 1950.
13. J. B. Buck, in "Insect Physiology" (K. D. Roeder, ed.), pp. 147–163. Wiley, New York, 1953.
14. A. P. Vinogradov, "The Elementary Composition of Marine Organisms," Memoirs, Sears Foundation for Marine Research No. 2. New Haven, Conn., 1953.
15. C. R. B. Joyce and M. Weatherall, *J. Physiol.* (*London*) **142**, 453 (1958); J. M. Barker, *Nature* **181**, 492–493 (1958).
16. W. F. Widdas, *J. Physiol.* (*London*) **125**, 18P (1954).
17. E. Epstein, *Ann. Rev. Plant. Physiol.* **7**, 1–24 (1956).
18. R. W. Eppley, *J. Gen. Physiol.* **41**, 901–911 (1958).
19. R. W. Eppley and C. R. Bovell, *Biol. Bull.* **115**, 101–106 (1958).
20. J. D. Robertson, in "Invertebrate Physiology" (B. Scheer, ed.), pp. 229–246. Univ. of Oregon Press, Eugene, Oregon, 1957.
21. H. B. Steinbach, *Ann. N. Y. Acad. Sci.* **47**, 849–874 (1947).
22. P. R. Lewis, *Biochem. J.* **52**, 330–338 (1952); M. N. Camien, H. Sarlet, G. Duchâteau, and M. Florkin, *J. Biol. Chem.* **193**, 881–885 (1955).
22a. G. G. Deffner, *Biophys. et Biochim. Acta* **47**, 378–388 (1961).
23. S. Lilly, *J. Exptl. Biol.* **32**, 423–439 (1955).
24. J. A. Kitching, *Symposia Soc. Exptl. Biol.* **8**, 63–75 (1954).
24a. M. Florkin, Congress Lecture. *Proc. 1st Intern. Congr. Biochem.*, *Cambridge* pp. 19–31 (1949).
25. W. A. Kratz and J. Myers, *Am. J. Botany* **42**, 282–287 (1955).
26. G. Schmidt, L. Hecht, and S. J. Thannhauser, *J. Biol. Chem.* **178**, 733–742 (1949); E. J. Conway, and P. T. Moore, *Nature* **57**, 527–528 (1954).
27. G. Bertrand, and D. Bertrand. *Ann. agron.* **17**, 149–153 (1947).
28. R. Collander, *Acta. Botan. Fennica* **29**, 1–12 (1941).
29. R. Kilpatrick, H. E. Renschler, D. S. Munro, and G. M. Wilson, *J. Physiol.* (*London*) **133**, 194–201 (1956).
30. P. H. Mitchell, J. W. Wilson, and R. E. Stanton, *J. Gen. Physiol.* **4**, 141–148 (1921).
31. G. O. Burr and D. Takahashi, *Hawaiian Planters' Record* **55**, 3–10 (1955).
32. W. S. McKerrow, S. R. Taylor, A. L. Blackburn, and L. H. Ahrens, *Nature* **178**, 204 (1956).
33. G. Bertrand and D. Bertrand, *Compt. rend. acad. sci.* **232**, 131–133 (1951).
34. G. Bertrand and D. Bertrand, *Compt. rend. acad. sci.* **229**, 609–610 (1949).
35. M. Schou, *Pharmacol. Revs.* **9**, 17–58 (1957).
36. H. J. M. Bowen, *J. Nuclear Energy* **2**, 255–263 (1956).
37. D. Bertrand, *Compt. rend. acad. sci.* **218**, 84–86 (1944).
38. See *Ann. Rev. Plant Physiol.*, *Ann. Rev. Physiol.*, *Ann. Rev. Microbiol.* Publ. by Annual Reviews, Inc., Palo Alto, California.
39. E. S. Snell, in "Trace Analysis" (J. H. Yoe and H. J. Koch, eds.), pp. 547–576. Wiley, New York, 1957.
40. R. W. Krauss, *Ann. Rev. Plant Physiol.* **9**, 207–244 (1958).
40a. H. M. Lenhoff and J. Bovaird, *Exptl. Cell Research* **20**, 284–294 (1960).
41. W. Reuther and T. W. Embleton, *Ann. Rev. Plant. Physiol.* **9**, 175–206 (1958).
42. W. J. Gross, *Biol. Bull.* **114**, 324–347 (1958).
43. D. M. Pace, *J. Cellular Comp. Physiol.* **18**, 243–255 (1941).
44. E. J. Ruth and J. R. Elkinton, *Am. J. Physiol.* **196**, 299–302 (1959).
45. H. Eagle, *Arch. Biochem. Biophys.* **61**, 356–366 (1956).

46. H. Vishniac, *J. Gen. Microbiol.* **12**, 455–463 (1955).
47. R. A. MacLeod, C. A. Claridge, A. Hori, and J. F. Murray, *J. Biol. Chem.* **232**, 829–834 (1958).
48. R. A. MacLeod and E. S. Snell, *J. Bacteriol.* **59**, 783–792 (1950).
49. R. H. Follis, *Am. J. Physiol.* **138**, 246–250 (1943).
50. M. R. Bovarnick, J. C. Miller, and J. C. Snyder, *J. Bacteriol.* **59**, 509–522 (1950).
51. R. B. McGhee, *Am. J. Hyg.* **52**, 42–47 (1950).
52. H. Takada, *J. Inst. Polytech., Osaka City Univ.* **D7**, 105–114 (1956).
53. N. Y. Kawamoto, T. Kondo, and T. Nishi, *Japan. J. Ecol.* **8**, 1–6 (1958).
54. N. E. Feeney, *Arch. Biochem.* **17**, 447–458 (1948).
55. R. G. Ham, D. C. Fitzgerald, Jr., and R. E. Eakin, *J. Exptl. Zool.* **133**, 559–572 (1956).
56. J. Gustafson and J. Hasselberg, *Exptl. Cell. Research* **2**, 642–672 (1951).
57. B. Haccius, *Ber. deut. botan. Ges.* **69**, 87–93 (1956).
58. G. von Bunge, "Textbook of Physiological and Pathological Chemistry." Blakiston, Philadelphia, 1902.
59. E. B. Forbes *et al.*, *Tech. Bull. Penn. State Coll.* **319**, (1935).
60. A. L. Kroeber, "Salt, Dogs and Tobacco." Univ. of California Press, Berkeley, Calif., 1941.
61. E. Jones, "Essays in Applied Psychoanalysis." Intern. Psychoanal. Press, London, 1923.
62. H. Kaunitz, *Nature* **178**, 1141–1144 (1956).
63. J. Castro, *Nutrition Revs.* **2**, 65–67 (1944).
64. M. J. Fregly, *Am. J. Physiol.* **195**, 645–653 (1958).
65. H. B. Steinbach, *Cold Spring Harbor Symposia Quant. Biol.* **8**, 242–254 (1940).
66. E. Epstein, *in* "Electrolytes in Biological Systems," Symposium, pp. 101–111. Marine Biol. Lab., Woods Hole, Mass., 1955. Publ. by American Physiological Society, Washington, D. C.
66a. A. Rothstein and R. Meier, *J. Cellular Comp. Physiol.* **38**, 245–270 (1951).
66b. D. B. Cowie and R. B. Roberts, *in* "Electrolytes in Biological Systems," Symposium, pp. 1–34. Marine Biol. Lab., Woods Hole, Mass., 1955. Publ. by American Physiological Society, Washington, D. C.
67. E. J. Conway, *Symposia Soc. Exptl. Biol.* **8**, 297–324 (1954).
68. A. K. Solomon, *J. Gen. Physiol.* **36**, 57–110 (1952).
69. D. C. Tosteson, *J. Gen. Physiol.* **39**, 55–67 (1955).
70. E. Ernst, J. Szabolcs, and P. T. Kovács, *Acta Physiol. Acad. Sci. Hung.* **6**, 155–170 (1954).
71. P. H. Mitchell and J. W. Wilson, *J. Gen. Physiol.* **4**, 45–56 (1921).
72. E. E. Daniel, *Can. J. Biochem. and Physiol.* **1**, p. 805 (1958).
73. E. Bozler, M. E. Calvin, and D. W. Watson, *Am. J. Physiol.* **195**, 38–44 (1958).
74. E. J. Harris and H. B. Steinbach, *J. Physiol. (London)*
75. S. E. Simon, F. H. Shaw, S. Bennett, and M. Muller, *J. Gen. Physiol.* **40**, 753–777 (1957).
76. G. Ling, *in* "Phosphorus Metabolism" (B. Glass, ed.). Johns Hopkins, Baltimore, 1957.
77. A. B. Macallum, *J. Physiol. (London)* **32**, 95–128 (1905).
78. M. Dubuisson, *Arch. intern. physiol.* **52**, 439–463 (1942).
79. H. B. Steinbach, *Ann. N. Y. Acad. Sci.* **47**, 849–874 (1947).
80. B. M. Johnstone, *Nature* **183**, 411 (1959).

81. P. H. Abelson and W. Duryea, *Biol. Bull.* **96**, 205–217 (1949).
82. A. L. Hodgkin and R. D. Keynes, *J. Physiol.* (*London*) **119**, 513–528 (1953).
83. E. J. Harris, *J. Physiol.* (*London*) **124**, 248–253 (1954).
84. H. Pauley, *Nature* **183**, 333–334 (1959).
85. J. R. van Wazer and C. F. Callis, *Chem. Revs.* **58**, 1011–1046 (1958).
86. H. B. Steinbach, *Am. J. Physiol.* **167**, 284–287 (1951).
87. R. Whittam, *J. Physiol.* (*London*) **140**, 479–496 (1958).
88. C. W. Carr and W. P. Engelstad, *Arch. Biochem. Biophys.* **77**, 158–167 (1958).
89. H. A. Saroff, *Arch. Biochem. Biophys.* **71**, 194–203 (1957).
90. L. V. Heilbrunn, "General Physiology," 3rd ed. Saunders, Philadelphia, 1952.
91. J. Folch, M. Lees, and G. H. Sloane-Stanley, *in* "Metabolism of the Nervous System" (D. Richter, ed.), pp. 174–181. Pergamon, New York, 1957.
91a. L. B. Kirschner, *J. Gen. Physiol.* **42**, 231 (1958).
92. R. Morris and R. D. Wright, *Australian J. Exptl. Biol. Med. Sci.* **32**, 669–676 (1954).
93. D. C. Tosteson, E. Carlsen, and E. T. Dunham, *J. Gen. Physiol.* **39**, 31–53 (1955).
94. T. Erdos, *Hung. Acta. Physiol.* **1**, 33 (1946).
95. L. G. Abood and S. K. Abul-Haj, *J. Neurochem.* **1**, 119–125 (1956).
96. B. I. Aldrich, *Biochem. J.* **70**, 236–244 (1958).
97. G. Zubay and P. Doty, *Biochim. et Biophys. Acta* **29**, 47–58 (1958).
98. B. Jardetsky and J. E. Wirtz, *Arch. Biochem. Biophys.* **65**, 569–572 (1956).
99. V. Myers and G. H. Mangun, *J. Biol. Chem.* **132**, 701–709 (1940).
100. A. Wassermann, *Ann. Botany* (*London*) **13**, 79–88 (1949).
101. I. M. Glynn, *Prog. in Biophys. and Biophys. Chem.* **8**, 241–308 (1958).
101a. J. Jarnefelt, *Biophys. et Biochim. Acta* **48**, 104–110 (1961).
102. D. Stone and S. Shapiro, *Am. J. Physiol.* **155**, 141–146 (1948).
103. J. E. Amoore and W. Bartley, *Biochem. J.* **69**, 223–236 (1958).
104. W. C. Holland and G. V. Auditore, *Am. J. Physiol.* **183**, 309–313 (1955).
105. L. Share, *Am. J. Physiol.* **194**, 47–52 (1958).
106. L. G. Abood and L. Romanchek, *Exptl. Cell. Research* **8**, 459–465 (1955).
107. D. B. Slautterback, *Exptl. Cell. Research* **5**, 173–186 (1955).
108. A. B. Macallum, *Proc. Roy. Soc.* **B104**, 440–458 (1928).
109. J. I. Bregman, *Ann. N. Y. Acad. Sci.* **57**, 125–143 (1953).
110. F. C. Happold and R. B. Beechey, *Biochem. Soc. Symposia* **15**, 52–63 (1958).
111. P. D. Boyer, *J. Cellular Comp. Physiol.* **42**, 71–78 (1953).
112. J. C. Skow, *Biochim. et Biophys. Acta* **23**, 394–401 (1957).
112a. E. T. Dunham and I. M. Glynn, *J. Physiol.* (*London*) **156**, 274–293 (1961).
113. D. S. Dittmer and R. M. Grebe, eds., "Handbook of Respiration," N.A.S. Series. Saunders, Philadelphia, 1958.
114. H. M. Pappius, H. Rosenfeld, D. M. Johnson, and K. A. C. Elliott, *Can. J. Biochem. and Physiol.* **36**, 217–226 (1958).
115. H. N. Christensen, T. R. Riggs, and B. A. Coyne, *J. Biol. Chem.* **209**, 413–427 (1954).
116. H. M. Pappius and K. A. C. Elliott, *Can. J. Biochem. and Physiol.* **34**, 1043–1067 (1956).
117. A. Sandow and H. Mandel, *J. Cellular Comp. Physiol.* **38**, 271–292 (1951).
118. "Handbuch der normalen und pathologischen Physiologie" (A. Bethe, G. v. Bergmann, *et al.*, eds.). Springer, Berlin, 1925 et seq.; "Handbuch der vergleichenden Physiologie" (H. Winterstein, ed.), Fischer, Jena; "Handbuch der

biologische Arbeitsmethoden" (E. Abderhalden, ed.). Urban & Schwarzenberg, Berlin, 1920 et seq.

119. A. Fleckenstein, "Der Kalium-Natrium-Austausch als Energieprinzip in Muskel und Nerv." Springer, Berlin, 1955.

120. A. M. Shanes, Pharmacol. Revs. 10, 59–164, 165–273 (1958).

121. J. Godeaux, Arch. intern. physiol. 55, 420–435 (1948).

122. D. W. Wood, J. Physiol. (London) 138, 119–139 (1957).

123. H. B. Steinbach, Physiol. Zoöl 14, 78–83 (1941).

124. J. M. Tobias, Ann. Rev. Physiol. 21, 299–324 (1959).

125. P. Fatt and B. L. Ginsburg, J. Physiol. (London) 142, 516 (1958).

126. C. T. Gaffey and L. J. Mullins, J. Physiol. (London) 144, 505–524 (1958).

127. T. S. Danowski and J. R. Elkinton, Pharmacol. Revs. 3, 42 (1951).

128. H. Grundfest, in "Electrochemistry in Biology and Medicine" (T. Shedlovsky, ed.). Wiley, New York, 1955.

129. A. L. Hodgkin and R. D. Keynes, J. Physiol. (London) 131, 592–615 (1956).

130. W. K. Stephenson, J. Cellular Comp. Physiol. 50, 105–128 (1957).

131. F. H. Shaw, S. E. Simon, B. H. Johnstone, and M. Holman, J. Gen. Physiol. 40, 263–288 (1956).

132. E. Ernst, J. Tigyi, and A. Niedetsky, Proc. 2nd Intern. Conf. on Peaceful Uses of Atomic Energy, Geneva, 1958 Paper P/1724 (1959).

133. A. P. Vinogradov, Nature 179, 308–309 (1957).

134. J. D. Robertson, J. Exptl. Biol. 26, 182–200 (1949).

135. J. D. Robertson, J. Exptl. Biol. 30, 277–296 (1953).

136. J. D. Robertson, J. Exptl. Biol. 31, 424–442 (1954).

137. J. D. Robertson, Biol. Revs. Cambridge Phil. Soc. 32, 156–187 (1957).

138. P. F. Scholander, L. van Dam, J. W. Kaniwiskes, H. T. Hammel, and M. S. Gordon, J. Cellular Comp. Physiol. 49, 5–24 (1958).

139. E. E. Selkurt, Ann. Rev. Physiol. 21, 117–150 (1959).

140. P. G. Prentiss, A. V. Wolf, and H. A. Eddy, Am. J. Physiol. 196, 626–632 (1959).

141. A. V. Wolf, "Thirst." Charles C Thomas, Springfield, Illinois, 1958.

142. B. Schmidt-Nielsen and K. Schmidt-Nielsen, Am. J. Physiol. 160, 291–294 (1950).

143. K. Schmidt-Nielsen and W. J. L. Sladen, Nature 181, 1217–1218 (1958).

144. A. V. Wolf, P. G. Prentiss, L. G. Douglas, and R. J. Swett, Am. J. Physiol. 196, 633–641 (1959).

145. D. A. Denton, J. Physiol. 131, 516–525 (1956).

146. T. Mann, "The Biochemistry of Semen." Methuen, London, 1954.

147. W. Howard, J. Cellular Comp. Physiol. 50, 451–470 (1957).

148. J. S. Barlow and J. F. Manery, J. Cellular Comp. Physiol. 43, 165–191 (1954).

149. G. Wald, Science 128, 1481–1489 (1958).

150. E. M. Widdowson and R. A. McCance, Clin. Sci. 15, 361–365 (1956).

151. R. A. MacLeod and E. Onofrey, J. Cellular Comp. Physiol. 50, 389–402 (1957).

152. D. Chalfin, J. Cellular Comp. Physiol. 47, 215–239 (1956).

153. W. F. Widdas, J. Physiol. 125, 18P (1954).

154. M. J. Karvonen, Ciba Foundation Colloquia on Ageing 4, 199–205 (1958).

155. C. R. B. Joyce, Quart. J. Exptl. Physiol. 43, 299–309 (1958).

156. B. Schmidt-Nielsen, Physiol. Revs. 38, 139 (1958).

157. J. D. Robertson, in "Invertebrate Physiology" (B. Scheer, ed.), Univ. of Oregon Press, Eugene, Oregon, 1957.

158. R. Adams, R. E. Johnson, and F. Sargent, *Quart. J. Exptl. Physiol.* **43**, 241–257 (1958).
159. D. C. Darrow and S. Hellerstein, *Physiol. Revs.* **38**, 114–137 (1958).
160. W. J. Gross, *Biol. Bull.* **114**, 334–347 (1958).
161. F. C. McLean and A. M. Budy, *Ann. Rev. Physiol.* **21**, 69–90 (1959).
162. H. C. Miller and D. C. Darrow, *Am. J. Physiol.* **130**, 747–758 (1940).
163. T. Teorell, *Proc. Natl. Acad. Sci. U. S.* **21**, 152–161 (1935).
164. H. B. Steinbach, *Biol. Bull.* **78**, 444–453 (1940).
165. A. S. Romer, *in* "Papers in Marine Biology and Oceanography" (M. Sears, ed.) pp. 261–280. Pergamon Press, London, 1956.
166. A. L. Hodgkin and R. D. Keynes, *Symposia Soc. Exptl. Biol.* **8**, 423–437 (1954).
167. J. W. Moore, *Nature* **183**, 265–266 (1959).
168. K. Koketsu, J. A. Cerf, and S. Nishi, *Nature* **181**, 1798 (1958).
169. J. S. Fruton and S. Simmonds, "General Biochemistry." Wiley, New York, 1953.
170. M. Lubin and D. Kessel, *Biochem. Biophys. Research Communs.* **2**, 249–255 (1960).
171. I. M. Klotz, Lecture, Marine Biological Laboratory, Woods Hole, Massachusetts; and personal communication (1961).
172. M. Eigen and L. De Maeyer, *Proc. Roy. Soc.* **A247**, 505–533 (1958).

AUTHOR INDEX

Numbers in parentheses are reference numbers and indicate that an author's work is referred to although his name is not cited in the text. Numbers in italic show the page on which the complete reference is listed.

A

Aach, H. G., 208(193), *238*
Abbo, F. E., 119(67), *176*
Abdel-Akher, M., 57, *63*
Abderhalden, E., 9(81), *23*, 258(64), 263(121), *328, 330*
Abderhalden, R., 9(81), *23*
Abdullah, M., 43, 44(124), *61*
Abel, J. J., 265(135), *330*
Abelson, P. H., 696(81), *718*
Aboliňš, L., 669(96, 97), *675*
Aboliňš-Krogis, A., 669(96), *675*
Abood, L. G., 698(95), 699(106), *718*
Abraham, E. P., 7(39, 40, 41), 22, 191 (26), *234*, 289(277), 292(277), 311(277), *334*
Abukumagawa, E., 216(316), *241*
Abul-Haj, S. K., 698(95), *718*
Acerbo, S. N., 86(62, 63), 88(63), 89 (63), 90(63), 95(63), 96(86, 87), 97(88), *104, 105*
Acher, R., 192(32, 36), 203(130), 231 (401), *234, 236, 244*
Ackermann, W. W., 622(51), *638*
Ada, G. L., 173(336), *183*
Adam, K. R., 323(504), *340*
Adams, E., 250(33), *327*
Adams, R., 710(158), *720*
Adelberg, E. A., 298(354), 299(363), *336*
Adinoifi, M., *552*
Adler, E., 84(57), 96(57), *104*
Adler, M., 162(290), *182*
Ahrens, L. H., 690(32), *716*
Akabori, S., 20, 25, 204(144, 146), 222 (358), *237, 242*
Åkesson, B., 451, 465(80), 471(80), *480*
Albert, A., 617(16, 17), 626(16, 17), 632(113), *637, 640*
Albert, P. W., 292(304), 306(304), *335*
Alberty, R. H., *697*
Albrecht, A. M., 617(19), 627(19), *637*
Albright, E. C., 10(88a), *23*

Alderton, G., 7(56), *23*
Aldrich, B. I., 698(96), *718*
Aldrich, R. A., 601(163), *612*
Aleschin, B., 546, 547, *556*
Alexander, C. S., 519, *555*
Alexander, H. E., 167(311), 173(329), *182, 183*
Alexander, P., 349(77), 358(114), 360, 361(114, 134, 135), 364, 367, *368*
Allard, C., 159(278), *181*
Allen, B. M., 495(32, 38), 496(32, 46, 48), *553, 554*
Allen, D. W., 214(296), *241*
Allen, E. H., 115(45), 116(49), *175, 176*, 246(2), *326*
Allen, F. W., 153(243), 161(284, 285), *180, 181*
Allen, M. B., 216(322), *242*, 655(32), 658(32), 662, *673*
Allfrey, V. G., 113(23, 27), *175*
Alsberg, C. L., 445, 468(57), *480*
Altenbern, R. A., 14(120), *25*
Altman, K. I., 273(206), 332, 565(18), 599, *608, 612*
Alvarez, W. C., 584, *610*
Ambrose, E. J., 347(67a), *367*
Aminoff, D., 6(22), *22*
Amoore, J. E., 699, *718*
Amos, H., 162(291), *182*
Anclair, J. L., 10(93), *23*
Anderer, F. A., 217(329), 232(426), *242, 244*
Anders, F., 668(90), *674*
Anderson, E. E., 202(108), *236*
Anderson, M. L., 621(44), *638*
Anderson, R. C., 314(439, 440), *339*, 618(25), *638*
Anderson, S. G., 173(336), *183*
Ando, T., 129, *178*, 203(138), 216(313, 314, 315, 316), *237, 241*
Anfinsen, C. B., 187(5), 202(109, 111, 113, 115, 119, 120, 121), 203(119), 226(394), *233, 236, 243*

721

(355, 356), 299(365), 328, 335, 336, 337
James, R., 344(6), 365
James, W. O., 279, 280(236), 333, 385 (58), 395
Jamikorn, M., 647(11), 662(51), 664 (57), 666(74), 672, 673, 674
Janes, R. G., 527, 555
Jansz, H. S., 199(87, 88b, 98, 99), 232 (406), 235, 236, 244
Jaques, R., 323(503), 340
Jardetsky, B., 699(98), 718
Jarnefelt, J., 699(101a), 718
Jarrett, A., 599(153), 612
Jeener, R., 126, 137(165), 177, 179
Jelinek, B., 540(124), 555
Jenkins, J. A., 654(27), 673
Jennings, B. E., 324(515), 341
Jensen, H., 323(506), 340
Jensen, S. L., 648(13), 672
Jensen, W. A., 123(89), 127(89), 177
Jermyn, M. A., 33(36), 59, 70, 103
Jerome, H., 631(102), 640
Jervis, G. A., 258, 260, 329
Jilke, I., 140(180), 179
Jönsson, B., 202(120), 236
Johnson, A. W., 7(32, 34), 22, 571 (33), 572(33), 608
Johnson, D. M., 702(114), 718
Johnson, E. A., 148(220), 180
Johnson, J. E., 219(343, 351), 242
Johnson, J. R., 7(51), 22
Johnson, M. L., 210(218), 239
Johnson, N. M., 323(509), 341
Johnson, R. E., 710(158), 720
Johnston, B. M., 696(80), 717
Johnstone, B. H., 705(131), 719
Jolivet, P., 444, 445, 446, 451, 456(49), 457(49), 458(49), 459(49), 461 (49), 467(49), 468(49), 469(49), 472(49), 480
Jollès, P., 203(134, 137, 139, 141), 237
Jolles-Thaureaux, J., 203(137), 237
Jones, A. S., 150(224, 226, 227), 151 (227), 180
Jones, B. M., 269(178), 270(178), 331
Jones, C. B., 359(127), 368
Jones, E., 694(61), 717
Jones, E. R. H., 315(457), 317(464), 339

Jones, F. T., 273(209), 332
Jones, G., 41(99, 101), 61
Jones, I. G., 47(148), 62
Jones, J. C., 454, 462(84), 481
Jones, J. D., 286(261), 334
Jones, J. K. N., 50, 63
Jones, K. M., 623(54), 639
Jones, O. T. G., 636(142), 641
Jones, P. J., 598(147), 611
Jones, R. G., 619(34), 638
Jones, R. T., 214(289, 291), 232(420), 241, 244
Jordan, K., 589(111), 611
Josephson, B., 210(242), 240
Joyce, A. E., 665(61), 674
Joyce, C. R. B., 684(15), 709(155), 716, 719
Joyeux-Laffuie, J., 583(66), 609
Jucker, E., 644(1), 646(1), 647(1), 652(1), 658(1), 672
Junqueira, P. B., 296(337), 336
Jurovcik, M., 213(274, 275), 240
Jutisz, M., 197(78), 203(130), 216 (319), 235, 236, 242

K

Kabal, E. A., 6(21), 22
Kaczka, E. A,, 7(26), 22, 618(25), 638
Kägi, J., 325(525), 341
Kämmerer, H., 600(155), 612
Kagawa, Y., 572(35), 609
Kahn, J. R., 196(72, 74), 222(72), 235
Kaihara, M., 302(382), 303(382), 337
Kajtar, M., 8(64), 23
Kakol, I., 232(409), 244
Kalan, E. B., 253(49), 328
Kalnitsky, G., 202(108), 236
Kaltenbach, J. C., 495(33), 500, 528, 545, 553, 554, 555
Kamahora, T., 305(391), 337
Kamen, M. D., 603, 613
Kaminsky, M., 679
Kaname, S., 474(141), 482
Kanamori, M., 222(362), 243
Kaneko, Y., 631(101), 640
Kaneman, G., 679(6), 698(6), 715(6), 715
Kaniwiskes, J. W., 706(138), 719
Kaper, J. M., 303(455), 315(455), 316, 339

(259), 221(9), 222(9), 226(104), 233, 236, 240

Kotake, M., 318(475), 340

Kotake, Y., 261(98), 288(270), 292 (299), 293, 295, 296(331), 297 (299), 299(368), 329, 334, 335, 336, 337

Kovacs, J., 8(64), 23

Kovács, P. T., 696(70), 717

Koval, G. J., 618(26), 621(46), 638

Kraft, R., 98(104), 101(104), 105

Kramer, M., 171, 182

Kratky, O., 404, 405, 432

Kratz, W. A., 688(25), 716

Kratzl, K., 88(66, 67), 95(81), 104, 105, 278(224), 333

Krauch, H., 18(138), 25

Kraus, Z., 210(226), 239

Krauss, R. W., 691(40), 692(40), 716

Krebs, E. G., 52(189, 191, 195, 196, 197), 63, 199(100), 232(407), 236, 244, 629(87), 639

Krebs, H. A., 3(12), 13(107), 21, 24

Krehl, W. A., 289(276), 334

Krekels, A., 129(113), 130(123, 124, 126), 131, 177, 178, 216(305, 317), 241

Kremers, R. E., 94(79, 80), 100, 104, 105, 278(224), 333

Kretchmer, N., 260(80), 261(93, 94), 294(94), 329

Kreuzer, L., 130(127), 178

Krieg, A., 466(108), 481

Krinsky, N. I., 655(29a), 673

Krishnan, G., 382(39), 395

Krishnaswamy, P. R., 246(2), 326, 636 (147), 641

Kritchevsky, D., 116(51), 158(265), 176, 181

Kritchevsky, J. L., 541, 555

Kroc, R. L., 499(55), 554

Kroeber, A. L., 694(60), 717

Krugelis-Macrae, E., 575(47), 580, 609

Kruhoffer, P., 677

Krukenberg, C., 605, 613

Krukenberg, C. F. W., 437(27), 440, 441, 442, 447, 454, 455(27), 462 (27), 479, 587, 589, 610

Kubowitz, P., 266(152), 331

Kudzin, S. F., 72(29). 103

Kuehl, F. A., 7(28, 29, 50), 22

Kühling, O., 616(2), 637

Kühn, K., 216(308), 222(366), 241, 243

Kühner, A., 600(155), 612

Kuh, E., 616(11), 618(11), 637

Kuhn, R., 633(127), 640

Kuhn, W., 4(17), 10(89, 90), 16(17), 21, 23

Kunisawa, R., 667(80), 674

Kunita, N., 287(268), 288(268), 334

Kuno, S., 304(389), 337

Kunst, P., 199(95), 236

Kuntz, A., 528, 555

Kuriyama, S., 404, 405(18), 432

Kurnick, N. B., 122(78), 176

Kuroda, Y., 130(125), 178

Kusama, K., 211(257), 240

Kuwada, S., 635(136, 138, 140), 636 (138), 641

L

Labbe, R. F., 572(35), 609

LaDu, B. N., 262(103, 112, 114), 263 (118), 330

Lafon, M., 381, 382(38), 395

Laki, K., 199(93), 207(174, 176), 215 (303), 235, 238, 241, 430(66), 433

Lalley, J. S., 471(134), 482

Lambrecht, R., 567(19), 608

Lamerton, L. F., 471(132), 482

Land, D. G., 659(42), 673

Landaburu, R. H., 464(97, 98, 99), 465 (97, 99), 481

Landmann, W., 13(106a), 24

Landmann, W. A., 194(48), 203(131), 234, 236

Landsteiner, K., 208, 211(179, 252), 226 (178), 238, 240

Lang, A. R., 347(61, 62), 348(62), 362 (62), 367

Lang, R. P., 199(96), 236

Langemann, H., 321(490), 325(525), 340, 341

Langham, W. H., 252(38), 327

Langhof, H., 349(86), 367

Langley, F. A., 603(179), 613

Langstein, L., 258(64), 328

Lankester, E. R., 577(90), 583, 584(64, 68), 587(90), 609, 610

Lardy, H. A., 496(52), 554, 701

W

SUBJECT INDEX

A

Absolute configuration,
 determination of, 5
Acalyptrata,
 sclerotin in, 384
Acanthodrilus annectans,
 coelomic fluid, coagulation of, 437
Accelerin, 464
 formation of, 463
Acer pseudoplanatus,
 carotenoids, senescence and, 661
Acetamide, flagellins and, 217
Acetate,
 activation, alkali metals and, 701
 aromatic biosynthesis and, 253
 flavonoid synthesis and, 275, 277–278
 glucose degradation and, 72–73
 glutarate metabolism and, 313–314
 kynurenic acid metabolism and, 304,
  306
 methoxycinnamate production and, 77
 tryptophan metabolism and, 311–314
Acetoacetate, 77
 glutarate metabolism and, 313–314
 phenylalanine and, 257–259, 263–264
 tyrosine degradation and, 286, 388
Acetobacter,
 cellulose synthesis by, 27, 28
Acetobacter acetigenum,
 cellulose synthesis by, 28
Acetobacter kützengianum,
 cellulose synthesis by, 28
Acetobacter pasteurianum,
 cellulose synthesis by, 28
Acetobacter rancens,
 cellulose synthesis by, 28
Acetobacter xylinum,
 cellulose synthesis by, 28–30
Acetoin, riboflavin synthesis from, 635
N-Acetyl alanine, cucumber virus and,
 217
Acetylcholine, porphyrin and, 605
N-Acetylglycine, 232
N^a-Acetylkynurenine,
 accumulation of, 292, 300, 302
 kynureninase and, 298

N-Acetylserine, 232
 intermedin and, 193
 tobacco mosaic virus and, 138, 217
N-Acetylthreonine, 232
Ac-globulin, 464
 thrombin and, 463
Acherontia atropos,
 porphyrin of, 579, 588
Acipenser sturio,
 protamine of, 130, 216
Acmoea, porphyrin of, 578
Acriquines, mollusks and, 20
Acteon, porphyrin of, 578
Actinia, porphyrin in, 573
Actinia equina, porphyrin in, 574, 580
Actiniohaematin,
 occurrence of, 574, 580
Actinomyces, antibiotic of, 7
Actinomycetes, melanin formation by, 288
Actinomycins, 191
 amino acids of, 7, 231
Active sites,
 amino acid sequences of, 199–206, 221
Actomyosin, alkali metals and, 698–700
Aculeata, silk of, 414, 428, 430
Adamsia palliata, porphyrin in, 574
Adenine, 139
 deoxyribonucleic acid composition and,
  140–143
 incorporation, enzyme induction and,
  171
 pteridine synthesis from, 632
 riboflavin synthesis from, 635, 636
Adenosine diphosphate,
 alkali metals and, 697
Adenosine monophosphate,
 alkali metals and, 697
Adenosine 3',5'-phosphate,
 phosphorylase and, 53
Adenosine triphosphatase,
 alkali metals and, 699, 701–702
 metamorphosis and, 543, 546, 549, 550
Adenosine triphosphate,
 alkali metals and, 697
 phosphorylase kinase and, 52

770

Liver,
  phosphorylase of, 53, 55
  porphyrins in, 599–600
  porphyrin metabolism by, 601–602
  ribonucleic acid in, 111–113, 115–
    116, 124–127, 155, 162
  ribonucleoprotein particles of, 114
  serum protein synthesis in, 519–520
  transglucosylase of, 56
  tryptophan peroxidase-oxidase of, 293–
    294
  tyrosine transaminase in, 261
Livona, porphyrin of, 578
Lobster, *see also Homarus*
  coagulation in, 447, 476
  fibrinogen of, 466, 476
Locusta migratoria,
  carotenoids in, 669
  coagulation in, 471
  deoxyribonucleic acid composition of,
    140
  sclerotin of, 390
Lombricine, derivation of, 10–11
Loricates, porphyrin in, 590
Lucapina, porphyrin of, 578
Lucilia,
  hydroxykynurenine in, 391
  puparia, phenols in, 378
Luidia ciliaris,
  porphyrins of, 579, 590
Lumbriconereis fragilis,
  hemoglobin of, 566
  porphyrin in, 576
Lumbricus,
  oxygen-carrying pigment of, 565
Lumbricus terrestris,
  coagulation in, 441, 442
  porphyrin in, 577, 586–587
Lung,
  hydroxytryptamine in, 323
  ribonucleic acid in, 113, 125
Lupine,
  indoleacetate oxidation by, 318
Lutein,
  occurrence of, 654, 656, 665, 669, 670
  senescence and, 661
  source of, 648
Lutein 5,6-epoxide, occurrence of, 665
Luteochrome, structure of, 651
Luteotropins, *see* Prolactins

Lycopene,
  derivatives of, 646
  occurrence of, 660, 661, 665, 666, 669
  shorthand formula of, 645
Lycophyll, source of, 648
Lycosa, coagulation in, 460
Lycoxanthin, source of, 648
Lygia oceanica, coagulation in, 448, 449
Lymantriidae, coagulation in, 452
Lymaria cymbalaria,
  alkali metals in, 689
Lymph, alkali metals in, 706
Lymphoma, deoxyribonucleic acid in,
  117
Lychnis dioica, alkali metals in, 689
Lysergic acid, biosynthesis of, 284–285
Lysine,
  cytochrome c. and, 205–206
  degradation of, 314
  frequency ranks of, 224–225
  hemoglobin and, 213, 214
  histones and, 132
  intermedin and, 193
  keratin and, 351, 359
  lysozyme and, 204
  nonhistone protein and, 134
  N-terminal, occurrence of, 223–224
  occurrence of, 189
  protamines and, 129
  ribonuclease and, 202–203
  vasopressin and, 192
D-Lysine, occurrence of, 8
Lysine racemase, occurrence of, 14
Lysozymes, amino acids of, 203–204,
  223
Lysylglycine dipeptidase,
  metamorphosis and, 546
Lytechinus,
  deoxyribonucleic acid in, 122

M

Mackerel, alkali metals in, 685, 686
Macromolecules,
  alkali metals and, 679–680
Macronucleus,
  deoxyribonucleic acid in, 117, 122
Magnesium,
  alkali metal binding and, 697–698
  chlorophylls and, 565

Sedoheptulose, 77
  methoxycinnamate production and, 78
Sedoheptulose 1,7-diphosphate,
  aromatic biosynthesis and, 253–254
Selachians, coagulins of, 475–477
Selaginella, carotenoids in, 655
Selenomethionine, protein and, 219
Semen, alkali metals in, 707
Seminal epithelia,
  cytoplasmic granules in, 114
Seminal vesicle, alkali metals in, 707
Semiquinone, riboflavin and, 634
Semliki forest virus,
  ribonucleic acid, infectivity of, 173
Senescence, carotenoids and, 661
Sepia, tropomyosin of, 207
Sepiapterins,
  drosopterins and, 630
  isolation of, 618
  occurrence of, 627
Sericin, 429
  amino acids of, 223, 420
  fibroin and, 400
  X-ray diffraction of, 420
Serine, 430
  active sites and, 199–201
  amino acid configuration and, 5
  collagen and, 416
  corticotropin and, 193–194
  cytochrome c and, 205–206
  fibroin and, 401–403, 404, 409, 412
  frequency ranks of, 224–225
  gliotoxin synthesis and, 285–286
  insulin and, 197–198
  keratin and, 350
  N-terminal, occurrence of, 223–224
  occurrence of, 189
  ribonuclease and, 202–203
  sericin and, 426
  tetrahydrofolic acid and, 622, 623
  tropomyosins and, 207
  tryptophan metabolism and, 311, 318
  tryptophan synthetase and, 251–252
Serine phosphate, active sites and, 231
D-Serine,
  lombricine formation from, 11
  occurrence of, 7
  toxin production and, 8
D-Serine dehydrase, occurrence of, 14

Serology,
  taxonomic problems and, 207–209
Serotonin, *see* 5-Hydroxytryptamine
Serpula vermicularis,
  hemoglobin of, 566
  porphyrins in, 576
Serratia marcescens,
  deoxyribonucleic acid of, 144, 149
  ribonucleic acid of, 156
Serum,
  alkali metals in, 686
  proteins of, 220
  transglucosylase of, 57
Serum albumin,
  adaptive role of, 519
  metamorphosis and, 503, 509–520, 540–541
Serum globulins,
  metamorphosis and, 516–520
Serum proteins,
  comparative embryology of, 519
  synthesis of, 519–520
Serum prothrombin conversion accelerator, 464
S factor, cellulose and, 35–36
Shales, alkali metals in, 682
Sheep,
  alkali metals in, 684, 686, 707, 709
  corticotropin of, 194–195
  deoxyribonucleic acid, 121
    composition of, 140
  fibrinogen of, 215
  hemoglobin of, 212
  insulin of, 197–198
  intermedins of, 193–194
  phenylalanine metabolism in, 273
  prolactin of, 195
  ribonuclease of, 202–203
  serum albumin of, 211
  somatotropin of, 195–196
  wool, amino acids of, 350
Sheep and cow,
  homologous proteins of, 229
Shigella dysenteriae,
  deoxyribonucleic acid of, 144
  ribonucleic acid of, 156
Shikimic acid,
  aromatic amino acid biosynthesis and, 74–75, 77, 248–249, 253, 256
  cambium and, 101